SO-BWS-649

SAYLOR
Publications, Inc.

2010

current construction costs

Editor-in-Chief:
Stanley J. Strychaz

Associate Editors:
Jody Brumfield
Anthony E. DiPaolo
James L. Horvath
Yuang Hsieh
Mike Kritscher
Cobus Malan
John G. McConville
Daniel J. McNicoll
Thomas C. Moe
John L. Moreno
Eugene E. Morrill
Frank W. Strychaz
James P. Sweeney
Mary Wallers

Special Consultants:
Anthony Nicoletti

Technical Services:
Andrew W. Strychaz
Renata Strychaz
Marianne Westenberg

Founder and Principal Advisor:
Leland S. Saylor, Saylor Consulting Group
San Francisco, California

Business Advisory Board:
James L. Horvath, Partner
Deloitte & Touche, Toronto, Ontario

James P. Sweeney, President
Cost Containment, Inc., Plymouth, Mass.

John M. Szymanski
New Bedford, Massachusetts

Sakan Yanagidaira, President
Group Dynamics Institute, Tokyo, Japan

47th ANNUAL EDITION
ISBN 978-1-933461-21-2

SAYLOR PUBLICATIONS, INC.
9420 Topanga Canyon Boulevard
Chatsworth, CA 91311

8 Bayview Avenue
Plymouth, MA 02360

110 Dunlop Street East
Barrie, Ontario L4M-1A5

800-624-3352   818-718-5966
Fax 818-718-8024
www.saylor.com

Jacobus & Yuang, Inc.

Construction Consultants

A major portion of the cost data, in this manual, is assembled and maintained by Jacobus & Yuang, Inc., Construction Consultants. As professional estimators and advisors, Mr. Jacobus Malan and Mr. Steve Hsieh are directly involved in major construction projects.

Subscribers are welcome to contact Jacobus & Yuang, Inc., on technical questions related to the data in this manual or on other construction services including; cost estimating, scheduling, project management and litigation support.

6477 Telephone Road
Suite 10
Ventura, CA 93003
213-688-1341 or 805-339-9434
Fax 213-688-1342 or 866-431-3256

CONSTRUCTION CONSULTANTS
SAYLOR
CONSULTING
GROUP

In Northern California, please contact Saylor Consulting Group for all estimating and project management needs. Mr. Leland Saylor, and the rest of the Saylor Consulting staff, may be reached at:

595 Market Street, 4th Floor
San Francisco, CA 94105
TEL 415-291-3200
FAX 415-291-3201

For additional information, especially, on international applications of the data in this cost resource please contact:

John G. McConville, C.C.C.
COMPASS International Consultants
PO Box 1295
Morrisville, PA 19067
215-504-9777

TABLE OF CONTENTS

CSI #	Division/Sub-Division	PAGE
	FOREWORD	I
	WAGE RATE RECAP	IV
	SEISMIC ZONE MAP	VI
	SAYLOR COST INDEXES	VII
	MAJOR CITIES COST RELATIONSHIP INDEX	X
	LIST OF ABBREVIATIONS	XII
	PLUMBING - Table of Contents	158
	HVAC - Table of Contents	177
	ELECTRICAL - Table of Contents	199
	ASSEMBLY COSTS - Table of Contents	243
	COMMERCIAL SQUARE FOOT BUILDING COSTS	325
	SAYLOR IN WINDOWS - QUICK START	339
	INDEX	361

CSI #	Division/Sub-Division	PAGE
01.0000 000	**GENERAL REQUIREMENTS:**	**1**
01.1000 000	GENERAL CONDITIONS:	1
01.1010 000	MOBILIZATION, ON & OFF:	1
01.1020 000	NON-DISTRIBUTABLE LABOR:	2
01.1030 000	PERMITS, LICENSES & FEES:	2
01.1040 000	TEMPORARY UTILITIES, STRUCTURES & FENCES:	3
01.1100 000	EQUIPMENT RENTAL:	3
01.1800 000	OTHER GENERAL CONDITIONS:	22
01.1900 000	NON-MANUAL LABOR DISTRIBUTABLES:	25
01.2000 000	OVERHEAD & PROFIT, BONDS:	25
01.3000 000	ESCALATION:	27
01.4000 000	CONTINGENCIES:	27
01.5000 000	GEOGRAPHICAL DIFFERENCES:	28
02.0000 000	**SITE WORK:**	**29**
02.1000 000	DEMOLITION:	29
02.1100 000	SITE DEMOLITION:	29
02.1200 000	GENERAL BUILDING DEMOLITION:	29
02.2000 000	EXCAVATION, FILL & GRADING:	33
02.3000 000	PILING:	34
02.3500 000	CAISSONS & DRILLING:	35
02.4000 000	SHORING & BULKHEADING:	35
02.5000 000	SITE UTILITIES:	37
02.5100 000	STORM DRAINAGE & SANITARY SEWER PIPE:	37
02.5300 000	WATER, STEAM & GAS DISTRIBUTION PIPING:	39
02.5400 000	VALVES & SPECIALTIES:	41
02.5500 000	MECHANICAL UTILITIES, ACCESSORIES:	43
02.5600 000	MISCELLANEOUS SITE EQUIPMENT:	43
02.5700 000	ELECTRICAL DISTRIBUTION, UNDERGROUND:	43
02.5800 000	ELECTRICAL DISTRIBUTION, OVERHEAD:	45
02.6000 000	GENERAL SITE WORK, PAVING & WALKS:	47
02.7000 000	MISCELLANEOUS SITE IMPROVEMENTS:	49
02.7400 000	IRRIGATION, SPRINKLER HEAD SYSTEMS:	49
02.7600 000	LANDSCAPING:	50
02.9100 000	RAILROAD WORK:	52
02.9500 000	MARINE WORK:	52

TABLE OF CONTENTS

CSI #	Division/Sub-Division	PAGE
03.0000 000	**CONCRETE:**	**53**
03.0500 000	CONCRETE, IN PLACE:	53
03.0600 000	PRECAST CONCRETE:	54
03.0700 000	SPECIALTY CONCRETE:	54
03.0800 000	EXCAVATION & BACKFILL:	55
03.1000 000	CONCRETE FORMS:	55
03.1100 000	FOUNDATION FORMS:	56
03.1200 000	FOOTING FORMS:	56
03.1300 000	FORMS, SLAB ON GRADE:	56
03.1400 000	CONSTRUCTION FORMS, VERTICAL:	56
03.1500 000	CONSTRUCTION FORMS, VERTICAL, HEAVY DUTY:	56
03.1600 000	COLUMN FORMS:	57
03.1700 000	CONSTRUCTION FORMS, HORIZONTAL:	58
03.1800 000	CONSTRUCTION FORMS, HORIZONTAL, HEAVY DUTY:	58
03.1900 000	MISC. CONCRETE FORMS & FORM SPECIALTIES	59
03.2000 000	REINFORCING STEEL:	59
03.2100 000	REINFORCING STEEL, IN PLACE:	59
03.2200 000	REINFORCING STEEL, BUILT/UP COST:	60
03.3000 000	READYMIX CONCRETE:	60
03.3100 000	CONCRETE PLACEMENT:	61
03.3600 000	SLAB FINISHES:	61
03.3700 000	VERTICAL SURFACE FINISHES:	61
03.3800 000	MISCELLANEOUS CONCRETE FINISHES:	62
03.3900 000	MISCELLANEOUS CONCRETE ITEMS & ACCESSORIES:	62
03.4000 000	TILT UP CONSTRUCTION:	62
03.4500 000	COMPILATION OF IN PLACE COST:	63
03.5100 000	INSULATING CONCRETE, INTERIOR:	63
03.5200 000	CONCRETE DECK, EXTERIOR:	64
03.5300 000	INSULATING DECKS:	64
03.5400 000	FIBER DECK:	64
03.6000 000	EPOXY INJECTION, REPAIR	64
04.0000 000	**MASONRY:**	**65**
04.1000 000	BRICK MASONRY:	65
04.2000 000	CONCRETE UNIT MASONRY:	65
04.3000 000	ARCHITECTURAL STONEWORK:	67
04.4000 000	MASONRY ACCESSORIES & MISCELLANEOUS WORK:	67
04.5000 000	FIREPLACES:	68
04.6000 000	PARGETING:	68
05.0000 000	**METALS:**	**69**
05.1000 000	STRUCTURAL STEEL:	69
05.1100 000	STRUCTURAL STEEL SPECIALTIES:	69
05.3000 000	DECKING & SIDING:	70
05.5000 000	MISCELLANEOUS IRON:	72
06.0000 000	**CARPENTRY:**	**75**
06.1000 000	ROUGH CARPENTRY:	75
06.1100 000	VERTICAL FRAMING, WALLS, PER 1,000 BOARD FEET:	75
06.1200 000	HORIZONTAL FRAMING, PER 1,000 BOARD FEET:	76
06.1300 000	MISCELLANEOUS FRAMING & MATERIALS:	77
06.1400 000	SHEATHING:	77
06.1500 000	CARPENTRY SPECIALTIES:	78
06.2000 000	FINISH CARPENTRY:	78
06.2100 000	CARPENTRY, INSTALLATION ONLY:	80
06.3000 000	GLU-LAM BEAMS, TRUSSES & HEAVY TIMBER:	80
06.5000 000	STAIRS, WOOD:	81
06.6000 000	ROUGH HARDWARE:	81

TABLE OF CONTENTS

CSI #	Division/Sub-Division	PAGE
07.0000 000	**THERMAL & MOISTURE PROTECTION:**	**83**
07.1000 000	WATERPROOFING:	83
07.2000 000	THERMAL & SOUND INSULATION:	84
07.3000 000	ROOFING:	85
07.3100 000	COMPOSITE BUILDING PANELS:	87
07.3200 000	STONE PANELS, MANUFACTURED:	88
07.3300 000	MINERAL FIBER PANELS, CURTAIN WALLS:	88
07.4000 000	EXTERIOR INSULATION FINISH SYSTEM (EIFS)	88
07.6000 000	SHEET METAL & FABRICATED SKYLIGHTS:	89
07.7000 000	ARCHITECTURAL SHEET METAL:	92
07.9000 000	CAULKING & SEALANTS:	92
08.0000 000	**DOORS, WINDOWS & GLASS:**	**95**
08.1000 000	HOLLOW METAL DOORS & FRAMES:	95
08.2000 000	WOOD DOORS & FRAMES:	96
08.2100 000	WOOD GARAGE DOORS:	98
08.2200 000	WOOD DOOR SPECIALTIES:	98
08.3000 000	SPECIAL DOORS:	99
08.4000 000	VINYL, WINDOWS AND DOORS:	100
08.5000 000	ALUMINUM, WINDOWS AND DOORS:	101
08.6000 000	WOOD, WINDOWS AND DOORS:	102
08.7000 000	FINISH HARDWARE:	103
08.8000 000	GLASS & GLAZING:	105
08.9000 000	CURTAIN WALL & STOREFRONT SYSTEMS:	105
08.9100 000	CURTAIN WALLS & EXTERIOR PANEL SYSTEMS:	107
09.0000 000	**FINISHES:**	**109**
09.1000 000	LATH, PLASTER, STUDDING & FURRING:	109
09.1100 000	STUDS	109
09.1200 000	FURRING:	110
09.1300 000	LATHING:	110
09.1400 000	PLASTER & LATH:	110
09.2000 000	GYPSUM WALL BOARD, STUDDING & FURRING:	112
09.2100 000	GYPSUM WALL BOARD SPECIALTIES:	114
09.3000 000	CERAMIC TILE:	114
09.4000 000	TERRAZZO:	115
09.5000 000	ACOUSTIC TREATMENT:	115
09.6000 000	WOOD FLOORING:	116
09.7000 000	RESILIENT FLOORING:	117
09.8000 000	PAINTING & WALL COVERING:	118
09.9000 000	PLASTIC & FACTORY FINISH WALL SURFACES:	120
10.0000 000	**SPECIALTIES:**	**123**
10.1000 000	CHALK & TACK BOARDS:	123
10.1500 000	TOILET PARTITIONS & COMPARTMENTS:	123
10.2000 000	PARTITIONS; FOLDING, RELOCATABLE & DEMOUNTABLE:	124
10.4000 000	TOILET ACCESSORIES:	125
10.5000 000	MISCELLANEOUS BUILDING SPECIALTIES:	126
11.0000 000	**EQUIPMENT:**	**131**
11.1100 000	BANK EQUIPMENT:	131
11.1200 000	ECCLESIASTICAL EQUIPMENT:	131
11.1300 000	EDUCATIONAL EQUIPMENT:	133
11.1400 000	OBSERVATORIES & PLANETARIUMS:	133
11.1500 000	VOCATIONAL SHOP EQUIPMENT:	134
11.1600 000	FOOD SERVICE EQUIPMENT:	134
11.1700 000	GYMNASIUM & PLAYGROUND EQUIPMENT:	137
11.1800 000	INDUSTRIAL EQUIPMENT:	138

TABLE OF CONTENTS

CSI #	Division/Sub-Division	PAGE
11.0000 000	**EQUIPMENT (Continued):**	
11.1900 000	PARKING LOT EQUIPMENT:	139
11.2000 000	MATERIAL HANDLING EQUIPMENT:	139
11.2100 000	LABORATORY EQUIPMENT:	140
11.2200 000	LIBRARY EQUIPMENT:	140
11.2300 000	HOSPITAL EQUIPMENT:	141
11.2400 000	DENTAL EQUIPMENT:	143
11.2500 000	MORTUARY EQUIPMENT:	144
11.2600 000	PRISON EQUIPMENT:	144
11.2700 000	CENTRAL VACUUM SYSTEM:	144
11.2800 000	STAGE EQUIPMENT:	144
11.2900 000	GARBAGE COMPACTORS:	145
11.3000 000	WINDOW WASHING EQUIPMENT, POWERED:	145
11.4000 000	VOCATIONAL EQUIPMENT:	146
12.0000 000	**FURNISHINGS:**	**147**
12.1100 000	BLINDS & SHADES:	147
12.3000 000	CABINETS & LAMINATED PLASTIC TOPS:	147
12.3500 000	LAMINATED PLASTIC & SIMULATED MARBLE TOPS:	148
12.4000 000	CARPETS:	148
12.5000 000	DRAPERIES & CURTAINS:	149
12.8000 000	OFFICE LANDSCAPE, FURNITURE BY STATION:	149
13.0000 000	**SPECIAL CONSTRUCTION:**	**151**
13.1000 000	SPECIAL CONSTRUCTION:	151
13.1100 000	PREFABRICATED STRUCTURES:	151
13.1201 000	RADIATION PROTECTION:	152
13.1203 000	SWIMMING POOLS:	153
14.0000 000	**CONVEYING SYSTEMS:**	**155**
14.1000 000	CONVEYING SYSTEMS:	155
15.0000 000	**MECHANICAL WORK - PLUMBING:**	**158**
15.1000 000	EQUIPMENT:	159
15.1200 000	FIXTURES:	160
15.1300 000	PIPING:	162
15.1400 000	VALVES & SPECIALTIES:	165
15.1500 000	INSULATION, PIPING:	168
15.1600 000	MISCELLANEOUS PLUMBING SPECIALTIES:	169
15.1700 000	MEDICAL & LABORATORY EQUIPMENT & PIPE:	171
15.1800 000	FEES, PERMITS & STERILIZATION:	172
15.1900 000	INDUSTRIAL PIPING:	173
15.2000 000	GATE, GLOBE & CHECK VALVES, CAST STEEL:	175
15.2100 000	INDUSTRIAL PIPING INSULATION:	176
15.3000 000	**MECHANICAL WORK - HVAC:**	**177**
15.3100 000	EQUIPMENT, FURNACES:	178
15.3200 000	EQUIPMENT, HOT WATER & STEAM BOILERS:	179
15.3300 000	EQUIPMENT, COOLING:	180
15.3400 000	EQUIPMENT, HEATING & COOLING COMBINATIONS:	182
15.3500 000	AUXILIARY HEATING & COOLING EQUIPMENT:	183
15.3600 000	AIR HANDLING EQUIPMENT, PRIMARY:	184
15.3700 000	DISTRIBUTION, TERMINAL EQUIPMENT:	185
15.3800 000	MISCELLANEOUS EQUIPMENT:	187
15.3900 000	CONTROLS:	188
15.4000 000	DUCT WORK, GRILLS & REGISTERS:	188
15.4100 000	PIPING & INSULATION:	190
15.4200 000	FITTINGS:	191

TABLE OF CONTENTS

CSI #	Division/Sub-Division	PAGE
15.3000 000	**MECHANICAL WORK - HVAC (Continued):**	
15.4300 000	VALVES & SPECIALTIES:	192
15.4400 000	INSULATION, PIPING:	194
15.5500 000	FIRE PROTECTION SYSTEMS:	195
16.0000 000	**ELECTRICAL WORK:**	**199**
16.0100 000	TOTAL ELECTRICAL WORK, BUILDINGS:	202
16.1000 000	ELECTRICAL COST, IN-PLACE, PRELIMINARY ESTIMATES:	202
16.1100 000	MAIN SWITCHBOARDS, 600V, SERVICE & DISTRIBUTION:	203
16.1200 000	DISTRIBUTION PANELS TO 600V:	203
16.1300 000	TRANSFORMERS:	204
16.1400 000	RACEWAY & WIRE, COMBINED:	204
16.1500 000	UNDERFLOOR DISTRIBUTION SYSTEMS:	205
16.1600 000	LIGHTING FIXTURES, IN-PLACE:	206
16.1700 000	BRANCH CIRCUIT RUNS, SPECIAL PURPOSE CONDUIT & WIRE:	206
16.1800 000	SIGNAL & COMMUNICATIONS SYSTEMS:	207
16.1900 000	BRANCH CIRCUIT OUTLETS & DEVICES:	207
16.2000 000	EQUIPMENT, UNIT SUBSTATIONS:	208
16.2100 000	EQUIPMENT, SWITCHGEAR & TRANSFORMERS:	209
16.2200 000	EQUIPMENT, HIGH VOLTAGE TRANSFORMERS:	209
16.2300 000	SERVICE SECTIONS:	209
16.2400 000	COMBINATION SERVICE & DISTRIBUTION SWITCHBOARDS:	211
16.3000 000	MOTOR CONTROL CENTERS:	214
16.4000 000	PANELBOARDS, 600V MAX, BOLT-ON BREAKERS:	215
16.4100 000	TRANSFORMERS, DRY, LOW VOLTAGE:	216
16.4200 000	PANELBOARDS FOR BOLT-ON BREAKERS, 120/240V, 1PH, 3W:	216
16.4300 000	LOAD CENTERS, MAIN LUG & CIRCUIT BREAKER TYPES, 240V MAX	217
16.4400 000	PLUG-IN CIRCUIT BREAKERS, TYPE QO:	218
16.4500 000	SPECIAL GEAR:	218
16.5000 000	PVC, RSC, IMC & ALUMINUM RACEWAY:	219
16.5100 000	PVC, RSC, IMC & ALUM CONDUIT TERMINALS, ELBOWS & FITTINGS:	221
16.5200 000	EMT RACEWAY, TERMINATIONS & ELBOWS:	222
16.5300 000	ENT, MI CABLE & TERMINATIONS:	224
16.5400 000	SPECIALTY FITTINGS, EXPLOSION PROOF:	224
16.5500 000	UNDERFLOOR & FLUSH TRENCH DUCT, CABLE TRAY:	225
16.5600 000	STEEL GUTTERS, PULL BOXES & UNISTRUT HANGERS:	226
16.5700 000	SPECIAL RACEWAY ASSEMBLY SYSTEMS:	226
16.5800 000	CONDUCTOR ONLY:	227
16.5900 000	BUSWAYS:	229
16.5950 000	RACEWAY & WIRE COMBINED:	231
16.6000 000	LIGHTING FIXTURES:	232
16.7000 000	ELECTRIC & SIGNAL DEVICES:	236
16.7100 000	COMMUNICATION, INTERCOM, PUBLIC ADDRESS:	238
16.7200 000	SPECIAL HOSPITAL SYSTEMS:	239
16.7500 000	SOFT WIRE SYSTEMS, 3 WIRE:	240
16.7600 000	ENERGY & BUILDING MANAGEMENT SYSTEMS:	241
16.7700 000	TESTING:	241
ASSEMBLY COSTS		**243**
COMMERCIAL SQUARE FOOT BUILDING COSTS		**325**
SAYLOR IN WINDOWS - QUICK START		**339**
INDEX		**361**

CD-ROM

Included, with this cost resource, is a CD with all of the cost data in the manual. The data is in two formats.

SAYLOR in Windows - an estimating program

Assembly Costs - a spreadsheet file

SAYLOR in Windows is a comprehensive estimating program that has two complete databases taken from the unit costs section of this resource (pages 1 -242). One database has union installation costs and the second has open shop installation costs. All of the commands, mouse techniques, icons and procedures that you learned to use with "Word for Windows" and "Excel" plus other Windows software make this extra-ordinary program a natural and comfortable estimating tool.

You use the built-in Saylor database, with the crews and man-hours to adjust installation costs (if you want to) and change the material costs (if necessary). Always add your own overhead and profit and produce a report that clearly communicates your estimate to your clients and colleagues.

The Quick Start instructions are on page 339.

Assembly Costs is in "Excel" spreadsheet format and consists of 2,800 assemblies taken from the Assembly Costs section (pages 243 - 323). Each assembly has a unique ID#, a "stand alone" description, a material cost, a union installation cost, an open shop installation cost and a total. This file can be read by spreadsheet and database programs from most vendors.

Microsoft "Excel" or another modern spreadsheet program is required to read this file.
The file name is ASM-CC10.XLS.

The CD setup procedure will copy both SAYLOR in Windows and the Assembly Costs file to a folder (directory) on your hard drive. The folder is named SAYLOR. You will be able to designate another folder name if you wish.

INTRODUCTION

The costs, in this resource, were compiled from the analysis of a large number of projects, interviews with material suppliers and subcontractors, and costs worked out with general contractors for labor items. In addition to the factual data derived from actual project costs, we routinely, solicit opinions from others involved in the construction industry.

In any resource, with more than ten thousand line items, there will always be differences of opinion on specific items. However, when used together over the spectrum of the sixteen divisions, they are found to be an accurate portrayal of construction costs for preparation of conceptual, schematic, preliminary and final estimates for architects, engineers, estimators in all trades, as well as, general building and engineering contractor estimators.

New items were added to the resource this year.

COMPONENTS

Four components make up this cost resource:

Unit Costs Section pages 1 - 242
Assembly Costs Section pages 243 - 323
Square Foot Costs Section pages 325 -337
CD-ROM with estimating program and data

ARRANGEMENT

The general arrangement of the **Unit Costs Section** follows the sixteen major division format of the Construction Specifications Institute (CSI). It is further broken down into the major sub-trade categories under the sixteen divisions. This arrangement is subsequently refined for logical use in estimating. The following deviations, from the standard CSI format, should be noted.

1. Where the standard format causes a split between disciplines involved in a single trade, the identity of the trade has been preserved. Plaster is an example, where light steel framing, lathing, plaster and fireproofing are collected under the title "Lathing, Plastering, Studding and Furring". Although, the trade discipline may be split in time or sequence, the sections are combined, for two basic reasons: first, because the trades normally work together; second, for the estimator's convenience in taking off the whole work that his firm may perform.

2. Where more separations are needed than allowed for in the Uniform Accounting System, some liberty has been taken, as in General Conditions.

3. Where divisions under the CSI format do not fit a logical trade pattern or flow of materials, we have deviated so that the patterns will better fit the trades. Specifically for the Mechanical and Electrical divisions

we have divided the patterns as we felt appropriate. We divide Mechanical into Plumbing, HVAC and Fire Protection, then follow a typical flow diagram. Electrical is divided into a pattern following a one line diagram.

4. Where the trades are so broken down that the sections become too small to conveniently handle in a cost resource, as in the Specialties Division, items used frequently are combined into one section called Building Specialties, Miscellaneous.

The **Assembly Costs Section** is arranged in eleven functional divisions with appropriate subdivisions. Each assembly component consists of several elements from the Unit Costs Section. For example one of the assemblies represents the installed cost of an exterior brick veneer wall on wood stud frame. The brick, building paper, sheathing, framing and insulation elements are included in this assembly. A complete building cost can be prepared by systematically adding the applicable assemblies.

BUDGET ESTIMATES VS BID ESTIMATES

Budget estimates are normally prepared for planning and feasibility analysis. These are also called conceptual, schematic and preliminary estimates. These kinds of estimates do not require or warrant extensive detail in the cost estimate. They seldom require a breakdown of material and installation, nor do they justify the time and expense of a detailed estimate. These types of estimates should be prepared using Assembly Costs.

For bidding and estimating costs of construction work the accuracy and documentation of detailed estimates is required and expected. These types of estimates should be prepared using Unit Costs.

It is not unusual for a conceptual estimate to be followed by a detailed estimate of the same project. The cost data, in this resource, accommodates both needs.

DETAIL GROUPINGS

Within the detail groupings, in the Unit Section, the items are, generally, arranged in the sequence of work, such as concrete, which is split into excavation for concrete, forms, pour and finish. Where no special construction sequence is required, the individual trade is broken down into it's logical components. For example, electrical work is arranged by equipment, fixtures, conduit, wire and miscellaneous electrical devices.

Groupings are, especially, valuable to the estimator who may not be familiar with all trades. The grouping is a "built-in" check list for the estimator.

UNIT COST COMPILATION

The unit costs of the various trade items are broken down into five columns: material, labor to install (Union and Open Shop) and total unit cost (Union and Open Shop). Material, in this resource, includes equipment, equipment rental, material and factory fabrication, combined with applied profit and overhead. Installation is defined as field installation and erection, applied subcontractor's overhead and profit, all applicable fringe benefits, payroll taxes and insurance. The only exception to this rule is for trade items not normally subcontracted by the general contractor.

Almost all the general contractor items are contained in divisions 1 (General Requirements), 3 (Concrete), and 6 (Carpentry). All of the above costs are included, in addition to profit for the trade involved.

We have done this because most general contractors treat these sections much like a subcontract, regardless, of the fact that the work is being performed by their own forces.

See the section on overhead and profit for further detail on how profit and overhead are included for the whole resource and for the general contractor. You will notice that divisions and sections which do not include subcontractor overhead and profit are labeled to further clarify cost breakdowns.

PECULIARITIES IN THE QUANTITY SURVEY

Each trade has formulas which are peculiar to the trade, usually developed over a period of years, to cover loose ends which contractors have experienced. For waste materials, job conditions and non-detailed trim items, the following quantities should be added:

10%

Sand (10-30% for compaction)
Crushed rock (10-20% for compaction)
Compacted fill (10-30% for compaction)
Foundation concrete (for waste and overpours)
Slab membranes (for laps)
Reinforcing (for laps and bends)
Plaster (for waste and clean-up)
Carpet (for waste and fitting)
Linoleum and sheet vinyl (for fitting and covers)
Tongue and groove lumber (10-33% depending on size)
Rough lumber (for miscellaneous backing and blocking)
Wire (for waste and pigtails)
Excavation, mass (10-30% for compaction)

5%

Concrete slabs on grade
Piping
Conduit
Mesh

Lath
Metal studding and furring
Structural steel, for details and clips (7%)
Ceramic Tile
Resilient flooring

In general, openings are deducted in the rough trades and not deducted in the finish trades.

OVERHEAD AND PROFIT

For the purposes of this resource, the subcontractor's overhead and profit is included in the trade prices for trades normally subcontracted. If this is not true, it is noted within the division title.

For trades which the general contractor does his own work, no home office overhead or profit is included. In general, these trades are concrete, building specialties and carpenter installed items of other trades.

All project overhead is combined in the division called General Conditions (1.1000), which includes all permits, temporary work, supervision, payroll taxes, union fringes for the non-distributable labor, and bonds.

Depending on the project, this division may make up from five to fifteen percent of the contract. Since general conditions make up such a large percentage of the project, it is imperative that it be given it's own section of the estimate and not be distributed into the trades. In addition, some of the make-up of project overhead is technically not distributable into the various trades. Fringes and payroll insurance for trade labor may be applied in the trade division applicable, or in the General Conditions section of the estimate, at the discretion of the estimator. Profit is added to the estimate summary after all other items have been determined. It is customary in the construction industry to absorb home office overhead in the profit item. The Overhead, Profit and Bonds sub-division (1.2000) details the typical general contractor profit structure and overhead relationships for various types and sizes of projects.

MAJOR CITIES COST RELATIONSHIP INDEX

The costs, in this resource, can be conveniently adjusted to 125 major cities in the United States and Canada using the indexes in **MAJOR CITIES COST RELATIONSHIP INDEX (MCCRI)**. The MCCRI uses San Francisco as base 100. All other cities in the U.S. and Canada are represented relative to that base. The indexes are computed from an analysis of both wage rates and productivity. The index should be applied to the total cost estimate. The editors recommend that users of these indexes make adjustments which reflect their local experience.

MAN HOURS

Man-hours is a measure of the productivity of the crews of workers involved in the installation of a component of construction. The man-hour rates, in this resource, reflect standard conditions of work and a normal construction environment. The man-hour column should be used as a guide to estimating the construction time and for scheduling of events in the construction process.

WAGES

Wage rates used, in this resource, represent the union and open shop wages in effect in the San Francisco area, at the time of publication plus applicable fringe benefits, payroll taxes, supervision, worker's compensation, overhead and profit. The union base wages and fringe benefits were derived from several sources and are not necessarily tied to a specific union local. The open shop wages with applicable taxes, insurance, supervision, overhead and profit were obtained from trade services, contractors and others, in the San Francisco area. The recaps of 31 trade rates used in the preparation, of this resource, are shown on pages IV and V.

PREPARATION OF THE ESTIMATE

An estimator should always prepare a complete summary for the estimate. The summary should contain all the trades included in the Table of Contents in this resource. Naturally, all of the trades may not be used for the project. Items not used are blanked out. The summary serves as a check list. The estimate is prepared from the ground up, with the estimator surveying the quantities and building the project in his mind just as the project would be built in the field.

Each of the trades in the summary are then relisted and, within each trade, the appropriate quantities are listed. A unit price is then applied. The trade is then totaled and inserted into the summary. In the case of the general contractor, general conditions, concrete and building specialties only, the balance of trade prices are provided by the subcontractors. General Conditions, escalation and profit are then added, completing the estimate. The estimate is then reviewed for items that may have been left out and mathematical errors.

BUDGET OR ENGINEERING ESTIMATES

See sub-division 1.4000 for contingencies.

The prices in this resource are based on normal bid practices, which average 4-5 bids for a project. The importance of the bid cannot be over-emphasized. The general contractor bidder will invite bids from several subcontractors in each of 63 trades or more. Since subcontracts on a typical project amount to 60-80% of the total dollar volume, the most important determinant of the total bid price is the subcontractor.

More general contractor bidding induces more subcontractor bidding.

Examination of a large number of bids received would indicate that the deviation from engineering estimates produced from complete drawings, using the pricing in this resource, is as follows:

1 bid	+15% to +40%
2-3 bids	+8% to +12%
4-5 bids	-4 to +4%
6-7 bids	-7 to -5%
8 or more bids	-12% to -8%

It is not unusual for subcontract bids to vary as much as 100% for an individual trade.

COMPUTER ASSISTED ESTIMATING

The enclosed CD-ROM has a complete and comprehensive estimating program which can be used immediately for unit estimating. Also included is the Assembly Cost Data in spreadsheet format.

Computers are now being used in nearly all construction cost estimating, drawing and scheduling. The data, in this resource is available in several well known estimating programs. It is also available in spreadsheet or database format for use in software available from most vendors.

CONCLUSION

The editors have carefully assembled and reviewed the information, in this resource, before publication. We have attempted to include costs for most materials in common use in modern construction. We have made every effort to be objective and scientific in our approach. We have always consulted several sources and have consistently verified the data presented.

We realize that economic conditions and location often indicate that, in reality, certain costs may appear to be significantly different from those shown, in this resource. We, respectfully, invite and request that users provide us with copies of any documentation related to apparent discrepancies of the information contained, in this resource.

SAYLOR PUBLICATIONS, INC.
9420 Topanga Canyon Blvd.
Suite 203
Chatsworth, CA 91311

818-718-5966
800-624-3352

www.saylor.com

UNION WAGE RATE RECAP

The wage rates in the "TOTAL" column (bold type) were used to calculate the Union Installation Costs in this cost resource.

TRADE	Base Wage	Total Fringe	Payroll Taxes	Super-vision	Workers Comp.	Sub Total	Overhead & Profit	TOTAL	% Wrk Cmp	% OHP
Bricklayer	35.33	23.02	4.61	1.77	5.14	69.87	18.86	**88.73**	14.55	27.00
Carpenter, General	36.50	21.15	4.79	1.83	10.32	74.59	20.14	**94.73**	28.28	27.00
Carpenter, hardwood floorer	36.65	21.15	4.81	1.83	4.87	69.31	18.71	**88.02**	13.28	27.00
Carpenter, Drywall	36.50	21.86	4.79	1.83	4.25	69.23	22.85	**92.08**	11.64	33.00
Cement Mason	28.65	16.76	4.02	1.43	4.17	55.03	14.86	**69.89**	14.55	27.00
Electrician	53.05	20.42	6.31	5.89	5.27	90.94	18.19	**109.13**	9.93	20.00
Elevator Constructor	53.66	22.76	6.90	2.68	3.10	89.10	29.40	**118.50**	5.77	33.00
Glazier	40.76	17.34	4.85	2.04	6.67	71.66	17.20	**88.86**	16.37	24.00
Hod Carrier, Brick	31.40	15.61	3.74	1.57	4.57	56.89	15.36	**72.25**	14.55	27.00
Hod Carrier, Plaster	28.83	14.38	3.43	1.44	5.22	53.30	14.92	**68.22**	18.12	28.00
Laborer, General	26.89	15.06	3.47	1.34	7.60	54.36	8.15	**62.51**	28.28	15.00
Laborer, Demolition	26.99	15.06	3.48	1.35	5.72	52.60	7.89	**60.49**	21.18	15.00
Lather	36.50	21.86	4.79	1.83	3.98	68.96	22.76	**91.72**	10.90	33.00
Operating Engineer, General	38.35	22.02	4.99	1.92	6.83	74.11	11.12	**85.23**	17.80	15.00
Operating Engineer, Oiler	32.54	22.02	4.30	1.63	5.79	66.28	9.94	**76.22**	17.80	15.00
Painter, General	37.57	16.30	4.47	1.88	7.31	67.53	16.88	**84.41**	19.45	25.00
Painter, Drywall (Taper)	37.11	19.94	4.89	1.86	7.22	71.02	17.76	**88.78**	19.45	25.00
Pile Driver	35.75	24.31	4.84	1.79	7.57	74.26	11.14	**85.40**	21.18	15.00
Plasterer	34.06	20.45	4.05	1.70	6.17	66.43	21.92	**88.35**	18.12	33.00
Plumber	53.25	34.69	6.34	2.66	6.17	103.11	15.47	**118.58**	11.59	15.00
Resilient Floorer	42.61	14.71	5.07	2.13	4.68	69.20	18.68	**87.88**	10.99	27.00
Roofer	32.12	14.05	4.20	1.61	12.78	64.76	14.25	**79.01**	39.79	22.00
Sheet Metal Worker, Deck&Siding	33.34	24.31	3.97	1.67	5.11	68.40	10.26	**78.66**	15.33	15.00
Sheet Metal Worker, Mechanical	47.73	27.25	5.68	2.39	7.32	90.37	19.88	**110.25**	15.33	22.00
Sprinkler Fitter	47.09	21.25	5.60	2.35	4.33	80.62	12.09	**92.71**	9.19	15.00
Structural Iron Worker	33.00	24.31	4.39	1.65	10.75	74.10	15.56	**89.66**	32.59	21.00
Teamster, 4 yard	27.13	19.07	3.52	1.36	7.67	58.75	8.81	**67.56**	28.28	15.00
Teamster, 95 yard	28.43	19.07	3.68	1.42	8.04	60.64	9.10	**69.74**	28.28	15.00
Terrazzo Mechanic	38.93	19.72	4.63	1.95	3.01	68.24	18.42	**86.66**	7.74	27.00
Tile Setter	36.16	15.05	4.58	1.81	2.80	60.40	15.10	**75.50**	7.74	25.00
Asbestos Worker	51.73	15.44	6.16	2.59	6.00	81.92	18.02	**99.94**	11.59	22.00

OPEN SHOP WAGE RATE RECAP

The wage rates in the "TOTAL" column (bold type) were used to calculate the Open Shop Installation Costs in this cost resource.

TRADE	Base Wage	Payroll Taxes	Super-vision	Workers Comp.	Sub Total	Overhead & Profit	TOTAL	% Wrk Cmp	% OHP
Bricklayer	29.97	3.57	1.80	4.36	39.70	16.77	**56.47**	14.55	42.25
Carpenter, General	33.27	3.96	2.00	9.41	48.64	20.55	**69.19**	28.28	42.25
Carpenter, hardwood floorer	32.94	3.92	1.98	4.37	43.21	18.26	**61.47**	13.28	42.25
Carpenter, Drywall	32.57	3.88	1.95	3.79	42.19	20.65	**62.84**	11.64	48.95
Cement Mason	27.06	3.22	1.62	3.94	35.84	15.14	**50.98**	14.55	42.25
Electrician	46.13	5.49	2.77	4.58	58.97	20.29	**79.26**	9.93	34.40
Elevator Constructor	45.44	5.41	2.73	2.62	56.20	27.51	**83.71**	5.77	48.95
Glazier	37.17	4.42	2.23	6.08	49.90	19.38	**69.28**	16.37	38.85
Hod Carrier, Brick	17.61	2.10	1.06	2.56	23.33	9.85	**33.18**	14.55	42.20
Hod Carrier, Plaster	16.47	1.96	.99	2.98	22.40	9.72	**32.12**	18.12	43.40
Laborer, General	14.42	1.72	.87	4.08	21.09	6.09	**27.18**	28.28	28.85
Laborer, Demolition	13.04	1.55	.78	2.76	18.13	5.22	**23.35**	21.18	28.80
Lather	31.24	3.72	1.87	3.41	40.24	19.70	**59.94**	10.90	48.95
Operating Engineer, General	34.33	4.09	2.06	6.11	46.59	13.42	**60.01**	17.80	28.80
Operating Engineer, Oiler	31.61	3.76	1.90	5.63	42.90	12.36	**55.26**	17.80	28.80
Painter, General	34.21	4.07	2.05	6.65	46.98	18.79	**65.77**	19.45	40.00
Painter, Drywall (Taper)	33.69	4.01	2.02	6.55	46.27	18.51	**64.78**	19.45	40.00
Pile Driver	34.74	4.13	2.08	7.36	48.31	13.91	**62.22**	21.18	28.80
Plasterer	31.32	3.73	1.88	5.67	42.60	20.87	**63.47**	18.12	49.00
Plumber	42.01	5.00	2.52	4.87	54.40	19.94	**74.34**	11.59	36.65
Resilient Floorer	39.98	4.76	2.40	4.39	51.53	21.77	**73.30**	10.99	42.25
Roofer	29.77	3.54	1.79	11.85	46.95	17.21	**64.16**	39.79	36.65
Sheet Metal Worker, Deck&Siding	27.20	3.24	1.63	4.17	36.24	10.44	**46.68**	15.33	28.80
Sheet Metal Worker, Mechanical	38.93	4.63	2.34	5.97	51.87	19.01	**70.88**	15.33	36.65
Sprinkler Fitter	37.44	4.46	2.25	3.44	47.59	13.71	**61.30**	9.19	28.80
Structural Iron Worker	32.91	3.92	1.97	10.73	49.53	17.61	**67.14**	32.59	35.55
Teamster, 4 yard	25.70	3.06	1.54	7.27	37.57	10.82	**48.39**	28.28	28.80
Teamster, 95 yard	26.61	3.17	1.60	7.53	38.91	11.21	**50.12**	28.28	28.80
Terrazzo Mechanic	31.58	3.76	1.89	2.44	39.67	16.76	**56.43**	7.74	42.25
Tile Setter	34.34	4.09	2.06	2.66	43.15	17.26	**60.41**	7.74	40.00
Asbestos Worker	49.57	5.90	2.97	5.74	64.18	23.52	**87.70**	11.59	36.65

SEISMIC ZONES

There are five seismic zones, in the United States. These are shown on the map. Because of the potential damage that can result from earthquakes and the likelihood of earthquake occurrence, construction practices and applicable codes vary in each zone. The differences in construction are generally attributed to the structural members of the building. In Zone 4 this means greater design emphasis on shearwalls and reinforcing. There is also a tendency, in the earthquake prone areas, to over-build or "beef-up" the safety factor as a precaution.

SEISMIC ZONE MAP OF THE UNITED STATES

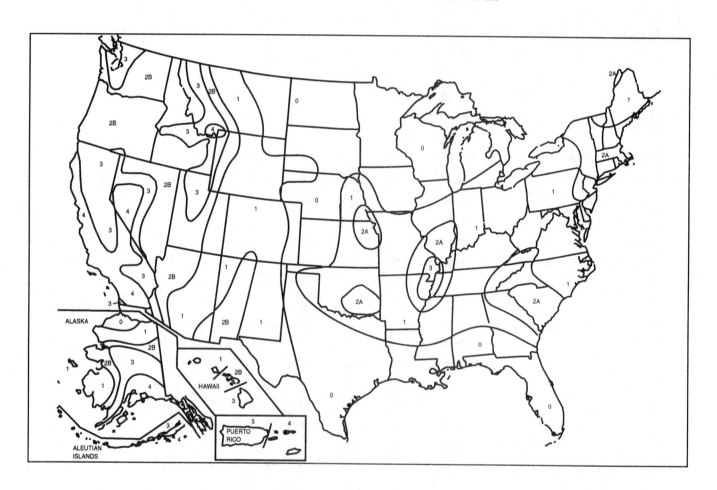

Reproduced from the 1988 edition of the Uniform Building Code, copyright 1988, with permission of the publishers, the International Conference of Building Officials.

COST INDEXES

MATERIAL/LABOR and SUBCONTRACT COSTS
ANNUAL CHANGES

CONTINUING INDEXES (1967 = 100) INCREASES FOR:	2005	2006	2007	2008	3 rd Qtr 2009
MATERIAL/LABOR INDEX (54% Labor, 46% Material)					
All Building Construction	5.4%	6.2%	2.5%	3.2%	0.7%
Concrete Construction Only	5.3%	6.2%	2.5%	3.0%	0.7%
Steel Construction Only	5.8%	6.8%	2.5%	3.5%	0.7%
Wood Frame Construction Only	5.3%	6.2%	2.4%	3.1%	0.7%
SUBCONTRACT COSTS INDEX (Non-weighted)	9.3%	6.5%	5.4%	1.6%	-0.4%

MATERIAL COSTS

MATERIALS COSTS INDEX (23 Selected Materials)	UNIT	2005	2006	2007	2008	9/30/09	9 Month % Change
Aluminum Sheet, H14, 36" x 96"	Cwt	161.54	180.10	182.96	190.73	186.96	-2.0%
Asphalt Felt, 15#	Cwt	19.19	20.73	20.73	21.12	21.12	0.0%
Block, Concrete, 8" x 8" x 16", Lightweight	Each	1.39	1.53	1.39	1.43	1.44	0.7%
Brick, Standard Modular	M	344.68	337.39	348.19	348.97	351.06	0.6%
Cement, Portland	Ton	89.71	96.15	101.09	101.76	101.29	-0.5%
Concrete Redimix, 3,000 PSI	CY	82.28	87.31	91.96	92.26	94.35	2.3%
Copper Tubing, 1/2" Diameter, Type 'L'	MLF	1298.75	2104.38	2123.75	2130.62	2129.38	-0.1%
Glass, 1/4" Float	SF	4.90	5.10	5.12	5.15	5.15	0.0%
GWB (Gypsum Wall Board), 1/2"	MSF	269.12	261.27	260.47	253.03	245.94	-2.8%
Insulation, Mineral Wool Batts, 3"	MSF	273.25	274.55	274.55	274.80	274.80	0.0%
Insulation, Rigid Fiberboard, 1/2"	MSF	298.41	301.02	303.74	303.98	303.98	0.0%
Lath, Metal, 3.4#, Galvanized	CSY	204.57	210.50	208.27	210.13	210.67	0.3%
Lumber, 2" x 4", 2" x 6"	MBF	467.05	451.31	438.77	427.74	415.38	-2.9%
Masons Lime	Ton	200.40	203.03	203.57	205.46	203.56	-0.9%
Paving, Asphalt, Tank Car	Ton	198.75	262.83	263.39	274.79	283.68	3.2%
Pipe, PVC, Water, 8" Diameter	LF	8.22	8.66	8.72	8.85	8.85	0.0%
Pipe, Reinforced Concrete, 24" Diameter	LF	23.01	23.38	24.50	24.96	25.98	4.1%
Plywood, 5/8", C-D, Interior	MBF	636.29	595.50	612.60	597.32	580.75	-2.8%
Steel Sheets, Stainless, 20 Gauge	Cwt	157.77	174.81	201.40	198.17	184.93	-6.7%
Steel, Reinforcing (Mill)	Cwt	35.19	34.56	35.00	40.90	39.71	-2.9%
Steel, Structural (Mill)	Cwt	36.58	39.64	40.38	44.67	43.43	-2.8%
Tar Pitch, #21	Ton	615.11	641.78	642.51	643.50	643.50	0.0%
Titanium Pigment	Cwt	118.97	125.88	126.01	126.09	126.09	0.0%
Total Average Material Change (Non-weighted)							**-0.6%**

COST INDEXES

LABOR COSTS

LABOR COSTS INDEX (9 Selected Trades)		2005	2006	2007	2008	9/30/09	9 Month % Change
Carpenters	$/Hour	41.87375	43.12	44.56	47.13	48.29	2.5%
Bricklayers	$/Hour	42.13625	43.8	45.54	47.66	47.85	0.4%
Iron Workers	$/Hour	45.70	48.00	49.70	51.97	54.34	4.6%
Laborers	$/Hour	33.44063	34.99	36.10	37.84	38.53	1.8%
Operating Engineers (Average)	$/Hour	43.55375	46.84	48.81	51.06	51.06	0.0%
Plasterers	$/Hour	38.82625	41.17	42.06	44.18	44.18	0.0%
Plumbers	$/Hour	46.95188	50.52	52.27	53.78	57.20	6.4%
Electricians	$/Hour	49.14	51.49	52.85	54.89	54.89	0.0%
Teamsters	$/Hour	36.62	37.84	39.08	40.89	40.89	0.0%
Total Average Wage Increase (Non-weighted)		**42.03**	**44.20**	**45.66**	**47.71**	**48.58**	**1.7%**

SUBCONTRACT COSTS

SUBCONTRACTS COSTS INDEX (21 Basic In-Place Materials)	Minimum Quantity	Unit	2005	2006	2007	2008	9/30/09	9 Month % Change
Acoustic Tile, 2' x 4' Grid, 3/8" Board	20,000 & up	SF	2.75	2.90	3.15	3.21	3.20	-0.3%
Brick Vener, Common, Commercial	2,000 & up	SF	13.40	14.10	15.25	15.60	15.55	-0.3%
Ceramic Tile, 4" x 4", Grout Set	1,000 & up	SF	10.80	11.40	11.63	11.63	11.61	-0.1%
Copper Tubing, 1/2" Diameter, Type 'L', Runs	2,000 & up	LF	7.85	10.45	10.50	10.51	10.49	-0.2%
Ductwork, Galvanized Iron	10,000 & up	#	8.20	8.25	8.60	8.66	8.65	-0.1%
Flooring, Terrazzo, Standard	3,000 & up	SF	13.75	15.05	15.40	15.90	15.85	-0.3%
Glass, Float, 1/4"	1,000 & up	SF	9.95	10.65	10.75	10.80	10.80	0.0%
Glu-lam Beams	10,000 & up	MBF	2850.00	3095.00	3125.00	3125.00	3125.00	0.0%
GWB, 5/8", Textured & Smooth, Institutional	20,000 & up	SF	2.05	2.05	2.50	2.50	2.49	-0.4%
Insulation, 1-1/2", Rigid	5,000 & up	SF	1.55	1.65	1.75	1.75	1.75	0.0%
Metal Roof Deck, 1-1/2", 20 Gauge, Painted	10,000 & up	SF	2.65	2.85	3.35	3.51	3.51	0.0%
Paint, Interior, 3 Coats on GWB	10,000 & up	SF	.70	.72	.75	.78	.78	0.0%
Piles, Concrete, 12", Precast	2,000 & up	LF	47.00	48.00	49.50	49.50	49.50	0.0%
Plywood Deck, 5/8", C-D, Machine, T & G	10,000 & up	SF	2.50	2.55	2.75	2.75	2.72	-1.1%
Roofing, 20 Year Built-up	5,000 & up	SF	2.92	3.25	3.35	3.45	3.50	1.4%
Steel, Reinforcing	20,000 & up	#	1.00	1.00	1.00	1.02	1.01	-1.0%
Steel, Structural	250,000 & up	#	1.65	1.65	1.85	1.98	1.89	-4.5%
Stucco, Exterior, Tract Quality	2,000 & up	SY	37.50	41.00	41.00	41.00	41.00	0.0%
Vinyl Composition Tile, 1/8"	10,000 & up	SF	2.90	3.05	3.10	3.20	3.22	0.6%
Wire, #12 TW, Pulled in Conduit	10,000 & up	LF	.96	1.10	1.20	1.23	1.25	1.6%
Wood Studs	10,000 & up	BF	3.30	3.30	3.30	3.30	3.20	-3.0%
Total Average Change, (Non-weighted)								**-0.4%**

COST INDEXES

Subcontract Index			Material/Labor Index		
Year	Index	Increase	Year	Index	Increase
1967	100.0	0.0%	1967	100.0	0.0%
1968	108.5	8.5%	1968	108.5	8.5%
1969	116.3	7.2%	1969	116.3	7.2%
1970	122.7	5.5%	1970	126.2	8.5%
1971	132.9	8.3%	1971	139.2	10.3%
1972	143.3	7.8%	1972	151.5	8.8%
1973	161.6	12.8%	1973	163.7	8.1%
1974	188.3	16.5%	1974	194.3	18.7%
1975	166.9	-11.4%	1975	208.5	7.3%
1976	182.3	9.2%	1976	221.2	6.1%
1977	209.3	14.8%	1977	242.0	9.4%
1978	241.3	15.3%	1978	263.0	8.7%
1979	281.3	16.6%	1979	285.4	8.5%
1980	296.4	5.4%	1980	310.3	8.7%
1981	331.4	11.8%	1981	335.0	8.0%
1982	343.3	3.6%	1982	354.2	5.7%
1983	350.8	2.2%	1983	370.6	4.6%
1984	370.0	5.5%	1984	386.5	4.3%
1985	367.1	-0.8%	1985	395.3	2.3%
1986	376.2	2.5%	1986	402.0	1.7%
1987	380.2	1.1%	1987	409.7	1.9%
1988	390.9	2.8%	1988	421.2	2.8%
1989	397.2	1.6%	1989	433.6	2.9%
1990	415.3	4.6%	1990	440.9	1.7%
1991	423.1	1.9%	1991	444.3	0.8%
1992	434.7	2.7%	1992	452.1	1.8%
1993	428.4	-1.4%	1993	468.9	3.7%
1994	442.8	3.4%	1994	492.3	5.0%
1995	459.4	3.7%	1995	503.2	2.2%
1996	482.8	5.1%	1996	511.9	1.7%
1997	499.9	3.5%	1997	522.0	2.0%
1998	522.6	4.5%	1998	533.0	2.1%
1999	534.3	2.2%	1999	552.1	3.6%
2000	585.0	9.5%	2000	575.5	4.2%
2001	602.7	3.0%	2001	587.1	2.0%
2002	645.4	7.1%	2002	609.9	3.9%
2003	651.6	1.0%	2003	639.0	4.8%
2004	743.2	14.1%	2004	685.7	7.3%
2005	811.8	9.2%	2005	724.9	5.7%
2006	864.3	6.5%	2006	769.5	6.2%
2007	910.4	5.3%	2007	790.2	2.7%
2008	926.7	1.8%	2008	816.1	3.3%
3rd Quarter 2009	918.5	-0.9%	3rd Quarter 2009	813.6	-0.3%

SUBCONTRACT and MATERIAL/LABOR INDEXES

MAJOR CITIES COST RELATIONSHIP INDEX

ALABAMA
Birmingham 71
Huntsville 71
Mobile 74
Montgomery 70

ALASKA
Anchorage 125

ALBERTA*
Calgary 83

ARIZONA
Phoenix 83

ARKANSAS
Little Rock 73

BRITISH COLUMBIA*
Vancouver 88

CALIFORNIA
Fremont 94
Fresno 90
Long Beach 93
Los Angeles 93
Oakland 96
Redding 90
Riverside 92
Sacramento 97
San Diego 93
San Francisco 100
San Jose 97
Santa Ana 94

COLORADO
Denver 78

CONNECTICUT
Hartford 91
New Haven 89
Stamford 91

WASHINGTON D.C. 87

DELAWARE
Wilmington 88

FLORIDA
Jacksonville 72
Miami 77
St. Petersburg 72
Tampa 74

GEORGIA
Atlanta 74
Savannah 69

HAWAII
Honolulu 135

IDAHO
Boise 84

ILLINOIS
Chicago 106
Peoria 105
Rock Island 104
Rockford 104

INDIANA
Evansville 98
Hammond 101
Indianapolis 99
South Bend 98

IOWA
Des Moines 87

KANSAS
Topeka 86
Wichita 85

KENTUCKY
Louisville 79

LOUISIANA
New Orleans 69
Shreveport 69

MAINE
Portland 93

MANITOBA*
Winnipeg 93

MARYLAND
Baltimore 85

MASSACHUSETTS
Boston 107
New Bedford 89
Reading 89
Springfield 84
Three Rivers 84
Worcester 87

MICHIGAN
Detroit 106
Flint 102
Grand Rapids 97
Lansing 99

MINNESOTA
Duluth 82
Minneapolis 102
St. Paul 100

MISSISSIPPI
Jackson 67

MISSOURI
Kansas City 92
St. Louis 93

MONTANA
Butte 80

NEBRASKA
Omaha 81

NEVADA
Las Vegas 88

NEW HAMPSHIRE
Hanover 81
Manchester 80

MAJOR CITIES COST RELATIONSHIP INDEX

NEW JERSEY
Newark..106
Trenton...103

NEW MEXICO
Albuquerque..78
Santa Fe..83

NEW YORK
Albany..101
Buffalo...105
New York..136
Rochester...103
Schenectady..99
Syracuse..100

NORTH CAROLINA
Charlotte..67
Raleigh..67

NORTH DAKOTA
Fargo...78

OHIO
Akron..87
Cincinnati..85
Cleveland...86
Columbus...80
Dayton...80
Toledo...84
Youngstown..82

OKLAHOMA
Oklahoma City..78
Tulsa...78

ONTARIO*
Toronto..99

OREGON
Portland...88

PENNSYLVANIA
Erie...90
Philadelphia..107
Pittsburgh...91
Scranton...86
York...83

QUEBEC*
Montreal...99

RHODE ISLAND
Providence..91

SOUTH CAROLINA
Charleston...69
Columbia...68

SOUTH DAKOTA
Sioux Falls..76

TENNESSEE
Chattanooga..73
Knoxville...71
Memphis...77
Nashville...72

TEXAS
Corpus Christi...73
Dallas...68
El Paso...69
Fort Worth...67
Houston..72
Lubbock..73
San Antonio...73

UTAH
Salt Lake City..78

VERMONT
Burlington..77

VIRGINIA
Norfolk..71
Richmond..73

WASHINGTON
Seattle..94
Spokane..93

WEST VIRGINIA
Charleston...79

WISCONSIN
Madison...88
Milwaukee..90

WYOMING
Cheyenne...80

US CITIES
Average...87

These city indexes are listed for comparison purposes only. Areas radiating out from the major cities to suburban cities usually have lower costs. Areas remote from labor and material supplies will usually have substantially higher prices compared to major cities, due to increases in shipping charges and travel and subsistence for the labor force.

* Canadian indexes reflect Canadian currency.

ABBREVIATIONS

A

"	INCHES
'	FEET
#	POUNDS
A	AMPERES
A/V	AUDIO VISUAL
AASHO	AM ASSN OF STATE HWY OFF
ABRAS	ABRASIVE
ABS	ABSORPTION
	ACRYLONITRILE BUTADIENE STYRENE
AC	ASPHALTIC CONCRETE
	ALTERNATING CURRENT
ACB	AIR CIRCUIT BREAKER
ACC	ACCORDION
ACP	ASBESTOS CEMENT PIPE
ACRY	ACRYLIC
ACU	AIR CONDITIONING UNIT
ADJ	ADJACENT
	ADJUSTABLE
AGG	AGGREGATE
AIC	AMPERE INTERRUPTED CAPACITY
AJ	ALUMINUM JACKET
AL	ALUMINUM
AMB	AMBER
AMP	AMPERE
ANOD	ANODIZED
APPD	APPROVED
APPL	APPLICATION
ARCH	ARCHITECTURAL
ARTIC	ARTICULATED
ASB	ASBESTOS
ASPH	ASPHALT
ASSEM	ASSEMBLY
ASS'T	ASSISTANT
ASTM	AM SOC FOR TESTING MATERIALS
AT	AIR TERMINAL
ATU	AIR TERMINAL UNIT
AV	AVERAGE
AVB	ATMOSPHERIC VACUUM BREAKER

B

B-O	BOLT-ON
B-U	BUILT-UP
B&B	BOARD & BATTEN

B&G	BOLT & GASKET
B&W	BLACK & WHITE
BARR	BARRICADE
BATT	BATT
	BATTEN
BCK	BACK
BCKSTP	BACKSTOP
BD	BOARD
BEL	BELOW
BF	BOARD FOOT
BFLY	BUTTERFLY
BFP	BACKFLOW PREVENTER
BHP	BRAKE HORSEPOWER
BITUM	BITUMINOUS
BK	BACK
BLDG	BUILDING
BLK	BLACK
	BLOCK
BLLWS	BELLOWS
BM	BEAM
BP	BLOOD PRESSURE
BPS	BOLTED PRESSURE SWITCH
BRCH	BIRCH
BRK	BREAK
	BRICK
BRKR	BREAKER
BRLAP	BURLAP
BRZ	BRONZE
BSBD	BASEBOARD
BSN	BASIN
BSP	BLACK STEEL PIPE
BTTN	BATTEN
BTU	BRITISH THERMAL UNITS

C

C/B	CIRCUIT BREAKER
CA	CALIFORNIA
CALSIL	CALCIUM SILICATE
CATH	CATHEDRAL
CC	CENTER TO CENTER
CCSS	COPPER CLAD STAINLESS STEEL
CCU	CORONARY CARE UNIT
CDR	CEDAR
CEM	CEMENT
CENT	CENTRIFUGAL

ABBREVIATIONS

CF	CUBIC FOOT
CFM	CUBIC FEET PER MINUTE
CFRD	COFFERED
CG	CONSTRUCTION GRADE
CHEM	CHEMICAL
CHK	CHECK
CHNNL	CHANNEL
CI	CAST IRON
CIP	CAST IN PLACE
CIP	CAST IRON PIPE
CIRC	CIRCULAR
CIRC	CIRCULATING
CKT	CIRCUIT
	CRICKET
CL	COIL
CL	CLASS
CLG	CEILING
CLNR	CLEANER
CLR	CLEAR
CLSD	CLOSED
CMP	CORRUGATED METAL PIPE
CMPLX	COMPLEX
CMPRSR	COMPRESSOR
CMU	CONCRETE MASONRY UNIT
CNDR	CINDER
CNT	CENTER
CNTR	COUNTER
CNTRL	CONTROL
COL	COLUMN
COMB	COMBINATION
COMM	COMMERCIAL
COMP	COMPUTER
	COMPOSITION
	COMPONENT
	COMPARTMENT
	COMPACT
COMPL	COMPLETE
CONC	CONCRETE
	CONCEALED
COND	CONDUIT
COND	CONDITIONING
CONGL	CONGLOMERATE
CONST	CONSTANT
	CONSTRUCTION
CONV	CONVEYOR
CORR	CORRUGATED

CPLG	COUPLING
CPP	CORRUGATED POLYETHYLENE PIPE
CR-MOLY	CHROME-MOLYBDENUM
CRB	CURB
CRYO	CRYOGENIC
CSMNT	CASEMENT
CT	COAT
CTD	COATED
CTRL	CENTRAL
CU	COPPER
CULT	CULTURED
CURR	CURRENT
CUST	CUSTOM
CVR	COVER
CW	COLD WATER
CY	CUBIC YARD

D

DB HNG	DOUBLE HUNG
DBLWL	DOUBLE WALL
DC	DIRECT CURRENT
DECON	DECONTAMINATION
DECOR	DECORATIVE
DEFIB	DEFIBRILLATOR
DEG	DEGREE
DESC	DESCENDING
DET	DETECTOR
DEV	DEVELOPING
	DEVICE
DF	DOUGLAS FIR
DIA	DIAMETER
DIAPH	DIAPHRAGM
DIM	DIMENSION
DIP	DUCTILE IRON PIPE
DIR	DIRECT
DISC	DISCONNECT
DISP	DISPOSE
	DISPOSAL
	DISPENSER
DIST	DISTRIBUTION
DIV	DIVIDER
DSL	DIESEL
DUMBWTR	DUMBWAITER
DWL	DOWEL
DWV	DRAINAGE, WASTE & VENT

ABBREVIATIONS

E

EA	EACH
ECON	ECONOMY
EJ	EXPANSION JOINT
	EJECTOR
ELEC	ELECTRIC
ELEV	ELEVATED
	ELEVATOR
ELLIP	ELLIPTICAL
EMB	EMBEDDED
EMERG	EMERGENCY
EMT	ELECTROMETALIC TUBING
EN	ENAMEL
ENC	ENCLOSURE
EQ	EQUAL
EP	EXPLOSION PROOF
EQUIP	EQUIPMENT
ERW	ELECTRIC RESISTANCE WELDED
ESC	ESCALATOR
EXC	EXCAVATE
EXH	EXHAUST
EXP	EXPOSED
	EXPANSION
EXT	EXTERIOR

F

F&S	FITTINGS & SUPPORTS
FAB	FABRICATED
	FABRIC
FBGLS	FIBERGLASS
FBR	FIBER
FBRBD	FIBERBOARD
FBRGLS	FIBERGLASS
FG	FOUNDATION GRADE
FIBREBD	FIBREBOARD
FIN	FINISHED
FISS	FISSURED
FIT	FITTINGS
FIX	FIXTURE
FL	FLOOR
	FLOAT
FLD	FIELD
FLL	FILL
FLNG	FLANGE
FLOT	FLOTATION

FLT

FLT	FLOAT
	FLIGHT
FLTR	FILTER
FLUOR	FLUORESCENT
FND	FOUNDATION
FOB	FREE ON BOARD
FOUNT	FOUNTAIN
FP	FIREPROOF
	FIRE PROTECTION
FPM	FEET PER MINUTE
FRC	GLASS FIBER REINFORCED CONCRETE
FRCN	FRACTIONAL
FRESNL	FRESNEL
FRKLFT	FORKLIFT
FRM	FRAME
FRNG	FURRING
FRP	FIBERGLASS REINFORCED PLASTIC
FRT	FREIGHT
FTG	FOOTING
	FITTING
FURN	FURNACE
FVNR	FULL VOLTAGE NON-REVERSING

G

G	GALLON
GA	GAUGE
GAL	GALLON
GALV	GALVANIZED
GD	GOOD
	GUARD
GFI	GROUND FAULT INTERRUPTER
GI	GALVANIZED IRON
GIP	GALVANIZED IRON PIPE
GL	GLASS
GLB	GLOBE
GLV	GALVANIZED
GLZ	GLAZE
GLZD	GLAZED
GPH	GALLONS PER HOUR
GPM	GALLONS PER MINUTE
GR	GROUP
GR-B	GRADE B
GRAN	GRANITE
GRAV	GRAVITY
	GRAVEL

ABBREVIATIONS

GRC.................................GALVANIZED RIGID CONDUIT
GRD...GROUND
GRT...GRATE
GSF...................................GROSS SQUARE FOOTAGE
GSM...........................GALVANIZED SHEET METAL
GSP............................GALVANIZED STEEL PIPE
GWB.......................GYPSUM WALL BOARD
GYP...GYPSUM

H

H..HIGH
HC..HOLLOW CORE
HD..HEAD
....HEAVY DUTY
HDBD..HARDBOARD
HDWR...HARDWARE
HI..HIGH
HI-CAP..HIGH CAPACITY
HNGD..HINGED
HNGR..HANGER
HO..HIGH OUTPUT
HORIZ..HORIZONTAL
HP..HORSEPOWER
....HIGH PRESSURE
HPS.........................HIGH PRESSURE SODIUM
HRDRK......................................HARDROCK
HS..HIGH STRENGTH
HTD...HEATED
HTR...HEATER
HV..HIGH VOLTAGE
HW..HOT WATER
HWY...HIGHWAY
HYD...HYDRAULIC
....HYDRANT
HZRD...HAZARD

I

IB..IRON BODY
IC..INTERCOM
ICU.....................................INTENSIVE CARE UNIT
ILLUM.......................................ILLUMINATOR
IMC............................INTERMEDIATE METAL CONDUIT
IN/DP...INCH OF DEPTH

INC...INCANDESCENT
INCAND...INCANDESCENT
INCL..INCLUDE
INS...INSULATION
....INSULATING
INSTR...INSTRUMENT
INT...INTERIOR
INTRCM...INTERCOM
INTRLCK...INTERLOCK
IOD...IODINE
IRRIG...IRRIGATION
ISO...ISOLATION

J

J-BOX.................................JUNCTION BOX
JKT...JACKET
JSF..........................JOB SQUARE FOOTAGE
JT...JOINT

K

K...THOUSAND
KD...KILN DRIED
KV..KILOVOLT
KVA..................................KILOVOLT AMPERES
KVAR........................KILOVOLT AMPERES RESISTANCE
KW...KILOWATT

L

LAM...LAMINATED
LAUN...LAUNDRY
LCK..LOCK
LD...LOAD
LDG...LOADING
LDGRS...LEDGERS
LF...LINEAL FOOT
LF/TR...........................LINEAL FOOT OF TREAD
LFT...LOFT
LG...LARGE
....LONG
LIQ..LIQUID
LL...LIVE LOAD
LMT...LIMIT
LP...LOW PRESSURE
....LOOP

XV

ABBREVIATIONS

LPH .... LITERS PER HOUR
LPM .... LITERS PER MINUTE
LS ....LUMP SUM
LT..LIGHT
LTS ....LIGHTS
LTWT ....LIGHTWEIGHT
LVL ....LEVEL
LYR ....LAYER

M

M.. THOUSAND
M/CFM .... THOUSAND CUBIC FOOT PER MINUTE
MACH ....MACHINE
MAG..MAGNETIC
MAHOG ....MAHOGANY
MAINT ....MAINTENANCE
MAST..MASTIC
MATL ....MATERIAL
MAX .... MAXIMUM
MBH........................... THOUSAND BTUS PER HOUR
MBTU..............................THOUSAND BTUS
MCB........................... MAIN CIRCUIT BREAKER
MCC........................... MOTOR CONTROL CENTER
MCMB ....MOLDED CASE MAIN BREAKER
MECH .... MECHANICAL
MED ....MEDIUM
.... MEDIAN
MEMB ....MEMBRANE
MERC .... MERCURY
MH ....MANHOLE
MI..MILE
MIN .... MINIMUM
MIN ....MINERAL
MIRR..MIRROR
MISC..................................MISCELLANEOUS
ML..MILLIMETER
MLO ....MAIN LUG ONLY
MM .... MILLION
MM ....MILLIMETER
MOD ....MODULAR
....MODERATE
MON ....MONTH
MONO...MONORAIL
....MONOLITHIC
MSF .... THOUSAND SQUARE FEET

MT ....MOUNT
MTD...MOUNTED
MTL ....METAL
MTR..METER
MU.......................................MASONRY UNIT
MULL .... MULLION
MUN ....MUNTIN
MVA .... MILLIVOLT AMPERES

N

N-R...NON-RATED
N-S...NON-SPOOLED
NEMA .... NAT'L ELECTRICAL MFR'S ASSOC
NEOP ....NEOPRENE
NLRS..NAILERS
NORM ....NORMAL
NR ....NEAR
NYL ....NYLON
NZ ....NOZZLE

O

O/R.......................................OPERATING ROOM
OC ....ON CENTER
OCBW ....ON CENTER BOTH WAYS
OH..OVERHEAD
OPER ....OPERATOR
OPER ....OPERATED
OPN .... OPENING
OS & Y ....OUTSIDE STEM & YOKE
OSM ....OSMOSIS
OZ ....OUNCE

P

P..POLE
P-T ....PASS-THRU
PA ....PUBLIC ADDRESS
PARG ....PARGETING
PART...PARTITION
PB ....PAPERBACK
....PANELBOARD
PC ....PRIME COAT
PE ....POLYETHYLENE
PERF...PERFORATED
PERM...PERMANENT

ABBREVIATIONS

PG...PAINT GRADE
PGBD..PEGBOARD
PH..PHASE
PHARM...PHARMACY
PHOTOELEC.................................PHOTOELECTRIC
PI..PRESSURE INJECTED
....PRESSURE INDICATOR
PIV..POST INDICATOR VALVE
PKG...PACKAGE
PL..PLACE
PLN..PLAN
PLSTC...PLASTIC
PLSTR..PLASTER
PLTS..PLANTS
PNEUM...PNEUMATIC
PNL..PANEL
POC...POINT OF CONNECTION
POLYPRO.......................................POLYPROPYLENE
PORC...PORCELAIN
PORT..PORTABLE
POS...POSITIVE
PRCST..PRECAST
PRE-FAB...PRE-FABRICATED
PRE-INS...PRE-INSULATED
PREFIN...PREFINISHED
PREH..PREHUNG
PREP..PREPARE
....PREPARATION
PREV..PREVENTER
PROJ..PROJECTOR
PRV..PRESSURE REDUCING VALVE
PS...POWER SUPPLY
PSF...POUNDS PER SQUARE FOOT
PSI..POUNDS PER SQUARE INCH
PSIG...POUNDS PER SQUARE INCH GAUGE
PT...PAPER TOWEL
PTD...PAINTED
PTRN...PATTERN
PURIF..PURIFICATION
PVC...POLYVINYL CHLORIDE

Q

QT...QUART

QTY...QUANTITY
QUAL...QUALITY

R

RAD...RADIUS
RCK...RACK
RDWY..ROADWAY
REC..RECREATION
....RECESSED
RECEPT..RECEPTACLE
RECIP...RECIPROCATING
RECPT..RECEPTACLE
RECT..RECTANGULAR
....RECTIFIER
REFER..REFRIGERATOR
REFL..REFLECTIVE
REG...REGISTER
REINF...REINFORCED
REL..RELIEF
RELOC...RELOCATABLE
REM...REMOVE
RES..RESIDENTIAL
RESUSC...RESUSCITATOR
RET..RETAINING
....RETAINER
REV...REVERSE
RF..ROOF
RIG...RIGID
RIP...RIP-RAP
RLLD...ROLLED
RSC...RIGID STEEL CONDUIT
RSR...RISER
RUBB..RUBBER
RW..REDWOOD

S

S/BY..STANDBY
S/O..SHUTOFF
S&P..SHIELDED & PULLED
SC...SOLID CORE
SCH..SCHEDULE
SCR..SCREEN
....SCREW
SCRW...SCREW

SD	SIDE
SECT	SECTION
SEL	SELECT
SEMIREC	SEMIRECESSED
SEP	SEPARATOR
SEW	SEWAGE
SF	SQUARE FOOT
SF/TR	SQUARE FOOT OF TRENCH
SFCA	SQUARE FOOT OF CONTACT AREA
SFFA	SQUARE FOOT FORM AREA
SFSA	SQUARE FOOT SURFACE AREA
SFWA	SQUARE FOOT WALL AREA
SG	SELECT GRADE
	SCOTCH GUARD
SH	SHEATH
SHK	SHACK
SHLVS	SHELVES
SHT	SHEET
SHTRPRF	SHATTERPROOF
SIM	SIMULATED
SK	SACK
SKYLT	SKYLIGHT
SLDG	SLIDING
SLPR	SLEEPER
SM	SHEET METAL
	SMALL
SMLS	SEAMLESS
SMPL	SIMPLEX
SND	SAND
SNDBLST	SANDBLAST
SNK	SINK
SOFF	SOFFIT
SOG	SLAB ON GRADE
SOL	SOLID
	SOLDER
SP	STEEL PIPE
	STATIC PRESSURE
	SPEC
	SPACE
SPAG	SPAGHETTI
SPEC	SPECIFICATION
SPL	SPLIT
SPLSH	SPLASH
SPRD	SPREAD
SPRNKLR	SPRINKLER
SQ	SQUARE (100 SF)

	SQUARE
SRVG	SERVING
SS	STAINLESS STEEL
STA	STATION
STC	SOUND TRANSMISSION COEFFICIENT
STD	STANDARD
STERIL	STERILIZER
STL	STEEL
STOR	STORAGE
STR	STRAIGHT
STR'L	STRUCTURAL
STRNR	STRAINER
STRT	STRAIGHT
STRUCT	STRUCTURE
STY	STORY
SUBFL	SUBFLOOR
SUBM	SUBMERGE
SUPT	SUPPORT
SURF	SURFACE
SURG	SURGERY
SUSP	SUSPENDED
SVC	SERVICE
SW	SWITCH
	SERVICE WEIGHT
SWBD	SWITCHBOARD
SWGR	SWITCHGEAR
SWPK	SWITCHPACK
SWR	SEWER
SYNTH	SYNTHETIC
SYS	SYSTEM

T

T	TON
T&B	TRENCHED & BURIED
T&C	THREADED AND CUT
T&G	TONGUE & GROOVE
TBL	TABLE
TC	THIN COAT
	THERMOCOUPLE
TEMP	TEMPORARY
	TEMPERED
	TEMPERATURE
TERR	TERRAZZO
TH	THICK
THRMPLSTC	THERMOPLASTIC

ABBREVIATIONS

THRSH...THRESHOLD
TNK...TANK
TP ....TOILET PAPER
TPL HNG ....TRIPLE HUNG
TRD ....TREAD
TRLR ....TRAILER
TRM ....TRIM
TRTD ....TREATED
TSTAT ....THERMOSTAT
TV ....TELEVISION
TWR ....TOWER

U

UG ....UNDERGROUND
UL ....UNITED LABS
UNCOMP ....UNCOMPACTED
UNDRCNTR...UNDERCOUNTER
UNDRPN...UNDERPIN
UNFIN ....UNFINISHED
UNMTD ....UNMOUNTED
UNTRTD ....UNTREATED
UPHOL...UPHOLSTERED
UPS ......................UNINTERRUPTIBLE POWER SUPPLY
URE ....URETHANE

V

V ....VOLT
VAC ....VACUUM
VAP..VAPOR
VERMIC...VERMICULITE
VERT ....VERTICAL
VF ....VERTICAL FOOT
VIB...VIBRATION
VIBR ....VIBRATOR
VICT..VICTAULIC
VLV...VALVE
VNT...VENT
VNYL ....VINYL
VOL...VOLUME
VWC ....VINYL WALL COVERING

W

W ....WIDE
W ....WATT

W/TR ....WITH TRENCH
WC ....WATER CLOSET
WD ....WOOD
WFR ....WAFER
WHT ....WHITE
WKND ....WEEKEND
WKWY ....WALKWAY
WL...WALL
WLD ....WELD
WP ....WATERPROOF
WT ....WEIGHT
....WATER TIGHT
WTHRSTRP ....WEATHERSTRIP
WTRPRF ....WATERPROOF

X

XFMR ....TRANSFORMER

Y

YD ....YARD
YR ....YEAR

Z

ZONO ....ZONOLITE

CSI#	DESCRIPTION
01.0 .1000	**GENERAL REQUIREMENTS:** **GENERAL CONDITIONS:** *Note: General conditions will range from 5.5% of project costs for large projects to 15% of project costs for small projects. If manual labor distributables are excluded, allow for 0.9% of project cost*

AMOUNT/SIZE	REPAIR OF FIRE DAMAGE	ALTERATIONS & ADDITIONS	UNIQUE STRUCTURE	INSTITUTIONAL STRUCTURE	COMMERCIAL STRUCTURE	PUBLIC WORKS HEAVY
	%	%	%	%	%	%
Under $200 Thousand	20.0	20.0	18.0	16.5	15.0	15.0
$200 to $500 Thousand	18.0	16.0	14.0	12.0	10.0	10.0
$500 Thousand to $1 Million	16.0	14.0	12.0	10.0	8.0	9.0
$1 to $2 Million	14.0	12.0	10.0	8.0	6.5	7.0
$2 to $5 Million	12.0	10.0	8.0	6.5	5.5	6.5
$5 to $10 Million	10.0	8.0	7.0	6.0	5.0	6.0
$10 to $20 Million	8.0	7.0	6.0	5.5	5.2	5.5
$20 to $50 Million	7.0	6.5	6.0	5.0	5.0	5.0
$50 to $100 Million	6.5	6.0	5.5	4.7	4.5	4.7
$100 Million and Up	6.0	5.5	5.0	4.5	4.5	4.5

AMOUNT/SIZE	HIGH RISE HOUSING	LOW RISE HOUSING	SINGLE FAMILY TRACT	SINGLE FAMILY CUSTOM	SINGLE FAMILY ARCHITECTURAL
	%	%	%	%	%
Under $200 Thousand	15.0	15.0	15.0	15.0	20.0
$200 to $500 Thousand	10.0	10.0	10.0	12.0	15.0
$500 Thousand to $1 Million	8.0	8.0	8.0	10.0	11.0
$1 to $2 Million	6.5	6.5	6.5	8.0	10.0
$2 to $5 Million	5.5	5.5	5.5	6.5	7.5
$5 to $10 Million	5.0	5.0	5.0	6.0	7.0
$10 to $20 Million	5.0	5.0	5.0	0.0	0.0
$20 to $50 Million	4.5	4.5	4.5	0.0	0.0
$50 to $100 Million	4.5	4.5	4.2	0.0	0.0
$100 Million and Up	4.5	4.5	0.0	0.0	0.0

BROAD CATEGORIES OF GENERAL REQUIREMENTS	SMALL JOBS *	LARGE JOBS **		
		HIGH	MEDIUM	LOW
Mobilization	2.0	1.0	0.3	0.2
Non-distributable labor and supervision	7.0	5.0	3.0	2.2
Permits, licenses & fees	0.4	0.3	0.2	0.1
Temporary utilities, structures, fences	1.5	1.0	0.5	0.2
Material handling equipment	2.0	1.0	0.5	0.2
Other general requirements: including trucks, safety, fuel, scaffolding	2.0	1.0	0.5	0.2
Non-manual labor, distributables, benefits, payroll tax, worker's compensation insurance	2.8	2.0	1.0	1.1
Insurances, comprehensive, builders risk	2.0	2.0	0.8	0.3
TOTAL	19.7	13.3	6.8	4.5

* SMALL JOB is less than $ 100,000.   ** Reflects typical average ranges for large jobs.

I.   NEGOTIATED PROJECT: Deduct home office overhead & profit and add 2 to 3% to general conditions.

II.   ADD TO GENERAL CONDITIONS:
   A.   Liquidated damages at specified amount, for duration of project or tight schedules.
   B.   Extra expenditures or supervision labor for calendar days short of normal.

Division 1 CSI #	01-GENERAL REQUIREMENTS Description	Unit	Material	Union Install	Union Total	Open Install	Open Total	Unit Man-Hrs
01.0000 000	**GENERAL REQUIREMENTS:**							
01.1000 000	**GENERAL CONDITIONS:**							
	Note: General conditions will range from 5.5% of project costs for large projects to 15% of project costs for small projects. If manual labor distributables are excluded, allow for 0.9% of project cost.							
01.1010 000	**MOBILIZATION, ON & OFF:**							
	Note: Mobilization ranges from 5% of project cost for large projects to 10% of project cost for small projects. Cost varies according to the type of work, site location and site conditions. This cost includes permits, fees, temporary structures, equipment rental and various miscellaneous items. This is a term usually confined to roadworks, dams, bridges or foreign works.							
01.1020 000	**NON-DISTRIBUTABLE LABOR:**							
	Note: The following percentages may be used in early stage estimating for supervision: *JOB SIZE . . . . PERCENTAGE OF JOB* *50,000 TO 2,000,000 SF . . . . 84%* *2,000,000 TO 5,000,000 SF . . . . 1.15%* *5,000,000 AND UP . . . . 1.73%* *For engineering and layout costs, Use .26% Of the overall job.*							
01.1021 000	**NON-DISTRIBUTABLE LABOR:**							
	Note: For fringes, payroll tax and insurance see section 01.1900.							
01.1021 011	Project Manager ($5 million & larger)	MONTH		12,295.11	12,295.11	12,295.11	12,295.11	173.0000
01.1021 021	Superintendent, large projects ($5 million & larger)	MONTH		11,530.45	11,530.45	11,530.45	11,530.45	173.0000
01.1021 031	Superintendent, medium projects ($2 to $5 million)	MONTH		10,203.54	10,203.54	10,203.54	10,203.54	173.0000
01.1021 041	Superintendent, small projects ($5,000 to $2 million)	MONTH		8,504.68	8,504.68	8,504.68	8,504.68	173.0000
01.1021 051	Assistant Superintendent, large projects	MONTH		8,281.51	8,281.51	8,281.51	8,281.51	173.0000
01.1021 061	Project Engineer	MONTH		7,172.58	7,172.58	7,172.58	7,172.58	173.0000
01.1021 071	Time Keeper	MONTH		4,709.06	4,709.06	4,709.06	4,709.06	173.0000
01.1021 081	Payroll Clerk	MONTH		4,145.08	4,145.08	4,145.08	4,145.08	173.0000
01.1021 091	Secretary	MONTH		3,577.64	3,577.64	3,577.64	3,577.64	173.0000
01.1021 101	Expediter	MONTH		5,089.66	5,089.66	5,089.66	5,089.66	173.0000
01.1021 111	Quality Control Engineer	MONTH		9,632.64	9,632.64	9,632.64	9,632.64	173.0000
01.1021 121	Safety Officer	MONTH		9,632.64	9,632.64	9,632.64	9,632.64	173.0000
01.1030 000	**PERMITS, LICENSES & FEES:**							
	Note: The charges for permits, licenses and meter fees vary. We recommend that you check with local authorities for more exact information. The charges in this section are representative only. Note that building permit and plan check is not required for schools or public projects.							
01.1031 000	**PERMITS, LICENSES & FEES:**							
	Note: The permit fees listed below may vary from one area to another. Please check with your local authorities. Plan check fees are usually based on a percentage of the permit fees. The recommended percentage is 65%, but this also may vary.							
01.1031 011	Permit, first $100,000	EA	1,133.86		1,133.86		1,133.86	
01.1031 021	Permit, each $1,000 over $100,000 to $500,000	M	6.24		6.24		6.24	
01.1031 031	Permit, first $500,000	EA	3,616.08		3,616.08		3,616.08	
01.1031 041	Permit, each $1,000 over $500,000 to $1 million	M	5.35		5.35		5.35	
01.1031 051	Permit, first $1million	EA	6,274.68		6,274.68		6,274.68	
01.1031 061	Permit, each $1,000 over $1 million	M	3.56		3.56		3.56	
01.1031 101	Water meter fee, 3/4" connection	EA	1,320.44		1,320.44		1,320.44	
01.1031 111	Water meter fee, 1" connection	EA	1,692.10		1,692.10		1,692.10	
01.1031 121	Water meter fee, 1-1/2" connection	EA	2,719.12		2,719.12		2,719.12	
01.1031 131	Water meter fee, 2" connection	EA	3,795.06		3,795.06		3,795.06	
01.1031 141	Water meter fee, 3" connection	EA	8,216.15		8,216.15		8,216.15	
01.1031 151	Water meter fee, 4" connection	EA	10,954.84		10,954.84		10,954.84	
01.1031 161	Water meter fee, 6" connection	EA	14,671.73		14,671.73		14,671.73	
01.1031 171	Sewer fee, 7 fixture house with laundry outlet	EA	880.29		880.29		880.29	
01.1031 181	Sewer fee, 5 fixture house with laundry outlet	EA	782.49		782.49		782.49	
01.1031 191	Sewer fee, major structure, average	/FIX	127.11		127.11		127.11	
01.1032 000	**PERMITS, MISCELLANEOUS (USE LOCAL CHARGES):**							
01.1032 011	Encroachment							
01.1032 021	Sidewalks							
01.1032 031	Power							
01.1032 041	Blasting							
01.1032 051	Demolition							
01.1032 061	Street & Alley							
01.1032 071	Land use							

Division 1 CSI #	01-GENERAL REQUIREMENTS Description	Unit	Material	Union Install	Union Total	Open Install	Open Total	Unit Man-Hrs
01.1040 000	**TEMPORARY UTILITIES, STRUCTURES & FENCES:**							
	Note: For compressors see section 01.1104. For early stage estimating, use 0.20% Of job cost to allow							
	for all temporary utilities.							
01.1041 000	**TEMPORARY UTILITIES:**							
01.1041 011	Temporary power pole, in & out only	EA	874.20		874.20		874.20	
01.1041 021	Temporary power pole, 50 amps	MONTH	221.50		221.50		221.50	
01.1041 031	Temporary power pole, 100 amps	MONTH	270.73		270.73		270.73	
01.1041 041	Temporary underground in & out charge	EA	984.46		984.46		984.46	
01.1041 051	Temporary underground, 100 amps	MONTH	85.08		85.08		85.08	
01.1041 061	Chemical toilets, serviced, fiberglass	MONTH	145.04		145.04		145.04	
01.1041 071	Chemical toilets, with sink, fiberglass	MONTH	175.59		175.59		175.59	
01.1041 081	Water, buy	M/GAL	1.54		1.54		1.54	
01.1041 091	Telephone	MONTH	440.16		440.16		440.16	
01.1042 000	**TEMPORARY STRUCTURES:**							
01.1042 011	Temporary shack, 8' x 12', rental	MONTH	137.58		137.58		137.58	
01.1042 021	Temporary shack, 8' x 12', on & off only	LS	712.98		712.98		712.98	
01.1042 031	Temporary shack, 8' x 16', rental	MONTH	160.21		160.21		160.21	
01.1042 041	Temporary shack, 8' x 16', on & off only	LS	806.08		806.08		806.08	
01.1043 000	**OFFICE TRAILER, RENTALS:**							
01.1043 011	Office trailer, 8' x 20', rental	MONTH	274.81		274.81		274.81	
01.1043 021	Office trailer, 8' x 20', on & off	LS	610.71		610.71		610.71	
01.1043 031	Office trailer, 10' x 55', rental	MONTH	650.42		650.42		650.42	
01.1043 041	Office trailer, 10' x 55', on & off	LS	1,050.24		1,050.24		1,050.24	
01.1044 000	**TEMPORARY STRUCTURES, BUY OUT:**							
01.1044 011	Temporary shack, 8' x 12', buy	EA	1,889.69		1,889.69		1,889.69	
01.1044 021	Temporary shack, 8' x 16', buy	EA	2,238.85		2,238.85		2,238.85	
01.1044 031	Temporary shack, 12' x 24', buy	EA	5,837.59		5,837.59		5,837.59	
01.1044 041	Temporary storage, 8' x 40', steel, buy	EA	14,504.35		14,504.35		14,504.35	
01.1044 051	Temporary tool bin, 4' x 8', buy	EA	555.56		555.56		555.56	
01.1045 000	**FENCING & RAILINGS:**							
01.1045 011	Temp wood fence, post in ground	LF	12.98	34.65	47.63	25.31	38.29	0.3658
01.1045 021	Temp barrier bolted to paving	LF	27.58	62.21	89.79	45.44	73.02	0.6567
01.1045 031	Add for sidewalk cover	LF	5.71	16.39	22.10	11.97	17.68	0.1730
01.1045 041	Temporary fence, architectural	LF	82.07	269.90	351.97	197.13	279.20	2.8491
01.1045 051	Temporary railing, wood	LF	6.16	19.58	25.74	14.30	20.46	0.2067
01.1045 061	Chain link 6ft high more than 801 ft, minimum 6 months	LF/MON	.57		.57		.57	
01.1045 071	Chain link 6ft high 501 to 800 ft, minimum 6 months	LF/MON	.64		.64		.64	
01.1045 081	Chain link 6ft high 201 to 500 ft, minimum 6 months	LF/MON	.90		.90		.90	
01.1045 091	Chain link 6ft high 100 to 200 ft, minimum 6 months	LF/MON	1.28		1.28		1.28	
01.1100 000	**EQUIPMENT RENTAL:**							
01.1101 000	**EQUIPMENT RENTAL, MATERIAL HANDLING:**							
	Note: For rental of crawler cranes over 30 days deduct 15% from the total material costs. Prices for							
	truck mounted cranes include on and off charges.							
01.1101 011	Elevator Tower to 200', material, operated	MONTH	7,023.15	14,744.79	21,767.94	10,381.73	17,404.88	173.0000
01.1101 021	Elevator Tower to 200', personnel, operated	MONTH	3,053.54	14,744.79	17,798.33	10,381.73	13,435.27	173.0000
01.1101 031	Erection (2 Hours/LF)	LF		1,219.54	1,219.54	902.02	902.02	14.0000
01.1101 041	Tower Crane to 138' Radius, medium load, operated	MONTH	22,901.61	14,744.79	37,646.40	10,381.73	33,283.34	173.0000
01.1101 051	Tower Crane to 138' Radius, heavy load, operated	MONTH	26,718.52	14,744.79	41,463.31	10,381.73	37,100.25	173.0000
01.1101 061	Tower crane, on & off only, easy access	LS	57,254.01		57,254.01		57,254.01	
01.1101 063	Tower crane, on & off only, average access	LS	64,887.87		64,887.87		64,887.87	
01.1101 065	Tower crane, on & off only, difficult access	LS	72,520.40		72,520.40		72,520.40	
01.1101 071	Stiff leg derrick, operated	MONTH	7,629.27	14,744.79	22,374.06	10,381.73	18,011.00	173.0000
01.1101 081	Guy derrick, 15 ton, 100' with hoist	MONTH	5,086.17	14,744.79	19,830.96	10,381.73	15,467.90	173.0000
01.1101 091	Gin poles, 2 at 250 ton	MONTH	8,900.84	29,489.58	38,390.42	20,763.46	29,664.30	346.0000
01.1101 101	Derrick, on & off charges	LS	11,189.60		11,189.60		11,189.60	
01.1101 111	Truck crane, 35 ton, operator/oiler	MONTH	11,886.85	27,932.58	39,819.43	19,943.44	31,830.29	346.0000
01.1101 121	Truck crane, 60 ton, operator/oiler	MONTH	20,600.25	27,932.58	48,532.83	19,943.44	40,543.69	346.0000
01.1101 131	Truck crane, 90 ton, operator/oiler	MONTH	27,595.23	27,932.58	55,527.81	19,943.44	47,538.67	346.0000
01.1101 141	Truck crane, 140 ton, operator/oiler	MONTH	38,825.73	27,932.58	66,758.31	19,943.44	58,769.17	346.0000
01.1101 151	Handy crane, 10 ton, operated	MONTH	3,563.30	13,966.29	17,529.59	9,971.72	13,535.02	173.0000
01.1101 161	Handy crane, 20 ton, operated	MONTH	10,216.15	6,983.15	17,199.30	4,985.86	15,202.01	86.5000
01.1101 171	Operator for phone on high rise	MONTH		14,744.79	14,744.79	10,381.73	10,381.73	173.0000

3

Division 1 CSI #	01-GENERAL REQUIREMENTS Description	Unit	Material	Union Install	Union Total	Open Install	Open Total	Unit Man-Hrs
01.1101 000	**EQUIPMENT RENTAL, MATERIAL HANDLING: (Cont.)**							
01.1101 181	Crawler crane, 70 ton, operator/oiler	MONTH	12,633.47	27,932.58	40,566.05	19,943.44	32,576.91	346.0000
01.1101 191	Crawler crane, 150 ton, operator/oiler	MONTH	23,060.16	27,932.58	50,992.74	19,943.44	43,003.60	346.0000
01.1101 201	Crawler crane, 200 ton, operator/oiler	MONTH	27,575.03	27,932.58	55,507.61	19,943.44	47,518.47	346.0000
01.1101 211	Crawler crane, 70 ton, on/off only	LS	18,221.39		18,221.39		18,221.39	
01.1101 221	Crawler crane, 150 ton, on/off only	LS	44,541.16		44,541.16		44,541.16	
01.1101 231	Crawler crane, 200 ton, on/off only	LS	53,437.08		53,437.08		53,437.08	
01.1101 251	Concrete conveyor, 20" x 42.5', gas, portable	MONTH	1,293.74		1,293.74		1,293.74	
01.1101 261	Concrete conveyor, 16" x 48', gas, portable	MONTH	1,789.53		1,789.53		1,789.53	
01.1101 271	Concrete pumping, first 50 CY	CY	11.57		11.57		11.57	
01.1101 281	Concrete pumping, 50-150 CY, add	CY	9.33		9.33		9.33	
01.1101 291	Concrete pumping, over 150 CY add	CY	7.60		7.60		7.60	
01.1101 301	Hydraulic Truck Crane, including operator, from yard 5 ton	HR	145.04		145.04		145.04	
01.1101 311	Hydraulic Truck Crane, including operator, from yard 10 ton	HR	190.88		190.88		190.88	
01.1101 321	Hydraulic Truck Crane, including operator, from yard 15 ton	HR	213.74		213.74		213.74	
01.1101 331	Hydraulic Truck Crane, including operator, from yard 30 ton	HR	297.73		297.73		297.73	
01.1101 341	Hydraulic Truck Crane, including operator, from yard 50 ton	HR	374.06		374.06		374.06	
01.1101 351	Hydraulic Truck Crane, including operator, from yard 65 ton	HR	435.13		435.13		435.13	
01.1101 361	Hydraulic Truck Crane, including operator, from yard 75 ton	HR	488.57		488.57		488.57	
01.1101 371	Lattice Boom Truck Crane, including operator, 65 ton	DAY	2,161.16		2,161.16		2,161.16	
01.1101 381	Lattice Boom Truck Crane, including operator, 75 ton	DAY	2,277.97		2,277.97		2,277.97	
01.1101 391	Lattice Boom Truck Crane, including operator, 90 ton	DAY	2,394.81		2,394.81		2,394.81	
01.1101 401	Lattice Boom Truck Crane, including operator, 150 ton	DAY	3,212.57		3,212.57		3,212.57	
01.1101 411	Lattice Boom Truck Crane, including operator, 200 ton	DAY	3,971.89		3,971.89		3,971.89	
01.1102 000	**TRUCK & FORKLIFT RENTAL:**							
01.1102 011	1/2 ton pickup rental	DAY	53.43		53.43		53.43	
01.1102 021	1/2 ton pickup rental	WEEK	213.74		213.74		213.74	
01.1102 031	1/2 ton pickup rental	MONTH	855.01		855.01		855.01	
01.1102 041	1 ton flatbed, stakeside, rental	DAY	70.38		70.38		70.38	
01.1102 051	1 ton flatbed, stakeside, rental	WEEK	351.82		351.82		351.82	
01.1102 061	1 ton flatbed, stakeside, rental	MONTH	1,055.49		1,055.49		1,055.49	
01.1102 071	1.5 ton flatbed, stakeside, 12' bed, rent	DAY	109.90		109.90		109.90	
01.1102 081	1.5 ton flatbed, stakeside, 12' bed, rent	WEEK	439.73		439.73		439.73	
01.1102 091	1.5 ton flatbed, stakeside, 12' bed, rent	MONTH	1,319.16		1,319.16		1,319.16	
01.1102 101	2 ton flatbed dump truck, 14' bed, rent	DAY	128.25		128.25		128.25	
01.1102 111	2 ton flatbed dump truck, 14' bed, rent	WEEK	513.03		513.03		513.03	
01.1102 121	2 ton flatbed dump truck, 14' bed, rent	MONTH	1,508.46		1,508.46		1,508.46	
01.1102 131	5 yard dump truck, rental	DAY	290.10		290.10		290.10	
01.1102 141	5 yard dump truck, rental	WEEK	1,160.34		1,160.34		1,160.34	
01.1102 142	Water truck 1,800 gal.	DAY	254.98		254.98		254.98	
01.1102 143	Water truck 1,800 gal.	WEEK	1,019.88		1,019.88		1,019.88	
01.1102 144	Water truck 1,800 gal.	MONTH	3,038.28		3,038.28		3,038.28	
01.1102 145	Water truck 2,500 gal.	DAY	354.21		354.21		354.21	
01.1102 146	Water truck 2,500 gal.	WEEK	1,416.86		1,416.86		1,416.86	
01.1102 147	Water truck 2,500 gal.	MONTH	4,250.56		4,250.56		4,250.56	
01.1102 148	Water truck 3,500 gal.	DAY	503.84		503.84		503.84	
01.1102 149	Water truck 3,500 gal.	WEEK	2,015.35		2,015.35		2,015.35	
01.1102 150	Water truck 3,500 gal.	MONTH	5,633.81		5,633.81		5,633.81	
01.1102 151	Vehicle trailer, double axle	DAY	80.15		80.15		80.15	
01.1102 152	Vehicle trailer, double axle	WEEK	320.63		320.63		320.63	
01.1102 153	Vehicle trailer, double axle	MONTH	961.87		961.87		961.87	
01.1102 154	Utility trailer, double axle	DAY	80.15		80.15		80.15	
01.1102 155	Utility trailer, double axle	WEEK	320.63		320.63		320.63	
01.1102 156	Utility trailer, double axle	MONTH	961.87		961.87		961.87	
01.1102 161	Mileage, 1/2-3/4 ton truck	MILE	.46		.46		.46	
01.1102 171	Mileage, 1 ton truck	MILE	.58		.58		.58	
01.1102 181	Mileage, 1-1/2 ton truck	MILE	.97		.97		.97	
01.1102 191	Mileage, 2 ton dump truck	MILE	1.12		1.12		1.12	
01.1102 201	Forklift, 8' lift, 4000#, gas flotation	DAY	190.10		190.10		190.10	
01.1102 211	Forklift, 8' lift, 4000#, gas flotation	WEEK	760.33		760.33		760.33	
01.1102 221	Forklift, 8' lift, 4000#, gas flotation	MONTH	1,900.81		1,900.81		1,900.81	
01.1102 231	Forklift, 12' lift, 5000#, gas flotation	DAY	221.37		221.37		221.37	

Division 1 CSI #	01-GENERAL REQUIREMENTS Description	Unit	Material	Union Install	Union Total	Open Install	Open Total	Unit Man-Hrs
01.1102 000	**TRUCK & FORKLIFT RENTAL: (Cont.)**							
01.1102 241	Forklift, 12' lift, 5000#, gas flotation	WEEK	885.54		885.54		885.54	
01.1102 251	Forklift, 12' lift, 5000#, gas flotation	MONTH	2,213.83		2,213.83		2,213.83	
01.1102 261	Forklift, 14' lift, 4000#, gas flotation	DAY	224.44		224.44		224.44	
01.1102 271	Forklift, 14' lift, 4000#, gas flotation	WEEK	897.73		897.73		897.73	
01.1102 281	Forklift, 14' lift, 4000#, gas flotation	MONTH	2,244.37		2,244.37		2,244.37	
01.1102 291	Forklift, 15' lift, 5000#, gas flotation	DAY	224.44		224.44		224.44	
01.1102 301	Forklift, 15' lift, 5000#, gas flotation	WEEK	897.73		897.73		897.73	
01.1102 311	Forklift, 15' lift, 5000#, gas flotation	MONTH	2,244.37		2,244.37		2,244.37	
01.1102 321	Forklift, 20' lift, 7000#, gas flotation	DAY	229.02		229.02		229.02	
01.1102 331	Forklift, 20' lift, 7000#, gas flotation	WEEK	908.42		908.42		908.42	
01.1102 341	Forklift, 20' lift, 7000#, gas flotation	MONTH	2,274.88		2,274.88		2,274.88	
01.1102 351	Forklift, 30' lift, 10,000#, gas flotation	DAY	335.90		335.90		335.90	
01.1102 361	Forklift, 30' lift, 10,000#, gas flotation	WEEK	1,343.56		1,343.56		1,343.56	
01.1102 371	Forklift, 30' lift, 10,000#, gas flotation	MONTH	3,351.31		3,351.31		3,351.31	
01.1102 381	Forklift, 16' lift, 6000#, reach	DAY	224.44		224.44		224.44	
01.1102 391	Forklift, 16' lift, 6000#, reach	WEEK	897.73		897.73		897.73	
01.1102 401	Forklift, 16' lift, 6000#, reach	MONTH	2,244.37		2,244.37		2,244.37	
01.1102 411	Forklift, 36' lift, 8000#, reach	DAY	367.22		367.22		367.22	
01.1102 421	Forklift, 36' lift, 8000#, reach	WEEK	1,468.76		1,468.76		1,468.76	
01.1102 431	Forklift, 36' lift, 8000#, reach	MONTH	3,671.92		3,671.92		3,671.92	
01.1102 441	Forklift, solid, gas, 4000#	DAY	195.43		195.43		195.43	
01.1102 451	Forklift, solid, gas, 4000#	WEEK	755.75		755.75		755.75	
01.1102 461	Forklift, solid, gas, 4000#	MONTH	2,149.71		2,149.71		2,149.71	
01.1102 471	Forklift, solid, gas, 5000#	DAY	229.02		229.02		229.02	
01.1102 481	Forklift, solid, gas, 5000#	WEEK	877.88		877.88		877.88	
01.1102 491	Forklift, solid, gas, 5000#	MONTH	2,519.16		2,519.16		2,519.16	
01.1102 501	Forklift, solid, propane, 8000#	DAY	247.35		247.35		247.35	
01.1102 511	Forklift, solid, propane, 8000#	WEEK	946.60		946.60		946.60	
01.1102 521	Forklift, solid, propane, 8000#	MONTH	2,778.73		2,778.73		2,778.73	
01.1102 531	Forklift, pneumatic, gas, 5000#	DAY	229.02		229.02		229.02	
01.1102 541	Forklift, pneumatic, gas, 5000#	WEEK	877.88		877.88		877.88	
01.1102 551	Forklift, pneumatic, gas, 5000#	MONTH	2,519.16		2,519.16		2,519.16	
01.1102 561	Forklift, pneumatic, gas, 6000#	DAY	247.35		247.35		247.35	
01.1102 571	Forklift, pneumatic, gas, 6000#	WEEK	946.60		946.60		946.60	
01.1102 581	Forklift, pneumatic, gas, 6000#	MONTH	2,778.73		2,778.73		2,778.73	
01.1102 591	Forklift, 12' lift, 15000#, pneumatic, gas	DAY	343.53		343.53		343.53	
01.1102 601	Forklift, 12' lift, 15000#, pneumatic, gas	WEEK	1,374.06		1,374.06		1,374.06	
01.1102 611	Forklift, 12' lift, 15000#, pneumatic, gas	MONTH	3,435.23		3,435.23		3,435.23	
01.1102 621	Forklift, 17.5' lift, 15m#, pneumatic, gas	DAY	358.80		358.80		358.80	
01.1102 631	Forklift, 17.5' lift, 15m#, pneumatic, gas	WEEK	1,450.44		1,450.44		1,450.44	
01.1102 641	Forklift, 17.5' lift, 15m#, pneumatic, gas	MONTH	3,587.91		3,587.91		3,587.91	
01.1102 651	Forklift, solid, electric, 4000#	DAY	195.43		195.43		195.43	
01.1102 661	Forklift, solid, electric, 4000#	WEEK	755.75		755.75		755.75	
01.1102 671	Forklift, solid, electric, 4000#	MONTH	2,149.71		2,149.71		2,149.71	
01.1102 681	Forklift platforms, 4' x 12'	DAY	87.96		87.96		87.96	
01.1102 691	Forklift platforms, 4' x 12'	WEEK	175.92		175.92		175.92	
01.1102 701	Forklift platforms, 4' x 12'	MONTH	299.10		299.10		299.10	
01.1102 711	Forklift boom jib	DAY	58.02		58.02		58.02	
01.1102 721	Forklift boom jib	WEEK	174.05		174.05		174.05	
01.1102 731	Forklift boom jib	MONTH	522.17		522.17		522.17	
01.1102 741	Forklift extension, 6'	DAY	61.07		61.07		61.07	
01.1102 751	Forklift extension, 6'	WEEK	109.90		109.90		109.90	
01.1102 761	Forklift extension, 6'	MONTH	183.21		183.21		183.21	
01.1102 771	Forklift self-dumping hopper	DAY	48.86		48.86		48.86	
01.1102 781	Forklift self-dumping hopper	WEEK	175.59		175.59		175.59	
01.1102 791	Forklift self-dumping hopper	MONTH	389.33		389.33		389.33	
01.1102 801	Rough terrain forward reach high lift loaders, 24 ft lift	DAY	473.34		473.34		473.34	
01.1102 811	Rough terrain forward reach high lift loaders, 24 ft lift	WEEK	1,801.56		1,801.56		1,801.56	
01.1102 821	Rough terrain forward reach high lift loaders, 24 ft lift	MONTH	4,733.00		4,733.00		4,733.00	
01.1102 831	Rough terrain forward reach high lift loaders, 36 ft lift	DAY	572.54		572.54		572.54	
01.1102 841	Rough terrain forward reach high lift loaders, 36 ft lift	WEEK	2,247.40		2,247.40		2,247.40	

Division 1 CSI #	01-GENERAL REQUIREMENTS Description	Unit	Material	Union Install	Union Total	Open Install	Open Total	Unit Man-Hrs
01.1102 000	**TRUCK & FORKLIFT RENTAL: (Cont.)**							
01.1102 851	Rough terrain forward reach high lift loaders, 36 ft lift	MONTH	6,180.40		6,180.40		6,180.40	
01.1102 861	Rough terrain forward reach high lift loaders, 40 ft lift	DAY	709.93		709.93		709.93	
01.1102 871	Rough terrain forward reach high lift loaders, 40 ft lift	WEEK	2,778.73		2,778.73		2,778.73	
01.1102 881	Rough terrain forward reach high lift loaders, 40 ft lift	MONTH	7,099.51		7,099.51		7,099.51	
01.1103 000	**SILENCED COMPRESSORS, RENTAL:**							
01.1103 011	Air compressor, 85-100 CFM, gas	DAY	145.77		145.77		145.77	
01.1103 021	Air compressor, 85-100 CFM, gas	WEEK	435.50		435.50		435.50	
01.1103 031	Air compressor, 85-100 CFM, gas	MONTH	1,066.53		1,066.53		1,066.53	
01.1103 041	Air compressor, 100 CFM, diesel	DAY	129.75		129.75		129.75	
01.1103 051	Air compressor, 100 CFM, diesel	WEEK	454.25		454.25		454.25	
01.1103 061	Air compressor, 100 CFM, diesel	MONTH	1,274.85		1,274.85		1,274.85	
01.1103 071	Air compressor, 125 CFM, diesel	DAY	195.52		195.52		195.52	
01.1103 081	Air compressor, 125 CFM, diesel	WEEK	666.60		666.60		666.60	
01.1103 091	Air compressor, 125 CFM, diesel	MONTH	1,377.58		1,377.58		1,377.58	
01.1103 101	Air compressor, 150/160 CFM, diesel	DAY	213.31		213.31		213.31	
01.1103 111	Air compressor, 150/160 CFM, diesel	WEEK	693.26		693.26		693.26	
01.1103 121	Air compressor, 150/160 CFM, diesel	MONTH	1,466.46		1,466.46		1,466.46	
01.1103 131	Air compressor, 150 CFM, gas	DAY	199.11		199.11		199.11	
01.1103 141	Air compressor, 150 CFM, gas	WEEK	657.67		657.67		657.67	
01.1103 151	Air compressor, 150 CFM, gas	MONTH	1,368.73		1,368.73		1,368.73	
01.1103 161	Air compressor, 160 CFM, gas	DAY	199.11		199.11		199.11	
01.1103 171	Air compressor, 160 CFM, gas	WEEK	657.67		657.67		657.67	
01.1103 181	Air compressor, 160 CFM, gas	MONTH	1,333.14		1,333.14		1,333.14	
01.1103 191	Air compressor, 190 CFM, gas	DAY	213.31		213.31		213.31	
01.1103 201	Air compressor, 190 CFM, gas	WEEK	693.26		693.26		693.26	
01.1103 211	Air compressor, 190 CFM, gas	MONTH	1,404.25		1,404.25		1,404.25	
01.1103 221	Air compressor, 190 CFM, diesel	DAY	183.21		183.21		183.21	
01.1103 231	Air compressor, 190 CFM, diesel	WEEK	633.60		633.60		633.60	
01.1103 241	Air compressor, 190 CFM, diesel	MONTH	1,679.46		1,679.46		1,679.46	
01.1103 251	Air compressor, 250 CFM, diesel	DAY	198.48		198.48		198.48	
01.1103 261	Air compressor, 250 CFM, diesel	WEEK	694.67		694.67		694.67	
01.1103 271	Air compressor, 250 CFM, diesel	MONTH	1,954.27		1,954.27		1,954.27	
01.1103 281	Air compressor, 365 CFM, diesel	DAY	277.89		277.89		277.89	
01.1103 291	Air compressor, 365 CFM, diesel	WEEK	992.41		992.41		992.41	
01.1103 301	Air compressor, 365 CFM, diesel	MONTH	2,611.53		2,611.53		2,611.53	
01.1103 311	Air compressor, 600 CFM, diesel	DAY	458.04		458.04		458.04	
01.1103 321	Air compressor, 600 CFM, diesel	WEEK	1,603.12		1,603.12		1,603.12	
01.1103 331	Air compressor, 600 CFM, diesel	MONTH	4,198.62		4,198.62		4,198.62	
01.1103 341	Air compressor, 750 CFM, diesel	DAY	523.67		523.67		523.67	
01.1103 351	Air compressor, 750 CFM, diesel	WEEK	1,793.96		1,793.96		1,793.96	
01.1103 361	Air compressor, 750 CFM, diesel	MONTH	4,572.68		4,572.68		4,572.68	
01.1103 371	Air compressor, 800 CFM, diesel	DAY	657.67		657.67		657.67	
01.1103 381	Air compressor, 800 CFM, diesel	WEEK	1,910.87		1,910.87		1,910.87	
01.1103 391	Air compressor, 800 CFM, diesel	MONTH	4,710.53		4,710.53		4,710.53	
01.1103 401	Air compressor, 1000 CFM, diesel	DAY	853.25		853.25		853.25	
01.1103 411	Air compressor, 1000 CFM, diesel	WEEK	2,577.42		2,577.42		2,577.42	
01.1103 421	Air compressor, 1000 CFM, diesel	MONTH	6,754.69		6,754.69		6,754.69	
01.1103 431	Air compressor, 1200 CFM, diesel	DAY	908.42		908.42		908.42	
01.1103 441	Air compressor, 1200 CFM, diesel	WEEK	2,748.20		2,748.20		2,748.20	
01.1103 451	Air compressor, 1200 CFM, diesel	MONTH	6,297.93		6,297.93		6,297.93	
01.1103 461	Air compressor, 1400 CFM, diesel	DAY	938.98		938.98		938.98	
01.1103 471	Air compressor, 1400 CFM, diesel	WEEK	2,824.52		2,824.52		2,824.52	
01.1103 481	Air compressor, 1400 CFM, diesel	MONTH	7,087.29		7,087.29		7,087.29	
01.1103 491	Air compressor, 1600 CFM, diesel	DAY	977.11		977.11		977.11	
01.1103 501	Air compressor, 1600 CFM, diesel	WEEK	3,114.63		3,114.63		3,114.63	
01.1103 511	Air compressor, 1600 CFM, diesel	MONTH	7,664.40		7,664.40		7,664.40	
01.1104 000	**PORTABLE AIR COMPRESSORS, RENTAL:**							
01.1104 011	Portable air compressor, 8 CFM, gas	DAY	53.43		53.43		53.43	
01.1104 021	Portable air compressor, 8 CFM, gas	WEEK	213.74		213.74		213.74	
01.1104 031	Portable air compressor, 8 CFM, gas	MONTH	534.37		534.37		534.37	
01.1104 041	Portable air compressor, 375 CFM, diesel	DAY	277.89		277.89		277.89	

Division 1 CSI #	01-GENERAL REQUIREMENTS Description	Unit	Material	Union Install	Union Total	Open Install	Open Total	Unit Man-Hrs
01.1104 000	**PORTABLE AIR COMPRESSORS, RENTAL: (Cont.)**							
01.1104 051	Portable air compressor, 375 CFM, diesel	WEEK	992.41		992.41		992.41	
01.1104 061	Portable air compressor, 375 CFM, diesel	MONTH	2,611.53		2,611.53		2,611.53	
01.1104 071	Portable air compressor, 800 CFM, diesel	DAY	523.67		523.67		523.67	
01.1104 081	Portable air compressor, 800 CFM, diesel	WEEK	1,793.96		1,793.96		1,793.96	
01.1104 091	Portable air compressor, 800 CFM, diesel	MONTH	4,572.68		4,572.68		4,572.68	
01.1104 101	Portable air compressor, 900 CFM, diesel	DAY	691.48		691.48		691.48	
01.1104 111	Portable air compressor, 900 CFM, diesel	WEEK	2,351.01		2,351.01		2,351.01	
01.1104 121	Portable air compressor, 900 CFM, diesel	MONTH	5,716.22		5,716.22		5,716.22	
01.1104 131	Portable air compressor, 1200 CFM, diesel	DAY	908.42		908.42		908.42	
01.1104 141	Portable air compressor, 1200 CFM, diesel	WEEK	2,748.20		2,748.20		2,748.20	
01.1104 151	Portable air compressor, 1200 CFM, diesel	MONTH	6,297.93		6,297.93		6,297.93	
01.1104 161	Portable air compressor, 1600 CFM, diesel	DAY	977.11		977.11		977.11	
01.1104 171	Portable air compressor, 1600 CFM, diesel	WEEK	3,114.63		3,114.63		3,114.63	
01.1104 181	Portable air compressor, 1600 CFM, diesel	MONTH	7,664.40		7,664.40		7,664.40	
01.1104 191	Portable air compressor, 1750 CFM, diesel	DAY	1,613.43		1,613.43		1,613.43	
01.1104 201	Portable air compressor, 1750 CFM, diesel	WEEK	4,148.83		4,148.83		4,148.83	
01.1104 211	Portable air compressor, 1750 CFM, diesel	MONTH	10,879.19		10,879.19		10,879.19	
01.1104 221	Portable air compressor, 2000 CFM, diesel	DAY	1,843.95		1,843.95		1,843.95	
01.1104 231	Portable air compressor, 2000 CFM, diesel	WEEK	4,886.42		4,886.42		4,886.42	
01.1104 241	Portable air compressor, 2000 CFM, diesel	MONTH	12,907.49		12,907.49		12,907.49	
01.1105 000	**ELECTRIC COMPRESSORS, RENTAL:**							
01.1105 011	Electric compressor, 6 CFM, 1.5HP, 110v	DAY	44.43		44.43		44.43	
01.1105 021	Electric compressor, 6 CFM, 1.5HP, 110v	WEEK	133.30		133.30		133.30	
01.1105 031	Electric compressor, 6 CFM, 1.5HP, 110v	MONTH	399.98		399.98		399.98	
01.1105 041	Electric compressor, 35-42 CFM, 10HP, skid	DAY	91.60		91.60		91.60	
01.1105 051	Electric compressor, 35-42 CFM, 10HP, skid	WEEK	391.04		391.04		391.04	
01.1105 061	Electric compressor, 35-42 CFM, 10HP, skid	MONTH	728.81		728.81		728.81	
01.1105 071	Compressor, 60 CFM, 15HP, skid, oil free	DAY	99.24		99.24		99.24	
01.1105 081	Compressor, 60 CFM, 15HP, skid, oil free	WEEK	711.00		711.00		711.00	
01.1105 091	Compressor, 60 CFM, 15HP, skid, oil free	MONTH	1,510.93		1,510.93		1,510.93	
01.1105 101	Electric compressor, 60 CFM, 15HP, skid	DAY	114.50		114.50		114.50	
01.1105 111	Electric compressor, 60 CFM, 15HP, skid	WEEK	450.40		450.40		450.40	
01.1105 121	Electric compressor, 60 CFM, 15HP, skid	MONTH	1,145.09		1,145.09		1,145.09	
01.1105 131	Electric compressor, 150 CFM, 40HP, trailer	DAY	167.94		167.94		167.94	
01.1105 141	Electric compressor, 150 CFM, 40HP, trailer	WEEK	671.79		671.79		671.79	
01.1105 151	Electric compressor, 150 CFM, 40HP, trailer	MONTH	1,603.12		1,603.12		1,603.12	
01.1105 161	Electric compressor, 250-260CFM, 60HP, skid	DAY	229.02		229.02		229.02	
01.1105 171	Electric compressor, 250-260CFM, 60HP, skid	WEEK	1,048.75		1,048.75		1,048.75	
01.1105 181	Electric compressor, 250-260CFM, 60HP, skid	MONTH	1,999.75		1,999.75		1,999.75	
01.1105 191	Electric compressor, 300 CFM, 75HP, skid	DAY	267.17		267.17		267.17	
01.1105 201	Electric compressor, 300 CFM, 75HP, skid	WEEK	1,119.84		1,119.84		1,119.84	
01.1105 211	Electric compressor, 300 CFM, 75HP, skid	MONTH	2,177.50		2,177.50		2,177.50	
01.1105 221	Electric compressor, 450-460 CFM, 100HP, skid	DAY	282.45		282.45		282.45	
01.1105 231	Electric compressor, 450-460 CFM, 100HP, skid	WEEK	1,306.49		1,306.49		1,306.49	
01.1105 241	Electric compressor, 450-460 CFM, 100HP, skid	MONTH	2,612.96		2,612.96		2,612.96	
01.1105 251	Electric compressor, 550-600 CFM, 125HP, skid	DAY	439.73		439.73		439.73	
01.1105 261	Electric compressor, 550-600 CFM, 125HP, skid	WEEK	1,910.87		1,910.87		1,910.87	
01.1105 271	Electric compressor, 550-600 CFM, 125HP, skid	MONTH	3,411.28		3,411.28		3,411.28	
01.1106 000	**AIR HOSE & ACCESSORIES, RENTAL:**							
01.1106 011	Air hose, 1/4" ID, 50', coupled	DAY	12.22		12.22		12.22	
01.1106 021	Air hose, 1/4" ID, 50', coupled	WEEK	30.55		30.55		30.55	
01.1106 031	Air hose, 1/4" ID, 50', coupled	MONTH	61.07		61.07		61.07	
01.1106 041	Air hose, 1/2" ID, 50', coupled	DAY	14.50		14.50		14.50	
01.1106 051	Air hose, 1/2" ID, 50', coupled	WEEK	43.50		43.50		43.50	
01.1106 061	Air hose, 1/2" ID, 50', coupled	MONTH	87.03		87.03		87.03	
01.1106 071	Air hose, 3/4" ID, 50', coupled	DAY	21.30		21.30		21.30	
01.1106 081	Air hose, 3/4" ID, 50', coupled	WEEK	48.86		48.86		48.86	
01.1106 091	Air hose, 3/4" ID, 50', coupled	MONTH	94.69		94.69		94.69	
01.1106 101	Air hose, 1" ID, 50', coupled	DAY	16.04		16.04		16.04	
01.1106 111	Air hose, 1" ID, 50', coupled	WEEK	48.09		48.09		48.09	
01.1106 121	Air hose, 1" ID, 50', coupled	MONTH	96.18		96.18		96.18	

Division 1 CSI #	01-GENERAL REQUIREMENTS Description	Unit	Material	Union Install	Union Total	Open Install	Open Total	Unit Man-Hrs
01.1106 000	**AIR HOSE & ACCESSORIES, RENTAL: (Cont.)**							
01.1106 131	Air hose, 1-1/2" ID, 50', coupled	DAY	53.35		53.35		53.35	
01.1106 141	Air hose, 1-1/2" ID, 50', coupled	WEEK	120.87		120.87		120.87	
01.1106 151	Air hose, 1-1/2" ID, 50', coupled	MONTH	213.31		213.31		213.31	
01.1106 161	Air hose, 2" ID, 50', coupled	DAY	56.49		56.49		56.49	
01.1106 171	Air hose, 2" ID, 50', coupled	WEEK	83.96		83.96		83.96	
01.1106 181	Air hose, 2" ID, 50', coupled	MONTH	251.89		251.89		251.89	
01.1106 191	Air hose, 3" ID, 50', coupled	DAY	133.30		133.30		133.30	
01.1106 201	Air hose, 3" ID, 50', coupled	WEEK	284.45		284.45		284.45	
01.1106 211	Air hose, 3" ID, 50', coupled	MONTH	666.60		666.60		666.60	
01.1106 221	Air manifold, 6 outlet	DAY	58.64		58.64		58.64	
01.1106 231	Air manifold, 6 outlet	WEEK	94.21		94.21		94.21	
01.1106 241	Air manifold, 6 outlet	MONTH	156.74		156.74		156.74	
01.1106 251	Aftercooler, AC2	DAY	88.89		88.89		88.89	
01.1106 261	Aftercooler, AC2	WEEK	158.19		158.19		158.19	
01.1106 271	Aftercooler, AC2	MONTH	284.45		284.45		284.45	
01.1107 000	**AIR TOOLS & ACCESSORIES, RENTAL:**							
01.1107 011	Paving breaker, 30#	DAY	67.19		67.19		67.19	
01.1107 021	Paving breaker, 30#	WEEK	235.14		235.14		235.14	
01.1107 031	Paving breaker, 30#	MONTH	705.38		705.38		705.38	
01.1107 041	Paving breaker, 60/70 #	DAY	70.23		70.23		70.23	
01.1107 051	Paving breaker, 60/70 #	WEEK	245.80		245.80		245.80	
01.1107 061	Paving breaker, 60/70 #	MONTH	737.42		737.42		737.42	
01.1107 071	Paving breaker, 80/90 #	DAY	73.30		73.30		73.30	
01.1107 081	Paving breaker, 80/90 #	WEEK	256.48		256.48		256.48	
01.1107 091	Paving breaker, 80/90 #	MONTH	769.49		769.49		769.49	
01.1107 101	Moil points/chisels, 5/8" to 1-1/4" shank	DAY	12.98		12.98		12.98	
01.1107 111	Moil points/chisels, 5/8" to 1-1/4" shank	WEEK	38.95		38.95		38.95	
01.1107 121	Moil points/chisels, 5/8" to 1-1/4" shank	MONTH	116.81		116.81		116.81	
01.1107 131	Wide chisels, 5/8" to 1-1/4" shank	DAY	16.79		16.79		16.79	
01.1107 141	Wide chisels, 5/8" to 1-1/4" shank	WEEK	50.38		50.38		50.38	
01.1107 151	Wide chisels, 5/8" to 1-1/4" shank	MONTH	151.17		151.17		151.17	
01.1107 161	Spades/asphalt cutter, 1" to 1-1/4" shank	DAY	17.53		17.53		17.53	
01.1107 171	Spades/asphalt cutter, 1" to 1-1/4" shank	WEEK	52.68		52.68		52.68	
01.1107 181	Spades/asphalt cutter, 1" to 1-1/4" shank	MONTH	151.91		151.91		151.91	
01.1107 191	Rock Drill - Jackhammer, 7-25 #	DAY	67.19		67.19		67.19	
01.1107 201	Rock Drill - Jackhammer, 7-25 #	WEEK	235.14		235.14		235.14	
01.1107 211	Rock Drill - Jackhammer, 7-25 #	MONTH	604.60		604.60		604.60	
01.1107 221	Rock Drill - Jackhammer, 30-40 #	DAY	73.30		73.30		73.30	
01.1107 231	Rock Drill - Jackhammer, 30-40 #	WEEK	256.48		256.48		256.48	
01.1107 241	Rock Drill - Jackhammer, 30-40 #	MONTH	659.56		659.56		659.56	
01.1107 251	Rock Drill - Jackhammer, 45 # & over	DAY	79.40		79.40		79.40	
01.1107 261	Rock Drill - Jackhammer, 45 # & over	WEEK	277.89		277.89		277.89	
01.1107 271	Rock Drill - Jackhammer, 45 # & over	MONTH	714.54		714.54		714.54	
01.1107 281	Drill steel, 3' long, 7/8" to 1" shank	DAY	14.19		14.19		14.19	
01.1107 291	Drill steel, 3' long, 7/8" to 1" shank	WEEK	24.92		24.92		24.92	
01.1107 301	Drill steel, 3' long, 7/8" to 1" shank	MONTH	40.88		40.88		40.88	
01.1107 311	Drill steel, 3'-5', 7/8"-1" shank	DAY	28.44		28.44		28.44	
01.1107 321	Drill steel, 3'-5', 7/8"-1" shank	WEEK	42.69		42.69		42.69	
01.1107 331	Drill steel, 3'-5', 7/8"-1" shank	MONTH	65.78		65.78		65.78	
01.1107 341	Drill steel, 5'-8', 7/8"-1" shank	DAY	58.64		58.64		58.64	
01.1107 351	Drill steel, 5'-8', 7/8"-1" shank	WEEK	104.89		104.89		104.89	
01.1107 361	Drill steel, 5'-8', 7/8"-1" shank	MONTH	133.30		133.30		133.30	
01.1107 371	Drill steel, over 8', 7/8-1" shank	DAY	133.30		133.30		133.30	
01.1107 381	Drill steel, over 8', 7/8-1" shank	WEEK	172.45		172.45		172.45	
01.1107 391	Drill steel, over 8', 7/8-1" shank	MONTH	276.57		276.57		276.57	
01.1107 401	Carbide bits, all sizes	DAY	35.53		35.53		35.53	
01.1107 411	Carbide bits, all sizes	WEEK	71.12		71.12		71.12	
01.1107 421	Carbide bits, all sizes	MONTH	124.45		124.45		124.45	
01.1107 431	Chipping hammer	DAY	65.65		65.65		65.65	
01.1107 441	Chipping hammer	WEEK	226.71		226.71		226.71	
01.1107 451	Chipping hammer	MONTH	633.60		633.60		633.60	

Division 1 CSI #	01-GENERAL REQUIREMENTS Description	Unit	Material	Union Install	Union Total	Open Install	Open Total	Unit Man-Hrs
01.1107 000	**AIR TOOLS & ACCESSORIES, RENTAL: (Cont.)**							
01.1107 461	Air impact wrench, 3/4" drive	DAY	47.34		47.34		47.34	
01.1107 471	Air impact wrench, 3/4" drive	WEEK	142.03		142.03		142.03	
01.1107 481	Air impact wrench, 3/4" drive	MONTH	425.96		425.96		425.96	
01.1107 491	Air concrete vibrator	DAY	133.30		133.30		133.30	
01.1107 501	Air concrete vibrator	WEEK	337.76		337.76		337.76	
01.1107 511	Air concrete vibrator	MONTH	648.84		648.84		648.84	
01.1107 521	Air grinders/drills	DAY	48.09		48.09		48.09	
01.1107 531	Air grinders/drills	WEEK	167.94		167.94		167.94	
01.1107 541	Air grinders/drills	MONTH	335.90		335.90		335.90	
01.1107 551	Clay Digger	DAY	68.71		68.71		68.71	
01.1107 561	Clay Digger	WEEK	206.13		206.13		206.13	
01.1107 571	Clay Digger	MONTH	618.37		618.37		618.37	
01.1107 581	Clay Digger Moil Points	DAY	12.22		12.22		12.22	
01.1107 591	Clay Digger Moil Points	WEEK	24.43		24.43		24.43	
01.1107 601	Clay Digger Moil Points	MONTH	48.86		48.86		48.86	
01.1107 611	Clay Digger Clay Spade	DAY	14.87		14.87		14.87	
01.1107 621	Clay Digger Clay Spade	WEEK	29.77		29.77		29.77	
01.1107 631	Clay Digger Clay Spade	MONTH	56.49		56.49		56.49	
01.1107 641	Clay Digger Chisels	DAY	13.37		13.37		13.37	
01.1107 651	Clay Digger Chisels	WEEK	26.73		26.73		26.73	
01.1107 661	Clay Digger Chisels	MONTH	46.93		46.93		46.93	
01.1107 671	Paving Crack Chaser, Bits Extra	DAY	125.95		125.95		125.95	
01.1107 681	Paving Crack Chaser, Bits Extra	WEEK	377.88		377.88		377.88	
01.1107 691	Paving Crack Chaser, Bits Extra	MONTH	1,198.51		1,198.51		1,198.51	
01.1108 000	**COMPACTION EQUIPMENT RENTAL:**							
01.1108 011	Air backfill tamper	DAY	72.88		72.88		72.88	
01.1108 021	Air backfill tamper	WEEK	175.95		175.95		175.95	
01.1108 031	Air backfill tamper	MONTH	506.60		506.60		506.60	
01.1108 041	Rammer - wacker 100-125 lb	DAY	103.83		103.83		103.83	
01.1108 051	Rammer - wacker 100-125 lb	WEEK	415.30		415.30		415.30	
01.1108 061	Rammer - wacker 100-125 lb	MONTH	1,142.03		1,142.03		1,142.03	
01.1108 071	Rammer - wacker 150 lb	DAY	138.19		138.19		138.19	
01.1108 081	Rammer - wacker 150 lb	WEEK	552.69		552.69		552.69	
01.1108 091	Rammer - wacker 150 lb	MONTH	1,435.18		1,435.18		1,435.18	
01.1108 101	Rammer - wacker 250 lb	DAY	149.61		149.61		149.61	
01.1108 111	Rammer - wacker 250 lb	WEEK	598.50		598.50		598.50	
01.1108 121	Rammer - wacker 250 lb	MONTH	1,570.28		1,570.28		1,570.28	
01.1108 131	Compactor, vibratory, plate type, 150-200 lb	DAY	99.24		99.24		99.24	
01.1108 141	Compactor, vibratory, plate type, 150-200 lb	WEEK	396.95		396.95		396.95	
01.1108 151	Compactor, vibratory, plate type, 150-200 lb	MONTH	992.41		992.41		992.41	
01.1108 161	Compactor, vibratory, plate type, 200-300 lb	DAY	125.95		125.95		125.95	
01.1108 163	Compactor, vibratory, plate type, 200-300 lb	WEEK	503.84		503.84		503.84	
01.1108 165	Compactor, vibratory, plate type, 200-300 lb	MONTH	1,259.61		1,259.61		1,259.61	
01.1108 167	Compactor, vibratory, plate type, 300-500 lb	DAY	164.11		164.11		164.11	
01.1108 169	Compactor, vibratory, plate type, 300-500 lb	WEEK	629.04		629.04		629.04	
01.1108 171	Compactor, vibratory, plate type, 300-500 lb	MONTH	1,641.30		1,641.30		1,641.30	
01.1108 173	Compactor, vibratory, plate type, 750 lb	DAY	171.01		171.01		171.01	
01.1108 175	Compactor, vibratory, plate type, 750 lb	WEEK	653.44		653.44		653.44	
01.1108 177	Compactor, vibratory, plate type, 750 lb	MONTH	1,709.98		1,709.98		1,709.98	
01.1108 179	Compactor, vibratory, plate type, 1000 lb	DAY	233.58		233.58		233.58	
01.1108 181	Compactor, vibratory, plate type, 1000 lb	WEEK	903.86		903.86		903.86	
01.1108 183	Compactor, vibratory, plate type, 1000 lb	MONTH	2,335.97		2,335.97		2,335.97	
01.1108 221	Roller, vibratory, single drum, walk behind, 30"	DAY	128.25		128.25		128.25	
01.1108 222	Roller, vibratory, single drum, walk behind, 30"	WEEK	513.03		513.03		513.03	
01.1108 223	Roller, vibratory, single drum, walk behind, 30"	MONTH	1,282.50		1,282.50		1,282.50	
01.1108 231	Roller, vibratory, double drum, walk behind, 21"	DAY	128.66		128.66		128.66	
01.1108 232	Roller, vibratory, double drum, walk behind, 21"	WEEK	514.53		514.53		514.53	
01.1108 233	Roller, vibratory, double drum, walk behind, 21"	MONTH	1,286.29		1,286.29		1,286.29	
01.1108 234	Roller, vibratory, double drum, walk behind, 22 to 27"	DAY	149.61		149.61		149.61	
01.1108 235	Roller, vibratory, double drum, walk behind, 22 to 27"	WEEK	598.50		598.50		598.50	
01.1108 236	Roller, vibratory, double drum, walk behind, 22 to 27"	MONTH	1,496.24		1,496.24		1,496.24	

Division 1 CSI #	01-GENERAL REQUIREMENTS Description	Unit	Material	Union Install	Union Total	Open Install	Open Total	Unit Man-Hrs
01.1108 000	**COMPACTION EQUIPMENT RENTAL: (Cont.)**							
01.1108 237	Roller, vibratory, double drum, walk behind, 28 to 29"	DAY	206.13		206.13		206.13	
01.1108 238	Roller, vibratory, double drum, walk behind, 28 to 29"	WEEK	778.67		778.67		778.67	
01.1108 239	Roller, vibratory, double drum, walk behind, 28 to 29"	MONTH	1,961.88		1,961.88		1,961.88	
01.1108 240	Roller, vibratory, double drum, walk behind, 30"	DAY	224.44		224.44		224.44	
01.1108 241	Roller, vibratory, double drum, walk behind, 30"	WEEK	845.83		845.83		845.83	
01.1108 242	Roller, vibratory, double drum, walk behind, 30"	MONTH	2,114.54		2,114.54		2,114.54	
01.1108 243	Roller, vibratory, double drum, walk behind, 31 to 36"	DAY	239.72		239.72		239.72	
01.1108 244	Roller, vibratory, double drum, walk behind, 31 to 36"	WEEK	908.42		908.42		908.42	
01.1108 245	Roller, vibratory, double drum, walk behind, 31 to 36"	MONTH	2,328.31		2,328.31		2,328.31	
01.1108 246	Roller, vibratory, double drum, walk behind, 39"	DAY	249.64		249.64		249.64	
01.1108 247	Roller, vibratory, double drum, walk behind, 39"	WEEK	946.60		946.60		946.60	
01.1108 248	Roller, vibratory, double drum, walk behind, 39"	MONTH	2,419.93		2,419.93		2,419.93	
01.1108 251	Roller, vibratory, double drum, riding, 36"	DAY	244.29		244.29		244.29	
01.1108 253	Roller, vibratory, double drum, riding, 36"	WEEK	732.85		732.85		732.85	
01.1108 255	Roller, vibratory, double drum, riding, 36"	MONTH	2,305.42		2,305.42		2,305.42	
01.1108 257	Roller, vibratory, double drum, riding, 48"	DAY	264.88		264.88		264.88	
01.1108 259	Roller, vibratory, double drum, riding, 48"	WEEK	794.69		794.69		794.69	
01.1108 261	Roller, vibratory, double drum, riding, 48"	MONTH	2,565.00		2,565.00		2,565.00	
01.1108 263	Roller, vibratory, double drum, riding, 66"	DAY	412.21		412.21		412.21	
01.1108 265	Roller, vibratory, double drum, riding, 66"	WEEK	1,442.81		1,442.81		1,442.81	
01.1108 267	Roller, vibratory, double drum, riding, 66"	MONTH	4,045.95		4,045.95		4,045.95	
01.1108 271	Roller, vibratory, double drum, riding, 84"	DAY	480.92		480.92		480.92	
01.1108 273	Roller, vibratory, double drum, riding, 84"	WEEK	1,580.21		1,580.21		1,580.21	
01.1108 275	Roller, vibratory, double drum, riding, 84"	MONTH	4,351.28		4,351.28		4,351.28	
01.1108 281	Roller, vibratory, double drum, riding, 96"	DAY	633.60		633.60		633.60	
01.1108 283	Roller, vibratory, double drum, riding, 96"	WEEK	217.55		217.55		217.55	
01.1108 285	Roller, vibratory, double drum, riding, 96"	MONTH	6,336.10		6,336.10		6,336.10	
01.1108 371	Roller, vibratory, sheepsfoot, 16 to 20 inch	DAY	338.93		338.93		338.93	
01.1108 373	Roller, vibratory, sheepsfoot, 16 to 20 inch	WEEK	1,016.82		1,016.82		1,016.82	
01.1108 375	Roller, vibratory, sheepsfoot, 16 to 20 inch	MONTH	3,389.43		3,389.43		3,389.43	
01.1108 381	Roller, vibratory, sheepsfoot, 24 to 33 inch	DAY	484.74		484.74		484.74	
01.1108 383	Roller, vibratory, sheepsfoot, 24 to 33 inch	WEEK	1,454.24		1,454.24		1,454.24	
01.1108 385	Roller, vibratory, sheepsfoot, 24 to 33 inch	MONTH	4,847.50		4,847.50		4,847.50	
01.1108 391	Roller, static, double drum, towable, sheepsfoot	DAY	141.24		141.24		141.24	
01.1108 393	Roller, static, double drum, towable, sheepsfoot	WEEK	496.21		496.21		496.21	
01.1108 395	Roller, static, double drum, towable, sheepsfoot	MONTH	1,270.27		1,270.27		1,270.27	
01.1108 401	Roller, vibratory, towable, 54", sheepsfoot	DAY	358.80		358.80		358.80	
01.1108 403	Roller, vibratory, towable, 54", sheepsfoot	WEEK	1,255.75		1,255.75		1,255.75	
01.1108 405	Roller, vibratory, towable, 54", sheepsfoot	MONTH	3,587.91		3,587.91		3,587.91	
01.1108 411	Roller, vibratory, towable, 54", smooth drum	DAY	335.90		335.90		335.90	
01.1108 413	Roller, vibratory, towable, 54", smooth drum	WEEK	1,175.61		1,175.61		1,175.61	
01.1108 415	Roller, vibratory, towable, 54", smooth drum	MONTH	335.90		335.90		335.90	
01.1108 421	Roller, vibratory, self propelled, 10 ton	DAY	485.52		485.52		485.52	
01.1108 423	Roller, vibratory, self propelled, 10 ton	WEEK	1,942.06		1,942.06		1,942.06	
01.1108 425	Roller, vibratory, self propelled, 10 ton	MONTH	5,328.46		5,328.46		5,328.46	
01.1108 431	Roller, vibratory, 35,000 lb, Force	DAY	629.04		629.04		629.04	
01.1108 433	Roller, vibratory, 35,000 lb, Force	WEEK	1,942.06		1,942.06		1,942.06	
01.1108 435	Roller, vibratory, 35,000 lb, Force	MONTH	5,328.46		5,328.46		5,328.46	
01.1108 441	Roller, asphalt, double drum, riding 1-2 ton	DAY	167.94		167.94		167.94	
01.1108 443	Roller, asphalt, double drum, riding 1-2 ton	WEEK	671.79		671.79		671.79	
01.1108 445	Roller, asphalt, double drum, riding 1-2 ton	MONTH	1,496.24		1,496.24		1,496.24	
01.1108 447	Roller, asphalt, double drum, riding 2-3 ton	DAY	201.56		201.56		201.56	
01.1108 449	Roller, asphalt, double drum, riding 2-3 ton	WEEK	793.91		793.91		793.91	
01.1108 451	Roller, asphalt, double drum, riding 2-3 ton	MONTH	1,908.46		1,908.46		1,908.46	
01.1108 453	Roller, asphalt, double drum, riding 6-8 ton	DAY	271.77		271.77		271.77	
01.1108 455	Roller, asphalt, double drum, riding 6-8 ton	WEEK	1,087.06		1,087.06		1,087.06	
01.1108 457	Roller, asphalt, double drum, riding 6-8 ton	MONTH	2,717.65		2,717.65		2,717.65	
01.1108 459	Roller, asphalt, double drum, riding 8-10 ton	DAY	282.45		282.45		282.45	
01.1108 461	Roller, asphalt, double drum, riding 8-10 ton	WEEK	1,129.80		1,129.80		1,129.80	
01.1108 463	Roller, asphalt, double drum, riding 8-10 ton	MONTH	2,824.52		2,824.52		2,824.52	
01.1108 465	Roller, asphalt, double drum, riding 10-12 ton	DAY	323.67		323.67		323.67	

Division 1 CSI #	01-GENERAL REQUIREMENTS Description	Unit	Material	Union Install	Union Total	Open Install	Open Total	Unit Man-Hrs
01.1108 000	COMPACTION EQUIPMENT RENTAL: (Cont.)							
01.1108 467	Roller, asphalt, double drum, riding 10-12 ton	WEEK	1,294.70		1,294.70		1,294.70	
01.1108 469	Roller, asphalt, double drum, riding 10-12 ton	MONTH	3,236.74		3,236.74		3,236.74	
01.1109 000	CONCRETE EQUIPMENT & ACCESSORIES, RENTAL:							
01.1109 011	Demolition hammer, electric 20 lb	DAY	88.56		88.56		88.56	
01.1109 013	Demolition hammer, electric 20 lb	WEEK	343.53		343.53		343.53	
01.1109 015	Demolition hammer, electric 20 lb	MONTH	992.41		992.41		992.41	
01.1109 021	Demolition hammer, electric 35 lb	DAY	99.24		99.24		99.24	
01.1109 023	Demolition hammer, electric 35 lb	WEEK	381.70		381.70		381.70	
01.1109 025	Demolition hammer, electric 35 lb	MONTH	1,129.80		1,129.80		1,129.80	
01.1109 031	Demolition hammer, electric 60 lb	DAY	131.31		131.31		131.31	
01.1109 033	Demolition hammer, electric 60 lb	WEEK	525.19		525.19		525.19	
01.1109 035	Demolition hammer, electric 60 lb	MONTH	1,575.64		1,575.64		1,575.64	
01.1109 041	Demolition hammer, electric 75 lb	DAY	145.79		145.79		145.79	
01.1109 043	Demolition hammer, electric 75 lb	WEEK	583.23		583.23		583.23	
01.1109 045	Demolition hammer, electric 75 lb	MONTH	1,749.68		1,749.68		1,749.68	
01.1109 051	Demolition hammer, hydraulic 750 foot/pounds per blow	DAY	687.06		687.06		687.06	
01.1109 053	Demolition hammer, hydraulic 750 foot/pounds per blow	WEEK	2,442.83		2,442.83		2,442.83	
01.1109 055	Demolition hammer, hydraulic 750 foot/pounds per blow	MONTH	8,244.59		8,244.59		8,244.59	
01.1109 061	Demolition hammer, hydraulic 1000 foot/pounds per blow	DAY	992.41		992.41		992.41	
01.1109 063	Demolition hammer, hydraulic 1000 foot/pounds per blow	WEEK	3,664.28		3,664.28		3,664.28	
01.1109 065	Demolition hammer, hydraulic 1000 foot/pounds per blow	MONTH	9,275.15		9,275.15		9,275.15	
01.1109 071	Demolition hammer, hydraulic 1400 foot/pounds per blow	DAY	1,145.09		1,145.09		1,145.09	
01.1109 073	Demolition hammer, hydraulic 1400 foot/pounds per blow	WEEK	3,816.93		3,816.93		3,816.93	
01.1109 075	Demolition hammer, hydraulic 1400 foot/pounds per blow	MONTH	9,924.04		9,924.04		9,924.04	
01.1109 081	Rotary hammer drills, 3/4 to 1"	DAY	61.07		61.07		61.07	
01.1109 083	Rotary hammer drills, 3/4 to 1"	WEEK	183.21		183.21		183.21	
01.1109 085	Rotary hammer drills, 3/4 to 1"	MONTH	366.45		366.45		366.45	
01.1109 091	Rotary hammer drills, 1 1/2"	DAY	83.96		83.96		83.96	
01.1109 093	Rotary hammer drills, 1 1/2"	WEEK	251.89		251.89		251.89	
01.1109 095	Rotary hammer drills, 1 1/2"	MONTH	503.84		503.84		503.84	
01.1109 101	Rotary hammer drills, 2"	DAY	106.86		106.86		106.86	
01.1109 103	Rotary hammer drills, 2"	WEEK	320.63		320.63		320.63	
01.1109 105	Rotary hammer drills, 2"	MONTH	641.24		641.24		641.24	
01.1109 111	Rotary drill core boring machine with vacuum rig, bits extra	DAY	140.42		140.42		140.42	
01.1109 113	Rotary drill core boring machine with vacuum rig, bits extra	WEEK	491.63		491.63		491.63	
01.1109 115	Rotary drill core boring machine with vacuum rig, bits extra	MONTH	1,264.17		1,264.17		1,264.17	
01.1109 121	Diamond core bit, 2"	DAY	83.96		83.96		83.96	
01.1109 123	Diamond core bit, 2"	WEEK	293.91		293.91		293.91	
01.1109 125	Diamond core bit, 2"	MONTH	702.32		702.32		702.32	
01.1109 131	Diamond core bit, 3"	DAY	114.50		114.50		114.50	
01.1109 133	Diamond core bit, 3"	WEEK	343.53		343.53		343.53	
01.1109 135	Diamond core bit, 3"	MONTH	839.71		839.71		839.71	
01.1109 141	Diamond core bit, 4"	DAY	145.04		145.04		145.04	
01.1109 143	Diamond core bit, 4"	WEEK	507.65		507.65		507.65	
01.1109 145	Diamond core bit, 4"	MONTH	1,160.34		1,160.34		1,160.34	
01.1109 151	Diamond core bit, 5"	DAY	178.63		178.63		178.63	
01.1109 153	Diamond core bit, 5"	WEEK	625.20		625.20		625.20	
01.1109 155	Diamond core bit, 5"	MONTH	1,487.07		1,487.07		1,487.07	
01.1109 161	Diamond core bit, 6"	DAY	213.74		213.74		213.74	
01.1109 163	Diamond core bit, 6"	WEEK	748.09		748.09		748.09	
01.1109 165	Diamond core bit, 6"	MONTH	1,740.54		1,740.54		1,740.54	
01.1109 171	Vibrators, air	DAY	111.46		111.46		111.46	
01.1109 173	Vibrators, air	WEEK	445.80		445.80		445.80	
01.1109 175	Vibrators, air	MONTH	1,053.46		1,053.46		1,053.46	
01.1109 181	Vibrators, electric, 1 to 2-1/2 HP	DAY	88.56		88.56		88.56	
01.1109 183	Vibrators, electric, 1 to 2-1/2 HP	WEEK	265.66		265.66		265.66	
01.1109 185	Vibrators, electric, 1 to 2-1/2 HP	MONTH	778.67		778.67		778.67	
01.1109 191	Mixer, concrete, electric knockdown, 2-1/2 CF	DAY	53.43		53.43		53.43	
01.1109 193	Mixer, concrete, electric knockdown, 2-1/2 CF	WEEK	189.31		189.31		189.31	
01.1109 195	Mixer, concrete, electric knockdown, 2-1/2 CF	MONTH	526.76		526.76		526.76	
01.1109 201	Mixer, concrete, electric knockdown, 3-1/2 CF	DAY	64.14		64.14		64.14	

Division 1 CSI #	01-GENERAL REQUIREMENTS Description	Unit	Material	Union Install	Union Total	Open Install	Open Total	Unit Man-Hrs
01.1109 000	**CONCRETE EQUIPMENT & ACCESSORIES, RENTAL: (Cont.)**							
01.1109 203	Mixer, concrete, electric knockdown, 3-1/2 CF	WEEK	225.93		225.93		225.93	
01.1109 205	Mixer, concrete, electric knockdown, 3-1/2 CF	MONTH	587.80		587.80		587.80	
01.1109 211	Mixer, gas, portable, 2-1/2 CF	DAY	53.43		53.43		53.43	
01.1109 213	Mixer, gas, portable, 2-1/2 CF	WEEK	189.31		189.31		189.31	
01.1109 215	Mixer, gas, portable, 2-1/2 CF	MONTH	526.76		526.76		526.76	
01.1109 221	Mixer, gas or electric portable, 3-1/2 CF	DAY	64.14		64.14		64.14	
01.1109 223	Mixer, gas or electric portable, 3-1/2 CF	WEEK	225.93		225.93		225.93	
01.1109 225	Mixer, gas or electric portable, 3-1/2 CF	MONTH	587.80		587.80		587.80	
01.1109 231	Mixer, gas or electric portable, 6 CF	DAY	73.30		73.30		73.30	
01.1109 233	Mixer, gas or electric portable, 6 CF	WEEK	262.62		262.62		262.62	
01.1109 235	Mixer, gas or electric portable, 6 CF	MONTH	722.15		722.15		722.15	
01.1109 241	Mixer, gas or electric portable 9 CF	DAY	83.96		83.96		83.96	
01.1109 243	Mixer, gas or electric portable 9 CF	WEEK	302.33		302.33		302.33	
01.1109 245	Mixer, gas or electric portable 9 CF	MONTH	831.35		831.35		831.35	
01.1109 251	Plaster Mixer, towable 6 CF	DAY	99.24		99.24		99.24	
01.1109 253	Plaster Mixer, towable 6 CF	WEEK	351.17		351.17		351.17	
01.1109 255	Plaster Mixer, towable 6 CF	MONTH	877.88		877.88		877.88	
01.1109 261	Plaster Mixer, towable 8 CF	DAY	106.86		106.86		106.86	
01.1109 263	Plaster Mixer, towable 8 CF	WEEK	366.45		366.45		366.45	
01.1109 265	Plaster Mixer, towable 8 CF	MONTH	916.07		916.07		916.07	
01.1109 271	Plaster Mixer 10 CF	DAY	114.50		114.50		114.50	
01.1109 273	Plaster Mixer 10 CF	WEEK	375.59		375.59		375.59	
01.1109 275	Plaster Mixer 10 CF	MONTH	938.98		938.98		938.98	
01.1109 281	Plaster Mixer 12 CF	DAY	119.08		119.08		119.08	
01.1109 283	Plaster Mixer 12 CF	WEEK	415.30		415.30		415.30	
01.1109 285	Plaster Mixer 12 CF	MONTH	1,038.19		1,038.19		1,038.19	
01.1109 291	Concrete bucket, 1/3 yard	DAY	53.43		53.43		53.43	
01.1109 293	Concrete bucket, 1/3 yard	WEEK	137.39		137.39		137.39	
01.1109 295	Concrete bucket, 1/3 yard	MONTH	259.54		259.54		259.54	
01.1109 301	Concrete bucket, 1/2 yard	DAY	42.75		42.75		42.75	
01.1109 303	Concrete bucket, 1/2 yard	WEEK	128.25		128.25		128.25	
01.1109 305	Concrete bucket, 1/2 yard	MONTH	256.48		256.48		256.48	
01.1109 311	Concrete bucket, 3/4 yard	DAY	44.25		44.25		44.25	
01.1109 313	Concrete bucket, 3/4 yard	WEEK	134.35		134.35		134.35	
01.1109 315	Concrete bucket, 3/4 yard	MONTH	267.17		267.17		267.17	
01.1109 321	Concrete bucket, 1 to 1-1/2 yard	DAY	45.81		45.81		45.81	
01.1109 323	Concrete bucket, 1 to 1-1/2 yard	WEEK	137.39		137.39		137.39	
01.1109 325	Concrete bucket, 1 to 1-1/2 yard	MONTH	274.81		274.81		274.81	
01.1109 331	Concrete bucket, 2 yards	DAY	58.02		58.02		58.02	
01.1109 333	Concrete bucket, 2 yards	WEEK	183.21		183.21		183.21	
01.1109 335	Concrete bucket, 2 yards	MONTH	335.90		335.90		335.90	
01.1109 341	Concrete troweling machine 20 to 24" electric	DAY	79.40		79.40		79.40	
01.1109 343	Concrete troweling machine 20 to 24" electric	WEEK	299.24		299.24		299.24	
01.1109 345	Concrete troweling machine 20 to 24" electric	MONTH	748.09		748.09		748.09	
01.1109 351	Concrete troweling machine, 36"	DAY	103.83		103.83		103.83	
01.1109 353	Concrete troweling machine, 36"	WEEK	415.30		415.30		415.30	
01.1109 355	Concrete troweling machine, 36"	MONTH	1,007.69		1,007.69		1,007.69	
01.1109 361	Concrete troweling machine, 44 to 48"	DAY	128.25		128.25		128.25	
01.1109 363	Concrete troweling machine, 44 to 48"	WEEK	454.99		454.99		454.99	
01.1109 365	Concrete troweling machine, 44 to 48"	MONTH	1,206.14		1,206.14		1,206.14	
01.1109 371	Concrete troweling machine, 48", two wheel riding	DAY	274.81		274.81		274.81	
01.1109 373	Concrete troweling machine, 48", two wheel riding	WEEK	1,045.85		1,045.85		1,045.85	
01.1109 375	Concrete troweling machine, 48", two wheel riding	MONTH	2,633.69		2,633.69		2,633.69	
01.1109 381	Concrete saw, gas, 10 HP	DAY	122.14		122.14		122.14	
01.1109 383	Concrete saw, gas, 10 HP	WEEK	427.50		427.50		427.50	
01.1109 385	Concrete saw, gas, 10 HP	MONTH	1,190.87		1,190.87		1,190.87	
01.1109 391	Concrete saw, gas, self propelled, 18 HP	DAY	175.59		175.59		175.59	
01.1109 393	Concrete saw, gas, self propelled, 18 HP	WEEK	603.09		603.09		603.09	
01.1109 395	Concrete saw, gas, self propelled, 18 HP	MONTH	1,709.98		1,709.98		1,709.98	
01.1109 401	Concrete saw, gas, self propelled, 36 HP	DAY	229.02		229.02		229.02	
01.1109 403	Concrete saw, gas, self propelled, 36 HP	WEEK	908.42		908.42		908.42	

Division 1 CSI #	01-GENERAL REQUIREMENTS Description	Unit	Material	Union Install	Union Total	Open Install	Open Total	Unit Man-Hrs
01.1109 000	CONCRETE EQUIPMENT & ACCESSORIES, RENTAL: (Cont.)							
01.1109 405	Concrete saw, gas, self propelled, 36 HP	MONTH	2,213.83		2,213.83		2,213.83	
01.1109 411	Concrete saw, gas, self propelled, 65 HP	DAY	358.80		358.80		358.80	
01.1109 413	Concrete saw, gas, self propelled, 65 HP	WEEK	1,255.75		1,255.75		1,255.75	
01.1109 415	Concrete saw, gas, self propelled, 65 HP	MONTH	3,511.59		3,511.59		3,511.59	
01.1109 421	Concrete cart, walk behind 6 CF	DAY	38.18		38.18		38.18	
01.1109 423	Concrete cart, walk behind 6 CF	WEEK	114.50		114.50		114.50	
01.1109 425	Concrete cart, walk behind 6 CF	MONTH	343.53		343.53		343.53	
01.1109 431	Concrete cart, riding, 13 CF	DAY	135.88		135.88		135.88	
01.1109 433	Concrete cart, riding, 13 CF	WEEK	509.94		509.94		509.94	
01.1109 435	Concrete cart, riding, 13 CF	MONTH	1,503.88		1,503.88		1,503.88	
01.1109 441	Wheelbarrow	DAY	21.37		21.37		21.37	
01.1109 443	Wheelbarrow	WEEK	64.14		64.14		64.14	
01.1109 445	Wheelbarrow	MONTH	128.25		128.25		128.25	
01.1109 451	Jitterbug (tamper)	DAY	16.79		16.79		16.79	
01.1109 453	Jitterbug (tamper)	WEEK	50.38		50.38		50.38	
01.1109 455	Jitterbug (tamper)	MONTH	100.78		100.78		100.78	
01.1109 461	Concrete floor grinder, 5" Cut	DAY	152.68		152.68		152.68	
01.1109 463	Concrete floor grinder, 5" Cut	WEEK	549.63		549.63		549.63	
01.1109 465	Concrete floor grinder, 5" Cut	MONTH	1,450.44		1,450.44		1,450.44	
01.1109 471	Concrete floor planer, 10" cut	DAY	167.94		167.94		167.94	
01.1109 473	Concrete floor planer, 10", gas, 9 HP	WEEK	603.09		603.09		603.09	
01.1109 475	Concrete floor planer, 10", gas, 9 HP	MONTH	1,595.49		1,595.49		1,595.49	
01.1109 481	Strip deck membrane remover	DAY	284.45		284.45		284.45	
01.1109 483	Strip deck membrane remover	WEEK	977.66		977.66		977.66	
01.1109 485	Strip deck membrane remover	MONTH	2,133.04		2,133.04		2,133.04	
01.1109 491	Concrete floor grinder, 3/4 HP, 100 lb	DAY	391.04		391.04		391.04	
01.1109 493	Concrete floor grinder, 3/4 HP, 100 lb	WEEK	1,279.81		1,279.81		1,279.81	
01.1109 495	Concrete floor grinder, 3/4 HP, 100 lb	MONTH	3,537.30		3,537.30		3,537.30	
01.1109 501	Concrete floor grinder, twin head 6 stone, gas	DAY	141.24		141.24		141.24	
01.1109 503	Concrete floor grinder, twin head 6 stone, gas	WEEK	564.89		564.89		564.89	
01.1109 505	Concrete floor grinder, twin head 6 stone, gas	MONTH	1,412.28		1,412.28		1,412.28	
01.1109 511	Concrete floor grinder, twin head 6 stone, electric	DAY	141.24		141.24		141.24	
01.1109 513	Concrete floor grinder, twin head 6 stone, electric	WEEK	564.89		564.89		564.89	
01.1109 515	Concrete floor grinder, twin head 6 stone, electric	MONTH	1,412.28		1,412.28		1,412.28	
01.1109 521	Concrete floor grinder, twin head 12 stone, gas	DAY	190.88		190.88		190.88	
01.1109 523	Concrete floor grinder, twin head 12 stone, gas	WEEK	748.09		748.09		748.09	
01.1109 525	Concrete floor grinder, twin head 12 stone, gas	MONTH	1,870.29		1,870.29		1,870.29	
01.1109 611	Air floor scrabbler, 7 piston	DAY	337.76		337.76		337.76	
01.1109 621	Air floor scrabbler, 7 piston	WEEK	1,102.08		1,102.08		1,102.08	
01.1109 631	Air floor scrabbler, 7 piston	MONTH	1,733.10		1,733.10		1,733.10	
01.1109 641	Air floor scrabbler, 3 piston	DAY	115.55		115.55		115.55	
01.1109 651	Air floor scrabbler, 3 piston	WEEK	373.28		373.28		373.28	
01.1109 661	Air floor scrabbler, 3 piston	MONTH	829.76		829.76		829.76	
01.1110 000	EARTH MOVING & EXCAVATING EQUIPMENT RENTAL:							
01.1110 011	Posthole digger, gas, 2 man	DAY	76.34		76.34		76.34	
01.1110 021	Posthole digger, gas, 2 man	WEEK	297.73		297.73		297.73	
01.1110 031	Posthole digger, gas, 2 man	MONTH	1,038.19		1,038.19		1,038.19	
01.1110 041	Posthole digger, hand, clamshell	DAY	13.73		13.73		13.73	
01.1110 051	Posthole digger, hand, clamshell	WEEK	41.20		41.20		41.20	
01.1110 061	Posthole digger, hand, clamshell	MONTH	82.45		82.45		82.45	
01.1110 071	Conveyor belt, electric or gas, 17'	DAY	128.25		128.25		128.25	
01.1110 081	Conveyor belt, electric or gas, 17'	WEEK	320.63		320.63		320.63	
01.1110 091	Conveyor belt, electric or gas, 17'	MONTH	908.42		908.42		908.42	
01.1110 101	Conveyor belt, electric or gas, 26'	DAY	175.59		175.59		175.59	
01.1110 111	Conveyor belt, electric or gas, 26'	WEEK	435.13		435.13		435.13	
01.1110 121	Conveyor belt, electric or gas, 26'	MONTH	1,183.27		1,183.27		1,183.27	
01.1110 131	Trencher, riding hydrostatic, 20 hp	DAY	335.90		335.90		335.90	
01.1110 133	Trencher, riding hydrostatic, 20 hp	WEEK	1,343.56		1,343.56		1,343.56	
01.1110 135	Trencher, riding hydrostatic, 20 hp	MONTH	3,358.88		3,358.88		3,358.88	
01.1110 141	Trencher, riding hydrostatic, 30 hp	DAY	396.95		396.95		396.95	
01.1110 143	Trencher, riding hydrostatic, 30 hp	WEEK	1,450.44		1,450.44		1,450.44	

Division 1 CSI #	01-GENERAL REQUIREMENTS Description	Unit	Material	Union Install	Union Total	Open Install	Open Total	Unit Man-Hrs
01.1110 000	**EARTH MOVING & EXCAVATING EQUIPMENT RENTAL: (Cont.)**							
01.1110 145	Trencher, riding hydrostatic, 30 hp	MONTH	3,458.14		3,458.14		3,458.14	
01.1110 151	Trencher, riding hydrostatic, 40 hp	DAY	557.26		557.26		557.26	
01.1110 153	Trencher, riding hydrostatic, 40 hp	WEEK	2,229.10		2,229.10		2,229.10	
01.1110 155	Trencher, riding hydrostatic, 40 hp	MONTH	5,496.40		5,496.40		5,496.40	
01.1110 161	Trencher, riding hydrostatic, 50 hp	DAY	610.71		610.71		610.71	
01.1110 163	Trencher, riding hydrostatic, 50 hp	WEEK	2,442.83		2,442.83		2,442.83	
01.1110 165	Trencher, riding hydrostatic, 50 hp	MONTH	6,084.20		6,084.20		6,084.20	
01.1110 171	Trencher, riding hydrostatic, 60 hp	DAY	625.97		625.97		625.97	
01.1110 173	Trencher, riding hydrostatic, 60 hp	WEEK	2,488.63		2,488.63		2,488.63	
01.1110 175	Trencher, riding hydrostatic, 60 hp	MONTH	6,259.77		6,259.77		6,259.77	
01.1110 181	Crawler tractor, angle dozer, 42 HP	DAY	488.57		488.57		488.57	
01.1110 183	Crawler tractor, angle dozer, 42 HP	WEEK	1,465.72		1,465.72		1,465.72	
01.1110 185	Crawler tractor, angle dozer, 42 HP	MONTH	4,885.68		4,885.68		4,885.68	
01.1110 191	Crawler tractor, 3/4 cy loader bucket, 42 HP	DAY	488.57		488.57		488.57	
01.1110 193	Crawler tractor, 3/4 cy loader bucket, 42 HP	WEEK	1,465.72		1,465.72		1,465.72	
01.1110 195	Crawler tractor, 3/4 cy loader bucket, 42 HP	MONTH	4,885.68		4,885.68		4,885.68	
01.1110 201	Crawler tractor, angle dozer, 65 HP	DAY	641.24		641.24		641.24	
01.1110 203	Crawler tractor, angle dozer, 65 HP	WEEK	1,923.74		1,923.74		1,923.74	
01.1110 205	Crawler tractor, angle dozer, 65 HP	MONTH	6,412.44		6,412.44		6,412.44	
01.1110 211	Crawler tractor, 1 1/4 cy loader bucket, 65 HP	DAY	641.24		641.24		641.24	
01.1110 213	Crawler tractor, 1 1/4 cy loader bucket, 65 HP	WEEK	1,923.74		1,923.74		1,923.74	
01.1110 215	Crawler tractor, 1 1/4 cy loader bucket, 65 HP	MONTH	6,412.44		6,412.44		6,412.44	
01.1110 221	Crawler tractor, dozer or loader, 72 HP	DAY	748.09		748.09		748.09	
01.1110 223	Crawler tractor, dozer or loader, 72 HP	WEEK	2,244.37		2,244.37		2,244.37	
01.1110 225	Crawler tractor, dozer or loader, 72 HP	MONTH	7,252.18		7,252.18		7,252.18	
01.1110 231	Crawler tractor, 30,000 lb	DAY	1,068.74		1,068.74		1,068.74	
01.1110 233	Crawler tractor, 30,000 lb	WEEK	3,969.60		3,969.60		3,969.60	
01.1110 235	Crawler tractor, 30,000 lb	MONTH	10,687.42		10,687.42		10,687.42	
01.1110 241	Crawler tractor, 80,000 lb	DAY	1,755.79		1,755.79		1,755.79	
01.1110 243	Crawler tractor, 80,000 lb	WEEK	7,023.15		7,023.15		7,023.15	
01.1110 245	Crawler tractor, 80,000 lb	MONTH	17,557.91		17,557.91		17,557.91	
01.1110 251	Wheel tractors, bare 40 HP	DAY	267.17		267.17		267.17	
01.1110 253	Wheel tractors, bare 40 HP	WEEK	801.54		801.54		801.54	
01.1110 255	Wheel tractors, bare 40 HP	MONTH	2,404.69		2,404.69		2,404.69	
01.1110 260	**TRACTOR ATTACHMENTS FOR ABOVE:**							
01.1110 261	Box scraper, rake or earth scraper	DAY	58.02		58.02		58.02	
01.1110 263	Box scraper, rake or earth scraper	WEEK	174.05		174.05		174.05	
01.1110 265	Box scraper, rake or earth scraper	MONTH	580.17		580.17		580.17	
01.1110 267	Disc harrow	DAY	102.30		102.30		102.30	
01.1110 269	Disc harrow	WEEK	358.03		358.03		358.03	
01.1110 271	Disc harrow	MONTH	1,022.93		1,022.93		1,022.93	
01.1110 273	Post hole digger	DAY	148.10		148.10		148.10	
01.1110 275	Post hole digger	WEEK	593.91		593.91		593.91	
01.1110 277	Post hole digger	MONTH	1,480.96		1,480.96		1,480.96	
01.1110 279	Roto tiller	DAY	198.48		198.48		198.48	
01.1110 281	Roto tiller	WEEK	793.91		793.91		793.91	
01.1110 283	Roto tiller	MONTH	1,984.80		1,984.80		1,984.80	
01.1110 285	Rotary mower	DAY	129.75		129.75		129.75	
01.1110 287	Rotary mower	WEEK	473.34		473.34		473.34	
01.1110 289	Rotary mower	MONTH	1,068.74		1,068.74		1,068.74	
01.1110 291	Mini Excavator, up to 10' digging depth	DAY	396.95		396.95		396.95	
01.1110 293	Mini Excavator, up to 10' digging depth	WEEK	1,519.14		1,519.14		1,519.14	
01.1110 295	Mini Excavator, up to 10' digging depth	MONTH	3,839.84		3,839.84		3,839.84	
01.1110 301	Excavator, 10,000 lb	DAY	374.06		374.06		374.06	
01.1110 303	Excavator, 10,000 lb	WEEK	1,496.24		1,496.24		1,496.24	
01.1110 305	Excavator, 10,000 lb	MONTH	4,488.70		4,488.70		4,488.70	
01.1110 311	Excavator, 40,000 lb	DAY	824.44		824.44		824.44	
01.1110 313	Excavator, 40,000 lb	WEEK	3,297.83		3,297.83		3,297.83	
01.1110 315	Excavator, 40,000 lb	MONTH	9,893.49		9,893.49		9,893.49	
01.1110 321	Excavator, 50,000 lb	DAY	992.41		992.41		992.41	
01.1110 323	Excavator, 50,000 lb	WEEK	3,969.60		3,969.60		3,969.60	

Division 1 CSI #	01-GENERAL REQUIREMENTS Description	Unit	Material	Union Install	Union Total	Open Install	Open Total	Unit Man-Hrs
01.1110 260	**TRACTOR ATTACHMENTS FOR ABOVE: (Cont.)**							
01.1110 325	Excavator, 50,000 lb	MONTH	11,908.83		11,908.83		11,908.83	
01.1110 331	Excavator, 80,000 lb	DAY	1,313.04		1,313.04		1,313.04	
01.1110 333	Excavator, 80,000 lb	WEEK	5,252.09		5,252.09		5,252.09	
01.1110 335	Excavator, 80,000 lb	MONTH	15,756.29		15,756.29		15,756.29	
01.1110 341	Excavator, 120,000 lb	DAY	2,519.16		2,519.16		2,519.16	
01.1110 343	Excavator, 120,000 lb	WEEK	10,076.72		10,076.72		10,076.72	
01.1110 345	Excavator, 120,000 lb	MONTH	27,176.56		27,176.56		27,176.56	
01.1110 351	Backhoe loader, wheel type 20 HP	DAY	267.17		267.17		267.17	
01.1110 353	Backhoe loader, wheel type 20 HP	WEEK	801.54		801.54		801.54	
01.1110 355	Backhoe loader, wheel type 20 HP	MONTH	2,366.49		2,366.49		2,366.49	
01.1110 361	Backhoe loader, wheel type 40 HP	DAY	328.27		328.27		328.27	
01.1110 363	Backhoe loader, wheel type 40 HP	WEEK	1,313.04		1,313.04		1,313.04	
01.1110 365	Backhoe loader, wheel type 40 HP	MONTH	3,282.54		3,282.54		3,282.54	
01.1110 371	Backhoe loader, wheel type 60-70 HP	DAY	381.70		381.70		381.70	
01.1110 373	Backhoe loader, wheel type 60-70 HP	WEEK	1,297.75		1,297.75		1,297.75	
01.1110 375	Backhoe loader, wheel type 60-70 HP	MONTH	3,816.93		3,816.93		3,816.93	
01.1110 381	Backhoe loader, wheel type 60-70 HP, 4wd	DAY	419.89		419.89		419.89	
01.1110 383	Backhoe loader, wheel type 60-70 HP, 4wd	WEEK	1,679.46		1,679.46		1,679.46	
01.1110 385	Backhoe loader, wheel type 60-70 HP, 4wd	MONTH	4,274.98		4,274.98		4,274.98	
01.1110 391	Backhoe loader, wheel type 60-70 HP, extended reach hoe	DAY	458.04		458.04		458.04	
01.1110 393	Backhoe loader, wheel type 60-70 HP, extended reach hoe	WEEK	1,832.11		1,832.11		1,832.11	
01.1110 395	Backhoe loader, wheel type 60-70 HP, extended reach hoe	MONTH	4,580.31		4,580.31		4,580.31	
01.1110 401	Backhoe loader, wheel type 100HP,	DAY	564.89		564.89		564.89	
01.1110 403	Backhoe loader, wheel type 100HP,	WEEK	2,252.00		2,252.00		2,252.00	
01.1110 405	Backhoe loader, wheel type 100HP,	MONTH	5,572.71		5,572.71		5,572.71	
01.1110 411	Skid steer loader, 700 lb capacity	DAY	297.73		297.73		297.73	
01.1110 413	Skid steer loader, 700 lb capacity	WEEK	1,038.19		1,038.19		1,038.19	
01.1110 415	Skid steer loader, 700 lb capacity	MONTH	3,252.02		3,252.02		3,252.02	
01.1110 421	Skid steer loader, 701 to 975 lb capacity	DAY	313.00		313.00		313.00	
01.1110 423	Skid steer loader, 701 to 975 lb capacity	WEEK	1,099.29		1,099.29		1,099.29	
01.1110 425	Skid steer loader, 701 to 975 lb capacity	MONTH	3,435.23		3,435.23		3,435.23	
01.1110 431	Skid steer loader, 976 to 1350 lb capacity	DAY	328.27		328.27		328.27	
01.1110 433	Skid steer loader, 976 to 1350 lb capacity	WEEK	1,160.34		1,160.34		1,160.34	
01.1110 435	Skid steer loader, 976 to 1350 lb capacity	MONTH	3,694.77		3,694.77		3,694.77	
01.1110 441	Skid steer loader, 1351 to1749 lb capacity	DAY	343.53		343.53		343.53	
01.1110 443	Skid steer loader, 1351 to1749 lb capacity	WEEK	1,244.33		1,244.33		1,244.33	
01.1110 445	Skid steer loader, 1351 to1749 lb capacity	MONTH	3,878.02		3,878.02		3,878.02	
01.1110 451	Skid steer loader, 1750 and over capacity	DAY	381.70		381.70		381.70	
01.1110 453	Skid steer loader, 1750 and over capacity	WEEK	1,366.45		1,366.45		1,366.45	
01.1110 455	Skid steer loader, 1750 and over capacity	MONTH	4,244.43		4,244.43		4,244.43	
01.1110 461	Skid steer loader trailer	DAY	53.43		53.43		53.43	
01.1110 463	Skid steer loader trailer	WEEK	160.30		160.30		160.30	
01.1110 465	Skid steer loader trailer	MONTH	335.90		335.90		335.90	
01.1110 470	**SKID STEER LOADER ACCESSORIES:**							
01.1110 471	Auger	DAY	91.60		91.60		91.60	
01.1110 473	Auger	WEEK	320.63		320.63		320.63	
01.1110 475	Auger	MONTH	877.88		877.88		877.88	
01.1110 477	Backhoe	DAY	91.60		91.60		91.60	
01.1110 479	Backhoe	WEEK	320.63		320.63		320.63	
01.1110 481	Backhoe	MONTH	877.88		877.88		877.88	
01.1110 483	Rotary broom	DAY	91.60		91.60		91.60	
01.1110 485	Rotary broom	WEEK	320.63		320.63		320.63	
01.1110 487	Rotary broom	MONTH	877.88		877.88		877.88	
01.1110 489	Forklift forks	DAY	119.08		119.08		119.08	
01.1110 491	Forklift forks	WEEK	419.89		419.89		419.89	
01.1110 493	Forklift forks	MONTH	1,213.78		1,213.78		1,213.78	
01.1110 501	Hydraulic hammer	DAY	244.29		244.29		244.29	
01.1110 503	Hydraulic hammer	WEEK	855.01		855.01		855.01	
01.1110 505	Hydraulic hammer	MONTH	2,565.00		2,565.00		2,565.00	
01.1110 511	Tree spade	DAY	206.13		206.13		206.13	
01.1110 513	Tree spade	WEEK	725.23		725.23		725.23	

Division 1 CSI #	01-GENERAL REQUIREMENTS Description	Unit	Material	Union Install	Union Total	Open Install	Open Total	Unit Man-Hrs
01.1110 470	**SKID STEER LOADER ACCESSORIES: (Cont.)**							
01.1110 515	Tree spade	MONTH	2,061.14		2,061.14		2,061.14	
01.1110 521	Cold planer attachment	DAY	633.60		633.60		633.60	
01.1110 523	Cold planer attachment	WEEK	2,369.54		2,369.54		2,369.54	
01.1110 525	Cold planer attachment	MONTH	5,458.22		5,458.22		5,458.22	
01.1110 621	Hydraulic jaw breaker	DAY	68.71		68.71		68.71	
01.1110 623	Hydraulic jaw breaker	WEEK	240.47		240.47		240.47	
01.1110 625	Hydraulic jaw breaker	MONTH	687.06		687.06		687.06	
01.1110 631	Wheel loader, 13,000 lb, 1.5 cy	DAY	366.45		366.45		366.45	
01.1110 633	Wheel loader, 13,000 lb, 1.5 cy	WEEK	1,465.72		1,465.72		1,465.72	
01.1110 635	Wheel loader, 13,000 lb, 1.5 cy	MONTH	4,287.17		4,287.17		4,287.17	
01.1110 641	Wheel loader, 20,000 lb, 2 cy	DAY	465.65		465.65		465.65	
01.1110 643	Wheel loader, 20,000 lb, 2 cy	WEEK	1,862.64		1,862.64		1,862.64	
01.1110 645	Wheel loader, 20,000 lb, 2 cy	MONTH	5,526.93		5,526.93		5,526.93	
01.1110 651	Wheel loader, 25,000 lb, 2.75 cy	DAY	549.63		549.63		549.63	
01.1110 653	Wheel loader, 25,000 lb, 2.75 cy	WEEK	2,198.55		2,198.55		2,198.55	
01.1110 655	Wheel loader, 25,000 lb, 2.75 cy	MONTH	6,381.90		6,381.90		6,381.90	
01.1110 661	Wheel loader, 30,000 lb, 3.5 cy	DAY	679.42		679.42		679.42	
01.1110 663	Wheel loader, 30,000 lb, 3.5 cy	WEEK	2,717.65		2,717.65		2,717.65	
01.1110 665	Wheel loader, 30,000 lb, 3.5 cy	MONTH	7,908.67		7,908.67		7,908.67	
01.1110 671	Motorgrader, blade, 30,000 lb	DAY	961.87		961.87		961.87	
01.1110 673	Motorgrader, blade, 30,000 lb	WEEK	3,847.50		3,847.50		3,847.50	
01.1110 675	Motorgrader, blade, 30,000 lb	MONTH	9,374.42		9,374.42		9,374.42	
01.1111 000	**PUMPS AND ACCESSORIES, RENTAL:**							
01.1111 011	Centrifugal pump, 2", gas	DAY	64.14		64.14		64.14	
01.1111 021	Centrifugal pump, 2", gas	WEEK	256.48		256.48		256.48	
01.1111 031	Centrifugal pump, 2", gas	MONTH	656.50		656.50		656.50	
01.1111 041	Centrifugal pump, 3", gas	DAY	67.19		67.19		67.19	
01.1111 051	Centrifugal pump, 3", gas	WEEK	268.71		268.71		268.71	
01.1111 061	Centrifugal pump, 3", gas	MONTH	806.12		806.12		806.12	
01.1111 071	Centrifugal pump, 6", gas	DAY	160.30		160.30		160.30	
01.1111 081	Centrifugal pump, 6", gas	WEEK	641.24		641.24		641.24	
01.1111 091	Centrifugal pump, 6", gas	MONTH	1,603.12		1,603.12		1,603.12	
01.1111 101	Trash pump, 2", gas	DAY	64.14		64.14		64.14	
01.1111 111	Trash pump, 2", gas	WEEK	256.48		256.48		256.48	
01.1111 121	Trash pump, 2", gas	MONTH	641.24		641.24		641.24	
01.1111 131	Trash pump, 3", gas	DAY	85.50		85.50		85.50	
01.1111 141	Trash pump, 3", gas	WEEK	341.99		341.99		341.99	
01.1111 151	Trash pump, 3", gas	MONTH	855.01		855.01		855.01	
01.1111 161	Trash pump, 4", gas	DAY	131.31		131.31		131.31	
01.1111 171	Trash pump, 4", gas	WEEK	525.19		525.19		525.19	
01.1111 181	Trash pump, 4", gas	MONTH	1,313.04		1,313.04		1,313.04	
01.1111 191	Trash pump, 4", diesel	DAY	131.31		131.31		131.31	
01.1111 201	Trash pump, 4", diesel	WEEK	525.19		525.19		525.19	
01.1111 211	Trash pump, 4", diesel	MONTH	1,313.04		1,313.04		1,313.04	
01.1111 221	Trash pump, low volume, 6", diesel	DAY	198.48		198.48		198.48	
01.1111 231	Trash pump, low volume, 6", diesel	WEEK	595.44		595.44		595.44	
01.1111 241	Trash pump, low volume, 6", diesel	MONTH	1,954.27		1,954.27		1,954.27	
01.1111 251	Trash pump, high volume, 6", diesel	DAY	198.48		198.48		198.48	
01.1111 261	Trash pump, high volume, 6", diesel	WEEK	595.44		595.44		595.44	
01.1111 271	Trash pump, high volume, 6", diesel	MONTH	1,954.27		1,954.27		1,954.27	
01.1111 281	Submersible, 2" pump, 110v, float	DAY	48.86		48.86		48.86	
01.1111 291	Submersible, 2" pump, 110v, float	WEEK	171.01		171.01		171.01	
01.1111 301	Submersible, 2" pump, 110v, float	MONTH	320.63		320.63		320.63	
01.1111 311	Diaphragm pump, 2", gas	DAY	73.30		73.30		73.30	
01.1111 321	Diaphragm pump, 2", gas	WEEK	293.15		293.15		293.15	
01.1111 331	Diaphragm pump, 2", gas	MONTH	732.85		732.85		732.85	
01.1111 341	Diaphragm pump, 3", gas	DAY	93.14		93.14		93.14	
01.1111 351	Diaphragm pump, 3", gas	WEEK	372.53		372.53		372.53	
01.1111 361	Diaphragm pump, 3", gas	MONTH	931.34		931.34		931.34	
01.1111 371	Sump pump, air, 115 GPM	DAY	76.44		76.44		76.44	
01.1111 381	Sump pump, air, 115 GPM	WEEK	225.77		225.77		225.77	

Division 1 CSI #	01-GENERAL REQUIREMENTS Description	Unit	Material	Union Install	Union Total	Open Install	Open Total	Unit Man-Hrs
01.1111 000	**PUMPS AND ACCESSORIES, RENTAL: (Cont.)**							
01.1111 391	Sump pump, air, 115 GPM	MONTH	506.60		506.60		506.60	
01.1111 401	Sump pump, air, 200 GPM	DAY	122.66		122.66		122.66	
01.1111 411	Sump pump, air, 200 GPM	WEEK	300.42		300.42		300.42	
01.1111 421	Sump pump, air, 200 GPM	MONTH	666.60		666.60		666.60	
01.1111 431	Hose suction, 2" x 20', coupled	DAY	19.84		19.84		19.84	
01.1111 441	Hose suction, 2" x 20', coupled	WEEK	59.54		59.54		59.54	
01.1111 451	Hose suction, 2" x 20', coupled	MONTH	119.08		119.08		119.08	
01.1111 461	Hose suction, 3" x 20', coupled	DAY	19.84		19.84		19.84	
01.1111 471	Hose suction, 3" x 20', coupled	WEEK	59.54		59.54		59.54	
01.1111 481	Hose suction, 3" x 20', coupled	MONTH	119.08		119.08		119.08	
01.1111 491	Hose suction, 4" x 20', coupled	DAY	22.14		22.14		22.14	
01.1111 501	Hose suction, 4" x 20', coupled	WEEK	67.19		67.19		67.19	
01.1111 511	Hose suction, 4" x 20', coupled	MONTH	134.35		134.35		134.35	
01.1111 521	Hose suction, 6" x 20', coupled	DAY	22.90		22.90		22.90	
01.1111 531	Hose suction, 6" x 20', coupled	WEEK	68.71		68.71		68.71	
01.1111 541	Hose suction, 6" x 20', coupled	MONTH	137.39		137.39		137.39	
01.1111 551	Suction hose, 10" x 25'	DAY	33.56		33.56		33.56	
01.1111 561	Suction hose, 10" x 25'	WEEK	94.69		94.69		94.69	
01.1111 571	Suction hose, 10" x 25'	MONTH	189.31		189.31		189.31	
01.1111 581	Hose, discharge, 3/4" x 50', coupled	DAY	22.86		22.86		22.86	
01.1111 591	Hose, discharge, 3/4" x 50', coupled	WEEK	47.52		47.52		47.52	
01.1111 601	Hose, discharge, 3/4" x 50', coupled	MONTH	52.78		52.78		52.78	
01.1111 611	Hose, discharge, 2" x 50', coupled	DAY	19.84		19.84		19.84	
01.1111 621	Hose, discharge, 2" x 50', coupled	WEEK	59.54		59.54		59.54	
01.1111 631	Hose, discharge, 2" x 50', coupled	MONTH	119.08		119.08		119.08	
01.1111 641	Hose, discharge, 3" x 50', coupled	DAY	22.90		22.90		22.90	
01.1111 651	Hose, discharge, 3" x 50', coupled	WEEK	68.71		68.71		68.71	
01.1111 661	Hose, discharge, 3" x 50', coupled	MONTH	137.39		137.39		137.39	
01.1111 671	Hose, discharge, 4" x 50', coupled	DAY	23.66		23.66		23.66	
01.1111 681	Hose, discharge, 4" x 50', coupled	WEEK	70.99		70.99		70.99	
01.1111 691	Hose, discharge, 4" x 50', coupled	MONTH	142.03		142.03		142.03	
01.1111 701	Hose, discharge, 6" x 50', coupled	DAY	25.18		25.18		25.18	
01.1111 711	Hose, discharge, 6" x 50', coupled	WEEK	75.56		75.56		75.56	
01.1111 721	Hose, discharge, 6" x 50', coupled	MONTH	151.17		151.17		151.17	
01.1111 731	Hose, discharge, 10" x 50'	DAY	34.35		34.35		34.35	
01.1111 741	Hose, discharge, 10" x 50'	WEEK	95.43		95.43		95.43	
01.1111 751	Hose, discharge, 10" x 50'	MONTH	190.88		190.88		190.88	
01.1112 000	**GENERATORS, RENTAL:**							
01.1112 011	Generator, 2750 watt, gas	DAY	59.54		59.54		59.54	
01.1112 021	Generator, 2750 watt, gas	WEEK	229.02		229.02		229.02	
01.1112 031	Generator, 2750 watt, gas	MONTH	687.06		687.06		687.06	
01.1112 041	Generator, 3000 watt, gas	DAY	64.14		64.14		64.14	
01.1112 051	Generator, 3000 watt, gas	WEEK	256.48		256.48		256.48	
01.1112 061	Generator, 3000 watt, gas	MONTH	769.49		769.49		769.49	
01.1112 071	Generator, 3500 watt, gas	DAY	93.91		93.91		93.91	
01.1112 081	Generator, 3500 watt, gas	WEEK	375.59		375.59		375.59	
01.1112 091	Generator, 3500 watt, gas	MONTH	1,126.78		1,126.78		1,126.78	
01.1112 101	Generator, 5000 watt, gas	DAY	99.24		99.24		99.24	
01.1112 111	Generator, 5000 watt, gas	WEEK	396.95		396.95		396.95	
01.1112 121	Generator, 5000 watt, gas	MONTH	1,190.87		1,190.87		1,190.87	
01.1112 131	Generator, 10,000 watt, diesel, trailer	DAY	145.79		145.79		145.79	
01.1112 141	Generator, 10,000 watt, diesel, trailer	WEEK	583.23		583.23		583.23	
01.1112 151	Generator, 10,000 watt, diesel, trailer	MONTH	1,749.68		1,749.68		1,749.68	
01.1112 191	Generator, 12,500 to 15,000 watt, diesel, trailer	DAY	161.83		161.83		161.83	
01.1112 201	Generator, 12,500 to 15,000 watt, diesel, trailer	WEEK	647.38		647.38		647.38	
01.1112 211	Generator, 12,500 to 15,000 watt, diesel, trailer	MONTH	1,942.06		1,942.06		1,942.06	
01.1112 221	Generator, 25,000 watt, diesel, trailer	DAY	195.43		195.43		195.43	
01.1112 231	Generator, 25,000 watt, diesel, trailer	WEEK	784.78		784.78		784.78	
01.1112 241	Generator, 25,000 watt, diesel, trailer	MONTH	2,354.29		2,354.29		2,354.29	
01.1112 251	Generator, 30,000 watt, diesel, trailer	DAY	201.56		201.56		201.56	
01.1112 261	Generator, 30,000 watt, diesel, trailer	WEEK	809.18		809.18		809.18	

Division 1 CSI #	01-GENERAL REQUIREMENTS Description	Unit	Material	Union Install	Union Total	Open Install	Open Total	Unit Man-Hrs
01.1112 000	**GENERATORS, RENTAL: (Cont.)**							
01.1112 271	Generator, 30,000 watt, diesel, trailer	MONTH	2,404.69		2,404.69		2,404.69	
01.1112 281	Generator, 40,000 watt, diesel, trailer	DAY	204.58		204.58		204.58	
01.1112 291	Generator, 40,000 watt, diesel, trailer	WEEK	818.37		818.37		818.37	
01.1112 301	Generator, 40,000 watt, diesel, trailer	MONTH	2,455.03		2,455.03		2,455.03	
01.1112 311	Generator, 50,000 watt, diesel, trailer	DAY	282.45		282.45		282.45	
01.1112 321	Generator, 50,000 watt, diesel, trailer	WEEK	1,129.80		1,129.80		1,129.80	
01.1112 331	Generator, 50,000 watt, diesel, trailer	MONTH	3,389.43		3,389.43		3,389.43	
01.1112 341	Generator, 100KW, diesel, trailer/skid	DAY	641.24		641.24		641.24	
01.1112 351	Generator, 100KW, diesel, trailer/skid	WEEK	2,565.00		2,565.00		2,565.00	
01.1112 361	Generator, 100KW, diesel, trailer/skid	MONTH	7,694.94		7,694.94		7,694.94	
01.1112 371	Generator, 135KW, diesel, trailer/skid	DAY	793.91		793.91		793.91	
01.1112 381	Generator, 135KW, diesel, trailer/skid	WEEK	2,717.65		2,717.65		2,717.65	
01.1112 391	Generator, 135KW, diesel, trailer/skid	MONTH	9,007.96		9,007.96		9,007.96	
01.1112 401	Generator, 150KW, diesel, skid	DAY	839.71		839.71		839.71	
01.1112 411	Generator, 150KW, diesel, skid	WEEK	2,824.52		2,824.52		2,824.52	
01.1112 421	Generator, 150KW, diesel, skid	MONTH	9,160.63		9,160.63		9,160.63	
01.1112 431	Generator, 200KW, diesel, skid	DAY	946.60		946.60		946.60	
01.1112 441	Generator, 200KW, diesel, skid	WEEK	3,313.10		3,313.10		3,313.10	
01.1112 451	Generator, 200KW, diesel, skid	MONTH	9,466.01		9,466.01		9,466.01	
01.1112 461	Generator, 300KW, diesel, skid	DAY	992.41		992.41		992.41	
01.1112 471	Generator, 300KW, diesel, skid	WEEK	3,473.42		3,473.42		3,473.42	
01.1112 481	Generator, 300KW, diesel, skid	MONTH	9,924.04		9,924.04		9,924.04	
01.1112 482	Generator, 600KW, diesel, skid	DAY	1,381.71		1,381.71		1,381.71	
01.1112 483	Generator, 600KW, diesel, skid	WEEK	4,809.32		4,809.32		4,809.32	
01.1112 484	Generator, 600KW, diesel, skid	MONTH	13,817.31		13,817.31		13,817.31	
01.1112 485	Generator, 1000KW, diesel, skid	DAY	1,648.91		1,648.91		1,648.91	
01.1112 486	Generator, 1000KW, diesel, skid	WEEK	5,771.19		5,771.19		5,771.19	
01.1112 487	Generator, 1000KW, diesel, skid	MONTH	16,489.16		16,489.16		16,489.16	
01.1112 488	Generator, 1135KW, diesel, skid	DAY	1,908.46		1,908.46		1,908.46	
01.1112 489	Generator, 1135KW, diesel, skid	WEEK	6,679.63		6,679.63		6,679.63	
01.1112 490	Generator, 1135KW, diesel, skid	MONTH	19,084.67		19,084.67		19,084.67	
01.1112 491	Electric extension cord, 50'	DAY	11.45		11.45		11.45	
01.1112 501	Electric extension cord, 50'	WEEK	34.35		34.35		34.35	
01.1112 511	Electric extension cord, 50'	MONTH	68.71		68.71		68.71	
01.1112 521	Electric extension cord, 100'	DAY	22.90		22.90		22.90	
01.1112 531	Electric extension cord, 100'	WEEK	68.71		68.71		68.71	
01.1112 541	Electric extension cord, 100'	MONTH	137.39		137.39		137.39	
01.1112 551	Electric Y's	DAY	6.88		6.88		6.88	
01.1112 561	Electric Y's	WEEK	20.63		20.63		20.63	
01.1112 571	Electric Y's	MONTH	41.20		41.20		41.20	
01.1112 581	Electric pigtail adapters	DAY	7.01		7.01		7.01	
01.1112 591	Electric pigtail adapters	WEEK	21.06		21.06		21.06	
01.1112 601	Electric pigtail adapters	MONTH	52.68		52.68		52.68	
01.1112 611	String lights with guards	DAY	62.21		62.21		62.21	
01.1112 621	String lights with guards	WEEK	97.75		97.75		97.75	
01.1112 631	String lights with guards	MONTH	151.10		151.10		151.10	
01.1112 641	Temporary power box, 4 & 7 receptacle	DAY	41.20		41.20		41.20	
01.1112 651	Temporary power box, 4 & 7 receptacle	WEEK	82.45		82.45		82.45	
01.1112 661	Temporary power box, 4 & 7 receptacle	MONTH	247.35		247.35		247.35	
01.1112 671	Temporary power cord, 6/4, 100'	DAY	44.43		44.43		44.43	
01.1112 681	Temporary power cord, 6/4, 100'	WEEK	119.10		119.10		119.10	
01.1112 691	Temporary power cord, 6/4, 100'	MONTH	160.00		160.00		160.00	
01.1112 701	Temporary power booster	DAY	62.21		62.21		62.21	
01.1112 711	Temporary power booster	WEEK	138.65		138.65		138.65	
01.1112 721	Temporary power booster	MONTH	257.76		257.76		257.76	
01.1113 000	**WELDING EQUIPMENT & ACCESSORIES, RENTAL:**							
01.1113 001	Acetylene outfit, does not include oxygen & acetylene	DAY	82.45		82.45		82.45	
01.1113 002	Acetylene outfit, does not include oxygen & acetylene	WEEK	328.27		328.27		328.27	
01.1113 003	Acetylene outfit, does not include oxygen & acetylene	MONTH	984.77		984.77		984.77	
01.1113 011	Welder, 175a, gas, with leads	DAY	99.24		99.24		99.24	
01.1113 021	Welder, 175a, gas, with leads	WEEK	396.95		396.95		396.95	

18

Division 1 CSI #	01-GENERAL REQUIREMENTS Description	Unit	Material	Union Install	Union Total	Open Install	Open Total	Unit Man-Hrs
01.1113 000	**WELDING EQUIPMENT & ACCESSORIES, RENTAL: (Cont.)**							
01.1113 031	Welder, 175a, gas, with leads	MONTH	1,190.87		1,190.87		1,190.87	
01.1113 041	Welder, 135a, gas	DAY	68.71		68.71		68.71	
01.1113 051	Welder, 135a, gas	WEEK	274.81		274.81		274.81	
01.1113 061	Welder, 135a, gas	MONTH	824.44		824.44		824.44	
01.1113 071	Welder, 200a, gas	DAY	99.24		99.24		99.24	
01.1113 081	Welder, 200a, gas	WEEK	396.95		396.95		396.95	
01.1113 091	Welder, 200a, gas	MONTH	1,190.87		1,190.87		1,190.87	
01.1113 101	Welder, 250a, diesel	DAY	118.32		118.32		118.32	
01.1113 111	Welder, 250a, diesel	WEEK	473.34		473.34		473.34	
01.1113 121	Welder, 250a, diesel	MONTH	1,183.27		1,183.27		1,183.27	
01.1113 131	Welder, 270a, diesel, 4KW generator	DAY	145.04		145.04		145.04	
01.1113 141	Welder, 270a, diesel, 4KW generator	WEEK	580.17		580.17		580.17	
01.1113 151	Welder, 270a, diesel, 4KW generator	MONTH	1,435.18		1,435.18		1,435.18	
01.1113 161	Welder, 400a, gas	DAY	157.25		157.25		157.25	
01.1113 171	Welder, 400a, gas	WEEK	629.04		629.04		629.04	
01.1113 181	Welder, 400a, gas	MONTH	1,523.74		1,523.74		1,523.74	
01.1113 191	Welder, 400a, diesel	DAY	167.94		167.94		167.94	
01.1113 201	Welder, 400a, diesel	WEEK	648.88		648.88		648.88	
01.1113 211	Welder, 400a, diesel	MONTH	1,557.30		1,557.30		1,557.30	
01.1113 221	Welder, 600a, gas	DAY	206.13		206.13		206.13	
01.1113 231	Welder, 600a, gas	WEEK	839.71		839.71		839.71	
01.1113 241	Welder, 600a, gas	MONTH	1,908.46		1,908.46		1,908.46	
01.1113 251	Welder, 500a, diesel, dual operator	DAY	229.02		229.02		229.02	
01.1113 261	Welder, 500a, diesel, dual operator	WEEK	946.60		946.60		946.60	
01.1113 271	Welder, 500a, diesel, dual operator	MONTH	2,137.48		2,137.48		2,137.48	
01.1113 273	Wire fed welders, 90 amp includes wire	DAY	83.96		83.96		83.96	
01.1113 275	Wire fed welders, 90 amp includes wire	WEEK	335.90		335.90		335.90	
01.1113 277	Wire fed welders, 90 amp includes wire	MONTH	916.07		916.07		916.07	
01.1113 281	Welding cable, copper, '00', 50'	DAY	19.09		19.09		19.09	
01.1113 291	Welding cable, copper, '00', 50'	WEEK	76.34		76.34		76.34	
01.1113 301	Welding cable, copper, '00', 50'	MONTH	229.02		229.02		229.02	
01.1113 311	Welder's hood	DAY	16.79		16.79		16.79	
01.1113 321	Welder's hood	WEEK	33.56		33.56		33.56	
01.1113 331	Welder's hood	MONTH	67.19		67.19		67.19	
01.1113 341	Arc air cutting torch	DAY	82.45		82.45		82.45	
01.1113 351	Arc air cutting torch	WEEK	328.27		328.27		328.27	
01.1113 361	Arc air cutting torch	MONTH	984.77		984.77		984.77	
01.1114 000	**SANDBLASTING EQUIPMENT & ACCESSORIES, RENTAL:**							
01.1114 011	Sandblaster, 20# cap, hose, nozzle	DAY	68.71		68.71		68.71	
01.1114 021	Sandblaster, 50# cap, hose, nozzle	WEEK	274.81		274.81		274.81	
01.1114 031	Sandblaster, 50# cap, hose, nozzle	MONTH	787.79		787.79		787.79	
01.1114 041	Sandblaster, 50 to 100# cap, remote control	DAY	76.34		76.34		76.34	
01.1114 051	Sandblaster, 50 to 100# cap, remote control	WEEK	305.35		305.35		305.35	
01.1114 061	Sandblaster, 50 to 100# cap, remote control	MONTH	1,209.18		1,209.18		1,209.18	
01.1114 071	Sandblaster, 150 to 200# cap, remote control	DAY	106.86		106.86		106.86	
01.1114 081	Sandblaster, 150 to 200# cap, remote control	WEEK	427.50		427.50		427.50	
01.1114 091	Sandblaster, 150 to 200# cap, remote control	MONTH	1,343.56		1,343.56		1,343.56	
01.1114 101	Sandblaster, 300# cap, remote control	DAY	106.86		106.86		106.86	
01.1114 111	Sandblaster, 300# cap, remote control	WEEK	427.50		427.50		427.50	
01.1114 121	Sandblaster, 300# cap, remote control	MONTH	1,419.90		1,419.90		1,419.90	
01.1114 131	Sandblaster, 600# cap, remote control	DAY	160.30		160.30		160.30	
01.1114 141	Sandblaster, 600# cap, remote control	WEEK	641.24		641.24		641.24	
01.1114 151	Sandblaster, 600# cap, remote control	MONTH	1,603.12		1,603.12		1,603.12	
01.1114 191	Sandblaster, 6 ton, 2 & 4 outlets	DAY	267.17		267.17		267.17	
01.1114 201	Sandblaster, 6 ton, 2 & 4 outlets	WEEK	801.54		801.54		801.54	
01.1114 211	Sandblaster, 6 ton, 2 & 4 outlets	MONTH	2,099.33		2,099.33		2,099.33	
01.1114 221	Sandblaster, 8 ton, 2 & 4 outlets	DAY	313.00		313.00		313.00	
01.1114 231	Sandblaster, 8 ton, 2 & 4 outlets	WEEK	977.11		977.11		977.11	
01.1114 241	Sandblaster, 8 ton, 2 & 4 outlets	MONTH	2,290.13		2,290.13		2,290.13	
01.1114 251	Twin line hose, 50', extra	DAY	50.38		50.38		50.38	
01.1114 261	Twin line hose, 50', extra	WEEK	151.17		151.17		151.17	

Division 1 CSI #	01-GENERAL REQUIREMENTS Description	Unit	Material	Union Install	Union Total	Open Install	Open Total	Unit Man-Hrs
01.1114 000	**SANDBLASTING EQUIPMENT & ACCESSORIES, RENTAL: (Cont.)**							
01.1114 271	Twin line hose, 50', extra	MONTH	335.90		335.90		335.90	
01.1114 281	Suction sandblaster	DAY	65.78		65.78		65.78	
01.1114 291	Suction sandblaster	WEEK	124.45		124.45		124.45	
01.1114 301	Suction sandblaster	MONTH	239.97		239.97		239.97	
01.1114 311	Pac unit	DAY	101.31		101.31		101.31	
01.1114 321	Pac unit	WEEK	204.43		204.43		204.43	
01.1114 331	Pac unit	MONTH	551.03		551.03		551.03	
01.1114 341	Pac discharge hose, 1-1/2" x 50'	DAY	186.63		186.63		186.63	
01.1114 351	Pac discharge hose, 1-1/2" x 50'	WEEK	471.03		471.03		471.03	
01.1114 361	Pac discharge hose, 1-1/2" x 50'	MONTH	622.13		622.13		622.13	
01.1114 371	Sandblast hose, 3/4" ID, 50', coupled	DAY	18.32		18.32		18.32	
01.1114 381	Sandblast hose, 3/4" ID, 50', coupled	WEEK	54.99		54.99		54.99	
01.1114 391	Sandblast hose, 3/4" ID, 50', coupled	MONTH	128.25		128.25		128.25	
01.1114 401	Sandblast hose, 3/4" whip hose	DAY	30.19		30.19		30.19	
01.1114 411	Sandblast hose, 3/4" whip hose	WEEK	51.53		51.53		51.53	
01.1114 421	Sandblast hose, 3/4" whip hose	MONTH	83.55		83.55		83.55	
01.1114 431	Sandblast hose, 1" ID, 50', coupled	DAY	56.87		56.87		56.87	
01.1114 441	Sandblast hose, 1" ID, 50', coupled	WEEK	101.31		101.31		101.31	
01.1114 451	Sandblast hose, 1" ID, 50', coupled	MONTH	195.52		195.52		195.52	
01.1114 461	Sandblast hose, 1-1/4" ID, 50', coupled	DAY	67.56		67.56		67.56	
01.1114 471	Sandblast hose, 1-1/4" ID, 50', coupled	WEEK	112.00		112.00		112.00	
01.1114 481	Sandblast hose, 1-1/4" ID, 50', coupled	MONTH	239.97		239.97		239.97	
01.1114 491	Sandblast hose, 1-1/2" ID, 50', coupled	DAY	186.63		186.63		186.63	
01.1114 501	Sandblast hose, 1-1/2" ID, 50', coupled	WEEK	453.27		453.27		453.27	
01.1114 511	Sandblast hose, 1-1/2" ID, 50', coupled	MONTH	622.13		622.13		622.13	
01.1114 521	Sandblast nozzle	DAY	38.18		38.18		38.18	
01.1114 531	Sandblast nozzle	WEEK	114.50		114.50		114.50	
01.1114 541	Sandblast nozzle	MONTH	343.53		343.53		343.53	
01.1114 551	Helmet with air filter	DAY	22.90		22.90		22.90	
01.1114 561	Helmet with air filter	WEEK	91.60		91.60		91.60	
01.1114 571	Helmet with air filter	MONTH	274.81		274.81		274.81	
01.1114 581	Sandblast helmet, air fed, with purifier	DAY	38.18		38.18		38.18	
01.1114 591	Sandblast helmet, air fed, with purifier	WEEK	114.50		114.50		114.50	
01.1114 601	Sandblast helmet, air fed, with purifier	MONTH	343.53		343.53		343.53	
01.1114 641	Wet blast head assembly	DAY	16.62		16.62		16.62	
01.1114 651	Wet blast head assembly	WEEK	31.32		31.32		31.32	
01.1114 661	Wet blast head assembly	MONTH	47.99		47.99		47.99	
01.1114 671	Moisture separator	DAY	62.21		62.21		62.21	
01.1114 681	Moisture separator	WEEK	103.09		103.09		103.09	
01.1114 691	Moisture separator	MONTH	302.19		302.19		302.19	
01.1115 000	**MISCELLANEOUS EQUIPMENT RENTAL:**							
01.1115 011	Pedestal floodlight, one 500w lamp	DAY	35.13		35.13		35.13	
01.1115 021	Pedestal floodlight, one 500w lamp	WEEK	140.42		140.42		140.42	
01.1115 031	Pedestal floodlight, one 500w lamp	MONTH	419.89		419.89		419.89	
01.1115 041	Pedestal floodlight, two 500w lamps	DAY	42.75		42.75		42.75	
01.1115 051	Pedestal floodlight, two 500w lamps	WEEK	151.17		151.17		151.17	
01.1115 061	Pedestal floodlight, two 500w lamps	MONTH	442.77		442.77		442.77	
01.1115 071	Mercury vapor, two 1000w, trailer with tower	DAY	175.59		175.59		175.59	
01.1115 081	Mercury vapor, two 1000w, trailer with tower	WEEK	526.76		526.76		526.76	
01.1115 091	Mercury vapor, two 1000w, trailer with tower	MONTH	1,312.27		1,312.27		1,312.27	
01.1115 101	4 1000w metal arc lamps	DAY	311.08		311.08		311.08	
01.1115 111	4 1000w metal arc lamps	WEEK	799.91		799.91		799.91	
01.1115 121	4 1000w metal arc lamps	MONTH	1,759.76		1,759.76		1,759.76	
01.1115 131	Port-a-lite, 1000w metal arc, 110v	DAY	101.31		101.31		101.31	
01.1115 141	Port-a-lite, 1000w metal arc, 110v	WEEK	337.76		337.76		337.76	
01.1115 151	Port-a-lite, 1000w metal arc, 110v	MONTH	622.13		622.13		622.13	
01.1115 161	Port-a-lite, 110v, with 10' tower	DAY	128.00		128.00		128.00	
01.1115 171	Port-a-lite, 110v, with 10' tower	WEEK	373.28		373.28		373.28	
01.1115 181	Port-a-lite, 110v, with 10' tower	MONTH	666.60		666.60		666.60	
01.1115 191	Space heater (lpg), 150,000 BTU	DAY	53.43		53.43		53.43	
01.1115 201	Space heater (lpg), 150,000 BTU	WEEK	213.74		213.74		213.74	

Division 1 CSI #	01-GENERAL REQUIREMENTS Description	Unit	Material	Union Install	Union Total	Open Install	Open Total	Unit Man-Hrs
01.1115 000	**MISCELLANEOUS EQUIPMENT RENTAL: (Cont.)**							
01.1115 211	Space heater (lpg), 150,000 BTU	MONTH	587.80		587.80		587.80	
01.1115 212	Space heater (lpg), 300,000 BTU	DAY	99.24		99.24		99.24	
01.1115 213	Space heater (lpg), 300,000 BTU	WEEK	396.95		396.95		396.95	
01.1115 214	Space heater (lpg), 300,000 BTU	MONTH	1,091.64		1,091.64		1,091.64	
01.1115 221	Space heater (lpg), 400,000 BTU	DAY	114.50		114.50		114.50	
01.1115 231	Space heater (lpg), 400,000 BTU	WEEK	458.04		458.04		458.04	
01.1115 241	Space heater (lpg), 400,000 BTU	MONTH	1,183.27		1,183.27		1,183.27	
01.1115 251	Cut off saw, gas	DAY	53.43		53.43		53.43	
01.1115 261	Cut off saw, gas	WEEK	187.01		187.01		187.01	
01.1115 271	Cut off saw, gas	MONTH	374.06		374.06		374.06	
01.1115 281	Cut off saw, electric	DAY	57.24		57.24		57.24	
01.1115 291	Cut off saw, electric	WEEK	198.48		198.48		198.48	
01.1115 301	Cut off saw, electric	MONTH	450.40		450.40		450.40	
01.1115 311	Concrete saw, 10 HP	DAY	122.14		122.14		122.14	
01.1115 321	Concrete saw, 10 HP	WEEK	427.50		427.50		427.50	
01.1115 331	Concrete saw, 10 HP	MONTH	1,190.87		1,190.87		1,190.87	
01.1115 341	Electromagnet, towable	DAY	399.98		399.98		399.98	
01.1115 351	Electromagnet, towable	WEEK	773.22		773.22		773.22	
01.1115 361	Electromagnet, towable	MONTH	2,488.57		2,488.57		2,488.57	
01.1115 371	Barrel pump	DAY	24.92		24.92		24.92	
01.1115 381	Barrel pump	WEEK	47.99		47.99		47.99	
01.1115 391	Barrel pump	MONTH	88.89		88.89		88.89	
01.1115 401	Hydrostatic tester, gas	DAY	163.55		163.55		163.55	
01.1115 411	Hydrostatic tester, gas	WEEK	462.16		462.16		462.16	
01.1115 421	Hydrostatic tester, gas	MONTH	711.00		711.00		711.00	
01.1115 431	Industrial truck, golf cart, electric	DAY	195.52		195.52		195.52	
01.1115 441	Industrial truck, golf cart, electric	WEEK	462.16		462.16		462.16	
01.1115 451	Industrial truck, golf cart, electric	MONTH	799.91		799.91		799.91	
01.1115 461	Machinery rollers (1 set)	DAY	53.35		53.35		53.35	
01.1115 471	Machinery rollers (1 set)	WEEK	115.55		115.55		115.55	
01.1115 481	Machinery rollers (1 set)	MONTH	373.28		373.28		373.28	
01.1115 491	Fuel storage tank, 200 & 350 gallon	DAY	115.55		115.55		115.55	
01.1115 501	Fuel storage tank, 200 & 350 gallon	WEEK	177.77		177.77		177.77	
01.1115 511	Fuel storage tank, 200 & 350 gallon	MONTH	337.76		337.76		337.76	
01.1115 521	Fuel storage tank, 350 & 420 gallon	DAY	138.65		138.65		138.65	
01.1115 531	Fuel storage tank, 350 & 420 gallon	WEEK	248.86		248.86		248.86	
01.1115 541	Fuel storage tank, 350 & 420 gallon	MONTH	479.96		479.96		479.96	
01.1115 551	Fuel storage tank, 500 gallon	DAY	168.85		168.85		168.85	
01.1115 561	Fuel storage tank, 500 gallon	WEEK	311.08		311.08		311.08	
01.1115 571	Fuel storage tank, 500 gallon	MONTH	533.28		533.28		533.28	
01.1115 581	Hot water washer, 4GPM @ 1000 psi	DAY	122.14		122.14		122.14	
01.1115 591	Hot water washer, 4GPM @ 1000 psi	WEEK	480.92		480.92		480.92	
01.1115 601	Hot water washer, 4GPM @ 1000 psi	MONTH	1,221.42		1,221.42		1,221.42	
01.1115 602	Hot water washer, 6GPM @ 3000 psi	DAY	221.37		221.37		221.37	
01.1115 603	Hot water washer, 6GPM @ 3000 psi	WEEK	885.54		885.54		885.54	
01.1115 604	Hot water washer, 6GPM @ 3000 psi	MONTH	2,274.88		2,274.88		2,274.88	
01.1115 605	Cold water pressure washer, 4 GPM @ 1500 psi	DAY	114.50		114.50		114.50	
01.1115 606	Cold water pressure washer, 4 GPM @ 1500 psi	WEEK	458.04		458.04		458.04	
01.1115 607	Cold water pressure washer, 4 GPM @ 1500 psi	MONTH	913.01		913.01		913.01	
01.1115 611	Cold water pressure washer, 7 GPM @ 3000 psi	DAY	302.33		302.33		302.33	
01.1115 621	Cold water pressure washer, 7 GPM @ 3000 psi	WEEK	1,209.18		1,209.18		1,209.18	
01.1115 631	Cold water pressure washer, 7 GPM @ 3000 psi	MONTH	3,023.00		3,023.00		3,023.00	
01.1115 711	Steam Cleaner, 150 to 240 GPH	DAY	145.04		145.04		145.04	
01.1115 721	Steam Cleaner, 150 to 240 GPH	WEEK	580.17		580.17		580.17	
01.1115 731	Steam Cleaner, 150 to 240 GPH	MONTH	1,603.12		1,603.12		1,603.12	
01.1115 741	Water blasters, 6,000 psi	DAY	439.73		439.73		439.73	
01.1115 751	Water blasters, 6,000 psi	WEEK	1,319.16		1,319.16		1,319.16	
01.1115 761	Water blasters, 6,000 psi	MONTH	3,297.83		3,297.83		3,297.83	
01.1115 771	Water blasters, 10,000 psi	DAY	587.80		587.80		587.80	
01.1115 781	Water blasters, 10,000 psi	WEEK	1,763.42		1,763.42		1,763.42	
01.1115 791	Water blasters, 10,000 psi	MONTH	4,408.57		4,408.57		4,408.57	

Division 1 CSI #	01-GENERAL REQUIREMENTS / Description	Unit	Material	Union Install	Union Total	Open Install	Open Total	Unit Man-Hrs
01.1115 000	MISCELLANEOUS EQUIPMENT RENTAL: (Cont.)							
01.1115 801	Water blasters, 20,000 psi	DAY	740.49		740.49		740.49	
01.1115 811	Water blasters, 20,000 psi	WEEK	2,221.45		2,221.45		2,221.45	
01.1115 821	Water blasters, 20,000 psi	MONTH	6,664.35		6,664.35		6,664.35	
01.1800 000	OTHER GENERAL CONDITIONS:							
01.1801 000	MISCELLANEOUS RENTAL & CLEAN-UP:							
	Note: Planking for scaffolding is usually furnished by the trade using it.							
01.1801 011	Safety nets, nylon, 4" mesh, rectangular	SFSA	12.26		12.26		12.26	
01.1801 021	Safety nets, nylon, 8" mesh, rectangular	SFSA	5.62		5.62		5.62	
01.1801 031	Scaffold, 1 month, with on/off	SFSA	1.11		1.11		1.11	
01.1801 041	Scaffold, each additional month	SFSA	.17		.17		.17	
01.1801 051	Scaffold over 1 story, add	FLOOR		.18	.18	.11	.11	0.0025
01.1801 061	Scaffold rolling towers, 5'-8'	MONTH	258.02		258.02		258.02	
01.1801 071	Scaffold rolling towers, 13'-15'	MONTH	372.53		372.53		372.53	
01.1801 081	Scaffold rolling towers, 21'-25'	MONTH	549.63		549.63		549.63	
01.1801 091	Scaffold rolling towers, 25'-30'	MONTH	641.24		641.24		641.24	
01.1801 101	Scaffold planks, 7'-10'	MONTH	15.88		15.88		15.88	
01.1801 111	Scaffold planks, aluminum, 10'	MONTH	18.54		18.54		18.54	
01.1801 121	Scaffold swing stage, 32', on/off, rental	MONTH	1,422.05		1,422.05		1,422.05	
01.1801 131	Scaffold swing stage, 32', on/off	LS	3,021.82		3,021.82		3,021.82	
01.1801 141	Clean up, progressive	JSF		.33	.33	.19	.19	0.0044
01.1801 151	Clean up, final	JSF		.24	.24	.16	.16	0.0030
01.1801 161	Clean up, glass, SF of glass	SF		.37	.37	.32	.32	0.0037
01.1801 171	Clean & wax resilient floors	JSF		.28	.28	.18	.18	0.0035
01.1801 181	Debris removal	SF		.27	.27	.16	.16	0.0037
01.1801 182	Debris boxes, 15 CY	LOAD	373.99		373.99		373.99	
01.1801 183	Debris boxes, 20 CY	LOAD	397.55		397.55		397.55	
01.1801 184	Debris boxes, 36 CY	LOAD	445.71		445.71		445.71	
01.1801 185	Debris boxes, 40 CY	LOAD	476.46		476.46		476.46	
01.1801 191	Sign, "construction", 4' x 8'	EA	1,188.68		1,188.68		1,188.68	
01.1801 201	Office expense, general	JSF	.09		.09		.09	
01.1801 211	Small tools	JSF	.08		.08		.08	
01.1801 221	Consumable supplies	JSF	.08		.08		.08	
01.1803 000	PLATFORMS, TELESCOPING AND SCISSOR:							
01.1803 011	Work platform, self propelled rotating, telescoping, 25 ft	DAY	297.73		297.73		297.73	
01.1803 021	Work platform, self propelled rotating, telescoping, 25 ft	WEEK	893.16		893.16		893.16	
01.1803 031	Work platform, self propelled rotating, telescoping, 25 ft	MONTH	2,679.50		2,679.50		2,679.50	
01.1803 041	Work platform, self propelled rotating, telescoping, 30 ft	DAY	381.70		381.70		381.70	
01.1803 051	Work platform, self propelled rotating, telescoping, 30 ft	WEEK	1,145.09		1,145.09		1,145.09	
01.1803 061	Work platform, self propelled rotating, telescoping, 30 ft	MONTH	3,435.23		3,435.23		3,435.23	
01.1803 071	Work platform, self propelled rotating, telescoping, 40 ft	DAY	435.13		435.13		435.13	
01.1803 081	Work platform, self propelled rotating, telescoping, 40 ft	WEEK	1,305.38		1,305.38		1,305.38	
01.1803 091	Work platform, self propelled rotating, telescoping, 40 ft	MONTH	3,916.18		3,916.18		3,916.18	
01.1803 101	Work platform, self propelled rotating, telescoping, 60 ft	DAY	763.37		763.37		763.37	
01.1803 111	Work platform, self propelled rotating, telescoping, 60 ft	WEEK	2,290.13		2,290.13		2,290.13	
01.1803 121	Work platform, self propelled rotating, telescoping, 60 ft	MONTH	6,870.46		6,870.46		6,870.46	
01.1803 131	Work platform, self propelled rotating, telescoping, 80 ft	DAY	1,374.06		1,374.06		1,374.06	
01.1803 141	Work platform, self propelled rotating, telescoping, 80 ft	WEEK	4,122.27		4,122.27		4,122.27	
01.1803 151	Work platform, self propelled rotating, telescoping, 80 ft	MONTH	12,366.86		12,366.86		12,366.86	
01.1803 161	Work platform, self propelled rotating, telescoping, 100 ft	DAY	2,419.93		2,419.93		2,419.93	
01.1803 171	Work platform, self propelled rotating, telescoping, 100 ft	WEEK	7,717.84		7,717.84		7,717.84	
01.1803 181	Work platform, self propelled rotating, telescoping, 100 ft	MONTH	25,321.52		25,321.52		25,321.52	
01.1803 191	Work platform, self propelled rotating, telescoping, 150 ft	DAY	3,893.28		3,893.28		3,893.28	
01.1803 201	Work platform, self propelled rotating, telescoping, 150 ft	WEEK	11,679.82		11,679.82		11,679.82	
01.1803 211	Work platform, self propelled rotating, telescoping, 150 ft	MONTH	35,039.43		35,039.43		35,039.43	
01.1803 221	Work platform, self propelled, scissor, slab type, 10 ft	DAY	128.25		128.25		128.25	
01.1803 231	Work platform, self propelled, scissor, slab type, 10 ft	WEEK	384.75		384.75		384.75	
01.1803 241	Work platform, self propelled, scissor, slab type, 10 ft	MONTH	1,152.72		1,152.72		1,152.72	
01.1803 251	Work platform, self propelled, scissor, slab type, 15 ft	DAY	175.59		175.59		175.59	
01.1803 261	Work platform, self propelled, scissor, slab type, 15 ft	WEEK	526.76		526.76		526.76	
01.1803 271	Work platform, self propelled, scissor, slab type, 15 ft	MONTH	1,397.00		1,397.00		1,397.00	
01.1803 281	Work platform, self propelled, scissor, slab type, 20 ft	DAY	190.88		190.88		190.88	

Division 1 CSI #	01-GENERAL REQUIREMENTS Description	Unit	Material	Union Install	Union Total	Open Install	Open Total	Unit Man-Hrs
01.1803 000	**PLATFORMS, TELESCOPING AND SCISSOR: (Cont.)**							
01.1803 291	Work platform, self propelled, scissor, slab type, 20 ft	WEEK	610.71		610.71		610.71	
01.1803 301	Work platform, self propelled, scissor, slab type, 20 ft	MONTH	1,832.11		1,832.11		1,832.11	
01.1803 311	Work platform, self propelled, scissor, slab type, 25 ft	DAY	244.29		244.29		244.29	
01.1803 321	Work platform, self propelled, scissor, slab type, 25 ft	WEEK	763.37		763.37		763.37	
01.1803 331	Work platform, self propelled, scissor, slab type, 25 ft	MONTH	2,213.83		2,213.83		2,213.83	
01.1803 341	Work platform, self propelled, scissor, slab type, 30 ft	DAY	305.35		305.35		305.35	
01.1803 351	Work platform, self propelled, scissor, slab type, 30 ft	WEEK	931.34		931.34		931.34	
01.1803 361	Work platform, self propelled, scissor, slab type, 30 ft	MONTH	2,794.01		2,794.01		2,794.01	
01.1803 371	Work platform, self propelled, scissor, slab type, 35 ft	DAY	335.90		335.90		335.90	
01.1803 381	Work platform, self propelled, scissor, slab type, 35 ft	WEEK	1,007.69		1,007.69		1,007.69	
01.1803 391	Work platform, self propelled, scissor, slab type, 35 ft	MONTH	3,023.00		3,023.00		3,023.00	
01.1803 401	Work platform, self propelled, scissor, slab type, 40 ft	DAY	366.45		366.45		366.45	
01.1803 411	Work platform, self propelled, scissor, slab type, 40 ft	WEEK	1,282.50		1,282.50		1,282.50	
01.1803 421	Work platform, self propelled, scissor, slab type, 40 ft	MONTH	3,847.50		3,847.50		3,847.50	
01.1803 431	Work platform, self propelled, scissor, slab type, 50 ft	DAY	389.33		389.33		389.33	
01.1803 441	Work platform, self propelled, scissor, slab type, 50 ft	WEEK	1,450.44		1,450.44		1,450.44	
01.1803 451	Work platform, self propelled, scissor, slab type, 50 ft	MONTH	4,351.28		4,351.28		4,351.28	
01.1803 461	Work platform, self propelled, scissor, rough terrain, 25 ft	DAY	244.29		244.29		244.29	
01.1803 471	Work platform, self propelled, scissor, rough terrain, 25 ft	WEEK	916.07		916.07		916.07	
01.1803 481	Work platform, self propelled, scissor, rough terrain, 25 ft	MONTH	2,290.13		2,290.13		2,290.13	
01.1803 491	Work platform, self propelled, scissor, rough terrain, 30 ft	DAY	305.35		305.35		305.35	
01.1803 501	Work platform, self propelled, scissor, rough terrain, 30 ft	WEEK	1,106.91		1,106.91		1,106.91	
01.1803 511	Work platform, self propelled, scissor, rough terrain, 30 ft	MONTH	3,206.24		3,206.24		3,206.24	
01.1803 521	Work platform, self propelled, scissor, rough terrain, 40 ft	DAY	358.80		358.80		358.80	
01.1803 531	Work platform, self propelled, scissor, rough terrain, 40 ft	WEEK	1,435.18		1,435.18		1,435.18	
01.1803 541	Work platform, self propelled, scissor, rough terrain, 40 ft	MONTH	3,587.91		3,587.91		3,587.91	
01.1803 551	Work platform, self propelled, scissor, rough terrain, 50 ft	DAY	393.92		393.92		393.92	
01.1803 561	Work platform, self propelled, scissor, rough terrain, 50 ft	WEEK	1,575.64		1,575.64		1,575.64	
01.1803 571	Work platform, self propelled, scissor, rough terrain, 50 ft	MONTH	3,939.08		3,939.08		3,939.08	
01.1803 581	Work platform, not propelled, scissor, slab type, 15 ft	DAY	115.27		115.27		115.27	
01.1803 591	Work platform, not propelled, scissor, slab type, 15 ft	WEEK	345.82		345.82		345.82	
01.1803 601	Work platform, not propelled, scissor, slab type, 15 ft	MONTH	1,037.45		1,037.45		1,037.45	
01.1803 611	Work platform, not propelled, scissor, slab type, 20 ft	DAY	160.30		160.30		160.30	
01.1803 621	Work platform, not propelled, scissor, slab type, 20 ft	WEEK	480.92		480.92		480.92	
01.1803 631	Work platform, not propelled, scissor, slab type, 20 ft	MONTH	1,442.81		1,442.81		1,442.81	
01.1803 641	Work platform, not propelled, scissor, slab type, 25 ft	DAY	200.79		200.79		200.79	
01.1803 651	Work platform, not propelled, scissor, slab type, 25 ft	WEEK	602.32		602.32		602.32	
01.1803 661	Work platform, not propelled, scissor, slab type, 25 ft	MONTH	1,806.96		1,806.96		1,806.96	
01.1803 671	Tower platform, not propelled telescoping, cable lift, 15 ft	DAY	76.34		76.34		76.34	
01.1803 681	Tower platform, not propelled telescoping, cable lift, 15 ft	WEEK	305.35		305.35		305.35	
01.1803 691	Tower platform, not propelled telescoping, cable lift, 15 ft	MONTH	763.37		763.37		763.37	
01.1803 701	Tower platform, not propelled telescoping, cable lift, 20 ft	DAY	45.81		45.81		45.81	
01.1803 711	Tower platform, not propelled telescoping, cable lift, 20 ft	WEEK	366.45		366.45		366.45	
01.1803 721	Tower platform, not propelled telescoping, cable lift, 20 ft	MONTH	916.07		916.07		916.07	
01.1803 731	Tower platform, not propelled telescoping, cable lift, 25 ft	DAY	106.86		106.86		106.86	
01.1803 741	Tower platform, not propelled telescoping, cable lift, 25 ft	WEEK	427.50		427.50		427.50	
01.1803 751	Tower platform, not propelled telescoping, cable lift, 25 ft	MONTH	1,068.74		1,068.74		1,068.74	
01.1803 761	Tower platform, not propelled telescoping, battery lift, 20 ft	DAY	99.24		99.24		99.24	
01.1803 771	Tower platform, not propelled telescoping, battery lift, 20 ft	WEEK	396.95		396.95		396.95	
01.1803 781	Tower platform, not propelled telescoping, battery lift, 20 ft	MONTH	992.41		992.41		992.41	
01.1803 791	Tower platform, not propelled telescoping, battery lift, 30 ft	DAY	129.75		129.75		129.75	
01.1803 801	Tower platform, not propelled telescoping, battery lift, 30 ft	WEEK	519.10		519.10		519.10	
01.1803 811	Tower platform, not propelled telescoping, battery lift, 30 ft	MONTH	1,297.75		1,297.75		1,297.75	
01.1803 821	Tower platform, not propelled telescoping, battery lift, 40 ft	DAY	190.88		190.88		190.88	
01.1803 831	Tower platform, not propelled telescoping, battery lift, 40 ft	WEEK	648.88		648.88		648.88	
01.1803 841	Tower platform, not propelled telescoping, battery lift, 40 ft	MONTH	1,679.46		1,679.46		1,679.46	

Division 1 CSI #	01-GENERAL REQUIREMENTS Description	Unit	Material	Union Install	Union Total	Open Install	Open Total	Unit Man-Hrs
01.1805 000	**PHOTOGRAPHY:**							
	Note: The following prices are based on 8" x 10" photos.							
01.1805 011	4 photos/month, 2 prints each	JSF	.08		.08		.08	
01.1805 021	4 photos, 2 prints each	SET	444.99		444.99		444.99	
01.1805 031	5 photos, aerial, 1 print, black & white	SET	802.21		802.21		802.21	
01.1805 041	5 photos, aerial, 1 print, color	SET	917.50		917.50		917.50	

Division 1 CSI#	01 - GENERAL REQUIREMENTS Description
01.1900 000	**NON-MANUAL LABOR DISTRIBUTABLES:** *Note: Payroll taxes, fringes and insurance are included with subcontractor labor prices in all trades except for supervision. The percentages listed below are derived from base pay scales, and are for informational purposes only.* Supervision: payroll taxes, insurance, vacation...54.97% Carpenters: payroll taxes, insurance, fringes ....68.14% Laborers: payroll taxes, insurance, fringes..69.84% Cement finishers: payroll taxes, insurance, fringes ....66.23% Subsistence/day (varies w/each trade)..$20.60 Travel allowance/mile (outside 35)...$ .23 Parking for field labor/month (urban) ....$92.70 **Derivation of above allowances:** FICA (Social Security)...7.65% FUTA (Federal Unemployment Tax) ....1.00% State Unemployment Insurance (AV.)..3.30% **Worker's compensation:** Supervision ....16.37% Carpenters...18.94% Laborers...18.94% Cement finishers ....14.33% **Average union fringe benefits:** *Note: Fringe benefits include vacation, holidays pension, health and welfare and miscellaneous benefits. Payroll taxes are not included.* Supervision ....23.30% Carpenters...33.90% Laborers ....35.60% Cement finishers..36.60% Insurance, comprehensive liability ....1.20% Course of construction insurance...1.75% Miscellaneous benefits...0.40%
01.2000 000	**OVERHEAD & PROFIT, BONDS:** *Note: Overhead, profit and bonds are placed at the end of the estimate summary. This section is for your convenience only.* **Bonds:** Performance bond, to 100 M...3.00% Performance bond, 100 M-l MM..2.40% Performance bond, 1 MM-2 MM..2.00% Performance bond, 2 MM-5 MM..1.60% Performance bond, 10 MM & Up...1.34% Subcontract bond, to 100 M..3.00% Subcontract bond, 100 M-l MM...2.40% Subcontract bond, 1 MM-2 MM...2.00% **Overhead:** *Note: Home office overhead is almost always included with the profit in the general contractor's estimate summary. The following are typical overhead costs, based on annual volume. (Consisting of executive, estimator and office salaries, rent, utilities, legal and accounting fees, taxes, license fees, etc.)* Annual volume, 600 M-2.5 MM ....5.00% Annual volume, 10 MM-20 MM 2.50% Annual volume, 2.5 MM-5 MM ....4.00% Annual volume, 20 MM & Up 2.00% Annual volume, 5 MM-10 MM ....3.50% **Profit:** *Note: The home office overhead from the table above, is included in the following figures.* **Average profit for new commercial structure:** **Average profit by type of structure;** 200 M or Less...............................16.00% Remodeling ....18.00% 200M-l MM....................................12.00% Custom house ....9.00% 1 MM-2.5 MM................................10.00% Multi-residential...................................6.00% 2.5 MM-5 MM..................................7.00% Institutional ....6.00% 5 MM-10 MM...................................5.00% Commercial ....5.00% 10 MM-50 MM.................................5.00% Educational..6.00% See typical breakouts for other structures on page 26.

Division 1 CSI #	01 - GENERAL REQUIREMENTS Description
01.2000 000	OVERHEAD & PROFIT, BONDS: (Cont.)

HOME OFFICE OVERHEAD AND PROFIT BASED ON BID PROJECT

	REPAIR OF FIRE DAMAGE	ALTERATIONS & ADDITIONS	UNIQUE STRUCTURE	INSTITUTIONAL STRUCTURE	COMMERCIAL STRUCTURE	PUBLIC WORKS HEAVY
AMOUNT/SIZE	%	%	%	%	%	%
Under $200 Thousand	25.0	23.0	20.0	18.0	16.0	18.0
$200 to $500 Thousand	20.0	18.0	16.0	15.0	13.0	15.0
$500 Thousand to $1 Million	18.0	16.0	15.0	14.0	11.0	11.0
$1 to $2 Million	16.0	14.0	13.0	10.0	10.0	10.0
$2 to $5 Million	14.0	12.0	11.0	8.0	7.0	7.0
$5 to $10 Million	12.0	100	9.0	6.0	5.0	5.0
$10 to $20 Million	10.0	9.0	8.0	5.5	5.0	5.0
$20 to $50 Million	10.0	8.5	7.0	5.5	5.0	5.0
$50 to $100 Million	10.0	8.0	6.5	5.0	5.0	5.0
$100 Million and Up	10.0	8.0	6.5	5.0	5.0	5.0
COMMON ADDERS AND DEDUCTORS						
Duration each year over two	1.0	1.0	1.0	1.0	1.0	1.0
Special Inspection Procedure	1.0	1.0	1.0	1.0	1.0	1.0
NEGOTIATED PROJECT, ADD OVERHEAD TO GENERAL CONDITIONS & DEDUCT FROM PROFIT:						
	-3.0	-3.0	-3.0	-3.0	-3.0	-2.0
SPECIAL AWARD-WINNING, ACCLAIMED ARCHITECTS:						
	3.0	3.0	3.0	3.0	3.0	3.0

	HIGH RISE HOUSING	LOW RISE HOUSING	SINGLE FAMILY TRACT	SINGLE FAMILY CUSTOM	SINGLE FAMILY ARCHITECTURAL
AMOUNT/SIZE	%	%	%	%	%
Under $200 Thousand	16.0	14.0	10.0	12.0	14.0
$200 to $500 Thousand	14.0	12.0	10.0	10.0	12.0
$500 Thousand to $1 Million	9.0	9.0	8.0	9.0	10.0
$1 to $2 Million	8.0	8.0	7.0	8.0	9.0
$2 to $5 Million	6.0	6.0	6.0	7.0	8.0
$5 to $10 Million	5.0	5.0	5.0	6.0	7.0
$10 to $20 Million	5.0	5.0	5.0	6.0	7.0
$20 to $50 Million	5.0	5.0	0.0	0.0	0.0
$50 to $100 Million	5.0	0.0	0.0	0.0	0.0
$100 Million and Up	5.0	0.0	0.0	0.0	0.0
COMMON ADDERS AND DEDUCTORS					
Duration each year over two	1.0	1.0	1.0	1.0	1.0
Special Inspection Procedure	0.5	0.5	1.0	2.0	2.0
NEGOTIATED PROJECT, ADD OVERHEAD TO GENERAL CONDITIONS & DEDUCT FROM PROFIT:					
	-2.0	-2.0	-3.0	-3.0	-3.0
SPECIAL AWARD-WINNING, ACCLAIMED ARCHITECTS:					
	3.0	3.0	3.0	3.0	5.0

Home office overhead is normally included with contractor's profit as a single item.

Home office overhead is separate and distinct from general conditions (Field Overhead) and consists of: Rent, Utilities, Legal, Accounting, Estimating, Travel, General Insurance, Taxes, Marketing, Advertising, Computer, Etc., and are distinctly not job related.

Division 1 CSI #	01 - GENERAL REQUIREMENTS Description
01.3000 000	**ESCALATION** This item is especially important on projects that will not start for some time, or that will be in construction over a long period of time. According to the Saylor material/labor index, the construction industry showed a -0.3% overall decrease, during the first nine months of 2009. In the same period, the Saylor subcontract index decreased -0.9%. Since most labor contracts are settled between May & August, estimates for projects that will extend beyond that period should allow for further increases. The subcontract bid includes escalation. Add escalation for your own work only. For architectural or engineering estimates, add escalation for the whole project. 2010 .... 4.0% 2011 .... 4.0% 2012 .... 4.0% **Remember:** Escalation is cumulative. Do not compute 2010 escalation until you have added escalation for 2009.
01.4000 000	**CONTINGENCIES:**

DRAWING STAGE	PERCENT - COMPLETE	CONTINGENCY
Conceptual Plans	0 - 15%	12%
Schematic Plans	15 - 30%	10%
Preliminary Plans	30 - 50%	5%
Semi-Final Plans	80 - 90%	2%
Final Working Drawings	100%	None

DESCRIPTION OF WORK	REPAIR OF FIRE DAMAGE	ALTERATIONS & ADDITIONS	UNIQUE STRUCTURE	INSTITUTIONAL STRUCTURE	COMMERCIAL STRUCTURE	PUBLIC WORKS HEAVY
STAGE OF DESIGN	%	%	%	%	%	%
Pre-Conceptual Stage 0%	30	20	18	15	15	15
Conceptual Stage 1 - 15%	25	15	15	12	12	12
Schematic 15 - 30%	20	12	12	10	10	10
Design Development 35%	15	7 - 9	7 - 9	5 - 7	5 - 7	5 - 7
Working Drawings 50%	10	5	5	4	4	4
Working Drawings 80%	5	4	3	2 - 3	2 - 3	2 - 3
Out for Bid 100%	3	2	0	0	0	0

DESCRIPTION OF WORK	HIGH RISE HOUSING	LOW RISE HOUSING	SINGLE FAMILY TRACT	SINGLE FAMILY CUSTOM	SINGLE FAMILY ARCHITECT	PARKING STRUCTURES	PROCESS INDUSTRY
STAGE OF DESIGN	%	%	%	%	%	%	%
Pre-Conceptual Stage 0%	15	15	10	15	20	10	30
Conceptual Stage 1 - 15%	12	12	7	12	15	7	25
Schematic 15 - 30%	10	10	8	10	12	5	20
Design Development 35%	5 - 7	5 - 7	4	5 - 7	7 - 8	3	15
Working Drawings 50%	4	4	3	3	5	2	10
Working Drawings 80%	2 - 3	2 - 3	2	2	3	2	5
Out for Bid 100%	0	0	0	0	0	0	0

Division 1 CSI #	**01 - GENERAL REQUIREMENTS** Description
01.5000 000	**GEOGRAPHICAL DIFFERENCES:** When compiling your estimates, Keep in mind that there are geographical differences. For architectural and engineering estimates (pre-bid), it is necessary to calculate a geographical difference for the entire estimate. For bidding, the general contractor will determine the differences for his own work. The subcontractor will generally be local, and will be familiar with local pricing. The major cities cost index in the front of this manual will provide guidelines for determining the percentage of change required. Please keep in mind that great differences will be experienced between rural and urban areas. In general, where wage rates are low, productivity is also decreased to some degree. States with right-to-work laws and non union conditions tend to have lower labor costs. Keep in mind that building codes can vary greatly between areas. Large cities tend to be more restrictive than rural or suburban areas. Most larger cities write their own building codes which are more stringent than the uniform building code. **MARKET FACTOR:** There are occasions when anomalies in the bidding marketplace that cannot be accounted for with normal contingencies like escalation and geographic differences. These anomalies, in the bidding marketplace, include the inability to get competitive bidders or sufficient bidders for a project. This includes General Contractors and major subcontractors, for instance Rough Carpentry, Mechanical, Plumbing or Electrical. Cost Consultants generally base their project cost estimates on competitive bidding. Competitive bidding means a minimum of five General Contractors and a minimum of three subcontractors in the major trades. If the above criteria are not met the overall cost of the project can be skewed to a higher cost for a project due to noncompetitive bids. The Architect is encouraged to notify the Owner or Project Manager to aggressively follow the bidding process to insure that there are sufficient bids by General Contractors and subcontractors to provide competitive bidding.

Division 2 CSI #	02 - SITEWORK Description	Unit	Material	Union Install	Union Total	Open Install	Open Total	Unit Man-Hrs
02.0000 000	SITE WORK:							
02.1000 000	DEMOLITION:							
	Note: Unless stated otherwise, demolition includes disposal. Other uncommon conditions, such as							
	excessive haul distances, unusual work hours, high voltage lines, limited access or volatile							
	materials must be accounted for by either increased costs or separate allowances.							
02.1100 000	SITE DEMOLITION:							
02.1101 000	PAVEMENT & MISCELLANEOUS CONCRETE REMOVAL:							
	Note: The following prices include disposal for short haul dumps. Adjustments are necessary for							
	long hauls.							
02.1101 011	Remove pavement, asphaltic concrete, 5,000 to 25,000	SF	.55	.29	.84	.21	.76	0.0038
02.1101 021	Remove pavement, asphaltic concrete, 25,000 to 50,000	SF	.35	.29	.64	.21	.56	0.0038
02.1101 031	Remove pavement, asphaltic concrete, over 50,000	SF	.24	.18	.42	.13	.37	0.0024
02.1101 033	Sawcut pavement, asphaltic concrete	LF	.75	1.53	2.28	1.08	1.83	0.0200
02.1101 035	Pulverize, asphaltic concrete, for recompaction, 4"	SF	.09	.11	.20	.08	.17	0.0015
02.1101 041	Remove concrete slab, 5" max, no rebar	SF	.51	.79	1.30	.36	.87	0.0128
02.1101 051	Remove concrete slab, 5" max, with rebar	SF	.57	1.02	1.59	.47	1.04	0.0165
02.1101 061	Remove concrete slab, 9"-12", with rebar	SF	2.75	4.43	7.18	2.03	4.78	0.0716
02.1101 071	Remove concrete slab, 13"-18", with rebar	SF	3.98	7.98	11.96	3.66	7.64	0.1289
02.1101 081	Remove concrete curb/gutter, no sawing	LF	.95	1.75	2.70	.80	1.75	0.0282
02.1101 091	Remove concrete curb-planter & batter board	SF	1.18	2.46	3.64	1.13	2.31	0.0397
02.1101 101	Remove concrete drive, with curb retainer & walk	LF	.55	1.03	1.58	.47	1.02	0.0166
02.1101 111	Remove concrete sidewalk, outside building	SF	.42	.91	1.33	.42	.84	0.0147
02.1101 121	Remove concrete catch basin, sump, dry well	EA	108.26	186.88	295.14	85.62	193.88	3.0190
02.1101 131	Dump charges, low	TON	18.44		18.44		18.44	
02.1101 141	Dump charges, mid	TON	26.43		26.43		26.43	
02.1101 151	Dump charges, high	TON	36.66		36.66		36.66	
02.1102 000	FENCE & GUARDRAIL REMOVAL:							
02.1102 011	Remove fence, chain link, 6', dispose	LF	.44	1.83	2.27	.84	1.28	0.0295
02.1102 021	Remove fence, chain link, 6', salvage	LF	.58	2.51	3.09	1.15	1.73	0.0406
02.1102 031	Remove fence, wood, 6', dispose	LF	.17	.97	1.14	.45	.62	0.0157
02.1102 041	Remove guardrail, dispose	LF	.56	3.88	4.44	2.45	3.01	0.0541
02.1102 051	Remove guardrail, salvage	LF	.77	3.08	3.85	1.41	2.18	0.0498
02.1103 000	MANHOLE REMOVAL:							
02.1103 011	Remove manhole, 6'	EA	133.40	320.38	453.78	201.77	335.17	4.4640
02.1103 021	Remove manhole, 7'-12'	EA	253.51	452.15	705.66	284.76	538.27	6.3000
02.1103 031	Remove manhole, break bellow collar, sand fill & plug	EA	105.42	133.49	238.91	84.07	189.49	1.8600
02.1103 041	Remove manhole, reset to grade, average	EA	124.57	83.90	208.47	52.84	177.41	1.1690
02.1104 000	TREE & POLE REMOVAL:							
	Note: Tree removal includes removal of stump.							
02.1104 011	Remove tree, 6"-8", off site disposal	EA	128.00	167.72	295.72	105.63	233.63	2.3369
02.1104 021	Remove tree, 10"-14", off site disposal	EA	166.99	167.72	334.71	105.63	272.62	2.3369
02.1104 031	Remove tree, 20"-30", off site disposal	EA	417.64	419.31	836.95	264.08	681.72	5.8424
02.1104 041	Remove tree, orchard clear	EA	48.59	41.87	90.46	26.37	74.96	0.5834
02.1104 051	Remove tree, walnut/tap root	EA	83.40	123.52	206.92	77.79	161.19	1.7210
02.1104 061	Remove tree, burning, large areas	EA	27.75	25.14	52.89	11.52	39.27	0.4061
02.1104 071	Remove pole, salvage condition	EA	29.41	339.67	369.08	155.62	185.03	5.4874
02.1105 000	MISC REMOVAL, RELOCATE TO FACILITATE ABOVE ITEMS:							
02.1105 011	Remove hydrant, with reset, thrust blocks	EA	118.33	418.38	536.71	191.69	310.02	6.7590
02.1105 021	Storm drain line to 15", dispose	LF	2.81	6.67	9.48	3.05	5.86	0.1077
02.1105 031	Sanitary line, 8"-12", complete	LF	3.26	6.56	9.82	3.01	6.27	0.1060
02.1200 000	GENERAL BUILDING DEMOLITION:							
02.1201 000	BUILDING DEMOLITION:							
	Note: For fireproofing on steel, add 30% to the total cost. For salvage of steel, add 50% to the total cost.							
02.1201 011	Frame building, single story	SF	.16	3.93	4.09	1.80	1.96	0.0635
02.1201 021	Frame building, two story	SF	.16	3.81	3.97	1.74	1.90	0.0615
02.1201 031	Frame building, three story	SF	.16	3.73	3.89	1.71	1.87	0.0602
02.1201 041	Concrete block building, 2 story, no concrete columns	SF	.76	7.74	8.50	3.55	4.31	0.1251
02.1201 051	Concrete block building, 3 story	SF	.70	7.48	8.18	3.43	4.13	0.1209
02.1201 061	Concrete building, monolithic, large	SF	3.44	8.73	12.17	4.00	7.44	0.1411
02.1201 071	Concrete building, precast panel , frame roof	SF	2.64	8.01	10.65	3.67	6.31	0.1294
02.1201 081	Steel frame building, no fireproof	SF	1.50	9.30	10.80	4.26	5.76	0.1502

Division 2 CSI #	02 - SITEWORK Description	Unit	Material	Union Install	Union Total	Open Install	Open Total	Unit Man-Hrs
02.1202 000	**CEILING REMOVAL:**							
02.1202 011	Remove ceiling, plaster/lath/frame	SF	.03	1.98	2.01	.91	.94	0.0320
02.1202 021	Remove ceiling, plaster suspended grid	SF	.03	1.49	1.52	.68	.71	0.0240
02.1202 031	Remove ceiling, acoustic suspended grid	SF	.03	.46	.49	.21	.24	0.0074
02.1202 041	Remove ceiling, acoustic, salvage	SF	.03	.86	.89	.39	.42	0.0139
02.1202 051	Remove ceiling, area light, salvage	SF	.03	1.60	1.63	.73	.76	0.0258
02.1202 061	Remove ceiling, tile, 12" x 12"	SF	.03	1.11	1.14	.51	.54	0.0180
02.1203 000	**ROOF REMOVAL:**							
	Note: For removal of rigid insulation, add 100% to the costs listed below.							
02.1203 011	Remove roof, built-up on plywood	SQ	1.87	57.96	59.83	26.56	28.43	0.9364
02.1203 021	Remove roof, built-up on metal deck	SQ	2.75	43.14	45.89	19.77	22.52	0.6970
02.1203 031	Remove roof, built-up on gypsum plank	SQ	1.87	44.12	45.99	20.21	22.08	0.7127
02.1203 041	Remove roof, built-up on concrete	SQ	1.87	50.67	52.54	23.21	25.08	0.8185
02.1203 061	Remove roof, asphalt shingle	SQ	1.87	37.56	39.43	17.21	19.08	0.6068
02.1203 071	Remove roof, wood shingle	SQ	1.87	35.57	37.44	16.30	18.17	0.5746
02.1203 081	Remove roof, skylight	SF	2.50	7.74	10.24	3.55	6.05	0.1250
02.1204 000	**CUT OPENINGS:**							
	Note: All openings 3' x 7'.							
02.1204 011	Cut opening, concrete wall, to 8"	EA	49.52	1,125.81	1,175.33	515.80	565.32	18.1876
02.1204 021	Cut opening, concrete masonry unit wall, to 8"	EA	36.02	997.98	1,034.00	728.45	764.47	12.1247
02.1204 031	Cut opening, plaster/metal stud	EA	14.63	552.77	567.40	403.48	418.11	6.7157
02.1204 041	Cut opening, drywall/wood stud	EA	2.80	363.00	365.80	264.96	267.76	4.4102
02.1204 051	Cut opening, suspended slab, to 8"	EA	39.50	653.63	693.13	477.10	516.60	7.9411
02.1205 000	**CONCRETE SAWING:**							
	Note: The following prices may be reduced as much as 50% if a large amount of sawing is to be done at one time. Add 50% if water control is needed. For angle cuts, add 5.5% to the total costs. For upside down cuts, add 103% to the total costs.							
02.1205 011	Sawing concrete slab, 1"	LF	.13	1.00	1.13	.43	.56	0.0160
02.1205 021	Sawing concrete slab, 1-1/2"	LF	.20	2.11	2.31	.92	1.12	0.0338
02.1205 031	Sawing concrete slab, 2"	LF	.30	6.31	6.61	2.75	3.05	0.1010
02.1205 041	Sawing concrete slab, 3"	LF	.49	8.22	8.71	3.57	4.06	0.1315
02.1205 051	Sawing concrete slab, 12"	LF	1.78	47.63	49.41	20.71	22.49	0.7620
02.1205 061	Sawing concrete wall, 6"	LF	4.84	19.92	24.76	8.66	13.50	0.3186
02.1205 071	Sawing concrete wall, 8"	LF	5.32	24.17	29.49	10.51	15.83	0.3867
02.1205 081	Sawing concrete wall, 10"	LF	6.65	30.22	36.87	13.14	19.79	0.4834
02.1205 091	Sawing concrete wall, 12"	LF	7.99	36.25	44.24	15.76	23.75	0.5799
02.1206 000	**DRILLING, DIAMOND BIT:**							
	Note: For angle holes, add 50% to the total costs. For upside down holes, add 100% to the total costs.							
02.1206 011	Core drilling, floor, 1" diameter	IN/DP	.98	3.28	4.26	1.42	2.40	0.0524
02.1206 021	Core drilling, floor, 3" diameter	IN/DP	.98	4.53	5.51	1.97	2.95	0.0724
02.1206 031	Core drilling, floor, 6" diameter	IN/DP	1.58	7.18	8.76	3.12	4.70	0.1148
02.1206 041	Core drilling, floor, 10" diameter	IN/DP	3.39	15.10	18.49	6.57	9.96	0.2416
02.1206 051	Core drilling, wall, 1" diameter	IN/DP	.98	10.13	11.11	4.41	5.39	0.1621
02.1206 061	Core drilling, wall, 3" diameter	IN/DP	1.32	35.89	37.21	15.60	16.92	0.5741
02.1206 071	Core drilling, wall, 6" diameter	IN/DP	2.07	56.81	58.88	24.70	26.77	0.9088
02.1206 081	Core drilling, wall, 10" diameter	IN/DP	4.40	119.61	124.01	52.01	56.41	1.9135
02.1207 000	**FOOTING REMOVAL & MISCELLANEOUS SALVAGE:**							
02.1207 011	Remove concrete foundations, no rebar	CY	43.71	67.01	110.72	42.20	85.91	0.9337
02.1207 021	Remove concrete foundation, with rebar	CY	51.10	98.99	150.09	62.34	113.44	1.3792
02.1207 031	Remove concrete foundation, residence	CY	38.02	41.43	79.45	26.09	64.11	0.5773
02.1207 041	Remove door & hardware, reuse, storage	EA	2.83	188.83	191.66	137.92	140.75	1.9934
02.1207 051	Remove wood surrounds, storage	EA	1.38	93.85	95.23	68.55	69.93	0.9907
02.1207 061	Remove lockset, butts, closer	SET	1.38	87.40	88.78	63.83	65.21	0.9226
02.1207 071	Remove locker, metal, surface mounted, save	TIER	1.38	103.53	104.91	75.62	77.00	1.0929
02.1207 081	Remove wire mesh enclosure, save	SF	.28	7.85	8.13	5.74	6.02	0.0829
02.1207 091	Remove sash, save glass	SF	.21	4.50	4.71	3.27	3.48	0.0412
02.1208 000	**DEMOLITION, WALLS ONLY, BUILDING TO REMAIN:**							
02.1208 011	Remove wall, concrete to 10", reinforced, machine	SF	2.53	3.77	6.30	2.37	4.90	0.0525
02.1208 021	Remove wall, concrete block, reinforced, machine	SF	1.35	2.71	4.06	1.71	3.06	0.0378
02.1208 031	Remove wall, stucco/plaster, metal stud	SF	.06	1.00	1.06	.63	.69	0.0139
02.1208 041	Remove wall, gypsum wall board, metal studs	SF	.02	.73	.75	.46	.48	0.0102
02.1208 051	Remove wall, brick veneer overlayed	SF	.23	6.81	7.04	4.29	4.52	0.0949

Division 2 CSI #	02 - SITEWORK Description	Unit	Material	Union Install	Union Total	Open Install	Open Total	Unit Man-Hrs
02.1208 000	**DEMOLITION, WALLS ONLY, BUILDING TO REMAIN: (Cont.)**							
02.1208 061	Remove wall, brick, 8" solid or 10" cavity	SF	.39	6.48	6.87	4.08	4.47	0.0903
02.1208 071	Remove wall, brick, 10-12", reinforced, grout	SF	.78	8.93	9.71	5.62	6.40	0.1244
02.1208 081	Remove wall, metal siding, no save	SF	.29	4.42	4.71	2.78	3.07	0.0616
02.1208 091	Remove wall, curtain wall, save glass	SF	.53	5.74	6.27	3.62	4.15	0.0800
02.1209 000	**DEMOLITION, FLOORS ONLY, BUILDING TO REMAIN:**							
02.1209 011	Remove slab on grade, 4"-5", with mesh	SF	.23	1.46	1.69	.92	1.15	0.0203
02.1209 021	Remove slab on grade, 4"-5", with #4 bars	SF	.34	1.53	1.87	.96	1.30	0.0213
02.1209 031	Remove suspended slab, 6"-8", free fall	SF	.41	2.71	3.12	1.71	2.12	0.0378
02.1209 041	Remove slab fill, lightweight concrete, metal deck	SF	.12	1.85	1.97	1.17	1.29	0.0258
02.1209 051	Remove insulated topping, no sand blast	SF	.09	1.39	1.48	.88	.97	0.0194
02.1209 061	Remove ceramic tile, brick plate	SF	.19	1.79	1.98	1.13	1.32	0.0249
02.1209 071	Remove resilient flooring	SF	.09	1.83	1.92	1.52	1.61	0.0208
02.1209 081	Remove wood floor, subfloor, wear layer	SF	.09	2.21	2.30	1.85	1.94	0.0252
02.1209 091	Remove carpet and pad	SF	.09	.98	1.07	.82	.91	0.0112
02.1210 000	**DEMOLITION ACCESSORIES:**							
02.1210 011	Chute	LF	12.70	19.65	32.35	8.77	21.47	0.3186
02.1210 021	Dust partition, 2" x 4" frame, 6 ml plastic	SF	2.56	1.46	4.02	.65	3.21	0.0237
02.1210 031	Debris bin, 20 CY, 2 days or 3 day weekend	PULL	475.00		475.00		475.00	
02.1210 041	Debris bin, 30 CY, 2 days or 3 day weekend	PULL	490.00		490.00		490.00	
02.1210 051	Concrete & asphalt debris bin, 7 CY	PULL	450.00		450.00		450.00	
02.1210 061	Dump charges, general bulk fill	TON	37.70		37.70		37.70	
02.1210 071	Dump charges, concrete, low	CY	26.43		26.43		26.43	
02.1210 073	Dump charges, concrete, mid	CY	39.61		39.61		39.61	
02.1210 075	Dump charges, concrete, high	CY	53.62		53.62		53.62	
02.1210 081	Remove waste oils, 200 gallon, including test	LS	86.38		86.38		86.38	
02.1211 000	**REMOVE ASBESTOS, FULL PROCEDURE AT PREMIUM TIME:**							
02.1211 011	Remove asbestos, pipe 6" diameter	LF	.32	9.49	9.81	8.33	8.65	0.0950
02.1211 021	Remove asbestos, pipe 16" diameter	LF	.42	13.59	14.01	11.93	12.35	0.1360
02.1211 031	Remove asbestos, column & beams only	SF	4.30	30.09	34.39	26.41	30.71	0.3011
02.1211 041	Remove Vinyl Asbestos Tile from floor	SF	.12	2.95	3.07	2.59	2.71	0.0295
02.1211 051	Remove asbestos fireproofing from ceiling	SF	.10	2.20	2.30	1.93	2.03	0.0220
02.1211 061	Debris bin for asbestos, 20 CY	PULL	1,565.82		1,565.82		1,565.82	
02.1213 000	**LEAD-BASE PAINT REMOVAL:**							
02.1213 011	Lead base paint removal, door surface	SF	1.63	5.82	7.45	4.53	6.16	0.0689
02.1213 021	Lead base paint removal, frames, jambs	SF	2.18	8.83	11.01	6.88	9.06	0.1046
02.1213 031	Lead base paint removal, door trim	SF	2.85	9.97	12.82	7.77	10.62	0.1181
02.1213 041	Lead base paint removal, window frames & trim	SF	5.27	13.35	18.62	10.40	15.67	0.1582
02.1213 051	Lead base paint removal, metal/wood siding	SF	1.62	5.13	6.75	4.00	5.62	0.0608
02.1213 061	Lead base paint removal, cabinet surface	SF	4.21	12.69	16.90	9.89	14.10	0.1503
02.1213 071	Lead base paint removal, cabinet trim	SF	5.33	15.86	21.19	12.36	17.69	0.1879
02.1213 081	Lead base paint removal, molding, simple	LF	3.50	10.48	13.98	8.17	11.67	0.1242
02.1213 091	Lead base paint removal, molding, ornate	LF	5.03	14.97	20.00	11.67	16.70	0.1774
02.1213 101	Lead base paint removal, base board, 4"	LF	3.05	9.94	12.99	7.74	10.79	0.1177
02.1213 111	Lead base paint removal, base board, 6"	LF	3.79	12.42	16.21	9.67	13.46	0.1471
02.1213 121	Lead base paint removal, pipes, railings & bars, to 2" dia	LF	2.32	7.72	10.04	6.01	8.33	0.0914
02.1213 131	Lead base paint removal, pipes, railings & bars, to 4" dia	LF	3.04	9.71	12.75	7.56	10.60	0.1150
02.1213 141	Lead base paint removal, pipes, railings & bars, to 6" dia	LF	3.74	11.75	15.49	9.16	12.90	0.1392
02.1213 151	Lead base paint removal, pipes, railings & bars, to 8" dia	LF	4.40	13.85	18.25	10.79	15.19	0.1641
02.1213 161	Lead base paint removal, pipes, railings & bars, to 10" dia	LF	5.08	15.66	20.74	12.20	17.28	0.1855
02.1213 171	Lead base paint removal, pipes, railings & bars, to 12" dia	LF	5.87	17.60	23.47	13.71	19.58	0.2085
02.1216 000	**MOVING STRUCTURES:**							
02.1216 011	Move concrete building, 1,000 to 2,000	SF	3.26	27.37	30.63	17.18	20.44	0.3382
02.1216 021	Move concrete building, 2,000 to 4,000	SF	3.03	25.07	28.10	15.73	18.76	0.3098
02.1216 031	Move frame building, 1 story, 1,000 to 2,000	SF	3.03	23.53	26.56	14.77	17.80	0.2908
02.1216 041	Move frame building, 1 story, 2,000 to 3,000	SF	2.93	22.77	25.70	14.29	17.22	0.2813
02.1216 051	Move frame building, 2 story, 1,000 to 4,000	SF	1.80	14.46	16.26	9.08	10.88	0.1787
02.1216 061	Move masonry building, 1,000 to 2,000	SF	3.60	30.30	33.90	19.02	22.62	0.3744
02.1216 071	Move steel frame building, 2,000 to 4,000	SF	4.48	13.63	18.11	6.08	10.56	0.2210
02.1301 000	**DEMOLITION, MISCELLANEOUS:**							
02.1301 011	Remove door, interior	EA		57.97	57.97	42.34	42.34	0.6120
02.1301 021	Remove door, exterior	EA		76.20	76.20	55.66	55.66	0.8044

Division 2 CSI #	02 - SITEWORK Description	Unit	Material	Union Install	Union Total	Open Install	Open Total	Unit Man-Hrs
02.1301 000	**DEMOLITION, MISCELLANEOUS: (Cont.)**							
02.1301 031	Remove door, glass	EA		186.37	186.37	136.12	136.12	1.9674
02.1301 041	Remove door, overhead	SF		4.33	4.33	3.16	3.16	0.0457
02.1301 051	Remove window, aluminum	SF		5.12	5.12	3.74	3.74	0.0541
02.1301 061	Remove window, wood	SF		3.85	3.85	2.81	2.81	0.0406
02.1301 071	Remove cabinet, base	LF		28.81	28.81	21.04	21.04	0.3041
02.1301 081	Remove cabinet, wall	LF		32.39	32.39	23.66	23.66	0.3419
02.1301 091	Remove cabinet, full height	LF		47.46	47.46	34.66	34.66	0.5010
02.1301 101	Remove counter top	LF		37.36	37.36	27.29	27.29	0.3944
02.1301 111	Remove shelving, single layer	LF		4.96	4.96	3.63	3.63	0.0524
02.1401 000	**DEMOLITION, PLUMBING:**							
02.1401 011	Remove bath tub	EA		217.15	217.15	114.72	114.72	2.6742
02.1401 021	Remove water closet	EA		152.37	152.37	80.50	80.50	1.8765
02.1401 031	Remove sink	EA		121.89	121.89	64.40	64.40	1.5011
02.1401 041	Remove lavatory	EA		114.51	114.51	60.50	60.50	1.4102
02.1401 051	Remove urinal	EA		165.75	165.75	87.57	87.57	2.0412
02.1401 061	Remove water fountain	EA		162.76	162.76	85.99	85.99	2.0044
02.1401 071	Remove shower	EA		136.20	136.20	71.96	71.96	1.6774
02.1401 081	Remove bidet	EA		144.28	144.28	76.23	76.23	1.7769
02.1401 091	Remove piping, to 2"	LF		4.69	4.69	2.48	2.48	0.0577
02.1401 101	Remove piping, to 4"	LF		5.64	5.64	2.98	2.98	0.0694
02.1401 111	Remove piping, to 6"	LF		7.42	7.42	3.92	3.92	0.0914
02.1401 121	Remove piping, to 8"	LF		16.18	16.18	8.55	8.55	0.1992
02.1401 131	Remove piping, to 10"	LF		18.21	18.21	9.62	9.62	0.2243
02.1501 000	**DEMOLITION, HVAC:**							
02.1501 011	Remove ductwork	#		1.11	1.11	.48	.48	0.0178
02.1501 021	Remove diffuser/register	EA		25.09	25.09	10.91	10.91	0.4014
02.1501 031	Remove grill	EA		20.85	20.85	9.07	9.07	0.3336
02.1501 041	Remove damper	EA		16.67	16.67	7.25	7.25	0.2667
02.1501 051	Remove flexible duct to 10"	LF		2.76	2.76	1.20	1.20	0.0441
02.1501 061	Remove flexible duct to 14"	LF		3.62	3.62	1.57	1.57	0.0579
02.1501 071	Remove flexible duct to 18"	LF		6.04	6.04	2.63	2.63	0.0967
02.1501 081	Remove piping, including insulation, to 1/2"	LF		2.86	2.86	1.24	1.24	0.0458
02.1501 091	Remove piping, including insulation, to 3"	LF		5.60	5.60	2.44	2.44	0.0896
02.1501 101	Remove piping, including insulation, to 6"	LF		12.16	12.16	5.29	5.29	0.1946
02.1501 111	Remove piping, including insulation, to 10"	LF		18.84	18.84	8.19	8.19	0.3014
02.1601 000	**DEMOLITION, ELECTRICAL:**							
02.1601 011	Remove main switchboard	AMP		3.39	3.39	2.46	2.46	0.0311
02.1601 021	Remove distribution board/panel	AMP		2.83	2.83	2.05	2.05	0.0259
02.1601 031	Remove transformer	KVA		8.45	8.45	6.13	6.13	0.0774
02.1601 041	Remove conduit, EMT, to 1"	LF		1.90	1.90	1.38	1.38	0.0174
02.1601 051	Remove conduit, EMT, to 2"	LF		3.24	3.24	2.35	2.35	0.0297
02.1601 061	Remove conduit, EMT, to 4"	LF		8.26	8.26	6.00	6.00	0.0757
02.1601 071	Remove conduit, RSC, to 1"	LF		3.81	3.81	2.77	2.77	0.0349
02.1601 081	Remove conduit, RSC, to 2"	LF		7.00	7.00	5.08	5.08	0.0641
02.1601 091	Remove conduit, RSC, to 4"	LF		15.05	15.05	10.93	10.93	0.1379
02.1601 101	Remove wire, 600v, #14	LF		.16	.16	.12	.12	0.0015
02.1601 111	Remove wire, 600v, #12	LF		.19	.19	.13	.13	0.0017
02.1601 121	Remove wire, 600v, #10	LF		.23	.23	.17	.17	0.0021
02.1601 131	Remove wire, 600v, #8	LF		.25	.25	.18	.18	0.0023
02.1601 141	Remove wire, 600v, #6	LF		.26	.26	.19	.19	0.0024
02.1601 151	Remove wire, 600v, #4	LF		.33	.33	.24	.24	0.0030
02.1601 161	Remove wire, 600v, #3	LF		.35	.35	.25	.25	0.0032
02.1601 171	Remove wire, 600v, #2	LF		.39	.39	.29	.29	0.0036
02.1601 181	Remove wire, 600v, 1/0	LF		.49	.49	.36	.36	0.0045
02.1601 191	Remove wire, 600v, 2/0	LF		.61	.61	.44	.44	0.0056
02.1601 201	Remove wire, 600v, 3/0	LF		.69	.69	.50	.50	0.0063
02.1601 211	Remove wire, 600v, 4/0	LF		.75	.75	.55	.55	0.0069
02.1601 221	Remove wire, 600v, 250 MCM	LF		.82	.82	.59	.59	0.0075
02.1601 231	Remove wire, 600v, 300 MCM	LF		.89	.89	.65	.65	0.0082
02.1601 241	Remove wire, 600v, 350 MCM	LF		.97	.97	.71	.71	0.0089
02.1601 251	Remove wire, 600v, 400 MCM	LF		1.07	1.07	.78	.78	0.0098

Division 2 CSI #	02 - SITEWORK Description	Unit	Material	Union Install	Union Total	Open Install	Open Total	Unit Man-Hrs
02.1601 000	**DEMOLITION, ELECTRICAL: (Cont.)**							
02.1601 261	Remove wire, 600v, 500 MCM	LF		1.10	1.10	.80	.80	0.0101
02.1601 271	Remove wire, 600v, 600 MCM	LF		1.21	1.21	.88	.88	0.0111
02.1601 281	Remove wire, 600v, 750 MCM	LF		1.46	1.46	1.06	1.06	0.0134
02.2000 000	**EXCAVATION, FILL & GRADING:**							
02.2001 000	**GRADING:**							
	Note: Material costs include machinery. Installation costs include labor and supervision. Costs do not							
	include auxiliary expenses such as staking, flagmen, lights, etc.							
02.2001 011	Clear, grub, brush, turf, roots, disposal	SF	.05	.09	.14	.06	.11	0.0010
02.2001 021	Clear & grub large area, no disposal	SF	.03	.09	.12	.06	.09	0.0010
02.2001 031	Clear & grub, large products	CY	1.19	1.25	2.44	.88	2.07	0.0147
02.2001 041	Strip & stock pile, 6"	CY	1.57	1.49	3.06	1.05	2.62	0.0175
02.2001 051	Scarify & compact top 6"	SF	.06	.20	.26	.14	.20	0.0024
02.2001 061	Rough grade, machine	SF	.03	.09	.12	.06	.09	0.0010
02.2001 071	Fine grade, machine	SF	.04	.16	.20	.11	.15	0.0019
02.2001 081	Fine grade, hand	SF		.79	.79	.56	.56	0.0093
02.2002 000	**ROADWAY EXCAVATION & FILL:**							
	Note: CAT & CAN, 1500' travel, fill in 6" lifts, compact to 95% AASHO standards.							
02.2002 011	Rdwy cut & fill, earth, 500,000 & up	CY	1.08	.20	1.28	.14	1.22	0.0026
02.2002 021	Rdwy cut & fill, earth, 100,000 to 500,000	CY	1.41	.29	1.70	.20	1.61	0.0037
02.2002 031	Rdwy cut & fill, earth, 50,000 to 100,000	CY	1.62	.35	1.97	.25	1.87	0.0045
02.2002 041	Rock & earth conglomerates, 50,000	CY	1.97	.35	2.32	.25	2.22	0.0045
02.2002 051	Ripable rock, large quantities	CY	3.79	4.17	7.96	2.97	6.76	0.0516
02.2003 000	**SITE CUT & FILL:**							
02.2003 011	Site cut & fill, earth, 250,000 & up	CY	1.18	1.12	2.30	.80	1.98	0.0139
02.2003 021	Site cut & fill, earth, 50,000 to 250,000	CY	1.35	1.34	2.69	.96	2.31	0.0166
02.2003 031	Site cut & fill, earth, 20,000 to 50,000	CY	1.66	1.72	3.38	1.23	2.89	0.0213
02.2003 041	Site cut & fill, earth, 5,000 to 20,000	CY	2.36	2.46	4.82	1.76	4.12	0.0305
02.2003 051	Site cut & fill, rock/earth mix	CY	5.75	5.43	11.18	3.88	9.63	0.0673
02.2004 000	**CUT FOR BUILDINGS, BACKHOE, TRUCKED:**							
	Note: For trenches 5 feet or deeper, shoring is required. Add 20% to 80% for shoring. Consult the							
	engineer for shoring requirements.							
02.2004 011	Building cut, earth, 500-1,000, site disposal	CY	2.84	3.00	5.84	2.14	4.98	0.0372
02.2004 021	Building cut, earth, 500-1,000, haul 1 mile	CY	7.80	4.82	12.62	3.42	11.22	0.0631
02.2004 031	Building cut, earth, 1,000 to 10,000, site disposal	CY	1.72	2.25	3.97	1.61	3.33	0.0279
02.2004 041	Building cut, earth, 1,000 to 10,000, haul 1 mile	CY	3.16	2.01	5.17	1.43	4.59	0.0263
02.2004 051	Building cuts, foundations, 100 to 500	CY	7.84	11.10	18.94	7.81	15.65	0.1302
02.2004 061	Building cuts, foundations, 500 to 2,000	CY	3.69	3.96	7.65	2.79	6.48	0.0465
02.2004 071	Building cuts, trench, grade beams	CY	4.17	9.50	13.67	6.69	10.86	0.1115
02.2004 081	Building cuts, hand excavate & trim	CY	1.70	125.02	126.72	54.36	56.06	2.0000
02.2004 091	Building cuts, rip rock, dispose	CY	2.92	3.75	6.67	2.68	5.60	0.0465
02.2004 101	Building cuts, rip rock, haul 1 mile	CY	4.71	2.49	7.20	1.77	6.48	0.0326
02.2004 111	Building cuts, rock, drill & blast	CY	21.49	37.82	59.31	23.82	45.31	0.5270
02.2004 121	Building cuts, rock, jackhammered	CY	46.96	52.14	99.10	28.37	75.33	0.7440
02.2004 131	Building cuts, rip trench, haul 1 mile	TON	19.55	4.63	24.18	3.28	22.83	0.0593
02.2004 141	Building cuts, hardrock trench, haul 1 mile	CY	17.90	10.90	28.80	7.72	25.62	0.1395
02.2004 151	Cut for buildings, levee	CY	.23	.75	.98	.54	.77	0.0093
02.2005 000	**ENGINEERED FILL FOR STRUCTURES:**							
02.2005 011	Fill, 1,000 to 2,500, imported one mile	CY	10.16	1.31	11.47	.92	11.08	0.0167
02.2005 021	Fill, 2,500 to 10,000, imported one mile	CY	9.87	.78	10.65	.55	10.42	0.0100
02.2005 031	Fill, 1,000 to 25,000, imported one mile	CY	9.50	1.02	10.52	.72	10.22	0.0130
02.2005 041	Fill, 25,000 to 50,000, imported one mile	CY	9.25	.90	10.15	.64	9.89	0.0115
02.2005 051	Fill, 100 to 2,500, on site	CY	7.01	.51	7.52	.36	7.37	0.0065
02.2005 061	Fill, 2,500 to 25,000, on site	CY	7.01	.34	7.35	.24	7.25	0.0043
02.2005 071	Fill, 25,000 to 50,000, on site	CY	7.01	.17	7.18	.12	7.13	0.0022
02.2005 081	Fill, compaction by roller	CY	.72	1.11	1.83	.78	1.50	0.0130
02.2005 091	Fill, compaction by sheepsfoot	CY	.94	1.41	2.35	1.00	1.94	0.0166
02.2005 101	Fill, dozer spread, no material	CY	.56	.75	1.31	.54	1.10	0.0093
02.2006 000	**BACKFILL, FOUNDATIONS, WALLS, ETC:**							
02.2006 011	Backfill, machine, no compaction	CY	3.31	11.97	15.28	8.43	11.74	0.1404
02.2006 021	Backfill, hand, no compaction	CY	5.65	62.51	68.16	27.18	32.83	1.0000
02.2006 031	Backfill, select import, compacted	CY	13.63	32.41	46.04	22.82	36.45	0.3803

Division 2 CSI #	02 - SITEWORK Description	Unit	Material	Union Install	Union Total	Open Install	Open Total	Unit Man-Hrs
02.2006 000	**BACKFILL, FOUNDATIONS, WALLS, ETC: (Cont.)**							
02.2006 041	Backfill, site material, compacted	CY	6.83	20.87	27.70	14.70	21.53	0.2449
02.2006 051	Backfill site material, compacted, bridges	CY	10.62	36.96	47.58	26.03	36.65	0.4337
02.2006 061	Add for lime treatment, 12" native soil, large areas	SF	.35	.27	.62	.17	.52	0.0038
02.2006 071	Lime bulk, material only	TON	115.20		115.20		115.20	
02.2006 100	**SOIL STABILIZATION - EROSION CONTROL**							
02.2006 111	Straw bale - Inlet barrier	LF	1.75	2.25	4.00	.98	2.73	0.0360
02.2006 121	Filter barrier 12" high filter fabric	LF	.95	2.69	3.64	1.17	2.12	0.0430
02.2006 131	Sediment fence- 36" wide mesh fabric	LF	3.65	7.19	10.84	3.13	6.78	0.1150
02.2006 141	Straw bale barrier	LF	3.65	2.25	5.90	.98	4.63	0.0360
02.2006 151	Straw wattles	LF	1.85	2.87	4.72	1.25	3.10	0.0459
02.2007 000	**SOIL POISONING:**							
	Note: The following prices assume large areas. For house with slab on grade, price assumes drilling							
	through footing to penetrate under slab area and treating soil.							
02.2007 011	Soil poison, permanent, inorganic base	SF	.08	.16	.24	.11	.19	0.0019
02.2007 021	Soil poison, temporary, organic base	SF	.08	.16	.24	.11	.19	0.0019
02.2007 031	Tent & fumigate	CF	.06		.06		.06	
02.2007 041	Soil treatment around house	SF	.32		.32		.32	
02.2007 051	Soil treatment at house on slab on grade	LF	6.14		6.14		6.14	
02.2008 000	**POROUS FILL & MISCELLANEOUS ROCK:**							
02.2008 011	Drain rock, 1/2"-3/4"	CY	11.15	18.96	30.11	13.54	24.69	0.2349
02.2008 021	Bankrun gravel	CY	7.09	17.54	24.63	12.53	19.62	0.2173
02.2008 031	Pea gravel	CY	16.44	18.96	35.40	13.54	29.98	0.2349
02.2008 041	Ornamental boulders, etc	CY	65.94	93.43	159.37	66.71	132.65	1.1573
02.2008 051	Rip rap, machine placed	TON	13.67	43.16	56.83	30.39	44.06	0.5064
02.2008 061	Rip rap, hand placed	CY	13.67	126.80	140.47	55.13	68.80	2.0284
02.2008 071	Rip rap, sacked, hand placed	CY	85.22	163.75	248.97	116.92	202.14	2.0284
02.3000 000	**PILING:**							
02.3001 000	**PILES, CONCRETE:**							
02.3001 011	Piles, precast, 10" square	LF	31.93	16.42	48.35	11.90	43.83	0.1953
02.3001 021	Piles, precast, 12" square	LF	37.14	18.74	55.88	13.58	50.72	0.2229
02.3001 031	Piles, precast, 14" square	LF	38.10	20.01	58.11	14.50	52.60	0.2381
02.3001 041	Piles, precast, 16" square	LF	41.14	21.06	62.20	15.26	56.40	0.2505
02.3001 051	Piles, precast, 18" square	LF	42.12	27.82	69.94	20.16	62.28	0.3310
02.3002 000	**PILES, STEEL H SECTION:**							
02.3002 011	Piles, steel H section, 8"x8"x36#	LF	25.81	20.52	46.33	14.87	40.68	0.2441
02.3002 021	Piles, steel H section, 10"x10"x57#	LF	40.54	23.07	63.61	16.71	57.25	0.2744
02.3002 031	Piles, steel H section, 12"x12"x74#	LF	49.76	24.31	74.07	17.62	67.38	0.2892
02.3002 041	Piles, steel H section, 14"x14"x89#	LF	58.02	25.62	83.64	18.57	76.59	0.3048
02.3002 051	Piles, steel H section, splice, average	EA	16.31	25.62	41.93	18.57	34.88	0.3048
02.3003 000	**PILES, PIPE:**							
02.3003 011	Piles, pipe, 12", concrete filled	LF	16.71	21.52	38.23	15.59	32.30	0.2560
02.3003 021	Piles, pipe, 12", unfilled	LF	14.38	19.20	33.58	13.91	28.29	0.2284
02.3003 031	Piles, pipe, 16", concrete filled	LF	24.14	23.07	47.21	16.71	40.85	0.2744
02.3003 041	Piles, pipe, 16", unfilled	LF	20.64	20.53	41.17	14.87	35.51	0.2442
02.3003 051	Piles, pipe, splicing, average	EA	14.76	156.35	171.11	113.29	128.05	1.8600
02.3003 061	Piles, pipe, points, average	EA	12.61	136.81	149.42	99.13	111.74	1.6275
02.3004 000	**PILES, STEEL STEP TAPERED:**							
02.3004 011	Piles, steel tip, 12" butt, concrete fill	LF	14.52	15.10	29.62	10.94	25.46	0.1796
02.3004 021	Piles, steel tip, 16" butt, concrete fill	LF	23.46	17.11	40.57	12.40	35.86	0.2035
02.3005 000	**PILES, WOOD:**							
02.3005 011	Piles, wood, 12" butt, untreated to 39'	LF	4.92	15.10	20.02	10.94	15.86	0.1796
02.3005 021	Piles, wood, 13" butt, untreated to 70'	LF	5.29	16.42	21.71	11.90	17.19	0.1953
02.3005 031	Piles, wood, 12" butt, treated to 39'	LF	6.96	15.10	22.06	10.94	17.90	0.1796
02.3005 041	Piles, wood, 13" butt, treated to 70'	LF	7.75	16.42	24.17	11.90	19.65	0.1953
02.3006 000	**PILES, MISCELLANEOUS ITEMS (INCLUDED ON ALL JOBS):**							
	Note: Make separate allowance for standby and idle time, access roads, rig mats and special							
	engineering.							
02.3006 011	Test piles	LS	11,805.33		11,805.33		11,805.33	
02.3006 021	Pile driver, truck crane, on/off	LS	10,224.14		10,224.14		10,224.14	
02.3006 031	Crane, crawler, 35 tons, on/off	LS	14,271.22		14,271.22		14,271.22	
02.3006 041	Crane, crawler, 65 tons, on/off	LS	20,022.28		20,022.28		20,022.28	

Division 2 CSI #	02 - SITEWORK Description	Unit	Material	Union Install	Union Total	Open Install	Open Total	Unit Man-Hrs
02.3006 000	**PILES, MISCELLANEOUS ITEMS (INCLUDED ON ALL JOBS): (Cont.)**							
02.3006 051	Crane, crawler, 100 tons, on/off	LS	28,755.39		28,755.39		28,755.39	
02.3006 061	Pile float rig, standby crew, on/off	LS	15,549.17		15,549.17		15,549.17	
02.3007 000	**PILES, SOLDIER, STEEL, RECOVERED, NO LAGGING:**							
02.3007 011	Piles, recovered, 15' max, pulled	LF	20.39	12.33	32.72	8.94	29.33	0.1467
02.3007 021	Piles, recovered, 20' max, pulled	LF	13.11	9.90	23.01	7.18	20.29	0.1178
02.3007 031	Piles, recovered, 30' max, pulled	LF	12.58	9.20	21.78	6.67	19.25	0.1095
02.3007 041	Piles, recovered, 50' max, pulled	LF	13.54	10.07	23.61	7.30	20.84	0.1198
02.3500 000	**CAISSONS & DRILLING:**							
02.3501 000	**BORING & PIERS, DRILLING ONLY, LARGE QUANTITY:**							
02.3501 011	Pier, drill only, 12", 4' deep	LF	1.22	1.11	2.33	.78	2.00	0.0130
02.3501 021	Pier, drill, add for each 1' to 6'	EA	.42	.24	.66	.17	.59	0.0028
02.3501 031	Pier, drill only, 16", 2' deep	LF	1.81	2.51	4.32	1.77	3.58	0.0295
02.3501 041	Pier, drill only, 16", 5' deep	LF	1.54	1.65	3.19	1.16	2.70	0.0194
02.3501 051	Test borings, 6"	LF	5.57	19.47	25.04	13.71	19.28	0.2284
02.3502 000	**AUGER HOLES, DRILLING ONLY, LARGE QUANTITY:**							
02.3502 011	Auger hole, drill only, 16"	LF	5.02	4.88	9.90	3.43	8.45	0.0572
02.3502 021	Auger hole, drill only, 24"	LF	5.61	4.95	10.56	3.49	9.10	0.0581
02.3502 031	Auger hole, drill only, 36"	LF	8.57	5.25	13.82	3.75	12.32	0.0650
02.3503 000	**ROCK DRILLING, ACCESSIBLE, NO DISPOSAL:**							
02.3503 011	Rock drilling, 24", no hard rock	LF	21.54	22.21	43.75	15.64	37.18	0.2606
02.3503 021	Rock drilling, 48", no hard rock	LF	51.72	44.41	96.13	31.27	82.99	0.5211
02.3503 031	Air tool mining, with rock drilling	CY	215.59	500.33	715.92	352.28	567.87	5.8704
02.3504 000	**CAISSONS, TO 45', 150 lbs per CY REBAR, NO DISPOSAL:**							
02.3504 011	Caisson, no casings, no ground water, 18"	LF	14.19	27.10	41.29	19.08	33.27	0.3180
02.3504 021	Caisson, no casings, no ground water, 24"	LF	24.54	28.55	53.09	20.10	44.64	0.3350
02.3504 031	Caisson, no casings, no ground water, 30"	LF	36.57	36.48	73.05	25.68	62.25	0.4280
02.3504 041	Caisson, no casings, no ground water, 36"	LF	54.05	43.81	97.86	30.85	84.90	0.5140
02.3504 051	Caisson, no casings, no ground water, 48"	LF	95.16	55.31	150.47	38.95	134.11	0.6490
02.3504 061	Caisson, no casings, no ground water, 60"	LF	145.89	61.45	207.34	43.27	189.16	0.7210
02.3504 071	Caisson, no casings, no ground water, 72"	LF	216.38	95.88	312.26	67.51	283.89	1.1250
02.3504 081	Caisson, casing temporary, ground water, 18"	LF	25.81	43.28	69.09	30.47	56.28	0.5078
02.3504 091	Caisson, casing temporary, ground water, 24"	LF	40.20	50.04	90.24	35.23	75.43	0.5871
02.3504 101	Caisson, casing temporary, ground water, 30"	LF	55.94	63.45	119.39	44.67	100.61	0.7444
02.3504 111	Caisson, casing temporary, ground water, 36"	LF	77.29	76.18	153.47	53.64	130.93	0.8938
02.3504 121	Caisson, casing temporary, ground water, 48"	LF	123.01	93.80	216.81	66.05	189.06	1.1006
02.3504 131	Caisson, casing temporary, ground water, 60"	LF	180.43	109.58	290.01	77.15	257.58	1.2857
02.3504 141	Caisson, casing temporary, ground water, 72"	LF	256.31	151.49	407.80	106.66	362.97	1.7774
02.3504 151	Caisson, casing in place, ground water, 18"	LF	46.55	82.85	129.40	58.34	104.89	0.9721
02.3504 161	Caisson, casing in place, ground water, 24"	LF	67.82	103.17	170.99	72.64	140.46	1.2105
02.3504 171	Caisson, casing in place, ground water, 30"	LF	96.75	123.14	219.89	86.70	183.45	1.4448
02.3504 181	Caisson, casing in place, ground water, 36"	LF	126.14	144.23	270.37	101.55	227.69	1.6922
02.3504 191	Caisson, casing in place, ground water, 48"	LF	184.55	172.12	356.67	121.19	305.74	2.0195
02.3504 201	Caisson, casing in place, ground water, 60"	LF	241.30	225.97	467.27	159.10	400.40	2.6513
02.3504 211	Caisson, casing in place, ground water, 72"	LF	342.71	271.82	614.53	191.38	534.09	3.1892
02.3505 000	**BELL FOOTING, ACCESSIBLE, NO DISPOSAL:**							
	Note: Adjust prices where unusual hazards exist.							
02.3505 011	Bell footing, 24", 5' shaft, 5' bell	EA	98.90	124.69	223.59	87.79	186.69	1.4630
02.3505 021	Add for concrete filled, above item	EA	322.62	28.48	351.10	15.50	338.12	0.4064
02.3505 031	Bell footing, 30", 6' shaft, 6' bell	EA	137.65	170.89	308.54	120.33	257.98	2.0051
02.3505 041	Add for concrete filled, above item	EA	361.39	31.34	392.73	17.05	378.44	0.4472
02.3505 051	Bell footing, 36", 10' shaft, 8' bell	EA	150.54	218.23	368.77	153.66	304.20	2.5605
02.3505 061	Add for concrete fill, above item	EA	1,239.22	280.54	1,519.76	197.53	1,436.75	3.2916
02.4000 000	**SHORING & BULKHEADING:**							
02.4001 000	**SHEET PILING:**							
	Note: Sheet piling is manufactured in many shapes and sizes. Gauges 7 through 12 are normally considered lightweight and are used primarily for trenching and stabilizing conditions. Material costs per square foot can be estimated based on weight and installation, with adjustments for unusual conditions. With lightweight sheet piling, allow for square set bracing as required.							
02.4001 011	Steel sheet piles, left in place, average	SF	25.66	5.57	31.23	4.02	29.68	0.0670
02.4001 021	Steel sheet piles, pull & save, average	SF	6.69	3.70	10.39	2.67	9.36	0.0445
02.4001 031	Steel sheet piles, 27#(Z-27), in place	SF	16.48	7.05	23.53	5.09	21.57	0.0849

Division 2 CSI #	02 - SITEWORK Description	Unit	Material	Union Install	Union Total	Open Install	Open Total	Unit Man-Hrs
02.4001 000	**SHEET PILING: (Cont.)**							
02.4001 041	Steel sheet piles, 27#, recycled	SF	7.76	11.71	19.47	8.45	16.21	0.1410
02.4001 051	Lightweight steel sheet piles, 9 ga, 86#	SF	10.03	10.39	20.42	7.50	17.53	0.1251
02.4001 061	Lightweight steel sheet piles, 12 ga, 654#	SF	11.04	8.90	19.94	6.42	17.46	0.1072
02.4001 071	Wood safety sheet pile to 8', braces	SF	2.77	8.43	11.20	6.08	8.85	0.1015
02.4001 081	Wood safety sheet pile to 12', braces	SF	4.75	10.50	15.25	7.58	12.33	0.1264
02.4001 091	Wood safety sheet pile to 16', braces	SF	5.52	11.06	16.58	7.98	13.50	0.1331
02.4002 000	**BULKHEADING & TIEBACK WALLS:**							
	Note: The following items include soldier piles 8' average space, 3" lagging, 2 rows of raker bracing.							
	Hydrostatic heads are not included.							
02.4002 011	Tie back wall, 10'-15', complete	SFWA	26.47	15.62	42.09	11.27	37.74	0.1881
02.4002 021	Tie back wall, 16'-20', complete	SFWA	28.51	16.37	44.88	10.56	39.07	0.2025
02.4002 031	Tie back wall, 21'-25', complete	SFWA	30.53	17.54	48.07	11.31	41.84	0.2170
02.4002 041	Tie back wall, 26'-35', complete	SFWA	34.65	19.87	54.52	12.82	47.47	0.2459
02.4002 051	Tie back wall, 36'-45', complete	SFWA	46.80	26.89	73.69	17.34	64.14	0.3327
02.4002 061	Tie backs, drilled, plug, with tie	LF	42.30	23.39	65.69	15.09	57.39	0.2894
02.4002 071	Rakers, steel	#	1.62	.94	2.56	.60	2.22	0.0116
02.4003 000	**SLURRY TRENCHING:**							
	Note: Prices do not include mats for rigs, traffic controls, bridging, resurfacing or unusual access							
	problems.							
02.4003 011	3,000 psi concrete, 36" trench	SF/TR	100.93	45.03	145.96	29.05	129.98	0.5572
02.4003 021	Disp waste excavation, short haul	CY	19.53	9.02	28.55	5.82	25.35	0.1116
02.4004 000	**PRESSURE INJECTED FOUNDATIONS:**							
02.4004 011	Pressure injected foundation, max 25'x18'x75 T, uncased	VF	42.75	24.55	67.30	15.84	58.59	0.3038
02.4004 021	Pressure injected foundation, max 25'x24'x150 T, uncased	VF	52.94	30.40	83.34	19.61	72.55	0.3761
02.4004 031	Pressure injected foundation, max 30'x14'x75 T, cased	VF	38.70	22.22	60.92	14.33	53.03	0.2749
02.4005 000	**DEWATERING:**							
02.4005 011	Deep well system, 12", cased & graded	VF	67.23	45.94	113.17	28.15	95.38	0.4774
02.4006 000	**WELL POINTS:**							
	Note: Well point spacing, header and pump size are determined by the expected flow. The following							
	prices assume a 2" well point system at 5' on center, and must be used based on the lineal feet of							
	perimeter of excavation. Prices include in and out costs and an operator 12 hrs per day.							
02.4006 011	Header system to 1000', 1 month	LF	13.39	40.05	53.44	24.54	37.93	0.4162
02.4006 021	Header system, to 1000', 2 month	LF	24.22	70.70	94.92	43.33	67.55	0.7347
02.4006 031	Header system, to 1000', 3 month	LF	35.16	101.31	136.47	62.08	97.24	1.0528
02.4006 041	Header system, to 1000', 4 month	LF	45.99	131.92	177.91	80.84	126.83	1.3709
02.4006 051	Header system, to 1000', 5 month	LF	56.86	162.44	219.30	99.54	156.40	1.6880
02.4006 061	Header system, to 1000', 6 month	LF	67.73	193.05	260.78	118.30	186.03	2.0061
02.4006 071	Header system, over 1000', 1 month	LF	11.71	24.48	36.19	15.00	26.71	0.2544
02.4006 081	Header system, over 1000', 2 month	LF	16.83	41.04	57.87	25.15	41.98	0.4265
02.4006 091	Header system, over 1000', 3 month	LF	22.03	57.61	79.64	35.31	57.34	0.5987
02.4006 101	Header system, over 1000', 4 month	LF	27.22	74.16	101.38	45.45	72.67	0.7707
02.4006 111	Header system, over 1000', 5 month	LF	32.46	90.75	123.21	55.61	88.07	0.9431
02.4006 121	Header system, over 1000', 6 month	LF	37.60	107.31	144.91	65.76	103.36	1.1151
02.4007 000	**UNDERPINNING:**							
02.4007 011	Underpinning, hand mining	CF		9.95	9.95	6.10	6.10	0.1034
02.4007 021	Underpinning, form, one side	SFFA	5.86	4.06	9.92	2.49	8.35	0.0422
02.4007 031	Underpinning, 35m# low slump concrete in place	CF	22.59	41.56	64.15	25.47	48.06	0.4319
02.4007 041	Underpinning, dry pack	CF	48.87	33.41	82.28	20.47	69.34	0.3472
02.4007 051	Underpinning, temp shoring, 4' oc	SFFA	16.75	11.53	28.28	7.06	23.81	0.1198
02.4007 061	Underpinning, perm shoring, 4' oc	SFFA	30.53	20.88	51.41	12.80	43.33	0.2170
02.4007 071	Water line blow off assem, 2"	EA	675.84	316.65	992.49	185.83	861.67	3.1700
02.4007 081	Valve, air release comb assem, 1"	EA	826.84	433.04	1,259.88	265.37	1,092.21	4.5000
02.4008 000	**PERMANENT DEWATERING SYSTEM:**							
	Note: A Permananet dewatering system consists of a network of perforated pipes, wrapped in filter							
	fabric and installed in a granular base under the slab. The pipes are in a grid in both directions under							
	the slab. They are connected to laterals that drain into the storm drainage system.							
02.4008 011	Permanent dewatering system, under slab	SF	5.89	6.44	12.33	3.95	9.84	0.0669
02.5000 000	**SITE UTILITIES:**							
	Note: Excavation and backfill are included with site utilities when applicable, with the exception of							
	conduit. No dewatering, shieldwork, clearing or demolition is included. All trenching is figured to cover							
	the top of pipe by 48". Spreaders are allowed for trenches over 5' deep. No off-site disposal of excess							

Division 2 CSI #	02 - SITEWORK Description	Unit	Material	Union Install	Union Total	Open Install	Open Total	Unit Man-Hrs
02.5000 000	**SITE UTILITIES: (Cont.)**							
	is included. Only conduit is included for electrical runs. See section 16.0000 For wire. Fitting allowance is included with pipe and conduit pricing. Equipment on and off charges are included for average jobs. These prices should be increased for small jobs or where trenching is over 6' deep.							
02.5001 000	**PIPE JACKING (ADD FOR CASING AND/OR PIPE):**							
02.5001 011	Pipe jacking, 2"	LF	17.20	29.33	46.53	17.21	34.41	0.2936
02.5001 021	Pipe jacking, 3"	LF	20.68	33.71	54.39	19.78	40.46	0.3375
02.5001 031	Pipe jacking, 4"	LF	26.92	45.80	72.72	26.88	53.80	0.4585
02.5001 041	Pipe jacking, 6"	LF	33.67	57.38	91.05	33.67	67.34	0.5744
02.5001 051	Pipe jacking, 8"	LF	45.60	77.50	123.10	45.48	91.08	0.7759
02.5001 061	Pipe jacking, 10"	LF	66.35	112.77	179.12	66.18	132.53	1.1289
02.5001 071	Pipe jacking, 12"	LF	82.02	143.83	225.85	84.41	166.43	1.4399
02.5001 081	Pipe jacking, 16"	LF	96.66	169.30	265.96	99.36	196.02	1.6949
02.5001 091	Pipe jacking, 18"	LF	109.51	191.64	301.15	112.46	221.97	1.9185
02.5001 101	Pipe jacking, 24"	LF	126.10	220.67	346.77	129.50	255.60	2.2091
02.5001 111	Pipe jacking, 30"	LF	164.45	287.32	451.77	168.61	333.06	2.8764
02.5001 121	Pipe jacking, 36"	LF	194.55	340.11	534.66	199.59	394.14	3.4048
02.5001 131	Pipe jacking, 42"	LF	214.96	376.30	591.26	220.83	435.79	3.7671
02.5001 141	Pipe jacking, 48"	LF	237.55	415.97	653.52	244.11	481.66	4.1643
02.5001 151	Pipe jacking, 54"	LF	257.75	451.33	709.08	264.86	522.61	4.5183
02.5001 161	Pipe jacking, 60"	LF	303.86	531.21	835.07	311.74	615.60	5.3179
02.5001 171	Pipe jacking, 66"	LF	317.72	555.60	873.32	326.05	643.77	5.5621
02.5001 181	Pipe jacking, 72"	LF	353.99	618.76	972.75	363.12	717.11	6.1944
02.5001 191	Pipe jacking, 84"	LF	426.76	749.12	1,175.88	439.61	866.37	7.4994
02.5100 000	**STORM DRAINAGE & SANITARY SEWER PIPE:**							
02.5102 000	**PIPE, PERFORATED & SOLID, CORRUGATED POLYETHYLENE UNDER DRAIN:**							
	Note: The following prices do not include trenching and backfill. For filter cloth on sizes 3" x 8" add 10% to material costs. For filter cloth on sizes 10" to 12" add 15% to the material costs.							
02.5102 011	Corrugated polytetheye pipe, perforated & solid, 3", under drain	LF	.44	8.47	8.91	5.19	5.63	0.0880
02.5102 021	Corrugated polytetheye pipe, perforated & solid, 4", under drain	LF	.58	8.68	9.26	5.32	5.90	0.0902
02.5102 031	Corrugated polytetheye pipe, perforated & solid, 6", under drain	LF	1.32	9.03	10.35	5.53	6.85	0.0938
02.5102 041	Corrugated polytetheye pipe, perforated & solid, 8", under drain	LF	2.38	9.28	11.66	5.68	8.06	0.0964
02.5102 051	Corrugated polytetheye pipe, perforated & solid, 10", under drain	LF	4.58	9.67	14.25	5.93	10.51	0.1005
02.5102 061	Corrugated polytetheye pipe, perforated & solid, 12", under drain	LF	6.53	9.96	16.49	6.10	12.63	0.1035
02.5103 000	**CAST IRON PIPE, SOIL, SERVICE WEIGHT, 1 HUB, WITH TRENCHING:**							
02.5103 011	Cast iron pipe, soil, 1 hub, 1-1/2", service weight	LF	9.15	15.74	24.89	9.65	18.80	0.1636
02.5103 021	Cast iron pipe, soil, 1 hub, 2", service weight	LF	10.10	16.24	26.34	9.95	20.05	0.1688
02.5103 031	Cast iron pipe, soil, 1 hub, 3", service weight	LF	12.29	17.32	29.61	10.61	22.90	0.1800
02.5103 041	Cast iron pipe, soil, 1 hub, 4", service weight	LF	16.31	18.12	34.43	11.10	27.41	0.1883
02.5103 051	Cast iron pipe, soil, 1 hub, 5", service weight	LF	23.05	21.26	44.31	13.03	36.08	0.2209
02.5103 061	Cast iron pipe, soil, 1 hub, 6", service weight	LF	28.22	24.41	52.63	14.96	43.18	0.2537
02.5103 071	Cast iron pipe, soil, 1 hub, 8", service weight	LF	54.33	28.08	82.41	17.21	71.54	0.2918
02.5103 081	Cast iron pipe, soil, 1 hub, 10", service weight	LF	71.12	30.50	101.62	18.69	89.81	0.3169
02.5104 000	**CAST IRON SOIL PIPE, NO HUB, SERVICE WEIGHT, WITH TRENCHING:**							
	Note: For extra heavy cast iron pipe, add 35% to the material costs.							
02.5104 011	Cast iron pipe, no hub, service weight, 2"	LF	10.48	16.22	26.70	9.94	20.42	0.1686
02.5104 021	Cast iron pipe, no hub, service weight, 3"	LF	11.81	17.84	29.65	10.93	22.74	0.1854
02.5104 031	Cast iron pipe, no hub, service weight, 4"	LF	15.78	19.97	35.75	13.37	29.15	0.1939
02.5104 041	Cast iron pipe, no hub, service weight, 5"	LF	24.58	23.43	48.01	15.69	40.27	0.2275
02.5104 051	Cast iron pipe, no hub, service weight, 6"	LF	28.97	26.92	55.89	18.02	46.99	0.2613
02.5104 061	Cast iron pipe, no hub, service weight, 8"	LF	51.99	30.95	82.94	20.72	72.71	0.3005
02.5104 071	Cast iron pipe, no hub, service weight, 10"	LF	74.81	33.60	108.41	22.49	97.30	0.3262
02.5105 000	**CONCRETE PIPE, NON-REINFORCED, WITH TRENCHING:**							
02.5105 011	Concrete pipe, non-reinforced, 6"	LF	11.76	20.32	32.08	12.45	24.21	0.2112
02.5105 021	Concrete pipe, non-reinforced, 8"	LF	12.86	21.24	34.10	13.01	25.87	0.2207
02.5105 031	Concrete pipe, non-reinforced, 10"	LF	14.78	22.16	36.94	13.58	28.36	0.2303
02.5105 041	Concrete pipe, non-reinforced, 12"	LF	16.52	23.09	39.61	14.15	30.67	0.2399
02.5105 051	Concrete pipe, non-reinforced, 15"	LF	20.55	26.79	47.34	16.42	36.97	0.2784
02.5105 061	Concrete pipe, non-reinforced, 18"	LF	24.58	34.17	58.75	20.94	45.52	0.3551
02.5105 071	Concrete pipe, non-reinforced, 21"	LF	28.59	37.87	66.46	23.20	51.79	0.3935
02.5105 081	Concrete pipe, non-reinforced, 24"	LF	32.56	43.41	75.97	26.60	59.16	0.4511

Division 2 CSI #	02 - SITEWORK Description	Unit	Material	Union Install	Union Total	Open Install	Open Total	Unit Man-Hrs
02.5106 000	**CONCRETE PIPE, REINFORCED, CLASS 3, WITH GASKETS, TRENCHING:**							
	Note: For class 2 pipe, deduct 5% from the material costs. For class 4, add 10%.							
02.5106 011	Concrete pipe, reinf, class 3, gaskets, 12"	LF	21.14	25.18	46.32	15.43	36.57	0.2617
02.5106 021	Concrete pipe, reinf, class 3, gaskets, 15"	LF	29.95	30.98	60.93	18.98	48.93	0.3219
02.5106 031	Concrete pipe, reinf, class 3, gaskets, 18"	LF	38.68	38.49	77.17	23.59	62.27	0.4000
02.5106 041	Concrete pipe, reinf, class 3, gaskets, 21"	LF	47.41	42.32	89.73	25.94	73.35	0.4398
02.5106 051	Concrete pipe, reinf, class 3, gaskets, 24"	LF	56.18	48.67	104.85	29.83	86.01	0.5058
02.5106 061	Concrete pipe, reinf, class 3, gaskets, 27"	LF	70.25	56.43	126.68	34.58	104.83	0.5864
02.5106 071	Concrete pipe, reinf, class 3, gaskets, 30"	LF	84.31	57.42	141.73	35.19	119.50	0.5967
02.5106 081	Concrete pipe, reinf, class 3, gaskets, 33"	LF	98.36	60.45	158.81	37.04	135.40	0.6282
02.5106 091	Concrete pipe, reinf, class 3, gaskets, 36"	LF	112.41	64.46	176.87	39.50	151.91	0.6699
02.5106 101	Concrete pipe, reinf, class 3, gaskets, 42"	LF	126.51	69.52	196.03	42.60	169.11	0.7224
02.5106 111	Concrete pipe, reinf, class 3, gaskets, 48"	LF	140.54	75.56	216.10	46.30	186.84	0.7852
02.5106 121	Concrete pipe, reinf, class 3, gaskets, 54"	LF	158.47	79.99	238.46	49.02	207.49	0.8312
02.5106 131	Concrete pipe, reinf, class 3, gaskets, 60"	LF	176.11	87.68	263.79	53.73	229.84	0.9112
02.5106 141	Concrete pipe, reinf, class 3, gaskets, 66"	LF	193.72	98.30	292.02	60.24	253.96	1.0215
02.5106 151	Concrete pipe, reinf, class 3, gaskets, 72"	LF	211.28	113.49	324.77	75.97	287.25	1.1017
02.5106 161	Concrete pipe, reinf, class 3, gaskets, 84"	LF	246.53	129.98	376.51	87.01	333.54	1.2618
02.5107 000	**CONCRETE PIPE, CAST-IN-PLACE:**							
	Note: The following prices include excavation, installation and backfill. Paving and grading is not included.							
02.5107 011	Concrete pipe, cast-in-place, 18"-24"	LF	20.39	22.12	42.51	13.56	33.95	0.2299
02.5107 021	Concrete pipe, cast-in-place, 30"	LF	24.48	28.40	52.88	19.01	43.49	0.2757
02.5107 031	Concrete pipe, cast-in-place, 36"	LF	28.57	33.13	61.70	22.18	50.75	0.3216
02.5107 041	Concrete pipe, cast-in-place, 42"	LF	33.66	39.43	73.09	26.40	60.06	0.3828
02.5107 051	Concrete pipe, cast-in-place, 48"	LF	42.86	53.74	96.60	35.98	78.84	0.5217
02.5107 061	Concrete pipe, cast-in-place, 60"	LF	56.14	70.38	126.52	47.11	103.25	0.6832
02.5107 071	Concrete pipe, cast-in-place, 72"	LF	71.46	83.67	155.13	51.27	122.73	0.8695
02.5107 081	Concrete pipe, cast-in-place, 84"	LF	91.88	107.58	199.46	65.92	157.80	1.1179
02.5108 000	**CORRUGATED METAL PIPE, BITUMINOUS COAT, 24" COVER, WITH TRENCH:**							
02.5108 011	Corrugated metal pipe, 10", 16 ga, bitum coat, 24" cover	LF	11.49	13.85	25.34	9.28	20.77	0.1345
02.5108 021	Corrugated metal pipe, 12", 16 ga, bitum coat, 24" cover	LF	14.05	18.78	32.83	12.57	26.62	0.1823
02.5108 031	Corrugated metal pipe, 15", 16 ga, bitum coat, 24" cover	LF	17.03	21.76	38.79	14.56	31.59	0.2112
02.5108 041	Corrugated metal pipe, 18", 16 ga, bitum coat, 24" cover	LF	19.95	24.01	43.96	14.71	34.66	0.2495
02.5108 051	Corrugated metal pipe, 24", 16 ga, bitum coat, 24" cover	LF	25.76	30.49	56.25	18.68	44.44	0.3168
02.5108 061	Corrugated metal pipe, 30", 16 ga, bitum coat, 24" cover	LF	25.76	36.01	61.77	22.07	47.83	0.3742
02.5108 071	Corrugated metal pipe, 15", 14 ga, bitum coat, 24" cover	LF	19.66	21.24	40.90	13.01	32.67	0.2207
02.5108 081	Corrugated metal pipe, 18", 14 ga, bitum coat, 24" cover	LF	23.11	24.01	47.12	14.71	37.82	0.2495
02.5108 091	Corrugated metal pipe, 24", 14 ga, bitum coat, 24" cover	LF	29.96	30.49	60.45	18.68	48.64	0.3168
02.5108 101	Corrugated metal pipe, 30", 14 ga, bitum coat, 24" cover	LF	37.06	34.36	71.42	20.20	57.26	0.3840
02.5108 111	Corrugated metal pipe, 30", 12 ga, bitum coat, 24" cover	LF	46.57	35.21	81.78	20.70	67.27	0.3935
02.5108 121	Corrugated metal pipe, 36", 12 ga, bitum coat, 24" cover	LF	55.74	42.94	98.68	25.25	80.99	0.4799
02.5108 131	Corrugated metal pipe, 48", 12 ga, bitum coat, 24" cover	LF	74.74	49.81	124.55	29.29	104.03	0.5567
02.5108 141	Corrugated metal pipe, 60", 12 ga, bitum coat, 24" cover	LF	92.52	75.57	168.09	44.43	136.95	0.8446
02.5108 151	Corrugated metal pipe, 72", 10 ga, bitum coat, 24" cover	LF	134.35	91.89	226.24	54.03	188.38	1.0269
02.5109 000	**CORRUGATED METAL PIPE, GALVANIZED, 24" COVER, WITH TRENCHING:**							
	Note: For aluminum pipe, deduct 15% from the labor costs.							
02.5109 011	Corrugated metal pipe, 8", 16 ga, galv, 24" cover	LF	7.41	17.54	24.95	10.75	18.16	0.1823
02.5109 021	Corrugated metal pipe, 10", 16 ga, galv, 24" cover	LF	8.22	18.47	26.69	11.32	19.54	0.1919
02.5109 031	Corrugated metal pipe, 12", 16 ga, galv, 24" cover	LF	9.08	20.77	29.85	13.90	22.98	0.2016
02.5109 041	Corrugated metal pipe, 15", 16 ga, galv, 24" cover	LF	10.11	23.83	33.94	15.95	26.06	0.2313
02.5109 051	Corrugated metal pipe, 18", 16 ga, galv, 24" cover	LF	12.58	26.92	39.50	18.02	30.60	0.2613
02.5109 061	Corrugated metal pipe, 24", 14 ga, galv, 24" cover	LF	15.24	33.86	49.10	22.67	37.91	0.3287
02.5109 071	Corrugated metal pipe, 30", 14 ga, galv, 24" cover	LF	21.21	39.07	60.28	26.16	47.37	0.3793
02.5109 081	Corrugated metal pipe, 36", 14 ga, galv, 24" cover	LF	30.11	50.18	80.29	33.59	63.70	0.4871
02.5109 091	Corrugated metal pipe, 42", 14 ga, galv, 24" cover	LF	33.14	52.09	85.23	34.87	68.01	0.5057
02.5109 101	Corrugated metal pipe, 48", 14 ga, galv, 24" cover	LF	38.32	60.60	98.92	40.57	78.89	0.5883
02.5109 111	Corrugated metal pipe, 54", 12 ga, galv, 24" cover	LF	59.20	75.10	134.30	50.28	109.48	0.7291
02.5109 121	Corrugated metal pipe, 60", 12 ga, galv, 24" cover	LF	61.88	95.52	157.40	63.95	125.83	0.9273
02.5109 131	Corrugated metal pipe, 66", 12 ga, galv, 24" cover	LF	67.43	99.86	167.29	66.85	134.28	0.9694
02.5109 141	Corrugated metal pipe, 72", 10 ga, galv, 24" cover	LF	92.62	107.07	199.69	65.61	158.23	1.1126
02.5109 151	Corrugated metal pipe, 78", 8 ga, galv, 24" cover	LF	137.42	119.16	256.58	79.77	217.19	1.1568

Division 2 CSI #	02 - SITEWORK Description	Unit	Material	Union Install	Union Total	Open Install	Open Total	Unit Man-Hrs
02.5109 000	**CORRUGATED METAL PIPE, GALVANIZED, 24" COVER, WITH TRENCHING: (Cont.)**							
02.5109 161	Corrugated metal pipe, 84", 8 ga, galv, 24" cover	LF	154.77	124.50	279.27	83.35	238.12	1.2086
02.5109 171	Corrugated metal pipe, 96", 8 ga, galv, 24" cover	LF	176.86	129.92	306.78	86.97	263.83	1.2612
02.5109 181	Corrugated metal pipe, 120", 8 ga, galv, 24" cover	LF	224.08	149.69	373.77	100.21	324.29	1.4532
02.5110 000	**PIPE, ABS, PLASTIC, WITH TRENCHING:**							
02.5110 011	Pipe, ABS, plastic, 2"	LF	9.26	16.38	25.64	10.04	19.30	0.1702
02.5110 021	Pipe, ABS, plastic, 3"	LF	13.47	17.17	30.64	10.52	23.99	0.1784
02.5110 031	Pipe, ABS, plastic, 4"	LF	23.14	19.05	42.19	11.68	34.82	0.1980
02.5110 041	Pipe, ABS, plastic, 6"	LF	38.17	23.15	61.32	15.50	53.67	0.2247
02.5110 051	Pipe Tap, ABS, 4"	EA	191.65	74.70	266.35	39.47	231.12	0.9200
02.5110 061	Pipe Tap, ABS, 6"	EA	255.57	109.62	365.19	57.92	313.49	1.3500
02.5110 071	Pipe Tap, PVC gravity sewer, 4", ASTM D3034	EA	192.03	75.15	267.18	39.70	231.73	0.9255
02.5110 081	Pipe Tap, PVC gravity sewer, 6", ASTM D3034	EA	252.67	110.22	362.89	58.23	310.90	1.3574
02.5110 091	Pipe Tap, PVC gravity sewer, 8", ASTM D3034	EA	535.71	150.30	686.01	79.41	615.12	1.8510
02.5110 101	Pipe Tap, PVC gravity sewer, 10", ASTM D3034	EA	707.56	200.39	907.95	105.87	813.43	2.4679
02.5110 111	Pipe Tap, PVC gravity sewer, 12", ASTM D3034	EA	980.47	250.49	1,230.96	132.34	1,112.81	3.0849
02.5110 121	Pipe Tap, PVC gravity sewer, 15", ASTM D3034	EA	1,314.05	350.69	1,664.74	185.28	1,499.33	4.3189
02.5111 000	**PIPE, PVC GRAVITY SEWER, ASTM D-3034, WITH TRENCH:**							
02.5111 011	Pipe, PVC gravity sewer, 4", ASTM D3034	LF	9.13	19.50	28.63	11.95	21.08	0.2026
02.5111 021	Pipe, PVC gravity sewer, 6", ASTM D3034	LF	11.20	21.76	32.96	13.33	24.53	0.2261
02.5111 031	Pipe, PVC gravity sewer, 8", ASTM D3034	LF	14.24	24.17	38.41	14.81	29.05	0.2512
02.5111 041	Pipe, PVC gravity sewer 10", ASTM D3034	LF	18.38	33.94	52.32	20.80	39.18	0.3527
02.5111 051	Pipe, PVC gravity sewer, 12", ASTM D3034	LF	26.43	43.78	70.21	26.83	53.26	0.4550
02.5111 061	Pipe, PVC gravity sewer, 15", ASTM D3034	LF	47.32	52.80	100.12	32.36	79.68	0.5487
02.5112 000	**VITRIFIED CLAY PIPE, RING SEAL, WITH TRENCHING:**							
02.5112 011	Clay pipe, 6", ring seal	LF	9.04	23.11	32.15	14.16	23.20	0.2402
02.5112 021	Clay pipe, 8", ring seal	LF	13.49	23.92	37.41	14.66	28.15	0.2486
02.5112 031	Clay pipe, 10", ring seal	LF	21.65	30.42	52.07	18.64	40.29	0.3161
02.5112 041	Clay pipe, 12", ring seal	LF	27.44	26.37	53.81	16.16	43.60	0.2740
02.5112 051	Clay pipe, 15", ring seal	LF	51.72	27.98	79.70	17.15	68.87	0.2908
02.5112 061	Clay pipe, 18", ring seal	LF	74.74	35.29	110.03	21.62	96.36	0.3667
02.5112 071	Clay pipe, 21", ring seal	LF	84.94	39.74	124.68	24.35	109.29	0.4130
02.5112 081	Clay pipe, 24", ring seal	LF	119.28	46.64	165.92	28.58	147.86	0.4847
02.5112 091	Clay pipe, 27", ring seal	LF	140.08	54.34	194.42	33.30	173.38	0.5647
02.5113 000	**PIPE, STORM DRAINAGE, PVC SDR-35, WITH TRENCHING:**							
02.5113 011	Pipe, PVC, SDR-35, 4"	LF	4.50	21.27	25.77	13.03	17.53	0.2210
02.5113 021	Pipe, PVC, SDR-35, 6"	LF	7.97	23.74	31.71	14.55	22.52	0.2467
02.5113 031	Pipe, PVC, SDR-35, 8"	LF	13.89	26.14	40.03	16.02	29.91	0.2716
02.5113 041	Pipe, PVC, SDR-35, 10"	LF	24.86	37.03	61.89	22.69	47.55	0.3848
02.5113 051	Pipe, PVC, SDR-35, 12"	LF	34.19	47.77	81.96	29.27	63.46	0.4964
02.5113 061	Pipe, PVC, SDR-35, 15"	LF	53.06	57.60	110.66	35.30	88.36	0.5986
02.5113 071	Pipe, PVC, SDR-35, 18"	LF	87.94	69.36	157.30	42.51	130.45	0.7208
02.5113 081	Pipe, PVC, SDR-35, 21"	LF	137.12	85.69	222.81	52.51	189.63	0.8905
02.5113 091	Pipe, PVC, SDR-35, 24"	LF	191.09	114.11	305.20	69.93	261.02	1.1858
02.5113 101	Pipe Tap, PVC, SDR-35, 4"	EA	192.03	75.15	267.18	39.70	231.73	0.9255
02.5113 111	Pipe Tap, PVC, SDR-35, 6"	EA	252.67	110.22	362.89	58.23	310.90	1.3574
02.5113 121	Pipe Tap, PVC, SDR-35, 8"	EA	535.71	150.30	686.01	79.41	615.12	1.8510
02.5113 131	Pipe Tap, PVC, SDR-35, 10"	EA	707.56	200.39	907.95	105.87	813.43	2.4679
02.5113 141	Pipe Tap, PVC, SDR-35, 12"	EA	980.47	250.49	1,230.96	132.34	1,112.81	3.0849
02.5113 151	Pipe Tap, PVC, SDR-35, 15"	EA	1,314.05	350.69	1,664.74	185.28	1,499.33	4.3189
02.5300 000	**WATER, STEAM & GAS DISTRIBUTION PIPING:**							
02.5302 000	**ACID WASTE PIPE, POLYPROPYLENE, WITH TRENCH:**							
02.5302 011	Polypropylene acid waste pipe, 2", with trench	LF	15.56	16.38	31.94	10.04	25.60	0.1702
02.5302 021	Polypropylene acid waste pipe, 3", with trench	LF	19.44	17.17	36.61	10.52	29.96	0.1784
02.5302 031	Polypropylene acid waste pipe, 4", with trench	LF	23.34	19.05	42.39	11.68	35.02	0.1980
02.5302 041	Polypropylene acid waste pipe, 6", with trench	LF	39.98	21.62	61.60	13.25	53.23	0.2247
02.5303 000	**COPPER TUBING, TYPE K HARD, WITH TRENCH:**							
	Note: For type 'I', deduct 20% from the material costs.							
02.5303 011	Copper pipe, 'K' hard, 1/2", with trench	LF	10.94	6.69	17.63	4.10	15.04	0.0695
02.5303 021	Copper pipe, 'K' hard, 3/4", with trench	LF	15.57	7.70	23.27	4.72	20.29	0.0800
02.5303 031	Copper pipe, 'K' hard, 1", with trench	LF	19.10	13.78	32.88	8.44	27.54	0.1432
02.5303 041	Copper pipe, 'K' hard, 1-1/4", with trench	LF	23.17	14.20	37.37	8.70	31.87	0.1476

Division 2 CSI #	02 - SITEWORK Description	Unit	Material	Union Install	Union Total	Open Install	Open Total	Unit Man-Hrs
02.5303 000	COPPER TUBING, TYPE K HARD, WITH TRENCH: (Cont.)							
02.5303 051	Copper pipe, 'K' hard, 1-1/2", with trench	LF	28.17	17.02	45.19	10.43	38.60	0.1769
02.5303 061	Copper pipe, 'K' hard, 2", with trench	LF	42.80	17.84	60.64	10.93	53.73	0.1854
02.5303 071	Copper pipe, 'K' hard, 3", with trench	LF	77.43	20.36	97.79	12.48	89.91	0.2116
02.5303 081	Copper pipe, 'K' hard, 4", with trench	LF	119.25	19.42	138.67	11.90	131.15	0.2018
02.5303 091	Copper pipe, 'K' hard, 5", with trench	LF	198.26	21.98	220.24	13.47	211.73	0.2284
02.5303 101	Copper pipe, 'K' hard, 6", with trench	LF	291.36	27.98	319.34	17.15	308.51	0.2908
02.5303 111	Pipe Tap, Copper pipe ,'K' hard, 4"	EA	332.13	75.11	407.24	39.68	371.81	0.9250
02.5304 000	PVC, SCHEDULE 40, SOLVENT WELD, WITH TRENCH:							
	Note: For schedule 80, add 26% to the material costs.							
02.5304 011	PVC, schedule 40, 1/2", weld, with trench	LF	.92	5.33	6.25	3.57	4.49	0.0517
02.5304 021	PVC, schedule 40, 3/4", weld, with trench	LF	1.27	6.99	8.26	4.68	5.95	0.0679
02.5304 031	PVC, schedule 40, 1", weld, with trench	LF	1.89	8.32	10.21	5.57	7.46	0.0808
02.5304 041	PVC, schedule 40, 1-1/2", weld, with trench	LF	3.05	9.60	12.65	6.43	9.48	0.0932
02.5304 051	PVC, schedule 40, 2", weld, with trench	LF	3.99	10.62	14.61	7.11	11.10	0.1031
02.5304 061	PVC, schedule 40, 2-1/2", weld, with trench	LF	6.36	12.01	18.37	8.04	14.40	0.1166
02.5304 071	PVC, schedule 40, 3", weld, with trench	LF	7.53	13.51	21.04	9.05	16.58	0.1312
02.5304 081	PVC, schedule 40, 4", weld, with trench	LF	9.91	14.63	24.54	9.79	19.70	0.1420
02.5305 000	PVC, MUNI WATER, AWWA C900, CLASS 150, WITH TRENCHING:							
02.5305 011	PVC municipal water pipe, 4", '150', C900	LF	24.14	15.12	39.26	10.12	34.26	0.1468
02.5305 021	PVC municipal water pipe, 6", '150', C900	LF	29.32	17.02	46.34	11.39	40.71	0.1652
02.5305 031	PVC municipal water pipe, 8", '150', C900	LF	38.73	18.78	57.51	12.57	51.30	0.1823
02.5305 041	PVC municipal water pipe, 10", '150', C900	LF	50.86	19.77	70.63	13.23	64.09	0.1919
02.5305 051	PVC municipal water pipe, 12", '150', C900	LF	62.64	20.77	83.41	13.90	76.54	0.2016
02.5305 061	Pipe Tap, municipal water pipe, 4",'150',C900	EA	192.03	75.15	267.18	39.70	231.73	0.9255
02.5305 071	Pipe Tap, municipal water pipe, 6",'150',C900	EA	252.67	110.22	362.89	58.23	310.90	1.3574
02.5305 081	Pipe Tap, municipal water pipe, 8",'150',C900	EA	535.71	150.30	686.01	79.41	615.12	1.8510
02.5305 091	Pipe Tap, municipal water pipe, 10",'150',C900	EA	707.56	200.39	907.95	105.87	813.43	2.4679
02.5305 101	Pipe Tap, municipal water pipe, 12",'150',C900	EA	980.47	250.49	1,230.96	132.34	1,112.81	3.0849
02.5305 111	Hot tap for 4" water pipe	EA	624.44	1,235.05	1,859.49	652.51	1,276.95	15.2100
02.5305 161	Thrust blocks for 4" water pipe	EA	71.88	97.44	169.32	51.48	123.36	1.2000
02.5305 171	Thrust blocks for 6" water pipe	EA	143.76	203.00	346.76	107.25	251.01	2.5000
02.5305 181	Thrust blocks for 8" water pipe	EA	164.73	324.80	489.53	171.60	336.33	4.0000
02.5305 191	Thrust blocks for 10" water pipe	EA	209.63	406.00	615.63	214.50	424.13	5.0000
02.5305 201	Thrust blocks for 12" water pipe	EA	299.49	609.00	908.49	321.75	621.24	7.5000
02.5305 121	Hot tap for 6" water pipe	EA	847.41	1,694.64	2,542.05	895.32	1,742.73	20.8700
02.5305 131	Hot tap for 8" water pipe	EA	893.99	1,962.60	2,856.59	1,036.89	1,930.88	24.1700
02.5305 141	Hot tap for 10" water pipe	EA	1,656.35	2,388.90	4,045.25	1,262.12	2,918.47	29.4200
02.5305 151	Hot tap for 12" water pipe	EA	2,445.23	3,140.82	5,586.05	1,659.37	4,104.60	38.6800
02.5306 000	DUCTILE IRON PIPE, WITH EXCAVATION & FILL:							
	Note: For class 52 pipe, sizes 3" to 4" add 7% to the material costs. For sizes 6" to 24" add 15%							
02.5306 011	Ductile iron pipe, 350 psi, class 50, 3", excavate & fill	LF	15.77	22.58	38.35	15.12	30.89	0.2192
02.5306 021	Ductile iron pipe, 350 psi, class 50, 4", excavate & fill	LF	16.57	22.58	39.15	15.12	31.69	0.2192
02.5306 031	Ductile iron pipe, 350 psi, class 50, 6", excavate & fill	LF	17.90	28.43	46.33	19.03	36.93	0.2760
02.5306 041	Ductile iron pipe, 350 psi, class 50, 8", excavate & fill	LF	19.81	28.43	48.24	19.03	38.84	0.2760
02.5306 051	Ductile iron pipe, 350 psi, class 50, 10", excavate & fill	LF	24.37	32.22	56.59	21.57	45.94	0.3128
02.5306 061	Ductile iron pipe, 350 psi, class 50, 12", excavate & fill	LF	29.65	40.75	70.40	27.28	56.93	0.3956
02.5306 071	Ductile iron pipe, 350 psi, class 50, 14", excavate & fill	LF	35.55	50.29	85.84	33.67	69.22	0.4882
02.5306 081	Ductile iron pipe, 350 psi, class 50, 16", excavate & fill	LF	40.72	54.09	94.81	36.21	76.93	0.5251
02.5306 091	Ductile iron pipe, 350 psi, class 50, 18", excavate & fill	LF	46.19	63.62	109.81	42.59	88.78	0.6176
02.5306 101	Ductile iron pipe, 350 psi, class 50, 20", excavate & fill	LF	51.91	70.49	122.40	47.19	99.10	0.6843
02.5306 111	Ductile iron pipe, 350 psi, class 50, 24", excavate & fill	LF	63.96	70.49	134.45	47.19	111.15	0.6843
02.5306 121	Ductile iron pipe, 350 psi, class 50, 30', excavate & fill	LF	84.47	70.49	154.96	47.19	131.66	0.6843
02.5306 131	Ductile iron pipe, 350 psi, class 50, 36", excavate & fill	LF	107.17	74.76	181.93	50.05	157.22	0.7258
02.5306 141	Ductile iron pipe, 350 psi, class 50, 42", excavate & fill	LF	132.29	80.62	212.91	53.97	186.26	0.7826
02.5306 151	Ductile iron pipe, 350 psi, class 50, 48", excavate & fill	LF	159.68	87.63	247.31	58.66	218.34	0.8507
02.5306 161	Ductile iron pipe, 350 psi, class 50, 54", excavate & fill	LF	187.54	92.76	280.30	62.10	249.64	0.9005
02.5306 171	Pipe Tap, Ductile iron pipe, 350psi, class 50, 4"	EA	241.69	260.51	502.20	137.64	379.33	3.2083
02.5306 181	Pipe Tap, Ductile iron pipe, 350psi, class 50, 6"	EA	599.40	260.51	859.91	137.64	737.04	3.2083
02.5306 191	Pipe Tap, Ductile iron pipe, 350psi, class 50, 8"	EA	667.05	455.91	1,122.96	240.87	907.92	5.6146
02.5306 201	Pipe Tap, Ductile iron pipe, 350psi, class 50, 10"	EA	763.73	455.91	1,219.64	240.87	1,004.60	5.6146
02.5306 211	Pipe Tap, Ductile iron pipe, 350psi, class 50, 12"	EA	937.74	716.41	1,654.15	378.50	1,316.24	8.8228

Division 2 CSI #	02 - SITEWORK Description	Unit	Material	Union Install	Union Total	Open Install	Open Total	Unit Man-Hrs
02.5307 000	**STEEL PIPE, GALVANIZED, SCH 40, TREADED & CUT, WITH TRENCHING:**							
02.5307 011	Steel pipe, galvanized, 1/2", schedule 40, threaded & cut	LF	2.46	7.66	10.12	4.50	6.96	0.0767
02.5307 021	Steel pipe, galvanized, 3/4", schedule 40, threaded & cut	LF	2.74	8.62	11.36	5.06	7.80	0.0863
02.5307 031	Steel pipe, galvanized, 1", schedule 40, threaded & cut	LF	3.47	9.60	13.07	5.63	9.10	0.0961
02.5307 041	Steel pipe, galvanized, 1-1/4", schedule 40, threaded & cut	LF	4.41	10.55	14.96	6.19	10.60	0.1056
02.5307 051	Steel pipe, galvanized, 1-1/2", schedule 40, threaded & cut	LF	5.25	11.50	16.75	6.75	12.00	0.1151
02.5307 061	Steel pipe, galvanized, 2", schedule 40, threaded & cut	LF	6.92	13.44	20.36	7.88	14.80	0.1345
02.5307 071	Steel pipe, galvanized, 2-1/2", schedule 40, threaded & cut	LF	9.72	15.33	25.05	9.00	18.72	0.1535
02.5307 081	Steel pipe, galvanized, 3", schedule 40, threaded & cut	LF	12.58	17.26	29.84	10.13	22.71	0.1728
02.5307 091	Steel pipe, galvanized, 4", schedule 40, threaded & cut	LF	18.30	21.10	39.40	12.38	30.68	0.2112
02.5307 101	Steel pipe, galvanized, 5", schedule 40, threaded & cut	LF	26.46	23.00	49.46	13.50	39.96	0.2303
02.5307 111	Steel pipe, galvanized, 6", schedule 40, threaded & cut	LF	31.95	23.96	55.91	14.06	46.01	0.2399
02.5307 121	Pipe Tap, Steel pipe galv., 4",sched 40, threaded & cut	EA	141.28	205.72	347.00	120.73	262.01	2.0595
02.5307 131	Pipe Tap, Steel pipe galv., 5",sched 40, threaded & cut	EA	199.11	257.15	456.26	150.91	350.02	2.5743
02.5307 141	Pipe Tap, Steel pipe galv., 6",sched 40, threaded & cut	EA	304.89	257.15	562.04	150.91	455.80	2.5743
02.5308 000	**STEEL PIPE, BLACK, SCH 40, WELDED, TREADED & CUT, WITH TRENCHING:**							
	Note: For schedule 80, add 39% to the material costs.							
02.5308 011	Steel pipe, black, A-120, schedule 40, weld, 1/2", threaded & cut	LF	2.53	7.66	10.19	4.50	7.03	0.0767
02.5308 021	Steel pipe, black, A-120, schedule 40, weld, 3/4", threaded & cut	LF	3.17	8.62	11.79	5.06	8.23	0.0863
02.5308 031	Steel pipe, black, A-120, schedule 40, weld, 1", threaded & cut	LF	3.94	9.60	13.54	5.63	9.57	0.0961
02.5308 041	Steel pipe, black, A-120, schedule 40, weld, 1-1/4", threaded & cut	LF	4.92	10.55	15.47	6.19	11.11	0.1056
02.5308 051	Steel pipe, black, A-120, schedule 40, weld, 1-1/2", threaded & cut	LF	5.37	11.50	16.87	6.75	12.12	0.1151
02.5308 061	Steel pipe, black, A-120, schedule 40, weld, 2", threaded & cut	LF	6.50	13.44	19.94	7.88	14.38	0.1345
02.5308 071	Steel pipe, black, A-120, schedule 40, weld, 2-1/2", threaded & cut	LF	8.69	15.33	24.02	9.00	17.69	0.1535
02.5308 081	Steel pipe, black, A-120, schedule 40, weld, 3", threaded & cut	LF	10.26	17.26	27.52	10.13	20.39	0.1728
02.5308 091	Steel pipe, black, A-120, schedule 40, weld, 4", threaded & cut	LF	14.58	19.39	33.97	12.61	27.19	0.2112
02.5308 101	Steel pipe, black, A-120, schedule 40, weld, 5", threaded & cut	LF	20.47	21.14	41.61	13.75	34.22	0.2303
02.5308 111	Steel pipe, black, A-120, schedule 40, weld, 6", threaded & cut	LF	25.66	22.02	47.68	14.33	39.99	0.2399
02.5309 000	**STEEL PIPE, BLACK, SCH 40, WITH XTRUCOAT, TREADED & CUT, WITH TRENCH:**							
02.5309 011	Steel pipe, black, wrapped, 1/2", schedule 40, threaded & cut	LF	2.73	13.09	15.82	8.17	10.90	0.1345
02.5309 021	Steel pipe, black, wrapped, 3/4", schedule 40, threaded & cut	LF	3.34	13.54	16.88	8.45	11.79	0.1391
02.5309 031	Steel pipe, black, wrapped, 1", schedule 40, threaded & cut	LF	4.13	14.03	18.16	8.75	12.88	0.1441
02.5309 041	Steel pipe, black, wrapped, 1-1/4", schedule 40, threaded & cut	LF	5.25	14.40	19.65	8.98	14.23	0.1479
02.5309 051	Steel pipe, black, wrapped, 1-1/2", schedule 40, threaded & cut	LF	5.70	15.50	21.20	9.68	15.38	0.1593
02.5309 061	Steel pipe, black, wrapped, 2", schedule 40, threaded & cut	LF	6.91	15.87	22.78	9.91	16.82	0.1631
02.5309 071	Steel pipe, black, wrapped, 2-1/2", schedule 40, threaded & cut	LF	9.20	16.35	25.55	10.21	19.41	0.1680
02.5309 081	Steel pipe, black, wrapped, 3", schedule 40, threaded & cut	LF	10.99	18.46	29.45	11.52	22.51	0.1897
02.5309 091	Steel pipe, black, wrapped, 4", schedule 40, threaded & cut	LF	15.46	21.95	37.41	13.70	29.16	0.2255
02.5310 000	**STEEL PIPE, MORTAR LINED, CEMENT COATED, WITH TRENCH:**							
02.5310 011	Steel pipe, mortar lined, 20", cement coated	LF	216.14	66.87	283.01	43.50	259.64	0.7284
02.5310 021	Steel pipe, mortar lined, 24", cement coated	LF	256.11	76.89	333.00	50.02	306.13	0.8376
02.5310 031	Steel pipe, mortar lined, 30", cement coated	LF	316.03	92.90	408.93	60.44	376.47	1.0120
02.5310 041	Steel pipe, mortar lined, 36", cement coated	LF	375.96	102.51	478.47	66.69	442.65	1.1167
02.5311 000	**STEEL PIPE, PRE-INSULATED, WITH STEEL JACKET, TRENCHING:**							
02.5311 011	Steel pipe, pre-insulated, steel jacket, 4"	LF	61.33	70.87	132.20	44.23	105.56	0.7281
02.5311 021	Steel pipe, pre-insulated, steel jacket, 6"	LF	80.05	93.23	173.28	58.19	138.24	0.9579
02.5311 031	Steel pipe, pre-insulated, steel jacket, 8"	LF	92.88	126.80	219.68	79.15	172.03	1.3028
02.5311 041	Steel pipe, pre-insulated, steel jacket, 10"	LF	109.24	151.42	260.66	94.51	203.75	1.5557
02.5311 051	Steel pipe, pre-insulated, steel jacket, 12"	LF	125.63	184.98	310.61	115.46	241.09	1.9005
02.5312 000	**STEEL PIPE, PRE-INSULATED, WITH PVC JACKET, TRENCHING:**							
02.5312 011	Steel pipe, pre-insulated, PVC jacket, 2"	LF	23.56	21.10	44.66	13.73	37.29	0.2299
02.5312 021	Steel pipe, pre-insulated, PVC jacket, 4"	LF	38.74	44.32	83.06	28.83	67.57	0.4828
02.5312 031	Steel pipe, pre-insulated, PVC jacket, 6"	LF	51.08	58.39	109.47	37.99	89.07	0.6361
02.5312 041	Steel pipe, pre-insulated, PVC jacket, 8"	LF	59.62	79.50	139.12	51.72	111.34	0.8660
02.5312 051	Steel pipe, pre-insulated, PVC jacket, 10"	LF	70.48	94.98	165.46	61.79	132.27	1.0346
02.5312 061	Steel pipe, pre-insulated, PVC jacket, 12"	LF	81.32	116.08	197.40	75.52	156.84	1.2645
02.5400 000	**VALVES & SPECIALTIES:**							
02.5401 000	**CHECK VALVE, BRASS, 125#, SCREWED:**							
02.5401 011	Check valve, brass, 125#, 1/2", screw	EA	33.03	23.84	56.87	13.99	47.02	0.2387
02.5401 021	Check valve, brass, 125#, 3/4", screw	EA	40.37	28.92	69.29	16.97	57.34	0.2895
02.5401 031	Check valve, brass, 125#, 1", screw	EA	55.22	35.29	90.51	20.71	75.93	0.3533
02.5401 041	Check valve, brass, 125#, 1-1/4", screw	EA	76.40	41.30	117.70	24.24	100.64	0.4135

Division 2 CSI #	02 - SITEWORK Description	Unit	Material	Union Install	Union Total	Open Install	Open Total	Unit Man-Hrs
02.5401 000	**CHECK VALVE, BRASS, 125#, SCREWED: (Cont.)**							
02.5401 051	Check valve, brass, 125#, 1-1/2", screw	EA	90.86	47.96	138.82	28.14	119.00	0.4801
02.5401 061	Check valve, brass, 125#, 2", screw	EA	132.70	77.58	210.28	45.53	178.23	0.7767
02.5402 000	**CHECK VALVE, IRON BODY, FLANGED, BOLT & GASKET SET:**							
	Note: For the following items, add for companion flanges.							
02.5402 011	Check valve, 125#, iron body, 2", flanged, bolt & gasket	EA	189.31	115.70	305.01	74.79	264.10	1.2100
02.5402 021	Check valve, 125#, iron body, 2-1/2", flanged, bolt & gasket	EA	238.63	129.09	367.72	83.44	322.07	1.3500
02.5402 031	Check valve, 125#, iron body, 3", flanged, bolt & gasket	EA	260.68	143.43	404.11	92.72	353.40	1.5000
02.5402 041	Check valve, 125#, iron body, 4", flanged, bolt & gasket	EA	483.76	229.49	713.25	148.34	632.10	2.4000
02.5402 051	Check valve, 125#, iron body, 5"-6", flanged, bolt & gasket	EA	699.73	349.62	1,049.35	205.17	904.90	3.5000
02.5402 061	Check valve, iron body, 8", weld flanged, bolt & gasket	EA	1,266.83	459.49	1,726.32	269.65	1,536.48	4.6000
02.5402 071	Check valve, iron body, 10", weld flanged, bolt & gasket	EA	2,163.63	679.25	2,842.88	398.62	2,562.25	6.8000
02.5402 081	Check valve, iron body, 12", weld flanged, bolt & gasket	EA	3,361.30	749.18	4,110.48	439.65	3,800.95	7.5000
02.5402 091	Check valve, iron body, 14", weld flanged, bolt & gasket	EA	3,897.68	1,228.65	5,126.33	721.03	4,618.71	12.3000
02.5403 000	**GATE OR GLOBE VALVE, BRASS, 125#, SCREWED:**							
02.5403 011	Gate/globe valve, brass, 125#, 1", screwed	EA	54.35	32.43	86.78	21.10	75.45	0.3533
02.5403 021	Gate/globe valve, brass, 125#, 1-1/2", screwed	EA	92.76	44.07	136.83	28.67	121.43	0.4801
02.5403 031	Gate/globe valve, brass, 125#, 2", screwed	EA	131.22	71.30	202.52	46.38	177.60	0.7767
02.5404 000	**GATE VALVE, IRON BODY, FLANGED, BOLT & GASKET SET:**							
	Note: For the following items, add for companion flanges.							
02.5404 011	Gate valve, 125#, iron body, flanged, 2", bolt & gasket	EA	312.72	120.87	433.59	70.93	383.65	1.2100
02.5404 021	Gate valve, 125#, iron body, flanged, 2-1/2", bolt & gasket	EA	342.57	134.85	477.42	79.14	421.71	1.3500
02.5404 031	Gate valve, 125#, iron body, flanged, 3", bolt & gasket	EA	390.87	149.84	540.71	87.93	478.80	1.5000
02.5404 041	Gate valve, 125#, iron body, flanged, 4", bolt & gasket	EA	572.46	239.74	812.20	140.69	713.15	2.4000
02.5404 051	Gate valve, 125#, iron body, flanged, 5"-6", bolt & gasket	EA	1,047.00	349.62	1,396.62	205.17	1,252.17	3.5000
02.5404 061	Gate valve, 125#, iron body, flanged, 8", bolt & gasket	EA	1,965.60	459.49	2,425.09	269.65	2,235.25	4.6000
02.5404 071	Gate valve, 125#, iron body, flanged, 10", bolt & gasket	EA	3,241.56	659.27	3,900.83	386.89	3,628.45	6.6000
02.5404 081	Gate valve, 125#, iron body, flanged, 12", bolt & gasket	EA	4,353.12	749.18	5,102.30	439.65	4,792.77	7.5000
02.5404 091	Gate valve, 125#, iron body, flanged, 14", bolt & gasket	EA	5,078.20	1,228.65	6,306.85	721.03	5,799.23	12.3000
02.5405 000	**GATE VALVE, IRON BODY, MECHANICAL JOINT, WITH ACCESSORIES:**							
02.5405 011	Gate valve, iron body, mech joint, 2", complete	EA	262.17	91.86	354.03	53.91	316.08	0.9196
02.5405 021	Gate valve, iron body, mech joint, 3", complete	EA	371.73	111.00	482.73	65.14	436.87	1.1112
02.5405 031	Gate valve, iron body, mech joint, 4", complete	EA	435.10	149.28	584.38	87.60	522.70	1.4944
02.5405 041	Gate valve, iron body, mech joint, 6", complete	EA	567.64	229.65	797.29	134.77	702.41	2.2990
02.5405 051	Gate valve, iron body, mech joint, 8", complete	EA	879.00	267.92	1,146.92	157.23	1,036.23	2.6822
02.5405 061	Gate valve, iron body, mech joint, 10", complete	EA	1,397.69	363.61	1,761.30	213.38	1,611.07	3.6401
02.5405 071	Gate valve, iron body, mech joint, 12", complete	EA	1,729.13	428.67	2,157.80	251.56	1,980.69	4.2914
02.5405 081	Gate valve, iron body, mech joint, 14", complete	EA	3,919.37	528.19	4,447.56	309.96	4,229.33	5.2877
02.5405 091	Gate valve, iron body, mech joint, 16", complete	EA	5,245.05	604.73	5,849.78	354.89	5,599.94	6.0540
02.5406 000	**GAS COCK, IRON BODY, SCREWED, 125#:**							
02.5406 011	Gas cock, iron body, 3/4", 125#, screwed	EA	26.39	37.89	64.28	22.23	48.62	0.3793
02.5406 021	Gas cock, iron body, 1", 125#, screwed	EA	37.94	53.05	90.99	31.13	69.07	0.5311
02.5406 031	Gas cock, iron body, 1-1/2", 125#, screwed	EA	74.07	68.20	142.27	40.03	114.10	0.6828
02.5406 041	Gas cock, iron body, 2", 125#, screwed	EA	116.34	98.51	214.85	57.81	174.15	0.9862
02.5406 051	Gas cock, iron body, 2-1/2", 125#, screwed	EA	197.72	121.26	318.98	71.16	268.88	1.2139
02.5406 061	Gas cock, iron body, 3", 125#, screwed	EA	314.52	156.30	470.82	104.63	419.15	1.5173
02.5406 071	Gas cock, iron body, 4", 125#, screwed	EA	487.11	218.82	705.93	146.49	633.60	2.1243
02.5407 000	**HOSE BIBB & HOSE GATE, WITH CAP:**							
02.5407 011	Hose bibb, 3/4", with cap	EA	17.53	30.43	47.96	17.86	35.39	0.3046
02.5407 021	Hose bibb, 1", with cap	EA	19.97	31.61	51.58	18.55	38.52	0.3164
02.5407 051	Hose gate, 1", with cap	EA	118.72	31.61	150.33	18.55	137.27	0.3164
02.5407 061	Hose gate, 1-1/2", with cap	EA	184.18	43.12	227.30	25.31	209.49	0.4317
02.5407 071	Hose gate, 2", with cap	EA	264.03	45.28	309.31	26.57	290.60	0.4533
02.5408 000	**SPECIALTIES:**							
02.5408 011	Fire hydrant, (2) 2-1/2" outlets	EA	1,062.46	744.94	1,807.40	437.16	1,499.62	7.4576
02.5408 021	Fire hydrant, (1) 2-1/2"/(1) 4/4 1/2"	EA	1,224.47	744.94	1,969.41	437.16	1,661.63	7.4576
02.5408 031	Fire hydrant, (2) 2-1/2"/(1) 4/4 1/2"	EA	1,588.83	863.16	2,451.99	506.54	2,095.37	8.6411
02.5408 041	Fire hydrant, bury	VF	369.01	329.66	698.67	193.46	562.47	3.3002
02.5408 051	Post indicator, for valve, 4"	EA	660.30	396.22	1,056.52	265.25	925.55	3.8464
02.5408 061	Post indicator, for valve, 6"	EA	1,009.94	542.36	1,552.30	363.08	1,373.02	5.2651
02.5408 071	Valve box, cast iron, 4" deep	EA	118.64	145.36	264.00	97.31	215.95	1.4111
02.5408 081	Add for each extra foot depth	VF	44.15	33.98	78.13	22.75	66.90	0.3299

Division 2 CSI #	02 - SITEWORK Description	Unit	Material	Union Install	Union Total	Open Install	Open Total	Unit Man-Hrs
02.5408 000	SPECIALTIES: (Cont.)							
02.5408 091	Thrust blocks for 6" water pipe	EA	143.76	203.00	346.76	107.25	251.01	2.5000
02.5408 101	Thrust blocks for 8" water pipe	EA	164.73	324.80	489.53	171.60	336.33	4.0000
02.5408 111	Thrust blocks for 10" water pipe	EA	209.63	406.00	615.63	214.50	424.13	5.0000
02.5408 121	Thrust blocks for 12" water pipe	EA	299.49	609.00	908.49	321.75	621.24	7.5000
02.5500 000	MECHANICAL UTILITIES, ACCESSORIES:							
02.5501 000	CATCH BASINS, WITH GRATE, LIGHT DUTY:							
	Note: For heavy duty grade, add 15% to the material costs.							
02.5501 011	Catch basin, 2'x2'x2', grate, light duty	EA	552.17	469.77	1,021.94	276.20	828.37	5.2500
02.5501 021	Catch basin, 2'x2'x4', grate, light duty	EA	697.79	731.12	1,428.91	429.87	1,127.66	8.1708
02.5501 031	Catch basin, 3'x3'x2', grate, light duty	EA	840.13	835.66	1,675.79	491.33	1,331.46	9.3391
02.5501 041	Catch basin, 3'x3'x4', grate, light duty	EA	989.16	871.63	1,860.79	512.48	1,501.64	9.7411
02.5501 051	Add for 6" grade ring	EA	118.53	156.81	275.34	92.20	210.73	1.7525
02.5502 000	DROP INLETS, PRECAST CONCRETE, THICK WALL, STANDARD GRATES:							
02.5502 011	Drop inlet, precast, 12"x12"x4", thick wall, grate	EA	348.59	306.19	654.78	179.69	528.28	3.0653
02.5502 021	Drop inlet, precast, 16"x16"x5", thick wall, grate	EA	458.19	382.74	840.93	224.61	682.80	3.8316
02.5502 031	Drop inlet, precast, 16"x24"x5", thick wall, grate	EA	537.94	459.29	997.23	269.53	807.47	4.5980
02.5502 041	Drop inlet, precast, 24"x24"x5", thick wall, grate	EA	652.45	612.39	1,264.84	359.38	1,011.83	6.1306
02.5502 051	Drop inlet, precast, 24"x30"x5", thick wall, grate	EA	801.88	688.93	1,490.81	404.30	1,206.18	6.8969
02.5502 061	Drop inlet, precast, 30"x30"x6", thick wall, grate	EA	856.65	765.48	1,622.13	449.22	1,305.87	7.6632
02.5502 071	Drop inlet, precast, 36"x36"x6", thick wall, grate	EA	911.53	918.58	1,830.11	539.06	1,450.59	9.1959
02.5502 081	Drop inlet, precast, 36"x48"x6", thick wall, grate	EA	1,185.37	1,071.67	2,257.04	628.90	1,814.27	10.7285
02.5502 091	Drop inlet, precast, 48"x48"x6", thick wall, grate	EA	1,559.00	1,224.77	2,783.77	718.75	2,277.75	12.2612
02.5503 000	CURB VALVE BOX, WITH CAST IRON LID:							
02.5503 011	Curb valve box, 8-1/2" dia x 12", cast iron lid	EA	47.11	48.88	95.99	28.74	75.85	0.5463
02.5503 021	Curb valve box, 8-1/2" diax30", cast iron lid	EA	70.78	77.39	148.17	45.50	116.28	0.8649
02.5504 000	MANHOLES, WITH LID & RUNGS:							
02.5504 011	Manhole, 4' dia x 6'-8' deep, lid, rungs	EA	1,574.07	1,264.69	2,838.76	743.58	2,317.65	14.1338
02.5504 021	Manhole, 4' dia x 9'-12' deep, lid, rungs	EA	1,967.67	1,616.34	3,584.01	950.33	2,918.00	18.0637
02.5504 031	Manhole, 4' dia x 13'-16' deep, lid, rungs	EA	2,439.89	1,967.98	4,407.87	1,157.08	3,596.97	21.9935
02.5505 000	CLEANOUTS:							
02.5505 011	Cleanout, 4" to grade	EA	229.23	78.74	307.97	46.30	275.53	0.8800
02.5505 021	Cleanout, 6" to grade	EA	375.09	89.48	464.57	52.61	427.70	1.0000
02.5505 031	Cleanout, 8" to grade	EA	428.11	100.22	528.33	58.92	487.03	1.1200
02.5506 000	AREA DRAINS, PRECAST, LANDSCAPE LIGHT TRAFFIC AREAS:							
02.5506 011	Precast area drain, 12x12x3, thick wall	EA	235.42	274.28	509.70	161.27	396.69	3.0653
02.5506 021	Precast area drain, 16x16x3, thick wall	EA	306.07	342.85	648.92	201.58	507.65	3.8316
02.5506 031	Add per foot over 3' high	LF	45.61		45.61		45.61	
02.5600 000	MISCELLANEOUS SITE EQUIPMENT:							
02.5601 000	FUEL STORAGE TANKS, UNDERGROUND:							
02.5601 011	Underground double wall oil tank, 500 gal, coated steel	EA	7,704.14	685.70	8,389.84	403.16	8,107.30	7.6632
02.5601 021	Underground tank, steel/glass, 1,000 gal, with access	EA	9,811.50	857.13	10,668.63	503.95	10,315.45	9.5790
02.5601 031	Underground tank, steel/glass, 2,000 gal, with access	EA	12,588.32	936.68	13,525.00	550.72	13,139.04	10.4680
02.5601 041	Underground tank, steel/glass, 4,000 gal, with access	EA	18,080.86	1,118.03	19,198.89	657.35	18,738.21	12.4948
02.5601 051	Underground tank, steel/glass, 6,000 gal, with access	EA	22,023.65	1,464.65	23,488.30	861.15	22,884.80	16.3685
02.5601 061	Underground tank, steel/glass, 10,000 gal, with access	EA	29,684.77	1,714.26	31,399.03	1,007.90	30,692.67	19.1580
02.5601 071	Underground tank, steel/glass, 12,000 gal, with access	EA	35,092.46	1,804.10	36,896.56	1,060.72	36,153.18	20.1620
02.5601 081	Underground tank, steel/glass, 20,000 gal, with access	EA	54,372.47	2,057.11	56,429.58	1,209.48	55,581.95	22.9896
02.5602 000	FIBERGLASS TANKS, UNDERGROUND, DOUBLEWALL, WITH ACCESS:							
02.5602 011	Underground tank, double wall fiberglass, 550 gal, with access	EA	12,823.09	274.28	13,097.37	161.27	12,984.36	3.0653
02.5602 021	Underground tank, double wall fiberglass, 1,000 gal, with access	EA	16,169.52	411.43	16,580.95	241.90	16,411.42	4.5980
02.5602 031	Underground tank, double wall fiberglass, 1,500 gal, with access	EA	18,640.69	548.57	19,189.26	322.53	18,963.22	6.1306
02.5602 041	Underground tank, double wall fiberglass, 2,000 gal, with access	EA	20,602.50	685.70	21,288.20	403.16	21,005.66	7.6632
02.5602 051	Underground tank, double wall fiberglass, 4,000 gal, with access	EA	31,299.81	822.85	32,122.66	483.80	31,783.61	9.1959
02.5602 061	Underground tank, double wall fiberglass, 6,000 gal, with access	EA	35,447.46	1,097.13	36,544.59	645.06	36,092.52	12.2612
02.5602 071	Underground tank, double wall fiberglass, 8,000 gal, with access	EA	44,211.90	2,057.11	46,269.01	1,209.48	45,421.38	22.9896
02.5602 081	Underground tank, double wall fiberglass, 10,000 gal, with access	EA	51,488.30	3,085.66	54,573.96	1,814.22	53,302.52	34.4844
02.5602 091	Underground tank, double wall fiberglass, 12,000 gal, with access	EA	62,966.62	3,771.37	66,737.99	2,217.39	65,184.01	42.1476
02.5602 101	Underground tank, double wall fiberglass, 15,000 gal, with access	EA	77,392.54	4,114.22	81,506.76	2,418.97	79,811.51	45.9792
02.5602 111	Underground tank, double wall fiberglass, 20,000 gal, with access	EA	97,138.57	4,799.92	101,938.49	2,822.13	99,960.70	53.6424
02.5602 121	Gage system, remote reading inventory	EA	8,273.06	380.29	8,653.35	223.59	8,496.65	4.2500
02.5602 131	Leak detection monitor	EA	2,522.38		2,522.38		2,522.38	

Division 2 CSI #	02 - SITEWORK Description	Unit	Material	Union Install	Union Total	Open Install	Open Total	Unit Man-Hrs
02.5700 000	**ELECTRICAL DISTRIBUTION, UNDERGROUND:**							
	Note: For wire and substation equipment, see section 16.0000.							
02.5701 000	**TRENCH FOR UNDERGROUND CONDUIT, BACKFILL & TAMPED:**							
02.5701 011	Trench, conduit, 1'x2' deep, fill, tamped	LF	1.06	2.14	3.20	1.39	2.45	0.0250
02.5701 021	Trench, conduit, 1'x3' deep, fill, tamped	LF	1.57	3.01	4.58	1.95	3.52	0.0352
02.5701 031	Trench, conduit, 2'x3' deep, fill, tamped	LF	3.18	3.90	7.08	2.52	5.70	0.0455
02.5701 041	Trench, conduit, 2'x4' deep, fill, tamped	LF	4.21	4.71	8.92	3.05	7.26	0.0550
02.5701 051	Trench, conduit, per cubic yard	CY	14.18	27.40	41.58	17.76	31.94	0.3200
02.5702 000	**CONCRETE ENVELOPES, COLORED RED:**							
02.5702 011	Concrete envelope, red, 9" x 9"	LF	4.71	2.79	7.50	1.81	6.52	0.0326
02.5702 021	Concrete envelope, red, 12" x 12"	LF	6.41	3.98	10.39	2.58	8.99	0.0465
02.5702 031	Concrete envelope, red, 12" x 24"	LF	9.38	5.57	14.95	3.61	12.99	0.0651
02.5702 041	Concrete envelope, red	CY	140.72	19.91	160.63	12.90	153.62	0.2325
02.5703 000	**PVC CONDUIT, SCH 40, CONCRETE ENCASED, TRENCH & COVER:**							
02.5703 011	PVC conduit, schedule 40, trenched & buried in concrete, 1-2"	LF	19.36	4.32	23.68	2.80	22.16	0.0504
02.5703 021	PVC conduit, schedule 40, trenched & buried in concrete, 2-2"	LF	23.80	5.30	29.10	3.43	27.23	0.0619
02.5703 031	PVC conduit, schedule 40, trenched & buried in concrete, 3-2"	LF	24.68	6.15	30.83	3.98	28.66	0.0718
02.5703 041	PVC conduit, schedule 40, trenched & buried in concrete, 4-2"	LF	25.57	7.10	32.67	4.60	30.17	0.0829
02.5703 051	PVC conduit, schedule 40, trenched & buried in concrete, 1-3"	LF	20.70	5.69	26.39	3.68	24.38	0.0664
02.5703 061	PVC conduit, schedule 40, trenched & buried in concrete, 2-3"	LF	25.07	7.10	32.17	4.60	29.67	0.0829
02.5703 071	PVC conduit, schedule 40, trenched & buried in concrete, 3-3"	LF	29.93	8.52	38.45	5.52	35.45	0.0995
02.5703 081	PVC conduit, schedule 40, trenched & buried in concrete, 4-3"	LF	31.66	9.46	41.12	6.13	37.79	0.1105
02.5703 091	PVC conduit, schedule 40, trenched & buried in concrete, 1-4"	LF	24.81	9.46	34.27	6.13	30.94	0.1105
02.5703 101	PVC conduit, schedule 40, trenched & buried in concrete, 2-4"	LF	30.12	12.30	42.42	7.97	38.09	0.1436
02.5703 111	PVC conduit, schedule 40, trenched & buried in concrete, 3-4"	LF	36.16	14.20	50.36	9.21	45.37	0.1659
02.5703 121	PVC conduit, schedule 40, trenched & buried in concrete, 4-4"	LF	38.94	15.62	54.56	10.12	49.06	0.1824
02.5703 131	PVC conduit, schedule 40, trenched & buried in concrete, 1-5"	LF	32.06	10.87	42.93	7.05	39.11	0.1270
02.5703 141	PVC conduit, schedule 40, trenched & buried in concrete, 2-5"	LF	38.18	15.15	53.33	9.82	48.00	0.1769
02.5703 151	PVC conduit, schedule 40, trenched & buried in concrete, 3-5"	LF	40.88	17.52	58.40	11.35	52.23	0.2046
02.5703 161	PVC conduit, schedule 40, trenched & buried in concrete, 4-5"	LF	43.17	19.89	63.06	12.89	56.06	0.2323
02.5703 171	PVC conduit, schedule 40, trenched & buried in concrete, 1-6"	LF	37.06	11.37	48.43	7.37	44.43	0.1328
02.5703 181	PVC conduit, schedule 40, trenched & buried in concrete, 2-6"	LF	43.19	15.73	58.92	10.19	53.38	0.1837
02.5703 191	PVC conduit, schedule 40, trenched & buried in concrete, 4-6"	LF	66.34	24.13	90.47	15.64	81.98	0.2818
02.5703 201	PVC conduit, schedule 40, trenched & buried in concrete, 6-6"	LF	88.68	32.24	120.92	20.89	109.57	0.3765
02.5703 211	PVC conduit, schedule 40, trenched & buried in concrete, 8-6"	LF	122.09	44.40	166.49	28.78	150.87	0.5186
02.5703 221	PVC conduit, schedule 40, trenched & buried in concrete, 10-6"	LF	142.49	51.83	194.32	33.59	176.08	0.6053
02.5703 231	PVC conduit, schedule 40, trenched & buried in concrete, 12-6"	LF	163.56	59.48	223.04	38.55	202.11	0.6947
02.5704 000	**FIBER CONDUIT, CLASS II, DIRECT BURIAL:**							
02.5704 011	Underground fiber conduit, class II, 2"	LF	2.05	9.49	11.54	6.90	8.95	0.0870
02.5704 021	Underground fiber conduit, class II, 3"	LF	2.59	10.05	12.64	7.30	9.89	0.0921
02.5704 031	Underground fiber conduit, class II, 3-1/2"	LF	3.56	11.16	14.72	8.11	11.67	0.1023
02.5705 000	**PVC CONDUIT, HEAVYWALL, WITH OUT TRENCHING:**							
02.5705 011	Heavywall PVC conduit, 1/2", no trench	LF	.44	2.79	3.23	2.03	2.47	0.0256
02.5705 021	Heavywall PVC conduit, 3/4", no trench	LF	.56	3.04	3.60	2.21	2.77	0.0279
02.5705 031	Heavywall PVC conduit, 1", no trench	LF	.85	3.31	4.16	2.40	3.25	0.0303
02.5705 041	Heavywall PVC conduit, 1-1/4", no trench	LF	1.13	3.56	4.69	2.58	3.71	0.0326
02.5705 051	Heavywall PVC conduit, 1-1/2", no trench	LF	1.44	3.81	5.25	2.77	4.21	0.0349
02.5705 061	Heavywall PVC conduit, 2", no trench	LF	1.86	4.06	5.92	2.95	4.81	0.0372
02.5705 071	Heavywall PVC conduit, 2-1/2", no trench	LF	3.07	4.57	7.64	3.32	6.39	0.0419
02.5705 081	Heavywall PVC conduit, 3", no trench	LF	4.02	5.07	9.09	3.69	7.71	0.0465
02.5705 091	Heavywall PVC conduit, 3-1/2", no trench	LF	4.78	6.09	10.87	4.42	9.20	0.0558
02.5705 101	Heavywall PVC conduit, 4", no trench	LF	5.64	7.10	12.74	5.16	10.80	0.0651
02.5705 111	Heavywall PVC conduit, 5", no trench	LF	8.04	8.12	16.16	5.90	13.94	0.0744
02.5705 121	Heavywall PVC conduit, 6", no trench	LF	10.38	10.15	20.53	7.37	17.75	0.0930
02.5706 000	**RIGID STEEL CONDUIT:**							
02.5706 011	Rigid steel conduit, 1/2"	LF	.92	4.20	5.12	3.05	3.97	0.0385
02.5706 021	Rigid steel conduit, 3/4"	LF	1.06	4.79	5.85	3.48	4.54	0.0439
02.5706 031	Rigid steel conduit, 1"	LF	1.47	6.29	7.76	4.57	6.04	0.0576
02.5706 041	Rigid steel conduit, 1-1/4"	LF	2.19	7.13	9.32	5.18	7.37	0.0653
02.5706 051	Rigid steel conduit, 1-1/2"	LF	2.62	8.56	11.18	6.21	8.83	0.0784
02.5706 061	Rigid steel conduit, 2"	LF	3.62	10.48	14.10	7.61	11.23	0.0960
02.5706 071	Rigid steel conduit, 2-1/2"	LF	5.34	13.40	18.74	9.73	15.07	0.1228

Division 2 CSI #	02 - SITEWORK Description	Unit	Material	Union Install	Union Total	Open Install	Open Total	Unit Man-Hrs
02.5706 000	**RIGID STEEL CONDUIT: (Cont.)**							
02.5706 081	Rigid steel conduit, 3"	LF	7.01	18.42	25.43	13.38	20.39	0.1688
02.5706 091	Rigid steel conduit, 3-1/2"	LF	9.50	22.62	32.12	16.43	25.93	0.2073
02.5706 101	Rigid steel conduit, 4"	LF	11.28	25.96	37.24	18.86	30.14	0.2379
02.5706 111	Rigid steel conduit, 5"	LF	12.81	29.12	41.93	21.15	33.96	0.2668
02.5706 121	Rigid steel conduit, 6"	LF	25.13	31.61	56.74	22.96	48.09	0.2897
02.5706 131	Rigid steel conduit, 2", 90 degree sweep	EA	74.64	67.66	142.30	49.14	123.78	0.6200
02.5706 141	Rigid steel conduit, 3", 90 degree sweep	EA	134.42	76.12	210.54	55.28	189.70	0.6975
02.5706 151	Rigid steel conduit, 4", 90 degree sweep	EA	226.53	202.98	429.51	147.42	373.95	1.8600
02.5706 161	Rigid steel conduit, 5", 90 degree sweep	EA	332.31	253.73	586.04	184.28	516.59	2.3250
02.5706 171	Rigid steel conduit, 6", 90 degree sweep	EA	349.04	304.47	653.51	221.14	570.18	2.7900
02.5706 181	Add for pipe wrapping	LF	2.79		2.79		2.79	
02.5707 000	**ELECTRICAL BOXES AND MANHOLES, CONCRETE:**							
02.5707 011	Pull/J-box, 12" x 12" x 18"	EA	37.48	171.27	208.75	124.39	161.87	1.5694
02.5707 021	Pull/J-box, 12" x 24" x 18"	EA	50.85	213.49	264.34	155.06	205.91	1.9563
02.5707 031	Pull/J-box, 12" x 18" round	EA	41.08	172.53	213.61	125.31	166.39	1.5810
02.5707 041	Pull/J-box, 18" x 24" round	EA	51.31	228.35	279.66	165.85	217.16	2.0925
02.5707 051	Concrete handhole, 2' x 2' x 3' deep	EA	698.43	199.07	897.50	129.01	827.44	2.3250
02.5707 061	Concrete handhole, 3' x 3' x 3' deep	EA	1,006.64	318.51	1,325.15	206.42	1,213.06	3.7200
02.5707 071	Concrete handhole, 4' x 4' x 4' deep	EA	2,249.55	457.85	2,707.40	296.73	2,546.28	5.3475
02.5707 081	Concrete manhole, 5'x5'x4', with cover	EA	2,204.77	477.76	2,682.53	309.63	2,514.40	5.5800
02.5707 091	Concrete manhole, 4'x6'x6', with cover	EA	2,748.73	557.39	3,306.12	361.24	3,109.97	6.5100
02.5707 101	Concrete manhole, 6'x8'x6', with cover	EA	4,372.96	676.83	5,049.79	438.65	4,811.61	7.9050
02.5707 111	Concrete manhole, 6'x10'x6', with cover	EA	5,259.37	796.27	6,055.64	516.06	5,775.43	9.3000
02.5707 121	Concrete vault, 8' x 10' x 9'	EA	5,659.36	1,804.48	7,463.84	1,169.47	6,828.83	21.0754
02.5707 131	Concrete vault, 8' x 14' x 9'	EA	8,671.26	2,243.22	10,914.48	1,453.82	10,125.08	26.1997
02.5707 141	Vault lid, 4' x 4' x 3'6", galv	EA	482.29	327.00	809.29	211.93	694.22	3.8192
02.5708 000	**TRANSFORMER PADS:**							
	Note: For pad mounted transformers, see section 16.0000.							
02.5708 011	Transformer pad, 3' x 4'	EA	324.13	273.06	597.19	179.40	503.53	3.2511
02.5708 021	Transformer pad, 4' x 5'	EA	492.14	309.07	801.21	203.05	695.19	3.6798
02.5708 031	Transformer pad, 6' x 8', slab box	EA	1,816.21	468.66	2,284.87	307.90	2,124.11	5.5800
02.5708 041	Transformer pad, 6' x 10'	EA	771.39	401.86	1,173.25	264.01	1,035.40	4.7846
02.5708 051	Transformer pad, 8' x 10'	EA	924.43	442.11	1,366.54	290.46	1,214.89	5.2638
02.5708 061	Transformer pad, large sizes	SF	10.14	6.84	16.98	4.49	14.63	0.0814
02.5709 000	**GROUNDING:**							
02.5709 011	Bare copper ground wire, soft #4	LF	1.25	.44	1.69	.32	1.57	0.0040
02.5709 021	Bare copper ground wire, soft #3/0	LF	3.85	2.62	6.47	1.90	5.75	0.0240
02.5709 031	Bare copper ground wire, soft #4/0	LF	4.85	3.06	7.91	2.22	7.07	0.0280
02.5709 041	Ground clamp, 1/2" - 1" ground rod	EA	10.98	16.37	27.35	11.89	22.87	0.1500
02.5709 051	Cadweld connection, average	EA	17.68	109.13	126.81	79.26	96.94	1.0000
02.5709 061	Copper ground rod, 5/8" x 10'	EA	26.07	81.85	107.92	59.45	85.52	0.7500
02.5709 071	Copper ground rod, 3/4" x 10'	EA	42.14	81.85	123.99	59.45	101.59	0.7500
02.5709 081	Ground rod well	EA	45.67	81.85	127.52	59.45	105.12	0.7500
02.5800 000	**ELECTRICAL DISTRIBUTION, OVERHEAD:**							
02.5801 000	**POLES, WOOD, BUTT TREATED, CLASS 5:**							
	Note: The following prices include setting with crane or boom and machine augered holes.							
02.5801 011	Pole, wood, 25', butt treated, class 5	EA	102.20	468.87	571.07	303.87	406.07	5.4762
02.5801 021	Pole, wood, 30', butt treated, class 5	EA	120.68	553.30	673.98	358.59	479.27	6.4623
02.5801 031	Pole, wood, 35', butt treated, class 5	EA	147.65	618.91	766.56	401.12	548.77	7.2286
02.5801 041	Pole, wood, 40', butt treated, class 5	EA	187.43	675.23	862.66	437.62	625.05	7.8864
02.5801 051	Pole, wood, 50', butt treated, class 5	EA	234.26	843.65	1,077.91	546.77	781.03	9.8534
02.5801 061	Pole, wood, 60', butt treated, class 5	EA	281.16	1,012.38	1,293.54	656.12	937.28	11.8241
02.5802 000	**CROSS ARMS, WOOD, WITH TYPICAL POLE LINE HARDWARE:**							
02.5802 011	Cross arm, 1 arm, 6', with hardware	EA	22.70	164.15	186.85	106.39	129.09	1.9172
02.5802 021	Cross arm, 1 arm, 8', with hardware	EA	28.39	168.79	197.18	109.39	137.78	1.9714
02.5802 031	Cross arm, 2 arm, 6', with hardware	EA	45.43	459.50	504.93	297.80	343.23	5.3667
02.5802 041	Cross arm, 2 arm, 8', with hardware	EA	56.80	473.60	530.40	306.94	363.74	5.5314
02.5803 000	**TRANSFORMERS, DISTRIBUTION, 1PH, 5KV, 120/240, OIL, POLE MOUNT:**							
02.5803 011	Transformer, 10kva, 1ph, 5kv, 120/240, pole	EA	548.90	711.16	1,260.06	516.51	1,065.41	6.5166
02.5803 021	Transformer, 15kva, 120/240v, 1ph, 5kv, pole	EA	717.83	914.44	1,632.27	664.15	1,381.98	8.3794
02.5803 031	Transformer, 25kva, 120/240v, 1ph, 5kv, pole	EA	900.86	1,093.74	1,994.60	794.38	1,695.24	10.0224

Division 2 CSI #	02 - SITEWORK Description	Unit	Material	Union Install	Union Total	Open Install	Open Total	Unit Man-Hrs
02.5803 000	**TRANSFORMERS, DISTRIBUTION, 1PH, 5KV, 120/240, OIL, POLE MOUNT: (Cont.)**							
02.5803 041	Transformer, 37.5kva, 120/240v, 1ph, 5kv	EA	1,257.44	1,296.92	2,554.36	941.94	2,199.38	11.8842
02.5803 051	Transformer, 50kva, 1ph, 5kv, 120/240v, pole	EA	1,421.65	1,571.79	2,993.44	1,141.57	2,563.22	14.4029
02.5803 061	Transformer, 75kv, 120/240v, 1ph, 5kv, pole	EA	2,125.47	1,828.78	3,954.25	1,328.22	3,453.69	16.7578
02.5803 071	Transformer, 100kva, 1ph, 5kv, 120/240v	EA	2,470.31	2,336.75	4,807.06	1,697.15	4,167.46	21.4125
02.5803 081	Transformer, 167kva, 1ph, 5kv, 120/240v	EA	3,659.80	2,743.22	6,403.02	1,992.37	5,652.17	25.1372
02.5803 091	Transformer, 250kva, 1ph, 5kv, 120/240v	EA	7,185.90	3,149.59	10,335.49	2,287.51	9,473.41	28.8609
02.5804 000	**FUSED CUTOUTS, POLE MOUNTED:**							
02.5804 011	Fused cutout, 50a, 5kv, pole mount	EA	100.96	220.94	321.90	160.47	261.43	2.0246
02.5804 021	Fused cutout, 100a, 5kv, pole mount	EA	100.96	220.94	321.90	160.47	261.43	2.0246
02.5804 031	Fused cutout, 250a, 5kv, pole mount	EA	115.78	281.12	396.90	204.17	319.95	2.5760
02.5805 000	**SWITCHES, DISCONNECT, POLE MOUNT, POLE ARM THROW & LOCK:**							
02.5805 011	Switches, disconnect, 400a, 5kv, set of 3, pole	EA	1,970.67	3,755.13	5,725.80	2,727.31	4,697.98	34.4097
02.5805 021	Switches, disconnect, 600a, 5kv, set of 3, pole	EA	2,955.96	3,755.13	6,711.09	2,727.31	5,683.27	34.4097
02.5805 031	Switches, disconnect, 1200a, 5kv, set of 3, pole	EA	5,912.00	4,216.98	10,128.98	3,062.75	8,974.75	38.6418
02.5806 000	**LIGHTNING ARRESTORS, POLE MOUNTED:**							
02.5806 011	Lightning arrester, pole mounted	EA	14.35	354.07	368.42	257.16	271.51	3.2445
02.5807 000	**OUTDOOR LIGHTING:**							
	Note: The following prices include base, pole and setting.							
02.5807 011	Light, mercury vapor, 175w, 30' pole	EA	1,209.63	2,389.66	3,599.29	1,735.59	2,945.22	21.8974
02.5807 021	Light, mercury vapor, 400w, 30' pole	EA	1,537.62	2,389.66	3,927.28	1,735.59	3,273.21	21.8974
02.5807 031	Light, mercury vapor, 1000w, 30' pole	EA	1,909.62	2,476.63	4,386.25	1,798.75	3,708.37	22.6943
02.5807 041	Light, mercury vapor, 175w, 10' pole	EA	814.21	1,137.95	1,952.16	826.48	1,640.69	10.4275
02.5807 051	Light, mercury vapor, 175w, on bldg	EA	436.41	615.81	1,052.22	447.26	883.67	5.6429
02.5807 061	Light, mercury vapor, 400w, on bldg	EA	620.88	615.81	1,236.69	447.26	1,068.14	5.6429
02.5808 000	**WALKWAY LIGHTING BOLLARDS:**							
02.5808 011	Wkwy light, 42", 175w mercury vapor	EA	900.42	304.47	1,204.89	221.14	1,121.56	2.7900
02.5808 021	Wkwy light, 42", 175w, metal halide	EA	1,029.07	304.47	1,333.54	221.14	1,250.21	2.7900
02.5808 031	Walkway light, 42", high pressure sodium to 150w	EA	1,098.33	304.47	1,402.80	221.14	1,319.47	2.7900
02.5808 041	Walkway light, 42", incandescent to 150w	EA	801.48	304.47	1,105.95	221.14	1,022.62	2.7900
02.5809 000	**SPECIALTY OUTDOOR LIGHTING:**							
02.5809 011	150 watt incandescent flush mounted landscape lighting	EA	363.37	171.27	534.64	124.39	487.76	1.5694
02.5809 021	200 watt incandescent flush mounted landscape lighting	EA	391.84	171.27	563.11	124.39	516.23	1.5694
02.5809 031	300 watt incandescent flush mounted landscape lighting	EA	407.17	171.27	578.44	124.39	531.56	1.5694
02.5809 071	Incandescent step light	EA	249.02	111.64	360.66	81.08	330.10	1.0230
02.5809 081	Fluorescent step light W1 PL-13 lamp	EA	253.65	111.64	365.29	81.08	334.73	1.0230
02.5809 111	Fluorescent, damp location, two lamp	EA	133.70	87.30	221.00	63.41	197.11	0.8000
02.5809 211	Adjust floodlight, 75w, PAR 38	EA	78.39	21.83	100.22	15.85	94.24	0.2000
02.5810 000	**RACEWAY AND WIRE FOR OUTDOOR LIGHTING:**							
02.5810 011	PVC & copper wire, 20 amps	LF	5.67	3.60	9.27	2.62	8.29	0.0330
02.5810 021	PVC & copper wire, 30 amps	LF	5.92	3.76	9.68	2.73	8.65	0.0345
02.5810 031	PVC & copper wire, 40 amps	LF	6.96	4.39	11.35	3.19	10.15	0.0402
02.5810 041	PVC & copper wire, 60 amps	LF	7.94	5.01	12.95	3.64	11.58	0.0459
02.5810 051	Copper wire, stranded, #12	LF	1.23	.72	1.95	.52	1.75	0.0066
02.5810 061	Copper wire, stranded, #10	LF	1.36	.82	2.18	.59	1.95	0.0075
02.5810 071	Copper wire, stranded, #8	LF	1.84	.88	2.72	.64	2.48	0.0081
02.5811 000	**PARKING LOT LIGHTING:**							
02.5811 011	Typical parking lot lighting, small	SF	.69	.83	1.52	.60	1.29	0.0076
02.5811 021	Typical parking lot lighting, large	SF	.44	.48	.92	.35	.79	0.0044
02.5812 000	**TRAFFIC SIGNALS:**							
02.5812 011	Signals, 4 lane - "T" intersection	LS	172,886.62		172,886.62		172,886.62	
02.5812 021	Signals, 4 lane - "X" intersection	LS	232,731.98		232,731.98		232,731.98	
02.5812 031	Signals, 6 lane - "T" intersection	LS	246,030.96		246,030.96		246,030.96	
02.5812 041	Signals, 6 lane - "X" intersection	LS	299,226.85		299,226.85		299,226.85	
02.5812 051	Traffic signal, pole mounted	LS	13,640.05		13,640.05		13,640.05	
02.5812 061	Traffic Controller	LS	16,623.72		16,623.72		16,623.72	
02.5814 000	**ATHLETIC FIELD LIGHTING:**							
02.5814 011	Lights, football field, 40 foot candles	LS	290,356.80		290,356.80		290,356.80	
02.5814 021	Lights, football field, 100 foot candles	LS	451,571.72		451,571.72		451,571.72	
02.5814 031	Playground, diamond, economy	LS	41,945.13		41,945.13		41,945.13	
02.5814 041	Tennis court, economy	LS	11,700.49		11,700.49		11,700.49	

Division 2 CSI #	02 - SITEWORK Description	Unit	Material	Union Install	Union Total	Open Install	Open Total	Unit Man-Hrs
02.5815 000	**HIGH MAST LIGHTING:**							
02.5815 011	Luminaire, pole top, 400 watt	EA	580.17	267.48	847.65	173.35	753.52	3.1240
02.5815 021	Luminaire, pole top, 750 watt	EA	612.25	294.62	906.87	190.94	803.19	3.4410
02.5815 031	Luminaire, pole top, 1,000 watt	EA	682.47	321.25	1,003.72	208.20	890.67	3.7520
02.5815 041	Luminaire, pole top, 1,500 watt	EA	885.54	343.85	1,229.39	222.85	1,108.39	4.0160
02.5815 051	Pole, galvanized steel, 70 feet high	EA	9,388.14	1,031.04	10,419.18	668.21	10,056.35	12.0420
02.5815 061	Pole, galvanized steel, 80 feet high	EA	11,186.67	1,151.59	12,338.26	746.34	11,933.01	13.4500
02.5815 071	Pole, galvanized steel, 90 feet high	EA	13,111.94	1,260.33	14,372.27	816.81	13,928.75	14.7200
02.5815 081	Pole, galvanized steel, 100 feet high	EA	15,018.86	1,390.55	16,409.41	901.21	15,920.07	16.2410
02.5815 091	Pole, footing system for 70 feet high	EA	341.99	787.31	1,129.30	502.65	844.64	11.6760
02.5815 101	Pole, footing system for 80 feet high	EA	400.02	918.40	1,318.42	586.34	986.36	13.6200
02.5815 111	Pole, footing system for 90 feet high	EA	499.23	1,115.56	1,614.79	712.22	1,211.45	16.5440
02.5815 121	Pole, footing system for 100 feet high	EA	571.01	1,311.99	1,883.00	837.62	1,408.63	19.4570
02.5815 131	Mounting hoist, 12 fixtures	EA	9,195.75	757.65	9,953.40	491.03	9,686.78	8.8490
02.5815 141	Mounting hoist, 16 fixtures	EA	10,953.06	1,073.76	12,026.82	695.90	11,648.96	12.5410
02.5815 151	Mounting hoist, 20 fixtures	EA	13,011.16	1,389.01	14,400.17	900.21	13,911.37	16.2230
02.5815 161	Mounting brackets for fixture	EA	103.83	55.65	159.48	36.07	139.90	0.6500
02.6000 000	**GENERAL SITE WORK, PAVING & WALKS:**							
02.6001 000	**PAVEMENTS, ASPHALTIC:**							
02.6001 011	Asphaltic concrete, 2", on 4" base	SF	1.67	1.53	3.20	.92	2.59	0.0221
02.6001 021	Asphaltic concrete, 2", on 6" base (parking lot)	SF	1.75	1.90	3.65	1.15	2.90	0.0274
02.6001 031	Asphaltic concrete, 3", on 8" base (truck & ramp)	SF	2.23	2.41	4.64	1.45	3.68	0.0348
02.6001 041	Asphaltic concrete, 3", 8" base, 10" sub (streets)	SF	2.87	3.31	6.18	2.00	4.87	0.0479
02.6001 051	Asphaltic concrete, armor coat, 2 shot, 4" base	SF	.89	1.05	1.94	.64	1.53	0.0152
02.6001 061	Sawcut pavement, asphaltic concrete	SF	.75	1.53	2.28	1.08	1.83	0.0200
02.6002 000	**PAVEMENTS, COMPILATION:**							
	Note: For headers see section 02.6007. The prices are based on quantities under 5,000 square feet.							
	For quantities under 2,000 square feet, add 25%.							
02.6002 011	Fine grading for roadbed	SF	.14	.18	.32	.13	.27	0.0021
02.6002 021	6" sub base for roadbed	SF	.71	.27	.98	.14	.85	0.0038
02.6002 031	4" base for roadbed	SF	.42	.27	.69	.14	.56	0.0038
02.6002 041	Tack coat	SF	.07	.03	.10	.02	.09	0.0004
02.6002 051	Pavement, 2" asphaltic concrete	SF	1.91	.58	2.49	.35	2.26	0.0084
02.6002 061	Pavement, sealer	SF	.07	.06	.13	.03	.10	0.0008
02.6002 071	Add or deduct per 1" of sub base	INCH	.15		.15		.15	
02.6002 081	Add or deduct per 1" base rock	INCH	.20		.20		.20	
02.6002 091	Add or deduct per 1" of asphaltic concrete	INCH	.78		.78		.78	
02.6003 000	**PAVEMENTS, MISCELLANEOUS:**							
02.6003 011	Tennis court, bases, Asphaltic concrete, color seal	SF	6.88		6.88		6.88	
02.6003 021	Tennis court, 7200 SF, fence/stripe	UNIT	72,017.08		72,017.08		72,017.08	
02.6003 031	Parking, gravel, 6" of 1-1/2" rock	SF	.53		.53		.53	
02.6004 000	**PAVING MATERIALS & SUPPORT ITEMS:**							
	Note: The following prices are based on quantities over 50,000 square feet. For quantities between							
	5,000 and 50,000 square feet, add 5%.							
02.6004 011	Fine grading	SF	.03	.12	.15	.08	.11	0.0014
02.6004 021	Aggregate, subbase, 1-1/2", class 2 & 3	TON	9.03	5.54	14.57	3.49	12.52	0.0772
02.6004 031	Aggregate rock, sub base, class 4	TON	8.13	5.54	13.67	3.49	11.62	0.0772
02.6004 041	Aggregate rock, sub base (non-spec)	TON	8.06	6.17	14.23	3.89	11.95	0.0860
02.6004 051	Aggregate rock, subbase, 8", class 2 & 3	SF	.39	.27	.66	.17	.56	0.0038
02.6004 061	Aggregate rock, sub base, 12", class 2&3	SF	.57	.27	.84	.17	.74	0.0038
02.6004 071	Aggregate rock, base, class 2 & 3	TON	11.49	5.54	17.03	3.49	14.98	0.0772
02.6004 081	Aggregate rock, base (non-spec)	TON	8.77	6.98	15.75	4.39	13.16	0.0972
02.6004 091	Engineered fill, sub base	TON	6.41	5.54	11.95	3.49	9.90	0.0772
02.6004 101	Aggregate base, chemical treated, 5% by dry weight	TON	15.13	10.78	25.91	6.79	21.92	0.1502
02.6004 111	Aggregate rock, base, 6", class 2 & 3	SF	.28	.27	.55	.17	.45	0.0038
02.6004 121	Aggregate base, 6", chemical treated, 5% by weight	SF	.46	.40	.86	.25	.71	0.0056
02.6004 131	Add for lime treatment, 12" native soil	SF	.30	.29	.59	.18	.48	0.0040
02.6004 141	Lime bulk, material only	TON	115.20		115.20		115.20	
02.6004 151	Cement	BBL	28.62		28.62		28.62	
02.6004 161	Base treatment cement, 134# CY	#	.03		.03		.03	
02.6004 171	Asphaltic concrete, 1,000 to 5,000	TON	105.62	12.22	117.84	7.38	113.00	0.1767
02.6004 181	Asphaltic concrete, more than 5,000	TON	98.46	12.22	110.68	7.38	105.84	0.1767

Division 2 CSI #	02 - SITEWORK Description	Unit	Material	Union Install	Union Total	Open Install	Open Total	Unit Man-Hrs
02.6004 000	**PAVING MATERIALS & SUPPORT ITEMS: (Cont.)**							
02.6004 191	Cut back, 1/2", bulk	TON	42.05	12.22	54.27	7.38	49.43	0.1767
02.6004 201	Cut back, 1/4", bulk	TON	43.17	12.22	55.39	7.38	50.55	0.1767
02.6004 211	Sheet asphalt	TON	90.06	12.22	102.28	7.38	97.44	0.1767
02.6004 221	Asphaltic concrete, open graded	TON	100.29	12.22	112.51	7.38	107.67	0.1767
02.6004 231	Cut back in sacks, 66# sacks	SACK	2.51	2.49	5.00	1.81	4.32	0.0356
02.6004 241	Seal coat, SC 70, penetrating	TON	396.17	19.32	415.49	14.09	410.26	0.2764
02.6004 251	Prime coat, MC 250	TON	396.17	19.32	415.49	14.09	410.26	0.2764
02.6004 261	Prime coat, MC 70-250, 1,000	SY	.44	.44	.88	.32	.76	0.0063
02.6004 271	Prime coat, MC 70-250, 2,000	SY	.26	.36	.62	.26	.52	0.0051
02.6004 281	Prime coat, MC 70-250, 2,500	SY	.20	.31	.51	.22	.42	0.0044
02.6004 291	Prime coat, MC 70-250, 5,000	SY	.17	.31	.48	.22	.39	0.0044
02.6005 000	**CURBS AND GUTTERS:**							
02.6005 011	Curb forms, fabricated, edge, 6" x 12"	LF	1.26	2.47	3.73	1.51	2.77	0.0314
02.6005 021	Curb forms, steel, long run, reuse	LF	1.26	1.39	2.65	.85	2.11	0.0177
02.6005 031	Curb/gutter, handwork	LF	9.11	5.00	14.11	3.06	12.17	0.0636
02.6005 041	Curb/gutter, machine work	LF	8.20	3.90	12.10	2.39	10.59	0.0496
02.6005 051	Curb, vertical face planter, 6"x18"	LF	9.92	6.16	16.08	3.78	13.70	0.0784
02.6005 061	Curb, vertical face, radial	LF	5.76	5.03	10.79	3.08	8.84	0.0640
02.6005 071	Curb, 6", asphaltic concrete	LF	2.95	7.24	10.19	5.10	8.05	0.0850
02.6005 081	Curb, 6", asphaltic concrete with ASB plain fiber	LF	4.88	7.63	12.51	5.37	10.25	0.0895
02.6005 091	Curb & gutter & 4' sidewalk, mono	LF	17.34	7.20	24.54	4.41	21.75	0.0916
02.6005 101	Split face granite curb, 6"x18", straight	LF	35.14	11.86	47.00	7.27	42.41	0.1508
02.6005 111	Split face granite curb, 6"x24", taper	LF	48.70	19.28	67.98	11.81	60.51	0.2452
02.6005 121	Split face granite curb, 6x24, radial	LF	62.20	15.21	77.41	9.32	71.52	0.1934
02.6005 131	Curb, driveway, concrete, apron, 4"	SF	1.91	2.65	4.56	1.62	3.53	0.0337
02.6005 141	Curb, driveway, concrete, apron, 5"	SF	2.41	2.65	5.06	1.62	4.03	0.0337
02.6006 000	**SIDEWALKS AND CONCRETE FINISHES:**							
02.6006 011	Brick pavers, sand bed 1" compact	SF	3.21	5.60	8.81	3.12	6.33	0.0696
02.6006 021	Brick pavers, grouted	SF	3.63	7.56	11.19	4.21	7.84	0.0939
02.6006 031	Precast paver, sand bed, 1" compact	SF	2.63	4.60	7.23	2.56	5.19	0.0572
02.6006 041	Precast pavers, grouted	SF	3.17	6.71	9.88	4.11	7.28	0.0854
02.6006 045	Turf stone pavers	SF	2.59	4.89	7.48	3.00	5.59	0.0622
02.6006 051	Concrete walk, 4", broom finish	SF	1.91	1.30	3.21	.79	2.70	0.0165
02.6006 061	Concrete walk, 4", exposed aggregate washed	SF	1.91	1.96	3.87	1.20	3.11	0.0249
02.6006 071	Concrete walk, 4"-24x24, score, lamp bl	SF	1.91	1.85	3.76	1.13	3.04	0.0235
02.6006 081	Walk, 4", sandblast, integral color	SF	1.91	2.59	4.50	1.59	3.50	0.0330
02.6006 091	Concrete walk 4", 80-100% seeded, agg	SF	2.21	3.24	5.45	1.99	4.20	0.0412
02.6006 101	Concrete walk 4", 100% seeded, color	SF	2.31	3.33	5.64	2.04	4.35	0.0423
02.6006 111	Concrete bands, 12-24" wide, 7" deep	SF	2.84	2.01	4.85	1.23	4.07	0.0256
02.6006 121	Finish, steel trowel	SF		.71	.71	.52	.52	0.0102
02.6006 131	Finish, broom	SF		.71	.71	.52	.52	0.0102
02.6006 141	Concrete hardener, chemical	SF	.09	.27	.36	.19	.28	0.0038
02.6006 151	Concrete hardener, granolithic	SF	.01	.27	.28	.19	.20	0.0038
02.6006 161	Concrete hardener, iron base	SF	.34	.52	.86	.38	.72	0.0074
02.6007 000	**SPECIALTIES (MEDIUM TO LARGE SITES):**							
02.6007 011	Header, redwood treated, 2" x 4"	LF	1.06	3.41	4.47	2.24	3.30	0.0406
02.6007 021	Header, redwood treated, 2" x 6"	LF	1.12	4.33	5.45	2.85	3.97	0.0516
02.6007 031	Headers, redwood, 2" x 6"	LF	1.41	4.33	5.74	2.85	4.26	0.0516
02.6007 041	Dividers, redwood, 2" x 4"	LF	.71	2.40	3.11	1.58	2.29	0.0286
02.6007 051	Benders, redwood, 3/8" x 4"	LF	.71	6.11	6.82	4.02	4.73	0.0728
02.6007 061	Parking bumper block, precast 3'	EA	25.82	15.72	41.54	6.83	32.65	0.2514
02.6007 071	Parking bumper block, precast 6'	EA	41.47	19.23	60.70	8.36	49.83	0.3076
02.6007 081	Bike lock, precast, lockable	EA	23.35	16.98	40.33	7.38	30.73	0.2717
02.6007 091	Street signs, with pole	EA	129.61	122.68	252.29	53.34	182.95	1.9625
02.6007 101	Striping, 2 coat, 4" wide	LF	.10	.29	.39	.13	.23	0.0047
02.6007 111	Striping, 2 ct, 4" wide, small quantity	LF	.10	.58	.68	.25	.35	0.0093
02.6007 121	Striping, 1 coat, single line	STALL	.10	9.90	10.00	4.31	4.41	0.1584
02.6007 131	Striping, thermoplastic, white bulk	SF	5.00	6.38	11.38	2.77	7.77	0.1020
02.6007 141	Striping, thermoplastic, yellow bulk	SF	6.62	6.38	13.00	2.77	9.39	0.1020
02.6007 151	Striping, thermoplastic, white, 4"	LF	.74	1.18	1.92	.51	1.25	0.0189
02.6007 161	Striping, thermoplastic, yellow, 4"	LF	1.31	1.18	2.49	.51	1.82	0.0189

Division 2 CSI #	02 - SITEWORK Description	Unit	Material	Union Install	Union Total	Open Install	Open Total	Unit Man-Hrs
02.6007 000	**SPECIALTIES (MEDIUM TO LARGE SITES): (Cont.)**							
02.6007 171	Striping, thermoplastic, white, 8"	LF	2.02	1.18	3.20	.51	2.53	0.0189
02.6007 181	Striping, thermoplastic, yellow, 8"	LF	3.24	1.18	4.42	.51	3.75	0.0189
02.6007 191	Striping, yellow base, glass embedded	LF	.28	.64	.92	.28	.56	0.0102
02.6007 201	A round buttons, large quantity	EA	1.64	3.06	4.70	1.33	2.97	0.0489
02.6007 211	B & D buttons, 2 way reflective, large quantity	EA	4.39	4.30	8.69	1.87	6.26	0.0688
02.6007 221	C buttons, 2 way reflective, large quantity	EA	5.36	4.30	9.66	1.87	7.23	0.0688
02.6007 231	G & H buttons, 1 way reflective, large quantity	EA	4.06	4.38	8.44	1.90	5.96	0.0700
02.6007 241	F reflector stake, steel to 6'	EA	20.78	8.75	29.53	3.81	24.59	0.1400
02.6007 251	Reverse amber reflector stake, type 1, 2 face	EA	25.57	8.75	34.32	3.81	29.38	0.1400
02.6007 261	Steel guard rail, type 9, state spec	LF	14.94	28.49	43.43	17.94	32.88	0.3969
02.6007 271	Guard rail, posts, wood treated	LF	12.56	24.13	36.69	15.20	27.76	0.3362
02.6007 281	Guard rail, anchors	LF	3.01	2.15	5.16	1.35	4.36	0.0299
02.6007 291	Guard rail, 2 side, channels & rails	LF	44.83	26.30	71.13	16.57	61.40	0.3665
02.6007 301	Add for sight screen	LF	3.29	1.95	5.24	1.23	4.52	0.0272
02.6007 311	Highway barrier/divider, concrete, type 25	LF	43.82	19.46	63.28	12.25	56.07	0.2711
02.6007 321	Deep beam median barrier-2 sides	LF	61.31	24.50	85.81	15.43	76.74	0.3414
02.6007 331	Deep beam guard rail	LF	43.68	17.15	60.83	10.80	54.48	0.2390
02.6007 341	Tri-guard guide rail	LF	52.98	17.15	70.13	10.80	63.78	0.2390
02.6007 351	W-beam guard rail	LF	39.91	17.15	57.06	10.80	50.71	0.2390
02.6007 361	Anchor guard rail	LF	47.64	17.15	64.79	10.80	58.44	0.2390
02.7000 000	**MISCELLANEOUS SITE IMPROVEMENTS:**							
	Note: All fencing prices are based on quantities between 500 and 2,000 lineal feet.							
02.7001 000	**METAL FENCING:**							
02.7001 011	Chain link, 9 gauge, 4'	LF	12.33	11.08	23.41	6.58	18.91	0.1409
02.7001 021	Chain link, 9 gauge, 6'	LF	13.45	14.55	28.00	8.64	22.09	0.1850
02.7001 031	Add for barbed wire outrigger	LF	.76	1.16	1.92	.69	1.45	0.0147
02.7001 041	Add for each foot to 10' high	LF	1.38	2.03	3.41	1.20	2.58	0.0258
02.7001 051	Add for rustake to 6' high	LF	4.54	2.90	7.44	1.72	6.26	0.0369
02.7001 061	Barbed wire, wood post	LF	4.54	12.82	17.36	7.61	12.15	0.1630
02.7001 071	Barbed wire, metal post	LF	4.82	4.71	9.53	2.80	7.62	0.0599
02.7001 081	Pass gate, 3' to 4'	EA	224.58	377.76	602.34	224.18	448.76	4.8024
02.7001 091	Single leaf gates to 8'	EA	449.19	412.08	861.27	244.55	693.74	5.2388
02.7001 101	Double leaf gates to 29'	EA	873.45	1,116.33	1,989.78	786.00	1,659.45	13.0979
02.7002 000	**WOOD FENCING:**							
02.7002 011	Wood fence, 4', economy	LF	4.23	3.02	7.25	1.98	6.21	0.0359
02.7002 021	Wood fence, 5', economy	LF	4.77	3.22	7.99	2.11	6.88	0.0383
02.7002 031	Wood fence, 6', economy	LF	5.26	3.49	8.75	2.29	7.55	0.0415
02.7002 041	Wood fence, 6', grape stake	LF	5.58	3.74	9.32	2.46	8.04	0.0445
02.7002 051	Wood fence, 6', cedar rough bd	LF	6.52	3.50	10.02	2.30	8.82	0.0417
02.7002 061	Wood fence, 6', resawn plywood	LF	8.86	4.02	12.88	2.64	11.50	0.0479
02.7002 071	Wood fence, 6', architectrual quality, plain	LF	16.21	7.53	23.74	4.94	21.15	0.0896
02.7002 081	Wood fence, 6', architectural quallty, decorative	LF	23.60	34.45	58.05	24.26	47.86	0.4042
02.7003 000	**MISCELLANEOUS IMPROVEMENTS:**							
02.7003 011	Guard rail, steel with wood posts	LF	8.48	1.77	10.25	1.13	9.61	0.0227
02.7003 021	Steel guard rail, channel 1 side	LF	13.01	1.77	14.78	1.13	14.14	0.0227
02.7003 031	Headlight glare shield, exposed metal	LF	2.61	10.55	13.16	6.73	9.34	0.1354
02.7003 041	Wall, precast, with posts, 8' high	LF	21.06	27.07	48.13	17.28	38.34	0.3474
02.7003 051	Add for barbed wire, 2 strands	LF	.69	1.86	2.55	1.19	1.88	0.0239
02.7004 000	**CONCRETE FENCING:**							
02.7004 011	Fence, precast concrete, 10' high	LF	37.59	38.13	75.72	16.58	54.17	0.6100
02.7004 021	Fence, precast concrete, 12' high	LF	47.88	55.01	102.89	23.92	71.80	0.8800
02.7004 031	Fence, precast concrete, 14' high	LF	61.04	71.89	132.93	31.26	92.30	1.1500
02.7400 000	**IRRIGATION, SPRINKLER HEAD SYSTEMS:**							
	Note: For automatic sprinkler systems, add 15% to the total cost. For hose bibbs in lieu of heads, deduct 5% from the total cost.							
02.7401 000	**IRRIGATE LARGE AREAS:**							
02.7401 011	Irrigate, 5,000	SF	.53	.71	1.24	.47	1.00	0.0077
02.7401 021	Irrigate, 10,000	SF	.45	.71	1.16	.47	.92	0.0077
02.7401 031	Irrigate, 25,000	SF	.39	.71	1.10	.47	.86	0.0077
02.7401 041	Irrigate, 50,000	SF	.36	.53	.89	.35	.71	0.0057
02.7401 051	Irrigate, 200,000	SF	.33	.45	.78	.29	.62	0.0048

Division 2 CSI #	02 - SITEWORK Description	Unit	Material	Union Install	Union Total	Open Install	Open Total	Unit Man-Hrs
02.7401 000	**IRRIGATE LARGE AREAS: (Cont.)**							
02.7401 061	Irrigate, 500,000	SF	.33	.45	.78	.29	.62	0.0048
02.7402 000	**IRRIGATE SMALL AREAS:**							
02.7402 011	Irrigate, strip, automatic	SF	1.54	2.04	3.58	1.35	2.89	0.0220
02.7402 021	Irrigate, lawn, automatic	SF	.85	.98	1.83	.65	1.50	0.0106
02.7402 031	Irrigate, commercial, manual	SF	.76	.71	1.47	.47	1.23	0.0077
02.7402 041	Irrigate, residential, manual	SF	.36	.53	.89	.35	.71	0.0057
02.7403 000	**POINT OF CONNECTIONS:**							
	Note: For meter fees see section 01.1031.							
02.7403 011	Meter, main line, point of connection	EA	71.80	133.21	205.01	88.08	159.88	1.4369
02.7404 000	**BACKFLOW PREVENTION ASSEMBLIES:**							
02.7404 011	Backflow preventer, 2" dia	EA	959.06	603.54	1,562.60	399.06	1,358.12	6.5100
02.7404 021	Backflow preventer, 3" dia	EA	1,956.31	948.42	2,904.73	627.10	2,583.41	10.2300
02.7404 031	Backflow preventer, 2" dia, commercial with box	EA	1,319.72	1,034.64	2,354.36	684.11	2,003.83	11.1600
02.7404 041	Backflow preventer, 3" dia, commercial with box	EA	1,604.57	2,791.65	4,396.22	1,845.84	3,450.41	30.1116
02.7405 000	**MAINLINE PIPE ONLY, WITH TRENCHING:**							
	Note: The following prices are based on pvc class 315 mainline pipe. For pvc schedule 40, add 10%.							
02.7405 011	Irrigation pipe, main, 1/2", trench	LF	.41	1.99	2.40	1.32	1.73	0.0215
02.7405 021	Irrigation pipe, main, 3/4", trench	LF	.55	2.23	2.78	1.48	2.03	0.0241
02.7405 031	Irrigation pipe, main, 1", trench	LF	1.06	2.72	3.78	1.80	2.86	0.0293
02.7405 041	Irrigation pipe, main, 1-1/2", trench	LF	1.27	2.91	4.18	1.92	3.19	0.0314
02.7405 051	Irrigation pipe, main, 2", trench	LF	1.67	3.39	5.06	2.24	3.91	0.0366
02.7405 061	Irrigation pipe, main, 2-1/2", trench	LF	2.70	3.73	6.43	2.46	5.16	0.0402
02.7405 071	Irrigation pipe, main, 3", trench	LF	3.20	4.23	7.43	2.80	6.00	0.0456
02.7405 081	Irrigation pipe, main, 4", trench	LF	4.44	4.72	9.16	3.12	7.56	0.0509
02.7405 091	Irrigation emitter spaghetti line, complete	LF	44.81	60.60	105.41	40.07	84.88	0.6537
02.7406 000	**LATERAL LINE PIPE ONLY, WITH TRENCHING:**							
	Note: The following prices are based on pvc class 200 lateral lines.							
02.7406 011	Irrigation pipe, lateral, 1/2", trench	LF	.36	1.99	2.35	1.32	1.68	0.0215
02.7406 021	Irrigation pipe, lateral, 3/4", trench	LF	.50	2.23	2.73	1.48	1.98	0.0241
02.7406 031	Irrigation pipe, lateral, 1", trench	LF	.98	2.72	3.70	1.80	2.78	0.0293
02.7406 041	Irrigation pipe, lateral, 1-1/2", trench	LF	1.18	2.91	4.09	1.92	3.10	0.0314
02.7406 051	Irrigation pipe, lateral, 2", trench	LF	1.51	3.39	4.90	2.24	3.75	0.0366
02.7406 061	Irrigation pipe, lateral, 2-1/2", trench	LF	2.11	3.73	5.84	2.46	4.57	0.0402
02.7407 000	**VALVES, REMOTE CONTROL, WITH ATMOSPHERIC VACUUM BREAKER:**							
02.7407 011	Valve, remote, 3/4", atmospheric vacuum breaker	EA	57.12	119.48	176.60	79.00	136.12	1.2887
02.7407 021	Valve, remote, 1", atmospheric vacuum breaker	EA	73.12	134.89	208.01	89.19	162.31	1.4550
02.7407 031	Valve, remote, 1-1/4", atmospheric vacuum breaker	EA	87.00	154.05	241.05	101.86	188.86	1.6616
02.7407 041	Valve, remote, 1-1/2", atmospheric vacuum breaker	EA	99.96	174.48	274.44	115.37	215.33	1.8820
02.7407 051	Valve, remote, 2", atmospheric vacuum breaker	EA	112.78	194.13	306.91	128.36	241.14	2.0939
02.7407 061	Valve, remote, 2-1/2", atmospheric vacuum breaker	EA	284.66	225.79	510.45	149.29	433.95	2.4354
02.7408 000	**VALVES, MANUAL CONTROL, WITH ATMOSPHERIC VACUUM BREAKER:**							
02.7408 011	Valve, manual, 3/4", atmospheric vacuum breaker	EA	33.30	46.49	79.79	30.74	64.04	0.5015
02.7408 021	Valve, manual, 1", atmospheric vacuum breaker	EA	46.50	77.71	124.21	51.38	97.88	0.8382
02.7408 031	Valve, manual, 1-1/4", atmospheric vacuum breaker	EA	96.27	92.83	189.10	61.38	157.65	1.0013
02.7408 041	Valve, manual, 1-1/2", atmospheric vacuum breaker	EA	175.09	109.32	284.41	72.28	247.37	1.1792
02.7408 051	Valve, manual, 2", atmospheric vacuum breaker	EA	211.55	139.39	350.94	92.16	303.71	1.5035
02.7408 061	Emitter valve assembly, with pressure reducing valve	EA	479.00	234.83	713.83	155.27	634.27	2.5330
02.7408 071	Quick coupling valves, 1", atmospheric vacuum breaker	EA	74.58	62.17	136.75	41.11	115.69	0.6706
02.7408 081	Add for concrete valve protector	EA	11.03	15.55	26.58	10.28	21.31	0.1677
02.7409 000	**SPRINKLER HEADS:**							
02.7409 011	Sprinkler head, bubble type	EA	4.87	15.55	20.42	10.28	15.15	0.1677
02.7409 021	Sprinkler head, spray type	EA	3.64	15.53	19.17	10.27	13.91	0.1675
02.7409 031	Sprinkler head, bird, #25	EA	16.14	18.66	34.80	12.34	28.48	0.2013
02.7409 041	Sprinkler head, bird, #35	EA	33.15	18.65	51.80	12.33	45.48	0.2012
02.7409 051	Sprinkler system control, residential, 3 station	EA	76.46	149.48	225.94	98.83	175.29	1.6123
02.7409 061	Sprinkler system control, residential, 6 station	EA	95.48	149.48	244.96	98.83	194.31	1.6123
02.7409 071	Sprinkler system control, commercial, 6 station	EA	265.94	623.01	888.95	411.94	677.88	6.7200
02.7409 081	Sprinkler system control, commercial, 12 station	EA	406.30	1,495.13	1,901.43	988.59	1,394.89	16.1270
02.7409 091	Sprinkler system master control, 24 station	EA	1,145.19	2,990.27	4,135.46	1,977.17	3,122.36	32.2540

Division 2 CSI #	02 - SITEWORK Description	Unit	Material	Union Install	Union Total	Open Install	Open Total	Unit Man-Hrs
02.7410 000	**WIRING FOR REMOTE CONTROL VALVES:**							
	Note: The following prices assume that wire is placed in trench with pipe.							
02.7410 011	Wire, #14, direct burial	LF	.12	.31	.43	.22	.34	0.0028
02.7410 021	Wire, #12, direct burial	LF	.17	.31	.48	.22	.39	0.0028
02.7410 031	Add for trench & backfill	LF	.74	1.01	1.75	.74	1.48	0.0093
02.7601 000	**LANDSCAPING:**							
	Note: For freeways, use one man per work day plus materials. For commercial work, pre-emergence							
	weed control, use $0.025 Per sf up to one acre.							
02.7601 011	Plant maintenance, automatic, 40,000 SF/30 day	LS	2,445.76		2,445.76		2,445.76	
02.7601 021	Plant maintenance, manual, 40,000 SF/30 day	LS	3,668.64		3,668.64		3,668.64	
02.7602 000	**GROUND COVER, SHRUBS & TREES:**							
02.7602 011	Ground cover, ice plant, rooted, large	SF	.17	.16	.33	.07	.24	0.0025
02.7602 021	Ground cover, all others, rooted, large	SF	.17	.23	.40	.10	.27	0.0037
02.7602 031	Ground cover, all others, rooted, small	SF	.25	.38	.63	.16	.41	0.0061
02.7602 041	Ground cover, ice plant, cutting, large	SF	.04	.16	.20	.07	.11	0.0025
02.7602 051	Gravel bed, 4" pea gravel	CY	19.82	42.08	61.90	17.80	37.62	0.6786
02.7602 061	Shrubs, 1 gallon, 1,000 & up	SF	3.48	4.73	8.21	2.00	5.48	0.0763
02.7602 071	Shrubs, 1 gallon, 500-1,000	EA	3.66	5.88	9.54	2.49	6.15	0.0948
02.7602 081	Shrubs, 1 gallon, less than 500	EA	9.79	16.17	25.96	6.84	16.63	0.2608
02.7602 091	Shrub, 5 gallon	EA	16.03	25.60	41.63	10.83	26.86	0.4128
02.7602 101	Tree, 5 gallon, single staked	EA	20.72	31.14	51.86	13.17	33.89	0.5022
02.7602 111	Tree, 5 gallon, double staked	EA	26.05	38.55	64.60	16.30	42.35	0.6216
02.7602 121	Tree, 15 gallon, single staked	EA	57.77	122.15	179.92	51.67	109.44	1.9698
02.7602 131	Tree, 15 gallon, double staked	EA	63.01	129.58	192.59	54.81	117.82	2.0897
02.7602 141	Tree, 20/40 box, guyed	EA	230.54	295.17	525.71	124.86	355.40	4.7601
02.7602 151	Tree, specimen size, 30" box, guyed	EA	528.11	403.80	931.91	170.81	698.92	6.5119
02.7602 161	Tree, 36" box, guyed	EA	883.14	484.62	1,367.76	204.99	1,088.13	7.8152
02.7602 171	Tree, 42" box, guyed	EA	1,266.25	536.36	1,802.61	226.88	1,493.13	8.6495
02.7602 181	Tree, 48" box, guyed	EA	1,766.83	506.98	2,273.81	214.45	1,981.28	8.1758
02.7602 191	Tree, fieldgrown	EA	467.81	363.94	831.75	153.94	621.75	5.8690
02.7602 201	Palm tree, 12' high	EA	414.38	548.48	962.86	232.00	646.38	8.8450
02.7602 211	Palm tree, 18' high	EA	690.63	617.00	1,307.63	260.99	951.62	9.9500
02.7602 221	Palm tree, 24' high	EA	1,139.56	1,096.96	2,236.52	464.01	1,603.57	17.6900
02.7602 231	Palm tree, 30' high	EA	1,553.91	1,477.70	3,031.61	625.06	2,178.97	23.8300
02.7603 000	**LOAM OR TOP SOIL, IN PLACE:**							
02.7603 011	Loam, under 1,000	CY	20.94	18.78	39.72	7.95	28.89	0.3029
02.7603 021	Loam, over 2,000	CY	20.15	16.10	36.25	6.81	26.96	0.2597
02.7603 031	Loam, cultivating	SY	.18	.23	.41	.10	.28	0.0037
02.7603 041	Loam, fine grading, manual	SY	.18	.44	.62	.19	.37	0.0071
02.7603 051	Loam, fine grading, machine	SY	.52	.59	1.11	.25	.77	0.0095
02.7604 000	**EDGING AND MULCH:**							
02.7604 011	Edging, redwood benders, 6"	LF	.92	4.83	5.75	2.04	2.96	0.0779
02.7604 021	Edging, redwood headers, 6"	LF	1.28	2.67	3.95	1.13	2.41	0.0430
02.7604 031	Edging, redwood headers, 4"	LF	.90	2.23	3.13	.94	1.84	0.0359
02.7604 041	Mulch, wood chips, 2", hand spread	SY	1.06	1.86	2.92	.79	1.85	0.0300
02.7604 051	Mulch, peat moss, 2", hand spread	SY	2.73	1.86	4.59	.79	3.52	0.0300
02.7605 000	**PLANT BED, 18" DEEP:**							
02.7605 011	Plant bed, 18", hand prepared	SF	1.25	3.48	4.73	1.47	2.72	0.0562
02.7605 021	Plant bed, 18", machine prepared	SF	1.25	2.97	4.22	1.26	2.51	0.0479
02.7606 000	**SEEDING, SOD & FERTILIZER:**							
02.7606 011	Seeding, highway areas, perennial	#	5.76	5.04	10.80	2.13	7.89	0.0813
02.7606 021	Seeding, highway areas, annual	#	1.25	2.38	3.63	1.01	2.26	0.0384
02.7606 031	Seeding, lawn, 5,000	SF	.03	.47	.50	.20	.23	0.0075
02.7606 041	Seeding, lawn, 10,000	SF	.02	.38	.40	.16	.18	0.0062
02.7606 051	Seeding, lawn, 50,000	SF	.02	.33	.35	.14	.16	0.0054
02.7606 061	Seeding, lawn, 100,000	SF	.02	.33	.35	.14	.16	0.0054
02.7606 071	Hydro-seeding, 50,000 to 250,000	SF	.03	.24	.27	.10	.13	0.0038
02.7606 081	Hydro-seeding, 250,000 to 500,000	SF	.02	.20	.22	.09	.11	0.0033
02.7606 091	Hydro-seeding, 500,000 and up	SF	.02	.16	.18	.07	.09	0.0026
02.7606 101	Fertilizer, commercial type	TON	279.78	318.56	598.34	134.75	414.53	5.1372
02.7606 111	Fertilizer, iron sulphate	#	.30	.38	.68	.16	.46	0.0061
02.7606 121	Fertilizer, manure	CY	13.59	8.99	22.58	3.80	17.39	0.1449

Division 2 CSI #	02 - SITEWORK Description	Unit	Material	Union Install	Union Total	Open Install	Open Total	Unit Man-Hrs
02.7606 000	SEEDING, SOD & FERTILIZER: (Cont.)							
02.7606 131	Fertilizer, rototiller mixing	SY	.24	.38	.62	.16	.40	0.0061
02.7606 141	Sodding, instant turf, small area	SF	.73	.79	1.52	.34	1.07	0.0128
02.7606 151	Sodding, instant turf, large area	SF	.54	.66	1.20	.28	.82	0.0106
02.7607 000	LANDSCAPING ACCESSORIES:							
02.7607 011	Wood & cast iron bench, 8'	EA	1,140.66		1,140.66		1,140.66	
02.7607 021	Precast concrete trash receptacle, 22'6"x3'	EA	527.40		527.40		527.40	
02.7607 031	Precast concrete planter, 5' x 15"	EA	1,161.63		1,161.63		1,161.63	
02.7607 041	Precast concrete planter, 4' x 36"	EA	1,165.76		1,165.76		1,165.76	
02.7607 051	Wire mesh arm chairs (set of 4)	SET	523.26		523.26		523.26	
02.7607 061	4' dia table, central support, base	EA	621.62		621.62		621.62	
02.7607 071	4' diameter table umbrella	EA	533.67		533.67		533.67	
02.7607 081	Logo for 4' diameter umbrella	EA	104.66		104.66		104.66	
02.7607 091	4' sq tree grate (2 piece set)	SET	339.05		339.05		339.05	
02.9101 000	RAILROAD WORK:							
02.9101 011	Spur track (90# rail/linear yd)	LF	58.57	35.92	94.49	18.64	77.21	0.5267
02.9101 021	Spur track bumper	EA	2,035.47	1,154.82	3,190.29	599.34	2,634.81	16.9354
02.9101 031	Derails	EA	651.30	359.31	1,010.61	186.48	837.78	5.2692
02.9101 041	Turn-out with switch points	EA	9,770.37	5,645.85	15,416.22	2,930.14	12,700.51	82.7958
02.9101 051	Railroad, grade & excavate roadbed	CY	2.03	1.58	3.61	.82	2.85	0.0231
02.9101 061	Railroad, ballast	CY	17.49	9.61	27.10	4.99	22.48	0.1409
02.9101 071	Railroad ties, replacement	EA	24.74	82.12	106.86	42.62	67.36	1.2043
02.9501 000	MARINE WORK:							
	Note: The following prices for berths include piling and all utilities. The following prices for wharves include fender systems and all utilities.							
02.9501 011	Covered berth, 28' to 36'	EA	7,503.46	20,026.43	27,529.89	14,607.94	22,111.40	222.3430
02.9501 021	Covered berth, 37' to 44'	EA	11,672.08	32,542.95	44,215.03	23,737.89	35,409.97	361.3073
02.9501 031	Open berth, 28' to 36'	EA	6,113.94	17,523.13	23,637.07	12,781.94	18,895.88	194.5501
02.9501 041	Open berth, 37' to 44'	EA	9,726.64	28,162.17	37,888.81	20,542.41	30,269.05	312.6698
02.9501 051	Timber wharf, wood deck	SF	136.98		136.98		136.98	
02.9501 061	Timber wharf, concrete deck	SF	124.68		124.68		124.68	
02.9501 071	Concrete pile & deck wharf	SF	149.61		149.61		149.61	
02.9501 081	Dolphin, 9 pile, wood, block & wrap	EA	24,142.48		24,142.48		24,142.48	
02.9501 091	Dredging, mobilization, maximum	LS	149,664.76		149,664.76		149,664.76	
02.9501 101	Dredging, mobilization, minimum	LS	14,966.46		14,966.46		14,966.46	
02.9501 111	Dredging	CY	6.11		6.11		6.11	
02.9501 121	Dredging, levee embankment	CY	4.88		4.88		4.88	
02.9501 131	Dredging, earthwork, unclassified	CY	4.57		4.57		4.57	
02.9501 141	Dredging, riprap, bulk	TON	34.67		34.67		34.67	
02.9501 151	Dredging, riprap, sacked	CY	179.16		179.16		179.16	
02.9501 161	Dredging, filter material	CY	30.69		30.69		30.69	

Division 3 CSI #	03 - CONCRETE Description	Unit	Material	Union Install	Union Total	Open Install	Open Total	Unit Man-Hrs
03.0000 000	CONCRETE:							
03.0500 000	CONCRETE, IN PLACE:							
	Note: The following prices include forms, rebar and excavation for concrete. For equipment see 1.1115.							
03.0501 000	FOUNDATIONS:							
03.0501 011	Foundations, tract housing	CY	194.23	181.79	376.02	114.96	309.19	2.2741
03.0501 021	Foundations, custom housing, flat lot	CY	327.24	330.54	657.78	209.02	536.26	4.1349
03.0501 031	Foundations, multi-residence, 2 story	CY	184.79	281.80	466.59	178.19	362.98	3.5251
03.0501 041	Foundations, school, 1 story, full form	CY	248.00	311.38	559.38	196.90	444.90	3.8952
03.0501 051	Foundations, school, 1 story, edge form	CY	288.01	203.16	491.17	128.47	416.48	2.5414
03.0501 061	Foundations, institutional, thru 3 story	CY	288.94	276.84	565.78	175.06	464.00	3.4631
03.0501 071	Foundations, multi-story commercial	CY	222.71	167.91	390.62	106.18	328.89	2.1005
03.0501 081	Foundations, heavy engineered structures	CY	286.54	383.20	669.74	242.32	528.86	4.7936
03.0502 000	CONCRETE WALLS, STRUCTURAL:							
03.0502 011	Concrete retaining walls, to 4'	CY	305.25	677.06	982.31	428.14	733.39	8.4696
03.0502 021	Concrete retaining walls, to 8'	CY	291.31	761.74	1,053.05	481.69	773.00	9.5289
03.0502 023	Precast, retaining sloped walls, to 35'	SF	14.82	13.64	28.46	7.08	21.90	0.2000
03.0502 025	Precast, retaining walls with geogrid, to 35'	SF	18.96	17.05	36.01	8.85	27.81	0.2500
03.0502 031	Concrete wall, 8", 12', reinforced	CY	307.54	785.39	1,092.93	496.64	804.18	9.8248
03.0502 041	Concrete wall, 10", 12', reinforced	CY	291.56	635.99	927.55	402.17	693.73	7.9559
03.0502 051	Concrete wall, 8", over 12', reinforced	CY	303.33	816.84	1,120.17	516.53	819.86	10.2182
03.0502 061	Concrete wall, 10", over 12', reinforced	CY	288.46	661.51	949.97	418.31	706.77	8.2751
03.0502 071	Concrete wall, slip form, 8"	CY	483.22	462.08	945.30	292.19	775.41	5.7803
03.0503 000	CONCRETE WALLS, TILT-UP:							
03.0503 011	Tilt-up walls, no pilasters, 6"	SF	7.10	7.85	14.95	5.84	12.94	0.0862
03.0503 021	Tilt-up walls, no pilasters, 8"	SF	8.25	8.02	16.27	5.96	14.21	0.0880
03.0503 031	Tilt-up walls, with pilasters, 6"	SF	7.54	9.13	16.67	6.79	14.33	0.1002
03.0503 041	Tilt-up walls, with pilasters, 8"	SF	8.82	9.96	18.78	7.40	16.22	0.1093
03.0503 051	Tilt-up walls, with pilasters, 6"	CY	356.11	448.82	804.93	333.64	689.75	4.9261
03.0503 061	Tilt-up walls, with pilasters, 8"	CY	370.15	467.23	837.38	347.33	717.48	5.1282
03.0503 071	Tilt-up walls, pilasters only	SFFA	14.79	13.70	28.49	10.19	24.98	0.1504
03.0503 081	Tilt-up walls, pilasters only	CY	446.49	695.50	1,141.99	517.02	963.51	7.6336
03.0504 000	SLABS, BEAMS & COLUMNS, STRUCTURAL:							
03.0504 011	Slab, 1 way beams, 6", with 200# rebar	CY	358.10	540.50	898.60	398.51	756.61	5.9737
03.0504 021	Slab, 2 way beams, 6", with 225# rebar	CY	427.41	646.29	1,073.70	476.50	903.91	7.1429
03.0504 031	Slab, flat, 8", with double mat	CY	265.68	402.13	667.81	296.49	562.17	4.4444
03.0504 041	Slab, flat, 12", with 250# rebar	CY	242.58	637.76	880.34	470.21	712.79	7.0486
03.0504 051	Slab, 7" post tensioned, 1#-1#, tempered bar	CY	311.91	474.53	786.44	352.76	664.67	5.2083
03.0504 061	Slab, 6"-8", with concurrent steel beam jacketing	CY	346.49	526.64	873.13	391.50	737.99	5.7803
03.0504 071	Slab, 6"-8", on permanent metal form	CY	323.39	492.49	815.88	366.11	689.50	5.4054
03.0504 081	Slab, 6"-8", lift slab construction	SF	16.07	12.31	28.38	9.15	25.22	0.1351
03.0504 091	Slab, 8", concurrent with slip form construction	CY	254.14	386.06	640.20	286.99	541.13	4.2373
03.0504 101	Slab, precast, 8"	SF	14.26	9.14	23.40	6.79	21.05	0.1003
03.0504 111	Pan, 30" square, 3"slab, 6" x 12" ribs	CY	346.93	526.64	873.57	391.50	738.43	5.7803
03.0504 121	Pan, 30" square, 3"slab, 6" x 16" ribs	CY	300.31	455.55	755.86	338.65	638.96	5.0000
03.0504 131	Pan, 30" square, 3"slab, 6" x 10" ribs	CY	265.68	403.14	668.82	299.69	565.37	4.4248
03.0504 141	Pan, 20" square, 4-1/2"slab, 6"x12" ribs	CY	277.35	421.80	699.15	313.56	590.91	4.6296
03.0504 151	Pan, 20" square, 4-1/2", 6"x16" ribs	CY	265.68	403.14	668.82	299.69	565.37	4.4248
03.0504 161	Pan, 20" square, 4-1/2"slab, 6"x20" ribs	CY	254.14	386.06	640.20	286.99	541.13	4.2373
03.0504 171	Dome slab, thin shell	SF	17.47	23.99	41.46	15.68	33.15	0.2941
03.0504 181	Stairs & stairways, concrete tread	CY	637.99	859.89	1,497.88	552.98	1,190.97	10.6383
03.0504 191	Stairs & stairways, concrete tread	LF	21.35	77.87	99.22	50.08	71.43	0.9634
03.0504 201	Stairs, concrete, 22 risers, 4' wide	FLOOR	1,995.58	7,216.96	9,212.54	4,641.07	6,636.65	89.2857
03.0504 211	Beams & girders, 12" x 24"	CY	612.31	815.60	1,427.91	533.20	1,145.51	10.0000
03.0504 221	Beams & girders, 18" x 24"	CY	491.85	679.66	1,171.51	444.33	936.18	8.3333
03.0504 231	Columns, Sonotube form, 425# rebar, 12-18" diameter	CY	369.63	505.19	874.82	324.88	694.51	6.2500
03.0504 241	Columns with chamfer, 550#/CY rebar, 12"square	CY	574.58	1,257.56	1,832.14	808.71	1,383.29	15.5581
03.0504 251	Columns with chamfer, 584#/CY rebar, 16"square	CY	551.20	893.12	1,444.32	574.35	1,125.55	11.0494
03.0504 261	Columns with chamfer, 598#/CY rebar, 18"square	CY	546.61	787.80	1,334.41	506.61	1,053.22	9.7463
03.0504 271	Columns with chamfer, 590#/CY rebar, 20"square	CY	532.86	699.99	1,232.85	450.15	983.01	8.6600
03.0504 281	Columns with chamfer, 578#/CY rebar, 24"square	CY	513.03	589.17	1,102.20	378.88	891.91	7.2890

Division 3 CSI #	03 - CONCRETE Description	Unit	Material	Union Install	Union Total	Open Install	Open Total	Unit Man-Hrs
03.0505 000	**REINFORCED CONCRETE, POURED IN PLACE:**							
03.0505 011	Poured in place, highway structures	CY	300.31	400.50	700.81	253.26	553.57	5.0100
03.0505 021	Poured in place, hospital wall/slab, steel frame	CY	346.49	462.08	808.57	292.19	638.68	5.7803
03.0505 031	Poured in place, hospital wall/slab, concrete frame	CY	311.91	416.35	728.26	263.28	575.19	5.2083
03.0505 041	Poured in place, office building concrete frame walls&slabs	CY	300.31	399.70	700.01	252.75	553.06	5.0000
03.0505 051	Poured in place, military structures	CY	292.97	399.70	692.67	252.75	545.72	5.0000
03.0505 061	Poured in place, parking structures	CY	302.80	416.35	719.15	263.28	566.08	5.2083
03.0505 071	Poured in place, stadiums & auditoriums	CY	325.23	446.59	771.82	282.40	607.63	5.5866
03.0505 081	Poured in place, college structures	CY	381.22	509.17	890.39	321.97	703.19	6.3694
03.0506 000	**MISCELLANEOUS ITEMS WITH STRUCTURAL CONCRETE:**							
03.0506 011	Lightweight concrete	CY	24.87	25.97	50.84	11.29	36.16	0.4154
03.0506 021	Waterproofing admix	CY	3.45	3.71	7.16	1.61	5.06	0.0594
03.0506 031	Color admix, black, 2-8#/sack	CY	8.29	11.46	19.75	7.24	15.53	0.1433
03.0506 041	Color admix, red/tan or green, 2-8#/sack	CY	17.47	23.72	41.19	15.00	32.47	0.2967
03.0506 051	Air entrainment, 6 sack mix	SF	1.24	1.81	3.05	1.14	2.38	0.0226
03.0506 061	Epoxy coat, squeegee applied	SF	2.26	3.11	5.37	1.97	4.23	0.0389
03.0506 071	Epoxy patch & grout mix	CY	73.41	99.77	173.18	63.09	136.50	1.2481
03.0506 081	Dust coating, mopped	SF	.05	.25	.30	.16	.21	0.0031
03.0507 000	**SLAB ON GRADE COMBOS:**							
	Note: The following prices include 2" of sand.							
03.0507 011	Slab on grade, 4", 4" rock, memb, 6x6 w1.4/w1.4 ewwm	SF	3.08	2.88	5.96	1.88	4.96	0.0353
03.0507 021	Slab on grade, 5", 4" rock, memb, 6x6 w1.4/w1.4 ewwm	SF	3.54	2.98	6.52	1.95	5.49	0.0366
03.0507 031	Slab on grade, 6", 6" rock, memb, 6x6 w2.9/w2.9 ewwm	SF	4.28	3.41	7.69	2.23	6.51	0.0418
03.0507 041	Slab on grade, 5", 4" rock, memb, #4 @ 18" on center each way	SF	3.95	3.28	7.23	2.14	6.09	0.0402
03.0507 051	Slab on grade, 6", 6" rock, memb, #4 @ 18" on center each way	SF	4.64	3.36	8.00	2.20	6.84	0.0412
03.0507 061	Kalman floor, 6"slab, 6" rock, #4@ 18" on center each way	SF	4.82	5.32	10.14	3.48	8.30	0.0653
03.0600 000	**PRECAST CONCRETE:**							
	Note: For caulking, see 7.9000. For precast utility items, see 2.5700.							
03.0601 011	Precast concrete, single tees	SF	11.00	4.75	15.75	3.50	14.50	0.0525
03.0601 021	Precast concrete, double tees	SF	9.04	3.25	12.29	2.39	11.43	0.0359
03.0601 031	Precast concrete, beams/girders	CY	876.26	117.55	993.81	86.67	962.93	1.2992
03.0601 041	Precast concrete, inverted tee	CY	1,022.01	146.88	1,168.89	108.29	1,130.30	1.6233
03.0601 051	Precast concrete, plank, solid, 6"	SF	6.14	2.59	8.73	1.91	8.05	0.0286
03.0601 061	Precast concrete, plank, hollow, 4"	SF	5.63	2.09	7.72	1.54	7.17	0.0231
03.0601 071	Precast concrete, plank, hollow, 6"	SF	5.95	2.33	8.28	1.72	7.67	0.0258
03.0601 081	Precast concrete, plank, hollow, 8"	SF	6.36	2.59	8.95	1.91	8.27	0.0286
03.0601 091	Precast concrete, plank, hollow, 10"	SF	6.76	2.92	9.68	2.15	8.91	0.0323
03.0602 000	**PRECAST CONCRETE, ARCHITECTURAL:**							
03.0602 011	Precast panel, vertical, single form	SF	19.55	10.91	30.46	8.11	27.66	0.1197
03.0602 021	Precast panel, vertical, double form	SF	26.14	10.91	37.05	8.11	34.25	0.1197
03.0602 031	Precast panel, vertical, single form, exp aggregate	SF	28.26	10.91	39.17	8.11	36.37	0.1197
03.0602 041	Precast panel, vertical, single form, sandblast	SF	28.26	10.91	39.17	8.11	36.37	0.1197
03.0602 051	Precast panel, vertical, double form, exp aggregate	SF	42.36	10.91	53.27	8.11	50.47	0.1197
03.0602 061	Precast panel, vertical, double form, sandblast	SF	42.36	10.91	53.27	8.11	50.47	0.1197
03.0602 071	Precast panel, vertical, single form, mo-sai fin	SF	26.85	10.91	37.76	8.11	34.96	0.1197
03.0602 081	Precast panel, vertical, single form, granite fin	SF	49.49	10.91	60.40	8.11	57.60	0.1197
03.0602 091	Precast coping, 8" wide, sandblast	SF	13.88	6.95	20.83	4.40	18.28	0.0870
03.0602 101	Precast sill, 12"x5", sandblasted	SF	25.95	13.33	39.28	8.43	34.38	0.1667
03.0700 000	**SPECIALTY CONCRETE:**							
03.0701 000	**GUNITE:**							
	Note: The following prices do not include form or bar.							
03.0701 011	Gunite, flat plane, 1" depth	SF	2.15	1.29	3.44	.83	2.98	0.0159
03.0701 021	Gunite, curved arch, 1" depth	SF	2.15	1.71	3.86	1.10	3.25	0.0211
03.0701 031	Gunite, pools, 1" depth	SF	2.15	1.10	3.25	.48	2.63	0.0176
03.0701 041	Gunite, bulk, small quantities	CY	231.70	569.23	800.93	366.06	597.76	7.0423
03.0701 051	Gunite, bulk, large quantities	CY	231.70	283.62	515.32	182.39	414.09	3.5088
03.0702 000	**PRESSURE GROUTING:**							
03.0702 011	Pressure grout, large quantity, 50/50 mix	CY	205.64	477.18	682.82	207.48	413.12	7.6336
03.0703 000	**DRY PACKING:**							
03.0703 011	Dry packing, 1" thick	SF	3.39	4.46	7.85	1.94	5.33	0.0714
03.0703 021	Dry packing, embeco, 1" thick	SF	5.06	6.25	11.31	2.72	7.78	0.1000

Division 3 CSI #	03 - CONCRETE Description	Unit	Material	Union Install	Union Total	Open Install	Open Total	Unit Man-Hrs
03.0704 000	**CONCRETE FINISHES:**							
03.0704 011	Concrete finish, exposed aggregate, washed	SF	.36	1.23	1.59	.90	1.26	0.0176
03.0704 021	Concrete finish, exposed aggregate, seeded 50%	SF	.44	1.47	1.91	1.08	1.52	0.0211
03.0704 031	Concrete finish, exposed aggregate, seeded 100%	SF	.77	2.33	3.10	1.70	2.47	0.0333
03.0704 041	Concrete finish, acid etch, 5% solution	SF	.05	.38	.43	.28	.33	0.0054
03.0705 000	**CONCRETE FIREPROOFING:**							
03.0705 011	Fireproofing, on steel beams to 8"	CY	227.57	770.55	998.12	506.24	733.81	9.1743
03.0705 021	Fireproofing, steel beams 10" & up	CY	196.89	666.59	863.48	437.94	634.83	7.9365
03.0800 000	**EXCAVATION & BACKFILL:**							
	Note: This section also includes grading and bases for concrete. For mass excavation, see section							
	2.2000. For trench over 5' deep, add for shoring, as in section 2.4000. The presence of groundwater,							
	sand, mud or hard pan must be covered by relative unit increases for footing drains.							
03.0801 000	**EXCAVATION, SPREAD FOOTINGS AND TRENCHING:**							
03.0801 011	Batter boards, foundation layout	EA	6.61	58.56	65.17	35.89	42.50	0.7449
03.0801 021	Foundations, structural	CY	8.99	10.93	19.92	7.69	16.68	0.1282
03.0801 031	Spread footings, structural	CY	11.29	13.64	24.93	9.60	20.89	0.1600
03.0801 041	Trench, structural	CY	10.87	13.11	23.98	9.23	20.10	0.1538
03.0801 051	Trenching, machine, 18" x 24" deep	LF	1.30	1.64	2.94	1.15	2.45	0.0192
03.0801 061	Trenching, machine, 24" x 36" deep	LF	2.38	2.84	5.22	2.00	4.38	0.0333
03.0801 071	Trenching, machine, 36" x 48" deep	LF	4.46	5.44	9.90	3.83	8.29	0.0638
03.0801 081	Trenching, machine, 48" x 60" deep	LF	6.77	8.16	14.93	5.74	12.51	0.0957
03.0801 091	Trench machine, minimum 4 hours with move	EACH	431.04		431.04		431.04	
03.0801 101	Hand labor, trench trimming	SF		1.44	1.44	.63	.63	0.0230
03.0801 111	Trenching, hand, hardpan, rock	CY	11.02	109.50	120.52	59.58	70.60	1.5625
03.0801 121	Trenching, hand, earth	CY		54.83	54.83	23.84	23.84	0.8772
03.0802 000	**FOOTING BACKFILL:**							
03.0802 011	Backfill, hand, no compaction	CY		23.42	23.42	10.18	10.18	0.3746
03.0802 021	Backfill, hand, water jetted	CY		23.95	23.95	10.41	10.41	0.3831
03.0802 031	Backfill, hand, rammer compacted	CY	3.19	24.61	27.80	10.70	13.89	0.3937
03.0802 041	Backfill, mach, no compaction	CY	7.16	7.47	14.63	5.26	12.42	0.0877
03.0802 051	Backfill, mach, compact 90% aasho	CY	13.40	16.01	29.41	11.28	24.68	0.1879
03.0803 000	**DISPOSAL, EXCESS EARTH:**							
03.0803 011	Earth, spot spread, machine	CY	2.38	2.43	4.81	1.71	4.09	0.0285
03.0803 021	Earth, on site, area spread, machine	CY	2.80	2.75	5.55	1.94	4.74	0.0323
03.0805 000	**GRADING FOR CONCRETE:**							
03.0805 011	Rough grading	SF	.01	.17	.18	.12	.13	0.0020
03.0805 021	Fine grading, hand	SF		.36	.36	.15	.15	0.0057
03.0805 031	Fine grading, machine	SF	.03	.09	.12	.06	.09	0.0010
03.0806 000	**FILL:**							
03.0806 011	Capillary fill	CY	12.52	31.85	44.37	17.33	29.85	0.4545
03.0806 021	Capillary fill, 4" hand grade & roll	SF	.22	.39	.61	.21	.43	0.0056
03.0806 031	Capillary fill, 4" machine grade & roll	SF	.30	.07	.37	.04	.34	0.0010
03.0806 041	Add for each added 1", hand grade	SF	.05	.10	.15	.05	.10	0.0014
03.0806 051	Add for each added 1", mach grade	SF	.06	.02	.08	.01	.07	0.0003
03.0806 061	Sand fill for concrete, large quantity	CY	11.22	17.86	29.08	7.77	18.99	0.2857
03.0806 071	Sand fill for concrete, 2" sand cushion	SF	.09	.11	.20	.05	.14	0.0018
03.0806 081	Add for each added 1" sand	SF	.03	.06	.09	.02	.05	0.0009
03.0807 000	**WATERPROOF MEMBRANE:**							
03.0807 011	Membrane, polyethylene, 4 mil	SF	.04	.14	.18	.06	.10	0.0023
03.0807 021	Membrane, polyethylene, 6 mil	SF	.06	.14	.20	.06	.12	0.0023
03.0807 031	Membrane, 2 ply, hot mop	SF	.17	1.36	1.53	1.10	1.27	0.0172
03.1000 000	**CONCRETE FORMS:**							
	Note: The following prices are for large quantities only. They are for quick budget type estimates. For							
	detailed estimates, see the flying forms listed in each section of this division. For full form stepped							
	foundations, add 51% to the material costs.							
03.1001 011	Foundations	CY	217.44		217.44		217.44	
03.1001 021	Structural walls gang formed	CY	358.28		358.28		358.28	
03.1001 031	Structural slabs gang formed	CY	426.54		426.54		426.54	
03.1001 041	Structural beams gang formed	CY	477.71		477.71		477.71	
03.1001 051	Structural columns gang formed	CY	597.13		597.13		597.13	
03.1001 061	Slab on grade	CY	272.12		272.12		272.12	

Division 3 CSI #	03 - CONCRETE Description	Unit	Material	Union Install	Union Total	Open Install	Open Total	Unit Man-Hrs
03.1100 000	**FOUNDATION FORMS:**							
03.1101 000	**FOUNDATION FORMS, TRACT/MULTI-UNIT:**							
03.1101 011	Foundation forms, edge	LF	.43	4.02	4.45	2.64	3.07	0.0479
03.1101 021	Foundation forms, full form, 16" panel	SFCA	.65	6.53	7.18	4.29	4.94	0.0777
03.1101 031	Foundation, full form, 2-3 story, 24" panel	SFCA	.55	5.78	6.33	3.80	4.35	0.0688
03.1102 000	**FOUNDATION FORMS, CUSTOM RESIDENTIAL:**							
03.1102 011	Foundation forms, custom, edge	LF	.59	6.30	6.89	4.14	4.73	0.0750
03.1102 021	Foundation full form, custom, 16-24" panel	SFCA	.84	10.15	10.99	6.67	7.51	0.1208
03.1103 000	**FOUNDATION FORMS, SCHOOL AND INSTITUTIONAL:**							
03.1103 011	Foundation forms, institutional, slab reveal	LF	1.22	8.69	9.91	5.71	6.93	0.1035
03.1103 021	Foundation forms, institutional, full form	SFCA	1.28	12.72	14.00	8.36	9.64	0.1515
03.1103 041	Foundation forms, institutional, keyway	LF	.31	1.55	1.86	1.02	1.33	0.0185
03.1200 000	**FOOTING FORMS:**							
03.1201 011	Footing forms, continuous spread, 12" high, 1 use	SFCA	2.48	10.97	13.45	7.21	9.69	0.1306
03.1201 021	Footing forms, continuous spread, 12" high, 3 uses	SFCA	.96	8.63	9.59	5.67	6.63	0.1028
03.1201 031	Footing forms, continuous spread, 12" high, 5 uses	SFCA	.61	8.16	8.77	5.36	5.97	0.0972
03.1201 041	Footing forms, pier type, 1 use	SFCA	2.37	11.14	13.51	7.32	9.69	0.1326
03.1201 051	Footing forms, pier type, 3 uses	SFCA	.89	8.80	9.69	5.78	6.67	0.1048
03.1201 061	Footing forms, pile cap, heavy material	SFCA	1.62	9.10	10.72	5.98	7.60	0.1083
03.1201 071	Footing forms, column & post	SFCA	2.37	14.00	16.37	9.20	11.57	0.1667
03.1201 081	Footing forms, pilaster/column	SFCA	2.37	14.00	16.37	9.20	11.57	0.1667
03.1201 091	Footing forms, curbs on foundations	SFCA	4.40	20.27	24.67	13.31	17.71	0.2413
03.1300 000	**FORMS, SLAB ON GRADE:**							
03.1301 011	Edge forms, 2" x 4"	LF	.46	4.20	4.66	2.76	3.22	0.0500
03.1301 021	Edge forms, 2" x 6"	LF	.64	4.96	5.60	3.26	3.90	0.0591
03.1301 031	Slab surface blockout, 1-1/2"x3/4" depressed	LF	.13	4.38	4.51	2.87	3.00	0.0521
03.1301 041	Cold joint forms, const/key, wood	LF	.39	4.20	4.59	2.76	3.15	0.0500
03.1301 051	Cold joint, const/key, metal	LF	.68	4.20	4.88	2.76	3.44	0.0500
03.1301 061	Cold joint forms, keyway, removable	LF	.38	5.60	5.98	3.68	4.06	0.0667
03.1301 071	Slab forms, chamfer strip	LF	.08	1.74	1.82	1.14	1.22	0.0207
03.1301 081	Set screed posts, hooks & bars	SF	.01	.23	.24	.15	.16	0.0027
03.1400 000	**CONSTRUCTION FORMS, VERTICAL:**							
	Note: These prices should be used for small quantities. Discount these prices up to 25% for larger quantities, depending on project set-up costs. For battered inside forms, add 5% to the material costs.							
03.1401 000	**FORMS, WOOD, RETAINING WALLS:**							
03.1401 011	Retaining wall forms, 4' height, 1 use	SFCA	2.30	14.00	16.30	9.20	11.50	0.1667
03.1401 021	Retaining wall forms, 4' height, 3 uses	SFCA	.93	11.67	12.60	7.66	8.59	0.1389
03.1401 031	Retaining wall forms, 4' height, 5 uses	SFCA	.64	11.20	11.84	7.36	8.00	0.1333
03.1401 041	Retaining wall forms, 8' height, 1 use	SFCA	2.00	14.00	16.00	9.20	11.20	0.1667
03.1401 051	Retaining wall forms, 8' height, 3 uses	SFCA	.80	11.67	12.47	7.66	8.46	0.1389
03.1401 061	Retaining wall forms, 8' height, 5 uses	SFCA	.57	11.20	11.77	7.36	7.93	0.1333
03.1401 071	Retaining wall forms, 12' height, 1 use	SFCA	2.14	15.50	17.64	10.18	12.32	0.1845
03.1401 081	Retaining wall forms, 12' height, 3 uses	SFCA	.86	12.53	13.39	7.92	8.78	0.1567
03.1401 091	Retaining wall forms, 12' height, 5 uses	SFCA	.62	12.09	12.71	7.64	8.26	0.1512
03.1402 000	**FORMS, WOOD, BUILDING WALLS:**							
03.1402 011	Wall forms, 8' height, 1 use	SFCA	2.00	14.00	16.00	9.20	11.20	0.1667
03.1402 021	Wall forms, 8' height, 3 uses	SFCA	.80	11.67	12.47	7.66	8.46	0.1389
03.1402 031	Wall forms, 8' height, 5 uses	SFCA	.57	11.20	11.77	7.36	7.93	0.1333
03.1402 041	Wall forms, 12' height, 1 use	SFCA	2.14	14.23	16.37	9.00	11.14	0.1780
03.1402 051	Wall forms, 12' height, 3 uses	SFCA	.88	12.01	12.89	7.60	8.48	0.1503
03.1402 061	Wall forms, 12' height, 5 uses	SFCA	.62	11.57	12.19	7.31	7.93	0.1447
03.1402 071	Wall forms, 16' height, 1 use	SFCA	2.05	15.63	17.68	9.88	11.93	0.1955
03.1402 081	Wall forms, 16' height, 3 uses	SFCA	.84	13.41	14.25	8.48	9.32	0.1677
03.1402 091	Wall forms, 16' height, 5 uses	SFCA	.60	12.97	13.57	8.20	8.80	0.1622
03.1402 101	Wall form, blockouts & offsets	SFCA	2.53	14.70	17.23	9.66	12.19	0.1750
03.1403 000	**WALLS, FLYING FORMS:**							
03.1403 011	Flying form, walls to 9', 1 use	SFCA	2.55	1.38	3.93	.87	3.42	0.0173
03.1403 021	Flying form, walls to 9', 3 uses	SFCA	1.87	1.38	3.25	.87	2.74	0.0173
03.1403 031	Flying form, walls to 9', 5 uses	SFCA	1.20	1.38	2.58	.87	2.07	0.0173
03.1403 041	Flying form, walls to 12', 1 use	SFCA	2.82	1.45	4.27	.92	3.74	0.0182
03.1403 051	Flying form, walls to 12', 3 uses	SFCA	2.14	1.45	3.59	.92	3.06	0.0182
03.1403 061	Flying form, walls to 12', 5 uses	SFCA	1.41	1.45	2.86	.92	2.33	0.0182

Division 3 CSI #	03 - CONCRETE Description	Unit	Material	Union Install	Union Total	Open Install	Open Total	Unit Man-Hrs
03.1403 000	WALLS, FLYING FORMS: (Cont.)							
03.1403 071	Flying form, walls to 16', 1 use	SFCA	3.05	1.57	4.62	.99	4.04	0.0196
03.1403 081	Flying form, walls to 16', 3 uses	SFCA	2.40	1.23	3.63	.78	3.18	0.0154
03.1403 091	Flying form, walls to 16', 5 uses	SFCA	1.72	.75	2.47	.48	2.20	0.0094
03.1600 000	COLUMN FORMS:							
	Note: These prices should be used for small quantities. Discount these prices up to 25% for larger quantities, depending on project set-up.							
03.1601 000	COLUMN FORMS, WOOD, BUILT-UP:							
03.1601 011	Column forms, square/rect, 1 use	SFCA	2.12	10.50	12.62	6.90	9.02	0.1250
03.1601 021	Column forms, square/rect, 3 uses	SFCA	.62	7.77	8.39	4.91	5.53	0.0972
03.1601 031	Column forms, square/rect, 5 uses	SFCA	.38	7.33	7.71	4.64	5.02	0.0917
03.1601 041	Add for 3/4" chamfer, column form	LF	.12	.93	1.05	.61	.73	0.0111
03.1602 000	STEEL FORMS, MULTI-USE:							
03.1602 011	Column forms, round/rect, rent	SFCA	1.17	5.00	6.17	3.16	4.33	0.0625
03.1603 000	FIBREBOARD FORMS:							
03.1603 011	Fibreform, circular column, 12"	LF	5.33	9.40	14.73	5.94	11.27	0.1176
03.1603 021	Fibreform, circular column, 14"	LF	7.43	9.40	16.83	5.94	13.37	0.1176
03.1603 031	Fibreform, circular column, 16"	LF	9.71	9.40	19.11	5.94	15.65	0.1176
03.1603 041	Fibreform, circular column, 20"	LF	15.97	10.21	26.18	6.46	22.43	0.1277
03.1603 051	Fibreform, circular column, 24"	LF	21.14	10.21	31.35	6.46	27.60	0.1277
03.1603 061	Fibreform, circular column, 30"	LF	31.89	10.95	42.84	6.93	38.82	0.1370
03.1603 071	Fibreform, circular column, 36"	LF	39.71	11.70	51.41	7.40	47.11	0.1464
03.1604 000	COLUMN FORMS, METAL (LOST FORM):							
03.1604 011	Form, circular, 12", lost	SFCA	7.96	4.96	12.92	3.14	11.10	0.0621
03.1604 021	Form, circular, 16", lost	SFCA	10.72	4.96	15.68	3.14	13.86	0.0621
03.1604 031	Form, circular, 20", lost	SFCA	13.55	5.04	18.59	3.18	16.73	0.0630
03.1604 041	Form, circular, 24", lost	SFCA	17.93	5.04	22.97	3.18	21.11	0.0630
03.1604 051	Form, circular, 30", lost	SFCA	25.15	5.11	30.26	3.23	28.38	0.0639
03.1604 061	Form, circular, 36", lost	SFCA	29.79	5.26	35.05	3.33	33.12	0.0658
03.1604 071	Form, circular, 42", lost	SFCA	38.77	5.41	44.18	3.42	42.19	0.0677
03.1605 000	COLUMNS FORMS, FLYING, METAL OR FIBERGLASS:							
	Note: The following prices assume 4 uses per month.							
03.1605 011	Column form, flying, 12"	SFCA	2.53	4.96	7.49	3.14	5.67	0.0621
03.1605 021	Column form, flying, 16"	SFCA	3.43	4.96	8.39	3.14	6.57	0.0621
03.1605 031	Column form, flying, 20"	SFCA	4.32	4.96	9.28	3.14	7.46	0.0621
03.1605 041	Column form, flying, 24"	SFCA	5.80	4.96	10.76	3.14	8.94	0.0621
03.1605 051	Column form, flying, 30"	SFCA	8.09	5.11	13.20	3.23	11.32	0.0639
03.1605 061	Column form, flying, 36"	SFCA	9.64	5.26	14.90	3.33	12.97	0.0658
03.1605 071	Column form, flying, 42"	SFCA	12.46	5.41	17.87	3.42	15.88	0.0677
03.1605 081	Capital column form, cone	SFCA	8.11	19.29	27.40	12.20	20.31	0.2413
03.1606 000	PILASTERS, TILT-UP:							
03.1606 011	Pilasters, wood formed	LF	2.37	27.99	30.36	18.39	20.76	0.3333
03.1700 000	CONSTRUCTION FORMS, HORIZONTAL:							
	Note: Discount these prices up to 25% for larger quantities, depending on project set-up costs.							
03.1701 000	SLAB FORMS:							
03.1701 011	Slab form, edge header	LF	1.05	4.98	6.03	3.27	4.32	0.0593
03.1701 021	Slab form, soffit, ply, 1 use	SFCA	2.47	16.75	19.22	10.27	12.74	0.2131
03.1701 031	Slab form, soffit, ply, 3 use	SFCA	1.40	10.55	11.95	6.35	7.75	0.1384
03.1701 041	Slab form, soffit, ply, 5 use	SFCA	1.05	9.41	10.46	5.66	6.71	0.1234
03.1701 051	Slab form, shoring, rent	SF	.53		.53		.53	
03.1701 061	Slab form, re-shoring	SF	.13	.81	.94	.46	.59	0.0111
03.1701 071	Slab form, drop head, soffit, 1 use	SFCA	1.83	27.99	29.82	18.39	20.22	0.3333
03.1701 081	Slab form, screeds	SF	.07	.34	.41	.23	.30	0.0041
03.1702 000	BEAM AND GIRDER FORMS:							
03.1702 011	Beam form, sides, 1 use	SFCA	2.03	27.58	29.61	18.12	20.15	0.3284
03.1702 021	Beam form, sides, 3 uses	SFCA	.97	19.69	20.66	12.45	13.42	0.2463
03.1702 031	Beam form, sides, 5 uses	SFCA	.73	18.38	19.11	11.62	12.35	0.2299
03.1702 041	Beam form, soffits, 1 use	SFCA	2.15	27.58	29.73	18.12	20.27	0.3284
03.1702 051	Beam form, soffits, 3 uses	SFCA	1.67	19.69	21.36	12.45	14.12	0.2463
03.1702 061	Beam form, soffits, 5 uses	SFCA	1.40	18.38	19.78	11.62	13.02	0.2299
03.1702 071	Beam form, cap head, side	SFCA	2.15	26.64	28.79	16.85	19.00	0.3333
03.1702 081	Beam form, cap head, soffit	SFCA	2.15	26.64	28.79	16.85	19.00	0.3333

Division 3 CSI #	03 - CONCRETE Description	Unit	Material	Union Install	Union Total	Open Install	Open Total	Unit Man-Hrs
03.1703 000	**PANS, WAFFLE AND JOIST, SUBCONTRACTOR ERECTED:**							
	Note: These prices include forms, rental, shoring at 12' height (including beams and girders to nearest							
	wall. General contractor provides ledgers at walls).							
03.1703 011	Metal pans, 1 use, 10-20,000 square feet	SFCA	4.96	6.17	11.13	4.55	9.51	0.0682
03.1703 021	Metal pans, 3 use, 10-20,000 square feet	SFCA	3.79	5.66	9.45	4.18	7.97	0.0626
03.1703 031	Metal pans, 5 use, 10-20,000 square feet	SFCA	2.87	5.58	8.45	4.12	6.99	0.0617
03.1703 041	Fiberglass pans, 1 use	SFCA	5.40	5.75	11.15	3.85	9.25	0.0682
03.1703 051	Fiberglass pans, 3 uses	SFCA	5.15	5.28	10.43	3.53	8.68	0.0626
03.1703 061	Fiberglass pans, 5 uses	SFCA	4.27	5.20	9.47	3.48	7.75	0.0617
03.1704 000	**STRUCTURAL SLABS WITH BEAMS, COMPOSITE, FORMS:**							
03.1704 011	Slab forms, 1 way beams, 1 use	SFCA	4.09	4.49	8.58	2.84	6.93	0.0562
03.1704 021	Slab forms, 1 way beams, 3 uses	SFCA	3.95	4.49	8.44	2.84	6.79	0.0562
03.1704 031	Slab forms, 2 way beams, 1 use	SFCA	4.87	5.38	10.25	3.40	8.27	0.0673
03.1704 041	Slab forms, 2 way beams, 3 uses	SFCA	4.51	5.38	9.89	3.40	7.91	0.0673
03.1705 000	**STRUCTURAL SLAB AND BEAM FLYING FORMS:**							
03.1705 011	Slab, flying forms, soffits, 1 use	SFCA	4.58	1.38	5.96	.87	5.45	0.0173
03.1705 021	Slab, flying forms, soffits, 3 uses	SFCA	3.33	1.35	4.68	.85	4.18	0.0169
03.1705 031	Slab, flying forms, soffits, 5 uses	SFCA	2.30	1.34	3.64	.85	3.15	0.0168
03.1705 041	Beam, flying forms, side, 1 use	SFCA	5.09	3.57	8.66	2.26	7.35	0.0447
03.1705 051	Beam, flying forms, side, 3 uses	SFCA	3.93	3.50	7.43	2.21	6.14	0.0438
03.1705 061	Beam, flying forms, side, 5 uses	SFCA	2.92	3.42	6.34	2.16	5.08	0.0428
03.1800 000	**CONSTRUCTION FORMS, HORIZONTAL, HEAVY DUTY:**							
	Note: Prices include stripping, cleaning, and oiling forms, and shoring erection. Add shoring material.							
	These prices should be used for small quantities. Discount these prices up to 25% for larger quantities							
	depending on project set-up costs.							
03.1801 000	**SLAB FORMS, HEAVY DUTY:**							
03.1801 011	Slab form, edge headers	LF	2.79	6.85	9.64	4.50	7.29	0.0816
03.1801 021	Slab form, soffit, ply, 1 use	SFCA	6.46	18.61	25.07	11.40	17.86	0.2367
03.1801 031	Slab form, soffit, ply, 3 uses	SFCA	3.72	12.34	16.06	7.43	11.15	0.1619
03.1801 041	Slab form, soffit, ply, 5 uses	SFCA	2.79	11.20	13.99	6.74	9.53	0.1469
03.1801 051	Slab form, shoring, rent	SF	1.38		1.38		1.38	
03.1801 061	Slab form, re-shoring	SF	.27	2.66	2.93	1.49	1.76	0.0363
03.1801 071	Slab form, drop head, soffit, 1 use	SFCA	4.74	29.87	34.61	19.62	24.36	0.3556
03.1801 081	Slab form, screeds	SF	.08	2.22	2.30	1.46	1.54	0.0264
03.1802 000	**BEAM AND GIRDER FORMS, HEAVY DUTY:**							
03.1802 011	Beam form, sides, 1 use	SFCA	5.28	29.46	34.74	19.35	24.63	0.3507
03.1802 021	Beam form, sides, 3 uses	SFCA	2.53	21.50	24.03	13.60	16.13	0.2690
03.1802 031	Beam form, sides, 5 uses	SFCA	1.95	20.19	22.14	12.77	14.72	0.2526
03.1802 041	Beam form, soffits, 1 use	SFCA	5.57	29.46	35.03	19.35	24.92	0.3507
03.1802 051	Beam form, soffits, 3 uses	SFCA	4.30	21.50	25.80	13.60	17.90	0.2690
03.1802 061	Beam form, soffits, 5 uses	SFCA	3.62	20.19	23.81	12.77	16.39	0.2526
03.1802 071	Beam form, cap head, side	SFCA	5.61	28.46	34.07	18.00	23.61	0.3560
03.1802 081	Beam form, cap head, soffit	SFCA	5.57	28.46	34.03	18.00	23.57	0.3560
03.1803 000	**PANS, WAFFLE & JOIST, SUBCONTRACTOR ERECTED, HEAVY DUTY:**							
	Note: These prices include forms, rental, shoring at 12' height (including beams and girders to nearest							
	wall. General contractor provides ledgers at walls).							
03.1803 011	Metal pans, 1 use, 10-20,000 square feet	SFCA	7.45	8.03	15.48	5.92	13.37	0.0888
03.1803 021	Metal pans, 3 use, 10-20,000 square feet	SFCA	5.68	7.53	13.21	5.55	11.23	0.0832
03.1803 031	Metal pans, 5 use, 10-20,000 square feet	SFCA	4.30	7.45	11.75	5.49	9.79	0.0823
03.1803 041	Fiberglass pans, 1 use	SFCA	8.11	7.57	15.68	5.06	13.17	0.0898
03.1803 051	Fiberglass pans, 3 uses	SFCA	7.70	7.10	14.80	4.75	12.45	0.0842
03.1803 061	Fiberglass pans, 5 uses	SFCA	6.40	7.02	13.42	4.70	11.10	0.0833
03.1804 000	**STRUCTURAL SLABS WITH BEAMS, COMPOSITE, FORMS, HEAVY DUTY:**							
03.1804 011	Slab forms, 1 way beams, 1 use	SFCA	6.94	6.31	13.25	3.99	10.93	0.0789
03.1804 021	Slab forms, 1 way beams, 3 uses	SFCA	6.60	6.31	12.91	3.99	10.59	0.0789
03.1804 031	Slab forms, 2 way beams, 1 use	SFCA	8.31	7.19	15.50	4.55	12.86	0.0900
03.1804 041	Slab forms, 2 way beams, 3 uses	SFCA	7.70	7.19	14.89	4.55	12.25	0.0900
03.1805 000	**STRUCTURAL SLAB & BEAM FLYING FORMS, HEAVY DUTY:**							
03.1805 011	Slab, flying forms, soffits, 1 use	SFCA	7.84	3.21	11.05	2.03	9.87	0.0401
03.1805 021	Slab, flying forms, soffits, 3 uses	SFCA	5.68	3.17	8.85	2.00	7.68	0.0396
03.1805 031	Slab, flying forms, soffits, 5 uses	SFCA	3.93	3.17	7.10	2.00	5.93	0.0396
03.1805 041	Beam, flying forms, side, 1 use	SFCA	8.60	5.39	13.99	3.41	12.01	0.0674

Division 3 CSI #	03 - CONCRETE Description	Unit	Material	Union Install	Union Total	Open Install	Open Total	Unit Man-Hrs
03.1805 000	STRUCTURAL SLAB & BEAM FLYING FORMS, HEAVY DUTY: (Cont.)							
03.1805 051	Beam, flying forms, side, 3 uses	SFCA	6.58	5.32	11.90	3.36	9.94	0.0665
03.1805 061	Beam, flying forms, side, 5 uses	SFCA	4.96	5.24	10.20	3.32	8.28	0.0656
03.1850 000	STAIR AND RAMP FORMS:							
03.1850 011	Stair forms, landing soffits	SFCA	3.95	17.66	21.61	12.16	16.11	0.2000
03.1850 021	Stair forms, sloping soffits	SFCA	4.30	25.97	30.27	17.88	22.18	0.2941
03.1850 031	Stair forms, risers	LF	4.29	25.97	30.26	17.88	22.17	0.2941
03.1900 000	MISCELLANEOUS CONCRETE FORMS & FORM SPECIALTIES:							
	Note: For architectural detail, multi-story batter walls, radial walls or architectural board forming,							
	add 150% to the total form costs.							
03.1901 000	CONSTRUCTION JOINTS:							
03.1901 011	Control joint	LF	1.25	2.17	3.42	1.42	2.67	0.0258
03.1901 021	Expansion joint	LF	1.35	7.00	8.35	4.60	5.95	0.0833
03.1901 031	Keyed 4" patent with stakes	LF	2.02	3.49	5.51	2.29	4.31	0.0415
03.1901 041	Key joints, recess form	LF	1.25	2.60	3.85	1.79	3.04	0.0295
03.1902 000	SPECIAL FORMS:							
03.1902 011	Fiberglass architectural forms	SFCA	18.65	8.88	27.53	5.62	24.27	0.1111
03.1903 000	FORMS, SPECIALTIES, GENERAL:							
03.1903 011	Forms, curbs, equipment bases	LF	2.06	12.44	14.50	8.17	10.23	0.1481
03.1903 021	Forms, slab depressions	LF	1.13	5.65	6.78	3.71	4.84	0.0673
03.1903 031	Add for rough board forms	SFCA	6.10	.88	6.98	.58	6.68	0.0105
03.1903 041	Form detailing	SFCA	.31		.31		.31	
03.1905 000	LINERS FOR FORMS:							
03.1905 011	Form liner, foam rubber	SFCA	6.96	14.70	21.66	9.66	16.62	0.1750
03.1905 021	Form liner, plastic	SFCA	7.53	14.70	22.23	9.66	17.19	0.1750
03.1905 031	Form liner, metal	SFCA	17.30	14.70	32.00	9.66	26.96	0.1750
03.1905 041	Form liner, architectural board	SFCA	10.96	14.70	25.66	9.66	20.62	0.1750
03.1905 051	Form liner, fiberglass, reusable	SFCA	10.75	14.70	25.45	9.66	20.41	0.1750
03.2000 000	REINFORCING STEEL:							
	Note: Average weight of post tensioned reinforcing slabs is as follows: Building Slabs 1#/SFSA							
	(50# Bridge Slabs 2.5#/SFSA; AASHO Standards). Balance as detailed.							
03.2100 000	REINFORCING STEEL, IN PLACE:							
03.2101 000	CAISSON, REINFORCING, WITH SPIRAL:							
03.2101 011	Caisson, 16" diameter, with 4 #6 bars	LF	8.14	1.66	9.80	1.24	9.38	0.0185
03.2101 021	Caisson, 24"diameter, with 6 #6 bars	LF	10.47	3.14	13.61	2.35	12.82	0.0350
03.2101 031	Caisson, 36" diameter, with 8 #8 bars	LF	19.06	6.36	25.42	4.76	23.82	0.0709
03.2102 000	PRE-STRESS AND POST TENSIONING:							
03.2102 011	Steel bars	#	1.10	1.41	2.51	1.05	2.15	0.0157
03.2102 021	Tubing & wire rope	#	1.52	1.74	3.26	1.30	2.82	0.0194
03.2102 031	Wire rope without tubing	#	1.25	1.66	2.91	1.24	2.49	0.0185
03.2200 000	REINFORCING STEEL, BUILT-UP COST:							
03.2201 000	BARS, LIGHTWEIGHT, #3-#5:							
03.2201 011	Rebar, lightweight, #3-#5, 0-5,000	#	.62	.71	1.33	.53	1.15	0.0079
03.2201 021	Rebar, lightweight, #3-#5, 5,000 to 20,000	#	.57	.60	1.17	.45	1.02	0.0067
03.2201 031	Rebar, lightweight, #3-#5, 20,000-50,000	#	.57	.55	1.12	.41	.98	0.0061
03.2201 041	Rebar, lightweight, #3-#5, 50,000-100,000	#	.57	.49	1.06	.37	.94	0.0055
03.2201 051	Rebar, lightweight, #3-#5, 100,000 & up	#	.57	.46	1.03	.34	.91	0.0051
03.2202 000	BARS, MEDIUM WT, #6-#8:							
03.2202 011	Rebar, medium wt, #6-#8, 5,000-50,000	#	.62	.55	1.17	.41	1.03	0.0061
03.2202 021	Rebar, medium wt, #6-#8, 50,000-100,000	#	.57	.49	1.06	.37	.94	0.0055
03.2202 031	Rebar, medium wt, #8-#8, 100,000-250,000 & up	#	.57	.46	1.03	.34	.91	0.0051
03.2203 000	BARS, HEAVY, #9 AND UP:							
03.2203 011	Rebar, heavy, #9 and up, less than 100,000	#	.57	.46	1.03	.34	.91	0.0051
03.2203 021	Rebar, heavy, #9 and up, 100,000-250,000	#	.57	.39	.96	.30	.87	0.0044
03.2203 031	Rebar, heavy, #9 and up, 250,000 and up	#	.57	.36	.93	.27	.84	0.0040
03.2204 000	REINFORCING STEEL, ACCESSORIES AND SPECIALTIES:							
03.2204 011	Reinforcing steel, chairs, average	EA	.56	.91	1.47	.68	1.24	0.0102
03.2204 021	Reinforcing steel, spirals	#	.80	.60	1.40	.45	1.25	0.0067
03.2204 031	Reinforcing steel, splices	EA	16.18	14.95	31.13	11.19	27.37	0.1667
03.2204 041	Reinforcing steel, stirrups	#	.73	2.24	2.97	1.68	2.41	0.0250

Division 3 CSI #	03 - CONCRETE Description	Unit	Material	Union Install	Union Total	Open Install	Open Total	Unit Man-Hrs
03.2205 000	**REINFORCING BAR, WELDING:**							
03.2205 011	Rebar, weld, #4 bar, 24 welds/day	WELD	4.64	44.83	49.47	33.57	38.21	0.5000
03.2205 021	Rebar, weld, #6 bar, 12 welds/day	WELD	9.47	59.78	69.25	44.76	54.23	0.6667
03.2205 031	Rebar, weld, #8 bar, 10 welds/day	WELD	11.36	71.73	83.09	53.71	65.07	0.8000
03.2205 041	Rebar, weld, #9 bar, 8 welds/day	WELD	14.28	89.66	103.94	67.14	81.42	1.0000
03.2205 051	Rebar, weld, #10 bar, 6 welds/day	WELD	19.09	119.54	138.63	89.52	108.61	1.3333
03.2205 061	Rebar, weld, #14 bar, 4 welds/day	WELD	28.69	179.32	208.01	134.28	162.97	2.0000
03.2205 071	Rebar, weld, #18 bar, 1 welds/day	WELD	38.22	717.28	755.50	537.12	575.34	8.0000
03.2206 000	**REINFORCING STEEL, WIRE MESH:**							
03.2206 011	Mesh, 4/4, W2/W2, for slab	SF	.21	.36	.57	.27	.48	0.0040
03.2206 021	Mesh, 4/4, W2.9/W2.9, for slab	SF	.35	.42	.77	.32	.67	0.0047
03.2206 031	Mesh, 6/6, W1.4/W1.4, for slab	SF	.35	.18	.53	.13	.48	0.0020
03.2206 041	Mesh, 6/6, W2/W2, for slab	SF	.16	.25	.41	.19	.35	0.0028
03.2206 051	Mesh, 6/6, W2.9/W2.9, for slab	SF	.18	.34	.52	.26	.44	0.0038
03.2206 061	Mesh, cut lengthwise	SF		.17	.17	.13	.13	0.0019
03.2206 071	Mesh, 2/2, 14/14, beams & columns, galvanized	SF	.21	2.80	3.01	2.09	2.30	0.0312
03.2206 081	Mesh, 2/2, 12/12, beams & columns, galvanized	SF	.36	2.80	3.16	2.09	2.45	0.0312
03.2208 000	**REBAR, NON-CORROSIVE, RESIN & FIBERGLASS:**							
03.2208 011	Rebar, non-corrosive, resin & fiberglass, #2, 1/4" diameter	SF	.47	.60	1.07	.45	.92	0.0067
03.2208 021	Rebar, non-corrosive, resin & fiberglass, #3, 3/8" diameter	SF	.70	.60	1.30	.45	1.15	0.0067
03.2208 031	Rebar, non-corrosive, resin & fiberglass, #4, 1/2" diameter	SF	1.02	.60	1.62	.45	1.47	0.0067
03.2208 041	Rebar, non-corrosive, resin & fiberglass, #5, 5/8" diameter	SF	1.33	.60	1.93	.45	1.78	0.0067
03.2208 051	Rebar, non-corrosive, resin & fiberglass, #6, 3/4" diameter	SF	1.80	.49	2.29	.37	2.17	0.0055
03.2208 061	Rebar, non-corrosive, resin & fiberglass, #7, 7/8" diameter	SF	2.19	.49	2.68	.37	2.56	0.0055
03.2208 071	Rebar, non-corrosive, resin & fiberglass, #8, 1" diameter	SF	2.77	.49	3.26	.37	3.14	0.0055
03.2208 081	Rebar, non-corrosive, resin & fiberglass, #9, 1-1/8" diameter	SF	3.12	.49	3.61	.37	3.49	0.0055
03.3000 000	**READYMIX CONCRETE:**							
	Note: The following prices do not include forms, finishing or rebar. Prices are subject to quoted discounts of 5 to 25%.							
03.3001 000	**DESIGN MIX POSTED PRICE & SALES TAX:**							
03.3001 011	Readymix, 2,000 PSI, 1-1/2" aggregate, 4.4 sack mix	CY	104.76		104.76		104.76	
03.3001 021	Readymix, 2,500 PSI, 1-1/2" aggregate, 4.8 sack mix	CY	107.51		107.51		107.51	
03.3001 031	Readymix, 3,000 PSI, 1-1/2" aggregate, 5.2 sack mix	CY	110.27		110.27		110.27	
03.3001 041	Readymix, 3,500 PSI, 1-1/2" aggregate, 5.8 sack mix	CY	114.41		114.41		114.41	
03.3001 051	Readymix, 4,000 PSI, 1-1/2" aggregate, 6.5 sack mix	CY	119.25		119.25		119.25	
03.3001 061	Readymix, 2,000 PSI, 3/4" aggregate, 4.7 sack mix	CY	106.81		106.81		106.81	
03.3001 071	Readymix, 2,500 PSI, 3/4" aggregate, 5.1 sack mix	CY	109.58		109.58		109.58	
03.3001 081	Readymix, 3,000 PSI, 3/4" aggregate, 5.5 sack mix	CY	112.36		112.36		112.36	
03.3001 091	Readymix, 3,500 PSI, 3/4" aggregate, 6.3 sack mix	CY	117.88		117.88		117.88	
03.3001 101	Readymix, 4,000 PSI, 3/4" aggregate, 6.8 sack mix	CY	121.32		121.32		121.32	
03.3002 000	**ADDERS FOR DESIGN MIX:**							
03.3002 011	Hi early strength	CY	11.16		11.16		11.16	
03.3002 021	Lightweight aggregate	CY	48.53		48.53		48.53	
03.3002 031	Granite aggregate	CY	12.48		12.48		12.48	
03.3002 041	White cement	CY	178.09		178.09		178.09	
03.3002 051	Calcium chloride, 1%	CY	.62		.62		.62	
03.3002 061	Short loads (add each cubic yard under 9)	EA	62.76		62.76		62.76	
03.3002 071	Stand-by charge (5 minutes per cubic yard-no charge)	MIN	1.52		1.52		1.52	
03.3002 081	Stand-by charge (over time)	HR	94.11		94.11		94.11	
03.3002 091	Pumping quality, mix	CY	8.59		8.59		8.59	
03.3002 101	Fiber reinforcement	CY	12.11		12.11		12.11	
03.3100 000	**CONCRETE PLACEMENT:**							
03.3101 000	**POUR FOUNDATIONS:**							
03.3101 001	Foundation, tract housing	CY	112.08	14.73	126.81	7.26	119.34	0.2222
03.3101 011	Foundation, residential, truck access	CY	112.08	18.78	130.86	10.56	122.64	0.2564
03.3101 021	Foundation, residential, hillside	CY	112.08	32.11	144.19	19.32	131.40	0.4211
03.3101 023	Foundations, multi-residence, 2 story	CY	115.05	17.00	132.05	8.37	123.42	0.2564
03.3101 025	Foundations, school, 1 story, full form	CY	120.12	47.35	167.47	23.33	143.45	0.7142
03.3101 027	Foundations, school, 1 story, edge form	CY	122.41	43.24	165.65	21.30	143.71	0.6522
03.3101 031	Foundation, institutional, thru 3 story	CY	120.12	69.79	189.91	34.38	154.50	1.0527
03.3101 041	Foundations, multi-story commercial	CY	120.12	49.73	169.85	24.50	144.62	0.7500
03.3101 051	Foundations, heavy engineered structures	CY	120.12	61.20	181.32	30.15	150.27	0.9231

Division 3 CSI #	03 - CONCRETE Description	Unit	Material	Union Install	Union Total	Open Install	Open Total	
03.3101 000	**POUR FOUNDATIONS: (Cont.)**							
03.3101 061	Foundations, retaining wall footing	CY	123.86	58.01	181.87	28.58	152.44	0.8750
03.3102 000	**POUR WALLS:**							
03.3102 011	Concrete retaining walls, to 4'	CY	124.99	49.73	174.72	24.50	149.49	0.7500
03.3102 021	Concrete retaining walls, to 8'	CY	124.99	54.65	179.64	26.92	151.91	0.8243
03.3102 031	Concrete wall, 8", to 12'	CY	121.38	43.63	165.01	21.49	142.87	0.6580
03.3102 041	Concrete wall, 10", to 12'	CY	121.38	37.36	158.74	18.40	139.78	0.5635
03.3102 051	Concrete wall, 12", to 12'	CY	121.38	32.67	154.05	16.09	137.47	0.4928
03.3102 061	Concrete wall, 8", over 12'	CY	121.38	43.63	165.01	21.49	142.87	0.6580
03.3102 071	Concrete wall, 10", over 12'	CY	121.38	37.36	158.74	18.40	139.78	0.5635
03.3103 000	**POUR STRUCTURAL:**							
03.3103 011	Slab, suspended, 1 story, pumped	CY	131.30	58.01	189.31	28.58	159.88	0.8750
03.3103 021	Slab, beam & flat slab, pumped	CY	131.30	56.91	188.21	28.03	159.33	0.8583
03.3103 031	Slab, pan joist & slab, pumped	CY	131.30	54.70	186.00	26.94	158.24	0.8250
03.3103 041	Slab, fill on metal deck, 3" to 5", pumped	CY	131.30	82.88	214.18	40.83	172.13	1.2500
03.3104 000	**OTHER CONCRETE POURS:**							
03.3104 011	Concrete basement walls, pumped	CY	126.65	87.24	213.89	42.97	169.62	1.3158
03.3104 021	Beams & slabs, suspended, pumped	CY	131.30	48.75	180.05	24.01	155.31	0.7353
03.3104 031	Columns, 1.8 square feet & under(cross-section), pumped	CY	131.30	99.45	230.75	48.99	180.29	1.5000
03.3104 035	Columns, 1.8 square feet & over(cross-section), pumped	CY	131.30	59.67	190.97	29.39	160.69	0.9000
03.3104 041	Mass concrete, on grade	CY	126.65	13.26	139.91	6.53	133.18	0.2000
03.3104 051	Pile caps & bases	CY	126.65	39.78	166.43	19.60	146.25	0.6000
03.3104 061	Slabs, on grade 4" to 5" thick, direct chute	CY	113.58	22.10	135.68	10.89	124.47	0.3333
03.3104 071	Increase for each added inch thick	SF	.31	.10	.41	.05	.36	0.0015
03.3104 081	Add for checkerboard pours	SF	.01	.16	.17	.11	.12	0.0020
03.3104 091	Stairs on grade, pumped	CY	131.30	127.72	259.02	92.70	224.00	1.6130
03.3104 095	Stairs & landings, suspended, pumped	CY	131.30	197.94	329.24	143.67	274.97	2.4999
03.3104 101	Steps, concrete	LF/TR	.51	13.21	13.72	9.59	10.10	0.1668
03.3104 111	Concrete test	EA	163.29		163.29		163.29	
03.3105 000	**LIGHTWEIGHT FILLS, METAL DECK:**							
03.3105 011	Lightweight fill, 2-1/4", 1-1/2" deck	SF	2.14	1.74	3.88	.86	3.00	0.0263
03.3105 021	Lightweight fill, 2-1/4", 3" deck	SF	2.72	1.90	4.62	.93	3.65	0.0286
03.3105 031	Lightweight fill, 3-1/4", 1-1/2" deck	SF	2.72	1.95	4.67	.96	3.68	0.0294
03.3105 041	Lightweight concrete fill, 3-1/4", 3" deck	SF	3.12	2.14	5.26	1.05	4.17	0.0323
03.3105 051	Lightweight fill, 3-1/4", 4-1/2" deck	SF	3.55	2.29	5.84	1.13	4.68	0.0345
03.3105 061	Lightweight concrete fills, pour	CY	195.41	33.15	228.56	16.33	211.74	0.5000
03.3600 000	**SLAB FINISHES:**							
03.3601 011	Float only	SF		.43	.43	.32	.32	0.0062
03.3601 021	Trowel, steel, by machine	SF		.65	.65	.47	.47	0.0093
03.3601 031	Trowel, steel, by hand	SF		.91	.91	.66	.66	0.0130
03.3601 033	Trowel small area, pour strips, etc.	SF		1.75	1.75	1.27	1.27	0.0250
03.3601 035	Trowel stair landings	SF		2.80	2.80	2.04	2.04	0.0400
03.3601 037	Trowel stair treads & nosing	SF		18.77	18.77	13.69	13.69	0.2685
03.3601 039	Trowel steel pan treads	SF		5.59	5.59	4.08	4.08	0.0800
03.3601 041	Broom finish	SF		.78	.78	.57	.57	0.0111
03.3601 051	Scoring	LF		.30	.30	.22	.22	0.0043
03.3601 061	Exposed aggregate, washed	SF	.04	1.12	1.16	.82	.86	0.0160
03.3601 071	Seeded aggregate, native material	SF	.13	1.24	1.37	.91	1.04	0.0178
03.3601 081	Non-slip finish	SF	.45	.09	.54	.07	.52	0.0013
03.3601 091	Hardener, sprayed	SF	.27	.04	.31	.03	.30	0.0006
03.3601 101	Color, tans and browns	SF	.99	.09	1.08	.07	1.06	0.0013
03.3601 111	Color, reds & greens	SF	1.97	.09	2.06	.07	2.04	0.0013
03.3601 121	Curing compound	SF	.03		.03		.03	
03.3601 131	Treads and risers	LF/TR		3.49	3.49	2.55	2.55	0.0500
03.3601 141	Treads & risers with abrasives	LF/TR	2.03	4.66	6.69	3.40	5.43	0.0667
03.3601 151	Wax	SF	.06	.13	.19	.10	.16	0.0019
03.3700 000	**VERTICAL SURFACE FINISHES:**							
03.3701 011	Cut back ties & patch	SF	.27	.58	.85	.25	.52	0.0093
03.3701 021	Patch & remove fins	LF	.02	.39	.41	.17	.19	0.0062
03.3701 031	Patch & grind smooth	SF	.02	1.16	1.18	.50	.52	0.0185
03.3701 041	Patch & sack, simple	SF	.06	.62	.68	.27	.33	0.0099
03.3701 051	Sandblast, light	SF	.16	1.68	1.84	.73	.89	0.0269

Division 3 CSI #	03 - CONCRETE Description	Unit	Material	Union Install	Union Total	Open Install	Open Total	Unit Man-Hrs
03.3700 000	**VERTICAL SURFACE FINISHES: (Cont.)**							
03.3701 061	Sandblast, medium	SF	.36	2.39	2.75	1.04	1.40	0.0383
03.3701 071	Sandblast, heavy	SF	.64	2.90	3.54	1.26	1.90	0.0464
03.3701 081	Bush hammer, light	SF	.64	1.69	2.33	.74	1.38	0.0271
03.3701 091	Bush hammer, medium	SF	1.34	2.91	4.25	1.26	2.60	0.0465
03.3701 101	Bush hammer, heavy	SF	2.53	4.12	6.65	1.79	4.32	0.0659
03.3701 111	Needle gun treatment	SF	1.68	2.91	4.59	1.26	2.94	0.0465
03.3701 121	Wire brush, green concrete	SF	.02	.96	.98	.42	.44	0.0154
03.3701 131	Wash with acid & rinse	SF	.05	.56	.61	.24	.29	0.0090
03.3800 000	**MISCELLANEOUS CONCRETE FINISHES:**							
03.3801 000	**ADDERS TO FINISHES:**							
03.3801 011	Monolithic topping 1/16"	SF	.07	1.33	1.40	.97	1.04	0.0190
03.3801 021	Monolithic topping 3/16"	SF	.29	1.40	1.69	1.02	1.31	0.0200
03.3801 031	Monolithic topping 1/2"	SF	.56	1.47	2.03	1.08	1.64	0.0211
03.3801 041	White cement	SACK	19.13		19.13		19.13	
03.3801 051	Felton sand	CY	64.11		64.11		64.11	
03.3801 061	Integral colors	#	1.88		1.88		1.88	
03.3802 000	**ADDERS FOR SPECIAL WEAR SURFACES:**							
03.3802 011	Mono rock, 3/8", wear course	SF	.38	1.29	1.67	.94	1.32	0.0184
03.3802 021	Kalman, 3/4", wear course	SF	.80	2.33	3.13	1.70	2.50	0.0333
03.3802 031	Commercial surface hardeners	SF	.01	.11	.12	.08	.09	0.0016
03.3802 035	Sealer, 1 coat	SF	.03	.03	.06	.01	.04	0.0004
03.3802 041	Traffic surface, waterproof	SF	1.11	2.83	3.94	1.23	2.34	0.0452
03.3802 051	Pressure grouting	CF	6.40	19.10	25.50	8.30	14.70	0.3055
03.3900 000	**MISCELLANEOUS CONCRETE ITEMS & ACCESSORIES:**							
03.3901 011	Sandblasting, whip clean up	SF	.24	.34	.58	.15	.39	0.0054
03.3901 021	Sandblasting, dust controlled	SF	.76	.94	1.70	.41	1.17	0.0150
03.3901 031	Inserts, unistrut, average	LF	4.30	2.48	6.78	1.81	6.11	0.0262
03.3901 041	Water stop, rubber, 9"	LF	6.21	4.58	10.79	3.34	9.55	0.0483
03.3901 051	Water stop, rubber, 12"	LF	9.36	6.61	15.97	4.83	14.19	0.0698
03.3901 061	Water stop, PVC, 9"	LF	6.71	6.55	13.26	4.78	11.49	0.0691
03.3901 071	Snap ties, average	EA	.62	.46	1.08	.34	.96	0.0049
03.3901 081	Hair pins, rental, month average	EA	.12		.12		.12	
03.3901 091	Saw cut concrete, 1" depth	LF	.13	1.00	1.13	.43	.56	0.0160
03.3901 101	Saw cut concrete, 1-1/2" depth	LF	.20	2.11	2.31	.92	1.12	0.0338
03.3901 111	Saw cut concrete, 2" depth	LF	.30	6.31	6.61	2.75	3.05	0.1010
03.3901 121	Saw cut concrete, 3" depth	LF	.49	8.22	8.71	3.57	4.06	0.1315
03.3901 131	Visqueen membrane, 6 mil	SF	.03	.14	.17	.06	.09	0.0023
03.3901 141	Embedded iron, install	#		5.92	5.92	4.32	4.32	0.0625
03.3901 151	Foundations, accessories	CY	12.28	1.26	13.54	.92	13.20	0.0133
03.3901 153	Bollards, pipe, 6", 8' long	LF	392.90	118.41	511.31	86.49	479.39	1.2500
03.3901 155	Bollards, pipe, 8", 8' long	LF	516.19	118.41	634.60	86.49	602.68	1.2500
03.3901 161	Wall, accessories	CY	14.30	4.98	19.28	3.64	17.94	0.0526
03.3901 171	Structural slab, accessories	CY	16.39	16.47	32.86	12.03	28.42	0.1739
03.3901 181	Column & beam, accessories	CY	18.40	18.47	36.87	13.49	31.89	0.1950
03.4000 000	**TILT UP CONSTRUCTION:**							
03.4001 000	**TILT UP CASTING:**							
03.4001 011	Tilt-up, bed preparation	SF		.13	.13	.06	.06	0.0021
03.4001 021	Tilt-up, edge forms, flat	LF	.96	5.42	6.38	3.67	4.63	0.0625
03.4001 031	Tilt-up, edge forms, with key way	LF	1.19	7.22	8.41	4.89	6.08	0.0833
03.4001 041	Tilt-up, blockout forms, plain	LF	1.71	17.34	19.05	11.74	13.45	0.2000
03.4001 051	Tilt-up, blockout forms, with key way	LF	1.80	21.67	23.47	14.67	16.47	0.2500
03.4001 061	Tilt-up, chamfers	LF	.33	.68	1.01	.46	.79	0.0078
03.4001 071	Tilt-up, bond breaker	SF	.13	.42	.55	.18	.31	0.0067
03.4001 081	Tilt-up, inserts, bracing	EA	13.59	44.15	57.74	30.40	43.99	0.5000
03.4001 091	Tilt-up, inserts, lifting	EA	16.39	44.15	60.54	30.40	46.79	0.5000
03.4001 101	Tilt-up, embedded metal, install	#		4.20	4.20	2.76	2.76	0.0500
03.4001 111	Tilt-up, set, door frames, install	EA		167.98	167.98	110.36	110.36	2.0000
03.4001 121	Tilt-up, pour concrete	CY		26.39	26.39	19.15	19.15	0.3333
03.4001 131	Tilt-up, finish concrete	SF	.02	1.12	1.14	.82	.84	0.0160

Division 3 CSI #	03 - CONCRETE Description	Unit	Material	Union Install	Union Total	Open Install	Open Total	Unit Man-Hrs
03.4002 000	**TILT-UP, SPECIAL FINISHES:**							
03.4002 011	Washed aggregate	SF	.34	1.59	1.93	1.05	1.39	0.0233
03.4002 021	Seeded aggregate, mexican pebbles	SF	.71	.50	1.21	.33	1.04	0.0074
03.4002 031	Seeded aggregate, palos verdes pebbles	SF	.38	.50	.88	.33	.71	0.0074
03.4002 041	Seeded aggregate, quartz pebbles	SF	.34	.32	.66	.21	.55	0.0047
03.4002 051	Aggregate, adhesive, 3/8"-3/4"	SF	.45	1.36	1.81	.90	1.35	0.0200
03.4002 061	Aggregate, adhesive, 3/4"-1"	SF	1.52	2.72	4.24	1.80	3.32	0.0400
03.4002 071	Exposed aggregate	SF	.33	.82	1.15	.54	.87	0.0120
03.4003 000	**TILT UP ERECTION, CREW OF 7 MEN, TRUCK CRANE:**							
03.4003 011	Tilt-up, panel lift, average	SF	.33	.92	1.25	.68	1.01	0.0102
03.4003 021	Tilt-up, panel lift, each lift	EA	133.24	261.53	394.77	192.83	326.07	2.8905
03.4003 031	Tilt-up shoring & bracing	SF	.07	.17	.24	.13	.20	0.0019
03.4003 041	Tilt-up, leveling pads	EA	6.71	24.43	31.14	14.70	21.41	0.3204
03.4003 051	Tilt-up, grout foundation to panel joint with embeco grout	LF	6.61	10.36	16.97	7.56	14.17	0.1483
03.4500 000	**COMPILATION OF IN PLACE COST:**							
03.4501 000	**FOUNDATIONS, INSTITUTIONAL:**							
03.4501 011	Foundations, institutional, forms, 1 use	SFCA	1.58	8.03	9.61	5.53	7.11	0.0909
03.4501 021	Foundations, institutional, forms, 3 uses	SFCA	1.11	6.43	7.54	4.43	5.54	0.0728
03.4501 031	Foundations, institutional, forms, 5 uses	SFCA	.99	6.67	7.66	4.60	5.59	0.0756
03.4501 041	Foundations, institutional, reinforced, 60#-90# per cubic yard	#	.50	.47	.97	.35	.85	0.0052
03.4501 051	Foundations, institutional, trench, machine, by subcontractor	CY	16.82	14.07	30.89	8.31	25.13	0.1905
03.4501 061	Foundations, institutional, trench/backfill, hand	CY	13.32	85.90	99.22	50.70	64.02	1.1628
03.4501 071	Foundations, institutional, concrete	CY	147.09	39.00	186.09	19.21	166.30	0.5882
03.4501 081	Foundations, institutional, embedded steel, install	#		5.24	5.24	3.92	3.92	0.0584
03.4501 091	Foundations, institutional, struct backfill, machine	CY	20.56	16.22	36.78	9.57	30.13	0.2196
03.4502 000	**CONCRETE STRUCTURAL WALL, INCLUDING ACCESSORIES:**							
03.4502 011	Wall, forms, 1 use	SFCA	2.63	10.09	12.72	6.95	9.58	0.1143
03.4502 021	Wall, forms, 3 uses	SFCA	1.47	9.54	11.01	6.57	8.04	0.1081
03.4502 031	Wall, forms, 5 uses	SFCA	.99	9.54	10.53	6.57	7.56	0.1081
03.4502 041	Wall, reinforced steel, 75#-100# per cubic yard	#	.51	.56	1.07	.42	.93	0.0062
03.4502 051	Wall, concrete, placed	CY	149.73	44.22	193.95	21.78	171.51	0.6670
03.4502 061	Strip & stock pile forms	SF		1.09	1.09	.72	.72	0.0130
03.4502 071	Wall, patch & sack, simple	SF	.06	1.33	1.39	.58	.64	0.0213
03.4502 081	Wall, embedded steel, install	#		5.21	5.21	3.90	3.90	0.0581
03.4502 091	Hoist or pump, average	CY	9.35	3.50	12.85	1.72	11.07	0.0528
03.4503 000	**STRUCTURAL BEAMS & SLAB COMBINED, 2 WAY BEAM:**							
03.4503 011	Beam & slab, forms, 1 use	SFCA	2.03	11.30	13.33	7.78	9.81	0.1280
03.4503 021	Beam & slab, forms, 3 uses	SFCA	1.44	10.17	11.61	7.00	8.44	0.1152
03.4503 031	Beam & slab, forms, 5 uses	SFCA	1.20	9.84	11.04	6.78	7.98	0.1115
03.4503 041	Beam & slab, forms, shoring, rent	SF	.29	.62	.91	.39	.68	0.0077
03.4503 061	Beam & slab, concrete, placed	CY	122.52	47.37	169.89	23.34	145.86	0.7145
03.4503 071	Beam & slab, finish	SF	.02	1.10	1.12	.80	.82	0.0157
03.4503 081	Strip & stockpile forms	SF		.86	.86	.56	.56	0.0102
03.4503 091	Beam & slab, patch & sack, simple	SF	.07	.46	.53	.20	.27	0.0074
03.4503 101	Beam & slab, embedded steel, install	#		4.71	4.71	3.52	3.52	0.0525
03.4503 111	Hoist or pump, concrete	CY	9.54	3.18	12.72	1.56	11.10	0.0479
03.5000 000	**CEMENTITIOUS DECKS, LIGHTWEIGHT & INSULATING CONCRETE:**							
03.5100 000	**INSULATING CONCRETE, INTERIOR:**							
03.5101 000	**INSULATING CONCRETE, RESIDENTIAL, 1-1/2":**							
03.5101 011	Insulating concrete, residential, under 3,000 square feet	SF	.54	.89	1.43	.61	1.15	0.0120
03.5101 021	Insulating concrete, residential, 3,000-10,000 square feet	SF	.54	.82	1.36	.57	1.11	0.0111
03.5101 031	Insulating concrete, residential, over 10,000 square feet	SF	.54	.55	1.09	.38	.92	0.0074
03.5102 000	**INSULATING CONCRETE, INCLUDING PUMPING:**							
03.5102 011	Insulating concrete, interior, 100# per cubic foot	CY	138.92	123.09	262.01	85.30	224.22	1.6667
03.5102 021	Insulating concrete, roof, 32# per cubic foot	CY	99.83	105.50	205.33	73.12	172.95	1.4286
03.5103 000	**INSULATING CONCRETE, 3-1/4":**							
03.5103 011	Lightweight concrete fill, trowel finish	SF	2.74	1.17	3.91	.85	3.59	0.0167
03.5103 021	Lightweight vermiculite, screed & float	SF	1.78	1.00	2.78	.73	2.51	0.0143
03.5103 031	Lightweight gypsum deck, screed & float	SF	1.67	1.00	2.67	.73	2.40	0.0143

Division 3 CSI #	03 - CONCRETE Description	Unit	Material	Union Install	Union Total	Open Install	Open Total	Unit Man-Hrs
03.5200 000	**CONCRETE DECK, EXTERIOR:**							
03.5201 000	**CONCRETE WALKING SURFACE, TROWELED:**							
03.5201 011	Walk, lightweight concrete, 2-5/8"	SF	1.39	2.17	3.56	1.58	2.97	0.0310
03.5201 021	Walk, lightweight concrete, 4"	SF	1.96	2.23	4.19	1.63	3.59	0.0319
03.5201 031	Add for 4, 000 psi mix	SF	.27		.27		.27	
03.5201 041	Add for 5, 000 psi mix	SF	.44		.44		.44	
03.5201 051	Cool-deck, pool side	SF	2.88	2.80	5.68	2.04	4.92	0.0400
03.5300 000	**INSULATING DECKS:**							
03.5301 000	**TWO HOUR SYSTEM, WITH 24 GA METAL DECK, REINFORCED & LIGHTWEIGHT:**							
03.5301 011	Zonolite, 2-1/2" thick	SF	2.60	4.28	6.88	2.92	5.52	0.0465
03.5301 021	Zonolite, 2-1/2", 1-1/2" styrene	SF	3.41	4.04	7.45	2.76	6.17	0.0439
03.5302 000	**TEE SYSTEM, 2-1/2" GYPSUM WALL BOARD WITH REINFORCING & CEILING BOARDS:**							
03.5302 011	Tee system, with 1/2" sheet rock	SF	2.86	4.36	7.22	2.98	5.84	0.0474
03.5302 021	Tee system, with 1" wood fiberboard	SF	3.19	4.36	7.55	2.98	6.17	0.0474
03.5302 031	Tee system, with 1" acoustical board	SF	3.62	4.36	7.98	2.98	6.60	0.0474
03.5302 041	Add for 1" urethane board	SF	.74	.39	1.13	.26	1.00	0.0042
03.5400 000	**FIBER DECK:**							
03.5401 000	**FIBER, T & G AND CEMENTITIOUS PLANKS:**							
03.5401 011	Fiber deck, 2" thickness	SF	2.66	1.45	4.11	.99	3.65	0.0157
03.5401 021	Fiber deck, 2-1/2" thickness	SF	3.07	1.45	4.52	.99	4.06	0.0157
03.5401 031	Fiber deck, 3" thickness	SF	4.47	1.45	5.92	.99	5.46	0.0157
03.6000 000	**EPOXY INJECTION, REPAIR:**							
03.6001 011	Epoxy injection, with ports & cap seal, 4"slab	LF	12.19	24.61	36.80	15.96	28.15	0.3250
03.6001 021	Epoxy injection, with ports & cap seal, 6"slab	LF	12.87	27.79	40.66	18.03	30.90	0.3670
03.6001 031	Epoxy injection, with ports & cap seal, 8"slab	LF	13.22	33.46	46.68	21.71	34.93	0.4420
03.6001 041	Epoxy injection, parking structure, 12", overhead	LF	19.83	44.29	64.12	28.74	48.57	0.5850
03.6001 051	Epoxy injection, stem wall, 4' high, easy access	MIN	381.24		381.24		381.24	
03.6001 061	Epoxy injection, stem wall, 4' high, difficult access	MIN	533.75		533.75		533.75	
03.6001 071	Epoxy injection, tilt-up, to 8' high	LF	12.87	41.64	54.51	27.02	39.89	0.5500
03.6001 081	Epoxy injection, tilt-up, above 8' high	LF	12.87	57.92	70.79	37.58	50.45	0.7650

Division 4 CSI #	04 - MASONRY Description	Unit	Material	Union Install	Union Total	Open Install	Open Total	Unit Man-Hrs
04.0000 000	**MASONRY:**							
	Note: Any condition other than ideal must be accounted for by increasing costs. Use the adders and deductors when applicable. The following costs include mortar and standard reinforcing. Cuts, lintels, coping and sills, jambs and heads must be included from the adders at the end of the section.							
04.1000 000	**BRICK MASONRY:**							
04.1001 000	**BRICK VENEER:**							
04.1001 011	Veneer, 4", standard brick, commercial	SF	5.98	7.01	12.99	3.90	9.88	0.0871
04.1001 021	Veneer, 4", standard brick, residential	SF	3.68	6.30	9.98	3.51	7.19	0.0783
04.1001 031	Veneer, 4", modular	SF	6.33	9.88	16.21	5.50	11.83	0.1228
04.1001 041	Veneer, jumbo brick, 4"x4"x12"	SF	4.25	6.95	11.20	3.87	8.12	0.0864
04.1001 051	Veneer, jumbo brick, 6"x4"x12"	SF	6.05	7.74	13.79	4.31	10.36	0.0961
04.1001 061	Veneer, jumbo brick, 8"x4"x12"	SF	7.89	8.56	16.45	4.76	12.65	0.1063
04.1001 071	Veneer, face brick, select modular	SF	6.94	10.63	17.57	5.92	12.86	0.1321
04.1001 081	Veneer, Norman brick	SF	5.77	10.50	16.27	5.85	11.62	0.1305
04.1001 091	Veneer, Roman brick	SF	6.68	14.94	21.62	8.32	15.00	0.1856
04.1001 101	Veneer, glazed brick	SF	10.69	16.90	27.59	9.41	20.10	0.2100
04.1002 000	**BRICK WALLS:**							
04.1002 011	Brick wall, 10" wall, cavity	SF	11.81	18.04	29.85	10.04	21.85	0.2241
04.1002 021	Brick wall, 10", reinforced #4/24", OCBW	SF	13.30	19.52	32.82	10.87	24.17	0.2425
04.1002 031	Brick wall, 13", reinforced #4/24", OCBW	SF	16.03	21.34	37.37	11.88	27.91	0.2651
04.1002 041	Brick wall, 16", reinforced #4/24", OCBW	SF	19.85	22.68	42.53	12.63	32.48	0.2818
04.1002 051	Brick wall, 20", reinforced #4/24", OCBW	SF	22.25	28.60	50.85	15.92	38.17	0.3553
04.1003 000	**ADDERS FOR BRICK MASONRY:**							
	Note: For extra reinforcing, see section 03.2000.							
	COMMON BOND, FULL HEADER EACH 7TH COURSE ..15%							
	SHORT RUNS AND/OR CUT-UP WORK 20%							
	PILASTERS, PER SQUARE FOOT OF PILASTER 10%							
	DEDUCT FOR RESIDENTIAL TRACTS 18%							
	BASKETWEAVE PATTERN 20%							
	FLEMISH BOND 33%							
	HERRINGBONE PATTERN 30%							
	SOLDIER COURSE 20%							
	STACKED BOND 15%							
	INSTITUTIONAL INSPECTION 20%							
	WALLS OVER ONE STORY 10%							
	MODULAR BRICK 15%							
	ARCHES 30%							
	CAPS & COPING............................... 15%							
	CUTS 50%							
	HEADER COURSE 33%							
	JAMBS 15%							
	LINTELS OVER OPENINGS 30%							
	SILLS, CUT 50%							
	DOVETAIL ANCHORS 5%							
04.1003 031	Add for zonolite filled walls	SF	.16	.47	.63	.26	.42	0.0058
04.2001 000	**CONCRETE MASONRY UNIT:**							
	Note:							
	SPECIAL COLORS 10%							
	STACK BOND 16%							
	SCORED BLOCK 9%							
	SCULPTURED BLOCK 14%							
	CUT UP PROJECTS 20%							
	INSTITUTIONAL INSPECTION 10%							
	SPECIAL GLAZING OF ENDS & SHAPING 100%							
04.2001 011	Concrete masonry unit, 4x8x16, #4 bar, 32" OCBW	SF	8.96	6.17	15.13	3.43	12.39	0.0766
04.2001 021	Concrete masonry unit, 6x8x16, #4 bar, 32" OCBW	SF	10.40	6.62	17.02	3.69	14.09	0.0823
04.2001 031	Concrete masonry unit, 8x8x16, #4 bar, 32" OCBW	SF	10.94	7.00	17.94	3.90	14.84	0.0870
04.2001 041	Concrete masonry unit, 12x8x16, #4 bar, 32" OCBW	SF	17.01	7.81	24.82	4.35	21.36	0.0970
04.2001 051	Concrete masonry unit, 4x8x16, #4 bar, 32" OCBW, filled	SF	9.49	6.63	16.12	3.69	13.18	0.0824
04.2001 061	Concrete masonry unit, 6x8x16, #4 bar, 32" OCBW, filled	SF	11.98	6.78	18.76	3.77	15.75	0.0842
04.2001 071	Concrete masonry unit, 8x8x16, #4 bar, 32" OCBW, filled	SF	12.87	7.16	20.03	3.98	16.85	0.0889
04.2001 081	Concrete masonry unit, 12x8x16, #4 bar, 32" OCBW, filled	SF	16.24	8.67	24.91	4.83	21.07	0.1077

Division 4 CSI #	04 - MASONRY Description	Unit	Material	Union Install	Union Total	Open Install	Open Total	Unit Man-Hrs
04.2001 000	**CONCRETE MASONRY UNIT: (Cont.)**							
04.2001 091	Concrete masonry unit, 8x4x16, #4 bar, 32" OCBW, filled	SF	18.44	9.43	27.87	5.25	23.69	0.1171
04.2001 101	Concrete masonry unit, 12x4x16, #4 bar, 32" OCBW, filled	SF	20.22	10.91	31.13	6.08	26.30	0.1356
04.2001 111	Concrete masonry unit, grout lock, 6x8x24, #4 bar, filled	SF	12.84	4.60	17.44	2.56	15.40	0.0571
04.2001 121	Concrete masonry unit, grout lock, 8x8x16, #4 bar, filled	SF	13.57	5.58	19.15	3.11	16.68	0.0693
04.2001 131	Concrete masonry unit, grout lock, 12x8x16, #4 bar, filled	SF	17.44	6.62	24.06	3.69	21.13	0.0823
04.2001 141	Concrete masonry unit, slumpstone, 8x4x16, #4 bar, filled	SF	22.31	10.16	32.47	5.66	27.97	0.1262
04.2001 151	Concrete masonry unit slumpstone, 8x8x16, #4 bar, filled	SF	17.36	8.54	25.90	4.76	22.12	0.1061
04.2001 161	Concrete masonry unit splitface, 8x4x16, #4 bar, filled	SF	20.16	10.15	30.31	5.65	25.81	0.1261
04.2001 171	Concrete masonry unit glazed 1 side, 4x8x16, reinforced, filled	SF	15.20	9.42	24.62	5.24	20.44	0.1170
04.2001 181	Concrete masonry unit glazed 1 side, 6x8x16, reinforced, filled	SF	17.49	10.07	27.56	5.61	23.10	0.1251
04.2001 191	Concrete masonry unit glazed 1 side, 8x8x16, reinforced, filled	SF	20.47	10.92	31.39	6.08	26.55	0.1357
04.2001 201	Concrete masonry unit glazed 1 side, 4x4x16, reinforced, filled	SF	22.52	10.77	33.29	6.00	28.52	0.1338
04.2001 211	Concrete masonry unit glazed 1 side, 6x4x16, reinforced, filled	SF	26.30	12.51	38.81	6.97	33.27	0.1554
04.2001 221	Concrete masonry unit glazed 1 side, 8x4x16, reinforced, filled	SF	30.05	13.30	43.35	7.41	37.46	0.1653
04.2001 231	Concrete masonry unit glazed 1 side, 12x8x16, reinforced, filled	SF	24.74	15.50	40.24	8.63	33.37	0.1926
04.2001 241	Add for glazing both sides	SF	8.19		8.19		8.19	
04.2001 251	Screen block 4" x 12" x 12"	SF	8.72	7.98	16.70	4.44	13.16	0.0991
04.2003 000	**ADDERS FOR CONCRETE MASONRY UNIT:**							
04.2003 021	Add for pilasters per SF of pilaster	SF	33.13		33.13		33.13	
04.2003 061	Add for sill blocks	LF	3.57	6.09	9.66	3.39	6.96	0.0756
04.2003 071	Add for cutting blocks	LF	4.12	10.01	14.13	5.58	9.70	0.1244
04.2003 081	Add for bond beams @ door and sash openings	LF	7.85	13.54	21.39	7.54	15.39	0.1682
04.2003 091	Add for lintels, over openings	LF	15.32	22.89	38.21	12.75	28.07	0.2844
04.2003 101	Add for concrete masonry unit, #5 bar, 32" OCBW	SF	.42	.38	.80	.21	.63	0.0047
04.2003 111	Add for concrete masonry unit, #5 bar, 24" OCBW	SF	.72	.56	1.28	.31	1.03	0.0069
04.2003 121	Add for concrete masonry unit, #5 bar, 16" OCBW	SF	1.25	.93	2.18	.52	1.77	0.0115
04.2004 000	**CLAY BACKING TILE:**							
	Note: Not used in critical seismic zones, may be used as blocking at columns as a plaster base.							
04.2004 011	Clay tile, load bearing, 4", 12" x 12"	SF	2.98	6.86	9.84	3.82	6.80	0.0852
04.2004 021	Clay tile, load bearing, 6", 12" x 12"	SF	3.46	7.53	10.99	4.19	7.65	0.0935
04.2004 031	Clay tile, load bearing, 8", 12" x 12"	SF	3.97	8.43	12.40	4.69	8.66	0.1047
04.2004 041	Clay tile, non-load bearing, 4", 12" x 12"	SF	2.92	6.18	9.10	3.44	6.36	0.0768
04.2004 051	Clay tile, non-load bearing, 6", 12" x 12"	SF	3.10	6.87	9.97	3.82	6.92	0.0853
04.2004 061	Clay tile, non-load bearing, 8", 12" x 12"	SF	4.89	7.52	12.41	4.19	9.08	0.0934
04.2005 000	**CLAY FACING TILE (GLAZED STRUCTURAL):**							
	Note: For large areas, deduct 15% from the total costs.							
04.2005 011	Tile, glazed 1 side, 2" x 6" x 12"	SF	6.23	11.61	17.84	6.46	12.69	0.1442
04.2005 021	Tile, glazed 1 side, 4" x 6" x 12"	SF	9.17	13.26	22.43	7.38	16.55	0.1647
04.2005 031	Tile, glazed 2 sides, 4" x 6" x 12"	SF	10.65	15.28	25.93	8.51	19.16	0.1898
04.2005 041	Tile, glazed 1 side, 6" x 6" x 12"	SF	8.81	13.99	22.80	7.79	16.60	0.1738
04.2005 051	Tile, glazed 1 side, 3" x 6" x 12"	SF	6.51	13.47	19.98	7.50	14.01	0.1673
04.2005 061	Tile, glazed 1 side, base	LF	8.85	13.47	22.32	7.50	16.35	0.1673
04.2005 071	Tile, glazed 2 sides, cap	SF	8.61	13.69	22.30	7.62	16.23	0.1701
04.2006 000	**CERAMIC VENEER:**							
04.2006 011	Ceramic veneer facing, vertical	SF	11.90	18.74	30.64	10.43	22.33	0.2328
04.2006 021	Ceramic veneer facing, horizontal on precast panels	SF	11.90	12.41	24.31	6.91	18.81	0.1542
04.2006 031	Brick plate, applied on walls	SF	6.91	11.87	18.78	6.61	13.52	0.1475
04.2007 000	**PAVERS AND FLOOR TILE:**							
	Note: For special brick patterns, add 30% to the labor costs.							
04.2007 011	Quarry tile, unglazed, floor, 16"	SF	4.76	13.17	17.93	7.33	12.09	0.1636
04.2007 021	Quarry tile, unglazed, floor, 12"	SF	4.98	11.37	16.35	6.33	11.31	0.1412
04.2007 031	Quarry tile, unglazed, base, 6"	LF	5.13	12.49	17.62	6.96	12.09	0.1552
04.2007 041	Quarry tile, glazed, floor, 6"	SF	6.26	13.18	19.44	7.34	13.60	0.1637
04.2007 051	Quarry tile, glazed, base, 6"	LF	6.10	12.49	18.59	6.96	13.06	0.1552
04.2007 061	Brick plate, glazed	SF	6.76	10.62	17.38	5.91	12.67	0.1319
04.2007 071	Brick, grouted on concrete substratum	SF	6.02	9.05	15.07	5.04	11.06	0.1124
04.2007 081	Brick, sand laid, no grout	SF	5.40	8.43	13.83	4.69	10.09	0.1047
04.2007 091	Brick pavers, grouted on concrete substratum	SF	6.78	8.75	15.53	4.87	11.65	0.1087
04.2007 101	Slate	SF	9.86	16.25	26.11	9.05	18.91	0.2019
04.2007 111	Terrazzo tiles, standard	SF	9.19	10.23	19.42	8.19	17.38	0.1355
04.2007 121	Terrazzo tiles, granite chips	SF	28.11	12.19	40.30	9.75	37.86	0.1614

Division 4 CSI #	04 - MASONRY Description	Unit	Material	Union Install	Union Total	Open Install	Open Total	Unit Man-Hrs
04.2007 000	**PAVERS AND FLOOR TILE: (Cont.)**							
04.2007 131	Brick steps	SF	8.62	18.51	27.13	14.81	23.43	0.2452
04.2008 000	**GLASS MASONRY UNIT:**							
	Note: For quantities between 1000 and 5000 sf, deduct 10% from the total costs. Quantities over 5000 sf, deduct 20% from the total costs. For special colors, add 10% to the total costs. For special decorations, add 400% to total cost.							
04.2008 011	Glass masonry unit, clear, 4" x 6" x 6"	SF	27.69	27.46	55.15	21.97	49.66	0.3637
04.2008 021	Glass masonry unit, clear, 4" x 8" x 8"	SF	26.54	18.84	45.38	15.08	41.62	0.2496
04.2008 031	Glass masonry unit, clear, 4" x 12" x 12"	SF	22.56	13.76	36.32	11.01	33.57	0.1823
04.3000 000	**ARCHITECTURAL STONEWORK:**							
04.3001 000	**STONE, ROUGH:**							
04.3001 011	Veneer, lava stone, average 4" thick	SF	7.27	16.65	23.92	13.32	20.59	0.2205
04.3001 021	Veneer, Arizona stone, average 4" thick	SF	12.75	18.73	31.48	14.99	27.74	0.2481
04.3001 031	Veneer, rubble stone, average 4" thick	SF	6.56	19.83	26.39	15.86	22.42	0.2626
04.3001 041	Veneer, Palos Verdes & driftwood	SF	6.36	15.25	21.61	12.20	18.56	0.2020
04.3001 051	Veneer, other common varieties	SF	9.50	17.37	26.87	13.89	23.39	0.2300
04.3001 061	Veneer, imported East Coast type	SF	13.65	17.71	31.36	14.17	27.82	0.2346
04.3002 000	**STONE, CUT:**							
	Note: Prices for cut stone are representative only. You can expect wide variations in price. For honed finish, add 10% to the total costs. For polished finish, add 30% to the total costs.							
04.3002 011	Granite, 3/4" thick	SF	24.96	25.56	50.52	20.45	45.41	0.3386
04.3002 021	Granite, 1-1/4" thick	SF	25.59	28.64	54.23	22.91	48.50	0.3793
04.3002 031	Limestone, 2" thick	SF	17.60	25.69	43.29	20.55	38.15	0.3402
04.3002 041	Limestone, 3" thick	SF	18.71	32.13	50.84	25.70	44.41	0.4255
04.3002 051	Marble, 7/8" thick	SF	23.86	25.31	49.17	20.25	44.11	0.3352
04.3002 061	Marble, 1-1/4" thick	SF	27.28	28.22	55.50	22.58	49.86	0.3738
04.3002 071	Travertine	SF	20.78	24.95	45.73	13.89	34.67	0.3100
04.3002 081	Base travertine 9" x 3/4"	SF	29.62	35.42	65.04	19.72	49.34	0.4400
04.3002 091	Columns, travertine (not curved)	SF	25.96	41.05	67.01	22.86	48.82	0.5100
04.3002 101	Base curved radius 4'6"	SF	43.48	52.32	95.80	29.13	72.61	0.6500
04.3002 111	Sandstone, 2" thick	SF	15.50	23.42	38.92	13.04	28.54	0.2910
04.3002 121	Sandstone, 3" thick	SF	18.38	26.06	44.44	14.51	32.89	0.3238
04.3003 000	**MASONRY AND STONE SPECIALTIES:**							
04.3003 011	Floor, marble, 7/8"	SF	23.97	14.09	38.06	7.84	31.81	0.1750
04.3003 021	Thresholds, marble, 1-1/4"	LF	20.82	17.20	38.02	9.58	30.40	0.2137
04.3003 031	Base, marble, 7/8" x 6" high	LF	21.52	17.20	38.72	9.58	31.10	0.2137
04.3003 041	Columns, marble, plain	CF	201.63	73.74	275.37	41.06	242.69	0.9162
04.3003 051	Columns, marble, fluted	CF	313.71	79.60	393.31	44.32	358.03	0.9889
04.3003 061	Window stools, marble	LF	20.12	11.71	31.83	6.52	26.64	0.1455
04.3003 071	Toilet partitions, marble	EA	942.35	766.20	1,708.55	426.65	1,369.00	9.5192
04.3003 081	Stair treads, 1-1/4" x 11", marble	LF	45.88	24.61	70.49	13.70	59.58	0.3057
04.3003 091	Limestone, roughcut, large block	CF	49.92	27.94	77.86	15.56	65.48	0.3471
04.3004 000	**ARTIFICIAL STONE WORK:**							
04.3004 011	Facing panel, terrazzo	SF	8.19	21.50	29.69	11.97	20.16	0.2671
04.3004 021	Palos Verdes, cast plaster	SF	4.33	11.71	16.04	6.52	10.85	0.1455
04.3004 031	Brick, all types	SF	3.44	9.86	13.30	5.49	8.93	0.1225
04.3004 041	Cast stone, facing	SF	8.83	21.50	30.33	11.97	20.80	0.2671
04.3004 051	Cast plaster, simulated stone, rough	SF	4.46	11.71	16.17	6.52	10.98	0.1455
04.4000 000	**MASONRY ACCESSORIES & MISCELLANEOUS WORK:**							
04.4001 000	**MASONRY WALL TIES & REINFORCING:**							
04.4001 011	Masonry wall ties, galvanized	EA	.15	.37	.52	.21	.36	0.0046
04.4001 021	Masonry wall ties, coppercoated	EA	.18	.37	.55	.21	.39	0.0046
04.4001 031	Masonry wall ties, z, galvanized	EA	.18	.37	.55	.21	.39	0.0046
04.4001 041	Masonry wall ties, z, copper coated	EA	.22	.37	.59	.21	.43	0.0046
04.4001 051	Masonry reinforced, truss, 6" wide	LF	.65	.19	.84	.11	.76	0.0024
04.4001 061	Masonry reinforced, ladder, 6" wide	LF	.44	.19	.63	.11	.55	0.0024
04.4001 071	Masonry reinforced, truss, 10" wide	LF	.73	.25	.98	.14	.87	0.0031
04.4001 081	Masonry reinforced, ladder, 10" wide	LF	.44	.25	.69	.14	.58	0.0031
04.4002 000	**MASONRY WALL FINISHES:**							
04.4002 011	Masonry, acid etch	SF	.05	.67	.72	.37	.42	0.0083
04.4002 021	Masonry, wash	SF	.05	.67	.72	.37	.42	0.0083
04.4002 031	Masonry, steam clean	SF	.31	1.26	1.57	.70	1.01	0.0157

Division 4 CSI #	04 - MASONRY Description	Unit	Material	Union Install	Union Total	Open Install	Open Total	Unit Man-Hrs
04.4002 000	**MASONRY WALL FINISHES: (Cont.)**							
04.4002 041	Masonry, existing, sandblasting	SF	.82	.94	1.76	.52	1.34	0.0117
04.4002 051	Masonry, new, light sandblasting	SF	.40	.76	1.16	.43	.83	0.0095
04.4002 061	Masonry, medium sandblasting	SF	.42	.88	1.30	.49	.91	0.0109
04.4002 071	Masonry, heavy sandblasting	SF	.59	1.32	1.91	.74	1.33	0.0164
04.4003 000	**MASONRY POINTING AND WATERPROOFING:**							
04.4003 011	Masonry pointing, brick	SF	.18	1.05	1.23	.58	.76	0.0130
04.4003 021	Masonry pointing, concrete block	SF	.18	.67	.85	.37	.55	0.0083
04.4003 031	Masonry repointing, brick	SF	.18	1.27	1.45	.71	.89	0.0158
04.4003 041	Masonry, waterproofing, flood coat	SF	.46	.38	.84	.21	.67	0.0047
04.5000 000	**FIREPLACES:**							
	Note: The following prices are based on fireplaces with 15' stacks. For prefabricated metal fireplaces,							
	see section 07.6023.							
04.5001 000	**COMMON BRICK FIREPLACES:**							
	Note: The following item uses 900 bricks.							
04.5001 011	Fireplace, 30" box, to mantle	EA	821.62	1,228.85	2,050.47	684.27	1,505.89	15.2671
04.5001 021	Fireplace, 36" box, to mantle	EA	941.12	1,731.37	2,672.49	964.10	1,905.22	21.5104
04.5001 031	Fireplace, 42" box, to 9'	EA	1,508.80	2,567.15	4,075.95	1,429.49	2,938.29	31.8940
04.5001 041	Fireplace, 48" box, to 9'	EA	1,762.79	3,014.91	4,777.70	1,678.82	3,441.61	37.4569
04.5002 000	**COMMON BRICK FIREPLACE, ADDERS:**							
04.5002 011	Add for full width stack to 15'	EA	315.10	557.22	872.32	310.28	625.38	6.9228
04.5002 021	Add for stone face to 9'	EA	351.13	621.27	972.40	345.95	697.08	7.7186
04.5002 031	Add for raised hearth	EA	133.16	235.66	368.82	131.22	264.38	2.9278
04.5002 041	Add for face brick mantle to ceiling	EA	133.16	235.66	368.82	131.22	264.38	2.9278
04.5002 051	Add for extra 10' stack (2 story)	EA	242.16	428.46	670.62	238.59	480.75	5.3232
04.5003 000	**PRE-FABRICATED FIREPLACES (QUANTITY):**							
04.5003 011	Fireplace, 30" box, simulated brick	EA	496.55	878.36	1,374.91	489.10	985.65	10.9126
04.5003 021	Add for face & hearth, pre-fabricated	EA	205.90	364.19	570.09	202.79	408.69	4.5246
04.5003 031	Add for carpentry, pre-fabricated	EA	78.68	139.24	217.92	77.53	156.21	1.7299
04.5004 000	**PRE-FABRICATED FIREPLACE, FLUES:**							
04.5004 011	Flues for pre-fab fireplace, average	EA	242.16	428.46	670.62	238.59	480.75	5.3232
04.5004 021	Patent flues, 12', average	EA	67.01	283.23	350.24	157.71	224.72	3.5188
04.5004 041	Pre-fabricated flue, 8"x10"x24" long	LF	4.94	10.29	15.23	5.73	10.67	0.1279
04.5004 051	Pre-fabricated flue, 12"x12"x24" long	LF	5.85	11.78	17.63	6.56	12.41	0.1463
04.5005 000	**FIREBRICK:**							
04.5005 011	Firebrick, industrial	SF	10.36	32.39	42.75	18.04	28.40	0.4024
04.6000 000	**PARGETING:**							
04.6001 000	**PARGET:**							
04.6001 011	Parget, cement, 2 coats, 1/2"	SF	.50	1.79	2.29	1.00	1.50	0.0223
04.6001 021	Parget, cement, waterproof, 2 coats, 1/2"	SF	.65	1.79	2.44	1.00	1.65	0.0223

Division 5 CSI #	05 - METALS Description	Unit	Material	Union Install	Union Total	Open Install	Open Total	Unit Man-Hrs
05.0000 000	**METALS:**							
05.1000 000	**STRUCTURAL STEEL:**							
05.1001 000	**STRUCTURAL SHAPES (A-36):**							
05.1001 011	Base US price, FOB Pittsburgh or Chicago, freight extra	CWT	51.85		51.85		51.85	
05.1001 021	Base price, foreign, FOB dock	CWT	51.28		51.28		51.28	
05.1001 031	Base price, FOB Fabrication shop (typical)	#	1.02		1.02		1.02	
05.1001 041	Fabrication charges, (paint, handling, cutting), typical	#	.17		.17		.17	
05.1001 051	Shop drawings (typical)	#	.17		.17		.17	
05.1001 061	Fabrication (typical)	#	.46		.46		.46	
05.1001 071	Administration, (overhead, sales, profit) typical	#	.63		.63		.63	
05.1001 081	Transportation (typical)	#	.04		.04		.04	
05.1001 091	Erection (typical)	#		.39	.39	.29	.29	0.0043
05.1002 000	**COLUMN SHAPES (A-36), 10" & LARGER:**							
05.1002 011	Column shapes, 10" & up, 5,000#	#	3.32	.47	3.79	.35	3.67	0.0052
05.1002 021	Column shapes, 10" & up, 5,000-10,000#	#	2.96	.42	3.38	.32	3.28	0.0047
05.1002 031	Column shapes, 10" & up, 10,000-20,000#	#	2.76	.39	3.15	.30	3.06	0.0044
05.1002 041	Column shapes, 10" & up, 20,000-50,000#	#	2.52	.38	2.90	.28	2.80	0.0042
05.1002 051	Column shapes, 10" & up, 50,000-300,000#	#	2.52	.34	2.86	.26	2.78	0.0038
05.1002 061	Column shapes, 10" & up, 300,000-1,000,000#	#	2.41	.30	2.71	.22	2.63	0.0033
05.1002 071	Column shapes, 10" & up, 1,000,000# & up	#	2.24	.26	2.50	.19	2.43	0.0029
05.1003 000	**BEAMS & GIRDERS, 8" & SMALLER, WELDED:**							
05.1003 011	Beams & girders, up to 8", under 5,000#	#	3.32	.73	4.05	.54	3.86	0.0081
05.1003 021	Beams & girders, up to 8", 5,000-10,000#	#	2.80	.62	3.42	.46	3.26	0.0069
05.1003 031	Beams & girders, up to 8", 10,000-20,000#	#	2.53	.55	3.08	.41	2.94	0.0061
05.1003 041	Beams & girders, up to 8", 20,000-50,000#	#	2.49	.51	3.00	.38	2.87	0.0057
05.1003 051	Beams & girders, up to 8", 50,000-300,000#	#	2.45	.48	2.93	.36	2.81	0.0053
05.1003 061	Beams & girders, up to 8", 300,000-1,000,000#	#	2.25	.46	2.71	.34	2.59	0.0051
05.1003 071	Deduct for bolted construction	#		.12	.12	.09	.09	0.0013
05.1004 000	**SHAPES, 10" & LARGER, WELDED:**							
05.1004 011	Shapes, 10" & up, under 5,000#	#	3.05	.62	3.67	.46	3.51	0.0069
05.1004 021	Shapes, 10" & up, 5,000-10,000#	#	2.53	.51	3.04	.38	2.91	0.0057
05.1004 031	Shapes, 10" & up, 10,000-20,000#	#	2.49	.51	3.00	.38	2.87	0.0057
05.1004 041	Shapes, 10" & up, 20,000-50,000#	#	2.45	.48	2.93	.36	2.81	0.0053
05.1004 051	Shapes, 10" & up, 50,000-300,000#	#	2.25	.46	2.71	.34	2.59	0.0051
05.1004 061	Shapes, 10" & up, 300,000-1,000,000#	#	1.98	.41	2.39	.31	2.29	0.0046
05.1004 071	Shapes, 10" & up, 1,000,000-3,000,000#	#	1.98	.39	2.37	.30	2.28	0.0044
05.1004 081	Shapes, 10" & up, 3,000,000# or more	#	1.96	.39	2.35	.30	2.26	0.0044
05.1004 091	Deduct for bolted construction	#		.12	.12	.09	.09	0.0013
05.1005 000	**ADDERS & DEDUCTORS FOR STRUCTURAL SHAPES:**							
05.1005 011	Deduct for jumbo columns	#	.04		.04		.04	
05.1005 021	Deduct for foreign steel	#	.04		.04		.04	
05.1005 031	Add for high strength steel, A-572	#	.04	.11	.15	.08	.12	0.0012
05.1005 041	Add for high strength steel, A-188	#	.04	.11	.15	.08	.12	0.0012
05.1005 051	Add for high strength steel, A-441, A-440, A-212	#	.04	.11	.15	.08	.12	0.0012
05.1005 061	Add for high strength steel, A-588 corten	#	.15	.11	.26	.08	.23	0.0012
05.1005 071	Add for light shapes & junior sizes	#	.41	.24	.65	.18	.59	0.0027
05.1005 081	Add for tube shapes	#	.44	.06	.50	.05	.49	0.0007
05.1005 091	Add for warehouse purchase	#	.13		.13		.13	
05.1005 101	Adder; 16 to 30 stories	#	.07	.12	.19	.09	.16	0.0013
05.1005 111	Adder; 31 to 45 stories	#	.07	.15	.22	.11	.18	0.0017
05.1005 121	Adder; 46 stories & over	#	.12	.18	.30	.13	.25	0.0020
05.1100 000	**STRUCTURAL STEEL SPECIALTIES:**							
05.1101 000	**TRUSSES:**							
05.1101 011	Trusses, light steel, bolted	#	2.76	.48	3.24	.36	3.12	0.0053
05.1101 021	Trusses, light steel, welded	#	2.85	.51	3.36	.38	3.23	0.0057
05.1101 031	Trusses, heavy steel, bolted	#	2.42	.31	2.73	.23	2.65	0.0035
05.1101 041	Trusses, heavy steel, welded	#	2.51	.41	2.92	.31	2.82	0.0046
05.1102 000	**SPACE FRAME SYSTEM, 10,000 SF & UP:**							
05.1102 011	Space frame, 4' modular, 20# live load	SF	11.18	8.22	19.40	6.16	17.34	0.0917
05.1102 021	Space frame, 5' modular, 20# live load	SF	9.69	6.90	16.59	5.17	14.86	0.0770
05.1102 031	Space frame, 4' modular, 35# live load	SF	13.27	8.83	22.10	6.61	19.88	0.0985
05.1102 041	Space frame, 5' modular, 35# live load	SF	11.59	7.50	19.09	5.62	17.21	0.0837

Division 5 CSI #	05 - METALS Description	Unit	Material	Union Install	Union Total	Open Install	Open Total	Unit Man-Hrs
05.1103 000	**DETAIL STEEL:**							
	Note: The following prices are based on 7% of shapes bolted, 5% welded.							
05.1103 011	Base plates, milled	#	2.81	.43	3.24	.32	3.13	0.0048
05.1103 021	Tie plates & angles	#	2.70	.73	3.43	.54	3.24	0.0081
05.1103 031	Gussets	#	2.70	.73	3.43	.54	3.24	0.0081
05.1103 041	Tie rod with clevis & turn buckles	#	2.71	.80	3.51	.60	3.31	0.0089
05.1103 051	Clips & angles, attached	#	2.97	.73	3.70	.54	3.51	0.0081
05.1103 061	Shear studs, welded	EA	1.36	5.15	6.51	3.85	5.21	0.0574
05.1103 071	Moment connections	EA	243.74	360.88	604.62	270.24	513.98	4.0250
05.1104 000	**MISCELLANEOUS COLUMNS:**							
05.1104 011	Pipe columns, 3"-6"	#	2.10	.67	2.77	.50	2.60	0.0075
05.1104 021	Pipe columns, 8"-12"	#	2.03	.33	2.36	.25	2.28	0.0037
05.1104 031	Tube columns, 3" x 4" x 5/16"	#	2.57	.49	3.06	.37	2.94	0.0055
05.1104 041	Concrete encasement for columns	CF	15.47	38.15	53.62	28.57	44.04	0.4255
05.1104 051	Fireproof jackets and fill	SF	17.70	4.33	22.03	3.24	20.94	0.0483
05.1104 061	False work support/ton supported	TON	520.56	398.73	919.29	298.58	819.14	4.4471
05.1105 000	**MISCELLANEOUS SUPPORT ITEMS:**							
05.1105 011	High strength bolts, 3/4" dia	EA	3.12	14.03	17.15	10.51	13.63	0.1565
05.1105 021	High strength bolts, 7/8" dia	EA	3.75	14.03	17.78	10.51	14.26	0.1565
05.1105 031	Welds, 1/8", 1 pass	LF	.15	10.22	10.37	7.65	7.80	0.1140
05.1105 041	Welds, 1/4", 3 pass	LF	.56	23.80	24.36	17.83	18.39	0.2655
05.1105 051	Welds, 3/8", 6 pass	LF	.94	49.04	49.98	36.72	37.66	0.5469
05.1105 061	Welds, 1/2", 10 pass	LF	1.33	81.82	83.15	61.27	62.60	0.9126
05.1105 071	Galvanizing, 2 oz	#	.34		.34		.34	
05.1105 091	Field paint, 1 coat	#	.15	.20	.35	.15	.30	0.0022
05.1105 101	Field touchup, painting	#	.16	.23	.39	.17	.33	0.0026
05.1106 000	**JOISTS, OPEN WEB:**							
05.1106 011	Joists, "H" series	#	2.74	.57	3.31	.43	3.17	0.0064
05.1106 021	Joists, "J" series	#	2.74	.45	3.19	.34	3.08	0.0050
05.1106 031	Joists, "H" series, high strength	#	2.89	.54	3.43	.40	3.29	0.0060
05.1106 041	Joists, "LH" or "LJ" series	#	2.36	.48	2.84	.36	2.72	0.0053
05.1106 051	Joists, "LH" or "LJ" series, high strength	#	2.72	.48	3.20	.36	3.08	0.0053
05.1106 061	Built/up heavy girders	#	2.14	.48	2.62	.36	2.50	0.0053
05.1106 071	Built/up heavy box girders	#	2.13	.66	2.79	.50	2.63	0.0074
05.1107 000	**STEEL BUILDING FRAME, 14' EAVE, NO FOUNDATIONS OR SLAB:**							
05.1107 011	Steel buildings, 40,000 SF and up	SF	17.44	7.24	24.68	5.42	22.86	0.0808
05.1107 021	Steel buildings, 10,000-40,000 SF	SF	19.50	7.54	27.04	5.65	25.15	0.0841
05.1107 031	Steel buildings, 5,000-10,000 SF	SF	20.36	7.82	28.18	5.85	26.21	0.0872
05.1107 041	Steel buildings, less than 5,000 SF	SF	20.65	8.03	28.68	6.02	26.67	0.0896
05.1108 000	**STEEL BUILDINGS, ADDERS:**							
	Note: For sheet metal siding or roofing, see section 07.6000. For sash see section 08.5000.							
05.1108 011	Steel building, frame, 3.8-4.4#/SF	#	1.93	.39	2.32	.30	2.23	0.0044
05.1108 021	Bents only	#	1.84	.31	2.15	.23	2.07	0.0035
05.1108 031	Purlins & eave struts only	#	2.05	.48	2.53	.36	2.41	0.0053
05.1108 041	Galvanized siding, 26 ga	SF	3.62	4.49	8.11	3.36	6.98	0.0501
05.1108 051	Galvanized roofing, 26 ga	SF	3.62	3.96	7.58	2.97	6.59	0.0442
05.1108 061	Steel building door & frame, 3' x 7', no hardware or paint	EA	663.21	200.99	864.20	150.51	813.72	2.2417
05.1108 071	Steel building door & frame, over head, 8' x 10', prime painted	EA	2,569.42	527.67	3,097.09	395.13	2,964.55	5.8852
05.3000 000	**DECKING & SIDING:**							
	Note: The installed prices are based on the square foot coverage shown in the 25,000 to 50,000 square foot range. Quantities under 15,000 square feet are subject to special pricing.							
	Quantities under 2,000 sf . . . . add 50%							
	Between 2,000 and 12,000 sf . . . . add 25%							
	Between 12,000 and 25,000 sf . . . . add 10%							
	For quantities over 50,000 sf . . . . . . .deduct 6%							
	For galvanizing . . . . add $.18 per sf.							
05.3001 000	**DECKING, 25M-50M SF:**							
05.3001 011	Roof decking, typical, 22 ga	#	2.29	.25	2.54	.19	2.48	0.0028
05.3001 021	Floor decking, typical, 18 ga	#	1.54	.29	1.83	.21	1.75	0.0032
05.3003 000	**FLOOR DECKING, STANDARD RIB, SIMPLE, 1-1/2":**							
	Note: The maximum span for the items below is 6'6".							
05.3003 011	Floor deck, 22 ga, Q-3, 1-1/2", simple	SF	2.72	.88	3.60	.66	3.38	0.0098

Division 5 CSI #	05 - METALS Description	Unit	Material	Union Install	Union Total	Open Install	Open Total	Unit Man-Hrs
05.3003 000	**FLOOR DECKING, STANDARD RIB, SIMPLE, 1-1/2": (Cont.)**							
05.3003 021	Floor deck, 20 ga, Q-3, 1-1/2", simple	SF	2.97	.94	3.91	.70	3.67	0.0105
05.3003 031	Floor deck, 18 ga, Q-3, 1-1/2", simple	SF	3.21	.99	4.20	.74	3.95	0.0110
05.3003 041	Floor deck, 16 ga, Q-3, 1-1/2", simple	SF	3.70	1.05	4.75	.79	4.49	0.0117
05.3004 000	**FLOOR DECKING, STANDARD RIB, SIMPLE 3":**							
	Note: The maximum span for the items below is 10'.							
05.3004 011	Floor deck, 22 ga, Q-21, 3", simple	SF	3.04	.94	3.98	.70	3.74	0.0105
05.3004 021	Floor deck, 20 ga, Q-21, 3", simple	SF	3.40	1.00	4.40	.75	4.15	0.0111
05.3004 031	Floor deck, 18 ga, Q-21, 3", simple	SF	3.70	1.03	4.73	.77	4.47	0.0115
05.3004 041	Floor deck, 16 ga, Q-21, 3", simple	SF	4.18	1.08	5.26	.81	4.99	0.0120
05.3004 051	Decking pour stops	LF	1.28	3.77	5.05	2.82	4.10	0.0420
05.3005 000	**FLOOR DECKING, DOUBLE FLUTED, CELLULAR, 3":**							
05.3005 011	Floor deck, 18-18 ga, 3", RK, cellular	SF	6.05	1.70	7.75	1.28	7.33	0.0190
05.3005 021	Floor deck, 18-16 ga, 3", RK, cellular	SF	6.97	1.79	8.76	1.34	8.31	0.0200
05.3006 000	**FLOOR DECKING, FLUTED & FLAT, CELLULAR, 1-1/2":**							
05.3006 011	Floor deck, 20-20 ga, 1-1/2", UKX	SF	5.12	1.47	6.59	1.10	6.22	0.0164
05.3006 021	Floor deck, 18-18 ga, 1-1/2", UKX	SF	5.57	1.53	7.10	1.15	6.72	0.0171
05.3006 031	Floor deck, 18-16 ga, 1-1/2", UKX	SF	6.32	1.61	7.93	1.21	7.53	0.0180
05.3006 041	Floor deck, 16-16 ga, 1-1/2", UKX	SF	6.79	1.73	8.52	1.30	8.09	0.0193
05.3007 000	**FLOOR DECKING, FLUTED & FLAT, CELLULAR, 3":**							
05.3007 011	Floor deck, 20-20 ga, 3", NKX, cellular	SF	5.82	1.55	7.37	1.16	6.98	0.0173
05.3007 021	Floor deck, 18-18 ga, 3", NKX, cellular	SF	6.38	1.60	7.98	1.20	7.58	0.0179
05.3007 031	Floor deck, 18-16 ga, 3", NKX, cellular	SF	7.33	1.70	9.03	1.28	8.61	0.0190
05.3008 000	**FLOOR DECKING, STANDARD, SIMPLE, 4-1/2":**							
	Note: The maximum span for the items below is 13'3".							
05.3008 011	Floor deck, 20 ga, 4 1/2", Q-21, simple	SF	5.46	1.23	6.69	.92	6.38	0.0137
05.3008 021	Floor deck, 18 ga, 4 1/2", Q-21, simple	SF	5.89	1.27	7.16	.95	6.84	0.0142
05.3008 031	Floor deck, 16 ga, 4 1/2", Q-21, simple	SF	6.71	1.36	8.07	1.02	7.73	0.0152
05.3009 000	**FLOOR DECKING, FLUTED & FLAT, CELLULAR, 4-1/2":**							
05.3009 011	Floor deck, 18-18 ga, 4-1/2", FKX, cellular	SF	8.28	1.65	9.93	1.24	9.52	0.0184
05.3009 021	Floor deck, 18-16 ga, 4-1/2", FKX, cellular	SF	8.47	1.87	10.34	1.40	9.87	0.0209
05.3009 031	Floor deck, 16-16 ga, 4-1/2", FKX, cellular	SF	8.89	1.95	10.84	1.46	10.35	0.0218
05.3010 000	**ROOF DECKING, STANDARD RIB, SIMPLE, 1-1/2":**							
05.3010 011	Roof deck, 22 ga, Q-3, 1-1/2", simple	SF	2.72	.94	3.66	.70	3.42	0.0105
05.3010 021	Roof deck, 20 ga, Q-3, 1-1/2", simple	SF	2.97	.94	3.91	.70	3.67	0.0105
05.3010 031	Roof deck, 18 ga, Q-3, 1-1/2", simple	SF	3.21	1.04	4.25	.78	3.99	0.0116
05.3010 041	Roof deck, 16 ga, Q-3, 1-1/2", simple	SF	3.70	1.08	4.78	.81	4.51	0.0121
05.3011 000	**ROOF DECKING, STANDARD RIB, SIMPLE, 3":**							
05.3011 011	Roof deck, 22 ga, Q-21, 3", simple	SF	3.04	.97	4.01	.73	3.77	0.0108
05.3011 021	Roof deck, 20 ga, Q-21, 3", simple	SF	3.40	1.00	4.40	.75	4.15	0.0112
05.3011 031	Roof deck, 18 ga, Q-21, 3", simple	SF	3.70	1.04	4.74	.78	4.48	0.0117
05.3011 041	Roof deck, 16 ga, Q-21, 3", simple	SF	4.18	1.12	5.30	.84	5.02	0.0125
05.3012 000	**ROOF DECKING, ACOUSTIC, SIMPLE 1-1/2":**							
05.3012 011	Roof deck, 22 ga, 'B', 1-1/2", simple	SF	4.35	.99	5.34	.74	5.09	0.0110
05.3012 021	Roof deck, 20 ga, 'B', 1-1/2", simple	SF	4.71	1.02	5.73	.77	5.48	0.0114
05.3012 031	Roof deck, 18 ga, 'B', 1-1/2", simple	SF	4.95	1.08	6.03	.81	5.76	0.0121
05.3012 041	Sheet metal toe board, 4"	LF	4.57	3.05	7.62	2.28	6.85	0.0340
05.3013 000	**ROOF DECKING, ACOUSTIC, SIMPLE 3":**							
05.3013 011	Roof deck, 20 ga, C-3, 3", simple	SF	5.09	.99	6.08	.74	5.83	0.0110
05.3013 021	Roof deck, 18 ga, C-3, 3", simple	SF	5.32	1.04	6.36	.78	6.10	0.0116
05.3013 031	Roof deck, 16 ga, C-3, 3", simple	SF	5.77	1.13	6.90	.85	6.62	0.0126
05.3013 041	Roof deck, 14 ga, C-3, 3", simple	SF	6.62	1.19	7.81	.89	7.51	0.0133
05.3014 000	**ROOF DECKING, CURRUFORM & TUFCOR, WITH REINFORCING:**							
05.3014 011	Roof deck, 26 ga, 5' span	SF	1.76	.94	2.70	.70	2.46	0.0105
05.3014 021	Roof deck, 20 ga, 8' span	SF	1.93	.99	2.92	.74	2.67	0.0110
05.3015 000	**SIDING, METAL WALLS:**							
05.3015 011	Siding, baked enamel	SF	39.54	4.17	43.71	3.12	42.66	0.0465
05.3015 031	Siding, porcelain	SF	43.92	4.39	48.31	3.29	47.21	0.0490
05.3016 000	**SIDING, INSULATED METAL WALLS:**							
05.3016 011	Siding, insulated metal, baked enamel	SF	40.89	6.28	47.17	4.70	45.59	0.0700
05.3016 021	Siding, insulated metal, porcelain	SF	56.62	7.08	63.70	5.30	61.92	0.0790

Division 5 CSI #	05 - METALS Description	Unit	Material	Union Install	Union Total	Open Install	Open Total	Unit Man-Hrs
05.5000 000	**MISCELLANEOUS IRON:**							
05.5001 000	**IRON, MISCELLANEOUS:**							
05.5001 011	Anchor bolts, hook, 1/2" x 8"	EA	4.14	14.79	18.93	11.08	15.22	0.1650
05.5001 021	Anchor bolts, hook, 5/8" x 10"	EA	4.68	15.60	20.28	11.68	16.36	0.1740
05.5001 031	Anchor bolts, hook, 3/4" x 12"	EA	7.16	16.77	23.93	12.56	19.72	0.1870
05.5001 041	Anchor bolts, hook, 1" x 15"	EA	12.03	17.21	29.24	12.89	24.92	0.1920
05.5001 051	Anchor bolts, hook, 1-1/4" x 18"	EA	27.84	17.93	45.77	13.43	41.27	0.2000
05.5001 061	Anchor bolts, hook, 1-1/2" x 24"	EA	51.55	18.92	70.47	14.17	65.72	0.2110
05.5001 071	Expansion bolt, 1/2"	EA	3.98	16.45	20.43	12.32	16.30	0.1835
05.5001 081	Expansion bolt, 5/8"	EA	4.83	17.21	22.04	12.89	17.72	0.1920
05.5001 091	Expansion bolt, 3/4"	EA	6.11	18.15	24.26	13.59	19.70	0.2024
05.5001 101	Expansion bolt, 7/8"	EA	7.67	20.01	27.68	14.99	22.66	0.2232
05.5001 111	Expansion bolt, 1"	EA	10.38	21.02	31.40	15.74	26.12	0.2344
05.5001 121	High strength bolt, ASTM 373, 3/4" x 2"	EA	4.83	10.37	15.20	7.77	12.60	0.1157
05.5001 131	High strength bolt, ASTM 373, 7/8" x 3"	EA	5.52	10.37	15.89	7.77	13.29	0.1157
05.5002 000	**STAIRS, WITHOUT RAILINGS:**							
05.5002 011	Steel stair, concrete tread, 44"	RISER	355.45	28.35	383.80	21.23	376.68	0.3162
05.5002 021	Steel stair, concrete tread, 44", switch	RISER	406.91	34.05	440.96	25.50	432.41	0.3798
05.5002 031	Steel pan, concrete fill, 44"	RISER	710.19	96.53	806.72	72.28	782.47	1.0766
05.5002 041	Steel pan, concrete fill, 48"	RISER	778.79	102.14	880.93	76.49	855.28	1.1392
05.5002 051	Steel stringer, ladder type	RISER	414.41	56.78	471.19	42.52	456.93	0.6333
05.5002 061	Cast iron stair, circular, 32"	RISER	490.18	39.76	529.94	29.77	519.95	0.4434
05.5002 071	Steel stair, concrete tread, 14 riser	FLT	4,976.32	606.18	5,582.50	453.93	5,430.25	6.7609
05.5002 081	Steel stair pan, concrete fill, 18 riser	FLT	12,783.42	1,389.73	14,173.15	1,040.67	13,824.09	15.5000
05.5002 091	Steel stair, steel tread, 18 riser	FLT	10,865.89	1,829.06	12,694.95	1,369.66	12,235.55	20.4000
05.5003 000	**LADDERS, GALVANIZED STEEL:**							
05.5003 011	Ladder, 2-1/2"x3/8" bar, 3/4" rung	LF	105.42	25.36	130.78	18.99	124.41	0.2829
05.5003 021	Ladder, hook bends only	EA	636.94	157.16	794.10	117.68	754.62	1.7528
05.5003 031	Ladder, protective cage only	LF	170.11	41.60	211.71	31.15	201.26	0.4640
05.5003 041	Ships ladder, plaster & tread, 4"	LF	125.32	26.21	151.53	19.63	144.95	0.2923
05.5004 000	**PIPE RAILING, WELDED, WITH KICK PLATE:**							
05.5004 011	Pipe rail, 2 high, 1-1/2", with kick	LF	69.12	16.32	85.44	12.22	81.34	0.1820
05.5004 021	Pipe rail, 3 high, 1-1/2", with kick	LF	88.90	16.32	105.22	12.22	101.12	0.1820
05.5004 031	Pipe rail, 4 high, 1-1/2", with kick	LF	108.68	16.32	125.00	12.22	120.90	0.1820
05.5004 041	Pipe rail, 1-1/2", wall type	LF	32.34	16.32	48.66	12.22	44.56	0.1820
05.5004 051	Pipe rail, 2 high, 1-1/2", kick, galvanized	LF	78.71	16.32	95.03	12.22	90.93	0.1820
05.5004 061	Pipe rail, 3 high, 1-1/2", kick, galvanized	LF	97.37	16.32	113.69	12.22	109.59	0.1820
05.5004 071	Pipe rail, 4 high, 1-1/2", kick, galvanized	LF	119.25	16.32	135.57	12.22	131.47	0.1820
05.5004 081	Pipe rail, 1-1/2", wall, galvanized	LF	31.98	16.32	48.30	12.22	44.20	0.1820
05.5005 000	**FLATBAR RAILING, WELDED:**							
05.5005 011	Angle & flatbar railing	LF	40.34	15.24	55.58	11.41	51.75	0.1700
05.5005 021	Flat & square bar, ornamental	LF	48.48	16.50	64.98	12.35	60.83	0.1840
05.5006 000	**WROUGHT IRON RAILINGS:**							
05.5006 011	Wrought iron rail, stock pattern, 6' high	LF	170.65	17.31	187.96	12.96	183.61	0.1931
05.5006 021	Wrought iron rail, custom pattern, 8' high	LF	377.76	36.73	414.49	27.51	405.27	0.4097
05.5006 031	Wrought iron rail, stair, 42" high	LF	117.52	17.95	135.47	13.44	130.96	0.2002
05.5007 000	**ALUMINUM & BRASS RAILING:**							
	Note: For anodizing, add 10% to the total costs. For bronze anodizing, add 20%. For black anodizing, add 30%.							
05.5007 011	Aluminum railing, stock patterns	LF	112.16	22.24	134.40	16.65	128.81	0.2480
05.5007 021	Aluminum railing, architectural designs	LF	162.55	26.36	188.91	19.74	182.29	0.2940
05.5007 031	Brass railing, architectural designs	LF	178.72	29.15	207.87	21.83	200.55	0.3251
05.5008 000	**DECORATIVE HANDRAILS, EASY DESIGNS:**							
05.5008 011	Rail, brass/bronze, floor mounted	LF	380.31	34.70	415.01	25.98	406.29	0.3870
05.5008 021	Rail, aluminum, floor mounted	LF	138.86	28.87	167.73	21.62	160.48	0.3220
05.5008 031	Rail, stainless steel, floor mounted	LF	232.57	38.15	270.72	28.57	261.14	0.4255
05.5008 041	Rail, brass/bronze, wall mounted	LF	133.39	23.10	156.49	17.30	150.69	0.2576
05.5008 051	Rail, aluminum, wall mounted	LF	50.04	19.28	69.32	14.44	64.48	0.2150
05.5008 061	Rail, stainless steel, wall mounted	LF	83.83	30.62	114.45	22.93	106.76	0.3415
05.5009 000	**WIRE MESH:**							
05.5009 011	Mesh & frame grill, heavy protection	SF	34.39	6.48	40.87	4.85	39.24	0.0723
05.5009 021	Mesh, partitions, heavy protection	SF	10.41	6.48	16.89	4.85	15.26	0.0723

Division 5 CSI #	05 - METALS Description	Unit	Material	Union Install	Union Total	Open Install	Open Total	Unit Man-Hrs
05.5009 000	WIRE MESH: (Cont.)							
05.5009 031	Mesh, standard partitions	SF	7.70	7.10	14.80	5.32	13.02	0.0792
05.5009 041	Mesh window guards, galvanized	SF	18.99	6.48	25.47	4.85	23.84	0.0723
05.5009 051	Grate, welded steel, 1"x1/8", galvanized, 50#/SF	SF	45.90	10.60	56.50	7.94	53.84	0.1182
05.5009 061	Grate, steel, 1-1/4"x3/16", 98#/SF	SF	54.75	13.34	68.09	9.99	64.74	0.1488
05.5009 071	Grate, steel, 1-1/2"x3/16", 105#/SF	SF	67.23	16.68	83.91	12.49	79.72	0.1860
05.5009 081	Grate, aluminum, 1" x 1/8", 19#/SF	SF	42.15	9.17	51.32	6.87	49.02	0.1023
05.5009 091	Grate, aluminum, 1-1/4" x 1/8", 33#/SF	SF	63.30	12.51	75.81	9.37	72.67	0.1395
05.5009 101	Grate, aluminum, 1-1/4" x 3/16", 38#/SF	SF	68.10	15.84	83.94	11.86	79.96	0.1767
05.5009 111	Add for edge banding, steel	LF	6.57	9.26	15.83	6.94	13.51	0.1033
05.5009 121	Add for edge banding, aluminum	LF	8.64	10.93	19.57	8.18	16.82	0.1219
05.5010 000	FRAMING:							
05.5010 011	Canopy framing	#	4.63	4.47	9.10	3.34	7.97	0.0498
05.5010 021	Frame supports, steel	#	3.84	1.65	5.49	1.24	5.08	0.0184
05.5010 031	Frame supports, aluminum	#	22.47	5.31	27.78	3.97	26.44	0.0592
05.5011 000	FIRE ESCAPES:							
05.5011 011	Fire escapes, ladder & balcony	FLOOR	4,600.09	650.22	5,250.31	486.91	5,087.00	7.2521
05.5012 000	EMBEDDED STEEL:							
05.5012 011	Light steel, embedded	#	4.94	2.58	7.52	1.93	6.87	0.0288
05.5012 021	Heavy steel, embedded	#	3.77	1.87	5.64	1.40	5.17	0.0209
05.5012 031	Trench covers with embedded frames	#	3.65	1.80	5.45	1.35	5.00	0.0201
05.5012 041	Carpenter's iron, general	#	4.31	2.82	7.13	2.11	6.42	0.0314
05.5012 051	Light door frames, U channel, anchor	#	5.41	2.58	7.99	1.93	7.34	0.0288
05.5012 061	Heavy door frames, U channel, anchor	#	4.07	1.87	5.94	1.40	5.47	0.0209
05.5012 071	Thresholds with anchors	#	5.41	2.58	7.99	1.93	7.34	0.0288
05.5012 081	Clips & L's, tiedowns, etc	#	4.70	2.82	7.52	2.11	6.81	0.0314
05.5013 000	COLUMNS, TUBE AND PIPE:							
05.5013 011	Column, pipe, 3", with plates	#	3.82	.90	4.72	.67	4.49	0.0100
05.5013 021	Column, pipe, 4", with plates	#	3.65	.84	4.49	.63	4.28	0.0094
05.5013 031	Column, pipe, 6", with plates	#	3.54	.81	4.35	.60	4.14	0.0090
05.5013 041	Column, tube, 4" x 4" x 3/8"	#	4.49	.65	5.14	.49	4.98	0.0073
05.5014 000	ROOF HATCHES:							
05.5014 011	Roof hatch, 30" x 48"	EA	1,593.99	229.56	1,823.55	171.90	1,765.89	2.5603
05.5014 021	Roof hatch, 30" x 72"	EA	2,523.84	292.99	2,816.83	219.40	2,743.24	3.2678
05.5014 031	Ceiling hatch, 30" x 30"	EA	902.15	195.12	1,097.27	146.11	1,048.26	2.1762
05.5015 000	CATCH BASIN AND MANHOLE ACCESSORIES:							
05.5015 011	Catch basin, grate & frame, 18" square, 500#	EA	524.99	74.70	599.69	55.93	580.92	0.8331
05.5015 021	Catch basin, grate & frame, 24" square, 500#	EA	636.79	125.08	761.87	93.66	730.45	1.3950
05.5015 031	Catch basin, grate & frame, 30" square, 500#	EA	1,292.52	175.20	1,467.72	131.19	1,423.71	1.9540
05.5015 041	Manhole, cover & frame, 24" dia	EA	1,253.31	175.20	1,428.51	131.19	1,384.50	1.9540
05.5015 051	Manhole, cover & frame, 30" dia	EA	707.07	125.08	832.15	93.66	800.73	1.3950
05.5015 071	Manhole, steps, wrought iron/aluminum	EA	28.73	37.82	66.55	28.32	57.05	0.4218
05.5015 081	Manhole ladder rungs, galvanized	EA	24.41	31.94	56.35	23.92	48.33	0.3562
05.5015 091	Trench drain, 8"	LF	98.53	19.18	117.71	14.36	112.89	0.2139
05.5016 000	MISCELLANEOUS SPECIALTIES:							
05.5016 011	Gray iron foundry items	#	2.62	1.09	3.71	.82	3.44	0.0122
05.5016 021	Stair nosings	LF	13.39	6.48	19.87	4.85	18.24	0.0723
05.5016 031	Stainless steel corridor wall rail, 1/2"	LF	88.82	8.34	97.16	6.24	95.06	0.0930
05.5016 041	Add for galvanizing	#	1.38		1.38		1.38	
05.5017 000	SUPPORTS, SPECIAL:							
05.5017 011	Toilet partition supports	EA	134.81	87.55	222.36	65.56	200.37	0.9765
05.5017 021	Surgical light supports, single	EA	343.15	104.23	447.38	78.05	421.20	1.1625
05.5017 031	Surgical light supports, double	EA	686.27	208.46	894.73	156.10	842.37	2.3250
05.5017 041	X-ray track supports, double	EA	1,293.38	510.31	1,803.69	382.13	1,675.51	5.6916
05.5017 051	Elevator beams	#	3.09	.96	4.05	.72	3.81	0.0107
05.5018 000	COLUMN BASES:							
05.5018 011	Column base, 16" x 16" x 2-1/2", cast iron	EA	172.13	55.13	227.26	41.28	213.41	0.6149
05.5018 021	Column base, 32" x 32" x 3-3/4", cast iron	EA	690.83	115.70	806.53	86.64	777.47	1.2904
05.5018 031	Wood column base, 8" x 8", cast aluminum	EA	186.78	16.53	203.31	12.38	199.16	0.1844
05.5018 041	Wood column base, 12" x 12", cast aluminum	EA	297.48	16.53	314.01	12.38	309.86	0.1844

Division 5 CSI #	05 - METALS Description	Unit	Material	Union Install	Union Total	Open Install	Open Total	Unit Man-Hrs
05.5019 000	**CORNER GUARDS:**							
05.5019 011	Corner guard, wheel, 2' 6" high	EA	71.41	22.41	93.82	16.78	88.19	0.2499
05.5019 021	Corner guard, wheel, 5' high	EA	142.77	44.81	187.58	33.56	176.33	0.4998
05.5020 000	**CASTINGS, MISCELLANEOUS:**							
05.5020 011	Iron casting, lightweight section	#	2.82	.36	3.18	.27	3.09	0.0040
05.5020 021	Iron casting, heavy section	#	2.55	.36	2.91	.27	2.82	0.0040
05.5021 000	**MISCELLANEOUS ORNAMENTAL METAL:**							
05.5021 011	Sight screen, aluminum	SF	58.46	11.78	70.24	8.82	67.28	0.1314
05.5021 021	Sight screen, extruded metal	SF	44.96	11.78	56.74	8.82	53.78	0.1314
05.5021 031	Sun screen, aluminum, manual	SF	58.82	5.85	64.67	4.38	63.20	0.0653
05.5021 041	Sun screen, aluminum, motorized	SF	106.11	7.73	113.84	5.79	111.90	0.0862
05.5021 051	Wrought iron gate, 6' x 7'	EA	2,705.18	336.65	3,041.83	252.09	2,957.27	3.7547
05.5021 061	Brass/bronze work	#	34.26	5.54	39.80	4.15	38.41	0.0618
05.5021 071	Aluminum work	#	29.93	11.00	40.93	8.24	38.17	0.1227
05.5021 081	Stainless steel, 300 series	#	15.98	5.54	21.52	4.15	20.13	0.0618
05.5022 000	**EXPANSION CONTROL & JOINTS:**							
	Note: For bronze or stainless, add 2% to the material costs.							
05.5022 011	Expansion joint, 1-1/2", floor	LF	59.47	10.34	69.81	7.74	67.21	0.1153
05.5022 021	Expansion joint, 1-1/2", wall	LF	41.94	12.59	54.53	9.43	51.37	0.1404
05.5022 031	Expansion joint, gymnasium base	LF	26.46	8.50	34.96	6.36	32.82	0.0948
05.5022 041	Expansion joint, roof, 1-1/2"	LF	83.40	12.19	95.59	9.13	92.53	0.1360
05.5022 051	Expansion joints, 4", floor	LF	115.46	20.75	136.21	15.54	131.00	0.2314
05.5022 061	Expansion joints, 4", wall	LF	80.94	25.18	106.12	18.85	99.79	0.2808
05.5022 071	Expansion joints, 4", roof	LF	122.46	23.36	145.82	17.49	139.95	0.2605

Division 6 CSI #	06 - CARPENTRY Description	Unit	Material	Union Install	Union Total	Open Install	Open Total	Unit Man-Hrs
06.0000 000	**CARPENTRY:**							
	Note: In the following section, material prices are based on commercial structures using standard or better grade lumber. Labor prices are based on institutional grade framing.							
06.1000 000	**ROUGH CARPENTRY:**							
	Note: The following percentages may be used to adjust the pricing in this section to fit job requirements:							
	Construction grade lumber . . . . add 19% to material							
	Select structural lumber . . . . add 40% to material							
	Forest Stewardship Council Approved (LEED) . . . . . add 15% to material							
	Kiln dried lumber . . . . add 15% to material							
	Hand selected lumber . . . . add 19% to material							
	Institutional structures . . . . add 25% to material							
	Residential by builder . . . . deduct 15% from labor							
	Residential by framer . . . . deduct 30% from labor							
	Note that the following sections (.1001, .1002, and .1003) are given in square foot area measure, and are pre-factored for board foot measure for quick estimates to eliminate board foot measure take-off by the estimator.							
06.1001 000	**STUD WALLS, 16" OC, INSTALLED:**							
	Note: The following prices include single plates, blocking, headers and diagonal bracing. Prices are by the square foot, already factored for board feet.							
06.1001 011	Wall, 2" x 4" x 8', 16" OC, 1.1 BF/SF	SF	1.10	2.34	3.44	1.63	2.73	0.0262
06.1001 021	Wall, 2" x 4" x 10', 16" OC, 1.0 BF/SF	SF	1.03	2.31	3.34	1.60	2.63	0.0258
06.1001 031	Wall, 3" x 4" x 8', 16" OC, 1.5 BF/SF	SF	1.47	3.17	4.64	2.21	3.68	0.0355
06.1001 041	Wall, 2" x 6" x 8', 16" OC, 1.7 BF/SF	SF	1.68	3.38	5.06	2.35	4.03	0.0378
06.1001 051	Wall, 2" x 6" x 10', 16" OC, 1.5 BF/SF	SF	1.51	3.60	5.11	2.51	4.02	0.0403
06.1001 061	Wall, 2" x 6" x 8', 12" OC, 2.0 BF/SF	SF	1.92	4.23	6.15	2.94	4.86	0.0473
06.1001 071	Wall, 2" x 4", 2" x 6" plate, staggered	SF	1.71	3.82	5.53	2.66	4.37	0.0428
06.1002 000	**JOIST, FLOOR, 16" OC, (MINIMUM 3000 SF):**							
	Note: The following prices include rim, joists and blocking. Prices are by square foot, already factored for board feet.							
06.1002 011	Floor joist, 2" x 6", 16" OC, 1.1 BF/SF	SF	.99	1.97	2.96	1.37	2.36	0.0220
06.1002 021	Floor joist, 2" x 8", 16" OC, 1.55 BF/SF	SF	1.41	3.10	4.51	2.16	3.57	0.0347
06.1002 031	Floor joist, 2" x 10", 16"oc, 1.85 BF/SF	SF	1.65	3.23	4.88	2.25	3.90	0.0361
06.1002 041	Floor joist, 2" x 12", 16" OC, 2.1 BF/SF	SF	1.87	3.55	5.42	2.47	4.34	0.0397
06.1002 051	Floor joist, 2" x 14", 16" OC, 2.42 BF/SF	SF	2.16	4.23	6.39	2.94	5.10	0.0473
06.1003 000	**RAFTERS, 24" OC:**							
	Note: The following prices include freeze block, ribbon & strong backs. Prices are by the square foot, already factored for board feet.							
06.1003 011	Rafters, 2" x 4", 24" OC, 0.46 BF/SF	SF	.64	3.25	3.89	2.26	2.90	0.0364
06.1003 021	Rafters, 2" x 6", 24" OC, 0.68 BF/SF	SF	.89	4.03	4.92	2.80	3.69	0.0451
06.1003 031	Rafters, 2" x 8", 24" OC, 0.90 BF/SF	SF	1.19	5.55	6.74	3.86	5.05	0.0621
06.1003 041	Rafters, 2" x 10", 24" OC, 1.16 BF/SF	SF	1.53	6.91	8.44	4.81	6.34	0.0773
06.1003 051	Rafters, 2" x 12", 24" OC, 1.37 BF/SF	SF	1.80	8.26	10.06	5.75	7.55	0.0924
06.1100 000	**VERTICAL FRAMING, WALLS, PER 1,000 BOARD FEET:**							
06.1101 000	**STUD WALLS, COMBINED, 16" OC:**							
	Note: The following prices include plates, blocks, bracing and mud sills.							
06.1101 011	Stud wall, 2" x 4", 2'-6', 16" OC	MBF	914.66	1,760.42	2,675.08	1,225.16	2,139.82	19.7003
06.1101 021	Stud wall, 2" x 4", 8', 16" OC	MBF	914.66	1,760.42	2,675.08	1,225.16	2,139.82	19.7003
06.1101 031	Stud wall, 3" x 4", 8', 16" OC	MBF	1,023.79	1,760.42	2,784.21	1,225.16	2,248.95	19.7003
06.1101 041	Stud wall, 2" x 6", 8', 16" OC	MBF	930.04	1,760.42	2,690.46	1,225.16	2,155.20	19.7003
06.1101 051	Stud wall, 2" x 4", 10'-16', 16" OC	MBF	914.66	1,921.24	2,835.90	1,337.09	2,251.75	21.5000
06.1101 061	Stud wall, 3" x 4", 10'-16', 16" OC	MBF	1,023.79	2,004.04	3,027.83	1,394.71	2,418.50	22.4266
06.1101 071	Stud wall, 2" x 6", 10'-16', 16" OC	MBF	930.04	2,004.04	2,934.08	1,394.71	2,324.75	22.4266
06.1102 000	**SLOPING STUD WALLS, COMBINED, 16" OC:**							
	Note: The following prices include blocks, bracing and mid blocks, with flat bottom plate and sloping top plate.							
06.1102 011	Stud wall, sloping, 2" x 4", 8'-16', 16" OC	MBF	914.66	2,751.28	3,665.94	1,914.75	2,829.41	30.7887
06.1102 021	Stud wall, sloping, 3" x 4", 8'-16', 16" OC	MBF	1,023.79	2,711.91	3,735.70	1,887.35	2,911.14	30.3481
06.1102 031	Stud wall, sloping, 2" x 6", 8'-16', 16" OC	MBF	930.04	2,711.91	3,641.95	1,887.35	2,817.39	30.3481
06.1103 000	**UNDERPINNING:**							
06.1103 011	Pier caps, field grade redwood, 2" x 6"	MBF	2,064.37	6,015.08	8,079.45	4,186.19	6,250.56	67.3129
06.1103 021	Jack studs, 2" x 4"	MBF	930.04	3,760.43	4,690.47	2,617.07	3,547.11	42.0818
06.1103 031	Jack post, 4" x 4"	MBF	1,406.83	3,468.69	4,875.52	2,414.03	3,820.86	38.8170

Division 6 CSI #	06 - CARPENTRY Description	Unit	Material	Union Install	Union Total	Open Install	Open Total	Unit Man-Hrs
06.1104 000	**MUD SILLS:**							
06.1104 011	Mud sill, bolt, 2" x 4" or 2" x 6", field grade redwood	MBF	2,091.58	1,760.16	3,851.74	1,224.98	3,316.56	19.6974
06.1104 021	Mud sill, bolt, 3" x 4", field grade redwood	MBF	2,576.70	3,524.38	6,101.08	2,452.79	5,029.49	39.4402
06.1104 031	Mud sill, shot, 2" x 4" or 2" x 6", field grade redwood	MBF	2,091.58	1,495.89	3,587.47	1,041.06	3,132.64	16.7400
06.1104 041	Mud sill, shot, 3" x 4", field grade redwood	MBF	2,576.70	2,596.90	5,173.60	1,807.31	4,384.01	29.0611
06.1104 051	Mud sill, grout, 2" x 4" or 2" x 6"	LF	2.40	6.07	8.47	4.22	6.62	0.0679
06.1104 061	Mud sill, grout, 2" x 8"	LF	2.67	6.50	9.17	4.52	7.19	0.0727
06.1104 071	Anchor bolt, embedded, 8" x 5/8"	EA	2.57	6.24	8.81	4.34	6.91	0.0698
06.1104 081	Shot fasteners	EA	1.60	3.25	4.85	2.26	3.86	0.0364
06.1105 000	**STUD WALL COMPONENTS:**							
06.1105 011	Plate, 2" x 4" or 2" x 6"	MBF	914.66	1,662.10	2,576.76	1,156.73	2,071.39	18.6000
06.1105 021	Studs, 2" x 4" or 2" x 6", 8'	MBF	914.66	1,828.31	2,742.97	1,272.41	2,187.07	20.4600
06.1105 031	Studs, 3" x 4", 8'	MBF	1,023.79	1,828.31	2,852.10	1,272.41	2,296.20	20.4600
06.1105 041	Studs, 2" x 4" or 2" x 6", 10'-16'	MBF	914.66	1,994.52	2,909.18	1,388.08	2,302.74	22.3200
06.1105 051	Studs, 3" x 4", 10'-16'	MBF	1,023.79	1,994.52	3,018.31	1,388.08	2,411.87	22.3200
06.1105 061	Blocking/brace, 2" x 4"	MBF	914.66	4,129.04	5,043.70	2,873.60	3,788.26	46.2068
06.1105 071	Blocking, 2" x 6"	MBF	930.04	3,986.16	4,916.20	2,774.17	3,704.21	44.6079
06.1105 081	Bracing, diagonal, let in, 1" x 4'	MBF	1,461.37	3,791.59	5,252.96	2,638.75	4,100.12	42.4305
06.1105 091	Headers, 4" x 12"	MBF	1,442.58	3,025.44	4,468.02	2,105.55	3,548.13	33.8568
06.1106 000	**POSTS AND COLUMNS:**							
	Note: The following prices include handling, unloading, cutting, notching, dapping, erecting and bolting.							
06.1106 011	Post, 4" x 4" to 4" x 8", construction grade	MBF	1,419.22	5,376.88	6,796.10	3,742.03	5,161.25	60.1710
06.1106 021	Post, 6" x 6" to 6" x 12", construction grade	MBF	1,377.95	4,032.66	5,410.61	2,806.53	4,184.48	45.1283
06.1106 031	Post, 8" x 8" to 8" x 12", construction grade	MBF	1,400.49	3,855.55	5,256.04	2,683.27	4,083.76	43.1463
06.1106 041	Post, 12" x 12", construction grade	MBF	1,558.47	3,573.51	5,131.98	2,486.98	4,045.45	39.9900
06.1106 051	Post, 4" x 4" to 4" x 8", select grade	MBF	1,861.17	5,376.88	7,238.05	3,742.03	5,603.20	60.1710
06.1106 061	Post, 6" x 6" to 6" x 12", select grade	MBF	1,558.47	4,032.66	5,591.13	2,806.53	4,365.00	45.1283
06.1106 071	Post, 8" x 8" to 8" x 12", select grade	MBF	1,878.28	3,855.55	5,733.83	2,683.27	4,561.55	43.1463
06.1106 081	Post, 12" x 12", select grade	MBF	1,976.53	3,573.51	5,550.04	2,486.98	4,463.51	39.9900
06.1200 000	**HORIZONTAL FRAMING, PER 1,000 BOARD FEET:**							
06.1201 000	**BEAMS:**							
06.1201 011	Beams, 4" x 6" to 4" x 12", to 20', construction grade	MBF	1,189.84	2,704.61	3,894.45	1,882.27	3,072.11	30.2665
06.1201 021	Beams, 6" x 6" to 6" x 12", to 20', construction grade	MBF	1,401.16	2,592.45	3,993.61	1,804.21	3,205.37	29.0113
06.1201 031	Beams, 8" x 8" to 8" x 12", to 20', construction grade	MBF	1,581.46	2,480.29	4,061.75	1,726.15	3,307.61	27.7561
06.1201 041	Beams, 4" x 6" to 4" x 12", to 20', select grade	MBF	1,517.08	2,704.61	4,221.69	1,882.27	3,399.35	30.2665
06.1201 051	Beams, 6" x 6" to 6" x 12", to 20', select grade	MBF	1,801.31	2,592.45	4,393.76	1,804.21	3,605.52	29.0113
06.1201 061	Beams, 8" x 8" to 8" x 12", to 20', select grade	MBF	2,043.70	2,480.29	4,523.99	1,726.15	3,769.85	27.7561
06.1202 000	**FLOOR JOISTS & BLOCKING INCLUDING RIM JOISTS:**							
06.1202 011	Floor joist, block, 2" x 6", rim joist	MBF	1,014.59	1,715.71	2,730.30	1,194.05	2,208.64	19.2000
06.1202 021	Floor joist, block, 2" x 8", rim joist	MBF	1,099.19	1,626.35	2,725.54	1,131.86	2,231.05	18.2000
06.1202 031	Floor joist, block, 2" x 10", rim joist	MBF	1,185.75	1,535.94	2,721.69	1,068.93	2,254.68	17.1882
06.1202 041	Floor joist, block, 2" x 12", rim joist	MBF	1,234.06	1,478.76	2,712.82	1,029.14	2,263.20	16.5483
06.1202 051	Floor joist, block, 2" x 14", rim joist	MBF	1,299.45	1,478.76	2,778.21	1,029.14	2,328.59	16.5483
06.1202 061	Floor joist, block, 4" x 14", rim joist	MBF	1,600.27	1,617.42	3,217.69	1,125.64	2,725.91	18.1000
06.1202 071	Floor joist, block, 3" x 14", rim joist	MBF	1,550.55	1,617.42	3,167.97	1,125.64	2,676.19	18.1000
06.1203 000	**PURLINS:**							
06.1203 011	Purlin, 4" x 14"-16" x 20'	MBF	1,749.43	1,758.17	3,507.60	1,223.59	2,973.02	19.6751
06.1203 021	Purlin, 4" x 14"-16" x 24'	MBF	1,749.43	1,728.57	3,478.00	1,203.00	2,952.43	19.3439
06.1203 031	Purlin, 6" x 10"	MBF	2,332.07	2,609.48	4,941.55	1,816.07	4,148.14	29.2019
06.1203 041	Purlin, 6" x 12"	MBF	2,533.32	2,539.39	5,072.71	1,767.28	4,300.60	28.4175
06.1204 000	**RAFTERS & OUTRIGGERS:**							
	Note: For 5, 6, 8 or 12/12 pitch, add 50% to the labor costs. For rafter framing with dormers and cut up sections, add 75% to the labor costs.							
06.1204 011	Rafter, 2" x 4", 4/12 pitch	MBF	997.81	3,655.64	4,653.45	2,544.14	3,541.95	40.9091
06.1204 021	Rafter, 2" x 6", 4/12 pitch	MBF	1,014.59	3,051.98	4,066.57	2,124.02	3,138.61	34.1538
06.1204 031	Rafter, 2" x 8", 4/12 pitch	MBF	1,181.03	3,117.21	4,298.24	2,169.42	3,350.45	34.8837
06.1204 041	Rafter, 2" x 10"-12", 4/12 pitch	MBF	1,185.75	3,080.02	4,265.77	2,143.53	3,329.28	34.4675
06.1205 000	**ROOF JOISTS & BLOCKING, INCLUDING RIM JOISTS:**							
06.1205 011	Roof joist, block, 2" x 4", rim joist	MBF	997.81	1,931.79	2,929.60	1,344.43	2,342.24	21.6181
06.1205 021	Roof joist, block, 2" x 6", rim joist	MBF	1,014.59	1,923.97	2,938.56	1,338.99	2,353.58	21.5306
06.1205 031	Roof joist, block, 2" x 8", rim joist	MBF	1,181.03	1,892.79	3,073.82	1,317.28	2,498.31	21.1816
06.1205 041	Roof joist, block, 2" x 10", rim joist	MBF	1,185.75	1,690.35	2,876.10	1,176.40	2,362.15	18.9162

Division 6 CSI #	06 - CARPENTRY Description	Unit	Material	Union Install	Union Total	Open Install	Open Total	Unit Man-Hrs
06.1205 000	**ROOF JOISTS & BLOCKING, INCLUDING RIM JOISTS: (Cont.)**							
06.1205 051	Roof joist, block, 2" x 12", rim joist	MBF	1,603.80	1,635.81	3,239.61	1,138.44	2,742.24	18.3058
06.1300 000	**MISCELLANEOUS FRAMING & MATERIALS:**							
06.1301 000	**FURRING:**							
06.1301 011	Furring, 2" x 4", nailed to masonry	MBF	896.71	3,842.48	4,739.19	2,674.17	3,570.88	43.0000
06.1301 021	Furring, 1" x 3", machine nailed, ceiling	MBF	1,455.12	3,482.39	4,937.51	2,423.56	3,878.68	38.9703
06.1301 031	Furring, 1" x 3", nailed to concrete	MBF	1,582.04	5,030.97	6,613.01	3,501.30	5,083.34	56.3000
06.1302 000	**INSULATION BOARD:**							
	Note: The following items are installed by carpenters. See also section 07.2001.							
06.1302 011	Insulation, fiberboard, 1/2", 4' x 8', wall	SF	.48	.88	1.36	.62	1.10	0.0099
06.1302 021	Insulation, fiberboard, 3/4", 4' x 8', wall	SF	.63	.96	1.59	.67	1.30	0.0107
06.1302 031	Insulation, fiberboard, 1", 2' x 8', roof	SF	1.05	1.39	2.44	.97	2.02	0.0156
06.1302 041	Insulation, fiberboard, 2", 2' x 8', roof	SF	1.33	1.68	3.01	1.17	2.50	0.0188
06.1303 000	**STRIPPING:**							
06.1303 011	Strip, 1" x 4"-6", machine nailed	MBF	1,306.73	3,959.59	5,266.32	2,755.67	4,062.40	44.3105
06.1303 021	Strip, 1" x 4"-6", soffit, machine nailed	MBF	1,306.73	4,941.15	6,247.88	3,438.79	4,745.52	55.2949
06.1304 000	**ADDERS & MISCELLANEOUS MATERIAL:**							
06.1304 011	Asphalt felt, 15#, walls	SF	.21	.36	.57	.25	.46	0.0040
06.1304 021	Backing for other trades	MBF	1,025.23	4,251.28	5,276.51	2,958.67	3,983.90	47.5747
06.1304 031	Beams, solid timbers, 6" and up	MBF	1,597.93	3,188.45	4,786.38	2,219.00	3,816.93	35.6810
06.1304 041	Sisalkraft flashing	SF	.21	.75	.96	.52	.73	0.0084
06.1304 051	Gypsum sheathing, 5/8"	SF	.47	1.42	1.89	.99	1.46	0.0159
06.1304 061	Headers, solid timbers, 4" & up	MBF	1,245.77	3,188.45	4,434.22	2,219.00	3,464.77	35.6810
06.1304 071	Ledgers/nailers, bolted, 2" x 6-8-10"	MBF	842.93	4,672.39	5,515.32	3,251.75	4,094.68	52.2873
06.1304 081	Post/mullion, solid timbers, to 16'	MBF	1,641.49	4,251.28	5,892.77	2,958.67	4,600.16	47.5747
06.1304 091	Ribbons and strong backs	MBF	845.51	3,589.57	4,435.08	2,498.16	3,343.67	40.1698
06.1304 101	Furring	MBF	1,267.44	3,573.51	4,840.95	2,486.98	3,754.42	39.9900
06.1304 111	Stripping	MBF	1,306.73	3,573.51	4,880.24	2,486.98	3,793.71	39.9900
06.1304 121	Grounds	MBF	845.51	4,570.76	5,416.27	3,181.02	4,026.53	51.1500
06.1304 131	Building paper	SF	.21	.25	.46	.17	.38	0.0028
06.1305 000	**ADDERS TO ROUGH FRAMING:**							
	Note: For backing and bracing add approximately 5% to total rough carpentry quantities and labor.							
	Attaching to metal frame, add 20% to the labor costs.							
06.1305 031	Add for bracing, miscellaneous	MBF	795.57	2,949.32	3,744.89	2,052.57	2,848.14	33.0049
06.1305 041	Add for framing, miscellaneous	MBF	795.57	2,949.32	3,744.89	2,052.57	2,848.14	33.0049
06.1400 000	**SHEATHING:**							
06.1401 000	**FLOOR SHEATHING:**							
06.1401 011	Floor sheathing, diagonal, 1" x 6"-8"	MBF	1,644.26	1,297.19	2,941.45	902.77	2,547.03	14.5164
06.1401 021	Floor sheathing, tongue & groove, 2" x 6"-8"	MBF	1,572.90	1,340.42	2,913.32	932.86	2,505.76	15.0002
06.1401 031	Floor sheathing, tongue & groove, 2" select Douglas fir	MBF	2,372.01	1,225.20	3,597.21	852.67	3,224.68	13.7108
06.1401 041	Deck, timber, 3"-4", laminated, tongue & groove	MBF	2,248.96	1,145.90	3,394.86	797.49	3,046.45	12.8234
06.1401 051	Deck, timber, 2" x 6", laminated, tongue & groove	MBF	1,955.82	1,474.44	3,430.26	1,026.14	2,981.96	16.5000
06.1401 061	Deck, composition board, (TREX) 2"x6", natural	LF	3.44	1.47	4.91	1.03	4.47	0.0165
06.1402 000	**WALL SHEATHING:**							
06.1402 011	Wall sheathing, diagonal, 1"	MBF	1,644.26	2,061.10	3,705.36	1,434.42	3,078.68	23.0651
06.1403 000	**ROOF SHEATHING:**							
06.1403 011	Roof sheathing, 1-1/8" plywood	MBF	1,770.20	1,340.42	3,110.62	932.86	2,703.06	15.0002
06.1404 000	**SHEATHING, FLOOR, PLYWOOD:**							
06.1404 011	Floor, 1/2", C-D exterior, hand nailed	MSF	1,047.26	864.42	1,911.68	601.59	1,648.85	9.6735
06.1404 021	Floor, 1/2", C-D exterior, machine nailed	MSF	1,047.26	734.76	1,782.02	511.36	1,558.62	8.2225
06.1404 031	Floor, 5/8", C-D exterior, hand nailed	MSF	1,213.40	913.66	2,127.06	635.86	1,849.26	10.2245
06.1404 041	Floor, 5/8", C-D exterior, machine nailed	MSF	1,213.40	776.61	1,990.01	540.48	1,753.88	8.6908
06.1404 051	Floor, 3/4", C-D exterior, hand nailed	MSF	1,485.01	997.99	2,483.00	694.55	2,179.56	11.1682
06.1404 061	Floor, 3/4", C-D exterior, machine nailed	MSF	1,485.01	848.29	2,333.30	590.37	2,075.38	9.4930
06.1404 071	Floor, 5/8", C-D exterior, tongue & groove, hand nailed	MSF	1,269.89	924.91	2,194.80	643.69	1,913.58	10.3504
06.1404 081	Floor, 5/8", C-D exterior, tongue & groove, machine nailed	MSF	1,269.89	786.17	2,056.06	547.14	1,817.03	8.7978
06.1404 091	Floor, 3/4", C-D exterior, tongue & groove, hand nailed	MSF	1,483.48	1,060.65	2,544.13	738.16	2,221.64	11.8694
06.1404 101	Floor, 3/4", C-D exterior, tongue & groove, machine nailed	MSF	1,483.48	901.55	2,385.03	627.43	2,110.91	10.0890
06.1404 111	Floor, 1-1/8", C-D exterior, tongue & groove, hand nailed	MSF	2,412.81	1,525.80	3,938.61	1,061.88	3,474.69	17.0748
06.1404 121	Floor, 1-1/8", C-D exterior, tongue & groove, machine nailed	MSF	2,412.81	1,435.92	3,848.73	999.32	3,412.13	16.0689
06.1404 131	Floor, 3/8", particle board underlay, hand nailed	MSF	766.68	864.42	1,631.10	601.59	1,368.27	9.6735
06.1404 141	Floor, 3/8", particle board underlay, machine nailed	MSF	766.68	734.76	1,501.44	511.36	1,278.04	8.2225

Division 6 CSI #	06 - CARPENTRY Description	Unit	Material	Union Install	Union Total	Open Install	Open Total	Unit Man-Hrs
06.1404 000	**SHEATHING, FLOOR, PLYWOOD: (Cont.)**							
06.1404 151	Floor, 1/2", particle board underlay, hand nailed	MSF	802.58	864.42	1,667.00	601.59	1,404.17	9.6735
06.1404 161	Floor, 1/2", particle board underlay, machine nailed	MSF	802.58	734.76	1,537.34	511.36	1,313.94	8.2225
06.1404 171	Floor, 3/4", particle board underlay, hand nailed	MSF	982.50	997.99	1,980.49	694.55	1,677.05	11.1682
06.1404 181	Floor, 3/4", particle board underlay, machine nailed	MSF	982.50	848.29	1,830.79	590.37	1,572.87	9.4930
06.1405 000	**SHEATHING, WALL, PLYWOOD:**							
	Note: Do not deduct for opening less than 6'8". For machine nailing, deduct 15% from the labor costs.							
06.1405 011	Wall, 5/16", C-D exterior, hand nailed	MSF	833.00	1,919.27	2,752.27	1,335.71	2,168.71	21.4779
06.1405 021	Wall, 3/8", C-D exterior, hand nailed	MSF	882.88	1,919.27	2,802.15	1,335.71	2,218.59	21.4779
06.1405 031	Wall, 1/2", C-D exterior, hand nailed	MSF	1,092.89	2,006.52	3,099.41	1,396.43	2,489.32	22.4543
06.1405 041	Wall, 5/8", C-D exterior, hand nailed	MSF	1,266.79	2,268.31	3,535.10	1,578.62	2,845.41	25.3839
06.1405 051	Wall, 3/4", C-D exterior, hand nailed	MSF	1,535.78	2,268.31	3,804.09	1,578.62	3,114.40	25.3839
06.1406 000	**SHEATHING, ROOF:**							
	Note: The following prices do not include stocking to roof.							
	For structural grade plywood . . . add 20% to material costs							
	For shear wall nailing . . . . add 20% to labor costs							
	For 9' sheets. . . . . add 15% to material costs							
	Allow 5% of material costs for waste.							
06.1406 011	Roof, 3/8", C-D exterior, hand nailed	MSF	882.88	1,203.98	2,086.86	837.91	1,720.79	13.4734
06.1406 021	Roof, 3/8", C-D exterior, machine nailed	MSF	882.88	963.18	1,846.06	670.33	1,553.21	10.7787
06.1406 031	Roof, 1/2", C-D exterior, hand nailed	MSF	1,092.89	1,221.41	2,314.30	850.04	1,942.93	13.6684
06.1406 041	Roof, 1/2", C-D exterior, machine nailed	MSF	1,092.89	977.12	2,070.01	680.03	1,772.92	10.9347
06.1406 051	Roof, 5/8", C-D exterior, hand nailed	MSF	1,266.79	1,352.24	2,619.03	941.09	2,207.88	15.1325
06.1406 061	Roof, 5/8", C-D exterior, machine nailed	MSF	1,266.79	1,134.15	2,400.94	789.31	2,056.10	12.6919
06.1406 071	Roof, 3/4", C-D exterior, hand nailed	MSF	1,535.78	1,413.36	2,949.14	983.63	2,519.41	15.8165
06.1406 081	Roof, 3/4", C-D exterior, machine nailed	MSF	1,535.78	1,195.15	2,730.93	831.77	2,367.55	13.3746
06.1406 091	Roof, 1-1/8", C-D exterior, machine nailed	MSF	2,028.32	1,525.73	3,554.05	1,061.83	3,090.15	17.0740
06.1500 000	**CARPENTRY SPECIALTIES:**							
	Note: The treatment for house on slab on grade includes drilling through footing to penetrate to							
	under-slab area and treating soil.							
06.1501 000	**WOOD TREATING:**							
06.1501 011	Fire proofing treatment	MBF	432.49		432.49		432.49	
06.1501 021	Fungus and termite treatment	MBF	364.09		364.09		364.09	
06.1501 031	Tent and fumigate existing house	MCF	125.70		125.70		125.70	
06.1501 041	Soil treatment around house	SF	.51		.51		.51	
06.1501 051	House on slab on grade (per running foot)	FT	12.58		12.58		12.58	
06.2000 000	**FINISH CARPENTRY:**							
	Note: The following percentages may be used to adjust pricing on this section to fit job requirements:							
	Residential by builder. . . . . deduct 15% from material							
	Residential by finish contractor . . . deduct 30% from material							
06.2001 000	**FACIA:**							
06.2001 011	Redwood facia, 2" x 3"-4", KD, clear heart	MBF	2,553.84	3,777.11	6,330.95	2,628.68	5,182.52	42.2685
06.2001 021	Redwood facia, 2" x 6"-8", KD, clear heart	MBF	2,638.60	3,777.11	6,415.71	2,628.68	5,267.28	42.2685
06.2001 031	Redwood facia, 2" x 10", KD, clear heart	MBF	2,829.48	3,777.11	6,606.59	2,628.68	5,458.16	42.2685
06.2001 041	Redwood facia, 2" x 12", KD, clear heart	MBF	3,233.63	3,777.11	7,010.74	2,628.68	5,862.31	42.2685
06.2001 051	Cedar facia, 2" x 4", KD, select	MBF	2,351.78	3,777.11	6,128.89	2,628.68	4,980.46	42.2685
06.2001 061	Cedar facia, 2" x 6", KD, select	MBF	2,419.13	3,777.11	6,196.24	2,628.68	5,047.81	42.2685
06.2001 071	Cedar facia, 2" x 8", KD, select	MBF	2,462.06	3,777.11	6,239.17	2,628.68	5,090.74	42.2685
06.2001 081	Cedar facia, 2" x 10", KD, select	MBF	2,480.37	3,777.11	6,257.48	2,628.68	5,109.05	42.2685
06.2001 091	Cedar facia, 2" x 12", KD, select	MBF	2,560.00	3,777.11	6,337.11	2,628.68	5,188.68	42.2685
06.2001 101	Douglas fir facia, 2", KD	MBF	2,431.39	3,777.11	6,208.50	2,628.68	5,060.07	42.2685
06.2002 000	**TRIM, VERTICAL & HORIZONTAL AVERAGE:**							
06.2002 011	Redwood trim, 1" x 4", clear heart	MBF	2,158.35	8,726.00	10,884.35	6,072.85	8,231.20	97.6500
06.2002 021	Redwood trim, 1" x 6", clear heart	MBF	2,248.00	6,108.20	8,356.20	4,251.00	6,499.00	68.3550
06.2002 031	Redwood trim, 1" x 8", clear heart	MBF	2,248.00	4,581.16	6,829.16	3,188.25	5,436.25	51.2663
06.2002 041	Redwood trim, 1" x 10", clear heart	MBF	2,486.10	4,581.16	7,067.26	3,188.25	5,674.35	51.2663
06.2002 051	Redwood trim, 1" x 12", clear heart	MBF	2,896.33	4,581.16	7,477.49	3,188.25	6,084.58	51.2663
06.2002 061	Redwood trim, 2", average	MBF	2,706.51	2,181.50	4,888.01	1,518.21	4,224.72	24.4125
06.2002 071	Redwood deck, 2 x 4, 2 x 6, construction heart	MSF	1,040.76	2,859.52	3,900.28	1,990.08	3,030.84	32.0000
06.2003 000	**SIDING, WOOD:**							
	Note: For green lumber, deduct 20% from the total costs.							
06.2003 011	Siding, redwood, bevel, rustic, 1", KD clear	MBF	3,509.51	2,948.88	6,458.39	2,052.27	5,561.78	33.0000

Division 6 CSI #	06 - CARPENTRY Description	Unit	Material	Union Install	Union Total	Open Install	Open Total	Unit Man-Hrs
06.2003 000	**SIDING, WOOD: (Cont.)**							
06.2003 021	Siding, cedar, bevel, rustic, 1", KD clear	MBF	1,889.79	2,859.52	4,749.31	1,990.08	3,879.87	32.0000
06.2003 031	Siding, redwood board & batten, rustic, KD clear	MBF	5,619.94	2,410.04	8,029.98	1,677.26	7,297.20	26.9700
06.2003 041	Siding, redwood tongue & groove, 1" x 6", KD clear	MBF	5,161.43	2,234.00	7,395.43	1,554.75	6,716.18	25.0000
06.2003 051	Add for mitred/pattern nailed	MBF		1,986.12	1,986.12	1,382.24	1,382.24	22.2261
06.2003 061	Add for resawn finish	MBF	122.05		122.05		122.05	
06.2004 000	**SIDING, PLYWOOD & MISCELLANEOUS:**							
	Note: The following prices are for premium grade siding.							
06.2004 011	Siding, redwood plywood, 3/8", plain, rough	MSF	2,342.48	2,685.59	5,028.07	1,869.03	4,211.51	30.0536
06.2004 021	Siding, redwood plywood, 3/8", planktex	MSF	2,342.48	2,685.59	5,028.07	1,869.03	4,211.51	30.0536
06.2004 031	Siding, redwood plywood, 3/8", prestain	MSF	2,424.48	2,685.59	5,110.07	1,869.03	4,293.51	30.0536
06.2004 041	Siding, redwood plywood, 5/8", T-1-11	MSF	2,594.15	2,758.70	5,352.85	1,919.91	4,514.06	30.8717
06.2004 051	Siding, cedar plywood, 5/8", T-1-11	MSF	2,233.05	2,758.70	4,991.75	1,919.91	4,152.96	30.8717
06.2004 061	Siding, redwood plywood, 5/8", board & batten shiplap	MSF	2,737.51	2,758.70	5,496.21	1,919.91	4,657.42	30.8717
06.2004 071	Siding, fir plywood, 3/8", rough sawn	MSF	1,411.30	2,685.59	4,096.89	1,869.03	3,280.33	30.0536
06.2004 081	Siding, fir plywood, 3/8" planktex	MSF	1,605.87	2,685.59	4,291.46	1,869.03	3,474.90	30.0536
06.2004 091	Siding, fir plywood, 5/8", board & batten, rough	MSF	1,687.48	2,685.59	4,373.07	1,869.03	3,556.51	30.0536
06.2004 101	Siding, fir plywood, 5/8", T-1-11, rough	MSF	1,687.48	2,685.59	4,373.07	1,869.03	3,556.51	30.0536
06.2004 111	Add for prefinish of plywood siding	MSF	294.98		294.98		294.98	
06.2004 121	Siding, hardboard, tempered & primed	MSF	1,370.24	3,185.99	4,556.23	2,217.28	3,587.52	35.6534
06.2004 131	Siding, cedar shingles, 7" exposed	SQ	261.14	562.24	823.38	391.29	652.43	6.2919
06.2004 141	Siding, cedar shingles, 3 ply-back	SQ	290.51	268.54	559.05	186.89	477.40	3.0051
06.2005 000	**SIDING, HARDBOARD:**							
06.2005 011	Siding, hardboard, 4' x 8', 1/8" tempered	SF	.69	3.22	3.91	2.24	2.93	0.0360
06.2005 021	Siding, hardboard, 4' x 8', 1/4" tempered	SF	.86	3.22	4.08	2.24	3.10	0.0360
06.2005 031	Siding, hardboard, 4' x 8', 3/8" tempered & prime coated	SF	1.31	3.22	4.53	2.24	3.55	0.0360
06.2006 000	**SIDING, GLASWELD PANELS, WOOD OR METAL STOPS:**							
06.2006 011	Siding, glasweld, 1/8", 1 side finished	SF	5.43	4.40	9.83	3.06	8.49	0.0492
06.2006 021	Siding, glasweld, 1/4", 2 side finished	SF	6.87	4.94	11.81	3.44	10.31	0.0553
06.2007 000	**MOLDING:**							
	Note: For horizontal molding, small forms, add 20% to the labor costs.							
06.2007 011	Base, 1-5/8", prefinished, hardwood	LF	1.65	2.20	3.85	1.53	3.18	0.0246
06.2007 021	Base, 2-1/4", softwood	LF	1.34	2.20	3.54	1.53	2.87	0.0246
06.2007 031	Base, 3-1/4", softwood	LF	1.55	2.20	3.75	1.53	3.08	0.0246
06.2007 041	Molding, chair rail	LF	1.43	3.42	4.85	2.38	3.81	0.0383
06.2007 051	Molding, cove, 3/4"	LF	.86	1.96	2.82	1.36	2.22	0.0219
06.2007 061	Molding, cove, 1-3/4"	LF	1.03	1.96	2.99	1.36	2.39	0.0219
06.2007 071	Molding, picture	LF	1.06	3.42	4.48	2.38	3.44	0.0383
06.2007 081	Molding, shoe	LF	.62	2.45	3.07	1.70	2.32	0.0274
06.2007 091	Molding, stucco	LF	.87	2.70	3.57	1.88	2.75	0.0302
06.2007 101	Molding, quarter round, 3/4"	LF	.76	2.08	2.84	1.45	2.21	0.0233
06.2008 000	**TRIM:**							
06.2008 011	Trim, apron, 1-3/8"	LF	.99	2.54	3.53	1.77	2.76	0.0284
06.2008 021	Trim, jamb, 2" pine with stop	LF	2.35	2.08	4.43	1.45	3.80	0.0233
06.2008 031	Trim, jamb, 4-5/8" pine	LF	3.49	8.91	12.40	6.20	9.69	0.0997
06.2008 041	Trim, oval casing, 2-1/4"	LF	1.34	3.57	4.91	2.48	3.82	0.0399
06.2008 051	Oval casing or streamline, 2-5/8"	LF	1.46	3.57	5.03	2.48	3.94	0.0399
06.2008 061	Trim, stool, 6" milled redwood	LF	9.98	4.75	14.73	3.31	13.29	0.0532
06.2008 071	Trim, stool, 4-1/2", flat pine	LF	1.58	4.75	6.33	3.31	4.89	0.0532
06.2008 081	Trim, stop, sash, 3/8" x 3/4"	LF	.64	2.54	3.18	1.77	2.41	0.0284
06.2008 091	Trim, stop, 1-3/8"	LF	.93	2.54	3.47	1.77	2.70	0.0284
06.2009 000	**MILLING CHARGES:**							
06.2009 011	Knife grinding, custom trim	SETUP	301.80		301.80		301.80	
06.2010 000	**FLOORING & SHELVING:**							
06.2010 011	Flooring, pine, 1" x 4"	MSF	1,940.87	1,815.59	3,756.46	1,263.56	3,204.43	20.3177
06.2010 021	Shelving, pine, 1" x 12", clear	LF	3.45	4.10	7.55	2.85	6.30	0.0459
06.2010 031	Hook strip, pine, 4-1/2", clear	LF	2.33	4.10	6.43	2.85	5.18	0.0459
06.2010 041	Shelving, particle board, 3/4 x 11-1/4	LF	1.49	4.10	5.59	2.85	4.34	0.0459

Division 6 CSI #	06 - CARPENTRY Description	Unit	Material	Union Install	Union Total	Open Install	Open Total	Unit Man-Hrs
06.2011 000	PANELING:							
	Note:							
	For book matched paneling . . . . . . add 40% to material costs							
	For top grade workmanship . . . . add 100% to labor costs							
	For 10' sheets . . . . add 30% to material costs							
06.2011 011	Panel, birch or ash, select	SF	1.85	4.11	5.96	2.86	4.71	0.0460
06.2011 021	Panel, birch or ash, economy	SF	1.20	3.77	4.97	2.62	3.82	0.0422
06.2011 031	Panel, mahogany, rotary cut, economy	SF	1.19	3.43	4.62	2.39	3.58	0.0384
06.2011 041	Panel, mahogany, ribbon cut, good	89	1.38	3.43	4.81	2.39	3.77	0.0384
06.2011 051	Panel, mahogany, Philippine, select	SF	1.34	3.43	4.77	2.39	3.73	0.0384
06.2011 061	Panel, mahogany, African, unfinished, good	SF	2.98	5.06	8.04	3.52	6.50	0.0566
06.2011 071	Panel, teak, unfinished, select	SF	2.53	5.06	7.59	3.52	6.05	0.0566
06.2011 081	Panel, teak, finished v plank, good	SF	4.24	5.14	9.38	3.58	7.82	0.0575
06.2011 091	Panel, walnut, finished, domestic	SF	4.03	4.80	8.83	3.34	7.37	0.0537
06.2011 101	Panel, walnut, finished, select	SF	6.56	5.14	11.70	3.58	10.14	0.0575
06.2011 111	Panel, hardboard, embossed/printed		1.13	3.74	4.87	2.61	3.74	0.0419
06.2011 121	Panel, hardboard, printed finish	SF	.86	3.74	4.60	2.61	3.47	0.0419
06.2011 131	Panel, Douglas fir, clear, vertical grain	SF	2.88	3.20	6.08	2.23	5.11	0.0358
06.2011 141	Panel, redwood, clear all heart	SF	2.96	.31	3.27	.22	3.18	0.0035
06.2101 000	CARPENTRY, INSTALLATION ONLY:							
06.2101 011	Cabinets, base, modular	LF		34.90	34.90	24.29	24.29	0.3906
06.2101 021	Cabinets, wall	LF		66.48	66.48	46.27	46.27	0.7440
06.2101 031	Cabinets, full height	LF		27.10	27.10	18.86	18.86	0.3033
06.2101 041	Doors, wood, pre-hung	EA		49.15	49.15	34.20	34.20	0.5500
06.2101 051	Doors, job hung, residential & commercial	EA		90.25	90.25	62.81	62.81	1.0100
06.2101 061	Doors, job hung, institutional	EA		94.98	94.98	66.10	66.10	1.0629
06.2101 071	Frames, wood, to 7' h & 6' w	EA		149.23	149.23	103.86	103.86	1.6700
06.2101 081	Hardware	DOOR		103.88	103.88	72.30	72.30	1.1625
06.2101 091	Sash	SF		3.32	3.32	2.31	2.31	0.0372
06.2101 101	Toilet accessories, average	EA		33.24	33.24	23.13	23.13	0.3720
06.2101 111	Frames, hollow metal, single	EA		72.72	72.72	50.61	50.61	0.8138
06.2101 121	Frames, hollow metal, pair	EA		96.29	96.29	67.02	67.02	1.0776
06.3000 000	GLU-LAM BEAMS, TRUSSES & HEAVY TIMBER:							
06.3001 000	GLU-LAMS, 7,000 BF OR MORE:							
	Note: For quantities under 7,000 bf, add 33% to total.							
06.3001 011	Glu-lams, industrial finish	MBF	2,166.55	557.87	2,724.42	388.25	2,554.80	6.2430
06.3001 021	Glu-lams, arch finish, wrapped	MBF	2,401.45	557.87	2,959.32	388.25	2,789.70	6.2430
06.3001 031	Glu-lam, arch, wrap, curved, 32' rad	MBF	4,449.14	603.34	5,052.48	419.89	4,869.03	6.7518
06.3001 041	Glu-lam, arch, Tudor, 10', 31' rad	MBF	5,869.84	804.45	6,674.29	559.86	6,429.70	9.0024
06.3001 051	Add for minor camber	EA	84.81		84.81		84.81	
06.3001 061	Add for delivery (min 40m#)	MILE	3.13		3.13		3.13	
06.3001 071	Add for delivery, 60' (min 40m#)	MILE	9.54		9.54		9.54	
06.3001 081	Add for steel connect, shoes, bolts	#	2.32		2.32		2.32	
06.3002 000	BOWSTRING TRUSSES:							
06.3002 011	Bowstring trusses, under 3,000 BF	MBF	2,109.25	1,005.57	3,114.82	699.82	2,809.07	11.2530
06.3002 021	Bowstring trusses, over 3,000 BF	MBF	2,109.25	887.32	2,996.57	617.53	2,726.78	9.9297
06.3003 000	TRUSSES, RESIDENTIAL, & HEAVY TIMBER:							
06.3003 011	Residential trusses, quantity	LF	4.31	1.93	6.24	1.34	5.65	0.0216
06.3003 021	Residential trusses, single house	LF	4.81	1.94	6.75	1.35	6.16	0.0217
06.3003 031	Heavy timber trusses	MBF	2,149.42	2,011.14	4,160.56	1,399.65	3,549.07	22.5060
06.3004 000	TRUSS JOISTS, IN PLACE:							
	Note:							
	Quantities under 2,000 LF . . . . add 50% to total cost							
	Between 2,000 and 3,000 LF . . . . . . add 20% to total cost							
06.3004 011	Truss joist, simple, over 3,000 lf	LF	7.01	4.76	11.77	3.31	10.32	0.0533
06.3004 021	Truss joist, compound, over 3000 lf	LF	10.12	6.79	16.91	4.73	14.85	0.0760
06.3004 031	Truss hardware, shoes, etc	#	5.40	89.36	94.76	62.19	67.59	1.0000
06.3005 000	HEAVY TIMBERS, MILLED & LAMS:							
06.3005 011	6" lumber & larger	MBF	2,467.99	900.20	3,368.19	626.50	3,094.49	10.0739
06.3005 021	2" & larger, mill constructed	MBF	1,460.27	1,173.09	2,633.36	816.41	2,276.68	13.1277
06.3005 031	2" laminates, mill constructed	MBF	1,537.29	2,079.12	3,616.41	1,446.96	2,984.25	23.2668

Division 6 CSI #	06 - CARPENTRY Description	Unit	Material	Union Install	Union Total	Open Install	Open Total	Unit Man-Hrs
06.5000 000	**STAIRS, WOOD:**							
	Note: For metal rails see section 05.5004000.							
06.5001 000	**STAIRS, CIRCULAR, 36" WIDE RISER:**							
	Note: Add for rail.							
06.5001 011	Stair, circular, hardwood, closed riser, mill	RISER	434.94	321.12	756.06	223.49	658.43	3.5936
06.5001 021	Stairs, circular, hardwood, open riser, mill	RISER	387.65	321.12	708.77	223.49	611.14	3.5936
06.5001 031	Stairs, semi-circular, 36" riser, job	RISER	144.79	106.98	251.77	74.45	219.24	1.1972
06.5002 000	**STAIRS, STRAIGHT & SWITCHBACK:**							
06.5002 011	Stair, straight, 36" riser, hardwood	RISER	113.11	106.98	220.09	74.45	187.56	1.1972
06.5002 021	Stair, switchback, 36" riser, hardwood	RISER	122.39	128.55	250.94	89.47	211.86	1.4386
06.5002 031	Stair, fourway, 36" riser, hardwood	RISER	161.37	160.63	322.00	111.79	273.16	1.7976
06.5003 000	**STAIR LANDINGS:**							
06.5003 011	Stair landings, finished hardwood	SF	20.85	26.83	47.68	18.68	39.53	0.3003
06.5004 000	**STAIR RAILINGS, HARDWARE NOT INCLUDED:**							
06.5004 011	Hand rail, fir, 1-5/8" x 1-3/4", wall	LF	1.86	16.47	18.33	11.46	13.32	0.1843
06.5004 021	Hand rail, fir, 1-5/8" x 2-5/8", wall	LF	2.42	16.47	18.89	11.46	13.88	0.1843
06.5004 031	Hand rail, custom, hardwood, straight	LF	26.97	26.83	53.80	18.68	45.65	0.3003
06.5004 041	Hand rail, custom, hardwood, curve	LF	120.32	53.67	173.99	37.35	157.67	0.6006
06.6000 000	**ROUGH HARDWARE:**							
	Note: Allow $60.00 Per 1,000 board feet of lumber for general construction.							
06.6001 000	**FRAMING HARDWARE:**							
06.6001 011	Joist hanger, 2" x 4", nails	EA	1.19	3.17	4.36	2.21	3.40	0.0355
06.6001 021	Joist hanger, 2" x 6"-8", nails	EA	1.47	3.93	5.40	2.74	4.21	0.0440
06.6001 031	Joist hanger, 2" x 12", nails	EA	1.81	4.49	6.30	3.12	4.93	0.0502
06.6001 041	Joist hanger, 4" x 10"-12"	EA	4.26	4.82	9.08	3.35	7.61	0.0539
06.6001 051	Joist hanger, 4" x 14"-16"	EA	4.57	5.92	10.49	4.12	8.69	0.0662
06.6001 061	Joist hanger, 6" x 10"-14", heavy duty	EA	14.58	5.92	20.50	4.12	18.70	0.0662
06.6001 071	Post anchor, 4" x 4"-6"	EA	7.38	6.45	13.83	4.49	11.87	0.0722
06.6001 081	Post cap, 16 ga, galvanized, 4" x 4"	EA	7.04	6.45	13.49	4.49	11.53	0.0722
06.6001 091	Post base	EA	7.58	7.77	15.35	5.40	12.98	0.0869
06.6001 101	Post base & cap combination	EA	14.35	4.82	19.17	3.35	17.70	0.0539
06.6001 111	Framing clips	EA	2.49	3.61	6.10	2.51	5.00	0.0404
06.6001 121	Ply clips, 1/2", 5/8", 3/4", aluminum	EA	.22	.88	1.10	.61	.83	0.0098
06.6001 131	Tie straps, 2-3/8" x 12", 20 ga	EA	2.33	18.17	20.50	12.64	14.97	0.2033
06.6001 141	Tie straps, 2-3/8" x 23", 16 ga	EA	3.98	18.17	22.15	12.64	16.62	0.2033
06.6001 151	Strap anchor, 3" x 33", 1/4" plate	EA	22.84	23.74	46.58	16.52	39.36	0.2657
06.6001 161	Strap anchor, 3" x 45", 1/4" plate	EA	33.84	24.30	58.14	16.91	50.75	0.2719
06.6001 171	Brace, 12 ga galvanized, 2" x 8'	EA	30.14	7.12	37.26	4.96	35.10	0.0797
06.6001 181	Brace, 12 ga galvanized, 1-1/4' x 12'	EA	35.16	7.12	42.28	4.96	40.12	0.0797
06.6001 191	Bridge, metal, 2" x 8", 12" OC	EA	.92	1.75	2.67	1.22	2.14	0.0196
06.6001 201	Bridge, metal, 2" x 8", 16" OC	EA	1.01	1.75	2.76	1.22	2.23	0.0196
06.6001 211	Bridge, metal, 2" x 8", 24" OC	EA	1.24	1.75	2.99	1.22	2.46	0.0196
06.6001 221	Bridge, metal, 2" x 16", 12" OC	EA	1.01	1.75	2.76	1.22	2.23	0.0196
06.6001 231	Bridge, metal, 2" x 16", 16" OC	EA	1.01	1.75	2.76	1.22	2.23	0.0196
06.6001 241	Bridge, metal, 2" x 16", 24" OC	EA	1.24	1.75	2.99	1.22	2.46	0.0196
06.6001 251	Hanger, stainless steel, 2" x 4"	EA	6.37	4.71	11.08	3.28	9.65	0.0527
06.6001 261	Hanger, stainless steel, 2" x 8"	EA	9.18	4.82	14.00	3.35	12.53	0.0539
06.6001 271	Hanger, stainless steel, 2"x14"	EA	18.85	5.36	24.21	3.73	22.58	0.0600
06.6001 281	Hanger, stainless steel, 4" x 4"	EA	7.74	4.82	12.56	3.35	11.09	0.0539
06.6001 291	Hanger, stainless steel, 4" x 8"	EA	13.04	5.36	18.40	3.73	16.77	0.0600
06.6001 301	Hanger, stainless steel, 4" x 16"	EA	27.02	6.24	33.26	4.34	31.36	0.0698
06.6001 311	Metal bridging, 16" OC	SET	1.54		1.54		1.54	
06.6001 321	Joist hanger, 4" x 4"	EA	3.03		3.03		3.03	
06.6001 331	Joist hanger, 4" x 16"	EA	8.05		8.05		8.05	
06.6002 000	**NAILS:**							
06.6002 011	Nails, common, average	100#	136.03		136.03		136.03	
06.6002 021	Nails, galvanized, average	100#	232.66		232.66		232.66	
06.6002 031	Nails, aluminum, average	100#	996.56		996.56		996.56	
06.6002 041	Nails, copper, average	100#	906.42		906.42		906.42	
06.6002 051	Nails, stainless steel, average	100#	1,142.66		1,142.66		1,142.66	
06.6002 061	Nails, add for cement coating	100#	13.94		13.94		13.94	
06.6002 071	Nails, add for zinc plating	100#	25.58		25.58		25.58	

Division 6 CSI #	06 - CARPENTRY Description	Unit	Material	Union Install	Union Total	Open Install	Open Total	Unit Man-Hrs
06.6003 000	**TIMBER CONNECTORS:**							
06.6003 011	Split rings, 2-5/8"	EA	2.60	5.35	7.95	3.73	6.33	0.0599
06.6003 021	Split rings, 4"	EA	3.73	5.84	9.57	4.07	7.80	0.0654
06.6003 031	Toothed rings, 2-5/8"	EA	1.13	4.45	5.58	3.10	4.23	0.0498
06.6003 041	Toothed rings, 4"	EA	1.24	4.86	6.10	3.38	4.62	0.0544
06.6003 051	Shear plates, 2-5/8"	EA	3.12	7.08	10.20	4.93	8.05	0.0792
06.6003 061	Shear plates, 4"	EA	6.81	8.97	15.78	6.24	13.05	0.1004
06.6003 071	Glu-lam beam seats, 5-1/4" x 1-1/2"	EA	30.68	38.98	69.66	27.13	57.81	0.4362
06.6003 081	Glu-lam beam seats, 6-3/4" x 1-3/4"	EA	34.81	44.23	79.04	30.78	65.59	0.4950
06.6003 091	Glu-lam beam seats, 8-3/4" x 1-3/4"	EA	48.00	49.49	97.49	34.44	82.44	0.5538
06.6003 101	Laminated hangers with nails, 3-1/8 x 13-1/2	EA	42.35	53.87	96.22	37.49	79.84	0.6028
06.6003 111	Laminated hangers with nails, 5-1/8 x 13-1/2	EA	45.53	59.12	104.65	41.14	86.67	0.6616
06.6003 121	Laminated hangers with nails, 6-3/4 x 13-1/2	EA	47.97	64.37	112.34	44.80	92.77	0.7204
06.6003 131	Laminated hangers with nails, 8-3/4 x 13-1/2	EA	52.08	69.63	121.71	48.46	100.54	0.7792
06.6003 141	Laminated saddle hangers, 3-1/8 x 13-1/2	EA	73.87	93.93	167.80	65.37	139.24	1.0511
06.6003 151	Laminated saddle hangers, 5-1/8 x 13-1/2	EA	98.66	99.18	197.84	69.02	167.68	1.1099
06.6003 161	Laminated saddle hangers, 6-3/4 x 13-1/2	EA	141.31	104.44	245.75	72.68	213.99	1.1687
06.6003 171	Laminated saddle hangers, 8-3/4 x 13-1/2	EA	156.01	109.69	265.70	76.34	232.35	1.2275
06.6003 181	Hinge connectors, 5-1/8" x 13"	EA	98.19	124.83	223.02	86.87	185.06	1.3969
06.6003 191	Hinge connectors, 6-3/4" x 13"	EA	196.76	130.08	326.84	90.53	287.29	1.4557
06.6003 201	Hinge connectors, 8-3/4" x 13"	EA	234.09	135.34	369.43	94.19	328.28	1.5145
06.6004 000	**BOLTS:**							
06.6004 011	Foundation bolts, 8" x 1/2" dia	EA	1.39	6.24	7.63	4.34	5.73	0.0698
06.6004 021	Foundation bolts, 8" x 5/8" dia	EA	2.77	6.24	9.01	4.34	7.11	0.0698
06.6004 031	Foundation bolts, 10" x 3/4" dia	EA	4.20	6.24	10.44	4.34	8.54	0.0698
06.6004 041	Foundation bolts, 10" x 1/2" dia	EA	1.45	6.24	7.69	4.34	5.79	0.0698
06.6004 051	Stud bolts, 4" x 1/2" dia	EA	2.09	8.40	10.49	5.85	7.94	0.0940
06.6004 061	Stud bolts, 8" x 3/4" dia	EA	4.49	10.62	15.11	7.39	11.88	0.1188
06.6004 071	Ledger bolts, 8" x 5/8" dia	EA	2.46	6.67	9.13	4.64	7.10	0.0746

Division 7 CSI #	07 - THERMAL & MOISTURE PROTECTION Description	Unit	Material	Union Install	Union Total	Open Install	Open Total	Unit Man-Hrs
07.0000 000	**THERMAL & MOISTURE PROTECTION:**							
07.1000 000	**WATERPROOFING:**							
	Note: For the following section, add 50% for small areas, such as small decks.							
07.1001 000	**WATERPROOFING, HOT COATINGS, VERTICAL SURFACES:**							
07.1001 011	Bitumals, walls, per coat	SF	.05	1.03	1.08	.83	.88	0.0130
07.1001 021	Hot mop, 15# felt, 1 ply	SF	.11	1.03	1.14	.83	.94	0.0130
07.1001 031	Hot mop, 15# felt, 2 ply	SF	.25	1.45	1.70	1.17	1.42	0.0183
07.1001 041	Hot mop, 15# felt, 3 ply	SF	.38	1.96	2.34	1.59	1.97	0.0248
07.1001 051	Hot mop, 30# felt, 1 ply	SF	.20	1.03	1.23	.83	1.03	0.0130
07.1001 061	Hot mop, 30# felt, 2 ply	SF	.33	1.45	1.78	1.17	1.50	0.0183
07.1001 071	Hot mop, 30# felt, 3 ply	SF	.43	1.96	2.39	1.59	2.02	0.0248
07.1001 081	Hot mop, glass fiber, 1 ply	SF	.11	1.03	1.14	.83	.94	0.0130
07.1001 091	Hot mop, glass fiber, 2 ply	SF	.27	1.45	1.72	1.17	1.44	0.0183
07.1001 101	Hot mop, glass fiber, 3 ply	SF	.41	1.96	2.37	1.59	2.00	0.0248
07.1001 111	Add for 1/2" asphalt fiberboard	SF	.35	.57	.92	.46	.81	0.0072
07.1002 000	**WATERPROOFING, COLD APPLICATION, VERTICALS:**							
07.1002 011	Waterproof, 1/32" butyl	SF	.75	1.79	2.54	1.45	2.20	0.0226
07.1002 021	Waterproof, 1/16" butyl	SF	1.10	1.79	2.89	1.45	2.55	0.0226
07.1002 031	Elastomeric membrane, 60 mil butyl, wall	SF	.96	.43	1.39	.35	1.31	0.0054
07.1002 051	Add for butyl with nylon	SF	.23	.40	.63	.32	.55	0.0050
07.1002 061	Waterproof, 1/32" neoprene	SF	.75	1.79	2.54	1.45	2.20	0.0226
07.1002 071	Waterproof, 1/16" neoprene	SF	1.13	1.79	2.92	1.45	2.58	0.0226
07.1002 081	Add for neoprene, nylon, extra coat	SF	.23	.40	.63	.32	.55	0.0050
07.1002 101	Waterproof, Kraft paper	SF	.01	.26	.27	.21	.22	0.0033
07.1002 111	Elastomeric polyurethane, 60 mil, horizontal	SF	1.33	1.79	3.12	1.45	2.78	0.0226
07.1002 121	Elastomeric polyurethane, 60 mil, vertical	SF	1.40	2.37	3.77	1.92	3.32	0.0300
07.1002 141	Waterproof, 60 mil Bituthene membrane	SF	1.13	1.79	2.92	1.45	2.58	0.0226
07.1003 000	**WATERPROOFING, EMULSION, VERTICAL SURFACES:**							
07.1003 011	Waterproof, asphalt mastic, 1/16"	SF	.11	.94	1.05	.76	.87	0.0119
07.1003 021	Waterproof, asphalt mastic, 1/8"	SF	.31	1.11	1.42	.90	1.21	0.0140
07.1003 031	Waterproof, asphalt paint, brush/coat	SF	.11	.43	.54	.35	.46	0.0054
07.1003 041	Waterproof, asphalt paint, spray/coat	SF	.11	.17	.28	.14	.25	0.0022
07.1003 051	Waterproof, silicone, spray/coat	SF	.11	.17	.28	.14	.25	0.0022
07.1003 061	Waterproof, silicone, spray, 2 coat	SF	.26	.43	.69	.35	.61	0.0054
07.1003 071	Add for each extra coat, silicone	SF	.06	.21	.27	.17	.23	0.0027
07.1003 081	Add for 1/2" fiberboard protection	SF	.31	.51	.82	.42	.73	0.0065
07.1004 000	**WATERPROOFING, SPECIALTIES, VERTICAL SURFACES:**							
07.1004 011	Waterproof, bentonite panels, 3/16"	SF	1.51	1.14	2.65	.92	2.43	0.0144
07.1004 021	Waterproof, bentonite panels, 3/16", coated	SF	1.80	1.14	2.94	.92	2.72	0.0144
07.1004 031	Waterproof, bentonite panel, 9/16"	SF	1.93	1.14	3.07	.92	2.85	0.0144
07.1004 051	Waterproof, bentonite, 3/8"	SF	2.61	1.26	3.87	1.02	3.63	0.0159
07.1004 061	Waterproof, interior, cement pargeting, 1/2", 2 coat	SF	.35	1.76	2.11	1.43	1.78	0.0223
07.1004 071	Waterproof, exterior, cement pargeting, 1/2", 2 coat	SF	.49	1.76	2.25	1.43	1.92	0.0223
07.1004 081	Waterproof, ironite, bushhammer preparation	SF	.11	1.70	1.81	1.38	1.49	0.0215
07.1004 091	Waterproof, ironite, 2 coats	SF	.77	2.92	3.69	2.37	3.14	0.0369
07.1004 101	Waterproof, ironite, 4 coats	SF	1.09	4.45	5.54	3.61	4.70	0.0563
07.1004 111	Waterproof, ironite, 6 coats	SF	2.19	5.58	7.77	4.53	6.72	0.0706
07.1004 121	Polymeric waterproof membrane, 1/16", vertical	SF	1.60	1.79	3.39	1.45	3.05	0.0226
07.1005 000	**WATERPROOFING, HOT COATINGS, HORIZONTAL SURFACE:**							
07.1005 011	Hot mop, deck, 15# felt, 2 ply	SF	.20	.95	1.15	.77	.97	0.0120
07.1005 021	Hot mop, deck, 15# felt, 3 ply	SF	.26	1.32	1.58	1.07	1.33	0.0167
07.1005 031	Hot mop, deck, 30# felt, 2 ply	SF	.26	.95	1.21	.77	1.03	0.0120
07.1005 041	Hot mop, deck, 30# felt, 3 ply	SF	.32	1.32	1.64	1.07	1.39	0.0167
07.1005 051	Add for fiberglass fabric	SF	.25		.25		.25	
07.1006 000	**WATERPROOFING, COLD APPLICATION, HORIZONTAL SURFACES:**							
07.1006 011	Waterproof, deck, 1/32" butyl	SF	.73	.43	1.16	.35	1.08	0.0054
07.1006 021	Waterproof, deck, 1/16" butyl	SF	.99	.43	1.42	.35	1.34	0.0054
07.1006 031	Add for butyl with nylon	SF	.25		.25		.25	
07.1006 041	Elastomeric membrane, 60 mil butyl, floor	SF	.98	.43	1.41	.35	1.33	0.0054
07.1006 051	Waterproof, deck, 1/32" neoprene	SF	1.42	.60	2.02	.49	1.91	0.0076
07.1006 061	Waterproof, deck, 1/16" neoprene	SF	.88	5.21	6.09	4.23	5.11	0.0660
07.1006 071	Add for neoprene with nylon	SF	.26		.26		.26	

Division 7 CSI #	07 - THERMAL & MOISTURE PROTECTION Description	Unit	Material	Union Install	Union Total	Open Install	Open Total	Unit Man-Hrs
07.1006 000	**WATERPROOFING, COLD APPLICATION, HORIZONTAL SURFACES: (Cont.)**							
07.1006 081	Waterproof, shower pans	SF	1.08	1.79	2.87	1.45	2.53	0.0226
07.1008 000	**WATERPROOFING, EMULSION, HORIZONTAL SURFACES:**							
07.1008 011	Waterproof, deck, asphalt mastic, 1/16"	SF	.05	.94	.99	.76	.81	0.0119
07.1008 021	Waterproof, deck, asphalt mastic, 1/8"	SF	.10	.94	1.04	.76	.86	0.0119
07.1008 031	Polyethylene asphalt, 60 mil, sheet, waterproof	SF	1.24	1.79	3.03	1.45	2.69	0.0226
07.1009 000	**WATERPROOFING, SPECIALTY, HORIZONTAL SURFACES:**							
07.1009 011	Waterproof, deck, Dex-o-tex, non-wear	SF	1.05	8.69	9.74	7.06	8.11	0.1100
07.1009 021	Waterproof, deck, Dex-o-tex, walk on	SF	2.60	7.11	9.71	5.77	8.37	0.0900
07.1009 041	Polyurethane traffic deck coat	SF	1.73	1.74	3.47	1.41	3.14	0.0220
07.1009 051	Siloxane sealer ultra violet protection	SF	.33	.23	.56	.19	.52	0.0029
07.1009 061	Siloxane sealer, economy, floor/wall	SF	.19	.13	.32	.11	.30	0.0017
07.1009 071	Siloxane sealer, best, floor/wall	SF	.38	.24	.62	.20	.58	0.0031
07.1009 081	Siloxane, anti graffiti/fungus	SF	.32	.21	.53	.17	.49	0.0027
07.1009 091	Polymeric waterproof membrane, 1/16", horizontal	SF	1.35	1.79	3.14	1.45	2.80	0.0226
07.1009 101	Waterproof, 60 mil bituthene membrane	SF	1.26	1.82	3.08	1.48	2.74	0.0230
07.2000 000	**THERMAL & SOUND INSULATION:**							
	Note: For prefab construction see section 13.0000. For insulating concrete, see section 3.5100.							
	For the following items,							
	Double prices for areas under 100 square feet;							
	Double prices for existing ceiling (attic);							
	Triple prices for existing wall or for flat ceiling (blown).							
	For overhead space . . . . add 10% to the total cost							
	For tight enclosed space . . . . add 15% to the total cost							
	For one hour fire rating . . . . .add 15% to the total cost							
07.2001 000	**INSULATION BOARD, DECKS:**							
07.2001 011	Insulation board deck, 1", rigid mineral fiber	SF	.70	.26	.96	.21	.91	0.0033
07.2001 021	Insulation board deck, 1-1/2", rigid mineral fiber	SF	1.00	.34	1.34	.28	1.28	0.0043
07.2001 031	Insulation board deck, 2", rigid mineral fiber	SF	1.35	.34	1.69	.28	1.63	0.0043
07.2001 041	Insulation board deck, 6", rigid mineral fiber	SF	4.15	.62	4.77	.50	4.65	0.0078
07.2001 051	Insulation board deck, 1-1/2", rigid fiberglass	SF	1.75	.36	2.11	.30	2.05	0.0046
07.2001 061	Insulation board deck, 2", rigid fiberglass	SF	2.32	.34	2.66	.28	2.60	0.0043
07.2001 071	Insulation board deck, 3", rigid fiberglass	SF	3.06	.36	3.42	.30	3.36	0.0046
07.2001 081	Insulation board deck, 2", rigid firtex, 32" OC	SF	1.71	.43	2.14	.35	2.06	0.0054
07.2001 091	Insulation board deck, 2", rigid tectum, painted	SF	3.06	.68	3.74	.55	3.61	0.0086
07.2001 101	Insulation board deck, 2-1/2", rigid tectum, painted	SF	3.56	.77	4.33	.62	4.18	0.0097
07.2001 111	Insulation board deck, 1-1/4", rigid urethane, R9	SF	1.75	.30	2.05	.24	1.99	0.0038
07.2001 121	Insulation board deck, 1-1/2", rigid urethane, R11	SF	2.25	.36	2.61	.30	2.55	0.0046
07.2001 131	Insulation board deck, 2", rigid urethane, R14	SF	2.89	.43	3.32	.35	3.24	0.0055
07.2001 141	Insulation board deck, 1", rigid urethane, R7	SF	1.28	.24	1.52	.19	1.47	0.0030
07.2001 151	Insulation board deck, 1-1/2", rigid urethane, R11	SF	2.01	.33	2.34	.27	2.28	0.0042
07.2001 161	Insulation board deck, 2", rigid urethane, R14	SF	2.25	.43	2.68	.35	2.60	0.0055
07.2001 171	Insulation board deck, 2-1/2", rigid urethane, R19	SF	2.88	.57	3.45	.46	3.34	0.0072
07.2001 181	Insulation board deck, 3", rigid urethane, R25	SF	3.79	.63	4.42	.51	4.30	0.0080
07.2001 191	Insulation board deck, 1-1/2" rigid Styrofoam	SF	1.71	.36	2.07	.30	2.01	0.0046
07.2001 201	Insulation board deck, 2" rigid Styrofoam	SF	2.18	.40	2.58	.33	2.51	0.0051
07.2001 211	Insulation board deck, 3" rigid Styrofoam	SF	3.30	.43	3.73	.35	3.65	0.0055
07.2002 000	**INSULATION, FIBERGLASS & MINERAL, BLOWN:**							
07.2002 011	Insulation, blown mineral, 4", R11	SF	.13	.20	.33	.15	.28	0.0022
07.2002 021	Insulation, blown mineral, 6", R17	SF	.19	.30	.49	.22	.41	0.0033
07.2002 031	Insulation, blown fiberglass, 4", R13	SF	.13	.20	.33	.15	.28	0.0022
07.2002 041	Insulation, blown fiberglass, 6", R19	SF	.19	.30	.49	.22	.41	0.0033
07.2002 051	Insulation, blown fiberglass, 9", R24	SF	.29	.39	.68	.29	.58	0.0043
07.2003 000	**INSULATION, PELLETIZED, LOOSE:**							
07.2003 011	Insulation, expanded glass beads, 4"	SF	.14	.30	.44	.22	.36	0.0033
07.2003 021	Insulation, expanded glass beads, 6"	SF	.19	.39	.58	.29	.48	0.0043
07.2003 031	Insulation, expanded shale beads, 4"	SF	.15	.30	.45	.22	.37	0.0033
07.2003 041	Insulation, expanded shale beads, 6"	SF	.19	.39	.58	.29	.48	0.0043
07.2003 051	Insulation, vermiculite beads, 4"	SF	.43	.31	.74	.23	.66	0.0033
07.2003 061	Insulation, vermiculite beads, 6"	SF	.63	.41	1.04	.30	.93	0.0043
07.2003 071	Insulation, polystyrene beads, 4"	SF	.46	.31	.77	.23	.69	0.0033
07.2003 081	Insulation, polystyrene beads, 6"	SF	.73	.41	1.14	.30	1.03	0.0043

Division 7 CSI #	07 - THERMAL & MOISTURE PROTECTION Description	Unit	Material	Union Install	Union Total	Open Install	Open Total	Unit Man-Hrs
07.2004 000	**INSULATION, BATT, WALL & CEILING:**							
07.2004 011	Batts, 2-1/2", mineral fiber, R7	SF	.24	.39	.63	.28	.52	0.0041
07.2004 021	Batts, 3", mineral fiber, R11	SF	.32	.39	.71	.28	.60	0.0041
07.2004 031	Batts, 3-1/2", mineral fiber, R13	SF	.34	.39	.73	.28	.62	0.0041
07.2004 041	Batts, 3-1/2", fiberglass, R13	SF	.41	.39	.80	.28	.69	0.0041
07.2004 051	Batts, 6", fiberglass, R19	SF	.51	.39	.90	.28	.79	0.0041
07.2004 061	Add for supporting batts on wire	SF	.01	.20	.21	.15	.16	0.0021
07.2004 071	Batts, 8-9" fiberglass, R30	SF	.44	.80	1.24	.58	1.02	0.0084
07.2004 081	Insulation blown fiber 11"	SF	.33	.54	.87	.39	.72	0.0057
07.2005 000	**INSULATION, FOAM OR SPRAYED:**							
07.2005 011	Insulation, urethane foam, 1", R7	SF	.71	1.02	1.73	.75	1.46	0.0108
07.2005 021	Insulation, urethane foam, 1-1/3", R9	SF	.79	1.13	1.92	.82	1.61	0.0119
07.2005 031	Insulation, urethane foam, 1-1/2", R11	SF	.92	1.13	2.05	.82	1.74	0.0119
07.2005 041	Insulation, urethane foam, 1 3/4", R13	SF	1.03	1.33	2.36	.97	2.00	0.0140
07.2005 051	Insulation, urethane foam, 2", R14	SF	1.14	1.53	2.67	1.11	2.25	0.0161
07.2005 061	Insulation, urethane foam, 2-1/4", R17	SF	1.26	1.53	2.79	1.11	2.37	0.0161
07.2005 071	Insulation, urethane foam, 2 3/4", R20	SF	1.49	1.73	3.22	1.27	2.76	0.0183
07.2005 081	Insulation, urethane foam, 3", R21	SF	1.59	1.93	3.52	1.41	3.00	0.0204
07.2005 091	Insulation, urethane foam, 3-1/4", R24	SF	1.87	1.93	3.80	1.41	3.28	0.0204
07.2005 101	Insulation, urethane foam, 4", R29	SF	2.16	2.51	4.67	1.83	3.99	0.0265
07.2006 000	**INSULATION, RIGID FIBERGLASS:**							
07.2006 011	Insulation, wall, rigid fiberglass, 1-1/2"	SF	.91	.44	1.35	.32	1.23	0.0046
07.2006 021	Insulation, wall, rigid fiberglass, 2"	SF	1.17	.44	1.61	.32	1.49	0.0046
07.2006 031	Insulation, wall, rigid fiberglass, 2-1/2"	SF	1.48	.44	1.92	.32	1.80	0.0046
07.2006 041	Insulation, wall, rigid fiberglass, 3"	SF	1.83	.44	2.27	.32	2.15	0.0046
07.2006 051	Insulation, wall, rigid fiberglass, 4"	SF	2.16	.44	2.60	.32	2.48	0.0046
07.2007 000	**INSULATION, RIGID STYROFOAM:**							
07.2007 011	Insulation, rigid Styrofoam, 1"	SF	.74	.44	1.18	.32	1.06	0.0046
07.2007 021	Insulation, rigid Styrofoam, 1-1/2"	SF	1.10	.44	1.54	.32	1.42	0.0046
07.2007 031	Insulation, rigid Styrofoam, 2"	SF	1.42	.44	1.86	.32	1.74	0.0046
07.2008 000	**INSULATION CORES:**							
07.2008 011	Vermiculite or Perlite, 4"	SF	.21	.21	.42	.15	.36	0.0022
07.2008 021	Vermiculite or Perlite, 6"	SF	.36	.27	.63	.20	.56	0.0029
07.2008 031	Vermiculite or Perlite, 8"	SF	.52	.35	.87	.26	.78	0.0037
07.2008 041	Vermiculite or Perlite, 10"	SF	.71	.42	1.13	.30	1.01	0.0044
07.2009 000	**ACOUSTIC INSULATION:**							
07.2009 011	Insulation, sound board, 1/2", vertical	SF	.22	.72	.94	.53	.75	0.0076
07.2009 021	Insulation, sound board, 1/2", horizontal	SF	.22	.62	.84	.45	.67	0.0065
07.2009 031	Insulation, acoustic board, 2", horizontal	SF	1.60	1.73	3.33	1.27	2.87	0.0183
07.2009 041	Insulation, cork, 1/2", horizontal	SF	.70	1.13	1.83	.82	1.52	0.0119
07.2009 051	Insulation, noise barrier, batt, 2-1/2"	SF	.45	.41	.86	.30	.75	0.0043
07.2009 061	Insulation, noise barrier, batt, 3-1/2"	SF	.48	.41	.89	.30	.78	0.0043
07.2010 000	**INSULATION, REFRIGERATION:**							
07.2010 011	Insulation, refrigeration, polystyrene, 2"	SF	.74	.77	1.51	.62	1.36	0.0097
07.2010 021	Insulation, refrigeration, polystyrene, 3 5/8"	SF	1.31	1.27	2.58	1.03	2.34	0.0161
07.2010 031	Insulation, refrigeration, polyurethane, 2"	SF	1.59	1.27	2.86	1.03	2.62	0.0161
07.2010 041	Insulation, refrigeration, polyurethane, 3 5/8"	SF	2.62	1.45	4.07	1.17	3.79	0.0183
07.2010 051	Insulation, refrigeration, cork, 1"	SF	1.19	.94	2.13	.76	1.95	0.0119
07.2010 061	Insulation, refrigeration, cork, 2"	SF	1.94	1.11	3.05	.90	2.84	0.0140
07.2010 071	Insulation, refrigeration, cork, 3"	SF	2.71	1.45	4.16	1.17	3.88	0.0183
07.2500 000	**FIREPROOFING, SPRAYED:**							
07.2500 011	Fireproofing, columns, 1-3/8", no finish	SYCA	11.21	22.80	34.01	14.81	26.02	0.2793
07.2500 021	Fireproofing metal deck, 1/2"	SYCA	8.25	14.61	22.86	9.49	17.74	0.1790
07.2500 031	Fireproofing beams & girders, 3/4"-1"	SYCA	10.20	17.90	28.10	11.62	21.82	0.2192
07.2500 041	Fireproofing, Monokote, per ton steel	TON	126.90	196.34	323.24	127.51	254.41	2.4049
07.2500 051	Fireproofing, Monokote, per SF building	SF	.80	1.49	2.29	.96	1.76	0.0182
07.3000 000	**ROOFING:**							
07.3001 000	**SHINGLES:**							
07.3001 011	Shingles, composition asphalt, 240#	SQ	76.39	87.95	164.34	71.42	147.81	1.1131
07.3001 021	Shingles, composition asphalt, 240#, 'A'	SQ	98.41	92.37	190.78	75.01	173.42	1.1691
07.3001 031	Shingles, composition asphalt, 300#	SQ	108.72	92.37	201.09	75.01	183.73	1.1691
07.3001 041	Shingles, composition asphalt, 325#, 'A'	SQ	124.28	92.37	216.65	75.01	199.29	1.1691

Division 7 CSI #	07 - THERMAL & MOISTURE PROTECTION Description	Unit	Material	Union Install	Union Total	Open Install	Open Total	Unit Man-Hrs
07.3001 000	**SHINGLES: (Cont.)**							
07.3001 051	Shingles, composition asphalt, president	SQ	169.10	84.54	253.64	68.65	237.75	1.0700
07.3001 061	Shingles, valley roll	LF	.52	1.37	1.89	1.11	1.63	0.0173
07.3001 071	Shingles, aluminum tabs, 020"	SF	3.02	2.74	5.76	2.23	5.25	0.0347
07.3001 081	Shingles, aluminum tabs, 030"	SF	3.51	2.74	6.25	2.23	5.74	0.0347
07.3001 091	Shingles, porcelain enamel, 18 ga	SQ	388.61	298.71	687.32	242.56	631.17	3.7806
07.3001 101	Shingles, fiberglass tabs, 300#	SQ	113.97	113.94	227.91	83.22	197.19	1.2028
07.3002 000	**TILE, CLAY:**							
07.3002 011	Tile, clay, Spanish, 2 piece	SQ	373.47	609.51	982.98	494.95	868.42	7.7143
07.3002 021	Tile, clay, flat red	SQ	158.81	339.49	498.30	275.68	434.49	4.2968
07.3002 031	Tile, clay, glazed, interlock	SQ	258.95	368.59	627.54	299.31	558.26	4.6651
07.3002 041	Tile, clay, Spanish	SQ	224.46	334.65	559.11	271.76	496.22	4.2356
07.3002 051	Add for 'riness system', galvanized iron	SQ	32.50	74.43	106.93	60.44	92.94	0.9420
07.3002 061	Add for 'tile-tie system', copper	SQ	48.81	74.43	123.24	60.44	109.25	0.9420
07.3002 091	Fire vent, skylight, 4'8" x 9'6"	EA	1,326.91	513.00	1,839.91	304.43	1,631.34	6.5217
07.3003 000	**TILE, CONCRETE:**							
07.3003 011	Tile, concrete, premium	SQ	325.10	361.88	686.98	293.87	618.97	4.5802
07.3003 021	Tile, concrete, flat	SQ	218.10	310.75	528.85	252.34	470.44	3.9330
07.3003 031	Tile, concrete, interlock	SQ	199.89	285.83	485.72	232.11	432.00	3.6177
07.3004 000	**STONE:**							
07.3004 011	Slate	SQ	619.96	233.44	853.40	189.56	809.52	2.9545
07.3005 000	**SHINGLES & SHAKES, WOOD, 30# FELT:**							
07.3005 011	Shingles, wood, 5" exposed, roof, premium	SQ	240.69	119.41	360.10	96.97	337.66	1.5113
07.3005 021	Shingles, wood, 5" exposed, roof, fireproof, premium	SQ	301.97	119.41	421.38	96.97	398.94	1.5113
07.3005 031	Shingles, roof, shakertown, panel	SQ	371.28	55.18	426.46	44.81	416.09	0.6984
07.3005 041	Shakes, wood, 1/2" butt, roof	SQ	188.75	102.35	291.10	83.11	271.86	1.2954
07.3005 051	Shakes, wood, 3/4" butt, roof	SQ	211.19	102.35	313.54	83.11	294.30	1.2954
07.3005 061	Shakes, wood, medium, B grade	SQ	214.55	139.06	353.61	112.92	327.47	1.7600
07.3005 071	Shakes, wood, heavy, C grade	SQ	262.20	152.49	414.69	123.83	386.03	1.9300
07.3005 081	Felt, 30#	SQ	19.70	3.29	22.99	2.68	22.38	0.0417
07.3006 000	**BUILT/UP ROOFING:**							
	Note: For chopped up work or multiple levels, add 100% to total costs.							
07.3006 011	Built-up, 3 ply, low rise	SQ	134.57	89.64	224.21	72.79	207.36	1.1345
07.3006 021	Built-up, 3 ply, high rise	SQ	134.57	201.67	336.24	163.77	298.34	2.5525
07.3006 031	Built-up, 4 ply, low rise	SQ	156.27	97.77	254.04	79.40	235.67	1.2375
07.3006 041	Built-up, 4 ply, high rise	SQ	156.27	220.00	376.27	178.65	334.92	2.7844
07.3006 051	Built-up, 5 ply, 20 year, low rise	SQ	183.79	111.32	295.11	90.40	274.19	1.4089
07.3006 061	Built-up, 5 ply, 20 year, high rise	SQ	183.79	250.46	434.25	203.39	387.18	3.1700
07.3006 071	Add for light rock dress off	SQ	9.23	5.59	14.82	4.54	13.77	0.0708
07.3006 081	Add for heavy rock dress off	SQ	10.41	5.59	16.00	4.54	14.95	0.0708
07.3006 091	Add for coal tar pitch roof	SQ	199.91	99.20	299.11	80.55	280.46	1.2555
07.3006 101	Add for aluminizing	SQ	31.68	6.03	37.71	4.90	36.58	0.0763
07.3006 111	Cap sheet, 90#, parapet walls	SQ	77.61	135.83	213.44	110.30	187.91	1.7191
07.3007 000	**PLASTIC ROOFING:**							
	Note: For the acrylic roof items listed below, prices are based on installation over existing roof, assuming acrylic polyester flashing. Allow 70% for elongation. Average tensile strength of fabric is 100 pounds per inch, 1914 psi minimum (Metacrylics).							
07.3007 011	Roof, elastomeric membrane, 1/16"	SQ	222.83	287.91	510.74	233.80	456.63	3.6440
07.3007 021	Roof, elastomeric membrane, 1/32"	SQ	198.15	287.91	486.06	233.80	431.95	3.6440
07.3007 031	Roof, elastomeric, loose, trocal	SQ	211.70	102.28	313.98	83.06	294.76	1.2945
07.3007 041	Roof, neoprene (gaco-auto guard)	SF	3.19	4.92	8.11	4.00	7.19	0.0623
07.3007 051	Roof, bituthene, 1/16", selfseal	SQ	208.03	287.91	495.94	233.80	441.83	3.6440
07.3007 061	Roof, silicone, 3 ply, rolled	SQ	282.41	353.03	635.44	286.68	569.09	4.4682
07.3007 071	Urethane foam, silicone cover, 1" thick	SQ	533.62	150.12	683.74	121.90	655.52	1.9000
07.3007 081	Roof, acrylic, existing cap sheet	SQ	251.51	66.36	317.87	53.89	305.40	0.8399
07.3007 091	Roof, acrylic, existing gravel	SQ	251.51	132.74	384.25	107.79	359.30	1.6800
07.3007 101	Roof, acrylic, existing deck	SQ	257.46	65.81	323.27	53.44	310.90	0.8329
07.3007 111	Roof, acrylic, existing corrugated metal	SQ	251.51	60.33	311.84	48.99	300.50	0.7636
07.3007 121	Roof, acrylic, new	SQ	251.51	132.74	384.25	107.79	359.30	1.6800
07.3008 000	**CORRUGATED ROOFING:**							
07.3008 011	Roof, corrugated aluminum, 020"	SF	1.42	2.17	3.59	1.76	3.18	0.0275
07.3008 021	Roof, corrugated aluminum, 032"	SF	2.37	2.52	4.89	2.05	4.42	0.0319

Division 7 CSI #	07 - THERMAL & MOISTURE PROTECTION Description	Unit	Material	Union Install	Union Total	Open Install	Open Total	Unit Man-Hrs
07.3008 000	**CORRUGATED ROOFING: (Cont.)**							
07.3008 031	Roof, corrugated composition, 3/16", non-walk	SF	2.07	2.95	5.02	2.39	4.46	0.0373
07.3008 041	Roof, corrugated composition, 3/8"	SF	2.50	3.26	5.76	2.65	5.15	0.0413
07.3008 051	Roof, corrugated fiberglass, 8 oz	SF	3.45	2.95	6.40	2.39	5.84	0.0373
07.3008 061	Roof, corrugated galvanized iron, 26 ga	SF	2.45	3.26	5.71	2.65	5.10	0.0413
07.3009 000	**CORRUGATED SIDING:**							
07.3009 011	Siding, corrugated aluminum, 032"	SF	3.50	3.26	6.76	2.65	6.15	0.0413
07.3009 021	Siding, corrugated aluminum, 032", painted	SF	4.19	3.26	7.45	2.65	6.84	0.0413
07.3009 031	Siding, aluminum, simulated wood, insulated	SF	3.91	3.26	7.17	2.65	6.56	0.0413
07.3009 041	Siding, corrugated composition, 3/8"	SF	2.72	4.36	7.08	3.54	6.26	0.0552
07.3009 051	Siding, corrugated fiberglass, 8 oz	SF	3.13	3.26	6.39	2.65	5.78	0.0413
07.3009 061	Siding, zip-rib, 032", over 100,000 SF	SF	3.50	2.17	5.67	1.76	5.26	0.0275
07.3009 071	Siding, zip-rib, 032", under 100,000 SF	SF	4.71	2.52	7.23	2.05	6.76	0.0319
07.3009 081	Siding, zip-rib, 032", under 15,000, painted	SF	5.16	4.03	9.19	3.27	8.43	0.0510
07.3009 091	Siding, corrugated galvanized iron, 26 ga	SF	2.45	3.59	6.04	2.92	5.37	0.0455
07.3010 000	**ROOF, COPPER CLAD STAINLESS STEEL:**							
07.3010 011	Roof, copper clad stainless steel, 16 oz panels	SF	9.28	5.95	15.23	4.83	14.11	0.0753
07.3010 021	Roof, copper clad stainless steel, 24 oz panels	SF	13.50	7.37	20.87	5.99	19.49	0.0933
07.3011 000	**ROOF, COPPER, STANDING SEAM:**							
07.3011 011	Roof, 16 oz copper, 16" panels	SF	8.25	5.95	14.20	4.83	13.08	0.0753
07.3012 000	**ROOFING, SHEET METAL, CUSTOM FABRICATED:**							
07.3012 011	Roof, fabricated, aluminum, .032", .456#/SF	SF	3.26	3.41	6.67	2.77	6.03	0.0432
07.3012 021	Roof, fabricated, 16 oz copper, .020", 1.0#/SF	SF	12.08	7.51	19.59	6.10	18.18	0.0951
07.3012 031	Roof, fabricated, .015" copper clad stainless steel, .787#/SF	SF	5.65	3.75	9.40	3.05	8.70	0.0475
07.3012 041	Roof, .020" lead coated copper, 1.25#/SF	SF	8.44	5.07	13.51	4.12	12.56	0.0642
07.3012 051	Roof, galvanized sheet metal, .026", .906#/SF	SF	2.43	3.48	5.91	2.83	5.26	0.0441
07.3012 061	Roof, fabricated, stainless steel, .018", .787#/SF	SF	4.62	4.84	9.46	3.93	8.55	0.0612
07.3012 071	Roof, fabricated, terne, .018", .787#/SF	SF	3.16	4.91	8.07	3.98	7.14	0.0621
07.3012 081	Roof, titanaloy, .027", 1.025#/SF	SF	3.48	3.77	7.25	3.06	6.54	0.0477
07.3012 091	Roof, fabricated, stainless steel, copper coated galvanized sheet metal	SF	4.72	4.73	9.45	3.84	8.56	0.0599
07.3013 000	**ROOFING SPECIALTIES:**							
07.3013 011	Cant strip, 3" fiber	LF	.41	1.44	1.85	1.17	1.58	0.0182
07.3013 021	Cant strip, 4" fiber, wood	LF	.51	1.44	1.95	1.17	1.68	0.0182
07.3013 031	Bonds, roof, 15 year	SQ	5.65		5.65		5.65	
07.3013 041	Bonds, roof, 20 year	SQ	6.85		6.85		6.85	
07.3100 000	**COMPOSITE BUILDING PANELS:**							
	Note: For storefront systems, see section 08.9000.							
07.3101 000	**ALUMINUM E-Z WALL SYSTEM:**							
07.3101 011	Aluminum E-Z wall, 1,000-4,000 SF	SF	11.62	9.41	21.03	7.64	19.26	0.1191
07.3101 021	Aluminum E-Z wall, 4,000-10,000 SF	SF	11.04	9.05	20.09	7.35	18.39	0.1145
07.3101 031	Aluminum E-Z wall, over 10,000 SF	SF	9.81	8.15	17.96	6.62	16.43	0.1032
07.3102 000	**COPPER VENEER PANELS:**							
	Note: For the following three sections, the standard panel size is 2' x 8'. Prices are based on 10,000 square feet or more and include all joint members.							
07.3102 011	Copper veneer panel, laminated, 3/8" ply	SF	24.42	5.29	29.71	4.29	28.71	0.0669
07.3102 021	Copper veneer panel, laminated, 3/4" ply	SF	35.44	5.29	40.73	4.29	39.73	0.0669
07.3103 000	**STRUCTURAL PANELS, HONEYCOMB CORE:**							
07.3103 011	Structural panel, 1", copper, paper core	SF	35.72	5.91	41.63	4.80	40.52	0.0748
07.3103 021	Structural panel, 2", copper, paper core	SF	37.66	5.91	43.57	4.80	42.46	0.0748
07.3103 031	Structural panel, 3", copper, paper core	SF	39.52	6.36	45.88	5.16	44.68	0.0805
07.3104 000	**INSULATED PANELS, FOAM CORE:**							
07.3104 011	Insulated panel, 1", copper, foam core	SF	37.66	5.91	43.57	4.80	42.46	0.0748
07.3104 021	Insulated panel, 2", copper, foam core	SF	39.52	5.91	45.43	4.80	44.32	0.0748
07.3104 031	Insulated panel, 3", copper, foam core	SF	41.56	6.36	47.92	5.16	46.72	0.0805
07.3105 000	**PANELS, COMPOSITION, EXPOSED AGGREGATE FACE:**							
	Note: The following panels are prefab units, made in fullwall, window and door components, 60' wide to 25' high.							
07.3105 011	Veneer panel, granowall, 1/4"	SF	4.36	4.20	8.56	3.41	7.77	0.0532
07.3105 021	Insulated panel, granowall, 1", color 1 side	SF	6.28	4.61	10.89	3.75	10.03	0.0584
07.3105 031	Structural wall unit, granostrut	SF	10.12	5.34	15.46	4.34	14.46	0.0676
07.3105 041	Projected facia, granostrut	SF	7.85	4.77	12.62	3.88	11.73	0.0604
07.3105 051	Facia/soffit assembly, granostrut	SF	7.71	5.34	13.05	4.34	12.05	0.0676

Division 7 CSI #	07 - THERMAL & MOISTURE PROTECTION Description	Unit	Material	Union Install	Union Total	Open Install	Open Total	Unit Man-Hrs
07.3200 000	**STONE PANELS, MANUFACTURED:**							
	Note: The following prices are based on 10,000 square feet or more. Panels are 24' wide to 20' high,							
	with a sandblasted finish.							
	Quantities under 10,000 SF . . . . . . add 15% to the total costs							
	For Smooth finish . . . . add 30% to the total costs							
07.3201 000	**FACESPAN PANELS, TO 15':**							
07.3201 011	Facespan panel, flat, 3/4"	SF	10.71	6.87	17.58	5.58	16.29	0.0870
07.3201 021	Facespan panel, rib one, 1"	SF	11.91	7.68	19.59	6.24	18.15	0.0972
07.3201 031	Facespan panel, rib 2-4, 1-1/2"	SF	15.28	7.68	22.96	6.24	21.52	0.0972
07.3201 041	Facespan panel, rib 5, 2 3/4"	SF	16.56	9.62	26.18	7.81	24.37	0.1218
07.3202 000	**CORSPAN WALL PANELS, TO 20':**							
07.3202 011	Corspan panel, striated, 1-1/2"	SF	14.85	6.72	21.57	5.45	20.30	0.0850
07.3202 021	Corspan panel, flat/recessed, 3"	SF	17.39	7.28	24.67	5.91	23.30	0.0921
07.3202 031	Corspan panel, rib 1, 3-1/4"	SF	20.70	7.28	27.98	5.91	26.61	0.0921
07.3202 041	Corspan panel, rib 2, 3-3/4"	SF	23.24	7.68	30.92	6.24	29.48	0.0972
07.3202 051	Corspan panel, rib 6, 2-1/2"	SF	21.58	6.87	28.45	5.58	27.16	0.0870
07.3203 000	**COMPOSITE BUILDING PANELS:**							
07.3203 011	Colorlith panel, 1/4"	SF	8.73	4.20	12.93	3.41	12.14	0.0532
07.3203 021	Colorlith panel, 5/8"	SF	13.24	6.87	20.11	5.58	18.82	0.0870
07.3203 031	Stonehenge panel	SF	13.37	6.87	20.24	5.58	18.95	0.0870
07.3203 041	Splitwood panel, natural	SF	7.79	3.89	11.68	3.16	10.95	0.0492
07.3203 051	Splitwood panel, factory coated	SF	9.07	3.89	12.96	3.16	12.23	0.0492
07.3203 061	Santone panel, 1/4"	SF	7.48	3.89	11.37	3.16	10.64	0.0492
07.3203 071	Kleftstone panel, 5/8"	SF	12.35	6.87	19.22	5.58	17.93	0.0870
07.3300 000	**MINERAL FIBER PANELS, CURTAIN WALLS:**							
	Note: The following items are laminated and pressed panels, sizes are 4' wide and from 4' to 10' high.							
07.3301 000	**GLASWELD PANELS:**							
07.3301 011	Glasweld panel, one face, 1/4"	SF	11.22	9.80	21.02	7.96	19.18	0.1240
07.3301 021	Glasweld panel, two face, 1/4"	SF	14.88	9.80	24.68	7.96	22.84	0.1240
07.3301 031	Glasweld panel, one face, 1", insulated	SF	15.52	11.76	27.28	9.55	25.07	0.1488
07.3301 041	Glasweld panel, two face, 1", insulated	SF	17.45	11.76	29.21	9.55	27.00	0.1488
07.3302 000	**PERMASTONE PANELS:**							
07.3302 011	Permastone panel, 1/8", color 1 side	SF	4.70	4.20	8.90	3.41	8.11	0.0532
07.3302 021	Permastone panel, 1/4", color 1 side	SF	7.47	4.20	11.67	3.41	10.88	0.0532
07.3302 031	Permastone panel, 1", insulated, color 1 side	SF	8.28	4.61	12.89	3.75	12.03	0.0584
07.3302 041	Permastone panel, 1/4", color 2 side	SF	9.20	4.20	13.40	3.41	12.61	0.0532
07.3302 051	Permastone panel, trim, aluminum, 1/8"/1/4"	SF	2.03	1.54	3.57	1.25	3.28	0.0195
07.3303 000	**SCULPTURED PANELS:**							
07.3303 011	Relief panel, facade, 2-1/2"	SF	12.89	8.08	20.97	6.56	19.45	0.1023
07.3303 021	Panel, qasal, 1/4"	SF	8.51	4.77	13.28	3.88	12.39	0.0604
07.3303 031	Panel, qasal, 1/2"	SF	10.21	4.77	14.98	3.88	14.09	0.0604
07.3303 041	Panel, qasal, 19/32"	SF	12.71	5.34	18.05	4.34	17.05	0.0676
07.3304 000	**PRE-CAST AGGREGATE CO-POLYMER PANELS:**							
07.3304 011	Panel, co-polymer, aggregate face, 1"	SF	16.21	8.08	24.29	6.56	22.77	0.1023
07.3305 000	**PORCELAIN METAL PANELS:**							
07.3305 011	Porcelain on steel, 1-1/2" insulated panel	SF	22.81	5.34	28.15	4.34	27.15	0.0676
07.3305 021	Porcelain on steel, 1/2" panel	SF	15.32	4.77	20.09	3.88	19.20	0.0604
07.3305 031	Porcelain on aluminum, 1-1/2" insulated panel	SF	24.23	5.34	29.57	4.34	28.57	0.0676
07.3305 041	Porcelain on aluminum, 1" panel	SF	21.49	4.77	26.26	3.88	25.37	0.0604
07.4000 000	**EXTERIOR INSULATION FINISH SYSTEM (EIFS):**							
07.4100 011	EIFS, Expanded polystyrene insulation, 1"	SF	2.90	10.61	13.51	6.89	9.79	0.1300
07.4100 021	EIFS, Expanded polystyrene insulation, 2"	SF	3.23	11.43	14.66	7.42	10.65	0.1400
07.4100 031	EIFS, Expanded polystyrene insulation, 3"	SF	3.55	11.84	15.39	7.69	11.24	0.1450
07.4100 041	EIFS, Expanded polystyrene insulation, 4"	SF	3.88	12.25	16.13	7.95	11.83	0.1500
07.4100 071	EIFS, Expanded polystyrene insulation, 1", on 3.4# metal lath	SF	3.29	19.35	22.64	12.57	15.86	0.2370
07.4100 081	EIFS, Expanded polystyrene insulation, 2", on 3.4# metal lath	SF	3.64	20.17	23.81	13.10	16.74	0.2470
07.4100 091	EIFS, Expanded polystyrene insulation, 3", on 3.4# metal lath	SF	3.97	20.57	24.54	13.36	17.33	0.2520
07.4100 101	EIFS, Expanded polystyrene insulation, 4", on 3.4# metal lath	SF	4.32	20.98	25.30	13.63	17.95	0.2570
07.6000 000	**SHEET METAL & FABRICATED SKYLIGHTS:**							
	Note: For the following section, you may deduct 25% from the total cost for residential tracts.							
07.6001 000	**COPING & WALL CAPS, ALL 16" GIRTH:**							
07.6001 011	Coping, galvanized sheet metal, 26 ga	LF	2.96	4.04	7.00	2.40	5.36	0.0514

88

Division 7 CSI #	07 - THERMAL & MOISTURE PROTECTION Description	Unit	Material	Union Install	Union Total	Open Install	Open Total	Unit Man-Hrs
07.6001 000	**COPING & WALL CAPS, ALL 16" GIRTH: (Cont.)**							
07.6001 021	Coping, aluminum, .032 ga	LF	2.21	4.04	6.25	2.40	4.61	0.0514
07.6001 031	Coping, copper, 16 oz	LF	7.40	4.18	11.58	2.48	9.88	0.0532
07.6001 041	Coping, copper clad stainless steel, .015 ga	LF	7.40	4.32	11.72	2.56	9.96	0.0549
07.6002 000	**GUTTERS:**							
07.6002 011	Gutter, galvanized iron facia, 5"	LF	1.56	4.04	5.60	2.40	3.96	0.0514
07.6002 021	Gutter, aluminum facia, 5"	LF	1.06	4.04	5.10	2.40	3.46	0.0514
07.6002 031	Gutter, copper facia, 5"	LF	7.60	4.18	11.78	2.48	10.08	0.0532
07.6002 041	Gutter, galvanized iron, 4" offset gutter, standard	LF	1.43	4.04	5.47	2.40	3.83	0.0514
07.6002 051	Gutter, aluminum, 4" offset gutter, standard	LF	1.12	4.04	5.16	2.40	3.52	0.0514
07.6002 061	Gutter, aluminum, 5" offset gutter, standard	LF	1.79	4.04	5.83	2.40	4.19	0.0514
07.6002 071	Gutter, copper, 4" offset gutter, standard	LF	7.70	4.18	11.88	2.48	10.18	0.0532
07.6002 081	Gutter, galvanized iron, 6" box, shop fabricated	LF	2.31	5.47	7.78	3.25	5.56	0.0696
07.6002 091	Gutter, copper, 6" box, shop fabricated	LF	10.01	5.47	15.48	3.25	13.26	0.0696
07.6003 000	**DOWNSPOUTS:**							
07.6003 011	Downspout, galvanized iron, 2" x 3", standard	LF	1.58	2.54	4.12	1.51	3.09	0.0323
07.6003 021	Downspout, aluminum, 2" x 3", standard	LF	1.19	2.54	3.73	1.51	2.70	0.0323
07.6003 031	Downspout, copper, 2"x3", standard	LF	6.02	2.54	8.56	1.51	7.53	0.0323
07.6003 041	Downspout, copper clad stainless steel, 2" x 3", standard	LF	6.02	3.08	9.10	1.83	7.85	0.0392
07.6003 051	Downspout, galvanized iron, 3" x 4", fabricated	LF	2.20	3.49	5.69	2.07	4.27	0.0444
07.6003 061	Downspout, aluminum, 3" x 4", fabricated	LF	1.63	3.49	5.12	2.07	3.70	0.0444
07.6003 071	Downspout, copper, 3" x 4", fabricated	LF	8.45	3.70	12.15	2.19	10.64	0.0470
07.6003 081	Downspout, copper clad stainless steel, 3" x 4", fabricated	LF	8.45	4.11	12.56	2.44	10.89	0.0522
07.6003 091	Downspout, galvanized iron, 2", round	LF	.87	2.54	3.41	1.51	2.38	0.0323
07.6003 101	Downspout, galvanized iron, 3" round	LF	1.10	2.54	3.64	1.51	2.61	0.0323
07.6003 111	Downspout, galvanized iron, 6" round	LF	5.34	5.47	10.81	3.25	8.59	0.0696
07.6003 121	Add for over 2 stories	LF		1.45	1.45	.86	.86	0.0184
07.6004 000	**GRAVEL STOP:**							
07.6004 011	Gravel stop, galvanized iron, 4"	LF	.60	1.10	1.70	.65	1.25	0.0140
07.6004 021	Gravel stop, aluminum, 4"	LF	.82	1.10	1.92	.65	1.47	0.0140
07.6004 031	Gravel stop, copper, 4"	LF	2.09	1.17	3.26	.70	2.79	0.0149
07.6004 041	Gravel stop, copper clad stainless steel, 4"	LF	2.09	1.23	3.32	.73	2.82	0.0157
07.6004 051	Gravel stop, facia, galvanized iron, 10"	LF	1.84	3.49	5.33	2.07	3.91	0.0444
07.6004 061	Gravel stop, facia, aluminum, 10"	LF	2.57	3.49	6.06	2.07	4.64	0.0444
07.6004 071	Gravel stop, facia, copper, 10"	LF	4.83	3.77	8.60	2.24	7.07	0.0479
07.6004 081	Gravel stop, facia, copper clad stainless steel, 10"	LF	4.83	4.18	9.01	2.48	7.31	0.0532
07.6005 000	**FLASHINGS:**							
07.6005 011	Flashing, galvanized iron, 6", 26 ga	LF	.82	2.12	2.94	1.26	2.08	0.0270
07.6005 021	Flashing, galvanized iron, 12", 26 ga	LF	1.22	2.33	3.55	1.38	2.60	0.0296
07.6005 031	Flashing, galvanized iron, 18", 26 ga	LF	1.64	2.54	4.18	1.51	3.15	0.0323
07.6005 041	Flashing, aluminum, 6", .024"	LF	1.01	2.12	3.13	1.26	2.27	0.0270
07.6005 051	Flashing, aluminum, 12", .024"	LF	1.43	2.33	3.76	1.38	2.81	0.0296
07.6005 061	Flashing, aluminum, 18", .024"	LF	1.84	2.54	4.38	1.51	3.35	0.0323
07.6005 071	Flashing, copper, 6", 16 oz	LF	2.85	2.12	4.97	1.26	4.11	0.0270
07.6005 081	Flashing, copper, 12", 16 oz	LF	4.34	2.33	6.67	1.38	5.72	0.0296
07.6005 091	Flashing, copper, 18", 16 oz	LF	5.78	2.54	8.32	1.51	7.29	0.0323
07.6005 101	Flashing, copper clad stainless steel, 6", .015"	LF	2.85	2.12	4.97	1.26	4.11	0.0270
07.6005 111	Flashing, copper clad stainless steel, 12", .015"	LF	4.34	2.33	6.67	1.38	5.72	0.0296
07.6005 121	Flashing, 18" wide	LF	5.78	2.54	8.32	1.51	7.29	0.0323
07.6005 131	Flashing, lead, 12", 12#/SF	LF	2.85	2.82	5.67	1.67	4.52	0.0358
07.6005 141	Flashing, lead, 12", 25#/SF	LF	5.52	3.49	9.01	2.07	7.59	0.0444
07.6006 000	**ROOF FLASHING MISCELLANEOUS:**							
07.6006 011	Roof flashing, galvanized iron, 26 ga	SF	1.64	3.43	5.07	2.04	3.68	0.0436
07.6006 021	Roof flashing, aluminum, .032"	SF	1.84	3.43	5.27	2.04	3.88	0.0436
07.6006 031	Roof flashing, copper, 16 oz	SF	5.80	3.43	9.23	2.04	7.84	0.0436
07.6006 041	Roof flashing, copper clad stainless steel, .015"	SF	4.40	3.43	7.83	2.04	6.44	0.0436
07.6006 051	Roof flashing, terne, 26 ga	SF	1.73	3.43	5.16	2.04	3.77	0.0436
07.6006 061	Roof flashing, lead, 25#/SF	SF	3.19	7.66	10.85	4.55	7.74	0.0974
07.6006 071	Roof flashing, fabric/copper, 5 oz	SF	1.31	1.51	2.82	.90	2.21	0.0192
07.6006 081	Roof flashing, fabric/aluminum, .005"	SF	.74	1.51	2.25	.90	1.64	0.0192
07.6006 091	Roof flashing, mastic/copper, 5 oz	SF	1.26	1.23	2.49	.73	1.99	0.0157
07.6006 101	Roof flashing, mastic/aluminum, .005"	SF	.60	1.23	1.83	.73	1.33	0.0157

Division 7 CSI #	07 - THERMAL & MOISTURE PROTECTION Description	Unit	Material	Union Install	Union Total	Open Install	Open Total	Unit Man-Hrs
07.6006 000	**ROOF FLASHING MISCELLANEOUS: (Cont.)**							
07.6006 111	Flash, 7 oz lead coated copper, fabric backing	SF	1.49	1.37	2.86	.81	2.30	0.0174
07.6006 121	Sheet metal, fabricated, 26 ga galvanized iron	SF	1.19	5.54	6.73	3.29	4.48	0.0704
07.6006 131	Sheet metal, fabricated, .032 aluminum	SF	2.04	5.54	7.58	3.29	5.33	0.0704
07.6006 141	Sheet metal, fabricated, 16 oz copper	SF	4.15	5.83	9.98	3.46	7.61	0.0741
07.6006 151	Sheet metal, fabricated, 12# lead	SF	2.82	5.54	8.36	3.29	6.11	0.0704
07.6006 161	Sheet metal, fabricated, .015 stainless steel	SF	5.70	7.00	12.70	4.15	9.85	0.0890
07.6007 000	**REGLETS:**							
07.6007 011	Reglets, galvanized iron, 26 ga	LF	.88	2.12	3.00	1.26	2.14	0.0270
07.6007 021	Reglets, aluminum, .032"	LF	1.10	2.12	3.22	1.26	2.36	0.0270
07.6007 031	Reglets, copper, 16 oz	LF	2.76	2.12	4.88	1.26	4.02	0.0270
07.6007 041	Reglets, copper clad stainless steel, .015"	LF	3.11	2.12	5.23	1.26	4.37	0.0270
07.6007 051	Reglets, PVC	LF	1.01	2.12	3.13	1.26	2.27	0.0270
07.6007 061	Add for neoprene gasket	LF	.54	.69	1.23	.41	.95	0.0088
07.6008 000	**COUNTER FLASH FOR REGLETS, ETC:**							
07.6008 011	Counter flashing, galvanized iron, 8", 26 ga	LF	1.44	4.32	5.76	2.56	4.00	0.0549
07.6008 021	Counter flashing, aluminum, 8", .032"	LF	1.52	4.25	5.77	2.52	4.04	0.0540
07.6008 031	Counter flashing, copper, 8", 16 oz	LF	4.19	4.59	8.78	2.73	6.92	0.0584
07.6008 041	Counter flashing, copper clad stainless steel, 8", .015"	LF	4.33	5.07	9.40	3.01	7.34	0.0644
07.6009 000	**SHEET METAL SPECIALTIES:**							
07.6009 011	Roof safe & cap, 4", 28 ga galvanized sheet metal	EA	9.72	11.63	21.35	6.90	16.62	0.1479
07.6009 021	Roof safe & cap, 4", aluminum, 032"	EA	11.36	11.63	22.99	6.90	18.26	0.1479
07.6009 031	Plumber's flashing cone, galvanized sheet metal, 2"	EA	6.73	14.37	21.10	8.53	15.26	0.1827
07.6009 041	Plumber's flashing cone, galvanized sheet metal, 3"	EA	9.04	14.78	23.82	8.77	17.81	0.1879
07.6009 051	Plumber's flashing cone, galvanized sheet metal, 4"	EA	12.76	15.19	27.95	9.01	21.77	0.1931
07.6009 061	Scupper, galvanized sheet metal, 28 ga	EA	14.83	22.58	37.41	13.40	28.23	0.2870
07.6009 071	Scupper, aluminum, .032"	EA	16.66	22.58	39.24	13.40	30.06	0.2870
07.6010 000	**SHEET METAL VENTS:**							
07.6010 011	Vent, foundation, galvanized iron, 6" x 16"	EA	1.91	3.29	5.20	1.95	3.86	0.0418
07.6010 021	Vent, foundation, galvanized iron, 8" x 16"	EA	2.17	3.29	5.46	1.95	4.12	0.0418
07.6010 031	Vent, foundation, galvanized iron, 10" x 16"	EA	2.65	3.29	5.94	1.95	4.60	0.0418
07.6010 041	Vent, foundation, aluminum, 6" x 16"	EA	1.80	3.29	5.09	1.95	3.75	0.0418
07.6010 051	Vent, foundation, aluminum, 8" x 16"	EA	2.01	3.29	5.30	1.95	3.96	0.0418
07.6010 061	Vent, foundation, aluminum, 10" x 16"	EA	2.49	3.29	5.78	1.95	4.44	0.0418
07.6010 071	Vent, frieze, galvanized sheet metal, 4" x 24"	EA	1.91	3.97	5.88	2.36	4.27	0.0505
07.6010 081	Vent, frieze, galvanized sheet metal, 6" x 24"	EA	2.17	3.97	6.14	2.36	4.53	0.0505
07.6010 091	Vent, frieze, aluminum, 4" x 24"	EA	1.80	3.97	5.77	2.36	4.16	0.0505
07.6010 101	Vent, frieze, aluminum, 6" x 24"	EA	2.01	3.97	5.98	2.36	4.37	0.0505
07.6010 111	Vent, attic, galvanized sheet metal, 14" x 24"	EA	16.06	23.26	39.32	13.80	29.86	0.2957
07.6010 121	Vent, block/brick, galvanized sheet metal, 8" x 16"	EA	15.96	30.10	46.06	17.86	33.82	0.3827
07.6010 131	Vent, block/brick, galvanized sheet metal, 12" x 16"	EA	20.65	30.10	50.75	17.86	38.51	0.3827
07.6010 141	Vent, block/brick, aluminum, 8" x 16"	EA	18.31	30.10	48.41	17.86	36.17	0.3827
07.6010 151	Vent, block/brick, aluminum, 12" x 16"	EA	22.96	30.10	53.06	17.86	40.82	0.3827
07.6011 000	**LOUVERS & SCREENS:**							
07.6011 011	Louvers, door	EA	30.64	63.62	94.26	37.75	68.39	0.8088
07.6011 021	Louvers, fixed, galvanized sheet metal	SF	7.67	14.37	22.04	8.53	16.20	0.1827
07.6011 031	Louvers, manual, galvanized sheet metal	SF	10.02	17.79	27.81	10.55	20.57	0.2261
07.6011 041	Screens, cooling tower, galvanized sheet metal	SF	7.97	17.79	25.76	10.55	18.52	0.2261
07.6011 051	Screens, bird	SF	1.59	2.06	3.65	1.22	2.81	0.0262
07.6011 061	Screens, insect	SF	1.06	1.71	2.77	1.02	2.08	0.0218
07.6012 000	**GRAVITY VENTILATORS:**							
07.6012 011	Gravity ventilator, 8", galvanized sheet metal	EA	152.05	42.41	194.46	25.17	177.22	0.5392
07.6012 021	Gravity ventilator, 18", galvanized sheet metal	EA	246.82	42.41	289.23	25.17	271.99	0.5392
07.6012 031	Gravity ventilator, 24", galvanized sheet metal	EA	344.02	55.41	399.43	32.88	376.90	0.7044
07.6012 041	Gravity ventilator, 36", galvanized sheet metal	EA	645.75	86.19	731.94	51.15	696.90	1.0957
07.6012 051	Gravity ventilator, 48", galvanized sheet metal	EA	1,029.77	143.64	1,173.41	85.24	1,115.01	1.8261
07.6012 061	Gravity ventilator, 60", galvanized sheet metal	EA	1,727.92	307.80	2,035.72	182.66	1,910.58	3.9130
07.6012 071	Add for hand damper	EA	51.21		51.21		51.21	
07.6012 081	Add for motor damper	EA	76.86		76.86		76.86	

Division 7 CSI #	07 - THERMAL & MOISTURE PROTECTION Description	Unit	Material	Union Install	Union Total	Open Install	Open Total	Unit Man-Hrs
07.6013 000	**MUSHROOM VENTILATORS, MOTORIZED:**							
	Note: For 2 speeds, add 25% to the material costs. For back draft damper, add 40% to the material costs.							
07.6013 011	Mushroom ventilator, 8", to 180 CFM	EA	378.72	220.25	598.97	130.70	509.42	2.8000
07.6013 021	Mushroom ventilator, 12", to 360 CFM	EA	613.81	220.25	834.06	130.70	744.51	2.8000
07.6013 031	Mushroom ventilator, 18", to 1000 CFM	EA	966.49	288.65	1,255.14	171.30	1,137.79	3.6696
07.6013 041	Mushroom ventilator, 24", to 1200 CFM	EA	1,358.29	360.47	1,718.76	213.92	1,572.21	4.5826
07.6014 000	**EXPANSION JOINTS:**							
07.6014 011	Expansion joint, dry wall, aluminum cover, 2"	LF	16.06	4.11	20.17	2.44	18.50	0.0522
07.6014 021	Expansion joint, plaster wall, aluminum cover, 2"	LF	14.22	4.11	18.33	2.44	16.66	0.0522
07.6014 031	Expansion joint, floor, aluminum cover, 2"	LF	16.06	4.11	20.17	2.44	18.50	0.0522
07.6014 041	Expansion joint, concrete wall, aluminum cover, 4"-6"	LF	33.82	24.63	58.45	14.62	48.44	0.3131
07.6014 051	Expansion joint, concrete floor, aluminum cover, 4"-6"	LF	32.62	24.63	57.25	14.62	47.24	0.3131
07.6014 061	Expansion joint, roof, neoprene & aluminum, 2"	LF	22.86	5.47	28.33	3.25	26.11	0.0696
07.6015 000	**ROOF HATCHES:**							
	Note: Add for curbs on hatches & skylights.							
07.6015 011	Hatch frame/cover, 3' x 3'6", galvanized	EA	462.95	384.34	847.29	228.08	691.03	4.8861
07.6015 021	Hatch frame/cover, 3' x 5'4", galvanized	EA	722.51	439.75	1,162.26	260.96	983.47	5.5905
07.6015 031	Hatch frame/cover, 3' x 9'6", galvanized	EA	1,166.84	495.07	1,661.91	293.79	1,460.63	6.2938
07.6016 000	**FIRE/SMOKE VENT, AUTOMATIC, 160 DEGREE:**							
07.6016 011	Smoke vent, 420#, 4'8" x 4'8", galvanized	EA	1,227.93	426.68	1,654.61	253.21	1,481.14	5.4243
07.6016 021	Smoke vent, 540#, 4'8" x 7'2", galvanized	EA	1,568.03	495.07	2,063.10	293.79	1,861.82	6.2938
07.6016 031	Smoke vent, 650#, 4'8" x 9', galvanized	EA	1,936.46	563.47	2,499.93	334.39	2,270.85	7.1634
07.6016 041	Smoke vent, 450#, 6' x 6', galvanized	EA	1,329.53	495.07	1,824.60	293.79	1,623.32	6.2938
07.6016 051	Smoke vent, 590#, 6' x 9'6", galvanized	EA	1,712.11	631.87	2,343.98	374.98	2,087.09	8.0329
07.6016 061	Smoke vent, 1075#, 6'6"x1'4", galvanized	EA	3,575.34	957.58	4,532.92	568.27	4,143.61	12.1737
07.6017 000	**FIRE VENT, AUTOMATIC, 160 DEGREE:**							
07.6017 011	Fire vent, 260#, 4'8" x 4'8", aluminum	EA	1,308.25	359.10	1,667.35	213.10	1,521.35	4.5652
07.6017 021	Fire vent, 320#, 4'8" x 7'2", aluminum	EA	1,485.37	427.50	1,912.87	253.70	1,739.07	5.4348
07.6017 031	Fire vent, 380#, 4'8" x 9'6", aluminum	EA	1,681.38	513.00	2,194.38	304.43	1,985.81	6.5217
07.6017 041	Fire vent, 330#, 6' x 6', aluminum	EA	1,511.30	444.59	1,955.89	263.84	1,775.14	5.6521
07.6017 051	Fire vent, 425#, 6' x 9'6", aluminum	EA	1,945.85	564.30	2,510.15	334.88	2,280.73	7.1739
07.6017 061	Fire vent, 800#, 6'6" x 1'4", aluminum	EA	3,667.46	889.19	4,556.65	527.68	4,195.14	11.3042
07.6018 000	**FIRE VENT, SKYLIGHT, MELT-OUT, 205 DEGREE:**							
07.6018 011	Fire vent, skylight, 3'x 3'	EA	340.01	273.60	613.61	162.36	502.37	3.4782
07.6018 021	Fire vent, skylight, 3' x 4'8"	EA	467.53	294.12	761.65	174.54	642.07	3.7391
07.6018 031	Fire vent, skylight, 3'6" x 6'	EA	557.28	314.64	871.92	186.72	744.00	4.0000
07.6018 041	Fire vent, skylight, 3'6" x 7'2"	EA	665.88	335.15	1,001.03	198.89	864.77	4.2608
07.6018 051	Fire vent, skylight, 4'8" x 4'8"	EA	580.88	359.10	939.98	213.10	793.98	4.5652
07.6018 061	Fire vent, skylight, 4'8" x 6'	EA	698.98	393.30	1,092.28	233.40	932.38	5.0000
07.6018 071	Fire vent, skylight, 4'8" x 7'2"	EA	826.52	427.50	1,254.02	253.70	1,080.22	5.4348
07.6019 000	**SKYLIGHTS, ALUMINUM FRAME, PLASTIC DOME:**							
07.6019 011	Skylight, 2'x2', aluminum frame, plastic dome	EA	137.44	89.06	226.50	52.85	190.29	1.1322
07.6019 021	Skylight, 4'x4', aluminum frame, plastic dome	EA	279.69	89.06	368.75	52.85	332.54	1.1322
07.6019 031	Skylight, 5'x5', aluminum frame, plastic dome	EA	529.24	89.06	618.30	52.85	582.09	1.1322
07.6019 041	Skylight, 3'x6', aluminum frame, plastic dome	EA	350.51	89.06	439.57	52.85	403.36	1.1322
07.6019 051	Skylight, 7'x7', aluminum frame, plastic dome	EA	1,367.12	120.18	1,487.30	71.32	1,438.44	1.5279
07.6019 061	Skylight, 8'x10', aluminum frame, plastic dome	EA	2,473.36	120.18	2,593.54	71.32	2,544.68	1.5279
07.6020 000	**SKYLIGHTS, ALUMINUM FRAME, PYRAMID DOME:**							
07.6020 011	Skylight, 2'x2', aluminum frame, pyramid dome	EA	199.52	89.06	288.58	52.85	252.37	1.1322
07.6020 021	Skylight, 3'x3', aluminum frame, pyramid dome	EA	224.73	89.06	313.79	52.85	277.58	1.1322
07.6020 031	Skylight, 4'x4', aluminum frame, pyramid dome	EA	405.91	89.06	494.97	52.85	458.76	1.1322
07.6021 000	**SKYLIGHTS, DOUBLE GLAZED ALUMINUM FRAME:**							
07.6021 011	Skylight, 2'x2', double glazed aluminum frame	EA	241.04	101.24	342.28	60.08	301.12	1.2870
07.6021 021	Skylight, 3'x3', double glazed aluminum frame	EA	389.91	127.22	517.13	75.50	465.41	1.6174
07.6021 031	Skylight, 4'x4', double glazed aluminum frame	EA	601.70	151.85	753.55	90.12	691.82	1.9305
07.6021 041	Skylight, 6'x6', double glazed aluminum frame	EA	1,505.40	180.58	1,685.98	107.16	1,612.56	2.2957
07.6021 051	Skylight, 4'x8', double glazed aluminum frame	EA	1,434.57	180.58	1,615.15	107.16	1,541.73	2.2957
07.6022 000	**FABRICATED SKYLIGHTS:**							
07.6022 011	Fabricated skylight, steel frame, laminated glass, 20' span	SF	88.42		88.42		88.42	
07.6022 021	Fabricated skylight, steel frame, laminated glass, 30' span	SF	109.02		109.02		109.02	
07.6022 031	Fabricated skylight, steel frame, laminated glass, 40' span	SF	127.64		127.64		127.64	

Division 7 CSI #	07 - THERMAL & MOISTURE PROTECTION Description	Unit	Material	Union Install	Union Total	Open Install	Open Total	Unit Man-Hrs
07.6023 000	**PREFAB METAL FIREPLACES:**							
07.6023 011	Prefabricated fireplace, 36"x24" opening	EA	2,602.98	293.98	2,896.96	174.46	2,777.44	3.7373
07.6023 021	Prefabricated fireplace, 42"x27" opening	EA	4,090.39	293.98	4,384.37	174.46	4,264.85	3.7373
07.6023 031	Prefabricated, free standing fireplace	EA	2,788.90	319.23	3,108.13	189.44	2,978.34	4.0583
07.6023 041	Add for log lighter	EA	47.94	251.98	299.92	149.53	197.47	3.2034
07.6023 051	Add for patent flue, from 6' up	EA	52.68	251.98	304.66	149.53	202.21	3.2034
07.6023 061	Add for exterior stack, simulated brick	LF	22.89	22.44	45.33	13.32	36.21	0.2853
07.6023 071	Add for extension, high rise	LF	15.36	11.16	26.52	6.62	21.98	0.1419
07.7000 000	**ARCHITECTURAL SHEET METAL:**							
07.7001 000	**PRE-FINISHED METAL FACIA & MANSARDS:**							
07.7001 011	Beam & batten, straight & simple	SF	5.71	5.45	11.16	3.23	8.94	0.0693
07.7001 021	Beam & batten, curved & complex	SF	6.17	10.90	17.07	6.47	12.64	0.1386
07.7001 031	Add for coping/gravel stop/flashing	LF	2.40	3.94	6.34	2.34	4.74	0.0501
07.7002 000	**WAINSCOT, GALVANIZED SHEET METAL:**							
07.7002 011	Wainscot, galvanized sheet metal	SF	1.31	2.09	3.40	1.24	2.55	0.0266
07.7003 000	**SCREENS & METAL LOUVERS:**							
07.7003 011	Louvers, aluminum, fixed blade	SF	14.59	4.73	19.32	2.81	17.40	0.0601
07.7003 021	Louvers, aluminum, manual	SF	17.42	5.88	23.30	3.49	20.91	0.0747
07.7003 031	Screens, insect, with frame	SF	1.21	1.97	3.18	1.17	2.38	0.0251
07.7003 041	Screens, bird, with frame	SF	1.88	1.97	3.85	1.17	3.05	0.0251
07.7004 000	**ARCHITECTURAL FACADE SCREENS:**							
07.7004 011	Screen, arch facade, aluminum	SF	19.76	6.81	26.57	4.04	23.80	0.0866
07.7004 021	Add for enamel or light anodizing	SF	6.24		6.24		6.24	
07.7004 031	Add for porcelain/heavy anodizing	SF	5.62		5.62		5.62	
07.7005 000	**DOOR LOUVERS & CORNER GUARDS:**							
07.7005 011	Louvers, door	EA	79.42	14.99	94.41	8.90	88.32	0.1906
07.7005 021	Corner guard, stainless steel, 40" length	LF	45.37	18.29	63.66	10.85	56.22	0.2325
07.7005 031	Corner guard, stainless steel, 48" length	LF	45.37	18.29	63.66	10.85	56.22	0.2325
07.7005 041	Ceiling access hatch, 30" x 30"	EA	228.61	85.71	314.32	50.86	279.47	1.0896
07.9000 000	**CAULKING & SEALANTS:**							
07.9001 000	**CAULKING, GUN GRADE:**							
	Note: For caulking above 14 stories, add 20% to the labor costs. For caulking between 6 and 14 stories, add 10% to the material costs. For 2 part caulk, add 15% to the labor costs.							
07.9001 011	Caulk, linseed oil base, per gallon	EA	15.09		15.09		15.09	
07.9001 021	Caulk, linseed oil base, per tube	EA	1.54		1.54		1.54	
07.9001 031	Caulk, linseed base, 1/8" x 1/8"	LF	.02	.98	1.00	.71	.73	0.0103
07.9001 041	Caulk, linseed base, 1/4" x 1/4"	LF	.09	1.46	1.55	1.07	1.16	0.0154
07.9001 051	Caulk, linseed base, 1/2" x 1/2"	LF	.22	1.94	2.16	1.42	1.64	0.0205
07.9001 061	Caulk, linseed base, 3/4" x 3/4"	LF	.35	2.91	3.26	2.12	2.47	0.0307
07.9001 071	Caulk, linseed base, 1" x 1"	LF	.95	3.88	4.83	2.84	3.79	0.0410
07.9001 081	Caulk, butyl base, per gallon	EA	25.38		25.38		25.38	
07.9001 091	Caulk, butyl base, per tube	EA	3.19		3.19		3.19	
07.9001 101	Caulk, butyl base, 1/8" x 1/8"	LF	.02	.98	1.00	.71	.73	0.0103
07.9001 111	Caulk, butyl base, 1/4" x 1/4"	LF	.09	1.46	1.55	1.07	1.16	0.0154
07.9001 121	Caulk, butyl base, 1/2" x 1/2"	LF	.37	1.94	2.31	1.42	1.79	0.0205
07.9001 131	Caulk, butyl base, 3/4" x 3/4"	LF	1.23	2.91	4.14	2.12	3.35	0.0307
07.9001 141	Caulk, butyl base, 1" x 1"	LF	1.58	3.88	5.46	2.84	4.42	0.0410
07.9001 151	Caulk, solvent acrylic, per gallon	EA	54.59		54.59		54.59	
07.9001 161	Caulk, solvent acrylic, per tube	EA	6.60		6.60		6.60	
07.9001 171	Caulk, acrylic, 1/8" x 1/8"	LF	.06	.98	1.04	.71	.77	0.0103
07.9001 181	Caulk, acrylic, 1/4" x 1/4"	LF	.28	1.46	1.74	1.07	1.35	0.0154
07.9001 191	Caulk, acrylic, 1/2" x 1/2"	LF	.90	1.94	2.84	1.42	2.32	0.0205
07.9001 201	Caulk, acrylic, 3/4" x 3/4"	LF	2.40	2.91	5.31	2.12	4.52	0.0307
07.9001 211	Caulk, acrylic, 1" x 1"	LF	3.27	3.88	7.15	2.84	6.11	0.0410
07.9001 221	Caulk, polysulfide/urethane, per gallon	EA	65.42		65.42		65.42	
07.9001 231	Caulk, polysulfide/urethane, per tube	EA	8.09		8.09		8.09	
07.9001 241	Caulk, polysulfide, 1/8" x 1/8"	LF	.32	.98	1.30	.71	1.03	0.0103
07.9001 251	Caulk, polysulfide, 1/4" x 1/4"	LF	.30	1.46	1.76	1.07	1.37	0.0154
07.9001 261	Caulk, polysulfide, 1/2" x 1/2"	LF	1.04	1.94	2.98	1.42	2.46	0.0205
07.9001 271	Caulk, polysulfide, 3/4" x 3/4"	LF	2.96	2.91	5.87	2.12	5.08	0.0307
07.9001 281	Caulk, polysulfide, 1" x 1"	LF	4.29	3.88	8.17	2.84	7.13	0.0410
07.9001 291	Caulk, silicone, per gallon	EA	85.88		85.88		85.88	

Division 7 CSI #	07 - THERMAL & MOISTURE PROTECTION Description	Unit	Material	Union Install	Union Total	Open Install	Open Total	Unit Man-Hrs
07.9001 000	**CAULKING, GUN GRADE: (Cont.)**							
07.9001 301	Caulk, silicone, per tube	EA	10.65		10.65		10.65	
07.9001 311	Caulk, silicone, 1/8" x 1/8"	LF	.09	.98	1.07	.71	.80	0.0103
07.9001 321	Caulk, silicone, 1/4" x 1/4"	LF	.32	1.46	1.78	1.07	1.39	0.0154
07.9001 331	Caulk, silicone, 1/2" x 1/2"	LF	1.40	1.94	3.34	1.42	2.82	0.0205
07.9001 341	Caulk, silicone, 3/4" x 3/4"	LF	3.77	2.91	6.68	2.12	5.89	0.0307
07.9001 351	Caulk, silicone, 1" x 1"	LF	5.54	3.88	9.42	2.84	8.38	0.0410
07.9001 361	Caulk, mildew resistant, per gallon	EA	110.52	.	110.52		110.52	
07.9001 371	Caulk, mildew resistant, per tube	EA	13.65		13.65		13.65	
07.9001 381	Caulk, mildew resistant, 1/8" x 1/8"	LF	.12	.98	1.10	.71	.83	0.0103
07.9001 391	Caulk, mildew resistant, 1/4" x 1/4"	LF	.35	1.46	1.81	1.07	1.42	0.0154
07.9001 401	Caulk, mildew resistant, 1/2" x 1/2"	LF	2.17	1.94	4.11	1.42	3.59	0.0205
07.9001 411	Caulk, mildew resistant, 3/4" x 3/4"	LF	4.85	2.91	7.76	2.12	6.97	0.0307
07.9001 421	Caulk, mildew resistant, 1" x 1"	LF	7.26	3.88	11.14	2.84	10.10	0.0410
07.9001 431	Caulk, elastomeric, for concrete	LF	2.54	1.62	4.16	1.18	3.72	0.0171
07.9002 000	**SEALANTS, SELF-LEVELING:**							
07.9002 011	Polysulfide polymer, 1/4" x 3/8"	LF	1.55	2.71	4.26	1.98	3.53	0.0286
07.9002 021	Acrylic latex polymer, 1/4"x3/8"	LF	1.37	2.71	4.08	1.98	3.35	0.0286
07.9002 031	Polyurethane, 1/4" x 3/8"	LF	1.72	2.71	4.43	1.98	3.70	0.0286
07.9003 000	**POLYISOBUTYLENE TAPES:**							
07.9003 011	Polybutene tape	LF	.30	2.19	2.49	1.60	1.90	0.0231
07.9003 021	Polisobutyl/butyl tape, preformed	LF	.17	1.66	1.83	1.21	1.38	0.0175
07.9004 000	**THERMOFIBER:**							
07.9004 011	Thermofiber, 1/8", 6"x8", glue back	SF	2.21	1.53	3.74	1.11	3.32	0.0161
07.9004 021	Thermofiber, 1" thick, 16" x 48"	SF	.30	3.95	4.25	2.89	3.19	0.0417
07.9004 031	Thermofiber, 1-1/2" thick, 16" x 48"	SF	.32	4.74	5.06	3.46	3.78	0.0500
07.9004 041	Thermofiber, 2" thick, 16" x 48"	SF	.49	5.52	6.01	4.03	4.52	0.0583
07.9004 051	Thermofiber, 3" thick, 16" x 48"	SF	.61	6.32	6.93	4.61	5.22	0.0667
07.9005 000	**CAULKING, ACOUSTICAL:**							
07.9005 011	Caulk, butyl rubber, 1/4" x 1/2"	LF	.49	2.19	2.68	1.60	2.09	0.0231
07.9006 000	**NEOPRENE GASKETS, CLOSED CELL:**							
07.9006 011	Neoprene gasket, 1/8" x 2"	LF	1.25	1.66	2.91	1.21	2.46	0.0175
07.9006 021	Neoprene gasket, 1/8" x 6"	LF	2.84	2.10	4.94	1.54	4.38	0.0222
07.9006 031	Neoprene gasket, 1/4" x 2"	LF	1.37	1.75	3.12	1.28	2.65	0.0185
07.9006 041	Neoprene gasket, 1/4" x 6"	LF	3.03	2.10	5.13	1.54	4.57	0.0222
07.9006 051	Neoprene gasket, 1/2" x 6"	LF	4.47	1.84	6.31	1.34	5.81	0.0194
07.9006 061	Neoprene gasket, 1/2" x 12"	LF	8.56	2.27	10.83	1.66	10.22	0.0240
07.9007 000	**BACKING RODS:**							
07.9007 011	Backing rod, butyl, 3/8"	LF	.22	2.10	2.32	1.54	1.76	0.0222
07.9007 021	Backing rod, butyl, 1/2"	LF	.35	2.19	2.54	1.60	1.95	0.0231
07.9007 031	Backing rod, polyethylene, 3/8"	LF	.21	1.66	1.87	1.21	1.42	0.0175
07.9007 041	Backing rod, polyethylene, 1/2"	LF	.24	1.75	1.99	1.28	1.52	0.0185
07.9008 000	**WEATHER-STRIPPING, METAL:**							
07.9008 011	Weatherstrip, exterior anodized aluminum, neoprene	LF	5.18	2.19	7.37	1.60	6.78	0.0231
07.9008 021	Weatherstrip, exterior anodized aluminum, neoprene, adjust	LF	11.53	3.23	14.76	2.36	13.89	0.0341
07.9008 031	Weatherstrip, bronze Y angle, neoprene	LF	9.51	5.06	14.57	3.69	13.20	0.0534
07.9008 041	Weatherstrip, bronze Z bar & angle	LF	7.53	5.06	12.59	3.69	11.22	0.0534
07.9008 051	Weatherstrip, astragal, adjust mortise	LF	17.82	8.03	25.85	5.87	23.69	0.0848

Division 8 CSI #	08 - DOORS, WINDOWS & GLASS Description	Unit	Material	Union Install	Union Total	Open Install	Open Total	Unit Man-Hrs
08.0000 000	**DOORS, WINDOWS & GLASS:**							
	Note: Materials are generally supplied FOB job, with labor supplied by the general contractor. The following prices are based on purchase of 25 or more per order. For larger amounts the cost may be reduced as much as 15%. For smaller amounts, add 5%. For installing metal doors in concrete, add 100% to unit man hours. Remember to include the costs for special work as shown in section 08.1000.							
08.1000 000	**HOLLOW METAL DOORS & FRAMES:**							
	Note: Door sizes are expressed in width then height, where the feet & inches are not expressed. For example, 2'8" by 6'8" is expressed "2868".							
08.1001 000	**FRAMES, 16 GA, 4-5/8", PRIME COAT, NON-RATED:**							
	Note: The following items are standard quality and are prefabricated.							
08.1001 011	Frame, 16 ga, to 2868, prime coat, non-rated	EA	82.79	77.09	159.88	56.31	139.10	0.8138
08.1001 021	Frame, 16 ga, 3068, prime coat, non-rated	EA	82.79	77.09	159.88	56.31	139.10	0.8138
08.1001 031	Frame, 16 ga, 4068, prime coat, non-rated	EA	104.02	84.80	188.82	61.94	165.96	0.8952
08.1001 041	Frame, 16 ga, to 2870, prime coat, non-rated	EA	99.80	77.09	176.89	56.31	156.11	0.8138
08.1001 051	Frame, 16 ga, 3070, prime coat, non-rated	EA	101.59	77.09	178.68	56.31	157.90	0.8138
08.1001 061	Frame, 16 ga, 4070, prime coat, non-rated	EA	104.12	84.80	188.92	61.94	166.06	0.8952
08.1001 071	Frame, 16 ga, 5070, prime coat, non-rated	EA	108.47	102.08	210.55	74.56	183.03	1.0776
08.1001 081	Frame, 16 ga, 6070, prime coat, non-rated	EA	118.07	102.08	220.15	74.56	192.63	1.0776
08.1001 091	Frame, 16 ga, 8080, prime coat, non-rated	EA	153.12	106.60	259.72	77.86	230.98	1.1253
08.1002 000	**FRAMES, 16 GA, 4-7/8", PRIME COAT, NON-RATED:**							
	Note: The following items are standard quality and are prefabricated.							
08.1002 011	Frame, custom, 16 ga, 2868, prime coat, non-rated	EA	128.15	77.09	205.24	56.31	184.46	0.8138
08.1002 021	Frame, custom, 16 ga, 3068, prime coat, non-rated	EA	99.41	77.09	176.50	56.31	155.72	0.8138
08.1002 031	Frame, custom, 16 ga, 4068, prime coat, non-rated	EA	105.27	84.80	190.07	61.94	167.21	0.8952
08.1002 041	Frame, custom, 16 ga, to 2870, prime coat, non-rated	EA	133.25	77.09	210.34	56.31	189.56	0.8138
08.1002 051	Frame, custom, 16 ga, 3070, prime coat, non-rated	EA	102.82	77.09	179.91	56.31	159.13	0.8138
08.1002 061	Frame, custom, 16 ga, 4070, prime coat, non-rated	EA	105.37	84.80	190.17	61.94	167.31	0.8952
08.1002 071	Frame, custom, 16 ga, 5070, prime coat, non-rated	EA	108.98	102.08	211.06	74.56	183.54	1.0776
08.1002 081	Frame, custom, 16 ga, 6070, prime coat, non-rated	EA	118.07	102.08	220.15	74.56	192.63	1.0776
08.1002 091	Frame, custom, 16 ga, 8080, prime coat, non-rated	PAIR	161.39	111.00	272.39	81.08	242.47	1.1718
08.1003 000	**FRAMES, 14 GA, 4-7/8", PRIME COAT, NON-RATED:**							
08.1003 011	Frame, to 3070, 14 ga, prime coat, non-rated	EA	153.43	77.09	230.52	56.31	209.74	0.8138
08.1003 021	Frame, 3670, 14 ga, prime coat, non-rated	EA	157.49	77.09	234.58	56.31	213.80	0.8138
08.1003 031	Frame, 3070, 14 ga, prime coat, non-rated	EA	155.03	77.09	232.12	56.31	211.34	0.8138
08.1003 041	Frame, 4070, 14 ga, prime coat, non-rated	EA	159.16	84.80	243.96	61.94	221.10	0.8952
08.1003 051	Frame, 5070, 14 ga, prime coat, non-rated	EA	176.25	102.08	278.33	74.56	250.81	1.0776
08.1003 061	Frame, 6070, 14 ga, prime coat, non-rated	EA	191.12	118.60	309.72	86.63	277.75	1.2520
08.1003 071	Frame, 8080, 14 ga, prime coat, non-rated	EA	200.42	137.08	337.50	100.12	300.54	1.4471
08.1003 090	**FRAMES, ROLL FORMED 20GA, PRE-FINISHED, NON-RATED, WITH EMBOSSED HARDBOARD DOORS:**							
	'Note: The doors in this section are 1-3/4" embossed hardboard, oak/walnut legacy, prefinished and prepared for cylinder lock. See 08.2012, "ADDERS FOR WOOD DOORS" for door upgrades and hardware. Frames are prefinished. The following prices are based on purchase of 25 or more per order. For larger amounts the cost may be reduced as much as 10%. For smaller amounts add 10%.							
08.1003 101	Hardboard door, with 20 ga frame 3068	EA	187.00	70.73	257.73	51.66	238.66	0.7467
08.1003 111	Hardboard door, with 20 ga frame 4068	EA	225.24	78.63	303.87	57.43	282.67	0.8300
08.1003 121	Hardboard door, with 20 ga frame 6068	EA	376.18	104.20	480.38	76.11	452.29	1.1000
08.1003 131	Hardboard door, with 20 ga frame 3070	EA	200.79	70.73	271.52	51.66	252.45	0.7467
08.1003 141	Hardboard door, with 20 ga frame 4070	EA	206.75	78.63	285.38	57.43	264.18	0.8300
08.1003 151	Hardboard door, with 20 ga frame 6070	EA	397.81	104.20	502.01	76.11	473.92	1.1000
08.1003 161	Hardboard door, with 20 ga frame 8080	EA	526.97	134.52	661.49	98.25	625.22	1.4200
08.1003 171	Hardboard door, with 18 ga frame 3068	EA	197.41	70.73	268.14	51.66	249.07	0.7467
08.1003 181	Hardboard door, with 18 ga frame 4068	EA	235.68	78.63	314.31	57.43	293.11	0.8300
08.1003 191	Hardboard door, with 18 ga frame 6068	EA	386.81	104.20	491.01	76.11	462.92	1.1000
08.1003 201	Hardboard door, with 18 ga frame 3070	EA	228.34	70.73	299.07	51.66	280.00	0.7467
08.1003 211	Hardboard door, with 18 ga frame 4070	EA	234.31	78.63	312.94	57.43	291.74	0.8300
08.1003 221	Hardboard door, with 18 ga frame 6070	EA	408.44	104.20	512.64	76.11	484.55	1.1000
08.1003 231	Hardboard door, with 18 ga frame 8080	EA	537.60	134.52	672.12	98.25	635.85	1.4200
08.1004 000	**DOORS, 18 GA, 1-3/4", PRIME COAT, NON-RATED:**							
	Note: The following items are custom fabricated.							
08.1004 011	Door, 18 ga, to 2868, prime coat, non-rated	EA	232.34	66.07	298.41	48.26	280.60	0.6975
08.1004 021	Door, 18 ga, 3068, prime coat, non-rated	EA	244.70	66.07	310.77	48.26	292.96	0.6975
08.1004 031	Door, 18 ga, 4068, prime coat, non-rated	EA	277.22	84.80	362.02	61.94	339.16	0.8952

Division 8 CSI #	08 - DOORS, WINDOWS & GLASS Description	Unit	Material	Union Install	Union Total	Open Install	Open Total	Unit Man-Hrs
08.1004 000	**DOORS, 18 GA, 1-3/4", PRIME COAT, NON-RATED: (Cont.)**							
08.1004 041	Door, 18 ga, to 2870, prime coat, non-rated	EA	241.33	66.07	307.40	48.26	289.59	0.6975
08.1004 051	Door, 18 ga, 3070, prime coat, non-rated	EA	241.33	66.07	307.40	48.26	289.59	0.6975
08.1004 061	Door, 18 ga, 4070, prime coat, non-rated	EA	286.95	79.29	366.24	57.91	344.86	0.8370
08.1004 071	Door, 18 ga, 4080, prime coat, non-rated	EA	295.63	107.48	403.11	78.50	374.13	1.1346
08.1005 000	**DOORS, 18 GA, CUSTOM, 1-3/4", PRIME COAT, NON-RATED:**							
08.1005 011	Door, custom, to 2868, prime coat, non-rated	EA	304.57	66.07	370.64	48.26	352.83	0.6975
08.1005 021	Door, custom, 3068, prime coat, non-rated	EA	319.41	66.07	385.48	48.26	367.67	0.6975
08.1005 031	Door, custom, 4068, prime coat, non-rated	EA	453.17	84.80	537.97	61.94	515.11	0.8952
08.1005 041	Door, custom, to 2870, prime coat, non-rated	EA	314.48	66.07	380.55	48.26	362.74	0.6975
08.1005 051	Door, custom, 3070, prime coat, non-rated	EA	368.97	66.07	435.04	48.26	417.23	0.6975
08.1005 061	Door, custom, 4070, prime coat, non-rated	EA	418.49	79.29	497.78	57.91	476.40	0.8370
08.1005 071	Door, custom, 4080, prime coat, non-rated	EA	474.19	107.48	581.67	78.50	552.69	1.1346
08.1006 000	**DOORS, 16 GA, 1-3/4" PRIME COATED, NON-RATED:**							
08.1006 011	Door, to 3070, 16 ga, prime coat, non-rated	EA	309.55	66.07	375.62	48.26	357.81	0.6975
08.1006 021	Door, 3670, 16 ga, prime coat, non-rated	EA	383.82	66.07	449.89	48.26	432.08	0.6975
08.1006 031	Door, 4070, 16 ga, prime coat, non-rated	EA	433.37	79.29	512.66	57.91	491.28	0.8370
08.1006 041	Door, 4080, 16 ga, prime coat, non-rated	EA	492.80	105.72	598.52	77.22	570.02	1.1160
08.1007 000	**MISCELLANEOUS ADDERS FOR FRAMES:**							
08.1007 011	Add for galvanizing	EA	71.43		71.43		71.43	
08.1007 021	Add for A label, 3 hours	EA	30.82		30.82		30.82	
08.1007 031	Add for B label, 1-1/2 hours	EA	26.92		26.92		26.92	
08.1007 041	Add for C label, 1 hour	EA	23.80		23.80		23.80	
08.1007 051	Add for stainless steel	EA	256.13		256.13		256.13	
08.1007 061	Add for baked enamel	EA	20.21		20.21		20.21	
08.1007 071	Add for porcelain enamel	EA	60.68	28.19	88.87	20.59	81.27	0.2976
08.1007 081	Add for special dapping	EA	27.97	66.07	94.04	48.26	76.23	0.6975
08.1007 091	Add for lengthening sections	SF	6.14		6.14		6.14	
08.1007 101	Add for bronze	EA	834.42		834.42		834.42	
08.1008 000	**MISCELLANEOUS ADDERS FOR DOORS:**							
08.1008 011	Add for galvanizing	EA	59.95		59.95		59.95	
08.1008 021	Add for A label, 3 hours	EA	145.77		145.77		145.77	
08.1008 031	Add for A label, 1-1/2 hours	EA	58.29		58.29		58.29	
08.1008 041	Add for C label, 1 hour	EA	29.21		29.21		29.21	
08.1008 051	Add for cutouts to 4 SF	EA	84.79		84.79		84.79	
08.1008 061	Add for cutouts over 4 SF	SF	18.81		18.81		18.81	
08.1008 071	Add for stainless steel	EA	497.28		497.28		497.28	
08.1008 081	Add for baked enamel	EA	20.21		20.21		20.21	
08.1008 091	Add for porcelain enamel	EA	166.18		166.18		166.18	
08.1008 101	Add for special dapping	EA	30.81		30.81		30.81	
08.1008 111	Add for bronze	EA	2,503.33		2,503.33		2,503.33	
08.1008 121	Add for 10" x 10" vision light	EA	87.98		87.98		87.98	
08.1008 131	Add for half glass opening	EA	109.87		109.87		109.87	
08.2000 000	**WOOD DOORS & FRAMES:**							
	Note: For the following sections, it is assumed that materials are supplied fob job site, with labor being supplied by the general contractor. Prices are for quantities of 25 or more. For quantities in excess of 250, cost may be reduced as much as 15%. For quantities less than 25, add 5%. The following prices for residential doors & frames are based on frames at 68, doors at 1-3/8" fj jambs and oval casing. Add 5% for 70 in lieu of 68, add 35% for 80 in lieu of 68. Dapping is included for all standard hardware, with hinges applied. No other hardware is included. The following prices for commercial doors and frames are based on 4-7/8" thick walls and 1-3/4" doors.							
08.2001 000	**DOORS & FRAMES, PREHUNG, HOLLOW, INTERIOR:**							
	Note: The following items are paint grade 1-3/8" thick.							
08.2001 011	Door, hollow core, to 2468, prehung, paint grade	EA	90.11	44.05	134.16	32.17	122.28	0.4650
08.2001 021	Door, hollow core, 2668, prehung, paint grade	EA	90.57	44.05	134.62	32.17	122.74	0.4650
08.2001 031	Door, hollow core, 2868, prehung, paint grade	EA	94.94	44.05	138.99	32.17	127.11	0.4650
08.2001 041	Door, hollow core, 3068, prehung, paint grade	EA	99.28	44.05	143.33	32.17	131.45	0.4650
08.2001 051	Door, hollow core, 3668, prehung, paint grade	EA	108.00	44.05	152.05	32.17	140.17	0.4650
08.2002 000	**DOORS & FRAMES, PREHUNG, 1-3/8", PAINT GRADE, INTERIOR:**							
	Note: The following are hollow core masonite.							
08.2002 011	Door, hollow core, interior, 2468x1-3/8", prehung, paint grade	EA	76.45	66.07	142.52	48.26	124.71	0.6975
08.2002 021	Door, hollow core, interior, 2668x1-3/8", prehung, paint grade	EA	79.06	66.07	145.13	48.26	127.32	0.6975

Division 8 CSI #	08 - DOORS, WINDOWS & GLASS Description	Unit	Material	Union Install	Union Total	Open Install	Open Total	Unit Man-Hrs
08.2002 000	**DOORS & FRAMES, PREHUNG,1-3/8", PAINT GRADE, INTERIOR: (Cont.)**							
08.2002 031	Door, hollow core, interior, 2868x1-3/8", prehung, paint grade	EA	81.64	66.07	147.71	48.26	129.90	0.6975
08.2002 041	Door, hollow core, interior, 3068x1-3/8", prehung, paint grade	EA	84.22	66.07	150.29	48.26	132.48	0.6975
08.2002 051	Door, hollow core, interior, 3668x1-3/8", prehung, paint grade	EA	86.81	66.07	152.88	48.26	135.07	0.6975
08.2003 000	**DOORS & FRAMES, PREHUNG, SOLID CORE, 1-3/8", PAINT GRADE, INTERIOR:**							
	Note: The following prices include solid jamb & casing.							
08.2003 011	Door, solid core, interior, 2468x1-3/8", prehung, paint grade	EA	146.63	66.07	212.70	48.26	194.89	0.6975
08.2003 021	Door, solid core, interior, 2668x1-3/8", prehung, paint grade	EA	150.17	66.07	216.24	48.26	198.43	0.6975
08.2003 031	Door, solid core, interior, 2868x1-3/8", prehung, paint grade	EA	163.34	66.07	229.41	48.26	211.60	0.6975
08.2003 041	Door, solid core, interior, 3068x1-3/8", prehung, paint grade	EA	158.96	66.07	225.03	48.26	207.22	0.6975
08.2003 051	Door, solid core, interior, 3668x1-3/8", prehung, paint grade	EA	167.82	66.07	233.89	48.26	216.08	0.6975
08.2004 000	**DOORS & FRAMES, PREHUNG, EXTERIOR:**							
	Note: The following prices include rabbet jamb, exterior molding and fir sill.							
08.2004 011	Door, solid core, exterior, 3068x1-3/8", prehung	EA	141.59	88.10	229.69	64.35	205.94	0.9300
08.2004 021	Door, solid core, exterior, 3068x1-3/4", prehung	EA	149.93	88.10	238.03	64.35	214.28	0.9300
08.2004 031	Door, exterior, 9 lite, x buck, 3'x1-3/4"	EA	193.24	88.10	281.34	64.35	257.59	0.9300
08.2004 041	Door, exterior, 12 lite, x buck, 3'x1-3/4"	EA	219.89	88.10	307.99	64.35	284.24	0.9300
08.2004 051	Door, exterior, Dutch, 3068x1-3/4", prehung	EA	320.38	132.15	452.53	96.52	416.90	1.3950
08.2004 061	Door, exterior, 12 lite, x buck, 3690x1-3/4"	EA	273.20	88.10	361.30	64.35	337.55	0.9300
08.2005 000	**DOORS & FRAMES, PREHUNG, PAINT GRADE, MISC:**							
08.2005 011	Door, pocket, 2870 x1-3/8", prehung, paint grade	EA	122.74	110.12	232.86	80.43	203.17	1.1625
08.2005 021	Door, by pass slide, to 50, prehung, paint grade	EA	147.71	132.15	279.86	96.52	244.23	1.3950
08.2005 031	Door, by pass slide, 60, prehung, paint grade	EA	166.15	132.15	298.30	96.52	262.67	1.3950
08.2005 041	Door, by pass slide, 80, prehung, paint grade	EA	175.37	149.77	325.14	109.39	284.76	1.5810
08.2005 051	Door, bifold, wood, 50, prehung, paint grade	EA	124.43	132.15	256.58	96.52	220.95	1.3950
08.2005 061	Door, bifold, wood, to 60, prehung, paint grade	EA	134.21	132.15	266.36	96.52	230.73	1.3950
08.2005 071	Door, bifold, wood, 80, prehung, paint grade	EA	174.30	149.77	324.07	109.39	283.69	1.5810
08.2005 081	Door, bifold, metal, 60, prehung, paint grade	EA	98.73	132.15	230.88	96.52	195.25	1.3950
08.2005 091	Door, bifold, metal, 80, prehung, paint grade	EA	119.15	132.15	251.30	96.52	215.67	1.3950
08.2005 101	Door, full louver, 2068, prehung, paint grade	EA	123.13	66.07	189.20	48.26	171.39	0.6975
08.2005 111	Door, full louver, 2668, prehung, paint grade	EA	131.61	66.07	197.68	48.26	179.87	0.6975
08.2005 121	Door, full louver, 3068, prehung, paint grade	EA	138.69	66.07	204.76	48.26	186.95	0.6975
08.2006 000	**DOORS & FRAMES, JOB HUNG, HOLLOW CORE, 1-3/8", INTERIOR:**							
08.2006 011	Door, hollow core, to 2470 x 1-3/8", paint grade	EA	69.37	110.12	179.49	80.43	149.80	1.1625
08.2006 021	Door, hollow core, 2670 x 1-3/8", paint grade	EA	73.30	110.12	183.42	80.43	153.73	1.1625
08.2006 031	Door, hollow core, 2870 x 1/3/8", paint grade	EA	73.54	110.12	183.66	80.43	153.97	1.1625
08.2006 041	Door, hollow core, 3070 x 1-3/8", paint grade	EA	75.81	110.12	185.93	80.43	156.24	1.1625
08.2006 051	Door, hollow core, 3670 x 1-3/8", paint grade	EA	78.92	110.12	189.04	80.43	159.35	1.1625
08.2007 000	**DOORS & FRAMES, JOB HUNG, SOLID CORE, 1-3/8", INTERIOR:**							
08.2007 011	Door, solid core, interior, to 2470 x 1-3/8", paint grade	EA	108.54	132.15	240.69	96.52	205.06	1.3950
08.2007 021	Door, solid core, interior, 2670 x 1-3/8", paint grade	EA	110.11	132.15	242.26	96.52	206.63	1.3950
08.2007 031	Door, solid core, interior, 2870 x 1-3/8", paint grade	EA	110.11	132.15	242.26	96.52	206.63	1.3950
08.2007 041	Door, solid core, interior, 3070 x 1-3/8", paint grade	EA	117.12	132.15	249.27	96.52	213.64	1.3950
08.2007 051	Door, solid core, interior, 3670 x 1-3/8", paint grade	EA	133.48	132.15	265.63	96.52	230.00	1.3950
08.2008 000	**ADDERS & DEDUCTORS FOR DOORS & FRAMES:**							
08.2008 011	Deduct for Philippine mahogany	EA	4.47		4.47		4.47	
08.2008 021	Add for stain grade birch	EA	9.74		9.74		9.74	
08.2008 031	Add for red oak	EA	11.02		11.02		11.02	
08.2008 041	Add for walnut	EA	42.28		42.28		42.28	
08.2008 051	Add for Formica clad	EA	89.08		89.08		89.08	
08.2008 061	Add for stain grade ash	EA	12.87		12.87		12.87	
08.2008 071	Add for plant-ons	EA	11.47		11.47		11.47	
08.2008 081	Add for prefinishing	EA	14.68	12.03	26.71	8.79	23.47	0.1270
08.2008 091	Deduct for hardboard	EA	12.40		12.40		12.40	
08.2008 101	Refinishing, average	EA	14.68	132.15	146.83	96.52	111.20	1.3950
08.2009 000	**DOORS & FRAMES, PREHUNG, SOLID CORE, PAINT GRADE, INTERIOR:**							
08.2009 011	Door, solid core, interior, to 2868, prehung, paint grade	EA	117.64	88.10	205.74	64.35	181.99	0.9300
08.2009 021	Door, solid core, interior, 3068, prehung, paint grade	EA	119.77	88.10	207.87	64.35	184.12	0.9300
08.2009 031	Door, solid core, interior, 3668, prehung, paint grade	EA	134.49	88.10	222.59	64.35	198.84	0.9300
08.2009 041	Door, solid core, interior, to 2870, prehung, paint grade	EA	130.13	96.91	227.04	70.78	200.91	1.0230
08.2009 051	Door, solid core, interior, 3070, prehung, paint grade	EA	134.46	96.91	231.37	70.78	205.24	1.0230
08.2009 061	Door, solid core, interior, 3670, prehung, paint grade	EA	139.97	96.91	236.88	70.78	210.75	1.0230

Division 8 CSI #	08 - DOORS, WINDOWS & GLASS Description	Unit	Material	Union Install	Union Total	Open Install	Open Total	Unit Man-Hrs
08.2009 000	**DOORS & FRAMES, PREHUNG, SOLID CORE, PAINT GRADE, INTERIOR: (Cont.)**							
08.2009 071	Door, solid core, interior, 3090, prehung, paint grade	EA	170.31	132.15	302.46	96.52	266.83	1.3950
08.2009 081	Door, solid core, interior, 3690, prehung, paint grade	EA	174.53	132.15	306.68	96.52	271.05	1.3950
08.2010 000	**DOORS, JOB HUNG, SOLID, 1-3/4", PAINT GRADE:**							
	Note: Prices include labor (not frame cost) for job fitting to hollow metal frames.							
08.2010 011	Door, solid core, to 2868, paint grade	EA	94.02	176.20	270.22	128.69	222.71	1.8600
08.2010 021	Door, solid core, 3068, paint grade	EA	96.18	176.20	272.38	128.69	224.87	1.8600
08.2010 031	Door, solid core, 3668, paint grade	EA	133.04	176.20	309.24	128.69	261.73	1.8600
08.2010 041	Door, solid core, to 2870, paint grade	EA	96.18	185.01	281.19	135.13	231.31	1.9530
08.2010 051	Door, solid core, 3070, paint grade	EA	102.74	185.01	287.75	135.13	237.87	1.9530
08.2010 061	Door, solid core, 3670, paint grade	EA	139.47	185.01	324.48	135.13	274.60	1.9530
08.2010 071	Door, solid core, 3090, paint grade	EA	170.23	220.25	390.48	160.87	331.10	2.3250
08.2010 081	Door, solid core, 3690, paint grade	EA	178.12	220.25	398.37	160.87	338.99	2.3250
08.2011 000	**DOORS, JOB HUNG, INSTITUTIONAL., SOLID CORE, 1-3/4" STAIN GRADE:**							
08.2011 011	Door, institutional, solid core, 2870, stain grade	EA	186.45	176.20	362.65	128.69	315.14	1.8600
08.2011 021	Door, institutional, solid core, 3070, stain grade	EA	194.79	176.20	370.99	128.69	323.48	1.8600
08.2011 031	Door, institutional, solid core, 3670, stain grade	EA	203.16	176.20	379.36	128.69	331.85	1.8600
08.2011 041	Door, institutional, solid core, 2880, stain grade	EA	278.30	185.01	463.31	135.13	413.43	1.9530
08.2011 051	Door, institutional, solid core, 3080, stain grade	EA	289.41	185.01	474.42	135.13	424.54	1.9530
08.2011 061	Door, institutional, solid core, 3680, stain grade	EA	300.57	185.01	485.58	135.13	435.70	1.9530
08.2011 071	Door, institutional, solid core, 3090, stain grade	EA	417.43	220.25	637.68	160.87	578.30	2.3250
08.2011 081	Door, institutional, solid core, 3690, stain grade	EA	431.34	220.25	651.59	160.87	592.21	2.3250
08.2012 000	**ADDERS FOR WOOD DOORS:**							
08.2012 011	Add for stain grade birch	EA	15.13	21.89	37.02	15.99	31.12	0.2311
08.2012 021	Add for stain grade ash	EA	17.69	28.64	46.33	20.92	38.61	0.3023
08.2012 031	Add for walnut	EA	68.28	64.80	133.08	47.33	115.61	0.6840
08.2012 041	Add for Formica clad	EA	89.51		89.51		89.51	
08.2012 051	Add for prefinishing	EA	22.77		22.77		22.77	
08.2012 061	Add for A label, 3 hour	EA	165.79		165.79		165.79	
08.2012 071	Add for B label, 1-1/2 hour	EA	127.33		127.33		127.33	
08.2012 081	Add for C label, 1 hour	EA	88.83		88.83		88.83	
08.2012 091	Add for X label, 20 minute	EA	9.28		9.28		9.28	
08.2012 101	Add for sound proof, STC 40	EA	175.06	8.02	183.08	5.86	180.92	0.0847
08.2012 111	Add for sound proof, STC 45	EA	212.19	10.75	222.94	7.85	220.04	0.1135
08.2012 121	Add for sound proof, STC 51	EA	424.41	32.69	457.10	23.88	448.29	0.3451
08.2013 000	**JAMB & TRIM SETS (FRAMES):**							
	Note: The following prices assume solid stock, integral stop, with matching wood casing.							
08.2013 011	Jamb & trim, paint grade pine/fir	EA	27.00	110.12	137.12	80.43	107.43	1.1625
08.2013 021	Jamb & trim, stain grade pine/fir	EA	33.73	110.12	143.85	80.43	114.16	1.1625
08.2013 031	Jamb & trim, birch or ash	EA	47.89	123.34	171.23	90.09	137.98	1.3020
08.2013 041	Jamb & trim, walnut	EA	74.98	132.15	207.13	96.52	171.50	1.3950
08.2100 000	**WOOD GARAGE DOORS:**							
08.2101 000	**GARAGE DOORS, WOOD, SPRING BALANCED:**							
08.2101 011	Garage door, 7' x 8', economy, spring	EA	193.10	391.29	584.39	285.80	478.90	4.1306
08.2101 021	Garage door, 7' x 16', economy, spring	EA	262.62	553.20	815.82	404.06	666.68	5.8398
08.2101 031	Garage door, 7' x 16', custom, spring	EA	326.96	586.93	913.89	428.69	755.65	6.1958
08.2101 041	Garage door, 7' x 16', premium, spring	EA	381.05	667.81	1,048.86	487.76	868.81	7.0496
08.2102 000	**GARAGE DOORS, WOOD, TRACK OPERATED:**							
08.2102 011	Garage door, 7' x 8', economy, track	EA	200.86	404.78	605.64	295.65	496.51	4.2730
08.2102 021	Garage door, 7' x 16', economy, track	EA	270.32	566.69	837.01	413.91	684.23	5.9822
08.2102 031	Garage door, 7' x 16', custom, track	EA	337.34	607.09	944.43	443.41	780.75	6.4086
08.2102 041	Garage door, 7' x 16', premium, track	EA	409.41	708.29	1,117.70	517.33	926.74	7.4769
08.2102 051	Garage door, 7' x 16', segment, track	EA	445.45	775.75	1,221.20	566.60	1,012.05	8.1891
08.2103 000	**ADDERS FOR WOOD GARAGE DOORS:**							
08.2103 011	Add for motor operation, premium grade	EA	354.98	264.30	619.28	193.04	548.02	2.7900
08.2103 021	Add for motor operation, standard grade	EA	213.55	264.30	477.85	193.04	406.59	2.7900
08.2200 000	**WOOD DOOR SPECIALTIES:**							
08.2201 000	**DOORS, DECORATOR, TO 3680, 1-3/4":**							
08.2201 011	Door, carved & relief fir	EA	529.78	249.61	779.39	182.32	712.10	2.6350
08.2201 021	Door, carved & relief hardwood	EA	953.64	249.61	1,203.25	182.32	1,135.96	2.6350
08.2201 031	Door, redwood slab	EA	180.09	249.61	429.70	182.32	362.41	2.6350
08.2201 041	French 1 lite or store door	EA	232.60	249.61	482.21	182.32	414.92	2.6350

Division 8 CSI #	08 - DOORS, WINDOWS & GLASS Description	Unit	Material	Union Install	Union Total	Open Install	Open Total	Unit Man-Hrs
08.2201 000	**DOORS, DECORATOR, TO 3680, 1-3/4": (Cont.)**							
08.2201 051	Door, French multi-lite	EA	198.63	249.61	448.24	182.32	380.95	2.6350
08.2201 061	Door, wardrobe, economy, per panel	EA	48.68	66.07	114.75	48.26	96.94	0.6975
08.2201 071	Door, wardrobe, custom, per panel	EA	63.53	66.07	129.60	48.26	111.79	0.6975
08.2202 000	**DOORS, FIR, TO 3070, 1-3/4":**							
08.2202 011	Door, fir, 1 panel, 1 lite	EA	203.86	132.15	336.01	96.52	300.38	1.3950
08.2202 021	Door, fir, 1 panel, 9 lite	EA	231.27	132.15	363.42	96.52	327.79	1.3950
08.2202 031	Door, fir, 1 panel, 12 diamond lite	EA	245.65	132.15	377.80	96.52	342.17	1.3950
08.2202 041	Door, fir, x buck, 1 lite	EA	223.43	132.15	355.58	96.52	319.95	1.3950
08.2202 051	Door, fir, x buck, 9 lite	EA	249.58	132.15	381.73	96.52	346.10	1.3950
08.2202 061	Door, fir, x buck, 12 diamond lite	EA	262.62	132.15	394.77	96.52	359.14	1.3950
08.2202 071	Add for Dutch door	EA	54.88	88.10	142.98	64.35	119.23	0.9300
08.2202 081	Add for Dutch shelf	EA	155.47	29.07	184.54	21.23	176.70	0.3069
08.3000 000	**SPECIAL DOORS:**							
08.3001 000	**ACCESS DOORS:**							
	Note: For roof hatches, see section 07.6015. The following items are installed in ceilings, walls or acoustic tile.							
08.3001 011	Access panel, aluminum, 12" x 12"	EA	30.83	15.24	46.07	11.41	42.24	0.1700
08.3001 021	Access panel, aluminum, 24" x 24"	EA	61.65	20.88	82.53	15.64	77.29	0.2329
08.3001 031	Access panel, galvanized sheet metal, 12" x 12"	EA	20.23	16.70	36.93	12.51	32.74	0.1863
08.3001 041	Access panel, galvanized sheet metal, 24" x 24"	EA	40.51	22.60	63.11	16.93	57.44	0.2521
08.3001 051	Access panel, fire rated, 12"x12"	EA	83.33	16.70	100.03	12.51	95.84	0.1863
08.3001 061	Access panel, fire rated, 24"x24"	EA	123.87	22.60	146.47	16.93	140.80	0.2521
08.3002 000	**ROLL-UP DOOR, CHAIN OPERATED, STEEL, 20 GA, GALVANIZED:**							
08.3002 011	Door, steel roll-up, 8'x10', 20 ga, galvanized	EA	999.17	2,043.12	3,042.29	1,529.95	2,529.12	22.7874
08.3002 021	Door, steel roll-up, 10'x10', 20 ga, galvanized	EA	792.31	2,075.05	2,867.36	1,553.85	2,346.16	23.1435
08.3002 031	Door, steel roll-up, 12'x10', 20 ga, galvanized	EA	883.49	2,138.90	3,022.39	1,601.67	2,485.16	23.8557
08.3002 041	Door, steel roll-up, 12'x12', 20 ga, galvanized	EA	1,084.53	2,170.82	3,255.35	1,625.57	2,710.10	24.2117
08.3002 051	Door, steel roll-up, 14'x14', 20 ga, galvanized	EA	1,355.61	2,170.82	3,526.43	1,625.57	2,981.18	24.2117
08.3002 061	Door, steel roll-up, 18'x14', 20 ga, galvanized	EA	1,923.61	2,777.42	4,701.03	2,079.81	4,003.42	30.9772
08.3002 071	Door, steel roll-up, large, 20 ga, galvanized	SF	9.98	12.18	22.16	9.12	19.10	0.1359
08.3002 081	Add for motor operation	EA	873.75	510.82	1,384.57	382.52	1,256.27	5.6973
08.3002 091	Add for fusible link	EA	222.02	134.10	356.12	100.41	322.43	1.4956
08.3003 000	**GRILL, ROLL-UP, CRANK OPERATED, ALUMINUM:**							
08.3003 011	Grill, aluminum roll-up, 8' x 8', crank	EA	1,238.84	1,085.42	2,324.26	812.80	2,051.64	12.1060
08.3003 021	Grill, aluminum roll-up, 10' x 10', crank	EA	1,437.78	1,436.60	2,874.38	1,075.77	2,513.55	16.0228
08.3003 031	Grill, aluminum roll-up, 10' x 12', crank	EA	1,774.14	2,170.82	3,944.96	1,625.57	3,399.71	24.2117
08.3003 041	Grill, aluminum roll-up, 18' x 8', crank	EA	2,018.13	2,330.46	4,348.59	1,745.12	3,763.25	25.9922
08.3003 051	Add for motor operation	EA	769.77	236.25	1,006.02	176.91	946.68	2.6350
08.3004 000	**DOOR, COUNTER, PUSH-UP, ALUMINUM:**							
08.3004 011	Door, push-up counter, aluminum, 4' x 4'	EA	497.36	667.07	1,164.43	499.52	996.88	7.4400
08.3004 021	Door, push-up counter, aluminum, 6' x 4'	EA	670.32	667.07	1,337.39	499.52	1,169.84	7.4400
08.3004 031	Door, push-up counter, aluminum, 10' x 4'	EA	734.27	750.45	1,484.72	561.96	1,296.23	8.3700
08.3004 041	Add for motor operation	EA	414.47	169.22	583.69	126.71	541.18	1.8873
08.3005 000	**OVERHEAD DOORS, SECTIONAL, PRIME COATED, MANUAL:**							
	Note: For bronze anodized aluminum, add 100% to the material costs.							
08.3005 011	Door, steel over head, 8' x 8', prime coat, manual	EA	432.39	440.59	872.98	329.93	762.32	4.9140
08.3005 021	Door, steel over head, 10'x10', prime coat, manual	EA	538.79	644.84	1,183.63	482.88	1,021.67	7.1921
08.3005 031	Door, steel over head, 12'x12', prime coat, manual	EA	595.55	734.23	1,329.78	549.82	1,145.37	8.1891
08.3005 041	Door, steel over head, 12'x14', prime coat, manual	EA	643.53	925.79	1,569.32	693.26	1,336.79	10.3256
08.3005 051	Add for chain operation	EA	65.43	67.06	132.49	50.21	115.64	0.7479
08.3005 061	Add for motor operation	EA	818.06	134.10	952.16	100.41	918.47	1.4956
08.3005 071	Sliding door with track, 12' x 14'	EA	823.06	341.87	1,164.93	256.00	1,079.06	3.8130
08.3005 081	Sliding door with track, 14' x 16'	EA	1,057.55	391.90	1,449.45	293.47	1,351.02	4.3710
08.3005 091	Sliding door with track, 16' x 20'	EA	1,344.69	475.29	1,819.98	355.91	1,700.60	5.3010
08.3005 101	Industrial door to 50' x 30', complete	SF	22.13	50.86	72.99	38.09	60.22	0.5673
08.3005 111	Industrial door, 90' x 30', complete	SF	25.67	54.20	79.87	40.59	66.26	0.6045
08.3006 000	**SLIDING FIRE DOORS WITH HARDWARE, FUSIBLE LINK:**							
08.3006 011	Fire door, sliding, 4' x 7', with hardware	EA	881.21	1,915.42	2,796.63	1,434.32	2,315.53	21.3631
08.3006 021	Fire door, sliding, 6' x 7', with hardware	EA	1,145.59	2,138.90	3,284.49	1,601.67	2,747.26	23.8557
08.3006 031	Fire door, sliding, 10' x 10', with hardware	EA	2,368.31	4,565.13	6,933.44	3,418.50	5,786.81	50.9160
08.3006 041	Fire door, sliding, with hardware	SF	25.95	47.10	73.05	35.27	61.22	0.5253

Division 8 CSI #	08 - DOORS, WINDOWS & GLASS Description	Unit	Material	Union Install	Union Total	Open Install	Open Total	Unit Man-Hrs
08.3006 000	**SLIDING FIRE DOORS WITH HARDWARE, FUSIBLE LINK: (Cont.)**							
08.3006 051	Fire shutter door, stainless steel center 4'x4'	EA	4,681.59	1,075.92	5,757.51	805.68	5,487.27	12.0000
08.3006 061	Fire shutter door, stainless steel center 4'x6'	EA	4,908.95	1,291.10	6,200.05	966.82	5,875.77	14.4000
08.3006 071	Fire shutter door, stainless steel center 4'x10'	EA	6,451.22	1,681.13	8,132.35	1,258.88	7,710.10	18.7500
08.3007 000	**FIRE DOORS, ROLL-UP:**							
08.3007 011	Fire door, roll-up, 6070, 4 hour	EA	913.37	2,075.05	2,988.42	1,553.85	2,467.22	23.1435
08.3007 021	Fire door, roll-up, 5080, 3 hour	EA	950.03	2,075.05	3,025.08	1,553.85	2,503.88	23.1435
08.3007 031	Fire door, roll-up	SF	26.65	49.91	76.56	37.38	64.03	0.5567
08.3008 000	**VAULT DOORS, MINIMUM SECURITY:**							
	Note: For bank vault doors, see section 11.1101.							
08.3008 011	Vault door, 3070, 2 hour	EA	1,957.69	1,500.91	3,458.60	1,123.92	3,081.61	16.7400
08.3008 021	Vault door, 4070, 2 hour	EA	2,799.48	1,500.91	4,300.39	1,123.92	3,923.40	16.7400
08.3008 031	Vault door, 3070, 4 hour	EA	2,194.12	1,667.68	3,861.80	1,248.80	3,442.92	18.6000
08.3008 041	Vault door, 4070, 4 hour	EA	2,969.65	1,667.68	4,637.33	1,248.80	4,218.45	18.6000
08.3009 000	**REVOLVING DOORS:**							
08.3009 011	Revolving door, 7', aluminum	EA	17,401.47	4,450.19	21,851.66	3,332.43	20,733.90	49.6341
08.3009 021	Revolving door, 7', stainless steel, satin finish	EA	34,986.17	4,450.19	39,436.36	3,332.43	38,318.60	49.6341
08.3009 031	Revolving door, 7', stainless steel, mirror finish	EA	42,313.12	6,626.15	48,939.27	4,961.85	47,274.97	73.9031
08.3009 041	Revolving door, 7', bronze satin finish	EA	34,535.05	6,499.69	41,034.74	4,867.15	39,402.20	72.4926
08.3009 051	Revolving door, 7', bronze mirror	EA	41,946.74	8,435.11	50,381.85	6,316.45	48,263.19	94.0788
08.3010 000	**REFRIGERATOR DOORS WITH HARDWARE & FRAME, 30 DEGREE:**							
08.3010 011	Refrigerator door, 3066, economy, plywood	EA	355.74	1,219.51	1,575.25	913.20	1,268.94	13.6015
08.3010 021	Refrigerator door, 3066, custom, galvanized face	EA	609.86	1,455.76	2,065.62	1,090.12	1,699.98	16.2365
08.3010 031	Refrigerator door, 3066, stainless steel, chrome	EA	1,086.37	1,557.92	2,644.29	1,166.62	2,252.99	17.3759
08.3010 041	Refrigerator door, 4066, economy, plywood	EA	441.46	1,423.84	1,865.30	1,066.21	1,507.67	15.8804
08.3010 051	Refrigerator door, 4066, custom, galvanized face	EA	746.43	1,557.92	2,304.35	1,166.62	1,913.05	17.3759
08.3010 061	Refrigerator door, 4066, stainless steel, chrome	EA	1,461.15	1,660.08	3,121.23	1,243.12	2,704.27	18.5153
08.4000 000	**WINDOWS & DOORS, GLAZED:**							
08.4001 000	**WINDOWS, VINYL, INSULATED GLASS WITH 1/2" AIR:**							
	Note: The following items are residential/light commercial grade Intermediate quality with white or almond vinyl; clear insulated glass with 1/2" air, no grid							
	Note: Apply all adder percentages to base price only.							
	Bronze or grey glass add: 15%							
	For low-E glazing add: 15%, Tempered add: 40%							
	For economy quality materials deduct 15%							
	Note: X means active panel, O means stationary panel							
	Window sizes are expressed in width then height, where the feet & inches are not shown.							
	For example, 2'8" by '6'8" is expressed "2868".							
08.4001 011	Window, vinyl, sliding, XO, 2016, clear insulated glass	EA	169.40	34.74	204.14	25.37	194.77	0.3667
08.4001 021	Window, vinyl, sliding, XO, 2630, clear insulated glass	EA	230.72	34.74	265.46	25.37	256.09	0.3667
08.4001 031	Window, vinyl, sliding, XO, 3040, clear insulated glass	EA	267.61	41.84	309.45	30.56	298.17	0.4417
08.4001 041	Window, vinyl, sliding, XO, 4040, clear insulated glass	EA	292.00	48.95	340.95	35.75	327.75	0.5167
08.4001 051	Window, vinyl, sliding, XO, 5050, clear insulated glass	EA	356.43	55.26	411.69	40.36	396.79	0.5833
08.4001 061	Window, vinyl, sliding, XO, 6040, clear insulated glass	EA	345.45	55.26	400.71	40.36	385.81	0.5833
08.4001 071	Window, vinyl, sliding, XO, 6050, clear insulated glass	EA	402.06	69.47	471.53	50.74	452.80	0.7333
08.4001 081	Window, vinyl, sliding, clear insulated glass, average cost	SF	24.25	2.43	26.68	1.78	26.03	0.0257
08.4002 000	**WINDOWS, VINYL, CASEMENT, INSULATED GLASS WITH 1/2" AIR, WITH SCREEN:**							
08.4002 011	Window, vinyl, casement, X, 1620, clear insulated glass	EA	276.44	34.74	311.18	25.37	301.81	0.3667
08.4002 021	Window, vinyl, casement, X, 2026, clear insulated glass	EA	357.71	34.74	392.45	25.37	383.08	0.3667
08.4002 031	Window, vinyl, casement, X, 2050, clear insulated glass	EA	391.05	34.74	425.79	25.37	416.42	0.3667
08.4002 041	Window, vinyl, casement, X, 2630, clear insulated glass	EA	337.83	34.74	372.57	25.37	363.20	0.3667
08.4002 051	Window, vinyl, casement, X, 2646, clear insulated glass	EA	389.56	41.84	431.40	30.56	420.12	0.4417
08.4002 061	Window, vinyl, casement, X, 3040, clear insulated glass	EA	382.57	41.84	424.41	30.56	413.13	0.4417
08.4002 071	Window, vinyl, casement, clear insulated glass, average cost	SF	50.46	2.43	52.89	1.78	52.24	0.0257
08.4003 000	**WINDOWS, VINYL, SINGLE HUNG, INSULATED GLASS WITH 1/2" AIR, WITH SCREEN:**							
08.4003 011	Window, vinyl, single hung, 2030, clear insulated glass	EA	205.60	34.74	240.34	25.37	230.97	0.3667
08.4003 021	Window, vinyl, single hung, 2650, clear insulated glass	EA	264.79	41.84	306.63	30.56	295.35	0.4417
08.4003 031	Window, vinyl, single hung, 3060, clear insulated glass	EA	309.28	48.95	358.23	35.75	345.03	0.5167
08.4003 041	Window, vinyl, single hung, 4070, clear insulated glass	EA	375.07	61.57	436.64	44.97	420.04	0.6500
08.4003 051	Window, vinyl, single hung, clear insulated glass, average cost	SF	21.52	2.43	23.95	1.78	23.30	0.0257

Division 8 CSI #	08 - DOORS, WINDOWS & GLASS Description	Unit	Material	Union Install	Union Total	Open Install	Open Total	Unit Man-Hrs
08.4004 000	**WINDOWS, VINYL, FIXED, INSULATED GLASS WITH 1/2" AIR:**							
08.4004 011	Window, vinyl, fixed, 2020, clear insulated glass	EA	99.61	27.78	127.39	20.29	119.90	0.2933
08.4004 021	Window, vinyl, fixed, 2650, clear insulated glass	EA	186.74	33.47	220.21	24.44	211.18	0.3533
08.4004 031	Window, vinyl, fixed, 3030, clear insulated glass	EA	150.56	27.78	178.34	20.29	170.85	0.2933
08.4004 041	Window, vinyl, fixed, 4040, clear insulated glass	EA	207.37	39.15	246.52	28.60	235.97	0.4133
08.4004 051	Window, vinyl, fixed, 5050, clear insulated glass	EA	286.85	44.21	331.06	32.29	319.14	0.4667
08.4004 061	Window, vinyl, fixed, 6060, clear insulated glass	EA	466.66	66.95	533.61	48.90	515.56	0.7067
08.4004 071	Window, vinyl, fixed, 7050, clear insulated glass	EA	461.60	66.95	528.55	48.90	510.50	0.7067
08.4004 081	Window, vinyl, fixed, 8050, clear insulated glass	EA	510.95	66.95	577.90	48.90	559.85	0.7067
08.4004 091	Window, vinyl, fixed, 10040, clear insulated glass	EA	527.54	66.95	594.49	48.90	576.44	0.7067
08.4004 101	Window, vinyl, fixed, clear insulated glass, average cost	SF	14.79	1.95	16.74	1.43	16.22	0.0206
08.4005 000	**DOORS, VINYL, SLIDING, INSULATED GLASS WITH 1/2" AIR, WITH SCREEN:**							
	Note: The following items are glazed with tempered glass.							
08.4005 011	Door, vinyl, sliding, 5068, XO, clear insulated glass	EA	659.90	198.32	858.22	144.85	804.75	2.0935
08.4005 021	Door, vinyl, sliding, 6068, XO, clear insulated glass	EA	715.48	222.63	938.11	162.61	878.09	2.3502
08.4005 031	Door, vinyl, sliding, 8068, XO, clear insulated glass	EA	891.07	249.19	1,140.26	182.00	1,073.07	2.6305
08.4005 041	Door, vinyl, sliding, 10068, OXXO, clear insulated glass	EA	1,497.42	269.86	1,767.28	197.10	1,694.52	2.8487
08.4005 051	Door, vinyl, sliding, 12068, OXO, clear insulated glass	EA	1,546.54	384.55	1,931.09	280.87	1,827.41	4.0594
08.4005 061	Door, vinyl, sliding, 12068, OXXO, clear insulated glass	EA	1,648.41	384.55	2,032.96	280.87	1,929.28	4.0594
08.4005 071	Door, vinyl, sliding, 6080, XO, clear insulated glass	EA	1,043.21	222.63	1,265.84	162.61	1,205.82	2.3502
08.4005 081	Door, vinyl, sliding, 8080, XO, clear insulated glass	EA	1,104.88	269.86	1,374.74	197.10	1,301.98	2.8487
08.4005 091	Door, vinyl, sliding, clear insulated glass, average cost	SF	19.40	4.98	24.38	3.64	23.04	0.0526
08.5000 000	**WINDOWS, ALUMINUM, INSULATED GLASS WITH 1/2" AIR SPACE:**							
	Note: The following items are residential/light commercial grade Intermediate quality with clear, white,							
	or bronze aluminum; clear insulated glass with 1/2" air, no grid							
	Note: Apply all adder percentages to base price only.							
	For clear single glazing deduct: 20%, Bronze or grey glass add: 20%							
	For low-E glazing add: 15%, Tempered add: 60%							
	For thermally broken frame add 20%							
	For economy quality materials deduct 20%, Premium add 50%							
08.5001 000	**WINDOWS, ALUMINUM, SLIDING, INSULATED GLASS WITH 1/2" AIR, WITH SCREEN:**							
08.5001 011	Window, aluminum, sliding, XO, 2016, clear insulated glass	EA	66.16	34.78	100.94	25.40	91.56	0.3671
08.5001 021	Window, aluminum, sliding, XO, 2030, clear insulated glass	EA	87.14	34.78	121.92	25.40	112.54	0.3671
08.5001 031	Window, aluminum, sliding, XO, 3040, clear insulated glass	EA	123.23	41.69	164.92	30.45	153.68	0.4401
08.5001 041	Window, aluminum, sliding, XO, 4040, clear insulated glass	EA	137.41	48.71	186.12	35.58	172.99	0.5142
08.5001 051	Window, aluminum, sliding, XO, 5040, clear insulated glass	EA	154.46	48.71	203.17	35.58	190.04	0.5142
08.5001 061	Window, aluminum, sliding, XO, 6040, clear insulated glass	EA	168.66	55.63	224.29	40.64	209.30	0.5873
08.5001 071	Window, aluminum, sliding, XOX, 8040, clear insulated glass	EA	252.97	69.54	322.51	50.79	303.76	0.7341
08.5001 081	Window, aluminum, sliding, XOX, 10040, clear insulated glass	EA	289.29	83.38	372.67	60.90	350.19	0.8802
08.5001 091	Window, aluminum, sliding, clear insulated glass, average cost	SF	10.66	2.43	13.09	1.77	12.43	0.0256
08.5002 000	**WINDOWS, ALUMINUM, CASEMENT, INSULATED GLASS WITH 1/2" AIR, WITH SCREEN:**							
08.5002 011	Window, aluminum, casement, X, 2026, clear insulated glass	EA	169.23	34.78	204.01	25.40	194.63	0.3671
08.5002 021	Window, aluminum, casement, X, 2640, clear insulated glass	EA	226.16	34.78	260.94	25.40	251.56	0.3671
08.5002 031	Window, aluminum, casement, XO, 4050, clear insulated glass	EA	295.70	48.71	344.41	35.58	331.28	0.5142
08.5002 041	Window, aluminum, casement, XX, 4050, clear insulated glass	EA	371.12	48.71	419.83	35.58	406.70	0.5142
08.5002 051	Window, aluminum, casement, XO, 6030, clear insulated glass	EA	272.99	48.71	321.70	35.58	308.57	0.5142
08.5002 061	Window, aluminum, casement, XX, 6030, clear insulated glass	EA	345.57	48.71	394.28	35.58	381.15	0.5142
08.5002 071	Window, aluminum, casement, clear insulated glass, average cost	SF	23.53	2.43	25.96	1.77	25.30	0.0256
08.5003 000	**WINDOWS, ALUMINUM, SINGLE HUNG, INSULATED GLASS WITH 1/2" AIR, WITH SCREEN:**							
08.5003 011	Window, aluminum, single hung, 2030, clear insulated glass	EA	107.14	34.78	141.92	25.40	132.54	0.3671
08.5003 021	Window, aluminum, single hung, 2640, clear insulated glass	EA	136.61	34.78	171.39	25.40	162.01	0.3671
08.5003 031	Window, aluminum, single hung, 3060, clear insulated glass	EA	177.78	48.71	226.49	35.58	213.36	0.5142
08.5003 041	Window, aluminum, single hung, 4080, clear insulated glass	EA	251.42	69.54	320.96	50.79	302.21	0.7341
08.5003 051	Window, aluminum, single hung, clear insulated glass, average cost	SF	12.30	1.58	13.88	.73	13.03	0.0256
08.5004 000	**WINDOWS, ALUMINUM, FIXED, INSULATED GLASS WITH 1/2" AIR:**							
08.5004 011	Window, aluminum, fixed, 2020, clear insulated glass	EA	52.34	27.78	80.12	20.29	72.63	0.2933
08.5004 021	Window, aluminum, fixed, 2650, clear insulated glass	EA	97.68	33.47	131.15	24.44	122.12	0.3533
08.5004 031	Window, aluminum, fixed, 3030, clear insulated glass	EA	78.72	27.78	106.50	20.29	99.01	0.2933
08.5004 041	Window, aluminum, fixed, 4040, clear insulated glass	EA	109.07	39.15	148.22	28.60	137.67	0.4133
08.5004 051	Window, aluminum, fixed, 5050, clear insulated glass	EA	160.55	44.21	204.76	32.29	192.84	0.4667
08.5004 061	Window, aluminum, fixed, 6060, clear insulated glass	EA	270.55	66.95	337.50	48.90	319.45	0.7067
08.5004 071	Window, aluminum, fixed, 7050, clear insulated glass	EA	270.73	55.58	326.31	40.59	311.32	0.5867

Division 8 CSI #	08 - DOORS, WINDOWS & GLASS Description	Unit	Material	Union Install	Union Total	Open Install	Open Total	Unit Man-Hrs
08.5004 000	**WINDOWS, ALUMINUM, FIXED, INSULATED GLASS WITH 1/2" AIR: (Cont.)**							
08.5004 081	Window, aluminum, fixed, 8050, clear insulated glass	EA	300.56	66.95	367.51	48.90	349.46	0.7067
08.5004 091	Window, aluminum, fixed, 10040, clear insulated glass	EA	308.58	66.95	375.53	48.90	357.48	0.7067
08.5004 101	Window, aluminum, fixed, clear insulated glass, average cost	SF	8.16	1.95	10.11	1.43	9.59	0.0206
08.5005 000	**DOORS, ALUMINUM, SLIDING, INSULATED GLASS WITH 1/2" AIR, WITH SCREEN:**							
	Note: The following items are glazed with tempered glass.							
	Note: X means active panel, O means stationary panel							
08.5005 011	Door, aluminum, sliding, 5068, XO, clear insulated glass	EA	410.30	198.32	608.62	144.85	555.15	2.0935
08.5005 021	Door, aluminum, sliding, 6068, XO, clear insulated glass	EA	444.86	222.63	667.49	162.61	607.47	2.3502
08.5005 031	Door, aluminum, sliding, 8068, XO, clear insulated glass	EA	554.02	249.61	803.63	182.32	736.34	2.6350
08.5005 041	Door, aluminum, sliding, 10068, OXXO, clear insulated glass	EA	931.02	269.86	1,200.88	197.10	1,128.12	2.8487
08.5005 051	Door, aluminum, sliding, 12068, OXO, clear insulated glass	EA	961.57	384.55	1,346.12	280.87	1,242.44	4.0594
08.5005 061	Door, aluminum, sliding, 12068, OXXO, clear insulated glass	EA	1,024.87	384.55	1,409.42	280.87	1,305.74	4.0594
08.5005 071	Door, aluminum, sliding, 6080, XO, clear insulated glass	EA	551.64	265.24	816.88	193.73	745.37	2.8000
08.5005 081	Door, aluminum, sliding, 8080, XO, clear insulated glass	EA	686.94	249.61	936.55	182.32	869.26	2.6350
08.5005 091	Door, aluminum, sliding, clear insulated glass, average cost	SF	11.82	4.98	16.80	3.64	15.46	0.0526
08.5006 000	**METAL SASH, UNGLAZED:**							
	Note: For commercial sash glazing, see section 08.8000 Glass & Glazing.							
08.5006 011	Sash, steel, industrial, vented 50%	SF	13.39	5.80	19.19	4.23	17.62	0.0612
08.5006 021	Sash, steel, projected, vented 100%	SF	16.10	5.80	21.90	4.23	20.33	0.0612
08.5006 031	Sash, steel, industrial, fixed 100%	SF	10.22	5.80	16.02	4.23	14.45	0.0612
08.5006 041	Sash, aluminum, industrial, vented 50%	SF	15.83	6.41	22.24	4.68	20.51	0.0677
08.5006 051	Sash, aluminum, projected, vented 100%	SF	20.39	6.41	26.80	4.68	25.07	0.0677
08.5006 061	Sash, aluminum, industrial, fixed 100%	SF	10.69	5.80	16.49	4.23	14.92	0.0612
08.5006 071	Add for screens	SF	3.79		3.79		3.79	
08.6000 000	**WINDOWS, WOOD, INSULATED GLASS:**							
08.6001 000	**WINDOWS, WOOD, INSULATED GLASS WITH 1/4" AIR, WITH SCREEN:**							
	Note: The following windows are unfinished softwood, built to order; prices include standard frame with							
	exterior mould, 1-3/8" sash, glazed clear, weatherstrip, hardware and screens							
08.6001 010	**WINDOWS, WOOD, DOUBLE HUNG, 2 LITE, INSULATED GLASS WITH 1/2" AIR, WITH SCREEN:**							
08.6001 021	Window, wood, double hung, 1626, 2 lite, clear insulated glass	EA	230.44	90.39	320.83	66.02	296.46	0.9542
08.6001 031	Window, wood, double hung, 2026, 2 lite, clear insulated glass	EA	233.51	90.39	323.90	66.02	299.53	0.9542
08.6001 041	Window, wood, double hung, 2030, 2 lite, clear insulated glass	EA	245.71	90.39	336.10	66.02	311.73	0.9542
08.6001 051	Window, wood, double hung, 2036, 2 lite, clear insulated glass	EA	282.31	90.39	372.70	66.02	348.33	0.9542
08.6001 061	Window, wood, double hung, 2640, 2 lite, clear insulated glass	EA	309.80	90.39	400.19	66.02	375.82	0.9542
08.6001 071	Window, wood, double hung, 2646, 2 lite, clear insulated glass	EA	331.17	97.31	428.48	71.07	402.24	1.0272
08.6001 081	Window, wood, double hung, 3040, 2 lite, clear insulated glass	EA	344.89	97.31	442.20	71.07	415.96	1.0272
08.6001 091	Window, wood, double hung, 3046, 2 lite, clear insulated glass	EA	369.32	97.31	466.63	71.07	440.39	1.0272
08.6001 101	Window, wood, double hung, 3050, 2 lite, clear insulated glass	EA	392.20	97.31	489.51	71.07	463.27	1.0272
08.6001 111	Window, wood, double hung, 3060, 2 lite, clear insulated glass	EA	486.82	111.23	598.05	81.24	568.06	1.1742
08.6001 121	Window, wood, double hung, 4046, 2 lite, clear insulated glass	EA	445.64	131.99	577.63	96.40	542.04	1.3933
08.6001 131	Window, wood, double hung, 4060, 2 lite, clear insulated glass	EA	595.18	131.99	727.17	96.40	691.58	1.3933
08.6001 141	Window, wood, double hung, 2 lite, clear insulated glass, average cost	SF	34.07		34.07		34.07	
08.6002 000	**WINDOWS, WOOD, CASEMENT, 2 LITE, INSULATED GLASS WITH 1/4" AIR, WITH SCREEN:**							
08.6002 011	Window, wood, casement, 1620, 1 lite, clear insulated glass	EA	186.19	97.31	283.50	71.07	257.26	1.0272
08.6002 021	Window, wood, casement, 2030, 1 lite, clear insulated glass	EA	239.59	104.22	343.81	76.12	315.71	1.1002
08.6002 031	Window, wood, casement, 5040, XX, 2 lite, clear insulated glass	EA	561.62	180.60	742.22	131.91	693.53	1.9065
08.6002 041	Window, wood, casement, 8050, XOX, 3 lite, clear insulated glass	EA	1,024.01	194.53	1,218.54	142.08	1,166.09	2.0535
08.6002 051	Window, wood, casement, 10050, XOX, 3 lite, clear insulated glass	EA	1,190.35	250.13	1,440.48	182.70	1,373.05	2.6405
08.6002 061	Window, wood, casement, 2 lite, clear insulated glass, average cost	SF	35.88		35.88		35.88	
08.6003 000	**WINDOWS, WOOD, FIXED, 1 LITE, INSULATED GLASS WITH 1/4" AIR, WITH SCREEN:**							
08.6003 011	Window, wood, fixed, 2020, 1 lite, clear insulated glass	EA	141.94	77.85	219.79	56.86	198.80	0.8218
08.6003 021	Window, wood, fixed, 3036, 1 lite, clear insulated glass	EA	231.98	77.85	309.83	56.86	288.84	0.8218
08.6003 031	Window, wood, fixed, 5060, 1 lite, clear insulated glass	EA	546.35	104.22	650.57	76.12	622.47	1.1002
08.6003 041	Window, wood, fixed, average cost/SF	SF	25.24		25.24		25.24	
08.6005 000	**WINDOWS, WOOD, VINYL CLAD, INSULATED GLASS WITH 1/2" AIR SPACE:**							
	Note: The following windows are white or tan vinyl clad exterior, unfinished softwood interior; prices							
	include standard frame depth, HP insulated glass, with strip, hardware and screen							
08.6005 010	**WINDOWS, WOOD, VINYL CLAD, DOUBLE HUNG, 2 LITE, INSULATED GLASS WITH 1/2" AIR, WITH SCREEN:**							
08.6005 011	Window, wood, vinyl clad, double hung, 18210, 2 lite, clear insulated glass	EA	238.86	34.74	273.60	25.37	264.23	0.3667
08.6005 021	Window, wood, vinyl clad, double hung, 2032, 2 lite, clear insulated glass	EA	254.60	34.74	289.34	25.37	279.97	0.3667
08.6005 031	Window, wood, vinyl clad, double hung, 24310, 2 lite, clear insulated glass	EA	287.94	34.74	322.68	25.37	313.31	0.3667

Division 8 CSI #	08 - DOORS, WINDOWS & GLASS Description	Unit	Material	Union Install	Union Total	Open Install	Open Total	Unit Man-Hrs
08.6005 010	**WINDOWS, WOOD, VINYL CLAD, DOUBLE HUNG, 2 LITE, INSULATED GLASS WITH 1/2" AIR, WITH SCREEN: (Cont.)**							
08.6005 041	Window, wood, vinyl clad, double hung, 2842, 2 lite, clear insulated glass	EA	326.84	41.84	368.68	30.56	357.40	0.4417
08.6005 051	Window, wood, vinyl clad, double hung, 3046, 2 lite, clear insulated glass	EA	361.09	41.84	402.93	30.56	391.65	0.4417
08.6005 061	Window, wood, vinyl clad, double hung, 3452, 2 lite, clear insulated glass	EA	413.85	48.95	462.80	35.75	449.60	0.5167
08.6005 071	Window, wood, vinyl clad, double hung, 3856, 2 lite, clear insulated glass	EA	455.50	55.26	510.76	40.36	495.86	0.5833
08.6005 081	Window, wood, vinyl clad, double hung, 3862, 2 lite, clear insulated glass	EA	517.54	55.26	572.80	40.36	557.90	0.5833
08.6005 091	Window, wood, vinyl clad, double hung, 2 lite, clear insulated glass, average	SF	30.93		30.93		30.93	
08.6006 000	**WINDOWS, WOOD, VINYL CLAD, CASEMENT, 2 LITE, INSULATED GLASS WITH 1/2" AIR, WITH SCREEN:**							
08.6006 011	Window, wood, vinyl clad, casement, 1818, 1 lite, clear insulated glass	EA	183.32	34.74	218.06	25.37	208.69	0.3667
08.6006 021	Window, wood, vinyl clad, casement, 18210, 1 lite, clear insulated glass	EA	203.67	34.74	238.41	25.37	229.04	0.3667
08.6006 031	Window, wood, vinyl clad, casement, 2333, 1 lite, clear insulated glass	EA	239.79	34.74	274.53	25.37	265.16	0.3667
08.6006 041	Window, wood, vinyl clad, casement, 23310, 1 lite, clear insulated glass	EA	274.05	34.74	308.79	25.37	299.42	0.3667
08.6006 051	Window, wood, vinyl clad, casement, 23410, 1 lite, clear insulated glass	EA	326.84	41.84	368.68	30.56	357.40	0.4417
08.6006 061	Window, wood, vinyl clad, casement, 23510, 1 lite, clear insulated glass	EA	378.66	41.84	420.50	30.56	409.22	0.4417
08.6006 071	Window, wood, vinyl clad, casement, 210510, 1 lite, clear insulated glass	EA	459.19	48.95	508.14	35.75	494.94	0.5167
08.6006 081	Window, wood, vinyl clad, casement, 1 lite, clear insulated glass, average	SF	36.46		36.46		36.46	
08.6007 000	**WINDOWS, WOOD, VINYL CLAD, FIXED, 1 LITE, INSULATED GLASS WITH 1/4" AIR, WITH SCREEN:**							
08.6007 011	Window, wood, vinyl clad, fixed, 3320, 1 lite, clear insulated glass	EA	237.95	27.78	265.73	20.29	258.24	0.2933
08.6007 021	Window, wood, vinyl clad, fixed, 31043, 1 lite, clear insulated glass	EA	382.37	39.15	421.52	28.60	410.97	0.4133
08.6007 031	Window, wood, vinyl clad, fixed, 310510, 1 lite, clear insulated glass	EA	509.22	44.21	553.43	32.29	541.51	0.4667
08.6007 041	Window, wood, vinyl clad, fixed, 510410, 1 lite, clear insulated glass	EA	680.49	49.26	729.75	35.98	716.47	0.5200
08.6007 051	Window, wood, vinyl clad, fixed, 1 lite, clear insulated glass, average	SF	26.78		26.78		26.78	
08.7000 000	**FINISH HARDWARE:**							
08.7001 000	**HARDWARE, IN PLACE COSTS, AVERAGE**							
08.7001 011	Hardware, tract, 3 bedroom, 2 bath	UNIT	2,754.63	775.27	3,529.90	566.25	3,320.88	8.1840
08.7001 021	Hardware, custom, 4 bedroom, 3 bath	UNIT	2,029.94	1,860.65	3,890.59	1,359.00	3,388.94	19.6416
08.7001 031	Hardware, commercial, economy	SF	.22	.27	.49	.19	.41	0.0028
08.7001 041	Hardware, commercial, standard	SF	.53	.44	.97	.32	.85	0.0046
08.7001 051	Hardware, institutional, with out panic hardware	DOOR	421.46	209.14	630.60	152.75	574.21	2.2077
08.7001 061	Hardware, hospital, with out panic hardware	DOOR	523.63	266.48	790.11	194.64	718.27	2.8131
08.7001 071	Hardware, office, with out panic hardware	DOOR	316.16	165.28	481.44	120.72	436.88	1.7448
08.7002 000	**GENERAL HARDWARE ITEMS:**							
	Note: Install prices are for labor to install in pre-machined doors. Commercial hardware is priced as dull chrome (26D). Residential locksets priced as polished brass (US3), hinges as dull brass (US4). Many other finishes are available.							
	Note: Letters in the lockset descriptions below refer to Schlage product codes for standard of quality.							
08.7002 011	Lockset, decorative entry, 'E/B'	EA	366.81	70.02	436.83	51.15	417.96	0.7392
08.7002 021	Lockset, commercial, mortise, 'L'	EA	266.79	39.79	306.58	29.06	295.85	0.4200
08.7002 031	Lockset, commercial, 'D'	EA	187.08	39.79	226.87	29.06	216.14	0.4200
08.7002 041	Lockset, commercial, 'S'	EA	110.24	32.03	142.27	23.39	133.63	0.3381
08.7002 051	Lockset, residential, good, 'A'	EA	79.67	25.70	105.37	18.77	98.44	0.2713
08.7002 061	Lockset, residential, economy, 'F'	EA	28.67	25.67	54.34	18.75	47.42	0.2710
08.7002 071	Latchset, commercial, mortise, 'L'	EA	202.87	37.89	240.76	27.68	230.55	0.4000
08.7002 081	Latchset, commercial, 'D'	EA	138.97	35.82	174.79	26.16	165.13	0.3781
08.7002 091	Latchset, commercial, 'S'	EA	66.82	32.03	98.85	23.39	90.21	0.3381
08.7002 101	Latchset, residential, 'A'	EA	37.96	25.70	63.66	18.77	56.73	0.2713
08.7002 111	Latchset, residential, privacy, 'A'	EA	44.49	25.70	70.19	18.77	63.26	0.2713
08.7002 112	Latchset, residential, 'F'	EA	15.30	25.70	41.00	18.77	34.07	0.2713
08.7002 121	Dummy trim, pair, 'L'	EA	192.67	35.82	228.49	26.16	218.83	0.3781
08.7002 131	Dummy trim, single, 'D'	EA	62.99	26.99	89.98	19.71	82.70	0.2849
08.7002 141	Add for electrified mortise lock	EA	143.57		143.57		143.57	
08.7002 151	Add for lead lined mortise lock	EA	111.15		111.15		111.15	
08.7002 161	Single cylinder, residential, economy, deadbolt, 'B16O'	EA	26.87	25.70	52.57	18.77	45.64	0.2713
08.7002 171	Double cylinder residential, economy, deadbolt, 'B162'	EA	37.96	25.70	63.66	18.77	56.73	0.2713
08.7002 181	Single cylinder, residential, standard, deadbolt, 'B46O'	EA	51.87	25.70	77.57	18.77	70.64	0.2713
08.7002 191	Double cylinder residential, standard, deadbolt, 'B462'	EA	65.79	25.70	91.49	18.77	84.56	0.2713
08.7002 201	Single cylinder, residential, standard, deadbolt, 'B56O'	EA	97.24	29.37	126.61	21.45	118.69	0.3100
08.7002 202	Double cylinder residential, standard, deadbolt, 'B562'	EA	115.80	29.37	145.17	21.45	137.25	0.3100
08.7002 211	Add lever handle, residential, economy, 'F'	EA	6.24		6.24		6.24	
08.7002 221	Add lever handle, residential, standard, 'A'	EA	19.42		19.42		19.42	
08.7002 231	Hinge, butt, 4.5x4.5, standard weight	PR	15.27	32.70	47.97	23.88	39.15	0.3452
08.7002 241	Hinge, butt, 4.5x4.5, standard weight, ball bearing	PR	27.71	32.70	60.41	23.88	51.59	0.3452

Division 8 CSI #	08 - DOORS, WINDOWS & GLASS Description	Unit	Material	Union Install	Union Total	Open Install	Open Total	Unit Man-Hrs
08.7002 000	**GENERAL HARDWARE ITEMS: (Cont.)**							
08.7002 251	Hinge, butt, 4.5x4.5, heavy weight, ball bearing	PR	60.04	32.70	92.74	23.88	83.92	0.3452
08.7002 261	Hinge, butt, 4.5x4.5, standard weight, ball bearing, brass	PR	62.18	32.70	94.88	23.88	86.06	0.3452
08.7002 271	Add elec thru wire or monitor	EA	152.40		152.40		152.40	
08.7002 281	Hinge, butt, 4" x 4", residential	PR	4.51	32.70	37.21	23.88	28.39	0.3452
08.7002 291	Hinge, butt, 3.5x3.5, residential	PR	3.18	25.70	28.88	18.77	21.95	0.2713
08.7002 301	Hinge, swing clear, 4.5, standard weight, ball bearing	PR	109.26	53.29	162.55	38.92	148.18	0.5625
08.7002 311	Hinge, butt, spring, 4.5x4.5 standard weight	EA	35.79	25.70	61.49	18.77	54.56	0.2713
08.7002 321	Hinge, butt, spring, 4x4, residential	EA	27.68	25.70	53.38	18.77	46.45	0.2713
08.7002 331	Hinge, double acting, 7"	PR	124.28	60.81	185.09	44.41	168.69	0.6419
08.7002 341	Hinge, pivot set, t & b, interior to 3'	EA	182.62	65.39	248.01	47.76	230.38	0.6903
08.7002 351	Hinge, pivot set, t & b, exterior to 3'	EA	262.12	65.39	327.51	47.76	309.88	0.6903
08.7002 361	Hinge, pivot set, t & b, exterior over 3'	EA	368.93	80.97	449.90	59.14	428.07	0.8547
08.7002 371	Intermediate pivot, standard	EA	131.49	25.70	157.19	18.77	150.26	0.2713
08.7002 381	Hinge, floor residential	ST	99.31	65.39	164.70	47.76	147.07	0.6903
08.7002 391	Closer, economy	EA	53.04	60.72	113.76	44.35	97.39	0.6410
08.7002 401	Closer, standard	EA	93.70	67.47	161.17	49.28	142.98	0.7122
08.7002 411	Closer, heavy duty	EA	170.83	87.71	258.54	64.06	234.89	0.9259
08.7002 421	Closer, floor mounted, hold open, w/cover	ST	757.90	118.06	875.96	86.23	844.13	1.2463
08.7002 422	Closer, floor mounted, non-hold open, w/cover	ST	702.11	118.06	820.17	86.23	788.34	1.2463
08.7002 423	Closer, floor mounted, install cement case	EA		189.46	189.46	138.38	138.38	2.0000
08.7002 431	Closer, smoke activated	EA	755.43	241.92	997.35	176.70	932.13	2.5538
08.7002 441	Panic devices, good, single door	EA	421.91	220.25	642.16	160.87	582.78	2.3250
08.7002 451	Panic devices, good, double door	PR	886.63	330.37	1,217.00	241.30	1,127.93	3.4875
08.7002 461	Panic devices, best, single door	EA	969.25	220.25	1,189.50	160.87	1,130.12	2.3250
08.7002 471	Panic devices, best, double door	PR	2,015.11	330.37	2,345.48	241.30	2,256.41	3.4875
08.7002 481	Panic device, best, fire labeled, single door	EA	1,064.45	220.25	1,284.70	160.87	1,225.32	2.3250
08.7002 491	Panic device, best, fire labeled, double door	PR	2,289.77	330.37	2,620.14	241.30	2,531.07	3.4875
08.7002 501	Kick plate, 10"x34", 16 ga bronze	EA	63.83	44.56	108.39	32.55	96.38	0.4704
08.7002 511	Kick plate, 10"x34", 18 ga stainless steel	EA	48.94	44.56	93.50	32.55	81.49	0.4704
08.7002 521	Push plate, 4"x16", wrought bronze	EA	16.95	18.95	35.90	13.84	30.79	0.2000
08.7002 531	Pull, 4" x 16', wrought bronze	EA	44.75	18.95	63.70	13.84	58.59	0.2000
08.7002 541	Pull bar, 30"	EA	119.38	12.81	132.19	9.35	128.73	0.1352
08.7002 551	Flush bolt, automatic, with label	EA	191.83	74.21	266.04	54.20	246.03	0.7834
08.7002 561	Flush bolt, extension	EA	32.49	35.03	67.52	25.59	58.08	0.3698
08.7002 571	Surface bolt, 4"	EA	7.54	31.66	39.20	23.12	30.66	0.3342
08.7002 581	Surface bolt, 6"	EA	10.19	31.66	41.85	23.12	33.31	0.3342
08.7002 591	Surface bolt, 12"brass, decorative	PR	212.45	37.89	250.34	27.68	240.13	0.4000
08.7002 601	Cremone bolt with egg handle, brass	EA	618.01	189.46	807.47	138.38	756.39	2.0000
08.7002 611	Dust proof strike	EA	18.76	27.69	46.45	20.22	38.98	0.2923
08.7002 621	Auto door bottom, aluminum, 36", rabbet	EA	42.57	49.57	92.14	36.21	78.78	0.5233
08.7002 631	Auto door bottom, residential, surface mounted	EA	22.51	27.69	50.20	20.22	42.73	0.2923
08.7002 641	Letter drop plate	EA	42.57	35.82	78.39	26.16	68.73	0.3781
08.7002 651	Door stop, rubber, tip, screw base	EA	7.21	5.98	13.19	4.37	11.58	0.0631
08.7002 661	Door stop & holder, floor mounted	EA	26.09	27.69	53.78	20.22	46.31	0.2923
08.7002 671	Door stop & holder, wall mounted	EA	26.09	27.69	53.78	20.22	46.31	0.2923
08.7002 681	Door stop/holder, overhead mounted	EA	165.22	57.36	222.58	41.89	207.11	0.6055
08.7002 691	Door privacy device, viewer	EA	18.88	18.95	37.83	13.84	32.72	0.2000
08.7002 701	Door interview panel, grill	EA	40.45	31.06	71.51	22.69	63.14	0.3279
08.7002 711	Threshold, anodized aluminum, 6" x3'	EA	27.71	18.95	46.66	13.84	41.55	0.2000
08.7002 721	Threshold, bronze, polished, 6"x3'	EA	102.88	18.95	121.83	13.84	116.72	0.2000
08.7002 731	Smoke seal, adhesive, 3x7 door	DOOR	16.17	.70	16.87	.51	16.68	0.0074
08.7002 741	Economy weatherstrip, threshold, 3x7 door	DOOR	20.39	151.80	172.19	110.88	131.27	1.6025
08.7002 742	Weatherstrip, with interlock threshold, 3x7 door	DOOR	45.49	151.80	197.29	110.88	156.37	1.6025
08.7002 751	Cabinet hardware, residential	LF	9.11	10.82	19.93	7.90	17.01	0.1142
08.7002 761	Cabinet hardware, commercial	LF	15.93	14.19	30.12	10.36	26.29	0.1498
08.7002 771	Cabinet hardware, institutional	LF	19.58	17.91	37.49	13.08	32.66	0.1891
08.7003 000	**ELECTRICALLY OPERATED HARDWARE DEVICES**							
	Note: Electrical connection extra.							
08.7003 011	Electromagnetic door lock	EA	689.52	359.97	1,049.49	262.92	952.44	3.8000
08.7003 021	Magnetic card reader	EA	626.81	331.56	958.37	242.17	868.98	3.5000
08.7003 031	Magnetic door holder	EA	121.78	161.04	282.82	117.62	239.40	1.7000

Division 8 CSI #	08 - DOORS, WINDOWS & GLASS Description	Unit	Material	Union Install	Union Total	Open Install	Open Total	Unit Man-Hrs
08.7003 000	**ELECTRICALLY OPERATED HARDWARE DEVICES (Cont.)**							
08.7003 041	Electric strike, economy	EA	87.17	35.82	122.99	26.16	113.33	0.3781
08.7003 051	Electric strike, good	EA	388.39	35.82	424.21	26.16	414.55	0.3781
08.8000 000	**GLASS & GLAZING:**							
	Note: The following prices are based on small quantities. For quantities over 300 square feet, see section 08.9000.							
08.8001 000	**JOB GLAZING, SINGLE GLAZED:**							
	Note: For lites under 2 SF, add 30% to the total costs.							
08.8001 011	Job, 3/32" (2.5mm) single strength, clear, float	SF	3.45	2.52	5.97	1.97	5.42	0.0284
08.8001 021	Job, 1/8" (3mm) double strength, clear, float	SF	3.68	2.52	6.20	1.97	5.65	0.0284
08.8001 031	Job, 1/8" (3mm) tempered float	SF	6.86	3.14	10.00	2.45	9.31	0.0353
08.8001 041	Job, 1/8" (3mm) obscure	SF	6.00	3.14	9.14	2.45	8.45	0.0353
08.8001 051	Job, 3/16" (5mm), clear, float	SF	5.53	4.30	9.83	3.35	8.88	0.0484
08.8001 061	Job, 3/16" (5mm), clear, tempered	SF	7.21	3.14	10.35	2.45	9.66	0.0353
08.8001 071	Job, 1/4" (6mm), clear, float	SF	5.76	4.30	10.06	3.35	9.11	0.0484
08.8001 081	Job, 1/4" (6mm) clear, wire	SF	27.44	4.30	31.74	3.35	30.79	0.0484
08.8001 091	Job, 1/4" (6mm), bronze/gray, float	SF	7.82	4.30	12.12	3.35	11.17	0.0484
08.8001 101	Job, 1/4" obscure	SF	11.96	4.30	16.26	3.35	15.31	0.0484
08.8001 111	Job, 1/4" obscure, wire	SF	13.62	4.30	17.92	3.35	16.97	0.0484
08.8001 121	Job, 1/4" (6mm) float, Solex	SF	10.02	4.30	14.32	3.35	13.37	0.0484
08.8001 131	Job, 1/4" clear laminated (.030)	SF	20.43	4.30	24.73	3.35	23.78	0.0484
08.8001 141	Job, 1/4" (6mm) clear, float, tempered	SF	7.56	4.30	11.86	3.35	10.91	0.0484
08.8001 161	Job, 1/4" spandrel, custom color	SF	24.78	4.97	29.75	3.87	28.65	0.0559
08.8001 171	Job, 1/4" spandrel, plain	SF	17.69	4.97	22.66	3.87	21.56	0.0559
08.8001 181	Job, 1/4" (6mm) float, temp, reflective, bronze/grey	SF	19.50	4.30	23.80	3.35	22.85	0.0484
08.8001 191	Job, 1/4" (6mm) float, reflective, solar bronze/grey	SF	17.84	4.30	22.14	3.35	21.19	0.0484
08.8001 201	Job, Greylite 14	SF	13.82	4.30	18.12	3.35	17.17	0.0484
08.8001 211	Job, Greylite 31	SF	13.22	4.30	17.52	3.35	16.57	0.0484
08.8001 221	Job, 3/8" clear, float, clear	SF	13.82	5.25	19.07	4.09	17.91	0.0591
08.8001 231	Job, 3/8" float, bronze/gray	SF	22.64	5.25	27.89	4.09	26.73	0.0591
08.8001 251	Job, 1/2" clear, float, tempered	SF	33.30	6.78	40.08	5.29	38.59	0.0763
08.8001 261	Job, 1/2" float, tempered bronze/gray	SF	38.35	6.78	45.13	5.29	43.64	0.0763
08.8002 000	**GLAZING SPECIALTIES:**							
08.8002 011	Glazing, acrylic sheet, 1/8" clear	SF	8.39	3.15	11.54	2.46	10.85	0.0355
08.8002 021	Glazing, acrylic sheet, 1/4" clear	SF	11.51	4.30	15.81	3.35	14.86	0.0484
08.8002 031	Glazing, acrylic sheet, 1/4" color	SF	13.37	4.30	17.67	3.35	16.72	0.0484
08.8002 041	Glazing, acrylic sheet, 1/4" shatterproof	SF	34.97	4.30	39.27	3.35	38.32	0.0484
08.8002 051	Glazing, 3/4" bullet resistant	SF	71.15	63.38	134.53	49.42	120.57	0.7133
08.8002 061	Glazing, 2" bullet resistant	SF	84.62	75.36	159.98	58.76	143.38	0.8481
08.8002 063	Glazing, service window, secure, 2'x3'	EA	3,486.89	142.18	3,629.07	110.85	3,597.74	1.6000
08.8002 065	Glazing, service window, secure, draft free	EA	4,674.09	142.18	4,816.27	110.85	4,784.94	1.6000
08.8002 071	Glazing, faceted glass, leaded	SF	148.98	49.45	198.43	38.55	187.53	0.5565
08.8002 081	Glazing, artistic murals, leaded	SF	163.10	49.45	212.55	38.55	201.65	0.5565
08.8002 091	Glazing, decor glass, small lites	SF	16.97	14.89	31.86	11.61	28.58	0.1676
08.8002 101	Glazing, decorative glass, panels	SF	8.39	4.97	13.36	3.87	12.26	0.0559
08.8002 111	Glazing, insulated glass, 1/8", B, 2 layer	SF	15.05	9.74	24.79	7.59	22.64	0.1096
08.8002 121	Glazing, insulated, 1/8" float, 2 layer	SF	21.04	9.74	30.78	7.59	28.63	0.1096
08.8002 131	Glazing, insulated, 1/4" float, 2 layer	SF	23.73	11.32	35.05	8.83	32.56	0.1274
08.8002 141	Glazing, insulated, 1/4" float, tempered, vented	SF	46.42	11.25	57.67	8.77	55.19	0.1266
08.8002 151	Glazing, insulated, 1/4" float, tinted	SF	38.93	11.27	50.20	8.78	47.71	0.1268
08.8002 161	Glazing, mirrors, sheet	SF	10.22	8.17	18.39	6.37	16.59	0.0919
08.8002 171	Glazing, mirrors, float	SF	15.42	8.86	24.28	6.91	22.33	0.0997
08.8002 181	Glazing, mirrors, wall	SF	14.55	8.17	22.72	6.37	20.92	0.0919
08.8002 191	Glazing, mirror, panel, 1-way, in wood	SF	20.52	9.71	30.23	7.57	28.09	0.1093
08.8002 201	Galzing, shower door, 24"x72", wire/tempered	EA	242.81		242.81		242.81	
08.8002 211	Glazing, shower door, panel & lite	EA	436.99		436.99		436.99	
08.8002 221	Glazing, shower door, average cost/SF	SF	21.74		21.74		21.74	
08.8002 231	Glazing, shower door, 24"x72", plastic	EA	200.25		200.25		200.25	
08.8002 241	Glazing, shower door, plastic, 1 pnl/lite	EA	309.46		309.46		309.46	
08.8002 251	Glazing, shower door, average cost/SF	SF	16.35		16.35		16.35	

Division 8 CSI #	08 - DOORS, WINDOWS & GLASS Description	Unit	Material	Union Install	Union Total	Open Install	Open Total	Unit Man-Hrs
08.9000 000	**CURTAIN WALL & STOREFRONT SYSTEMS:**							
08.9001 000	**STOREFRONT, CLEAR GLASS & CLEAR ANODIZED ALUMINUM:**							
08.9001 011	Storefront system, stub wall to 8'	SF	24.71	8.63	33.34	6.73	31.44	0.0971
08.9001 021	Storefront system, floor 8' to 10'	SF	27.32	10.09	37.41	7.86	35.18	0.1135
08.9002 000	**ADDERS:**							
08.9002 011	Add for tint	SF	2.02		2.02		2.02	
08.9002 021	Add for bronze anodized aluminum	SF	2.21		2.21		2.21	
08.9002 031	Add for black anodized aluminum	SF	5.38		5.38		5.38	
08.9002 041	Add for extra aluminum sections	LF	12.98		12.98		12.98	
08.9003 000	**ENTRANCES, CONCEALED CLOSER, CENTER PIVOT:**							
	Note: The following items should be added to those in the sections immediately preceding, without credit for square foot of contact area.							
08.9003 011	Entry, to 3' x 7', narrow stile	EA	840.94	525.05	1,365.99	409.35	1,250.29	5.9087
08.9003 021	Entrance, to 3' x 7', heavy section	EA	987.28	552.39	1,539.67	430.67	1,417.95	6.2164
08.9003 031	Entrance, to 3' x 7', 1/2" tempered	EA	2,085.78	683.57	2,769.35	532.95	2,618.73	7.6927
08.9003 041	Add for center stop	EA	27.68	20.80	48.48	16.22	43.90	0.2341
08.9003 051	Add for floor check	EA	224.71	109.38	334.09	85.28	309.99	1.2309
08.9003 061	Add for bronze anodized aluminum	EA	165.48		165.48		165.48	
08.9003 071	Add for black anodized aluminum	EA	240.38		240.38		240.38	
08.9003 081	Add for large sizes	SF	18.47	10.40	28.87	8.11	26.58	0.1170
08.9003 091	Add for automatic opener	EA	3,170.29	1,776.77	4,947.06	1,297.73	4,468.02	18.7561
08.9004 000	**STOREFRONT, CLEAR POLISHED PLATE, CLEAR ANODIZED ALUMINUM:**							
08.9004 011	Storefront system, stub wall to 9'	SF	21.67	10.24	31.91	7.98	29.65	0.1152
08.9004 021	Storefront system, stub wall to 13'	SF	22.43	11.15	33.58	8.69	31.12	0.1255
08.9004 031	Storefront system, floor to 9'	SF	23.30	10.54	33.84	8.22	31.52	0.1186
08.9004 041	Storefront system, floor to 13'	SF	25.06	11.84	36.90	9.23	34.29	0.1332
08.9005 000	**ADDERS:**							
08.9005 011	Add for tint	SF	1.66		1.66		1.66	
08.9005 021	Add for bronze anodized aluminum	SF	1.99		1.99		1.99	
08.9005 031	Add for black anodized aluminum	SF	4.22		4.22		4.22	
08.9005 041	Add for extra aluminum sections	LF	11.33	7.21	18.54	5.27	16.60	0.0761
08.9006 000	**ENTRANCES, CONCEALED CLOSER:**							
	Note: The following items should be added to those in the sections immediately preceding, without credit for square feet of contact area.							
08.9006 011	Entrance, 3070, aluminum & glass, hidden closer	EA	1,084.71	639.82	1,724.53	498.84	1,583.55	7.2003
08.9006 021	Entrance, 3070, 5/8" tempered, herculite	EA	2,312.52	749.24	3,061.76	584.15	2,896.67	8.4317
08.9006 031	Add for floor check	EA	267.78	119.78	387.56	93.39	361.17	1.3480
08.9006 041	Add for black anodized aluminum	EA	249.82		249.82		249.82	
08.9006 051	Add for bronze anodized aluminum	EA	187.34		187.34		187.34	
08.9006 061	Add for larger sizes	SF	21.55	15.64	37.19	12.19	33.74	0.1760
08.9006 071	Add for automatic opener	EA	3,170.29	1,666.67	4,836.96	1,299.42	4,469.71	18.7561
08.9007 000	**STOREFRONT, CLEAR PLATE GLASS ANODIZED ALUMINUM:**							
08.9007 011	Storefront system, floor to 9'	SF	31.95	12.07	44.02	9.41	41.36	0.1358
08.9007 021	Storefront system, floor to 11'	SF	32.71	12.90	45.61	10.06	42.77	0.1452
08.9007 031	Storefront system, floor to 13'	SF	33.66	13.75	47.41	10.72	44.38	0.1547
08.9007 041	Anod bronze frame, 1/4" tint plate	SF	23.82	13.75	37.57	10.72	34.54	0.1547
08.9007 051	Decorative storefront	SF	25.76	14.86	40.62	11.58	37.34	0.1672
08.9007 061	Decorative curved storefront	SF	48.95	28.28	77.23	22.05	71.00	0.3183
08.9008 000	**ADDERS:**							
08.9008 011	Add for tint	SF	1.76		1.76		1.76	
08.9008 021	Add for bronze anodized aluminum	SF	2.14		2.14		2.14	
08.9008 031	Add for black anodized aluminum	SF	4.77		4.77		4.77	
08.9008 041	Add for extra aluminum sections	LF	16.00		16.00		16.00	
08.9008 051	Add for lacquered bronze	SF	11.09	6.26	17.35	4.88	15.97	0.0705
08.9008 061	Add for oil-rubbed bronze	SF	11.77	7.28	19.05	5.67	17.44	0.0819
08.9008 071	Add for seismic bracing	SF	3.11	2.10	5.21	1.54	4.65	0.0222
08.9008 081	Add for automatic opener	EA	4,232.20	1,776.77	6,008.97	1,297.73	5,529.93	18.7561
08.9009 000	**FRAMING, STEEL STOREFRONT:**							
	Note: For steel glazing, use the adders given for aluminum.							
08.9009 011	Storefront, primed steel framing	SF	17.58	5.51	23.09	4.30	21.88	0.0620
08.9009 021	Storefront, stainless steel framing	SF	47.48	8.26	55.74	6.44	53.92	0.0929

Division 8 CSI #	08 - DOORS, WINDOWS & GLASS Description	Unit	Material	Union Install	Union Total	Open Install	Open Total	Unit Man-Hrs
08.9010 000	**STEEL STOREFRONT FRAMING, DOOR & SASH INSERTION:**							
08.9010 011	Storefront, stainless steel door, 1 lite, frame	EA	3,396.36	656.23	4,052.59	511.63	3,907.99	7.3850
08.9010 021	Storefront, stainless steel door, 1 lite, frame, pair	EA	6,586.91	911.51	7,498.42	710.66	7,297.57	10.2578
08.9010 031	Automatic opener	EA	3,168.90	1,666.67	4,835.57	1,299.42	4,468.32	18.7561
08.9100 000	**CURTAIN WALLS & EXTERIOR PANEL SYSTEMS:**							
	Note: The following items are for mid-rise and high-rise construction.							
08.9101 000	**CURTAIN WALLS, IN PLACE WITH OUT GLAZING (FRAME ONLY):**							
	Note: The following prices include installation and fasteners, but do not include structural steel, see							
	section 05.0000. Prices are based on the gross square footage of exterior skin. Glazing must be added							
	to determine total system cost. For sloped or butt glazing, add 30% to the total costs.							
08.9101 011	Curtain wall frame, bronze anodized aluminum	SF	22.59		22.59		22.59	
08.9101 021	Curtain wall frame, black anodized aluminum	SF	26.01		26.01		26.01	
08.9101 031	Curtain wall frame, aluminum, sloping section	SF	36.02		36.02		36.02	
08.9101 041	Curtain wall frame, steel, painted	SF	21.93		21.93		21.93	
08.9101 051	Curtain wall frame, steel, porcelain enamel	SF	23.67		23.67		23.67	
08.9102 000	**CURTAIN WALL GLAZING:**							
	Note: The following items are for glazed installation in the frames listed above. Most systems include a							
	combination of two or more of the following items. Determine the gross square footage of surface area							
	for each item used and add the resultant cost to the cost of frames. The total square footage of these							
	items should equal the total square footage of the frame.							
08.9102 011	Plate, 1/4", clear	SF	7.86		7.86		7.86	
08.9102 021	Plate, 1/4", tinted	SF	9.66		9.66		9.66	
08.9102 031	Plate, 1/4" solarcool, reflective	SF	18.11		18.11		18.11	
08.9102 041	Plate, 1/4", veri-tran, reflective	SF	24.18		24.18		24.18	
08.9102 051	Tempered plate, 1/4", clear	SF	14.46		14.46		14.46	
08.9102 061	Tempered plate, 1/4", tinted	SF	16.94		16.94		16.94	
08.9102 071	Tempered plate, 1/4", solarcool reflective	SF	27.22		27.22		27.22	
08.9102 081	Double glazed, 5/8", clear	SF	14.46		14.46		14.46	
08.9102 091	Double glazed, 5/8", tinted	SF	15.71		15.71		15.71	
08.9102 101	Double glazed, 5/8", solarcool reflective	SF	19.29		19.29		19.29	
08.9102 111	Double glazed, tempered, 5/8", clear	SF	24.79		24.79		24.79	
08.9102 121	Double glazed, tempered, 5/8", tinted	SF	26.60		26.60		26.60	
08.9102 131	Double glazed, tempered, 5/8", solarcool	SF	37.53		37.53		37.53	
08.9102 141	Double glazed, 1", clear	SF	15.71		15.71		15.71	
08.9102 151	Double glazed, 1", tinted	SF	16.94		16.94		16.94	
08.9102 161	Double glazed, 1", solarcool reflective	SF	22.38		22.38		22.38	
08.9102 171	Double glazed, tempered, 1", clear	SF	28.42		28.42		28.42	
08.9102 181	Double glazed, tempered, 1", tinted	SF	30.85		30.85		30.85	
08.9102 191	Double glazed, tempered, 1", solarcool	SF	15.71		15.71		15.71	
08.9102 201	Spandrel	SF	16.94		16.94		16.94	
08.9102 211	Glasweld, 1/4", finished 1 side	SF	29.67		29.67		29.67	
08.9102 221	Glasweld, 1", insulated, finished 1 side, dual	SF	38.57		38.57		38.57	
08.9102 231	Mirawal, 5/16", finished 1 side, dual	SF	30.24		30.24		30.24	
08.9102 241	Mirawal, 1", insulated, finished 1 side, dual	SF	39.63		39.63		39.63	
08.9102 251	Aluca bond, glazed installation	SF	43.52		43.52		43.52	
	Add for sloped glazing 30%							
	Add for butt glazing 30%							
08.9103 000	**PREFINISHED & INSULATED BUILDING PANELS WITH SUPPORT FRAME:**							
08.9103 011	Aluca bond	SF	88.96		88.96		88.96	
08.9104 000	**PREFINISHED & INSULATED BUILDING PANELS, STRUCTURAL STUDS:**							
	Note: The following prices do not include structural studs unless otherwise noted. For studs see							
	section 09.1100. For sash see section 08.9106. The glasweld item below is installed over gwb or ply							
	sheathing. The price does not include sheathing but does include adhesive and matching trim.							
08.9104 011	Aluca bond	SF	48.16		48.16		48.16	
08.9104 021	Dryvit, with studs & 3" insulation	SF	29.21		29.21		29.21	
08.9104 031	Glasweld, 1/4" finished 1 side	SF	20.99		20.99		20.99	
08.9105 000	**PRECAST CONCRETE & FIBERGLASS REINFORCED CONCRETE PANELS:**							
	Note: The following prices are for furnished and installed panels including fasteners. Structural steel							
	supports are not included. For structural steel see section 05.1000. For sash see section 08.9106.							
08.9105 011	Precast panel, 1 form, standard finish	SF	35.38		35.38		35.38	
08.9105 021	Precast panel, 2 form, standard finish	SF	47.32		47.32		47.32	
08.9105 031	Precast panel, 1 form, sandblast	SF	57.05		57.05		57.05	

Division 8 CSI #	08 - DOORS, WINDOWS & GLASS Description	Unit	Material	Union Install	Union Total	Open Install	Open Total	Unit Man-Hrs
08.9105 000	**PRECAST CONCRETE & FIBERGLASS REINFORCED CONCRETE PANELS: (Cont.)**							
08.9105 041	Precast panel, 2 form, sandblast	SF	62.91		62.91		62.91	
08.9105 051	Precast panel, 1 form, mo-sai finish	SF	49.26		49.26		49.26	
08.9105 061	Precast panel, 1 form, granite overlay	SF	72.63		72.63		72.63	
08.9105 071	GFRC panel, 1 form, standard finish	SF	40.40		40.40		40.40	
08.9105 081	GFRC panel, 2 form, standard finish	SF	47.28		47.28		47.28	
08.9105 091	GFRC panel, 1 form, sandblast	SF	58.00		58.00		58.00	
08.9105 101	GFRC panel, 2 form, sandblast	SF	61.66		61.66		61.66	
08.9105 111	GFRC panel, 1 form, mo-sai finish	SF	47.32		47.32		47.32	
08.9105 121	GFRC panel, 1 form, granite overlay	SF	72.74		72.74		72.74	
08.9106 000	**SASH, METAL, GLAZED, IN EXTERIOR PANEL SYSTEMS:**							
	Note: The following items are to be used with all systems except curtain walls.							
08.9106 011	Sash, steel, fixed, 1/4" clear	SF	16.96	9.75	26.71	7.60	24.56	0.1097
08.9106 021	Sash, steel, fixed, 1/4" tint	SF	18.09	9.75	27.84	7.60	25.69	0.1097
08.9106 031	Sash, steel, fixed, 1/4" reflective	SF	20.92	9.75	30.67	7.60	28.52	0.1097
08.9106 041	Sash, steel, 50% vent, 1/4" clear	SF	20.23	9.75	29.98	7.60	27.83	0.1097
08.9106 051	Sash, steel, 50% vent, 1/4" tint	SF	21.36	9.75	31.11	7.60	28.96	0.1097
08.9106 061	Sash, steel, 50% vent, 1/4" reflective	SF	24.18	9.75	33.93	7.60	31.78	0.1097
08.9106 071	Sash, steel, 100% vent, 1/4" clear	SF	23.03	9.75	32.78	7.60	30.63	0.1097
08.9106 081	Sash, steel, 100% vent, 1/4" tint	SF	24.15	9.75	33.90	7.60	31.75	0.1097
08.9106 091	Sash, steel, 100% vent, 1/4" reflective	SF	26.96	9.75	36.71	7.60	34.56	0.1097
08.9106 101	Sash, aluminum, fixed, 1/4" clear	SF	17.42	9.75	27.17	7.60	25.02	0.1097
08.9106 111	Sash, aluminum, fixed, 1/4" tint	SF	18.55	9.75	28.30	7.60	26.15	0.1097
08.9106 121	Sash, aluminum, fixed, 1/4" reflective	SF	21.42	9.75	31.17	7.60	29.02	0.1097
08.9106 131	Sash, aluminum, 50% vent, 1/4" clear	SF	22.69	10.32	33.01	8.04	30.73	0.1161
08.9106 141	Sash, aluminum, 50% vent, 1/4" tint	SF	23.86	10.32	34.18	8.04	31.90	0.1161
08.9106 151	Sash, aluminum, 50% vent, 1/4" reflective	SF	26.70	10.32	37.02	8.04	34.74	0.1161
08.9106 161	Sash, aluminum, 100% vent, 1/4" clear	SF	27.39	10.32	37.71	8.04	35.43	0.1161
08.9106 171	Sash, aluminum, 100% vent, 1/4" tint	SF	28.53	10.32	38.85	8.04	36.57	0.1161
08.9106 181	Sash, aluminum, 100% vent, 1/4" reflective	SF	31.33	10.32	41.65	8.04	39.37	0.1161

Division 9 CSI #	09 - FINISHES Description	Unit	Material	Union Install	Union Total	Open Install	Open Total	Unit Man-Hrs
09.0000 000	FINISHES:							
09.1000 000	LATH, PLASTER, STUDDING & FURRING:							
	Note: Remember to add 5% to all material for laps and waste. The studs listed below are spaced 16"							
	on center unless otherwise noted. Prices include top and bottom track and bridging. For drywall studs							
	see section 09.2001. In plaster and stucco, scaffolding is assumed to be provided by the subcontractor							
	up to 12', by the general contractor above 12'. Planks are assumed to be provided by the subcontractor.							
	Note that stucco prices may vary greatly if configurations are irregular.							
	For areas under 1,000 sf . . . . . add 20% to the material costs							
	For galvanized studs . . . . add 5% to the material costs							
	For painted sfs studs . . . . deduct 15% from the material costs							
	For 24" spacing . . . . deduct 20% from the material costs							
09.1100 000	STUDS:							
09.1101 000	STUDS, STANDARD, 'C' STRUCTURAL, 1-5/8", 16"OC:							
09.1101 011	Studs, 'C' structural, 1-5/8", 16"OC, 14 ga, 2-1/2"	SF	1.67	3.73	5.40	2.29	3.96	0.0475
09.1101 021	Studs, 'C' structural, 1-5/8", 16"OC, 14 ga, 3-5/8"	SF	2.19	3.93	6.12	2.41	4.60	0.0500
09.1101 031	Studs, 'C' structural, 1-5/8", 16"OC, 14 ga, 4"	SF	2.30	4.20	6.50	2.57	4.87	0.0534
09.1101 041	Studs, 'C' structural, 1-5/8", 16"OC, 14 ga, 6"	SF	2.87	4.41	7.28	2.70	5.57	0.0561
09.1101 051	Studs, 'C' structural, 1-5/8", 16"OC, 14 ga, 8"	SF	3.50	4.84	8.34	2.96	6.46	0.0615
09.1101 111	Studs, 'C' structural, 1-5/8", 16"OC, 16 ga, 2-1/2"	SF	1.46	3.73	5.19	2.29	3.75	0.0475
09.1101 121	Studs, 'C' structural, 1-5/8", 16"OC, 16 ga, 3-5/8"	SF	1.68	3.93	5.61	2.41	4.09	0.0500
09.1101 131	Studs, 'C' structural, 1-5/8", 16"OC, 16 ga, 4"	SF	1.76	4.20	5.96	2.57	4.33	0.0534
09.1101 141	Studs, 'C' structural, 1-5/8", 16"OC, 16 ga, 6"	SF	2.20	4.41	6.61	2.70	4.90	0.0561
09.1101 151	Studs, 'C' structural, 1-5/8", 16"OC, 16 ga, 8"	SF	2.62	4.84	7.46	2.96	5.58	0.0615
09.1101 211	Studs, 'C' structural, 1-5/8", 16"OC, 18 ga, 2-1/2"	SF	1.22	3.73	4.95	2.29	3.51	0.0475
09.1101 221	Studs, 'C' structural, 1-5/8", 16"OC, 18 ga, 3-5/8"	SF	1.44	3.93	5.37	2.41	3.85	0.0500
09.1101 231	Studs, 'C' structural, 1-5/8", 16"OC, 18 ga, 4"	SF	1.52	4.20	5.72	2.57	4.09	0.0534
09.1101 241	Studs, 'C' structural, 1-5/8", 16"OC, 18 ga, 6"	SF	1.87	4.41	6.28	2.70	4.57	0.0561
09.1101 251	Studs, 'C' structural, 1-5/8", 16"OC, 18 ga, 8"	SF	2.33	4.84	7.17	2.96	5.29	0.0615
09.1101 311	Studs, 'C' structural, 1-5/8", 16"OC, 20 ga, 2-1/2"	SF	1.25	3.73	4.98	2.29	3.54	0.0475
09.1101 321	Studs, 'C' structural, 1-5/8", 16"OC, 20 ga, 3-5/8"	SF	1.37	3.93	5.30	2.41	3.78	0.0500
09.1101 331	Studs, 'C' structural, 1-5/8", 16"OC, 20 ga, 4"	SF	1.39	4.20	5.59	2.57	3.96	0.0534
09.1101 341	Studs, 'C' structural, 1-5/8", 16"OC, 20 ga, 6"	SF	1.62	4.41	6.03	2.70	4.32	0.0561
09.1101 351	Studs, 'C' structural, 1-5/8", 16"OC, 20 ga, 8"	SF	1.81	4.84	6.65	2.96	4.77	0.0615
09.1102 000	STUDS, 'C' STRUCTURAL, 1-3/8", 16"OC:							
09.1102 011	Studs, 'C' structural, 1-3/8", 16"OC, 14 ga, 2-1/2"	SF	1.70	3.73	5.43	2.29	3.99	0.0475
09.1102 021	Studs, 'C' structural, 1-3/8", 16"OC, 14 ga, 3-5/8"	SF	2.04	3.93	5.97	2.41	4.45	0.0500
09.1102 031	Studs, 'C' structural, 1-3/8", 16"OC, 14 ga, 4"	SF	2.17	4.20	6.37	2.57	4.74	0.0534
09.1102 041	Studs, 'C' structural, 1-3/8", 16"OC, 14 ga, 6"	SF	2.71	4.41	7.12	2.70	5.41	0.0561
09.1102 051	Studs, 'C' structural, 1-3/8", 16"OC, 14 ga, 8"	SF	3.25	4.84	8.09	2.96	6.21	0.0615
09.1102 111	Studs, 'C' structural, 1-3/8", 16"OC, 16 ga, 2-1/2"	SF	1.34	3.73	5.07	2.29	3.63	0.0475
09.1102 121	Studs, 'C' structural, 1-3/8", 16"OC, 16 ga, 3-5/8"	SF	1.60	3.93	5.53	2.41	4.01	0.0500
09.1102 131	Studs, 'C' structural, 1-3/8", 16"OC, 16 ga, 4"	SF	1.65	4.20	5.85	2.57	4.22	0.0534
09.1102 141	Studs, 'C' structural, 1-3/8", 16"OC, 16 ga, 6"	SF	2.05	4.41	6.46	2.70	4.75	0.0561
09.1102 151	Studs, 'C' structural, 1-3/8", 16"OC, 16 ga, 8"	SF	2.53	4.84	7.37	2.96	5.49	0.0615
09.1102 211	Studs, 'C' structural, 1-3/8", 16"OC, 18 ga, 2-1/2"	SF	1.13	3.73	4.86	2.29	3.42	0.0475
09.1102 221	Studs, 'C' structural, 1-3/8", 16"OC, 18 ga, 3-5/8"	SF	1.36	3.93	5.29	2.41	3.77	0.0500
09.1102 231	Studs, 'C' structural, 1-3/8", 16"OC, 18 ga, 4"	SF	1.44	4.20	5.64	2.57	4.01	0.0534
09.1102 241	Studs, 'C' structural, 1-3/8", 16"OC, 18 ga, 6"	SF	1.79	4.41	6.20	2.70	4.49	0.0561
09.1102 251	Studs, 'C' structural, 1-3/8", 16"OC, 18 ga, 8"	SF	2.13	4.84	6.97	2.96	5.09	0.0615
09.1103 000	STUDS OR TRACK, STANDARD FLANGE STRUCTURAL, 1-1/4", 16"OC:							
09.1103 011	Studs, channel, 1", 16"OC, 14 ga, 2-1/2"	SF	1.40	3.73	5.13	2.29	3.69	0.0475
09.1103 021	Studs, channel, 1", 16"OC, 14 ga, 3-5/8"	SF	1.59	3.93	5.52	2.41	4.00	0.0500
09.1103 031	Studs, channel, 1", 16"OC, 14 ga, 4"	SF	1.70	4.20	5.90	2.57	4.27	0.0534
09.1103 041	Studs, channel, 1", 16"OC, 14 ga, 6"	SF	2.30	4.41	6.71	2.70	5.00	0.0561
09.1103 051	Studs, channel, 1", 16"OC, 14 ga, 8"	SF	2.86	4.84	7.70	2.96	5.82	0.0615
09.1103 061	Studs, channel, 1", 16"OC, 16 ga, 2-1/2"	SF	.98	3.73	4.71	2.29	3.27	0.0475
09.1103 071	Studs, channel, 1", 16"OC, 16 ga, 3-5/8"	SF	1.25	3.93	5.18	2.41	3.66	0.0500
09.1103 081	Studs, channel, 1", 16"OC, 16 ga, 4"	SF	1.34	4.20	5.54	2.57	3.91	0.0534
09.1103 091	Studs, channel, 1", 16"OC, 16 ga, 6"	SF	1.76	4.41	6.17	2.70	4.46	0.0561
09.1103 101	Studs, channel, 1", 16"OC, 16 ga, 8"	SF	2.20	4.84	7.04	2.96	5.16	0.0615
09.1103 111	Studs, channel, 1", 16"OC, 18 ga, 2-1/2"	SF	.86	3.73	4.59	2.29	3.15	0.0475
09.1103 121	Studs, channel, 1", 16"OC, 18 ga, 3-5/8"	SF	1.05	3.93	4.98	2.41	3.46	0.0500

Division 9 CSI #	09 - FINISHES Description	Unit	Material	Union Install	Union Total	Open Install	Open Total	Unit Man-Hrs
09.1103 000	STUDS OR TRACK, STANDARD FLANGE STRUCTURAL, 1-1/4", 16"OC: (Cont.)							
09.1103 131	Studs, channel, 1", 16"OC, 18 ga, 4"	SF	1.13	4.20	5.33	2.57	3.70	0.0534
09.1103 141	Studs, channel, 1", 16"OC, 18 ga, 6"	SF	1.52	4.41	5.93	2.70	4.22	0.0561
09.1103 151	Studs, channel, 1", 16"OC, 18 ga, 8"	SF	1.87	4.84	6.71	2.96	4.83	0.0615
09.1103 161	Studs, channel, 1", 16"OC, 20 ga, 2-1/2"	SF	.85	3.73	4.58	2.29	3.14	0.0475
09.1103 171	Studs, channel, 1", 16"OC, 20 ga, 3-5/8"	SF	1.01	3.93	4.94	2.41	3.42	0.0500
09.1103 181	Studs, channel, 1", 16"OC, 20 ga, 4"	SF	1.02	4.20	5.22	2.57	3.59	0.0534
09.1103 191	Studs, channel, 1", 16"OC, 20 ga, 6"	SF	1.31	4.41	5.72	2.70	4.01	0.0561
09.1103 201	Studs, channel, 1", 16"OC, 20 ga, 8"	SF	1.53	4.84	6.37	2.96	4.49	0.0615
09.1104 000	SHAFTWALL, STUDS, CH, 24" OC:							
	Note: Costs include finished gypsum wall board							
09.1104 011	Shaftwall, studs, CH, 24"OC, 20 ga, 2-1/2"	SF	1.76	3.73	5.49	2.29	4.05	0.0475
09.1104 021	Shaftwall, studs, CH, 24"OC, 20 ga, 4"	SF	1.81	4.20	6.01	2.57	4.38	0.0534
09.1104 031	Shaftwall, studs, CH, 24"OC, 20 ga, 6"	SF	2.30	4.41	6.71	2.70	5.00	0.0561
09.1104 041	Shaftwall, studs, CH, 24"OC, 25 ga, 2-1/2"	SF	1.07	3.73	4.80	2.29	3.36	0.0475
09.1104 051	Shaftwall, studs, CH, 24"OC, 25 ga, 4"	SF	1.21	4.20	5.41	2.57	3.78	0.0534
09.1104 061	Shaftwall, studs, CH, 24"OC, 25 ga, 6"	SF	1.53	4.41	5.94	2.70	4.23	0.0561
09.1200 000	FURRING:							
09.1201 000	FURRING CHANNELS, CEILINGS:							
09.1201 011	Furring, channels, ceiling, 1-1/2" x 3/4", 16" OC	SF	.83	1.62	2.45	.99	1.82	0.0206
09.1201 021	Hat channel, ceiling, 1-1/2"x7/8", 16" OC	SF	.91	1.67	2.58	1.02	1.93	0.0212
09.1201 031	Furring, ceiling, 3-1/4x1-1/2x3/4, triple hung	SF	1.20	3.10	4.30	1.90	3.10	0.0394
09.1201 041	Furring, ceiling, 1-1/2"x3/4", coffered, double hung	SF	1.12	4.03	5.15	2.47	3.59	0.0513
09.1201 051	Furring, ceiling, 2 layers gypsum wall board, studs, 25ga	SF	1.52	5.85	7.37	3.58	5.10	0.0744
09.1201 061	Furring, ceiling, 3 layers gypsum wall board, studs, 25ga	SF	2.06	8.73	10.79	5.35	7.41	0.1111
09.1201 071	Furring, ceiling, 4 layers gypsum wall board, studs, 25ga	SF	2.65	11.64	14.29	7.14	9.79	0.1481
09.1202 000	FURRING CHANNEL, WALL:							
09.1202 011	Hat channel, 3/4" x 5/8", 16" OC	SF	.64	1.08	1.72	.66	1.30	0.0137
09.1202 021	Furring, channels, wall, 3/4"x 3/4", 16" OC	SF	.56	1.08	1.64	.66	1.22	0.0137
09.1202 031	Furring, hat channel, articulated wall	SF	.64	3.90	4.54	2.39	3.03	0.0496
09.1202 041	Furring, wall, 2 layers gypsum wall board, studs, 25ga	SF	1.52	5.85	7.37	3.58	5.10	0.0744
09.1202 051	Furring, wall, 3 layers gypsum wall board, studs, 25ga	SF	2.06	8.73	10.79	5.35	7.41	0.1111
09.1202 061	Furring, wall, 4 layers gypsum wall board, studs, 25ga	SF	2.63	11.64	14.27	7.14	9.77	0.1481
09.1300 000	LATHING:							
09.1301 000	METAL LATH:							
09.1301 011	Lath, metal, 2.5#, painted, wood frame	SY	3.21	6.80	10.01	4.42	7.63	0.0833
09.1301 021	Lath, metal, 3.4#, painted, wood frame	SY	3.66	6.80	10.46	4.42	8.08	0.0833
09.1301 031	Lath, metal, 3.4#, galvanized, wood frame	SY	4.43	6.80	11.23	4.42	8.85	0.0833
09.1302 000	WIRE MESH & SPECIAL LATH:							
	Note: For wiring to steel frames or screwing to steel studs, add 5% to the total costs. For wiring to steel ceiling frame, add 15% to the total costs.							
09.1302 011	Mesh, 1" x 18 ga, 15# felt, wire	SY	3.68	6.33	10.01	4.11	7.79	0.0775
09.1302 021	Mesh, 1-1/2"x17 ga, 15# felt, wire	SY	2.95	6.33	9.28	4.11	7.06	0.0775
09.1302 031	Lath, stucco rite, 2" x 16 ga	SY	3.33	6.19	9.52	4.02	7.35	0.0758
09.1302 041	Lath, paperback with felt, mesh, wire	SY	3.29	5.05	8.34	3.28	6.57	0.0618
09.1302 051	Lath, aqua, 2" x 16 ga	SY	3.57	6.19	9.76	4.02	7.59	0.0758
09.1302 061	Lath, rock, 3/8", wood frame	SY	2.64	5.33	7.97	3.46	6.10	0.0653
09.1302 071	Lath, rock, 3/8", steel frame	SY	2.64	6.19	8.83	4.02	6.66	0.0758
09.1302 081	Lath, gypsum, asphalt coated, 1/2", nailed	SY	3.44	4.48	7.92	2.91	6.35	0.0549
09.1302 091	Lath, gypsum, lead lined, 4#	SY	56.69	23.68	80.37	15.38	72.07	0.2901
09.1302 101	Lath, gypsum, lead lined, 2#	SY	45.01	23.68	68.69	15.38	60.39	0.2901
09.1302 111	Lath, gypsum, lead lined, 1#	SY	45.01	23.68	68.69	15.38	60.39	0.2901
09.1400 000	PLASTER & LATH:							
	Note: Scaffolding is provided by the subcontractor to 12'. Above 12' scaffolding is provided by the general contractor. Planks are supplied by the subcontractor. Remember to add 5% to materials for waste. With irregular configurations, stucco may vary greatly in cost.							
09.1401 000	PLASTER & LATH, IN PLACE, AVERAGE COSTS:							
09.1401 011	Plaster & lath, tract, residential	SY	21.59	23.09	44.68	14.99	36.58	0.2828
09.1401 021	Plaster & lath, condo & apartment 2 story	SY	21.59	34.63	56.22	22.49	44.08	0.4242
09.1401 031	Plaster & lath, condo & apartment 3 story	SY	21.59	40.82	62.41	26.51	48.10	0.5000
09.1401 041	Plaster & lath, residential, 3 coat exterior, custom	SY	32.39	46.18	78.57	29.99	62.38	0.5656
09.1401 051	Plaster & lath, commercial, 3 coat exterior	SY	42.63	46.62	89.25	30.27	72.90	0.5710

Division 9 CSI #	09 - FINISHES Description	Unit	Material	Union Install	Union Total	Open Install	Open Total	Unit Man-Hrs
09.1401 000	PLASTER & LATH, IN PLACE, AVERAGE COSTS: (Cont.)							
09.1401 061	Plaster & lath, commercial, 3 coat interior	SY	30.40	51.08	81.48	33.17	63.57	0.6257
09.1401 071	Plaster & lath, commercial, 3 coat exterior soffits	SY	34.01	53.15	87.16	34.52	68.53	0.6510
09.1401 081	Plaster & lath, partitions	SY	35.72	66.17	101.89	42.97	78.69	0.8105
09.1402 000	EXTERIOR STUCCO & PLASTER, WITHOUT LATH OR FURRING:							
	Note: Because of current propensity for complicated plaster interior and exterior shapes, plaster is given without furring or lath. Both must be added to complete the plaster price. Do not forget shaping of plaster requires extensive plaster accessories and trim.							
09.1402 011	Stucco, residential, textured, soffit, wide & low	SY	20.33	36.04	56.37	23.40	43.73	0.4414
09.1402 021	Stucco, residential, textured, soffit, high & narrow	SY	20.63	46.83	67.46	30.41	51.04	0.5736
09.1402 031	Stucco, residential, textured	SY	20.88	26.55	47.43	17.24	38.12	0.3252
09.1402 041	Stucco, residential, float finish	SY	26.07	31.43	57.50	20.41	46.48	0.3850
09.1402 051	Stucco, institutional, float finish	SY	50.12	34.18	84.30	22.20	72.32	0.4187
09.1402 061	Stucco, institutional, dash finish	SY	57.17	34.63	91.80	22.49	79.66	0.4242
09.1402 071	Stucco, institutional, float finish, soffit, wide & low	SY	32.58	28.57	61.15	18.56	51.14	0.3500
09.1402 081	Stucco, institutional, float finish, soffit, high & narrow	SY	32.58	37.93	70.51	24.63	57.21	0.4646
09.1402 091	Stucco, institutional, float finish, articulated, wood	SY	32.58	72.77	105.35	47.26	79.84	0.8913
09.1402 101	Cement plaster, 2 coat, for paint	SY	17.09	21.13	38.22	13.72	30.81	0.2588
09.1402 111	Add for dash coat	SY	.86	3.89	4.75	2.52	3.38	0.0476
09.1402 121	Stucco, run mold, ogee 6"	LF	18.37	12.86	31.23	8.35	26.72	0.1575
09.1402 131	Stucco, run mold, ogee 9"	LF	22.63	18.78	41.41	12.19	34.82	0.2300
09.1402 141	Stucco, run mold, ogee 12"	LF	26.88	24.49	51.37	15.91	42.79	0.3000
09.1402 151	Stucco, run mold, ogee 15"	LF	33.25	26.94	60.19	17.50	50.75	0.3300
09.1402 161	Stucco, rustication, 1"	LF	7.53	6.53	14.06	4.24	11.77	0.0800
09.1402 171	Stucco, rustication, 2"	LF	9.43	7.35	16.78	4.77	14.20	0.0900
09.1402 181	Stucco, quoins, 12"x12"	LF	26.38	44.38	70.76	28.82	55.20	0.5436
09.1402 191	Stucco, quoins, 16"x16"	LF	26.38	40.00	66.38	25.98	52.36	0.4900
09.1403 000	INTERIOR PLASTER WALLS, WITHOUT LATH OR FURRING:							
	Note: Because of current propensity for complicated plaster interior and exterior shapes. Plaster is given without furring or lath. Both must be added to complete the plaster price. Do not forget shaping of plaster requires extensive plaster accessories and trim.							
09.1403 011	Plaster, gypsum, interior	SY	7.01	22.19	29.20	14.41	21.42	0.2718
09.1403 021	Cement plaster, Keenes, interior	SY	8.37	22.19	30.56	14.41	22.78	0.2718
09.1403 031	Plaster, structo lite, interior	SY	8.03	22.19	30.22	14.41	22.44	0.2718
09.1403 041	Cement plaster, interior	SY	6.27	15.05	21.32	9.77	16.04	0.1843
09.1403 051	Stucco, interior, 2 coat, residential	SY	7.19	12.86	20.05	8.35	15.54	0.1575
09.1403 061	Plaster, acoustic, 1/2" on brown coat	SY	12.37	27.81	40.18	18.06	30.43	0.3407
09.1403 071	Plaster, scratch coat, for tile	SY	4.51	12.40	16.91	8.05	12.56	0.1519
09.1403 081	Plaster, brown coat, for tile	SY	6.15	17.72	23.87	11.51	17.66	0.2171
09.1404 000	INTERIOR PLASTER CEILINGS, WITHOUT LATH OR FURRING:							
	Note: Because of current propensity for complicated plaster interior and exterior shapes. Plaster is given without furring or lath. Both must be added to complete the plaster price. Do not forget shaping of plaster requires extensive plaster accessories and trim.							
09.1404 011	Plaster, gypsum, ceilings	SY	6.22	22.19	28.41	14.41	20.63	0.2718
09.1404 021	Plaster, Keenes cement, ceilings	SY	7.72	22.19	29.91	14.41	22.13	0.2718
09.1404 031	Plaster, structo lite, ceilings	SY	7.24	22.19	29.43	14.41	21.65	0.2718
09.1404 041	Plaster, cement, ceilings	SY	5.61	22.19	27.80	14.41	20.02	0.2718
09.1404 051	Plaster, acoustic, 4 coat, ceilings	SY	15.08	50.01	65.09	32.48	47.56	0.6126
09.1404 061	Stucco, 2 coat, board lath, ceiling	SY	9.06	15.10	24.16	9.80	18.86	0.1849
09.1405 000	PLASTER, THIN COAT, WITHOUT LATH OR FURRING:							
09.1405 011	Plaster, thin, 1/2" board, wood studs	SY	7.20	16.87	24.07	10.95	18.15	0.2066
09.1405 021	Plaster, thin, 5/8" board, wood studs	SY	9.53	16.87	26.40	10.95	20.48	0.2066
09.1405 031	Plaster, thin, 1/2" board, metal stud	SY	8.12	19.15	27.27	12.44	20.56	0.2346
09.1405 041	Plaster, thin, 5/8" board, metal stud	SY	10.61	19.15	29.76	12.44	23.05	0.2346
09.1406 000	INTERIOR THIN COAT PLASTER CEILINGS, WITHOUT LATH, FURRING:							
09.1406 011	Plaster, thin, ceiling, 1/2" gypsum wall board, nailed	SY	7.20	21.57	28.77	14.72	21.92	0.2343
09.1406 021	Plaster, thin, ceiling, 5/8" gypsum wall board, nailed	SY	9.53	21.57	31.10	14.72	24.25	0.2343
09.1406 031	Plaster, thin, ceiling, 1/2" gypsum wall board, screw	SY	8.12	23.98	32.10	16.36	24.48	0.2604
09.1406 041	Plaster, thin, ceiling, 5/8" gypsum wall board, screw	SY	10.61	23.98	34.59	16.36	26.97	0.2604
09.1406 051	Add for bonding, concrete or masonry	SF	.33		.33		.33	

Division 9 CSI #	09 - FINISHES Description	Unit	Material	Union Install	Union Total	Open Install	Open Total	Unit Man-Hrs
09.1408 000	**PLASTERING ACCESSORIES, MISCELLANEOUS:**							
09.1408 011	Bullnose, 3/4"	LF	.70	3.75	4.45	2.43	3.13	0.0459
09.1408 021	Bullnose, 1-1/2", galvanized	LF	2.26	3.72	5.98	2.42	4.68	0.0456
09.1408 031	Bullnose, 1-1/2", stainless	LF	5.64	6.36	12.00	4.13	9.77	0.0779
09.1408 041	Casing/stop, square nose, galvanized	LF	.40	2.61	3.01	1.70	2.10	0.0320
09.1408 051	Corner bead, short nose	LF	.39	2.90	3.29	1.88	2.27	0.0355
09.1408 061	Corner bead, expanded, galvanized, zinc nose	LF	.69	2.90	3.59	1.88	2.57	0.0355
09.1408 071	Expansion joint, 3/4", galvanized	LF	1.26	2.90	4.16	1.88	3.14	0.0355
09.1408 081	Expansion joint, 1-1/2", galvanized	LF	1.70	3.09	4.79	2.00	3.70	0.0378
09.1408 091	Screed, base	LF	.31	2.90	3.21	1.88	2.19	0.0355
09.1408 101	Vent, 1-1/2", galvanized	LF	2.10	3.89	5.99	2.52	4.62	0.0476
09.1408 111	Vent, 4", galvanized	LF	2.48	5.52	8.00	3.58	6.06	0.0676
09.1408 121	Drip pacific #2	LF	.40	2.90	3.30	1.88	2.28	0.0355
09.1409 000	**ACCESS DOORS:**							
09.1409 000	**ACCESS DOOR, 24"X30":**							
09.1409 011	Access door, 12" x 12"	EA	163.51	106.30	269.81	69.03	232.54	1.3020
09.1409 021	Access door, 18" x 18"	EA	203.67	106.30	309.97	69.03	272.70	1.3020
09.1409 031	Access door, 20" x 30"	EA	222.98	106.30	329.28	69.03	292.01	1.3020
09.1409 041	Access door, 24" x 24"	EA	237.87	106.30	344.17	69.03	306.90	1.3020
09.1409 051	Access door, 24" x 30"	EA	245.27	106.30	351.57	69.03	314.30	1.3020
09.1410 000	**PLASTER MOLDINGS & ORNAMENTS, INTERIOR:**							
09.1410 011	Plaster molding, 2"	LF	6.63	8.80	15.43	5.72	12.35	0.1078
09.1410 021	Plaster molding, 4"	LF	12.34	10.47	22.81	6.80	19.14	0.1283
09.1410 031	Plaster molding, 6"	LF	14.77	12.26	27.03	7.96	22.73	0.1502
09.2000 000	**GYPSUM WALL BOARD, STUDDING & FURRING:**							
	Note: For metal studs see section 09.1000. For wood studs see section 06.0000.							
09.2001 000	**STUDS, METAL DRYWALL, 16" OC:**							
	Note: For galvanized studs, add 5% to the material costs. This section, 09.2000, relates to interior partition work not exceeding 12' above floor level.							
09.2001 011	Drywall stud, 25 ga, 16" OC, 1-5/8"	SF	.53	1.62	2.15	1.11	1.64	0.0176
09.2001 021	Drywall stud, 25 ga, 16" OC, 2-1/2"	SF	.55	1.72	2.27	1.18	1.73	0.0187
09.2001 031	Drywall stud, 25 ga, 16" OC, 3-5/8"	SF	.67	1.82	2.49	1.24	1.91	0.0198
09.2001 041	Drywall stud, 25 ga, 16" OC, 4"	SF	.73	1.98	2.71	1.35	2.08	0.0215
09.2001 051	Drywall stud, 25 ga, 16" OC, 6"	SF	.85	2.08	2.93	1.42	2.27	0.0226
09.2001 061	Drywall stud, 20 ga, 16" OC, 1-5/8"	SF	1.06	1.81	2.87	1.24	2.30	0.0197
09.2001 071	Drywall stud, 20 ga, 16" OC, 2-1/2"	SF	1.12	1.81	2.93	1.24	2.36	0.0197
09.2001 081	Drywall stud, 20 ga, 16" OC, 3-5/8"	SF	1.19	2.01	3.20	1.37	2.56	0.0218
09.2001 091	Drywall stud, 20 ga, 16" OC, 4"	SF	1.34	2.17	3.51	1.48	2.82	0.0236
09.2001 101	Drywall stud, 20 ga, 16" OC, 6"	SF	1.56	2.29	3.85	1.56	3.12	0.0249
09.2004 000	**RESIDENTIAL GYPSUM WALL BOARD, WALLS, HANG, TAPE, TEXTURE:**							
	Note: All gypsum wall board prices are given for 8' heights. You must add for structural studs and height as shown in section 09.2013.							
09.2004 011	Gypsum wall board, 1/4", wall, residential, taped & textured	SF	.35	.68	1.03	.47	.82	0.0074
09.2004 021	Gypsum wall board, 3/8", wall, residential, taped & textured	SF	.53	.68	1.21	.47	1.00	0.0074
09.2004 031	Gypsum wall board, 1/2", wall, residential, taped & textured	SF	.58	.76	1.34	.52	1.10	0.0082
09.2004 041	Gypsum wall board, fire resistant, 1/2", wall, residential, taped & textured	SF	.66	.76	1.42	.52	1.18	0.0082
09.2004 051	Gypsum wall board, water resistant, 1/2", wall, residential, taped & textured	SF	.78	.76	1.54	.52	1.30	0.0082
09.2004 061	Gypsum wall board, 5/8", wall, residential, taped & textured	SF	.64	.76	1.40	.52	1.16	0.0082
09.2004 071	Gypsum wall board, fire resistant, 5/8", wall, residential, taped & textured	SF	.76	.76	1.52	.52	1.28	0.0082
09.2004 081	Gypsum wall board, water resistant, 5/8", wall, residential, taped & textured	SF	.82	.76	1.58	.52	1.34	0.0082
09.2004 091	Gypsum wall board, 2 hour, 5/8", wall, residential, taped & textured	SF	1.42	1.29	2.71	.88	2.30	0.0140
09.2005 000	**RESIDENTIAL, GYPSUM BOARD, CEILINGS, HANG, TAPE, TEXTURE:**							
09.2005 011	Gypsum wall board, 1/4", ceilings, residential, tape & texture	SF	.35	.75	1.10	.51	.86	0.0081
09.2005 021	Gypsum wall board, 3/8", ceilings, residential, tape & texture	SF	.53	.75	1.28	.51	1.04	0.0081
09.2005 031	Gypsum wall board, 1/2", ceilings, residential, tape & texture	SF	.58	.75	1.33	.51	1.09	0.0081
09.2005 041	Gypsum wall board, fire resistant, 1/2", ceilings, residential, tape & texture	SF	.66	.75	1.41	.51	1.17	0.0081
09.2005 051	Gypsum wall board, water resistant, 1/2", ceilings, residential, tape & texture	SF	.78	.75	1.53	.51	1.29	0.0081
09.2005 061	Gypsum wall board, 5/8", ceilings, residential, tape & texture	SF	.64	.76	1.40	.52	1.16	0.0083
09.2005 071	Gypsum wall board, fire resistant, 5/8", ceilings, residential, tape & texture	SF	.76	.76	1.52	.52	1.28	0.0083
09.2005 081	Gypsum wall board, water resistant, 5/8", ceilings, residential, tape & texture	SF	.82	.76	1.58	.52	1.34	0.0083
09.2005 091	Gypsum wall board, 2 hour, 5/8", ceilings, residential, tape & texture	SF	1.42	.78	2.20	.53	1.95	0.0085

Division 9 CSI #	09 - FINISHES Description	Unit	Material	Union Install	Union Total	Open Install	Open Total	Unit Man-Hrs
09.2006 000	**RESIDENTIAL GYPSUM BOARD, MISCELLANEOUS:**							
09.2006 011	Gypsum wall board, asphalt core sheathing, 1/2", residential	SF	.66	.38	1.04	.26	.92	0.0041
09.2006 021	Gypsum wall board, vinyl clad, good, 5/8", residential	SF	2.38	.91	3.29	.62	3.00	0.0099
09.2006 031	Gypsum wall board, vinyl clad, best, 5/8", residential	SF	2.81	.91	3.72	.62	3.43	0.0099
09.2006 041	Gypsum sound board, 1/4", residential	SF	.35	.53	.88	.36	.71	0.0058
09.2006 051	Fiber sound board, 1/2", residential	SF	.61	.53	1.14	.36	.97	0.0058
09.2006 061	Gypsum wall board, partition, 5/8" each side, residential	SF	2.72	4.68	7.40	3.19	5.91	0.0508
09.2007 000	**COMMERCIAL GYPSUM WALL BOARD, WALLS, HANG, TAPE, TEXTURE:**							
	Note: All gypsum wall board prices are given in 8' heights. You must add adders under section 09.2013							
	for both height and structural studs.							
09.2007 011	Gypsum wall board, 1/4", 8', commercial, wall, tape & texture	SF	.35	1.06	1.41	.72	1.07	0.0115
09.2007 021	Gypsum wall board, 3/8", 8', commercial, wall, tape & texture	SF	.53	1.13	1.66	.77	1.30	0.0123
09.2007 031	Gypsum wall board, 1/2", 8', commercial, wall, tape & texture	SF	.58	1.29	1.87	.88	1.46	0.0140
09.2007 041	Gypsum wall board, fire resistant, 1/2", 8', commercial, wall, tape & texture	SF	.66	1.29	1.95	.88	1.54	0.0140
09.2007 051	Gypsum wall board, water resistant, 1/2", 8', commercial, wall, tape & texture	SF	.78	1.29	2.07	.88	1.66	0.0140
09.2007 061	Gypsum wall board, 5/8", 8', commercial, wall, tape & texture	SF	.64	1.29	1.93	.88	1.52	0.0140
09.2007 071	Gypsum wall board, fire resistant, 5/8", 8', commercial, wall, tape & texture	SF	.76	1.29	2.05	.88	1.64	0.0140
09.2007 081	Gypsum wall board, water resistant, 5/8", 8', commercial, wall, tape & texture	SF	.82	1.29	2.11	.88	1.70	0.0140
09.2007 091	Gypsum wall board, 2 hour, 5/8", 8', commercial, wall, tape & texture	SF	1.42	1.73	3.15	1.18	2.60	0.0188
09.2008 000	**COMMERCIAL GYPSUM BOARD, CEILINGS, HANG, TAPE, TEXTURE:**							
09.2008 011	Gypsum wall board, 1/4", ceilings, commercial, tape & texture	SF	.35	1.11	1.46	.76	1.11	0.0121
09.2008 021	Gypsum wall board, 3/8", ceilings, commercial, tape & texture	SF	.53	1.20	1.73	.82	1.35	0.0130
09.2008 031	Gypsum wall board, 1/2", ceilings, commercial, tape & texture	SF	.58	1.37	1.95	.94	1.52	0.0149
09.2008 041	Gypsum wall board, fire resistant, 1/2", ceilings, commercial	SF	.66	1.37	2.03	.94	1.60	0.0149
09.2008 051	Gypsum wall board, water resistant, 1/2", ceilings, commercial	SF	.78	1.37	2.15	.94	1.72	0.0149
09.2008 061	Gypsum wall board, 5/8", ceilings, commercial	SF	.64	1.37	2.01	.94	1.58	0.0149
09.2008 071	Gypsum wall board, fire resistant, 5/8", ceilings, commercial	SF	.76	1.37	2.13	.94	1.70	0.0149
09.2008 081	Gypsum wall board, water resistant, 5/8", ceilings, commercial	SF	.82	1.37	2.19	.94	1.76	0.0149
09.2008 091	Gypsum wall board, 2 hour, 5/8", ceilings, commercial	SF	1.42	1.80	3.22	1.23	2.65	0.0196
09.2009 000	**COMMERCIAL GYPSUM BOARD, MISCELLANEOUS:**							
	Note: All gypsum wall board prices are given in 8' heights. You must add adders under section 09.2013							
	for both height and structural studs.							
09.2009 011	Gypsum wall board, 1/2" asphalt core sheath, commercial	SF	.66	.61	1.27	.41	1.07	0.0066
09.2009 021	Gypsum wall board, vinyl clad, good, 5/8", commercial	SF	2.38	1.35	3.73	.92	3.30	0.0147
09.2009 031	Gypsum wall board, vinyl clad, best, 5/8", commercial	SF	2.81	1.59	4.40	1.09	3.90	0.0173
09.2009 041	Gypsum sound board, 1/4", commercial	SF	.35	.61	.96	.41	.76	0.0066
09.2009 051	Fiber sound board, 1/2", commercial	SF	.61	.61	1.22	.41	1.02	0.0066
09.2009 061	Gypsum wall board, partition, 5/8" each side, commercial	SF	2.72	5.13	7.85	3.50	6.22	0.0557
09.2010 000	**INSTITUTIONAL GYPSUM BOARD, WALL, HANG, TAPE, TEXTURE:**							
	Note: All gypsum wall board prices are given in 8' heights. You must add adders under section 09.2013							
	for both height and structural studs.							
09.2010 011	Gypsum wall board, 1/4", 8', institutional, wall, tape & texture	SF	.42	1.44	1.86	.98	1.40	0.0156
09.2010 021	Gypsum wall board, 3/8", 8', institutional, wall, tape & texture	SF	.58	1.44	2.02	.98	1.56	0.0156
09.2010 031	Gypsum wall board, 1/2", 8', institutional, wall, tape & texture	SF	.62	1.51	2.13	1.03	1.65	0.0164
09.2010 041	Gypsum wall board, fire resistant, 1/2", 8', institutional, wall, tape & texture	SF	.75	1.51	2.26	1.03	1.78	0.0164
09.2010 051	Gypsum wall board, water resistant, 1/2", 8', institutional, wall, tape & texture	SF	.81	1.51	2.32	1.03	1.84	0.0164
09.2010 061	Gypsum wall board, 5/8", 8', institutional, wall, tape & texture	SF	.75	1.51	2.26	1.03	1.78	0.0164
09.2010 071	Gypsum wall board, fire resistant, 5/8", 8', institutional, wall, tape & texture	SF	.81	1.51	2.32	1.03	1.84	0.0164
09.2010 081	Gypsum wall board, water resistant, 5/8", 8', institutional, wall, tape & texture	SF	.92	1.51	2.43	1.03	1.95	0.0164
09.2010 091	Gypsum wall board, 2 hour, 5/8", 8', institutional, wall, tape & texture	SF	1.55	1.81	3.36	1.24	2.79	0.0197
09.2010 101	Gypsum wall board, 2 hour, shaft liner, 1", institutional	SF	2.33	.63	2.96	.43	2.76	0.0068
09.2011 000	**INSTITUTIONAL GYPSUM BOARD, CEILINGS, HANG, TAPE TEXTURE:**							
09.2011 011	Gypsum wall board, 1/4", ceilings, institutional, tape & texture	SF	.42	1.55	1.97	1.06	1.48	0.0168
09.2011 021	Gypsum wall board, 3/8", ceilings, institutional, tape & texture	SF	.58	1.55	2.13	1.06	1.64	0.0168
09.2011 031	Gypsum wall board, 1/2", ceilings, institutional, tape & texture	SF	.62	1.63	2.25	1.11	1.73	0.0177
09.2011 041	Gypsum wall board, fire X, 1/2", ceilings, institutional, tape & texture	SF	.75	1.63	2.38	1.11	1.86	0.0177
09.2011 051	Gypsum wall board, water resistant, 1/2", ceilings, institutional, tape & texture	SF	.81	1.63	2.44	1.11	1.92	0.0177
09.2011 061	Gypsum wall board, 5/8", ceilings, institutional, tape & texture	SF	.75	1.63	2.38	1.11	1.86	0.0177
09.2011 071	Gypsum wall board, fire X, 5/8", ceilings, institutional, tape & texture	SF	.81	1.63	2.44	1.11	1.92	0.0177
09.2011 081	Gypsum wall board, water resistant, 5/8", ceilings, institutional, tape & texture	SF	.92	1.63	2.55	1.11	2.03	0.0177
09.2011 091	Gypsum wall board, 2 hour, 5/8", ceilings, institutional, tape & texture	SF	1.55	1.89	3.44	1.29	2.84	0.0205

Division 9 CSI #	09 - FINISHES Description	Unit	Material	Union Install	Union Total	Open Install	Open Total	Unit Man-Hrs
09.2012 000	**INSTITUTIONAL GYPSUM BOARD, MISCELLANEOUS:**							
09.2012 011	Gypsum wall board, asphalt core sheath, 1/2", institutional	SF	.66	.76	1.42	.52	1.18	0.0082
09.2012 021	Gypsum wall board, vinyl clad, good, 5/8", institutional	SF	2.38	1.81	4.19	1.24	3.62	0.0197
09.2012 031	Gypsum wall board, vinyl clad, best, 5/8", institutional	SF	2.81	1.81	4.62	1.24	4.05	0.0197
09.2012 041	Gypsum sound board, 1/4", institutional	SF	.35	.61	.96	.41	.76	0.0066
09.2012 051	Fiber sound board, 1/2", institutional	SF	.61	.61	1.22	.41	1.02	0.0066
09.2012 061	Gypsum wall board, partition, 5/8", each side, institutional	SF	2.72	5.65	8.37	3.86	6.58	0.0614
09.2013 000	**ADDERS FOR ALL GRADES OF GYPSUM WALL BOARD:**							
09.2013 011	Add for fire rated back taping	SF	.09	.30	.39	.21	.30	0.0033
09.2013 021	Add for 10' wall	SF	.09	.16	.25	.11	.20	0.0017
09.2013 031	Add for 12' wall	SF	.09	.30	.39	.21	.30	0.0033
09.2013 041	Add for 16' wall	SF	.09	.38	.47	.26	.35	0.0041
09.2013 051	Add for application to metal studs, 25 ga	SF	.09	.17	.26	.12	.21	0.0019
09.2013 061	Add for application to metal studs, 20 ga	SF	.09	.25	.34	.17	.26	0.0027
09.2013 071	Add for application to metal studs, 16 ga	SF	.12	.38	.50	.26	.38	0.0041
09.2013 081	Add for resilient clip system	SF	.44	.91	1.35	.62	1.06	0.0099
09.2100 000	**GYPSUM WALL BOARD SPECIALTIES:**							
09.2101 000	**GYPSUM BOARD, ACOUSTICAL TEXTURES:**							
09.2101 011	Gypsum wall board, simulated acoustic sprayed	SF	.17	.22	.39	.15	.32	0.0024
09.2102 000	**GYPSUM BOARD, TAPING & TEXTURING ONLY:**							
09.2102 011	Gypsum wall board, taping	SF	.15	.30	.45	.21	.36	0.0033
09.2102 021	Gypsum wall board, taping and sanding	SF	.15	.53	.68	.36	.51	0.0058
09.2102 031	Gypsum wall board, tape & texture, residential	SF	.15	.30	.45	.21	.36	0.0033
09.2102 041	Gypsum wall board, tape & sand, institutional	SF	.15	.61	.76	.41	.56	0.0066
09.2102 051	Gypsum wall board, tape & texture, 15' or more	SF	.15	.61	.76	.41	.56	0.0066
09.2102 061	Add for sand finish, no texture	SF		.30	.30	.21	.21	0.0033
09.2103 000	**GYPSUM WALL BOARD TRIM:**							
09.2103 011	Gypsum wall board, trim, corner beads	LF	.30	1.35	1.65	.92	1.22	0.0147
09.2103 021	Gypsum wall board, trim, stop/casing	LF	.53	2.04	2.57	1.40	1.93	0.0222
09.2103 031	Gypsum wall board, trim, jamb casing	LF	.62	2.11	2.73	1.44	2.06	0.0229
09.2104 000	**DRAFTSTOP:**							
09.2104 011	Draftstop, gypsum wall board, 5/8", taped only	SF	.76	1.01	1.77	.69	1.45	0.0110
09.3000 000	**CERAMIC TILE:**							
	Note: For brown and scratch coat see section 09.1403. For institutional applications, material costs may increase from 60 to 200%, depending on specification of the tile. The following prices reflect standard utility grade materials, standard colors and size from manufacturer's palettes.							
09.3001 000	**CERAMIC TILE, RESIDENTIAL:**							
	Note: For single family custom residence, add 60% to the material costs.							
09.3001 011	Tile, ceramic, residential, shower & tub, mastic	SF	5.95	4.98	10.93	3.98	9.93	0.0659
09.3001 021	Tile, ceramic, residential, shower & tub, mortar	SF	6.54	6.12	12.66	4.90	11.44	0.0811
09.3001 031	Tile, ceramic, residential, counter & splash, mastic	SF	10.12	24.61	34.73	19.69	29.81	0.3259
09.3001 041	Tile, ceramic, residential, counter & splash, mortar	SF	15.20	32.69	47.89	26.16	41.36	0.4330
09.3001 051	Tile, ceramic, residential, wall hung, counter, splash, mastic	SF	36.81	63.25	100.06	50.61	87.42	0.8377
09.3001 061	Tile, ceramic, residential, wall hung, counter, splash, mortar	SF	46.56	78.78	125.34	63.04	109.60	1.0435
09.3002 000	**CERAMIC TILE, FLOORS, COMMERCIAL & INSTITUTIONAL:**							
09.3002 011	Tile, ceramic, commercial & institutional, floor, unglazed, 1"x1", mortar	SF	5.68	6.89	12.57	5.51	11.19	0.0912
09.3002 021	Tile, ceramic, commercial & institutional, floor, glazed, 1" x 1", mortar	SF	5.73	7.49	13.22	5.99	11.72	0.0992
09.3002 031	Tile, ceramic, commercial & institutional, floor, glazed, 4" x 4", mortar	SF	5.55	6.79	12.34	5.43	10.98	0.0899
09.3002 041	Tile, ceramic, commercial & institutional, floor, glazed, 4" x 4", mastic	SF	5.40	4.13	9.53	3.30	8.70	0.0547
09.3002 051	Tile, ceramic, commercial & institutional, bull nose base, 4", mortar	LF	7.38	4.91	12.29	3.93	11.31	0.0650
09.3002 061	Tile, ceramic, commercial & institutional, bull nose base, 4", mastic	LF	6.42	3.15	9.57	2.52	8.94	0.0417
09.3003 000	**CERAMIC TILE, WALL, COMMERCIAL & INSTITUTIONAL:**							
09.3003 011	Tile, ceramic, commercial & institutional, wall, 1" x 1", mortar	SF	5.82	9.60	15.42	7.68	13.50	0.1271
09.3003 021	Tile, ceramic, commercial & institutional, wall, 1" x 1", mastic	SF	5.73	4.98	10.71	3.98	9.71	0.0659
09.3003 031	Tile, ceramic, commercial & institutional, wall, 2" x 1", mortar	SF	5.51	7.89	13.40	6.31	11.82	0.1045
09.3003 041	Tile, ceramic, commercial & institutional, wall, 2" x 1", mastic	SF	5.38	4.42	9.80	3.53	8.91	0.0585
09.3003 051	Tile, ceramic, commercial & institutional, wall, 4" x 4", mortar	SF	5.13	7.69	12.82	6.16	11.29	0.1019
09.3003 061	Tile, ceramic, commercial & institutional, wall, 4" x 4", mastic	SF	5.04	4.42	9.46	3.53	8.57	0.0585
09.3003 071	Tile, ceramic, commercial & institutional, wall, 6" x 3", mortar	SF	5.51	7.49	13.00	5.99	11.50	0.0992
09.3003 081	Tile, ceramic, commercial & institutional, wall, 6" x 3", mastic	SF	5.38	3.81	9.19	3.05	8.43	0.0505
09.3003 091	Tile, ceramic, commercial & institutional, wall, 6" x 4", mortar	SF	5.38	6.89	12.27	5.51	10.89	0.0912
09.3003 101	Tile, ceramic, commercial & institutional, wall, 6" x 4", mastic	SF	5.38	3.68	9.06	2.94	8.32	0.0487

Division 9 CSI #	09 - FINISHES Description	Unit	Material	Union Install	Union Total	Open Install	Open Total	Unit Man-Hrs
09.3004 000	**TILE ACCESSORIES:**							
09.3004 011	Soap & grab, mortar	EA	13.33	17.38	30.71	11.32	24.65	0.2006
09.3004 021	Soap & grab, mastic	EA	12.80	12.68	25.48	8.26	21.06	0.1463
09.3004 031	Paper holder, mortar	EA	13.33	16.38	29.71	13.10	26.43	0.2169
09.3004 041	Paper holder, mastic	EA	12.80	12.05	24.85	9.64	22.44	0.1596
09.3004 051	Epoxy grout, 1/16" joint	SF	1.22	.87	2.09	.56	1.78	0.0100
09.4000 000	**TERRAZZO:**							
09.4001 000	**STANDARD TERRAZZO, MUD:**							
	Note: The following prices are based on amounts of 3200 square feet or more.							
	For quantities between 200 & 1600 SF . . . . add 100% to labor cost							
	For quantities between 1600 & 3200 SF . . . . add 25% to labor cost							
09.4001 011	Terrazzo floor, mud, bonded, 2", bed only	SF	5.10		5.10		5.10	
09.4001 021	Terrazzo floor, mud, bonded, 2", conductive	SF	6.51	11.24	17.75	7.32	13.83	0.1297
09.4001 031	Terrazzo floor, mud, bonded, 2", decorative	SF	8.88	12.14	21.02	7.91	16.79	0.1401
09.4001 041	Terrazzo floor, mud, bonded, 3", 15#, with felt	SF	5.56	11.69	17.25	7.61	13.17	0.1349
09.4001 051	Terrazzo floor, mono, 3-1/2", with mesh	SF	6.02	11.39	17.41	7.41	13.43	0.1314
09.4001 061	Terrazzo wainscot, mud	SF	8.88	23.37	32.25	15.22	24.10	0.2697
09.4002 000	**ADDERS FOR TERRAZZO FLOORS:**							
09.4002 011	Add for white cement grout	SF	.37		.37		.37	
09.4002 021	Add for non-slip abrasive, heavy	SF	.80		.80		.80	
09.4002 031	Add for non-slip abrasive, light	SF	.34		.34		.34	
09.4002 041	Add for stairs, mud set	LF	7.28		7.28		7.28	
09.4002 051	Add for countertops, mud set	LF	25.78		25.78		25.78	
09.4002 061	Add for cove base, mud set	LF	12.38		12.38		12.38	
09.4003 000	**THINSET TERRAZZO:**							
	Note: The following prices are based on amounts of 1000 square feet or more.							
09.4003 011	Floor, polyester, 3/8", polished	SF	5.75	10.73	16.48	6.99	12.74	0.1238
09.4003 021	Floor, epoxy, conductive, 3/8", polish	SF	6.20	9.93	16.13	6.47	12.67	0.1146
09.4003 031	Floor, polyester, 3/8", unpolished	SF	3.66	6.92	10.58	4.50	8.16	0.0798
09.4003 041	Floor, polyester, 3/8", industrial	SF	3.34	6.21	9.55	4.05	7.39	0.0717
09.4003 051	Floor, latex, polished, 3/8"	SF	7.04	13.13	20.17	8.55	15.59	0.1515
09.4003 061	Floor, neoprene, 3/8", polished	SF	6.87	12.68	19.55	8.26	15.13	0.1463
09.4003 071	Floor, epoxy, 3/8", chemical resistant, polish	SF	5.66	10.47	16.13	6.82	12.48	0.1208
09.4003 081	Base, neoprene, 6"	LF	6.74	12.42	19.16	8.09	14.83	0.1433
09.4003 091	Wainscot, neoprene	SF	7.15	13.22	20.37	8.61	15.76	0.1525
09.4003 101	Add for waterproof membrane	SF	.98	2.05	3.03	1.33	2.31	0.0236
09.4004 000	**TERRAZZO ACCESSORIES:**							
09.4004 011	Divider strip, brass, 12 ga	LF	4.05	.46	4.51	.30	4.35	0.0053
09.4004 021	Divider strip, white metal, 12 ga	LF	1.61	.46	2.07	.30	1.91	0.0053
09.4004 031	Divider strip, brass, 4' OC, each way	SF	2.27	.26	2.53	.17	2.44	0.0030
09.4004 041	Divider strip, brass, 2' OC, each way	SF	4.29	.49	4.78	.32	4.61	0.0056
09.5000 000	**ACOUSTIC TREATMENT:**							
	Note: The following prices are based on amounts of 5000 square feet or more. Prices are based on							
	non-rated ceilings unless otherwise noted.							
	For quantities between 2500 and 5000 square feet . . . . add 50%							
	For quantities under 2500 square feet . . . . add 80%							
09.5001 000	**ACOUSTIC ADDERS:**							
09.5001 011	Add for earthquake sway bracing	SF	.20		.20		.20	
09.5002 000	**CEILING SYSTEM, SUSPENDED T BAR, 5/8" BD, STC 40:**							
09.5002 011	T-bar, 2x2, 5/8" board, 55 NRC, STC 40	SF	1.73	1.59	3.32	1.16	2.89	0.0168
09.5002 021	T-bar, 2x4, 5/8" board, 55 NRC, STC 40	SF	1.52	1.15	2.67	.84	2.36	0.0121
09.5002 031	T-bar, 4x4, 5/8" board, 55 NRC, STC 40	SF	1.82	1.09	2.91	.80	2.62	0.0115
09.5002 041	T-bar, 2x2, each room divided	SF	1.73	2.56	4.29	1.87	3.60	0.0270
09.5002 051	T-bar, 2x4, each room divided	SF	1.52	2.41	3.93	1.76	3.28	0.0254
09.5002 061	T-bar, 4x4, each room divided	SF	1.82	2.53	4.35	1.85	3.67	0.0267
09.5002 071	Deduct for no STC rating	SF	.08		.08		.08	
09.5002 081	Ceiling, suspended, coffered, 4x5, with fixture	SF	5.00	4.27	9.27	3.12	8.12	0.0451
09.5003 000	**SUSPENDED CEILING, DIRECT HUNG, CONCEALED SPLINE:**							
09.5003 011	T-bar, 1x1, mineral board, direct hung	SF	3.32	2.56	5.88	1.87	5.19	0.0270
09.5003 021	T-bar, 2x2, mineral board, direct hung	SF	5.19	2.41	7.60	1.76	6.95	0.0254
09.5003 031	T-bar, 1x1, 6# fiberboard, direct hung	SF	4.68	3.11	7.79	2.27	6.95	0.0328
09.5003 041	T-bar, 1x1, metal pan tile, direct hung	SF	5.80	3.33	9.13	2.44	8.24	0.0352

Division 9 CSI #	09 - FINISHES Description	Unit	Material	Union Install	Union Total	Open Install	Open Total	Unit Man-Hrs
09.5003 000	**SUSPENDED CEILING, DIRECT HUNG, CONCEALED SPLINE: (Cont.)**							
09.5003 051	T-bar, 1x1, aluminum pan tile direct hung	SF	8.56	2.95	11.51	2.15	10.71	0.0311
09.5003 061	T-bar, 1x1, vinyl diaphragm, direct hung	SF	4.39	2.88	7.27	2.10	6.49	0.0304
09.5003 071	T-bar, 2x2, tile, pop-out, direct hung	SF	4.39	2.88	7.27	2.10	6.49	0.0304
09.5004 000	**TILE, WOOD FIBER, RANDOM PERFORATION, ADHESIVE:**							
09.5004 011	Tile, wood fiber, 1/2"x12"x12"	SF	1.48	1.06	2.54	.77	2.25	0.0112
09.5004 021	Tile, wood fiber, 1/2"x12"x24"	SF	1.40	1.06	2.46	.77	2.17	0.0112
09.5004 031	Tile, wood fiber, 3/4"x12"x12"	SF	1.92	1.06	2.98	.77	2.69	0.0112
09.5004 041	Tile, wood fiber, 1/2"x12"x12", fissured	SF	1.48	1.06	2.54	.77	2.25	0.0112
09.5004 051	Tile, wood fiber, 3/4"x12"x12", fissured	SF	2.12	1.06	3.18	.77	2.89	0.0112
09.5004 061	Add for fireproofing	SF	.12		.12		.12	
09.5005 000	**TILE, MINERAL FIBER, FISSURED, ADHESIVE:**							
09.5005 011	Tile, mineral, 1/2"x12"x12", fissured	SF	2.26	1.06	3.32	.77	3.03	0.0112
09.5005 021	Tile, mineral, 5/8"x12"x12", fissured	SF	2.63	1.06	3.69	.77	3.40	0.0112
09.5005 031	Tile, mineral, 3/4"x12"x12", fissured	SF	2.69	1.06	3.75	.77	3.46	0.0112
09.5006 000	**TILE, VINYL DIAPHRAGM, WASHABLE, ADHESIVE:**							
09.5006 011	Tile, vinyl, 1/2x12x12, spray paint	SF	2.12	1.33	3.45	.97	3.09	0.0140
09.5006 021	Tile, vinyl, 1/2"x12"x12", bonded	SF	2.69	1.33	4.02	.97	3.66	0.0140
09.5006 031	Add for 1 hour fire rating	SF	.28		.28		.28	
09.5006 041	Add for stapling tile to furring	SF	.01	.24	.25	.17	.18	0.0025
09.5006 051	Add for plastic overlay, acoustic tile	SF	.13		.13		.13	
09.5006 061	Add for enamel paint, acoustic tile	SF	.66		.66		.66	
09.5006 071	Add for colored steel grid	SF	.42		.42		.42	
09.5006 081	Add for colored aluminum grid	SF	1.00		1.00		1.00	
09.5007 000	**BOARD, ACOUSTIC:**							
	Note: The following prices must be added to grid prices to determine total system cost.							
09.5007 011	Board, fiberglass, 5/8"	SF	1.00	.39	1.39	.28	1.28	0.0041
09.5007 021	Board, fiberglass, 3/4"	SF	1.04	.47	1.51	.35	1.39	0.0050
09.5007 031	Board, mineral fiber, 5/8"	SF	1.00	.39	1.39	.28	1.28	0.0041
09.5007 041	Board, mineral fiber, 5/8, vinyl face	SF	2.26	.55	2.81	.40	2.66	0.0058
09.5007 051	Board, mineral fiber, 5/8", 1-2 hour	SF	1.17	.47	1.64	.35	1.52	0.0050
09.5007 061	Board, mineral fiber, 5/8", 4 hour	SF	1.63	.55	2.18	.40	2.03	0.0058
09.5007 071	Board, wood fiber, 3/4"	SF	1.29	.55	1.84	.40	1.69	0.0058
09.5007 081	Board, mineral fiber, 5/8", air distribution	SF	1.40	.55	1.95	.40	1.80	0.0058
09.5007 091	Board, mineral fiber, 5/8", aluminum face	SF	1.89	.77	2.66	.56	2.45	0.0081
09.5008 000	**CEILING, T BAR SUSPENSION, GRID ONLY:**							
09.5008 011	T-bar ceiling, 2'x2', no divisions	SF	.91	.63	1.54	.46	1.37	0.0066
09.5008 021	T-bar ceiling, 2'x4', no divisions	SF	.85	.55	1.40	.40	1.25	0.0058
09.5008 031	T-bar ceiling, 4'x4', no divisions	SF	.81	.47	1.28	.35	1.16	0.0050
09.5008 041	T-bar ceiling, 2'x2', each room divided	SF	.91	1.60	2.51	1.17	2.08	0.0169
09.5008 051	T-bar ceiling, 2'x4', each room divided	SF	.85	1.50	2.35	1.09	1.94	0.0158
09.5008 061	T-bar ceiling, 4'x4', each room divided	SF	.81	1.24	2.05	.91	1.72	0.0131
09.5009 000	**CEILING, T BAR SPLINE, CONCEALED, GRID ONLY:**							
09.5009 011	T-bar spline, 1' x 1', grid only	SF	1.07	2.56	3.63	1.87	2.94	0.0270
09.5009 021	T-bar spline, 1' x 2', grid only	SF	1.12	2.56	3.68	1.87	2.99	0.0270
09.5009 031	T-bar spline, 2'x2', grid, pop-out	SF	1.63	2.56	4.19	1.87	3.50	0.0270
09.5009 041	T-bar spline, 2'x2', grid, pop-out	SF	1.63	2.56	4.19	1.87	3.50	0.0270
09.5009 051	T-bar spline, 1'x1', one room	SF	1.07	3.52	4.59	2.57	3.64	0.0372
09.5009 061	T-bar spline, 1'x2', one room	SF	1.12	3.55	4.67	2.59	3.71	0.0375
09.5009 071	T-bar spline, 2'x2', one room	SF	1.05	3.48	4.53	2.54	3.59	0.0367
09.5009 091	Add for second suspension system	SF	.40	1.39	1.79	1.02	1.42	0.0147
09.5009 101	Add for hanging wire, 12 ga, 4'	SQ	.12	14.71	14.83	10.75	10.87	0.1553
09.5009 111	Add for hanging wire, 12 ga, 8'	SQ	.21	14.71	14.92	10.75	10.96	0.1553
09.5700 000	**WOOD CEILINGS:**							
	Note: The following prices are based on amounts of 5000 square feet or more. Prices do not reflect custom work, but include suspension system							
09.5700 011	Celing System, wood, proprietory system, average	SF	13.64	15.08	28.72	10.53	24.17	0.1713
09.6000 000	**WOOD FLOORING:**							
	Note: The following prices are based on amounts of 5000 square feet or more. Prices do not reflect custom work.							
09.6001 011	Oak floor, commercial, 25/32"x2-1/4", unfinished	SF	4.12	3.69	7.81	2.58	6.70	0.0419
09.6001 021	Oak floor, select, 25/32"x2-1/4", unfinished	SF	4.19	3.92	8.11	2.74	6.93	0.0445

Division 9 CSI #	09 - FINISHES Description	Unit	Material	Union Install	Union Total	Open Install	Open Total	Unit Man-Hrs
09.6000 000	**WOOD FLOORING: (Cont.)**							
09.6001 031	Oak plank floor, 25/32", tract	SF	5.89	3.92	9.81	2.74	8.63	0.0445
09.6001 041	Oak plank floor, 25/32", institutional	SF	4.34	4.13	8.47	2.88	7.22	0.0469
09.6001 051	1/2" pre-finish plank floor	SF	3.62	4.92	8.54	3.44	7.06	0.0559
09.6001 061	Oak parquet floor, 5/16", prefinished	SF	4.17	4.92	9.09	3.44	7.61	0.0559
09.6001 071	Oak parquet floor, 25/32", prefinished	SF	4.50	5.06	9.56	3.53	8.03	0.0575
09.6001 081	Maple parquet floor, 5/16", prefinished	SF	6.97	5.28	12.25	3.69	10.66	0.0600
09.6001 091	Walnut parquet floor, 5/16", prefinished	SF	7.12	5.49	12.61	3.84	10.96	0.0624
09.6001 101	Teak parquet floor, 5/16", prefinished	SF	7.42	5.84	13.26	4.08	11.50	0.0664
09.6001 111	Maple gym floor, 25/32", 2x4 sleepers	SF	7.74	5.48	13.22	3.83	11.57	0.0623
09.6001 121	Gym floor, 25/32" on steel springs	SF	8.93	8.00	16.93	5.59	14.52	0.0909
09.6001 131	Gym floor, 25/32", on steel channels	SF	7.96	7.14	15.10	4.99	12.95	0.0811
09.6001 141	Floor, Douglas fir, 'B'	SF	3.10	4.13	7.23	2.88	5.98	0.0469
09.6001 151	Floor, Douglas fir, 'C'	SF	2.61	4.13	6.74	2.88	5.49	0.0469
09.6001 161	Floor, mill, 2x4", 20-30d, 5.3 BF/SF	SF	2.73	3.53	6.26	2.46	5.19	0.0401
09.6001 171	Floor, mill, 2x6, 20-30 d, 8 BF/SF	SF	4.36	5.77	10.13	4.03	8.39	0.0655
09.6001 181	Mill, knock down, sanding	SF	.07	.51	.58	.36	.43	0.0058
09.6002 000	**FLOORING, WOOD BLOCK:**							
09.6002 011	Floor, wood block, natural, 1-1/2"	SF	3.29	3.40	6.69	2.37	5.66	0.0386
09.6002 021	Floor, wood block, treated, 2"	SF	3.55	1.52	5.07	1.06	4.61	0.0173
09.6002 031	Floor, wood block, treated, 2-1/2"	SF	3.74	1.65	5.39	1.16	4.90	0.0188
09.6002 041	Floor, wood block, treated, 3"	SF	3.96	1.73	5.69	1.21	5.17	0.0197
09.6003 000	**FLOOR SANDING & FINISHING ONLY:**							
09.6003 011	Floor, sand, fill, 2 coats lacquer	SF	.37	1.16	1.53	.81	1.18	0.0132
09.6003 021	Floor, waxing	SF	.13	.51	.64	.36	.49	0.0058
09.6003 031	Floor, pegging	SF	.09	.51	.60	.36	.45	0.0058
09.6003 041	Floor, institutional, total finishing	SF	.27	3.04	3.31	2.12	2.39	0.0345
09.6003 051	Floor, refinish existing, average	SF	.86	2.92	3.78	2.04	2.90	0.0332
09.7000 000	**RESILIENT FLOORING:**							
	Note: The labor prices in this section are based on the following productivity figures:							
	Tile . . . . 450 SF PER MAN DAY							
	Linoleum, Coved . . . . . . 30 SY PER MAN DAY							
	Linoleum, Flat . . . . 60 SY PER MAN DAY							
09.7001 000	**TILE, RESILIENT:**							
09.7001 011	Tile, asphalt, 1/8", 'B'	SF	1.45	1.56	3.01	1.30	2.75	0.0178
09.7001 021	Tile, asphalt, 1/8", 'C'	SF	1.61	1.56	3.17	1.30	2.91	0.0178
09.7001 031	Tile, vinyl, 1/8", grease resistant	SF	4.62	1.56	6.18	1.30	5.92	0.0178
09.7001 041	Tile, cork, 5/16"	SF	6.58	1.56	8.14	1.30	7.88	0.0178
09.7001 051	Tile, cork, 3/16"	SF	4.38	1.56	5.94	1.30	5.68	0.0178
09.7001 061	Tile, vinyl composition, 1/16", standard	SF	1.23	1.56	2.79	1.30	2.53	0.0178
09.7001 071	Tile, vinyl composition, 3/32", standard	SF	1.61	1.56	3.17	1.30	2.91	0.0178
09.7001 081	Tile, vinyl composition, 1/8", standard	SF	1.80	1.56	3.36	1.30	3.10	0.0178
09.7001 091	Tile, vinyl composition, 1/16", metallic	SF	1.53	1.56	3.09	1.30	2.83	0.0178
09.7001 101	Tile, vinyl solid, 1/16", standard	SF	4.29	1.56	5.85	1.30	5.59	0.0178
09.7001 111	Tile, vinyl solid, 1/8", heavy duty	SF	6.35	1.56	7.91	1.30	7.65	0.0178
09.7001 121	Tile, vinyl, decorative, 125", best	SF	13.01	3.13	16.14	2.61	15.62	0.0356
09.7002 000	**SHEET GOODS, RESILIENT:**							
09.7002 011	Vinyl, .065", with cove	SY	22.99	13.75	36.74	11.47	34.46	0.1565
09.7002 021	Vinyl, good, .040", with cove	SY	18.81	13.75	32.56	11.47	30.28	0.1565
09.7002 031	Vinyl, metallic, .065", with cove	SY	29.13	13.75	42.88	11.47	40.60	0.1565
09.7002 041	Vinyl, metallic, .090", custom	SY	40.54	3.30	43.84	2.75	43.29	0.0375
09.7002 051	Vinyl, flat, with out cove, labor only	SY		7.91	7.91	6.60	6.60	0.0900
09.7002 061	Vinyl, flat, cove, labor only	LF		31.32	31.32	26.12	26.12	0.3564
09.7002 071	Linoleum, inlaid, standard grade with out cove	SY	24.86	13.74	38.60	11.46	36.32	0.1564
09.7002 081	Linoleum, inlaid, heavy duty, 1/8", with out cove	SY	32.07	16.76	48.83	13.98	46.05	0.1907
09.7002 091	Border, linoleum	LF	2.87	10.64	13.51	8.88	11.75	0.1211
09.7002 101	Floor, PVC, edge sealed, hot weld, small area	SF	2.06	5.31	7.37	4.43	6.49	0.0604
09.7002 111	Floor, PVC, edge sealed, small area	SF	2.63	6.39	9.02	5.33	7.96	0.0727
09.7003 000	**FLOORING, RESILIENT, BASE:**							
	Note: For wood in combination with resilient flooring see section 06.2000.							
09.7003 011	Base, top set, vinyl, 6"	LF	1.53	1.29	2.82	1.08	2.61	0.0147
09.7003 021	Base, top set, vinyl, 4"	LF	1.05	1.29	2.34	1.08	2.13	0.0147

117

Division 9 CSI #	09 - FINISHES Description	Unit	Material	Union Install	Union Total	Open Install	Open Total	Unit Man-Hrs
09.7003 000	**FLOORING, RESILIENT, BASE: (Cont.)**							
09.7003 031	Base, top set, vinyl, 2-1/2"	LF	.66	1.29	1.95	1.08	1.74	0.0147
09.7003 041	Base, top set, rubber, 6"	LF	2.12	1.29	3.41	1.08	3.20	0.0147
09.7003 051	Base, cove set, rubber, 4"	LF	1.52	1.29	2.81	1.08	2.60	0.0147
09.7003 061	Base, top set, rubber, 2-1/2"	LF	1.05	1.29	2.34	1.08	2.13	0.0147
09.7004 000	**FLOORING, SEAMLESS:**							
09.7004 011	Floor, seamless resilient, large area	SF	1.47	4.41	5.88	3.68	5.15	0.0502
09.7004 021	Floor, seamless resilient, small area	SF	4.27	12.15	16.42	10.13	14.40	0.1382
09.7004 031	Floor, seamless, 4" base, chemical resistant	SF	1.79	5.31	7.10	4.43	6.22	0.0604
09.7004 041	Elastomeric/poly cove base, large area	SF	1.47	4.41	5.88	3.68	5.15	0.0502
09.7004 051	Elastomeric/poly cove base, small area	SF	1.73	5.13	6.86	4.28	6.01	0.0584
09.7004 061	Wainscot, seamless, cove, large area	SF	1.47	5.13	6.60	4.28	5.75	0.0584
09.7004 071	Wainscot, seamless, cove, small area	SF	1.73	6.48	8.21	5.40	7.13	0.0737
09.7004 081	Tread, seamless, riser, nosing, large	LF	2.30	8.18	10.48	6.82	9.12	0.0931
09.7004 091	Tread, seamless, riser, nosing, small	LF	2.90	8.18	11.08	6.82	9.72	0.0931
09.7005 000	**FLOORING, RESILIENT, SPECIALTIES:**							
09.7005 011	Floor, magnesite, medium area	SF	3.35	5.13	8.48	4.28	7.63	0.0584
09.7005 021	Floor, magnesite, large area	SF	2.94	3.96	6.90	3.31	6.25	0.0451
09.7005 031	Base, magnesite, medium area	LF	3.37	5.31	8.68	4.43	7.80	0.0604
09.7005 041	Base, magnesite, large area	LF	3.06	4.41	7.47	3.68	6.74	0.0502
09.7005 051	Treads, rubber, molded, 12" x 5/16"	LF	9.64	7.29	16.93	6.08	15.72	0.0829
09.7005 061	Treads, rubber, molded, 12" x 3/16"	LF	9.17	6.39	15.56	5.33	14.50	0.0727
09.7005 071	Treads, rubber, grip strip, 5/16"	LF	14.18	13.67	27.85	11.40	25.58	0.1555
09.7005 081	Treads, rubber, grip strip, 3/16"	LF	10.51	11.78	22.29	9.83	20.34	0.1341
09.7005 091	Treads, vinyl, molded, 12" x 1/8"	LF	3.80	3.06	6.86	2.55	6.35	0.0348
09.7005 101	Treads, vinyl, molded, 12" x 1/4"	LF	6.56	5.76	12.32	4.80	11.36	0.0655
09.7005 111	Risers, rubber, 7" x 1/8"	LF	2.85	3.60	6.45	3.01	5.86	0.0410
09.7005 121	Risers, vinyl, 7" x 1/8"	LF	2.45	3.78	6.23	3.15	5.60	0.0430
09.7005 131	Underlayment, particle board	SF	.30	.51	.81	.43	.73	0.0058
09.7005 141	Asphalt plank, 1/2" x 12" x 24"	SF	2.27	1.16	3.43	.97	3.24	0.0132
09.7005 151	Corner guards, rubber, 2-3/4"x1/4"	LF	4.22	3.27	7.49	2.73	6.95	0.0372
09.7005 161	Corner guard, vinyl, 2-3/4"x1-1/4"	LF	4.22	3.27	7.49	2.73	6.95	0.0372
09.8000 000	**PAINTING & WALL COVERING:**							
09.8001 000	**PAINTING & WALL COVERING, IN PLACE:**							
	Note: The following production rates are used:							
	Brush Painting . . . . . 2,000 SF MAN DAY							
	Roller Painting . . . . . 3,000 SF MAN DAY							
	Spray Painting . . . . . 5,000 SF MAN DAY							
	Airless Painting . . . . 8,000 SF MAN DAY							
	SF/GAL TYPICAL: PRIME COAT 200,FINISH COATS 250							
09.8001 011	Multi residential, economy, 1 flat, 2 enamel	SF	.32	1.01	1.33	.79	1.11	0.0120
09.8001 021	Multi residential, economy, 2 flat, 3 enamel	SF	.52	1.43	1.95	1.12	1.64	0.0170
09.8001 031	Custom residential, 2 flat, 3 enamel	SF	.76	2.11	2.87	1.64	2.40	0.0250
09.8001 041	Commercial & industrial, 2 flat, 2 enamel	SF	.32	1.01	1.33	.79	1.11	0.0120
09.8001 051	Frame & schools, 2 flat, 3 enamel	SF	.76	1.52	2.28	1.18	1.94	0.0180
09.8002 000	**PAINTING, EXTERIOR, NO HAND CUT-IN, LARGE AREAS:**							
09.8002 011	Paint, concrete, prime	SF	.09	.35	.44	.28	.37	0.0042
09.8002 021	Paint, concrete, prime + 1 finish	SF	.17	.68	.85	.53	.70	0.0080
09.8002 031	Paint, concrete, prime + 2 finish	SF	.24	.99	1.23	.77	1.01	0.0117
09.8002 041	Paint, plaster, prime	SF	.09	.35	.44	.28	.37	0.0042
09.8002 051	Paint, plaster, prime + 1 finish	SF	.14	.68	.82	.53	.67	0.0080
09.8002 061	Paint, plaster, prime + 2 finish	SF	.24	.99	1.23	.77	1.01	0.0117
09.8002 071	Paint, masonry, prime	SF	.14	.40	.54	.31	.45	0.0047
09.8002 081	Paint, masonry, prime + 1 finish	SF	.14	.71	.85	.55	.69	0.0084
09.8002 091	Paint, masonry, prime + 2 finish	SF	.24	1.01	1.25	.79	1.03	0.0120
09.8002 101	Paint, wood siding, prime	SF	.08	.32	.40	.25	.33	0.0038
09.8002 111	Paint, wood siding, prime + 1 finish	SF	.14	.68	.82	.53	.67	0.0080
09.8002 121	Paint, wood siding, prime + 2 finish	SF	.24	.99	1.23	.77	1.01	0.0117
09.8002 131	Stain, wood siding	SF	.09	.32	.41	.25	.34	0.0038
09.8002 141	Stain, wood siding, + 2 seal coats	SF	.09	.95	1.04	.74	.83	0.0112
09.8002 151	Stain, shingle siding	SF	.08	.32	.40	.25	.33	0.0038
09.8002 161	Stain, shingle siding, + 2 seal coats	SF	.09	.95	1.04	.74	.83	0.0112

Division 9 CSI #	09 - FINISHES Description	Unit	Material	Union Install	Union Total	Open Install	Open Total	Unit Man-Hrs
09.8002 000	**PAINTING, EXTERIOR, NO HAND CUT-IN, LARGE AREAS: (Cont.)**							
09.8002 171	Silicone seal spray, 1 coat	SF	.26	.32	.58	.25	.51	0.0038
09.8002 181	Silicone seal spray, 2 coat	SF	.63	.59	1.22	.46	1.09	0.0070
09.8002 191	Polyurethane coating, 1/8"	SF	1.62	3.14	4.76	2.45	4.07	0.0372
09.8002 201	Paint, sheet metal, prime	SF	.08	.63	.71	.49	.57	0.0075
09.8002 211	Paint, sheet metal, prime + 1 finish	SF	.14	1.06	1.20	.83	.97	0.0126
09.8002 221	Paint, sheet metal, prime + 2 finish	SF	.20	1.57	1.77	1.22	1.42	0.0186
09.8002 231	Paint, wood trim, prime	LF	.09	.40	.49	.31	.40	0.0047
09.8002 241	Paint, wood trim, prime + 1 finish	LF	.20	.69	.89	.54	.74	0.0082
09.8002 251	Paint, wood trim, prime + 2 finish	LF	.26	1.11	1.37	.86	1.12	0.0131
09.8003 000	**INTERIOR PAINTING:**							
	Note: C-G-P = Concrete, gypsum wall board, plaster							
09.8003 011	Paint, c-g-p, interior, prime, brush	SF	.04	.32	.36	.25	.29	0.0038
09.8003 021	Paint, c-g-p, interior, prime+1 finish, brush	SF	.12	.59	.71	.46	.58	0.0070
09.8003 031	Paint, c-g-p, interior, prime+2 finish, brush	SF	.22	.95	1.17	.74	.96	0.0112
09.8003 041	Paint, c-g-p, interior, prime, roller	SF	.04	.21	.25	.16	.20	0.0025
09.8003 051	Paint, c-g-p, interior, prime+1 finish, roll	SF	.12	.40	.52	.31	.43	0.0047
09.8003 061	Paint, c-g-p, interior, prime+2 finish, roll	SF	.22	.63	.85	.49	.71	0.0075
09.8003 071	Paint, c-g-p, interior, prime, spray	SF	.04	.13	.17	.10	.14	0.0015
09.8003 081	Paint, c-g-p, interior, prime+1 finish, spray	SF	.12	.24	.36	.18	.30	0.0028
09.8003 091	Paint, c-g-p, interior, prime+2 finish, spray	SF	.22	.38	.60	.30	.52	0.0045
09.8003 101	Paint, c-g-p, interior, prime, airless	SF	.08	.08	.16	.07	.15	0.0010
09.8003 111	Paint, c-g-p, interior, prime+1 finish, airless	SF	.14	.15	.29	.12	.26	0.0018
09.8003 121	Paint, c-g-p, interior, prime+2 finish, airless	SF	.24	.24	.48	.18	.42	0.0028
09.8003 123	Paint, cmu, interior, prime, brush	SF	.04	.35	.39	.28	.32	0.0042
09.8003 125	Paint, cmu, interior, prime + 1 finish, brush	SF	.14	.68	.82	.53	.67	0.0080
09.8003 127	Paint, cmu, interior, prime + 2 finish, brush	SF	.24	1.00	1.24	.78	1.02	0.0118
09.8003 131	Paint, cmu, interior, prime, rolled	SF	.04	.24	.28	.18	.22	0.0028
09.8003 141	Paint, cmu, interior, prime + 1 finish, roll	SF	.14	.45	.59	.35	.49	0.0053
09.8003 151	Paint, cmu, interior, prime + 2 finish, roll	SF	.24	.67	.91	.52	.76	0.0079
09.8003 161	Stain, paneling, brush	SF	.08	.32	.40	.25	.33	0.0038
09.8003 171	Stain, paneling, + 2 seal coats, brush	SF	.09	.95	1.04	.74	.83	0.0112
09.8003 181	Paint, sheet metal, interior, prime, brush	SF	.08	.59	.67	.46	.54	0.0070
09.8003 191	Paint, sheet metal, interior, prime+1 finish, brush	SF	.14	1.02	1.16	.80	.94	0.0121
09.8003 201	Paint, sheet metal, interior, prime+2 finish, brush	SF	.20	1.54	1.74	1.20	1.40	0.0182
09.8003 211	Paint, wood trim, interior, prime, brush	LF	.09	.35	.44	.28	.37	0.0042
09.8003 221	Paint, wood trim, interior, prime+1 finish, brush	LF	.20	.65	.85	.51	.71	0.0077
09.8003 231	Paint, wood trim, interior, prime+2 finish, brush	LF	.26	.99	1.25	.77	1.03	0.0117
09.8004 000	**MISCELLANEOUS PAINTING ITEMS:**							
	Note: For institutional finish on cabinets, add 30% to the total costs. Price does not include painting							
	interior of cabinets.							
09.8004 011	Cabinets, exterior, stain & varnish	LF	4.54	17.61	22.15	13.72	18.26	0.2086
09.8004 021	Cabinets, exterior, lacquer, 2 coats	LF	3.43	16.01	19.44	12.48	15.91	0.1897
09.8004 031	Cabinets, stain & varnish, 3 coats	LF	9.17	23.26	32.43	18.13	27.30	0.2756
09.8004 041	Door & trim, lacquer, spray 2 coats	EA	4.54	34.92	39.46	27.21	31.75	0.4137
09.8004 051	Door & trim, 2 coats, residential	EA	5.72	18.92	24.64	14.74	20.46	0.2241
09.8004 061	Door & trim, 3 coats, institutional	EA	13.68	40.73	54.41	31.73	45.41	0.4825
09.8004 071	Sash & trim, wood sash, 2 coats	SF	.59	2.18	2.77	1.70	2.29	0.0258
09.8004 081	Sash & trim, steel sash, 2 coats	SF	.76	2.91	3.67	2.27	3.03	0.0345
09.8004 091	Hand rail, architectural, 3 coats	LF	1.12	3.79	4.91	2.95	4.07	0.0449
09.8004 101	Hand rail, pipe, 3 coats	LF	1.12	3.79	4.91	2.95	4.07	0.0449
09.8004 111	Paint wall louver, 24" x 8"	EA	6.90	23.97	30.87	18.68	25.58	0.2840
09.8004 121	Paint roll-up doors, 2 sides	LF	1.12	2.28	3.40	1.78	2.90	0.0270
09.8004 131	Ceraglazed e-p coating on gypsum wall board	SF	1.12	1.18	2.30	.92	2.04	0.0140
09.8004 141	Paint guard rail	LF	1.12	2.95	4.07	2.30	3.42	0.0350
09.8004 151	Paint ladder	LF	1.12	5.06	6.18	3.95	5.07	0.0600
09.8004 161	Graffiti resistant coating	SF	.64	1.23	1.87	.96	1.60	0.0146
09.8005 000	**PAINTING STEEL:**							
09.8005 011	Paint, structural steel, average cost/ton	TON	101.01	292.73	393.74	228.09	329.10	3.4680
09.8005 021	Paint, structural steel, average cost/SF building	SF	.09	.35	.44	.28	.37	0.0042
09.8005 031	Paint, structural steel, 1 coat, brush	SF	.03	.47	.50	.37	.40	0.0056
09.8005 041	Paint, structural steel, 2 coats, brush	SF	.09	.87	.96	.68	.77	0.0103

Division 9 CSI #	09 - FINISHES Description	Unit	Material	Union Install	Union Total	Open Install	Open Total	Unit Man-Hrs
09.8005 000	**PAINTING STEEL: (Cont.)**							
09.8005 051	Paint, structural steel, 1 coat, spray	SF	.10	.24	.34	.18	.28	0.0028
09.8005 061	Paint, structural steel, 2 coats, spray, airless	SF	.24	.44	.68	.34	.58	0.0052
09.8005 071	Paint, structural steel, 1 epoxy, touch up	SF	.29	.59	.88	.46	.75	0.0070
09.8005 081	Paint, pipe to 6", prime	LF	.04	.59	.63	.46	.50	0.0070
09.8005 091	Paint, pipe to 6", prime + 1 finish	LF	.13	1.11	1.24	.86	.99	0.0131
09.8005 101	Paint, pipe to 6", prime + 2 finish	LF	.22	1.57	1.79	1.22	1.44	0.0186
09.8005 111	Paint, pipe to 12", prime	LF	.04	1.18	1.22	.92	.96	0.0140
09.8005 121	Paint, pipe to 12", prime + 1 finish	LF	.13	2.16	2.29	1.68	1.81	0.0256
09.8005 131	Paint, pipe to 12", prime + 2 finish	LF	.24	2.75	2.99	2.14	2.38	0.0326
09.8005 141	Paint, pipe over 12", prime	SF	.03	.56	.59	.43	.46	0.0066
09.8005 151	Paint, pipe over 12", prime + 1 finish	SF	.09	1.18	1.27	.92	1.01	0.0140
09.8005 161	Paint, pipe over 12", prime + 2 finish	SF	.13	1.57	1.70	1.22	1.35	0.0186
09.8005 171	Paint, steel tank, prime	SF	.03	.47	.50	.37	.40	0.0056
09.8005 181	Paint, steel tank, prime + 1 finish	SF	.09	.87	.96	.68	.77	0.0103
09.8005 191	Paint, steel tank, prime + 2 finish	SF	.13	1.02	1.15	.80	.93	0.0121
09.8006 000	**SANDBLASTING, IN CONJUNCTION WITH PAINTING:**							
	Note: Prices include compressor time. Material prices are based on sand, a b & c pattern Swedish pictorial. For cost of clean blast abrasive multiply sand cost by 3. Codes sp1 through sp10 refer to steel structures painting council coding.							
09.8006 011	Whip blast, SP 7, 6000 SF/day	SF	.16	.21	.37	.16	.32	0.0025
09.8006 021	Sandblast, commercial, SP 6, 3200 SF/day	SF	.34	.32	.66	.25	.59	0.0038
09.8006 031	Sandblast, near white, SP 10, 2200 SF/day	SF	.78	.62	1.40	.49	1.27	0.0074
09.8006 041	Sandblast, white metal, SP 5, 1400 SF/day	SF	1.04	.84	1.88	.65	1.69	0.0099
09.8006 051	Wire brush, incidental, SP 1	SF		.29	.29	.22	.22	0.0034
09.8006 061	Wire brush, power, SP 2	SF		.44	.44	.34	.34	0.0052
09.8006 071	Acid clean & etch, water rinse	SF		.41	.41	.32	.32	0.0048
09.8007 000	**WALL COVERINGS:**							
	Note: For quantities under 500 sf, add 20% to the total costs, less than 250 sf double time.							
09.8007 021	Paper hanging, labor, normal conditions	SF		.89	.89	.69	.69	0.0105
09.8007 031	Wall paper, 36 SF/roll, average	ROLL	32.06	26.17	58.23	20.39	52.45	0.3100
09.8007 041	Wall cover, vinyl, 7 oz, light	SF	1.72	.57	2.29	.45	2.17	0.0068
09.8007 051	Wall cover, vinyl, 14 oz, medium	SF	1.88	.73	2.61	.57	2.45	0.0086
09.8007 061	Wall cover, vinyl, 22 oz, heavy	SF	2.14	.84	2.98	.65	2.79	0.0099
09.8007 071	Fiber board backing for vinyl	SF	.20	.21	.41	.16	.36	0.0025
09.8007 081	Wall cover, vinyl, 14 oz, aluminum back	SF	1.58	2.14	3.72	1.66	3.24	0.0253
09.8007 091	Wall cover, linen, acrylic back	SF	1.34	1.14	2.48	.89	2.23	0.0135
09.8007 101	Wall cover, glass cloth	SF	1.46	.79	2.25	.61	2.07	0.0093
09.8007 111	Wall cover, felt	SF	2.54	1.61	4.15	1.26	3.80	0.0191
09.8007 121	Wall cover, cork sheathing, 1/8"	SF	2.02	1.61	3.63	1.26	3.28	0.0191
09.8007 131	Wall cover, flexible wood, veneer	SF	4.81	2.91	7.72	2.27	7.08	0.0345
09.9000 000	**PLASTIC & FACTORY FINISH WALL SURFACES:**							
09.9001 000	**LAM PLASTICS, STD PATTERNS & COLORS, WITHOUT BACKING:**							
09.9001 011	Laminated plastic cover, adhesive, 1/16"	SF	2.22	2.08	4.30	1.62	3.84	0.0246
09.9001 021	Laminated plastic, adhesive, 1/32", vertical surface	SF	2.34	2.08	4.42	1.62	3.96	0.0246
09.9001 031	Laminated plastic, adhesive, 1/16", acid resistant	SF	2.22	2.08	4.30	1.62	3.84	0.0246
09.9001 041	Laminated plastic, adhesive, .020", back sheet	SF	.59	.89	1.48	.69	1.28	0.0105
09.9001 051	Add for post formed	SF	.17	.21	.38	.16	.33	0.0025
09.9002 000	**WALL COVER, HARDBOARD, PHOTO REPRODUCTION WITHOUT BACKING:**							
	Note: For patterns and deep colors, add 20% to the material costs.							
09.9002 011	Wall cover, plastic/hardboard, 1/8", trim	SF	2.58	1.30	3.88	1.01	3.59	0.0154
09.9002 021	Wall cover, plastic/hardboard, 1/4", trim	SF	3.42	1.30	4.72	1.01	4.43	0.0154
09.9002 031	Wall cover, plastic/pegboard, 1/8", trim	SF	.85	1.30	2.15	1.01	1.86	0.0154
09.9002 041	Wall cover, plastic/pegboard, 1/4", trim	SF	.78	1.30	2.08	1.01	1.79	0.0154
09.9003 000	**WALL COVERING, TILE:**							
09.9003 011	Plastic tile, 4-1/4"x4-1/4"x.11"	SF	1.68	2.08	3.76	1.62	3.30	0.0246
09.9003 021	Plastic tile, 4-1/4"x4-1/4"x.05"	SF	1.08	2.08	3.16	1.62	2.70	0.0246
09.9003 031	Aluminum tile, 4-1/2" x 4-1/2"	SF	7.53	2.49	10.02	1.94	9.47	0.0295
09.9003 041	Copper/aluminum tile, 4-1/4"x4-1/4"	SF	7.53	2.49	10.02	1.94	9.47	0.0295
09.9003 051	Stain steel tile, 4-1/4"x4-1/4"	SF	15.31	2.95	18.26	2.30	17.61	0.0350

residential construction costs

This manual is arranged in the 16 Division system and lists more than 6,000 unit cost items and 1,600 assemblies found in Residential Construction. Using the man-hours, the installation costs can be quickly adjusted to reflect local conditions. The illustrations help you identify items of construction and the glossary helps you to standardize terminology. The material costs and labor rates are not cluttered with unrealistic overhead and profit factors.
...................And the man-hours make sense!

With assemblies and CD-ROM

$79.95

**Open Shop and Union
Examine the differences**

SAYLOR Publications, Inc.

2010

residential construction costs

29th ANNUAL EDITION
SAYLOR PUBLICATIONS, INC.

29th Annual Edition
$79.95
over 300 pages!

- Illustrations
- Material Costs
- Installation Costs
- Unit Costs
- Assembly Costs
- Man-Hours
- Labor Indexes
- Material Indexes
- Subcontractor Indexes
- Glossary
- Location Multipliers

The CD-ROM has our Saylor in Windows estimating program with two databases (Open Shop and Union). Also included is the Assemblies Database in Microsoft Excel spreadsheet format.

Sample Page

Division 4 CSI #	Description	Unit Man-Hrs	Material	Union Install	Union Total	Open Install	Open Total	Unit
04.0000 000	MASONRY:							
	Note: The following costs include mortar and standard reinforcing. Cuts, lintels, coping ... bs and heads must be included from the adders at the end of the section.							
04.1001 000	BRICK VENEER:							
04.1001 011	VENEER,4",STANDARD BRICK,COMM	0.0871	4.39	4.64	9.03	3.57	7.96	SF
04.1001 021	VENEER,4",STANDARD BRICK,RES	0.0783	2.71	4.17	6.88	3.21	5.92	SF
04.1001 031	VENEER,4",MODULAR	0.1228	4.66	6.54	11.20	5.03	9.69	SF
04.1001 041	VENEER,JUMBO BRICK,4"X4"X12"	0.0864	3.11	4.60	7.71	3.54	6.65	SF
04.1001 051	VENEER,JUMBO BRICK,6"X4"X12"	0.0961	4.46	5.12	9.58			SF
04.1001 061	VENEER,JUMBO BRICK,8"X4"X12"		5.80	5.66	11.46	4.50	10.16	SF
04.1001 071	VENEER,FACE BRICK,SEL MODULAR		5.11	7.03	12.14	5.42	10.53	SF
04.1001 081	VENEER,NORMAN BRICK		4.23	6.95	11.18	5.35	9.58	SF
04.1001 091	VENEER,ROMAN BRICK	0.1856	4.92	9.88	14.80	7.61	12.53	SF

Callouts: **CSI Numbers** · **Man-Hours**  · **Material Costs** · **Union Installation and Total** · **Open Shop Installation and Total** · **"Stand Alone" Descriptions** · **Unit of Measure**

Division 10 CSI #	10 - SPECIALTIES Description	Unit	Material	Union Install	Union Total	Open Install	Open Total	Unit Man-Hrs
10.0000 000	SPECIALTIES:							
10.1000 000	CHALK & TACK BOARDS:							
10.1001 000	CHALK & TACK BOARD, IN PLACE:							
10.1001 011	Chalk board, institutional, with trim, map, rail	SF	21.78	4.96	26.74	3.63	25.41	0.0524
10.1001 021	Chalk board, institutional, without trim, average	SF	9.14	2.49	11.63	1.82	10.96	0.0263
10.1001 041	Chalk board, vertical sliding	SF	86.85	23.49	110.34	17.16	104.01	0.2480
10.1001 051	Chalk board, horizontal sliding	SF	56.44	15.36	71.80	11.22	67.66	0.1621
10.1001 061	Chalk board, swing leaf panels	SF	190.88	13.41	204.29	9.80	200.68	0.1416
10.1001 071	Chalk board, reversible, roll, 4x8	EA	897.96	438.58	1,336.54	320.34	1,218.30	4.6298
10.1002 000	CHALK BOARDS, WITHOUT FRAME:							
10.1002 011	Chalk board, hardboard, tempered, 1/4"	SF	13.98	1.71	15.69	1.25	15.23	0.0181
10.1002 021	Chalk board, hardboard, tempered, 1/2"	SF	15.84	2.31	18.15	1.69	17.53	0.0244
10.1002 031	Chalk board, metal, 24 ga, 1/4"	SF	17.94	2.31	20.25	1.69	19.63	0.0244
10.1002 041	Chalk board, metal, 24 ga, 1/2"	SF	18.22	2.71	20.93	1.98	20.20	0.0286
10.1002 051	Chalk board, slate, 3/8"	SF	23.87	5.02	28.89	3.67	27.54	0.0530
10.1002 061	Chalk board, adhesive	GAL	10.58		10.58		10.58	
10.1003 000	TACK BOARDS, WITHOUT FRAME:							
10.1003 011	Tack board, cork, unbacked, 1/8"	SF	6.27	.63	6.90	.46	6.73	0.0066
10.1003 021	Tack board, cork, unbacked, 1/4"	SF	12.01	1.09	13.10	.80	12.81	0.0115
10.1003 031	Tack board, cork, 1/8", burlap back	SF	12.70	1.33	14.03	.97	13.67	0.0140
10.1003 041	Tack board, cork, 1/4", burlap back	SF	12.98	2.33	15.31	1.70	14.68	0.0246
10.1003 051	Tack board, vinyl cork, 1/4", burlap back	SF	13.84	2.41	16.25	1.76	15.60	0.0254
10.1003 061	Tack board, vinyl/fiberboard, 1/2"	SF	12.86	1.87	14.73	1.36	14.22	0.0197
10.1003 071	Tack board, 1/4" vinyl cork, 1/4" hardboard	SF	22.77	3.11	25.88	2.27	25.04	0.0328
10.1003 081	Tack board, 1/8" vinyl cork, 3/8" fiberboard	SF	13.84	2.41	16.25	1.76	15.60	0.0254
10.1003 091	Tack board, adhesive	GAL	19.58		19.58		19.58	
10.1004 000	FRAMES, TRIM, TRAYS & RAILS:							
10.1004 011	Chalk board, aluminum frame, trim	LF	4.63	.80	5.43	.58	5.21	0.0084
10.1004 021	Aluminum chalk tray	LF	10.54	2.31	12.85	1.69	12.23	0.0244
10.1004 031	Aluminum map & display rail, deluxe	LF	5.59	1.00	6.59	.73	6.32	0.0106
10.1500 000	TOILET PARTITIONS & COMPARTMENTS:							
10.1501 000	TOILET PARTITIONS:							
10.1501 011	Toilet partition, baked enamel, floor mounted	EA	630.17	123.68	753.85	90.33	720.50	1.3056
10.1501 021	Toilet partition, baked enamel, ceiling mounted	EA	665.22	144.27	809.49	105.38	770.60	1.5230
10.1501 031	Toilet partition, porcelain enamel, floor mounted	EA	931.02	151.19	1,082.21	110.43	1,041.45	1.5960
10.1501 041	Toilet partition, porcelain enamel, ceiling mounted	EA	980.24	176.37	1,156.61	128.82	1,109.06	1.8618
10.1501 051	Toilet partition, laminated plastic, floor mounted	EA	814.88	151.19	966.07	110.43	925.31	1.5960
10.1501 061	Toilet partition, laminated plastic, ceiling mounted	EA	827.90	176.37	1,004.27	128.82	956.72	1.8618
10.1501 071	Toilet partition, stainless steel, floor mounted	EA	2,137.48	151.19	2,288.67	110.43	2,247.91	1.5960
10.1501 081	Toilet partition, stainless steel, ceiling mounted	EA	1,984.80	176.37	2,161.17	128.82	2,113.62	1.8618
10.1501 091	Add for best quality	EA	143.29		143.29		143.29	
10.1502 000	URINAL SCREENS:							
10.1502 011	Urinal screen, baked enamel, wall mounted	EA	227.42	42.53	269.95	31.07	258.49	0.4490
10.1502 021	Urinal screen, porcelain enamel, wall mounted	EA	427.95	51.98	479.93	37.96	465.91	0.5487
10.1502 031	Urinal screen, laminated plastic, wall mounted	EA	315.51	51.98	367.49	37.96	353.47	0.5487
10.1502 041	Urinal screen, stainless steel, wall mounted	EA	579.48	51.98	631.46	37.96	617.44	0.5487
10.1502 051	Add for best quality	EA	39.84		39.84		39.84	
10.1502 061	Add for floor mounted	EA	57.96	21.24	79.20	15.51	73.47	0.2242
10.1503 000	SIGHT SCREENS, 3' X 7':							
10.1503 011	Sight screen, baked enamel, floor mounted	EA	358.19	89.25	447.44	65.18	423.37	0.9421
10.1503 021	Sight screen, porcelain enamel, floor mounted	EA	475.97	109.11	585.08	79.69	555.66	1.1518
10.1503 031	Sight screen, laminated plastic, floor mounted	EA	465.68	109.11	574.79	79.69	545.37	1.1518
10.1503 041	Sight screen, stainless steel, floor mounted	EA	730.57	109.11	839.68	79.69	810.26	1.1518
10.1503 051	Add for best quality	EA	77.72		77.72		77.72	
10.1504 000	ACCESSORIES:							
10.1504 011	Coat hooks & door stop	EA	16.14		16.14		16.14	
10.1504 021	Purse shelf, chrome, 5" x 14"	EA	33.65	12.41	46.06	9.06	42.71	0.1310
10.1504 031	Toilet paper dispenser, chrome	EA	20.08	7.46	27.54	5.45	25.53	0.0788
10.1504 041	Seat cover dispenser, chrome	EA	117.76	43.52	161.28	31.79	149.55	0.4594
10.1505 000	DRESSING CUBICLES, 80" HIGH, W/CURTAIN:							
10.1505 011	Dressing cubicle, baked enamel, floor mounted	EA	1,164.47	99.33	1,263.80	72.55	1,237.02	1.0486
10.1505 021	Dressing cubicle, porcelain enamel, floor mounted	EA	1,724.11	121.44	1,845.55	88.70	1,812.81	1.2820

Division 10 CSI #	10 - SPECIALTIES Description	Unit	Material	Union Install	Union Total	Open Install	Open Total	Unit Man-Hrs
10.1505 000	**DRESSING CUBICLES, 80" HIGH, W/CURTAIN: (Cont.)**							
10.1505 031	Dressing cubicle, laminated plastic, floor mounted	EA	1,513.86	121.44	1,635.30	88.70	1,602.56	1.2820
10.1505 041	Dressing cubicle, stainless steel, floor mounted	EA	2,157.64	121.44	2,279.08	88.70	2,246.34	1.2820
10.1506 000	**SHOWER COMPARTMENTS, WITH RECEPTOR, WITHOUT PLUMBING:**							
10.1506 011	Shower compartment, baked enamel, 1 entry	EA	1,154.40	652.88	1,807.28	409.30	1,563.70	5.5058
10.1506 021	Shower compartment, porcelain enamel, 1 entry	EA	1,499.73	730.64	2,230.37	458.05	1,957.78	6.1616
10.1506 031	Shower compartment, fiberglass, 1 entry	EA	1,374.39	652.88	2,027.27	409.30	1,783.69	5.5058
10.1506 041	Shower compartment, stainless steel, 1 entry	EA	2,068.38	1,243.64	3,312.02	779.66	2,848.04	10.4878
10.1506 051	Add for soap dish	EA	13.12	5.82	18.94	4.25	17.37	0.0614
10.1506 061	Add for curtain rod	LF	10.30	4.56	14.86	3.33	13.63	0.0481
10.1506 071	Add for shower door	EA	196.32	86.93	283.25	63.50	259.82	0.9177
10.2000 000	**PARTITIONS; FOLDING, RELOCATABLE & DEMOUNTABLE:**							
	Note: The prices listed below for relocatable partitions are for preliminary estimates only. They							
	are based on a minimum of 100 lineal feet of partition, 8-12' ceilings, 3 doors and frames, 5 starters,							
	4 corners and 4' high base. The prices for folding partitions do not include structural supports,							
	architectural trim, placement of track in concrete floor or electric circuits.							
10.2001 000	**STANDARD RELOCATABLE PARTITIONS:**							
10.2001 011	Relocatable partition, 1/2" gypsum wall board, STC 38	SF	7.62	2.24	9.86	1.63	9.25	0.0236
10.2001 021	Relocatable partition, 5/8" gypsum wall board, STC 40	SF	8.49	2.52	11.01	1.84	10.33	0.0266
10.2001 031	Relocatable partition, 1/2"-5/8" gypsum wall board, STC 45	SF	12.34	3.59	15.93	2.62	14.96	0.0379
10.2001 041	Relocatable partition, 1/2" gypsum wall board, vinyl wall cover, 2 sides	SF	12.56	3.68	16.24	2.69	15.25	0.0389
10.2001 051	Relocatable partition, 5/8" gypsum wall board, vinyl wall cover, 2 sides	SF	16.13	4.76	20.89	3.47	19.60	0.0502
10.2001 061	Relocatable partition, metallic gypsum wall board, baked enamel	SF	15.30	4.46	19.76	3.26	18.56	0.0471
10.2001 071	Relocatable partition, 5/8" gypsum wall board, STC 30	SF	23.47	6.89	30.36	5.03	28.50	0.0727
10.2001 081	Relocatable partition, 5/8" gypsum wall board, STC 43, 2 hour	SF	25.58	7.46	33.04	5.45	31.03	0.0788
10.2001 091	Relocatable partition, gypsum wall board, studs, unfinished	SF	8.04	2.33	10.37	1.70	9.74	0.0246
10.2001 101	Relocatable partition, gypsum wall board, stud, 3", unfinished	SF	10.14	3.01	13.15	2.20	12.34	0.0318
10.2001 111	Add for factory vinyl, 15-22 oz	SF	3.77	1.17	4.94	.85	4.62	0.0123
10.2001 121	Cubicle/welding booth, 5'x5'x5'	SF	6.17	5.82	11.99	4.25	10.42	0.0614
10.2001 131	Divider, 5'-6', 18" glass top, 2" vinyl	SF	5.27	4.94	10.21	3.61	8.88	0.0522
10.2002 000	**RELOCATABLE PARTITIONS, ACCESSORIES:**							
10.2002 011	Windows, frame & glass, 3'6" x 2'	EA	430.75	44.28	475.03	34.52	465.27	0.4983
10.2002 021	Windows, frame & glass, 3'6" x 4'	EA	710.40	58.27	768.67	45.43	755.83	0.6558
10.2002 031	Door, hollow core, prefinished, 3' x 7'	EA	271.82	99.33	371.15	72.55	344.37	1.0486
10.2002 041	Door jamb, metal, 3' x 7'	EA	326.21	74.52	400.73	54.43	380.64	0.7867
10.2002 051	Door jamb, metal, 6' x 7'	EA	398.68	117.94	516.62	86.14	484.82	1.2450
10.2002 061	Add for passage set	EA	57.96	28.59	86.55	20.88	78.84	0.3018
10.2002 071	Add for lock set	EA	75.36	37.22	112.58	27.18	102.54	0.3929
10.2002 081	Corner	EA	92.98	45.94	138.92	33.56	126.54	0.4850
10.2002 091	Corner, metal	EA	176.05	86.93	262.98	63.50	239.55	0.9177
10.2002 101	Starter	EA	32.60	16.19	48.79	11.82	44.42	0.1709
10.2002 111	Starter, metal	EA	67.86	33.53	101.39	24.49	92.35	0.3540
10.2002 121	Metal base, not supplied with wall	LF	2.00	.98	2.98	.71	2.71	0.0103
10.2003 000	**ACCORDION PARTITIONS:**							
10.2003 011	Accordion partition, vinyl, 8', STC 36, economy	SF	19.14	5.63	24.77	4.11	23.25	0.0594
10.2003 021	Accordion partition, vinyl, 30x17, STC 41, economy	SF	24.95	7.37	32.32	5.38	30.33	0.0778
10.2003 031	Accordion partition, vinyl, 30x17, STC 43, good	SF	29.64	8.72	38.36	6.37	36.01	0.0921
10.2003 041	Accordion partition, vinyl, 30x17, STC 44, better	SF	32.72	9.60	42.32	7.01	39.73	0.1013
10.2003 051	Accordion partition, vinyl, large opening, STC 45, better	SF	36.08	10.57	46.65	7.72	43.80	0.1116
10.2003 061	Accordion partition, vinyl, large opening, STC 47, best	SF	42.35	10.86	53.21	7.93	50.28	0.1146
10.2003 071	Accordion partition, wood slat, birch or ash, prefinished	SF	19.14	5.63	24.77	4.11	23.25	0.0594
10.2004 000	**FOLDING PARTITIONS, OPERABLE WALLS, LEAF:**							
10.2004 011	Folding partition, vinyl and metal panel, STC 52	SF	59.84	23.65	83.49	17.28	77.12	0.2497
10.2004 021	Folding partition, vinyl and metal panel, STC 48	SF	54.68	23.84	78.52	17.42	72.10	0.2517
10.2004 031	Folding partition, vinyl and wood panel, STC 40	SF	44.03	17.35	61.38	12.68	56.71	0.1832
10.2004 041	Add for laminated plastic	SF	3.67	1.17	4.84	.85	4.52	0.0123
10.2004 051	Add for wood veneer	SF	4.81	1.46	6.27	1.07	5.88	0.0154
10.2004 061	Add for chalk board	SF	3.92	1.17	5.09	.85	4.77	0.0123
10.2005 000	**FOLDING PARTITIONS, OPERABLE WALLS, COMMERCIAL:**							
	Note: The following prices are based on 60' x 25' walls, top hung, with no bottom track required.							
10.2005 011	Folding partition, aluminum slat, 13#/SF	SF	19.86	7.95	27.81	5.81	25.67	0.0839
10.2005 021	Folding partition, steel slat, 16#/SF	SF	13.59	5.43	19.02	3.96	17.55	0.0573

Division 10 CSI #	10 - SPECIALTIES Description	Unit	Material	Union Install	Union Total	Open Install	Open Total	Unit Man-Hrs
10.2005 000	**FOLDING PARTITIONS, OPERABLE WALLS, COMMERCIAL: (Cont.)**							
10.2005 031	Folding partition, wood, side coil, single, crank	SF	27.87	11.15	39.02	8.14	36.01	0.1177
10.2005 041	Folding partition, wood, side coil, single, motor	SF	59.12	23.65	82.77	17.28	76.40	0.2497
10.2005 051	Folding partition, wood, side coil, 2 crank	SF	49.73	19.87	69.60	14.52	64.25	0.2098
10.2005 061	Folding partition, wood, side coil, 2 motor	SF	99.65	39.74	139.39	29.03	128.68	0.4195
10.2005 071	Folding partition, motor, under 30' x 9'	EA	1,714.75	683.02	2,397.77	498.87	2,213.62	7.2102
10.2005 081	Folding partition, motor drive, over 30'	EA	3,429.49	1,366.04	4,795.53	997.74	4,427.23	14.4203
10.2006 000	**DEMOUNTABLE PARTITIONS:**							
10.2006 011	Demountable partitions, air wall	SF	26.18	9.98	36.16	7.29	33.47	0.1054
10.2006 021	Demountable modular panels, spring mount	SF	15.83	5.63	21.46	4.11	19.94	0.0594
10.2006 031	Add for 1 hour doors & hardware	SF	15.83	5.63	21.46	4.11	19.94	0.0594
10.4000 000	**TOILET ACCESSORIES:**							
	Note: Labor costs for the following items can be found in section 06.2101.							
10.4001 000	**PAPER TOWEL & WASTE COMBINATION:**							
10.4001 011	Paper towel & waste combination, stainless steel, laminated, 14"x24", recess	EA	455.71		455.71		455.71	
10.4001 021	Paper towel & waste combination, stainless steel, 17"x54", semi-recessed	EA	687.12		687.12		687.12	
10.4001 031	Paper towel & waste combination, stainless, laminated, 12"x72", recessed	EA	794.58		794.58		794.58	
10.4001 041	Paper towel & waste combination, 12"x72", stainless steel trim, surface	EA	1,145.18		1,145.18		1,145.18	
10.4002 000	**PAPER TOWEL DISPENSERS:**							
10.4002 011	Towel dispenser, stainless steel, 12"x17", surface	EA	112.17		112.17		112.17	
10.4002 021	Towel dispenser, stainless steel, 12" x 15", recessed	EA	217.39		217.39		217.39	
10.4002 031	Towel dispenser, stainless steel, 14" x 26", recessed	EA	324.83		324.83		324.83	
10.4002 041	Towel dispenser, laminated, 14"x26", recessed	EA	490.77		490.77		490.77	
10.4002 051	Towel dispenser, stainless steel trim, 17"x28"	EA	773.61		773.61		773.61	
10.4002 061	Towel & soap combination, stainless steel	EA	490.81		490.81		490.81	
10.4002 071	Towel & soap combination, laminated	EA	577.25		577.25		577.25	
10.4002 081	Towel, soap & mirror, stainless steel	EA	687.12		687.12		687.12	
10.4002 091	Towel, soap & mirror, laminated	EA	740.87		740.87		740.87	
10.4003 000	**WASTE RECEPTACLES:**							
10.4003 011	Waste receptacle, stainless steel, 3 gal, recessed	EA	335.94		335.94		335.94	
10.4003 021	Waste receptacle, stainless steel, 12 gal, semi-recessed	EA	422.65		422.65		422.65	
10.4003 031	Waste receptacle, stainless steel, 18 gal, semi-recessed	EA	509.39		509.39		509.39	
10.4003 041	Waste receptacle, stainless steel, 10 gal, recessed	EA	509.39		509.39		509.39	
10.4003 051	Waste receptacle, laminated, 3 gal, recessed	EA	535.36		535.36		535.36	
10.4003 061	Waste receptacle, laminated, 10 gal, recessed	EA	669.73		669.73		669.73	
10.4003 071	Waste receptacle, stainless steel, 13 gal, top, unmounted	EA	335.94		335.94		335.94	
10.4004 000	**TOILET SEAT COVER DISPENSERS:**							
10.4004 011	Seat cover dispenser, stainless steel, surface	EA	70.11		70.11		70.11	
10.4004 021	Seat cover dispenser, stainless steel, recessed	EA	160.57		160.57		160.57	
10.4004 031	Seat cover dispenser, laminated, recess	EA	307.61		307.61		307.61	
10.4004 041	Seat cover dispenser, stainless steel, partition mounted	EA	327.94		327.94		327.94	
10.4005 000	**TOILET PAPER DISPENSERS:**							
10.4005 011	Toilet paper dispenser, aluminum, single, surface	EA	24.86		24.86		24.86	
10.4005 021	Toilet paper dispenser, stainless steel, single, surface	EA	45.24		45.24		45.24	
10.4005 031	Toilet paper dispenser, stainless steel, single, recessed	EA	33.92		33.92		33.92	
10.4005 041	Folded tissue cabinet, stainless steel, surface	EA	45.24		45.24		45.24	
10.4005 051	Toilet paper dispenser, aluminum, double, surface	EA	42.97		42.97		42.97	
10.4005 061	Toilet paper dispenser, stainless steel, double, surface	EA	74.60		74.60		74.60	
10.4005 071	Toilet paper dispenser, stainless steel, double, recessed	EA	76.90		76.90		76.90	
10.4005 081	Toilet paper & seat cover dispenser combination, recessed	EA	662.69		662.69		662.69	
10.4005 091	Toilet paper, seat cover & napkin dispenser combination, recessed	EA	737.30		737.30		737.30	
10.4006 000	**FEMININE NAPKIN DISPENSERS:**							
10.4006 011	Napkin dispenser, stainless steel, surface	EA	678.50		678.50		678.50	
10.4006 021	Napkin dispenser, stainless steel, recessed	EA	741.86		741.86		741.86	
10.4006 031	Napkin dispenser, laminated, recessed	EA	877.53		877.53		877.53	
10.4006 041	Napkin, dispenser & disposal, stainless steel	EA	1,024.56		1,024.56		1,024.56	
10.4007 000	**FEMININE NAPKIN DISPOSAL:**							
10.4007 011	Napkin disposal, stainless steel, surface	EA	79.17		79.17		79.17	
10.4007 021	Napkin disposal, stainless steel, recessed, small	EA	185.45		185.45		185.45	
10.4007 031	Napkin disposal, stainless steel, partition mounted	EA	287.26		287.26		287.26	
10.4007 041	Napkin disposal, stainless steel, recessed, large	EA	287.26		287.26		287.26	
10.4007 051	Napkin disposal, laminated, recessed	EA	418.38		418.38		418.38	

Division 10 CSI #	10 - SPECIALTIES Description	Unit	Material	Union Install	Union Total	Open Install	Open Total	Unit Man-Hrs
10.4008 000	**SOAP DISPENSERS:**							
10.4008 011	Soap dispenser, plastic, liquid, surface, stainless steel lid	EA	42.97		42.97		42.97	
10.4008 021	Soap dispenser, stainless steel, liquid & powder, surface	EA	88.26		88.26		88.26	
10.4008 031	Soap dispenser, counter mounted, tank below	EA	101.79		101.79		101.79	
10.4008 041	Soap dispenser, stainless steel, liquid, recessed	EA	146.99		146.99		146.99	
10.4008 051	Soap dispenser, stainless steel, powder, recessed	SS	223.88		223.88		223.88	
10.4008 061	Soap dispenser, laminated, liquid, recessed	EA	223.88		223.88		223.88	
10.4008 071	Soap dispenser, stainless steel, liquid, recessed, shelf	EA	287.26		287.26		287.26	
10.4008 081	Soap dispenser, stainless steel, leaf, surface	EA	289.51		289.51		289.51	
10.4008 091	Soap dispenser, stainless steel, leaf, recessed	EA	314.39		314.39		314.39	
10.4009 000	**FACIAL TISSUE DISPENSERS:**							
10.4009 011	Tissue dispenser, stainless steel, recessed	EA	33.92		33.92		33.92	
10.4009 021	Tissue dispenser, stainless steel, surface	EA	36.20		36.20		36.20	
10.4009 031	Tissue dispenser, laminated, recessed	EA	110.83		110.83		110.83	
10.4009 041	Tissue dispenser, stainless steel, recessed, electric outlet	EA	167.33		167.33		167.33	
10.4009 051	Tissue dispenser, stainless steel, recessed, with shelf	EA	203.56		203.56		203.56	
10.4009 061	Tissue dispenser, stainless steel, recessed, shelf, outlet	EA	244.26		244.26		244.26	
10.4010 000	**GRAB BARS:**							
	Note: For concealed mounting, add 10% to the total costs. For peened grip, add 20% to the total costs.							
10.4010 011	Grab bar, stainless steel, 1-1/2" x 24", exposed mounted	EA	72.39		72.39		72.39	
10.4010 021	Grab bar, stainless steel, 1-1/2" x 48", exposed mounted	EA	108.57		108.57		108.57	
10.4010 031	Grab bar, swing away, exposed, floor mounted	EA	802.89		802.89		802.89	
10.4010 041	Wheel chair compartment, exposed mounted	EA	140.22		140.22		140.22	
10.4010 051	Grab bar, horizontal tub, exposed mounted	EA	174.13		174.13		174.13	
10.4010 061	Grab bar, 2 way tub, exposed mounted	EA	294.07		294.07		294.07	
10.4011 000	**MISCELLANEOUS TOILET ACCESSORIES:**							
10.4011 011	Towel bar, stainless steel, 18"	EA	63.32		63.32		63.32	
10.4011 021	Towel bar, stainless steel, 24"	EA	67.85		67.85		67.85	
10.4011 031	Towel bar, stainless steel, 30"	EA	72.39		72.39		72.39	
10.4011 041	Shower rod, stainless steel, 1" x 6'	EA	47.48		47.48		47.48	
10.4011 051	Shower rod flanges, pair	PAIR	33.92		33.92		33.92	
10.4011 061	Shower curtain, 70"x7'2", with hooks	EA	54.30		54.30		54.30	
10.4011 071	Robe hook	EA	40.66		40.66		40.66	
10.4011 081	Mirror, stainless steel frame, tilt	EA	181.84		181.84		181.84	
10.4011 091	Mirror, stainless steel frame, 16" x 24"	EA	89.57		89.57		89.57	
10.4011 101	Mirror, stainless steel frame, 16" x 24", shelf	EA	130.33		130.33		130.33	
10.4011 111	Medicine cabinet & mirror, baked enamel, surface	EA	142.48		142.48		142.48	
10.4011 121	Medicine cabinet & mirror, baked enamel, recessed	EA	199.38		199.38		199.38	
10.4011 131	Medicine cabinet & mirror, stainless steel, recessed	EA	578.67		578.67		578.67	
10.4011 141	Clothes line, retractable	EA	43.75		43.75		43.75	
10.4011 151	Shower seat, stainless steel	EA	213.95		213.95		213.95	
10.4011 161	Ash tray, stainless steel, wall mounted	EA	56.90		56.90		56.90	
10.4011 171	Ash tray, stainless steel, surface, small	EA	167.72		167.72		167.72	
10.4011 181	Ash tray, stainless steel, surface, large	EA	248.59		248.59		248.59	
10.4011 191	Ash tray, stainless steel, recessed	EA	269.54		269.54		269.54	
10.4011 201	Ash tray, laminated, recessed	EA	407.29		407.29		407.29	
10.4011 211	Towel ring, stainless steel	EA	44.92		44.92		44.92	
10.4011 221	Towel fin, stainless steel	EA	32.96		32.96		32.96	
10.4011 231	Shelf, stainless steel, 18"	EA	95.83		95.83		95.83	
10.4011 241	Shelf, stainless steel, 24"	EA	104.81		104.81		104.81	
10.4011 251	Shelf, stainless steel, 30"	EA	113.82		113.82		113.82	
10.4011 261	Towel shelf, stainless steel, 18"	EA	125.76		125.76		125.76	
10.4011 271	Towel shelf, stainless steel, 24"	EA	137.78		137.78		137.78	
10.4011 281	Bottle opener, stainless steel	EA	9.01		9.01		9.01	
10.4011 291	Blade disposal, stainless steel	EA	38.95		38.95		38.95	
10.4011 301	Electric hand dryer, surface, 40 second cycle	EA	1,818.52		1,818.52		1,818.52	
10.5000 000	**MISCELLANEOUS BUILDING SPECIALTIES:**							
10.5001 000	**LINEN & GARBAGE CHUTES:**							
	Note: The following prices assume prefab units with roof vents, 1 1/2 hour 'B' doors, discharge and *sprinkler systems.*							
10.5001 011	Chute, aluminum, 20', light duty	FLOOR	828.62	445.55	1,274.17	325.43	1,154.05	4.7034
10.5001 021	Chute, 18 ga galvanized steel, 24"	FLOOR	1,022.40	445.55	1,467.95	325.43	1,347.83	4.7034

Division 10 CSI #	10 - SPECIALTIES Description	Unit	Material	Union Install	Union Total	Open Install	Open Total	Unit Man-Hrs
10.5001 000	**LINEN & GARBAGE CHUTES: (Cont.)**							
10.5001 031	Chute, 18 ga galvanized steel, 30"	FLOOR	1,226.25	445.55	1,671.80	325.43	1,551.68	4.7034
10.5001 041	Chute, 18 ga stainless steel, 24", heavy duty	FLOOR	1,701.66	445.55	2,147.21	325.43	2,027.09	4.7034
10.5001 051	Chute, 18 ga stainless steel, 30", heavy duty	FLOOR	1,873.67	445.55	2,319.22	325.43	2,199.10	4.7034
10.5001 061	Chute door, stainless steel rim, manual	EA	417.58	159.09	576.67	116.20	533.78	1.6794
10.5001 071	Pneumatic vertical	FLOOR	9,537.97	1,527.51	11,065.48	1,115.68	10,653.65	16.1249
10.5001 081	Pneumatic horizontal	LF	1,402.75	159.09	1,561.84	116.20	1,518.95	1.6794
10.5002 000	**FLAG POLES WITH FOUNDATIONS:**							
10.5002 011	Flag pole, fiberglass, 30', with foundation	EA	1,949.36	1,639.65	3,589.01	1,197.59	3,146.95	17.3087
10.5002 021	Flag pole, fiberglass, 35', with foundation	EA	2,983.55	2,191.62	5,175.17	1,600.74	4,584.29	23.1354
10.5002 031	Flag pole, fiberglass, 39', with foundation	EA	3,383.58	2,465.59	5,849.17	1,800.85	5,184.43	26.0276
10.5002 041	Flag pole, fiberglass, 60', with foundation	EA	8,216.83	3,287.46	11,504.29	2,401.14	10,617.97	34.7035
10.5002 051	Flag pole, aluminum, 30', with foundation	EA	2,087.98	1,639.65	3,727.63	1,197.59	3,285.57	17.3087
10.5002 061	Flag pole, aluminum, 35', with foundation	EA	2,962.06	2,191.62	5,153.68	1,600.74	4,562.80	23.1354
10.5002 071	Flag pole, aluminum, 40', with foundation	EA	3,886.79	2,465.59	6,352.38	1,800.85	5,687.64	26.0276
10.5002 081	Flag pole, aluminum, 50', with foundation	EA	6,084.23	3,013.48	9,097.71	2,201.02	8,285.25	31.8113
10.5002 091	Flag pole, aluminum, 60', with foundation	EA	11,604.09	3,287.46	14,891.55	2,401.14	14,005.23	34.7035
10.5002 101	Flag pole, aluminum, 70', with foundation	EA	13,420.61	4,018.01	17,438.62	2,934.72	16,355.33	42.4154
10.5003 000	**DIRECTORIES:**							
	Note:							
	For bronze or stainless steel . . . . add 100% to total costs							
	For illumination . . . . add 50% to total costs							
	For lettered header . . . . add 15% to total costs							
	For recessing . . . . add 10% to total costs							
10.5003 011	Directory, aluminum & glass, 24" x 36"	EA	837.73	299.88	1,137.61	219.03	1,056.76	3.1656
10.5003 021	Directory, aluminum & glass, 48" x 36"	EA	1,210.07	449.89	1,659.96	328.60	1,538.67	4.7492
10.5003 031	Directory, aluminum & glass, 60" x 36"	EA	1,675.44	499.82	2,175.26	365.07	2,040.51	5.2763
10.5003 041	Directory, aluminum & glass, 72" x 48"	EA	2,010.60	649.84	2,660.44	474.64	2,485.24	6.8599
10.5004 000	**DISPLAY CASES:**							
10.5004 011	Display case, glass, wood pedestal, 48x36 no frame	EA	6,068.72	374.93	6,443.65	273.85	6,342.57	3.9579
10.5004 021	Display case, glass, wood pedestal, 72x48 no frame	EA	6,961.20	449.89	7,411.09	328.60	7,289.80	4.7492
10.5004 031	Display case, glass, 72x48, recessed front	EA	2,320.39	474.85	2,795.24	346.83	2,667.22	5.0127
10.5005 000	**METAL LETTERS & PLAQUES:**							
	Note:							
	For black aluminum or satin bright face . . . add 10% to total cost							
	For gold and black aluminum . . . . add 15%							
	For duranodic color or hard coat finish . . . . add 20%							
	For chrome plate or verdigris . . . . add 15%							
	For nickel silver . . . . add 20%							
10.5005 011	Letters, aluminum, 2", gothic block	EA	16.07	39.64	55.71	28.96	45.03	0.4185
10.5005 021	Letters, aluminum, 6", gothic block	EA	26.89	39.64	66.53	28.96	55.85	0.4185
10.5005 031	Letters, aluminum, 12", gothic block	EA	65.89	39.64	105.53	28.96	94.85	0.4185
10.5005 041	Letters, bronze, 2", gothic	EA	19.28	39.64	58.92	28.96	48.24	0.4185
10.5005 051	Letters, bronze, 6", gothic	EA	59.71	39.64	99.35	28.96	88.67	0.4185
10.5005 061	Letters, bronze, 12", gothic	EA	149.32	39.64	188.96	28.96	178.28	0.4185
10.5005 071	Letters, stainless steel, 6"	EA	189.72		189.72		189.72	
10.5005 081	Plaque, aluminum, 24" x 24"	EA	1,517.18	66.07	1,583.25	48.26	1,565.44	0.6975
10.5005 091	Plaque, aluminum, 24" x 36"	EA	2,347.61	66.07	2,413.68	48.26	2,395.87	0.6975
10.5005 101	Plaque, bronze, 24" x 24"	EA	1,857.08	66.07	1,923.15	48.26	1,905.34	0.6975
10.5005 111	Plaque, bronze, 24" x 36"	EA	2,859.26	66.07	2,925.33	48.26	2,907.52	0.6975
10.5006 000	**GRAPHICS, SIGNS:**							
10.5006 011	Letters & numbers, plastic, 1"	PLATE	2.12	16.99	19.11	12.41	14.53	0.1793
10.5006 021	Sign, engraved brass	PLATE	2.61	16.99	19.60	12.41	15.02	0.1793
10.5006 031	Sign, hand lettered	SQ IN	2.49	16.77	19.26	12.25	14.74	0.1770
10.5006 041	Sign, hand painted, gold leaf	SQ IN	3.94	34.41	38.35	25.13	29.07	0.3632
10.5006 051	Sign, porcelain enamel, 12"x2-1/2"x6", neon	EA	238.18	66.91	305.09	48.87	287.05	0.7063
10.5006 061	Sign, porcelain enamel, 24"x5"x8", neon	EA	501.33	133.90	635.23	97.80	599.13	1.4135
10.5006 071	Sign, porcelain enamel, 36"x6 1/2"x10", neon	EA	783.81	267.78	1,051.59	195.59	979.40	2.8268
10.5006 081	Sign, baked enamel, 12"x3" deep, neon	EA	134.26	66.91	201.17	48.87	183.13	0.7063
10.5006 091	Sign, baked enamel, 24"x6" deep, neon	EA	296.37	111.56	407.93	81.49	377.86	1.1777
10.5006 101	Sign, baked enamel, 36"x8" deep, neon	EA	540.07	200.80	740.87	146.66	686.73	2.1197

Division 10 CSI #	10 - SPECIALTIES Description	Unit	Material	Union Install	Union Total	Open Install	Open Total	Unit Man-Hrs
10.5007 000	**TURNSTILES:**							
10.5007 011	Turnstile, non-register	EA	1,212.80	127.53	1,340.33	93.15	1,305.95	1.3463
10.5007 021	Turnstile, register	EA	1,664.93	127.53	1,792.46	93.15	1,758.08	1.3463
10.5007 031	Turnstile, register, portable	EA	1,901.71	28.88	1,930.59	21.10	1,922.81	0.3049
10.5007 041	Turnstile ticket collection box	EA	362.31	28.88	391.19	21.10	383.41	0.3049
10.5008 000	**EXTINGUISHERS:**							
	Note: The following prices are based on quantities of 20 or more.							
10.5008 011	Extinguisher, CO2, 5#, swivel horn	EA	182.75	32.96	215.71	24.07	206.82	0.3479
10.5008 021	Extinguisher, CO2, 10#, hose & 'H' horn	EA	278.45	32.96	311.41	24.07	302.52	0.3479
10.5008 031	Extinguisher, CO2, 15#, hose & 'H' horn	EA	312.20	32.96	345.16	24.07	336.27	0.3479
10.5008 041	Extinguisher, CO2, 20#, hose & 'H' horn	EA	388.87	32.96	421.83	24.07	412.94	0.3479
10.5008 051	Extinguisher, CO2, 50#, wheeled cart	EA	1,547.14	32.96	1,580.10	24.07	1,571.21	0.3479
10.5008 061	Extinguisher, monoamm phos, 5#, nozzle	EA	94.16	32.96	127.12	24.07	118.23	0.3479
10.5008 071	Extinguisher, monoamm, 10#, short hose	EA	150.45	32.96	183.41	24.07	174.52	0.3479
10.5008 081	Extinguisher, monoamm phos, 20#, nozzle	EA	192.68	32.96	225.64	24.07	216.75	0.3479
10.5008 091	Extinguisher, halon 1211, 5#, nozzle	EA	167.32	32.96	200.28	24.07	191.39	0.3479
10.5008 101	Extinguisher, halon 1211, 10#, tall hose	EA	257.33	32.96	290.29	24.07	281.40	0.3479
10.5008 111	Extinguisher, halon 1211, 20#, hose	EA	374.09	32.96	407.05	24.07	398.16	0.3479
10.5009 000	**EXTINGUISHER CABINETS:**							
10.5009 011	Extinguisher cabinet, steel, 12" x 27"	EA	122.37	90.01	212.38	65.74	188.11	0.9502
10.5009 021	Extinguisher cabinet, steel, 20" x 30"	EA	153.27	90.01	243.28	65.74	219.01	0.9502
10.5009 031	Extinguisher cabinet, aluminum, 12" x 27"	EA	159.06	90.01	249.07	65.74	224.80	0.9502
10.5009 041	Extinguisher cabinet, aluminum, 20" x 30"	EA	199.21	90.01	289.22	65.74	264.95	0.9502
10.5009 051	Extinguisher cabinet, stainless steel, 12" x 27"	EA	367.12	90.01	457.13	65.74	432.86	0.9502
10.5009 061	Extinguisher cabinet, stainless steel, 20" x 30"	EA	459.84	90.01	549.85	65.74	525.58	0.9502
10.5010 000	**FIRE HOSE CABINETS, WITH GLASS DOOR:**							
10.5010 011	Hose cabinet, steel, 22" x 30" x 5"	EA	218.89	109.93	328.82	80.29	299.18	1.1605
10.5010 021	Hose cabinet, steel, 22x30x5, 50' hose & nozzle	EA	500.67	109.93	610.60	80.29	580.96	1.1605
10.5010 031	Hose cabinet, steel, 24" x 30" x 8"	EA	229.60	109.93	339.53	80.29	309.89	1.1605
10.5010 041	Hose cabinet, steel, 24x30x8, 75' hose & nozzle	EA	621.68	109.93	731.61	80.29	701.97	1.1605
10.5010 051	Hose cabinet, aluminum, 24" x 30" x 8"	EA	298.54	109.93	408.47	80.29	378.83	1.1605
10.5010 061	Hose cabinet, aluminum, 24x30x8, 75' hose & nozzle	EA	690.54	109.93	800.47	80.29	770.83	1.1605
10.5010 071	Hose cabinet, stainless steel, 24" x 30" x 8"	EA	689.01	109.93	798.94	80.29	769.30	1.1605
10.5010 081	Hose cabinet, stainless steel, 24x30x8, 75' hose & nozzle	EA	1,081.01	109.93	1,190.94	80.29	1,161.30	1.1605
10.5011 000	**MAIL CHUTES & COLLECTION BOXES:**							
	Note: For bronze mail chutes, use prices given for stainless steel.							
10.5011 011	Mail chute, aluminum & glass, 8-3/4"x3-1/2"	FLOOR	705.07	394.49	1,099.56	253.62	958.69	3.5781
10.5011 021	Mail chute, aluminum & glass, 14-1/4"x4-5/8"	FLOOR	1,159.97	473.44	1,633.41	304.37	1,464.34	4.2942
10.5011 031	Mail chute, aluminum & glass, 14-1/4"x8-5/8"	FLOOR	1,484.22	473.44	1,957.66	304.37	1,788.59	4.2942
10.5011 041	Mail chute, stainless steel, 8-3/4" x 3-1/2"	FLOOR	967.75	394.49	1,362.24	253.62	1,221.37	3.5781
10.5011 051	Mail chute, stainless steel, 14-1/4" x 4-5/8"	FLOOR	1,711.44	535.42	2,246.86	344.22	2,055.66	4.8564
10.5011 061	Mail chute, stainless steel, 14-1/4" x 8-5/8"	FLOOR	2,066.61	535.42	2,602.03	344.22	2,410.83	4.8564
10.5011 071	Collection boxes, aluminum	EA	1,430.13	439.60	1,869.73	282.62	1,712.75	3.9873
10.5011 081	Collection boxes, stainless steel or bronze	EA	1,771.04	79.85	1,850.89	51.34	1,822.38	0.7243
10.5012 000	**MAIL BOXES:**							
10.5012 011	Mail box, aluminum, gang, front load	EA	20.43	13.57	34.00	9.91	30.34	0.1433
10.5012 021	Mail box, aluminum, gang, front load, intercom	EA	27.97	18.80	46.77	13.73	41.70	0.1985
10.5012 031	Add for bronze or stainless steel	EA	9.33	6.89	16.22	5.03	14.36	0.0727
10.5013 000	**SEATING:**							
10.5013 011	Seating, theater, economy	EA	118.47	29.27	147.74	21.38	139.85	0.3090
10.5013 021	Seating, theater, loge, rocking	EA	186.19	46.32	232.51	33.83	220.02	0.4890
10.5013 031	Seating, auditorium	EA	232.73	57.96	290.69	42.33	275.06	0.6118
10.5013 041	Bleachers, 18" aluminum seat, steel support	EA	131.06	33.53	164.59	24.49	155.55	0.3540
10.5013 051	Bleachers, plastic seat, steel support	EA	20.56	5.63	26.19	4.11	24.67	0.0594
10.5013 061	Bleachers, 18" folding seat, lacquer	EA	43.55	11.63	55.18	8.50	52.05	0.1228
10.5013 071	Add for under structure	EA	32.29	9.41	41.70	6.87	39.16	0.0993
10.5013 081	Table, folding, with seats	EA	1,005.00	198.22	1,203.22	144.78	1,149.78	2.0925
10.5014 000	**METAL LOCKERS:**							
10.5014 011	Locker, 12" x 12" x 72", 1 tier	EA	207.55	17.77	225.32	10.55	218.10	0.2259
10.5014 021	Locker, 15" x 18" x 72", 1 tier	EA	225.90	21.76	247.66	12.91	238.81	0.2766
10.5014 031	Locker, 12" x 12" x 30", 2 tier	TIER	262.76	17.77	280.53	10.55	273.31	0.2259
10.5014 041	Locker, 12" x 12" x 24", 3 tier	TIER	299.74	17.77	317.51	10.55	310.29	0.2259

Division 10 CSI #	10 - SPECIALTIES Description	Unit	Material	Union Install	Union Total	Open Install	Open Total	Unit Man-Hrs
10.5014 000	**METAL LOCKERS: (Cont.)**							
10.5014 051	Locker, 12" x 12" x 12", 5 high	TIER	276.49	22.72	299.21	13.49	289.98	0.2889
10.5014 061	Locker, 15" x 15" x 12", 5 high	TIER	327.48	22.72	350.20	13.49	340.97	0.2889
10.5015 000	**SHELVING & BINS:**							
10.5015 011	Shelves, metal, 5, 30"x8"x84", library	EA	485.77	80.32	566.09	58.67	544.44	0.8479
10.5015 021	Shelves, metal, 7, 36"x8"x84", library	EA	497.46	89.24	586.70	65.18	562.64	0.9420
10.5015 031	Shelves, metal, 7, 36"x12"x84", industrial	EA	268.87	80.32	349.19	58.67	327.54	0.8479
10.5015 041	Shelves, metal, 5, 36"x24"x84", industrial	EA	374.51	89.24	463.75	65.18	439.69	0.9420
10.5016 000	**SCALES, STEEL, PLATFORM:**							
10.5016 011	Scale, 5 ton, 6' x 8', dial/readout	EA	15,958.32	3,311.50	19,269.82	2,418.69	18,377.01	34.9572
10.5016 021	Scale, 25 ton, 10'x24', dial/readout	EA	23,556.97	5,355.49	28,912.46	3,911.61	27,468.58	56.5343
10.5016 031	Scale, 50 ton, 10'x60', dial/readout	EA	38,099.36	8,479.52	46,578.88	6,193.37	44,292.73	89.5125
10.5016 041	Scale, 80 ton, 10'x60', dial/readout	EA	46,401.72	8,479.52	54,881.24	6,193.37	52,595.09	89.5125
10.5017 000	**TELEPHONE ENCLOSURES:**							
10.5017 011	Phone enclosure, shelf style	EA	1,382.69	144.30	1,526.99	105.40	1,488.09	1.5233
10.5017 021	Phone enclosure, desk style	EA	899.15	93.91	993.06	68.59	967.74	0.9913
10.5017 031	Phone enclosure, full height	EA	3,585.89	374.17	3,960.06	273.29	3,859.18	3.9499
10.5018 000	**CHAIN LINK PARTITIONS & GATES:**							
10.5018 011	Chain link partition with pipe frame	SF	1.72	2.53	4.25	1.50	3.22	0.0322
10.5018 021	Chain link gate, 3'x4'	EA	435.25	377.76	813.01	224.18	659.43	4.8024
10.5019 000	**RACKING, INDUSTRIAL:**							
	Note: Codes may require in-rack sprinklers. See section 15.5500.							
10.5019 011	Racking, 2-tier, single row	LF	75.49	58.63	134.12	42.82	118.31	0.6189
10.5019 021	Racking, 2-tier, back to back	LF	151.01	117.27	268.28	85.65	236.66	1.2379
10.5019 031	Racking, 3-tier, single row	LF	100.64	78.18	178.82	57.10	157.74	0.8253
10.5019 041	Racking, 3-tier, back to back	LF	201.30	156.36	357.66	114.21	315.51	1.6506
10.5019 051	Add for wall brackets	LF	2.02	1.56	3.58	1.14	3.16	0.0165
10.5020 000	**AWNINGS & CANOPIES:**							
10.5020 011	Awning, canvas, with frame, average	SF	18.59	15.63	34.22	11.42	30.01	0.1650
10.5020 021	Awning, canvas, with frame, custom	SF	27.85	24.63	52.48	17.99	45.84	0.2600
10.5020 031	Canopy, entrance, aluminum	SF	11.62	14.21	25.83	10.38	22.00	0.1500
10.5020 041	Canopy, wall hung, aluminum	SF	6.96	8.53	15.49	6.23	13.19	0.0900

Division 11 CSI #	11 - EQUIPMENT Description	Unit	Material	Union Install	Union Total	Open Install	Open Total	Unit Man-Hrs
11.0000 000	**EQUIPMENT:**							
11.1100 000	**BANK EQUIPMENT:**							
11.1101 000	**VAULTS & VAULT DOORS:**							
	Note: The vault doors listed below are for safekeeping, such as in safe deposit boxes.							
11.1101 011	Vault door, 78"x44"x3-1/2", steel, class 1	EA	33,229.32	1,101.02	34,330.34	824.48	34,053.80	12.2800
11.1101 021	Vault door, 78"x44"x3-1/2", steel, class 2	EA	37,516.96	1,101.02	38,617.98	824.48	38,341.44	12.2800
11.1101 031	Vault door, 78"x44"x3-1/2", steel, class 3	EA	45,020.37	1,101.02	46,121.39	824.48	45,844.85	12.2800
11.1101 041	Vault door, 78"x44"x3-1/2", 6 hour	EA	25,078.71	1,101.02	26,179.73	824.48	25,903.19	12.2800
11.1101 051	Vault, 78" x 33", 1 hour, single	EA	4,414.62	569.34	4,983.96	426.34	4,840.96	6.3500
11.1101 061	Vault, 84" x 51-1/8", 2 hour, single	EA	5,380.36	569.34	5,949.70	426.34	5,806.70	6.3500
11.1101 071	Vault, 84" x 51-1/8", 4 hour, single	EA	5,623.89	558.58	6,182.47	418.28	6,042.17	6.2300
11.1101 081	Vault, 84" x 51-1/8", 6 hour, single	EA	6,527.19	565.75	7,092.94	423.65	6,950.84	6.3100
11.1101 091	Modular vaults, class I, 15 minute	EA	31,220.79	9,281.60	40,502.39	6,950.33	38,171.12	103.5200
11.1101 101	Modular vaults, class II, 1 hour	EA	52,034.64	9,280.71	61,315.35	6,949.66	58,984.30	103.5100
11.1101 111	Modular vaults, class III, 2 hour	EA	72,848.47	9,285.19	82,133.66	6,953.02	79,801.49	103.5600
11.1102 000	**DRIVE- & WALK-UP TELLER WINDOWS:**							
11.1102 011	Teller window, drive-up, manual	EA	10,257.18	1,219.79	11,476.97	913.41	11,170.59	13.6046
11.1102 021	Teller window, drive-up, motorized	EA	11,552.12	1,219.79	12,771.91	913.41	12,465.53	13.6046
11.1102 031	Teller window, walk-up, one teller	EA	7,051.67	975.81	8,027.48	730.72	7,782.39	10.8835
11.1102 041	Teller window, walk-up, 2 teller	EA	7,790.85	975.81	8,766.66	730.72	8,521.57	10.8835
11.1103 000	**NIGHT DEPOSIT DOORS:**							
11.1103 011	Night deposit, bag/envelope, illuminated	EA	5,807.06	1,010.47	6,817.53	756.67	6,563.73	11.2700
11.1103 021	Night deposit, envelope	EA	2,399.79	278.83	2,678.62	208.80	2,608.59	3.1099
11.1103 031	Night deposit, bag, flush mount	EA	2,932.62	458.25	3,390.87	343.15	3,275.77	5.1110
11.1104 000	**TELLER COUNTERS & CHECK DESKS:**							
11.1104 011	Teller counter, modular component	LF	350.47	92.35	442.82	69.15	419.62	1.0300
11.1104 021	Check desk, round, 48", 4 person	EA	2,568.44	559.21	3,127.65	418.75	2,987.19	6.2370
11.1104 031	Check desk, square, 48", 4 person	EA	2,164.59	528.75	2,693.34	347.38	2,511.97	6.2954
11.1104 041	Check desk, 72" x 24", 4 person	EA	2,572.58	320.17	2,892.75	210.35	2,782.93	3.8120
11.1104 051	Check desk, 72" x 36", 8 person	EA	3,197.00	418.86	3,615.86	275.18	3,472.18	4.9870
11.1105 000	**SAFE DEPOSIT BOXES, MODULAR UNITS:**							
11.1105 011	Safe deposit, 42 openings, 2" x 5"	MOD	3,425.93	333.78	3,759.71	219.29	3,645.22	3.9740
11.1105 021	Safe deposit, 30 openings, 2" x 5"	MOD	2,447.66	249.29	2,696.95	163.78	2,611.44	2.9681
11.1105 031	Safe deposit, 18 openings, 5" x 5"	MOD	1,769.16	207.72	1,976.88	136.47	1,905.63	2.4731
11.1105 041	Safe deposit, base, 32" x 24" x 3"	EA	228.94	75.57	304.51	49.65	278.59	0.8998
11.1105 051	Safe deposit, canopy top	EA	58.78	41.58	100.36	27.31	86.09	0.4950
11.1105 061	Safe deposit, 9 openings, 5"x10 3/8"	EA	1,332.06	260.20	1,592.26	194.85	1,526.91	2.9021
11.1105 071	Safe deposit, 15 openings, 3"x10 3/8"	EA	1,540.23	257.86	1,798.09	193.09	1,733.32	2.8760
11.1105 081	Safe deposit, 1 section, 3 openings, 5"x10"	EA	1,352.90	468.92	1,821.82	351.14	1,704.04	5.2300
11.1105 091	Deposit, 1 section, 3 openings, 10"x10 3/8"	EA	1,352.90	477.08	1,829.98	357.25	1,710.15	5.3210
11.1106 000	**SAFES:**							
11.1106 011	Safe, floor, 10"x24", minimum security	EA	558.46	111.56	670.02	81.49	639.95	1.1777
11.1106 021	Safe, wall, minimum security	EA	2,924.69	794.76	3,719.45	580.48	3,505.17	8.3897
11.1106 031	Safe, cabinet, medium security, full door	EA	4,214.40	1,145.28	5,359.68	836.50	5,050.90	12.0899
11.1106 041	Book drop, minimum security	EA	1,045.91	284.24	1,330.15	207.60	1,253.51	3.0005
11.1106 051	Night depository	EA	1,706.01	463.62	2,169.63	338.62	2,044.63	4.8941
11.1200 000	**ECCLESIASTICAL EQUIPMENT:**							
11.1201 000	**LECTERNS:**							
11.1201 011	Lectern, economy, 16" x 24"	EA	720.38	277.01	997.39	181.99	902.37	3.2981
11.1201 021	Lectern, good, 16" x 24"	EA	1,355.98	277.01	1,632.99	181.99	1,537.97	3.2981
11.1201 031	Lectern, best, 16" x 24"	EA	2,542.56	277.01	2,819.57	181.99	2,724.55	3.2981
11.1202 000	**PULPITS:**							
11.1202 011	Pulpit, economy	EA	805.06	296.79	1,101.85	194.98	1,000.04	3.5336
11.1202 021	Pulpit, good	EA	1,412.54	296.79	1,709.33	194.98	1,607.52	3.5336
11.1202 031	Pulpit, best	EA	3,107.62	296.79	3,404.41	194.98	3,302.60	3.5336
11.1203 000	**ARKS:**							
11.1203 011	Ark, with curtain, economy	EA	833.37	356.11	1,189.48	233.96	1,067.33	4.2399
11.1203 021	Ark, with curtain, good	EA	1,101.80	356.11	1,457.91	233.96	1,335.76	4.2399
11.1203 031	Ark, with curtain, best	EA	1,836.32	356.11	2,192.43	233.96	2,070.28	4.2399
11.1203 041	Ark, with doors, economy	EA	946.34	553.94	1,500.28	363.93	1,310.27	6.5953
11.1203 051	Ark, with doors, good	EA	1,638.56	553.94	2,192.50	363.93	2,002.49	6.5953
11.1203 061	Ark, with doors, best	EA	2,570.82	553.94	3,124.76	363.93	2,934.75	6.5953

Division 11 CSI #	11 - EQUIPMENT Description	Unit	Material	Union Install	Union Total	Open Install	Open Total	Unit Man-Hrs
11.1204 000	**PEWS:**							
11.1204 011	Pew, bench, economy	LF	49.39	21.80	71.19	14.32	63.71	0.2596
11.1204 021	Pew, bench, good	LF	53.64	21.80	75.44	14.32	67.96	0.2596
11.1204 031	Pew, bench, best	LF	62.09	21.80	83.89	14.32	76.41	0.2596
11.1204 041	Pew, seat, economy	LF	62.09	25.70	87.79	16.89	78.98	0.3060
11.1204 051	Pew, seat, good	LF	76.21	25.70	101.91	16.89	93.10	0.3060
11.1204 061	Pew, seat, best	LF	90.38	25.70	116.08	16.89	107.27	0.3060
11.1205 000	**KNEELERS:**							
11.1205 011	Kneeler, good	LF	13.45	10.68	24.13	7.02	20.47	0.1272
11.1205 021	Kneeler, best	LF	17.02	10.68	27.70	7.02	24.04	0.1272
11.1205 031	Kneeler, serenity	LF	26.24	10.68	36.92	7.02	33.26	0.1272
11.1206 000	**CATHEDRAL CHAIRS, SERENITY:**							
11.1206 011	Cathedral chair, shaped wood, economy	EA	169.47	13.87	183.34	9.11	178.58	0.1651
11.1206 021	Cathedral chair, shaped wood, book rack	EA	183.55	13.87	197.42	9.11	192.66	0.1651
11.1206 031	Cathedral chair, wood, book rack, kneeler	EA	211.82	13.87	225.69	9.11	220.93	0.1651
11.1206 041	Cathedral chair, upholstered, economy	EA	177.97	15.81	193.78	10.38	188.35	0.1882
11.1206 051	Cathedral chair, upholstered, book rack	EA	192.13	15.81	207.94	10.38	202.51	0.1882
11.1206 061	Cathedral chair, upholstered, book rack, kneeler	EA	220.30	15.81	236.11	10.38	230.68	0.1882
11.1207 000	**CONFESSIONALS, SINGLE:**							
11.1207 011	Confessional, single, with curtain, economy	EA	3,107.62	553.94	3,661.56	363.93	3,471.55	6.5953
11.1207 021	Confessional, single, with curtain, good	EA	3,672.64	553.94	4,226.58	363.93	4,036.57	6.5953
11.1207 031	Confessional, single, with curtain, best	EA	4,237.67	553.94	4,791.61	363.93	4,601.60	6.5953
11.1207 041	Confessional, single, with door, economy	EA	3,813.89	553.94	4,367.83	363.93	4,177.82	6.5953
11.1207 051	Confessional, single, with door, good	EA	4,308.31	553.94	4,862.25	363.93	4,672.24	6.5953
11.1207 061	Confessional, single, with door, best	EA	4,802.75	553.94	5,356.69	363.93	5,166.68	6.5953
11.1208 000	**CONFESSIONALS, DOUBLE:**							
11.1208 011	Confessional, double, with curtain, economy	EA	4,944.01	830.95	5,774.96	545.92	5,489.93	9.8934
11.1208 021	Confessional, double, with curtain, good	EA	5,975.17	830.95	6,806.12	545.92	6,521.09	9.8934
11.1208 031	Confessional, double, with curtain, best	EA	7,062.88	830.95	7,893.83	545.92	7,608.80	9.8934
11.1208 041	Confessional, double, with doors, economy	EA	6,215.38	830.95	7,046.33	545.92	6,761.30	9.8934
11.1208 051	Confessional, double, with doors, good	EA	7,062.88	830.95	7,893.83	545.92	7,608.80	9.8934
11.1208 061	Confessional, double, with doors, best	EA	8,192.89	830.95	9,023.84	545.92	8,738.81	9.8934
11.1209 000	**COMMUNION RAILS, HARDWOOD, WITH STANDARDS:**							
11.1209 011	Communion rail, hardwood, economy	LF	56.44	19.78	76.22	12.99	69.43	0.2355
11.1209 021	Communion rail, hardwood, good	LF	70.53	19.78	90.31	12.99	83.52	0.2355
11.1209 031	Communion rail, hardwood, best	LF	84.66	19.78	104.44	12.99	97.65	0.2355
11.1210 000	**COMMUNION RAILS, CARVED, WITH STANDARDS:**							
11.1210 011	Communion rail, carved oak, economy	LF	98.80	19.78	118.58	12.99	111.79	0.2355
11.1210 021	Communion rail, carved oak, good	LF	141.20	19.78	160.98	12.99	154.19	0.2355
11.1210 031	Communion rail, carved oak, best	LF	197.72	19.78	217.50	12.99	210.71	0.2355
11.1211 000	**COMMUNION RAILS, METAL, WITH STANDARDS:**							
11.1211 011	Communion rail, bronze or stainless steel	LF	124.27	25.36	149.63	18.99	143.26	0.2828
11.1212 000	**ALTARS, HARDWOOD:**							
11.1212 011	Altar, hardwood, economy	EA	988.74	383.83	1,372.57	280.34	1,269.08	4.0518
11.1212 021	Altar, hardwood, good	EA	1,197.79	383.83	1,581.62	280.34	1,478.13	4.0518
11.1212 031	Altar, hardwood, best	EA	1,553.80	423.95	1,977.75	309.65	1,863.45	4.4754
11.1213 000	**ALTARS, HARDWOOD, CARVED:**							
11.1213 011	Altar, carved hardwood, economy	EA	3,994.76	383.83	4,378.59	280.34	4,275.10	4.0518
11.1213 021	Altar, carved hardwood, good	EA	7,102.39	383.83	7,486.22	280.34	7,382.73	4.0518
11.1213 031	Altar, carved hardwood, best	EA	8,207.02	423.95	8,630.97	309.65	8,516.67	4.4754
11.1214 000	**ALTARS, MARBLE OR GRANITE:**							
11.1214 011	Altar, marble or granite, economy	EA	5,650.26	2,090.10	7,740.36	1,330.19	6,980.45	23.5557
11.1214 021	Altar, marble or granite, good	EA	8,475.44	2,090.10	10,565.54	1,330.19	9,805.63	23.5557
11.1214 031	Altar, marble or granite, best	EA	12,713.22	2,090.10	14,803.32	1,330.19	14,043.41	23.5557
11.1215 000	**ALTARS, HARDWOOD, WITH MARBLE BASE & LEGS:**							
11.1215 011	Altar, hardwood, marble base, good	EA	3,107.62	1,672.11	4,779.73	1,064.17	4,171.79	18.8449
11.1215 021	Altar, hardwood, marble base, best	EA	4,520.17	1,672.11	6,192.28	1,064.17	5,584.34	18.8449
11.1216 000	**STAINED GLASS, INCLUDING ARTWORK:**							
11.1216 011	Stained glass, simple artwork	SF	59.79	14.87	74.66	11.59	71.38	0.1673
11.1216 021	Stained glass, moderate artwork	SF	80.72	24.76	105.48	19.30	100.02	0.2786
11.1216 031	Stained glass, elaborate artwork	SF	104.65	49.42	154.07	38.53	143.18	0.5562

Division 11 CSI #	11 - EQUIPMENT Description	Unit	Material	Union Install	Union Total	Open Install	Open Total	Unit Man-Hrs
11.1217 000	**FACET GLASS, INCLUDING ART WORK:**							
11.1217 011	Facet glass, with simple artwork	SF	44.83	14.87	59.70	11.59	56.42	0.1673
11.1217 021	Facet glass, with moderate artwork	SF	68.71	24.76	93.47	19.30	88.01	0.2786
11.1217 031	Facet glass, with elaborate artwork	SF	95.64	49.42	145.06	38.53	134.17	0.5562
11.1218 000	**COLORED GLASS:**							
11.1218 011	Colored glass, single pane	SF	5.90	4.96	10.86	3.87	9.77	0.0558
11.1218 021	Colored glass, patterned	SF	11.92	14.87	26.79	11.59	23.51	0.1673
11.1218 031	Colored glass, small pieces	SF	32.87	19.80	52.67	15.44	48.31	0.2228
11.1300 000	**EDUCATIONAL EQUIPMENT:**							
	Note: For chalk & tack boards see section 10.1000.							
11.1301 000	**WARDROBES:**							
11.1301 011	Wardrobe, teacher, 40"x78"x26-1/4"	EA	1,128.72	66.71	1,195.43	49.95	1,178.67	0.7440
11.1301 021	Wardrobe, student, 40"x78"x26-1/4"	EA	739.66	50.03	789.69	37.46	777.12	0.5580
11.1302 000	**SEATING:**							
11.1302 011	Seating, pedestal, folding arm	EA	124.76	22.19	146.95	16.20	140.96	0.2342
11.1302 021	Seating, horizontal 2 section, 5 chair	SEAT	134.09	23.82	157.91	17.39	151.48	0.2514
11.1303 000	**TABLES:**							
11.1303 011	Table, fixed pedestal, 48" x 16"	EA	520.10	92.39	612.49	67.48	587.58	0.9753
11.1303 021	Table, fixed pedestal, chair, 48"x16"	EA	716.51	127.30	843.81	92.98	809.49	1.3438
11.1304 000	**PROJECTION SCREENS:**							
11.1304 011	Slide screen, pull, 70"x70", ceiling	SF	6.06	1.31	7.37	.95	7.01	0.0138
11.1304 021	Slide screen, electric, ceiling	SF	52.09	5.37	57.46	3.92	56.01	0.0567
11.1305 000	**DRAFTING FURNITURE:**							
11.1305 011	Draft table, steel base, 60"x37-1/2"	EA	579.97		579.97		579.97	
11.1305 021	Draft table, hardwood, 60"x37-1/2"	EA	1,196.85		1,196.85		1,196.85	
11.1305 031	Draft table, 2 station, 10 drawer, flexible	EA	810.49		810.49		810.49	
11.1305 041	Draft table, 1 station, 6 drawer, flexible	EA	647.63		647.63		647.63	
11.1305 051	Desk, metal frame, mechanical drawing	EA	869.10		869.10		869.10	
11.1305 061	Desk, wood, mechanical drawing	EA	434.51		434.51		434.51	
11.1305 071	Tracing table, pedestal, 24" x 22"	EA	775.81		775.81		775.81	
11.1306 000	**FILES:**							
11.1306 011	File cabinet, steel, 10 drawer	EA	2,107.23		2,107.23		2,107.23	
11.1306 021	File cabinet, wood, 10 drawer	EA	1,638.02		1,638.02		1,638.02	
11.1306 031	Files, modular, 8 tube, 48"	EA	128.23		128.23		128.23	
11.1306 041	Files, vertical, 26 binder, 44 3/4"	EA	2,339.01		2,339.01		2,339.01	
11.1307 000	**AUDIO-VISUAL EQUIPMENT:**							
11.1307 011	Video tape recorder	EA	4,638.35	393.68	5,032.03	287.54	4,925.89	4.1558
11.1307 021	Camera	EA	1,854.67	421.76	2,276.43	308.05	2,162.72	4.4522
11.1307 031	Monitor	EA	821.62	398.31	1,219.93	290.92	1,112.54	4.2047
11.1308 000	**STUDY CARREL, PLASTIC LAMINATED WOOD:**							
11.1308 011	Study carrel, 48"x30"x54", 1 station	EA	885.56	93.70	979.26	68.44	954.00	0.9891
11.1308 021	Study carrel, 73"x30"x47", 2 station	EA	1,549.99	140.59	1,690.58	102.68	1,652.67	1.4841
11.1308 031	Study carrel, 66"x66"x47", 4 station	EA	1,834.55	210.84	2,045.39	154.00	1,988.55	2.2257
11.1309 000	**AUDIO-VISUAL EQUIPMENT:**							
11.1309 011	Tape recorder	EA	512.56		512.56		512.56	
11.1309 021	Head set	SET	49.49		49.49		49.49	
11.1309 031	Projector, movie, 8 mm	EA	605.78		605.78		605.78	
11.1309 041	Projector, slide, carousel	EA	465.96		465.96		465.96	
11.1310 000	**AUDIO-VISUAL CENTER, MOBILE, WITH CONTROL PANELS:**							
	Note: The following item has 10 listening stations with earphones.							
11.1310 011	Folding table, elect, ear phone, 4x8	EA	1,276.68		1,276.68		1,276.68	
11.1310 021	Stack chairs	EA	136.34		136.34		136.34	
11.1311 000	**ACCESSORIES FOR CARRELS:**							
11.1311 011	Rear projection module with light	EA	309.81		309.81		309.81	
11.1311 021	Power column, study carrel	EA	61.92		61.92		61.92	
11.1400 000	**OBSERVATORIES & PLANETARIUMS:**							
11.1401 000	**DOME, OBSERVATION, REVOLVING, SHELL ONLY:**							
11.1401 011	Dome, observation, revolving, 12', 800#, shell	EA	9,029.69	2,928.81	11,958.50	2,139.18	11,168.87	30.9175
11.1401 021	Dome, observation, revolving, 12' base, shell	EA	3,353.84	1,288.71	4,642.55	941.26	4,295.10	13.6040
11.1401 031	Dome, observation, revolving, 18', 2500#, shell	EA	24,896.17	4,662.62	29,558.79	3,405.54	28,301.71	49.2201
11.1401 041	Dome, observation, revolving, 18' base, shell	EA	9,803.59	2,343.04	12,146.63	1,711.34	11,514.93	24.7339
11.1401 051	Dome, observation, revolving, 20', 4500#, shell	EA	44,632.58	8,669.23	53,301.81	6,331.93	50,964.51	91.5151

Division 11 CSI #	11 - EQUIPMENT Description	Unit	Material	Union Install	Union Total	Open Install	Open Total	Unit Man-Hrs
11.1401 000	DOME, OBSERVATION, REVOLVING, SHELL ONLY: (Cont.)							
11.1401 061	Dome, observation, revolving, 20' base, shell	EA	14,963.51	3,163.10	18,126.61	2,310.30	17,273.81	33.3907
11.1402 000	TELESCOPES:							
11.1402 011	Telescope, reflector, 6", portable	EA	1,911.00		1,911.00		1,911.00	
11.1402 021	Telescope, reflector, 8", stationary	EA	6,536.06		6,536.06		6,536.06	
11.1402 031	Telescope, refraction, 4", portable	EA	3,693.23		3,693.23		3,693.23	
11.1402 041	Telescope, refraction 4", stationary	EA	3,822.95		3,822.95		3,822.95	
11.1402 051	Telescope, refraction, 6", stationary	EA	15,234.85		15,234.85		15,234.85	
11.1403 000	PLANETARIUM CLASS ROOM EQUIPMENT:							
11.1403 011	Instrument control console system 512	EA	90,030.88		90,030.88		90,030.88	
11.1403 021	Add for automatic controls	EA	46,535.39		46,535.39		46,535.39	
11.1403 031	Hemispherical screen, 30' dia	EA	58,169.32		58,169.32		58,169.32	
11.1403 041	Seating, table arm & reclinable	EA	335.73		335.73		335.73	
11.1403 051	Special effects projector	EA	2,123.93		2,123.93		2,123.93	
11.1403 061	Stereo sound system	ROOM	9,062.78		9,062.78		9,062.78	
11.1403 071	Cove lighting	ROOM	17,121.39		17,121.39		17,121.39	
11.1501 000	VOCATIONAL SHOP EQUIPMENT:							
11.1501 011	Welding booth, glassweld panel	SF	14.11		14.11		14.11	
11.1501 021	Welding booth, fireproof panel	SF	11.57		11.57		11.57	
11.1600 000	FOOD SERVICE EQUIPMENT:							
	Note: The prices for commercial and institutional equipment do not include final electrical or mechanical connections. Note that for preliminary and schematic estimates, the unit price for food service equipment must be at least $90 per square foot.							
11.1601 000	FOOD SERVICE EQUIPMENT, RESIDENTIAL:							
	Note: The following prices are based on quantities of 100 to 500 each purchased over one year. For more than 500, deduct 10%.							
11.1601 011	Oven, single, self clean	EA	1,166.96		1,166.96		1,166.96	
11.1601 021	Oven, double, self clean	EA	1,359.53		1,359.53		1,359.53	
11.1601 031	Oven, microwave, built-in	EA	2,163.09		2,163.09		2,163.09	
11.1601 041	Cook top	EA	785.86		785.86		785.86	
11.1601 051	Range & oven, drop-in	EA	1,125.70		1,125.70		1,125.70	
11.1601 061	Range hood with microwave	EA	799.58		799.58		799.58	
11.1601 071	Hood	EA	137.53		137.53		137.53	
11.1601 081	Hood with microwave	EA	799.58		799.58		799.58	
11.1601 091	Electric grill	EA	805.50		805.50		805.50	
11.1601 101	Refrigerator, 12 CF	EA	823.16		823.16		823.16	
11.1601 111	Refrigerator, 18 CF	EA	1,074.63		1,074.63		1,074.63	
11.1601 121	Refrigerator with icemaker	EA	1,035.34		1,035.34		1,035.34	
11.1601 131	Freezer, 16 CF	EA	760.29		760.29		760.29	
11.1601 141	Dishwasher, built-in	EA	654.19		654.19		654.19	
11.1601 151	Garbage disposal	EA	192.54		192.54		192.54	
11.1601 161	Trash compactor	EA	575.62		575.62		575.62	
11.1601 171	Washer	EA	719.06		719.06		719.06	
11.1601 181	Dryer, electric	EA	571.69		571.69		571.69	
11.1601 191	Dryer, gas	EA	1,037.34		1,037.34		1,037.34	
11.1602 000	IN-PLACE COST, FABRICATED ITEMS:							
	Note: Prices for fabricated food service fixtures may vary as much as $200.00 Per foot, depending on style, materials, accessories and built-in items. The following prices are mean average costs for most common configurations. Factory manufactured buy-out items are listed in the latter part of this section. The price for sandwich preparation with open storage does not include ductwork or exhaust fan.							
11.1602 021	Tables, counter with sink, shelves & racks, economy	LF	354.33	77.17	431.50	52.73	407.06	0.7530
11.1602 031	Tables, counter with sink, shelves & racks, best	LF	570.90	117.78	688.68	80.48	651.38	1.1492
11.1602 041	Pot washer table, loading apron & sink, economy	LF	314.96	64.99	379.95	44.41	359.37	0.6341
11.1602 051	Pot washer table, loading apron & sink, best	LF	393.66	81.23	474.89	55.51	449.17	0.7926
11.1602 061	Sandwich prep, open storage	LF	511.80	105.61	617.41	72.16	583.96	1.0304
11.1602 071	Sandwich prep, closed storage, undercounter refrigerator	LF	869.63	174.63	1,044.26	119.32	988.95	1.7039
11.1602 081	Sandwich prep, closed storage, plastic laminated face, refrigerator	LF	885.83	182.76	1,068.59	124.88	1,010.71	1.7832
11.1602 091	Service counter, open storage	LF	869.63	174.63	1,044.26	119.32	988.95	1.7039
11.1602 101	Service center, closed storage	LF	869.63	223.38	1,093.01	152.63	1,022.26	2.1795
11.1602 131	Cook's table, with sink, 6'	EA	4,990.60	528.08	5,518.68	360.83	5,351.43	5.1525
11.1602 141	Vegetable preparation table, with sink, 12'	EA	5,238.76	678.51	5,917.27	463.62	5,702.38	6.6203

Division 11 CSI #	11 - EQUIPMENT Description	Unit	Material	Union Install	Union Total	Open Install	Open Total	Unit Man-Hrs
11.1602 000	**IN-PLACE COST, FABRICATED ITEMS: (Cont.)**							
11.1602 151	Food service equipment, average cost	SF	445.50		445.50		445.50	
11.1603 000	**FABRICATED FIXTURES, BUILT-UP, UNIT COST:**							
	Note: The following basic fixtures are 30" x 32" x 6'-21', free standing or wall mounted with top and frame. Combine these items with the adders listed below for complete cost.							
11.1603 011	Table & counter, stainless steel, rolled edge, 6" splash	LF	347.91	105.26	453.17	71.92	419.83	1.0270
11.1603 021	Table & counter, stainless steel, straight edge, 6" splash	LF	273.41	105.26	378.67	71.92	345.33	1.0270
11.1603 031	Serving fixture, stainless steel top, galvanized frame stiles, economy	LF	298.24	140.30	438.54	95.86	394.10	1.3689
11.1603 041	Serving fixture, all stainless steel, best	LF	422.55	140.30	562.85	95.86	518.41	1.3689
11.1604 000	**ADDERS FOR BASIC BUILT-UP FIXTURES:**							
11.1604 011	Shelves, stainless steel, 85/SF, base	LF	69.09		69.09		69.09	
11.1604 021	Shelves, galvanized iron, 375/SF, base	LF	37.69		37.69		37.69	
11.1604 031	Angle or pipe stretchers	LF	23.53		23.53		23.53	
11.1604 041	Tray slide, stainless steel	LF	80.12		80.12		80.12	
11.1604 051	Display shelf, sneeze guard	LF	97.41		97.41		97.41	
11.1604 061	Each additional shelf	LF	58.15		58.15		58.15	
11.1604 071	Plastic laminate on plywood	LF	48.80		48.80		48.80	
11.1604 081	Stainless steel facing, 18 ga, 3' high	LF	72.36		72.36		72.36	
11.1604 091	Stainless steel facing, 22 ga, 3' high	LF	45.92		45.92		45.92	
11.1604 101	Marine front coping	LF	18.15		18.15		18.15	
11.1604 111	Stainless steel dirty dish table, 12" splash	LF	36.16		36.16		36.16	
11.1604 121	Slop gutter, 4" square, with sump	LF	68.90		68.90		68.90	
11.1605 000	**SHOP INSTALLED ACCESSORIES:**							
	Note: The following items should be added separately to the basic fixture costs above.							
11.1605 011	Joint & miter, weld & polish	EA	210.18		210.18		210.18	
11.1605 021	Door, stainless steel, to 24"	EA	303.76		303.76		303.76	
11.1605 031	Drawer, stainless steel face, removable pan	EA	276.48		276.48		276.48	
11.1605 041	Drawer, stainless steel face, galvanized iron pan	EA	192.25		192.25		192.25	
11.1605 051	Punch-out	EA	69.15		69.15		69.15	
11.1605 061	Ventilating grill, 24" x 12"	EA	102.07		102.07		102.07	
11.1605 071	Maple cutting board, laminated, 2"	EA	29.78		29.78		29.78	
11.1605 081	Richlite cutting board, laminated, 2"	EA	40.60		40.60		40.60	
11.1605 091	Pot washer sink, 24" x 24" x 24"	EA	1,113.06		1,113.06		1,113.06	
11.1605 101	Vegetable sink	EA	1,038.91		1,038.91		1,038.91	
11.1605 111	Mixer valve	EA	163.94		163.94		163.94	
11.1605 121	Lever operated drain valve	EA	132.46		132.46		132.46	
11.1605 131	Disposer, with stainless steel cone, 1 hp	EA	1,688.22	473.61	2,161.83	323.61	2,011.83	4.6210
11.1605 141	Disposer, with stainless steel cone, 1-1/2 hp	EA	2,316.58	473.61	2,790.19	323.61	2,640.19	4.6210
11.1605 151	Disposer, with stainless steel cone, 3 hp	EA	3,525.23	473.61	3,998.84	323.61	3,848.84	4.6210
11.1605 161	Pot washer, sink mounted	EA	2,060.57	552.57	2,613.14	377.57	2,438.14	5.3915
11.1605 171	Water heater, electric, sink mounted	EA	984.75	473.61	1,458.36	323.61	1,308.36	4.6210
11.1605 181	Conveyors, soiled dish, 16'	EA	9,323.96	6,512.09	15,836.05	4,449.62	13,773.58	63.5388
11.1605 191	Electric sub panel, 100a, prewired case	EA	577.89		577.89		577.89	
11.1605 201	Display, fluorescent fixture, 6"	EA	243.30		243.30		243.30	
11.1605 211	Shelf heater, infra-red	EA	341.03	315.77	656.80	215.76	556.79	3.0810
11.1605 221	Pot & pan rack, 6', table mounted	EA	614.36		614.36		614.36	
11.1605 231	Shelf rack, 12', table mounted	LF	72.21		72.21		72.21	
11.1605 241	Shelf, stainless steel, wall mounted	SF	35.49	23.69	59.18	16.18	51.67	0.2311
11.1605 251	Equipment base, 4", galvanized iron channel	LF	12.92	41.03	53.95	28.03	40.95	0.4003
11.1605 261	Glass rack dispenser, self level	EA	895.29	252.57	1,147.86	172.57	1,067.86	2.4643
11.1605 271	Cup & plate dispenser, heated	EA	682.10	157.84	839.94	107.85	789.95	1.5401
11.1605 281	Hot food well, electric, 12" x 20"	EA	554.18	236.80	790.98	161.80	715.98	2.3105
11.1605 291	Bain marie, gas or steam, 6'	EA	3,538.56	355.22	3,893.78	242.72	3,781.28	3.4659
11.1605 301	Bain marie, electric	EA	3,368.00	355.22	3,723.22	242.72	3,610.72	3.4659
11.1605 311	Drop-in deep fryer, electric	EA	1,492.06	315.77	1,807.83	215.76	1,707.82	3.0810
11.1605 321	Griddle, built-in, 4', electric	EA	2,984.29	355.22	3,339.51	242.72	3,227.01	3.4659
11.1605 331	Hotplate, built-in, 12"x20", electric	EA	255.71	157.84	413.55	107.85	363.56	1.5401
11.1605 341	Drop-in water cooler	EA	1,449.50	157.84	1,607.34	107.85	1,557.35	1.5401
11.1606 000	**REFRIGERATOR, UNDER THE COUNTER:**							
11.1606 011	Refrigerator, without compressor	LF	358.94		358.94		358.94	
11.1606 021	Add for each door	EA	424.74		424.74		424.74	
11.1606 031	Add for each drawer	EA	375.09		375.09		375.09	

Division 11 CSI #	11 - EQUIPMENT Description	Unit	Material	Union Install	Union Total	Open Install	Open Total	Unit Man-Hrs
11.1606 000	**REFRIGERATOR, UNDER THE COUNTER: (Cont.)**							
11.1606 041	Add for each 16" x 16" coil	EA	244.05		244.05		244.05	
11.1606 051	Add for remote compressor, 1/4 hp	EA	937.88	1,499.79	2,437.67	1,024.78	1,962.66	14.6335
11.1606 061	Refrigerator, 5 CF, undercounter, with compressor	EA	1,875.82	355.22	2,231.04	242.72	2,118.54	3.4659
11.1606 071	Cold pan, 6', non-refrigerating	EA	682.10	197.38	879.48	134.86	816.96	1.9258
11.1606 081	Cold pan, 6', refrigerating	EA	1,065.82	552.57	1,618.39	377.57	1,443.39	5.3915
11.1606 091	Soft drink dispenser, 4 spout, 1 remote	EA	9,464.61	3,157.31	12,621.92	2,157.34	11,621.95	30.8060
11.1607 000	**BUY-OUT EQUIPMENT:**							
	Note: The item canopy hood, ss, 4'3" x 9'6" listed below includes filters, automatic fire extinguisher							
	and detergent washdown.							
11.1607 011	Cart, self level, glass, dish, cup	EA	2,465.67		2,465.67		2,465.67	
11.1607 021	Cart, clean dish stacking	EA	925.06		925.06		925.06	
11.1607 031	Cart, delivery, hot & cold tray	EA	10,325.86		10,325.86		10,325.86	
11.1607 041	Coffee urn, twin, 8 gallon	EA	3,282.69	157.88	3,440.57	107.87	3,390.56	1.5404
11.1607 051	Coffee urn, twin, 12 gallon	EA	5,050.35	219.31	5,269.66	149.85	5,200.20	2.1398
11.1607 061	Coffee urn, twin, 20 gallon	EA	6,924.10	241.21	7,165.31	164.82	7,088.92	2.3535
11.1607 071	Coffee urn, twin, 40 gallon	EA	8,040.22	265.33	8,305.55	181.29	8,221.51	2.5888
11.1607 081	Cart, utility	EA	518.58		518.58		518.58	
11.1607 091	Canopy hood, stainless steel, with filters	SFSA	121.94	38.68	160.62	26.43	148.37	0.3774
11.1607 101	Canopy hood, stainless steel, 4'3" x 9'6"	EA	10,165.74	1,879.05	12,044.79	1,283.93	11,449.67	18.3340
11.1607 111	Can washer	EA	2,398.86	252.57	2,651.43	172.57	2,571.43	2.4643
11.1607 121	Can crusher	EA	4,250.60	142.09	4,392.69	97.09	4,347.69	1.3864
11.1607 131	Deep fryer, electric	EA	1,683.41	205.21	1,888.62	140.21	1,823.62	2.0022
11.1607 141	Freezer, roll-in, thru, 1 section	EA	6,843.99	190.63	7,034.62	130.26	6,974.25	1.8600
11.1607 151	Freezer, roll-in, thru, 2 section	EA	9,916.21	190.63	10,106.84	130.26	10,046.47	1.8600
11.1607 161	Freezer, roll-in, thru, 3 section	EA	12,185.39	190.63	12,376.02	130.26	12,315.65	1.8600
11.1607 171	Hot food cab, roll-in, thru, 1 section	EA	11,653.67	190.63	11,844.30	130.26	11,783.93	1.8600
11.1607 181	Hot food cab, roll-in, thru, 2 section	EA	8,121.52	190.63	8,312.15	130.26	8,251.78	1.8600
11.1607 191	Hot food cab, roll-in, thru, 3 section	EA	10,859.15	190.63	11,049.78	130.26	10,989.41	1.8600
11.1607 201	Griddle & skillet, 4', electric, tilt	EA	7,752.20	473.61	8,225.81	323.61	8,075.81	4.6210
11.1607 211	Glass rack dispenser	EA	1,186.29		1,186.29		1,186.29	
11.1607 221	Hose reel & spray	EA	778.53	189.44	967.97	129.44	907.97	1.8484
11.1607 231	Ice machine	EA	5,681.56	268.41	5,949.97	183.40	5,864.96	2.6189
11.1607 241	Kettle filler, wall standard	EA	589.13	236.80	825.93	161.80	750.93	2.3105
11.1607 251	Mixer, 20 quart, bench mounted	EA	2,575.61	189.44	2,765.05	129.44	2,705.05	1.8484
11.1607 261	Milk dispenser, refrigerated, self-level cart	EA	4,124.43	315.77	4,440.20	215.76	4,340.19	3.0810
11.1607 271	Micro spray cart washer, without drain	EA	799.58	378.90	1,178.48	258.89	1,058.47	3.6969
11.1607 281	Oven, microwave, large, with timer	EA	3,345.93	197.38	3,543.31	134.86	3,480.79	1.9258
11.1607 291	Oven, microwave, small, with timer	EA	1,367.72	197.38	1,565.10	134.86	1,502.58	1.9258
11.1607 301	Oven, gas, convection, 3 deck, bake	EA	13,467.56	852.50	14,320.06	582.50	14,050.06	8.3179
11.1607 311	Oven, gas, convection, 2 deck, bake	EA	10,479.39	489.37	10,968.76	334.38	10,813.77	4.7748
11.1607 321	Oven, gas, convection, 1 deck, bake	EA	7,365.05	489.37	7,854.42	334.38	7,699.43	4.7748
11.1607 331	Oven, convection, 3 deck, roast	EA	18,938.83	1,010.34	19,949.17	690.35	19,629.18	9.8579
11.1607 341	Oven, convection, 2 deck, roast	EA	13,888.45	836.74	14,725.19	571.73	14,460.18	8.1641
11.1607 351	Oven, convection, 1 deck, roast	EA	9,258.97	678.80	9,937.77	463.82	9,722.79	6.6231
11.1607 361	Pot sink, single	EA	631.25	197.38	828.63	134.86	766.11	1.9258
11.1607 371	Pot sink, double	EA	1,009.98	315.77	1,325.75	215.76	1,225.74	3.0810
11.1607 381	Pot filler	EA	189.29	355.22	544.51	242.72	432.01	3.4659
11.1607 391	Peeler, vegetable	EA	4,145.47	394.65	4,540.12	269.66	4,415.13	3.8506
11.1607 401	Pot rack, mobile	EA	1,788.58	94.72	1,883.30	64.72	1,853.30	0.9242
11.1607 411	Pan rack, roll-in	EA	1,241.51	94.72	1,336.23	64.72	1,306.23	0.9242
11.1607 421	Refrigerator, 1 section reach-in, pass thru	EA	3,516.25	285.95	3,802.20	195.38	3,711.63	2.7900
11.1607 431	Refrigerator, 2 section, reach-in, pass thru	EA	4,733.02	285.95	5,018.97	195.38	4,928.40	2.7900
11.1607 441	Refrigerator, 3 section, reach-in, pass thru	EA	6,010.58	285.95	6,296.53	195.38	6,205.96	2.7900
11.1607 451	Range match, gas, fryer, 36"	EA	2,739.79	426.26	3,166.05	291.25	3,031.04	4.1590
11.1607 461	Range, electric, hot top, oven 36" deep	EA	3,366.82	631.45	3,998.27	431.46	3,798.28	6.1611
11.1607 471	Range, hot top, oven under, gas	EA	2,567.19	426.26	2,993.45	291.25	2,858.44	4.1590
11.1607 481	Range, spreader plate, cabinet, 24"	EA	799.58	157.84	957.42	107.85	907.43	1.5401
11.1607 491	Range, spreader plate, cabinet, 18"	EA	673.33	157.84	831.17	107.85	781.18	1.5401
11.1607 501	Roll warmer, 2 drawer	EA	1,376.20	142.09	1,518.29	97.09	1,473.29	1.3864
11.1607 511	Roll warmer, 3 drawer	EA	1,586.65	142.09	1,728.74	97.09	1,683.74	1.3864
11.1607 521	Racks, chrome wire, 2x5, 5 shelves	EA	659.10		659.10		659.10	

Division 11 CSI #	11 - EQUIPMENT Description	Unit	Material	Union Install	Union Total	Open Install	Open Total	Unit Man-Hrs
11.1607 000	**BUY-OUT EQUIPMENT: (Cont.)**							
11.1607 531	Racks, stainless steel, per shelf to 5 shelves	LF	26.74		26.74		26.74	
11.1607 541	Steam kettle, 40 gal, tilt, motor	EA	10,193.23	426.26	10,619.49	291.25	10,484.48	4.1590
11.1607 551	Steam kettle, 20 gal, tilt, motor	EA	7,996.35	426.26	8,422.61	291.25	8,287.60	4.1590
11.1607 561	Steam kettle, 10 gal, tilt, motor	EA	1,809.62	284.17	2,093.79	194.17	2,003.79	2.7727
11.1607 571	Steam kettle, 40 gal, wall mounted	EA	7,769.06	426.26	8,195.32	291.25	8,060.31	4.1590
11.1607 581	Steam kettle, 60 gal, wall mounted	EA	8,602.36	426.26	9,028.62	291.25	8,893.61	4.1590
11.1607 591	Steam cooker, 1 compartment, small	EA	2,661.51	426.26	3,087.77	291.25	2,952.76	4.1590
11.1607 601	Steam cooker, 1 compartment, large	EA	5,472.14	426.26	5,898.40	291.25	5,763.39	4.1590
11.1607 611	Steam cooker, 2 compartment, large	EA	10,050.06	426.26	10,476.32	291.25	10,341.31	4.1590
11.1607 621	Soak sink, mobile, 24" x 24"	EA	1,165.72	157.84	1,323.56	107.85	1,273.57	1.5401
11.1607 631	Slicing machine	EA	1,999.08	118.42	2,117.50	80.91	2,079.99	1.1554
11.1607 641	Soft ice cream & shake machine	EA	11,826.20	536.72	12,362.92	366.73	12,192.93	5.2368
11.1607 651	Mobile stand, mixer & slicer	EA	1,262.54	252.57	1,515.11	172.57	1,435.11	2.4643
11.1607 661	Steam table, 6 well, heated over shelf	EA	5,892.02	426.26	6,318.28	291.25	6,183.27	4.1590
11.1607 671	Baker's table, 6', refrigerated	EA	9,258.97	489.37	9,748.34	334.38	9,593.35	4.7748
11.1607 681	Toaster, conveyor	EA	2,735.53	252.57	2,988.10	172.57	2,908.10	2.4643
11.1607 691	Tray dispenser, self level, mobile	EA	1,704.47	142.09	1,846.56	97.09	1,801.56	1.3864
11.1607 701	Tray maker conveyor, 36'	EA	19,780.50	378.90	20,159.40	258.89	20,039.39	3.6969
11.1607 711	Table, stainless steel, 6', with shelf under	EA	2,440.96	142.09	2,583.05	97.09	2,538.05	1.3864
11.1607 721	Work center & cabinet stainless steel, 6'	EA	5,647.89	426.26	6,074.15	291.25	5,939.14	4.1590
11.1607 731	Water station, chilled	EA	3,661.45	489.37	4,150.82	334.38	3,995.83	4.7748
11.1607 741	Washer, utensil, pass-thru	EA	18,100.33		18,100.33		18,100.33	
11.1607 751	Washer, glassware, pass-thru	EA	18,014.14		18,014.14		18,014.14	
11.1607 761	Dishwasher, peg-belt type	EA	21,548.00		21,548.00		21,548.00	
11.1607 771	Dishwasher, 30' flight, without access	EA	48,668.69		48,668.69		48,668.69	
11.1607 781	Dishwasher, 26' flight, without access	EA	46,235.29		46,235.29		46,235.29	
11.1607 791	Dishwasher, 22' flight, without access	EA	43,801.82		43,801.82		43,801.82	
11.1607 801	Dishwasher, 18' flight, without access	EA	41,368.37		41,368.37		41,368.37	
11.1607 811	Refrigerator, wall, stainless steel, glass door, 5', no compressor	EA	3,556.32		3,556.32		3,556.32	
11.1607 821	Walk-in cooler, metal, 8', prefab	SF	251.60		251.60		251.60	
11.1607 831	Refrigerator shelving	LF	21.55		21.55		21.55	
11.1608 000	**PREFAB KITCHEN, WITH ELECT RANGE, REFER & TOP:**							
11.1608 011	Kitchen unit, 60", no wall cabinets	EA	3,528.49	238.29	3,766.78	162.82	3,691.31	2.3250
11.1608 021	Kitchen unit, 72", no wall cabinets	EA	3,832.62	285.95	4,118.57	195.38	4,028.00	2.7900
11.1608 031	Kitchen unit, 84", no wall cabinets	EA	4,331.47	333.60	4,665.07	227.95	4,559.42	3.2550
11.1608 041	Add for disposal	EA	304.16		304.16		304.16	
11.1608 051	Add for microwave	EA	2,798.44		2,798.44		2,798.44	
11.1608 061	Add for hot water dispenser	EA	365.00		365.00		365.00	
11.1608 071	Add for porcelain colors	EA	182.51		182.51		182.51	
11.1700 000	**GYMNASIUM & PLAYGROUND EQUIPMENT:**							
11.1701 000	**FIELD EQUIPMENT:**							
11.1701 011	Basketball, post & steel backstop, single	EA	958.11	398.79	1,356.90	291.09	1,249.20	4.8450
11.1701 021	Basketball, post & steel backstop, double	EA	1,345.28	427.76	1,773.04	312.23	1,657.51	5.1969
11.1701 031	Add for fiberglass backstop	EA	58.02		58.02		58.02	
11.1701 041	Baseball backstop, 34x10, with hood	EA	2,893.84	1,193.47	4,087.31	871.14	3,764.98	14.4997
11.1701 051	Baseball backstop, 60x15, with hood	EA	8,100.86	2,094.64	10,195.50	1,528.93	9,629.79	25.4482
11.1701 061	Football goal, single post, two	SET	3,449.38	974.26	4,423.64	711.14	4,160.52	11.8365
11.1701 071	Soccer goal, two	SET	2,680.90	1,266.55	3,947.45	924.49	3,605.39	15.3876
11.1701 081	Tennis post, two	SET	338.74	204.59	543.33	149.33	488.07	2.4856
11.1701 091	Tennis net, nylon	EA	292.25		292.25		292.25	
11.1701 101	Tennis net, metal	EA	619.38		619.38		619.38	
11.1701 111	Volley ball post, two	SET	290.31	214.81	505.12	156.80	447.11	2.6098
11.1701 121	Tether ball post	EA	121.72	112.53	234.25	82.14	203.86	1.3672
11.1701 131	Add for ground sock, tether ball	EA	93.17	112.53	205.70	82.14	175.31	1.3672
11.1701 141	Court striping, tennis, basketball	EA	303.96		303.96		303.96	
11.1701 151	Court striping, volleyball	EA	182.36		182.36		182.36	
11.1701 161	Swings, 10' high, 4 seats	SET	1,254.30	664.94	1,919.24	485.36	1,739.66	8.0785
11.1701 171	Swings, 10' high, 6 seats	SET	1,538.81	792.83	2,331.64	578.70	2,117.51	9.6322
11.1701 181	Horizontal ladder, 8' x 16'	EA	809.11	409.18	1,218.29	298.67	1,107.78	4.9712
11.1701 191	Horizontal bar, single, 6-1/2'	EA	239.02	194.37	433.39	141.87	380.89	2.3614

Division 11 CSI #	11 - EQUIPMENT Description	Unit	Material	Union Install	Union Total	Open Install	Open Total	Unit Man-Hrs
11.1702 000	**BLEACHERS, ON CONCRETE RISER, BENCHES ONLY:**							
11.1702 011	Benches, fiberglass	SEAT	28.83		28.83		28.83	
11.1702 021	Benches, wood	SEAT	54.65		54.65		54.65	
11.1702 031	Benches, aluminum	SEAT	60.75		60.75		60.75	
11.1702 041	Benches, fiberglass, with back	SEAT	72.94		72.94		72.94	
11.1702 051	Individual seats	SEAT	103.28		103.28		103.28	
11.1702 061	Benches, port, 16 rows, 500 minimum	SEAT	57.72		57.72		57.72	
11.1703 000	**OUTDOOR EQUIPMENT, MISCELLANEOUS:**							
11.1703 011	Benches, wood slats, 6'	EA	712.80	38.27	751.07	27.94	740.74	0.4650
11.1703 021	Benches, precast concrete, 6'	EA	1,603.80	57.41	1,661.21	41.91	1,645.71	0.6975
11.1703 031	Picnic table & benches, 6'	EA	1,602.90	76.55	1,679.45	55.87	1,658.77	0.9300
11.1703 041	Bicycle rack, galvanized iron, 10', 1 side	EA	1,236.44	76.55	1,312.99	55.87	1,292.31	0.9300
11.1703 051	Bicycle rack, galvanized iron, 10', 2 side	EA	1,419.66	76.55	1,496.21	55.87	1,475.53	0.9300
11.1703 061	Bicycle rack, precast concrete, single	EA	201.36		201.36		201.36	
11.1704 000	**ATHLETIC FIELD, SYNTHETIC SURFACE:**							
11.1704 011	Uniturf, embossed, running, 3/8"	SF	8.91		8.91		8.91	
11.1704 021	Turf, 3 layer	SF	13.42		13.42		13.42	
11.1704 031	Turf, 2 layer	SF	11.73		11.73		11.73	
11.1704 041	Running track, volcanic cinder, 7"	SF	2.30		2.30		2.30	
11.1704 051	Running track, bitumen/cork, 2"	SF	3.67		3.67		3.67	
11.1704 061	Track, asphaltic concrete, 1/4 mi, 55,000 SF, 1/4" synthetic	EA	563,091.48		563,091.48		563,091.48	
11.1704 071	Track, 1/4 mi, 55,000 SF, 2" cinder, 6" curb	EA	158,474.83		158,474.83		158,474.83	
11.1704 081	Track, bitumen & cork, 1/4 mi, 55,000 SF	EA	202,308.32		202,308.32		202,308.32	
11.1704 091	Tennis court, asphaltic concrete base, all weather	SF	4.18		4.18		4.18	
11.1704 101	Score board	EA	16,858.97		16,858.97		16,858.97	
11.1705 000	**BASKETBALL BACKSTOPS:**							
11.1705 011	Backstop, wall, out-rigger, fixed	EA	722.32	692.00	1,414.32	505.10	1,227.42	8.4072
11.1705 021	Backstop, wall, out-rigger, swing	EA	2,214.36	1,321.69	3,536.05	964.73	3,179.09	16.0575
11.1705 031	Backstop, ceiling, swing up, manual	EA	4,453.35	1,770.35	6,223.70	1,292.22	5,745.57	21.5083
11.1705 041	Add for glass, fan backstop	EA	1,011.25		1,011.25		1,011.25	
11.1705 051	Add for glass, rectangular backs	EA	1,207.73		1,207.73		1,207.73	
11.1705 061	Add for power operation	EA	803.19		803.19		803.19	
11.1706 000	**GYM WALLS:**							
11.1706 011	Padded gym wall	SF	9.51		9.51		9.51	
11.1707 000	**GYM FLOORS, NO SUB-FLOOR OR BASE INCLUDED:**							
11.1707 011	Synthetic gym floor, 3/16"	SF	7.84		7.84		7.84	
11.1707 021	Synthetic gym floor, 3/8"	SF	8.59		8.59		8.59	
11.1707 031	Gym floor, maple, wood, spring	SF	22.63		22.63		22.63	
11.1707 041	Gym floor, rubber cushion, maple	SF	12.67		12.67		12.67	
11.1707 051	Gym floor, maple over sleepers	SF	18.18		18.18		18.18	
11.1707 061	Add for apparatus inserts	EA	60.65		60.65		60.65	
11.1708 000	**GYM SEATING:**							
11.1708 011	Bleachers, telescoping, manual	SEAT	74.13	16.70	90.83	12.20	86.33	0.1763
11.1708 021	Bleachers, portable, hydraulic	SEAT	75.35		75.35		75.35	
11.1709 000	**SCORE BOARDS:**							
11.1709 011	Score board, basketball, economy	EA	2,806.70	679.83	3,486.53	496.54	3,303.24	7.1765
11.1709 021	Score board, basketball, good	EA	2,819.87	1,246.35	4,066.22	910.33	3,730.20	13.1569
11.1709 031	Score board, basketball, best	EA	4,197.05	1,982.90	6,179.95	1,448.29	5,645.34	20.9321
11.1800 000	**INDUSTRIAL EQUIPMENT:**							
11.1801 000	**SERVICE STATION:**							
	Note: The prices for the next two items are rough averages. The price for the first item does not include the cost of land.							
11.1801 011	Service station, 3 island, 4 tanks	EA	652,398.49		652,398.49		652,398.49	
11.1801 021	Service station, remold to selfserve, conversion	EA	186,399.57		186,399.57		186,399.57	
11.1801 031	Air compressor, 2 hp, with receiver	EA	3,280.60	321.73	3,602.33	139.89	3,420.49	5.1469
11.1801 041	Air compressor, 3 hp, with receiver	EA	3,448.37	321.73	3,770.10	139.89	3,588.26	5.1469
11.1801 051	Gas pump, full size, 1/2 hp	EA	2,423.17	160.83	2,584.00	69.93	2,493.10	2.5729
11.1801 061	Gas pump, submerged turbine, 1/3 hp	EA	1,146.30	86.36	1,232.66	50.77	1,197.07	0.9651
11.1801 071	Gas pump, submerged turbine, 3/4 hp	EA	1,327.15	86.36	1,413.51	50.77	1,377.92	0.9651
11.1801 081	Gas dispenser, computing, single hose	EA	4,072.81	87.05	4,159.86	45.99	4,118.80	1.0720
11.1801 091	Add to above for vapor recovery	EA	838.77		838.77		838.77	
11.1801 101	Gas dispenser, computing, dual hose	EA	8,145.65	87.05	8,232.70	45.99	8,191.64	1.0720

Division 11 CSI #	11 - EQUIPMENT Description	Unit	Material	Union Install	Union Total	Open Install	Open Total	Unit Man-Hrs
11.1801 000	**SERVICE STATION: (Cont.)**							
11.1801 111	Fill boxes, 12", cast iron	EA	64.29	78.15	142.44	41.29	105.58	0.9624
11.1801 121	Air & water, bibbs, underground reels	EA	438.00	69.67	507.67	36.81	474.81	0.8580
11.1801 131	Add for electric thermal unit	EA	177.08		177.08		177.08	
11.1801 141	Hoist, 1 post, 8000#, semihydraulic	EA	3,700.04	720.46	4,420.50	473.33	4,173.37	8.5779
11.1801 151	Hoist, 2 post, 8000#, semihydraulic	EA	6,100.05	1,545.73	7,645.78	1,015.52	7,115.57	18.4037
11.1801 155	Truck lift, 50,000 lb, 4 post	EA	103,772.37	17,772.28	121,544.65	11,676.09	115,448.46	211.6000
11.1801 161	Cash box & pedestal stand	EA	177.08	80.43	257.51	34.97	212.05	1.2866
11.1801 171	Tire changer, air operated	EA	1,781.44	104.46	1,885.90	55.19	1,836.63	1.2864
11.1801 181	Lube, oil & air, reels & remote pump	EA	2,143.56	783.53	2,927.09	413.96	2,557.52	9.6494
11.1801 183	Trapeze, air & electrical, drop	EA	1,596.50	292.32	1,888.82	154.44	1,750.94	3.6000
11.1801 185	Reel bank, 3 services	EA	5,205.98	958.16	6,164.14	506.22	5,712.20	11.8000
11.1801 186	Reel bank, 4 services	EA	7,808.94	1,437.24	9,246.18	759.33	8,568.27	17.7000
11.1801 187	Reel bank, 5 services	EA	10,411.96	1,916.32	12,328.28	1,012.44	11,424.40	23.6000
11.1801 191	Exhaust fume system, underground	STA.	1,160.32		1,160.32		1,160.32	
11.1801 201	Island metal furring for 3 island	ONE S	1,118.34	156.22	1,274.56	102.63	1,220.97	1.8600
11.1801 211	Dynamometer	EA	70,150.32	9,629.46	79,779.78	6,780.05	76,930.37	112.9820
11.1801 221	Tank, waste oil with pump, 240 gal	EA	5,466.28	1,006.88	6,473.16	531.96	5,998.24	12.4000
11.1802 000	**SHOP EQUIPMENT, MISCELLANEOUS:**							
11.1802 011	Sawdust collector	EA	12,899.83	927.32	13,827.15	609.23	13,509.06	11.0408
11.1802 021	Sawdust collector, large capacity	EA	17,098.08	927.32	18,025.40	609.23	17,707.31	11.0408
11.1802 031	Paint spray booths	SF	13.27		13.27		13.27	
11.1802 041	Paint spray booth car	EA	58,124.60	2,526.34	60,650.94	1,659.76	59,784.36	30.0790
11.1802 051	Paint spray booth, 60' bus	EA	250,537.07	61,524.13	312,061.20	43,318.82	293,855.89	721.8600
11.1803 000	**VEHICLE MAINTENANCE EQUIPMENT, HEAVY DUTY:**							
11.1803 011	Cabinet, storage, shop	EA	807.03	109.62	916.65	57.92	864.95	1.3500
11.1803 021	Workbench, steel top, 6'	EA	461.13	63.90	525.03	33.76	494.89	0.7870
11.1803 031	Vise, machinist, swivel base, 4"	EA	428.21	59.33	487.54	31.35	459.56	0.7307
11.1803 041	Pump, air piston	EA	4,199.81	581.95	4,781.76	307.46	4,507.27	7.1669
11.1803 051	Pump, air piston, with hoist	EA	5,929.16	821.58	6,750.74	434.06	6,363.22	10.1180
11.1803 061	Tank, storage, cube, 500 gal	EA	1,646.99	228.22	1,875.21	120.57	1,767.56	2.8106
11.1803 071	Tank, storage, cube, 1,000 gal	EA	2,305.79	319.51	2,625.30	168.80	2,474.59	3.9348
11.1803 081	Washer, vehicle, gantry	EA	64,232.40	8,900.50	73,132.90	4,702.36	68,934.76	109.6121
11.1803 091	Water reclamation system	EA	11,528.85	1,597.53	13,126.38	844.01	12,372.86	19.6740
11.1803 101	Washer, high pressure, hot water	EA	16,058.08	2,225.12	18,283.20	1,175.59	17,233.67	27.4030
11.1803 111	Lift, ramp, surface mounted, 50,000#	EA	98,489.68	13,647.45	112,137.13	7,210.29	105,699.97	168.0720
11.1803 121	Buffer & grinder, 10", with dust collector	EA	7,576.12	1,049.80	8,625.92	554.64	8,130.76	12.9286
11.1803 131	Drill press variable speed, 20"	EA	9,223.13	1,278.02	10,501.15	675.21	9,898.34	15.7392
11.1803 141	Lathe, brake drum/rotor	EA	54,350.51	7,531.19	61,881.70	3,978.92	58,329.43	92.7487
11.1803 151	Hoist, chain, electric, 2 ton	EA	6,423.24	890.05	7,313.29	470.24	6,893.48	10.9612
11.1803 161	Hoist, chain, electric, 3 ton	EA	7,823.17	1,084.04	8,907.21	572.72	8,395.89	13.3502
11.1803 171	Tank, water oil, with pump, 240 gal	EA	5,187.96	718.89	5,906.85	379.81	5,567.77	8.8533
11.1803 181	Mounter & demounter, tire, truck	EA	17,869.78	2,476.17	20,345.95	1,308.22	19,178.00	30.4947
11.1901 000	**PARKING LOT EQUIPMENT:**							
11.1901 011	Automatic gate, automatic arm, 8'	EA	3,735.45	156.22	3,891.67	102.63	3,838.08	1.8600
11.1901 021	Traffic detector	EA	1,195.35	195.28	1,390.63	128.29	1,323.64	2.3250
11.1901 031	Ticket dispenser, control unit	EA	4,452.69	130.18	4,582.87	85.53	4,538.22	1.5500
11.1901 041	Gate operator card or coin	EA	1,195.35	475.58	1,670.93	334.86	1,530.21	5.5800
11.2000 000	**MATERIAL HANDLING EQUIPMENT:**							
	Note: Dock levelers don't include forms, concrete reinforcing or embedded metal.							
11.2001 000	**MATERIAL HANDLING EQUIPMENT:**							
11.2001 011	Conveyor power riser, 12' floors	EA	7,984.17	3,171.56	11,155.73	2,316.48	10,300.65	33.4800
11.2001 021	Conveyor, roller, 12"	LF	37.27		37.27		37.27	
11.2001 031	Conveyor, roller, 24"	LF	44.43		44.43		44.43	
11.2001 041	Dock bumper, 10" x 4-1/2" x 2'	EA	92.45	55.60	148.05	40.61	133.06	0.5869
11.2001 051	Dock bumper, 10" x 4-1/2" x 3'	EA	131.95	55.60	187.55	40.61	172.56	0.5869
11.2001 061	Dock bumper, 12" x 4-1/2" x 6'	EA	238.87	143.60	382.47	104.89	343.76	1.5159
11.2001 071	Dock leveler, medium duty, manual	EA	5,999.13	914.38	6,913.51	667.86	6,666.99	9.6525
11.2001 081	Dock leveler, heavy duty, hydraulic	EA	7,647.21	722.41	8,369.62	527.64	8,174.85	7.6260
11.2001 091	Dock leveler, heavy duty, hydraulic	EA	7,647.21	722.41	8,369.62	527.64	8,174.85	7.6260
11.2001 101	Scissor lift, 56", 2000#, 4x4 deck	EA	8,813.01		8,813.01		8,813.01	
11.2001 111	Scissors lift, 56", 2000#, 4x7 deck	EA	11,460.84		11,460.84		11,460.84	

Division 11 CSI #	11 - EQUIPMENT Description	Unit	Material	Union Install	Union Total	Open Install	Open Total	Unit Man-Hrs
11.2001 000	MATERIAL HANDLING EQUIPMENT: (Cont.)							
11.2001 121	Scissors lift, 60", 5000#, 6x8 deck	EA	13,436.86		13,436.86		13,436.86	
11.2001 131	Load dock, accordion door, 7'6"x8'	EA	1,192.43	746.86	1,939.29	545.50	1,737.93	7.8841
11.2100 000	LABORATORY EQUIPMENT:							
11.2101 000	LAB FURNITURE:							
	Note: The prices on following items include sink, fixtures & acid resistant tops.							
11.2101 011	Instructor's table, 12'x36"x36"	EA	3,044.73	264.30	3,309.03	193.04	3,237.77	2.7900
11.2101 021	Table, 8 student, 15' x 5' x 36"	EA	6,422.53	264.30	6,686.83	193.04	6,615.57	2.7900
11.2102 000	LABORATORY CABINETS, BASE UNITS:							
11.2102 011	Steel laboratory cabinet, base	LF	262.82	152.52	415.34	111.40	374.22	1.6100
11.2102 021	Wood laboratory cabinet, base	LF	216.75	152.52	369.27	111.40	328.15	1.6100
11.2102 031	Plastic laminated laboratory cabinet, base	LF	196.63	152.52	349.15	111.40	308.03	1.6100
11.2103 000	LAB CABINETS, KNEE SPACE DRAWER UNITS:							
11.2103 011	Steel laboratory cabinet, knee space, drawers	LF	168.37	96.91	265.28	70.78	239.15	1.0230
11.2103 021	Wood laboratory cabinet, knee space, drawers	LF	140.26	96.81	237.07	70.71	210.97	1.0220
11.2103 031	Plastic laminated laboratory cab, knee space, drawers	LF	126.24	96.72	222.96	70.64	196.88	1.0210
11.2104 000	LAB CABINETS, WALL HUNG:							
11.2104 011	Steel laboratory cabinet, wall hung	LF	193.14	74.08	267.22	54.11	247.25	0.7820
11.2104 021	Wood laboratory cabinet, wall hung	LF	201.16	74.08	275.24	54.11	255.27	0.7820
11.2104 031	Plastic laminated laboratory cabinet, wall hung	LF	127.00	74.08	201.08	54.11	181.11	0.7820
11.2105 000	LABORATORY CABINETS, TOPS, REAGENT SHELF, IN PLACE:							
	Note: Labor charges for the following items are included in the prices for base units.							
11.2105 011	Plastic laminate laboratory cabinet top	LF	72.16		72.16		72.16	
11.2105 021	Epoxy resin, acid resistant cabinet top	LF	168.37		168.37		168.37	
11.2105 031	Stainless steel laboratory cabinet top	LF	242.52		242.52		242.52	
11.2105 041	Chemical resist laboratory cabinet top	LF	96.18		96.18		96.18	
11.2106 000	CENTRIFUGES:							
11.2106 011	Centrifuge, high speed, portable	EA	2,465.28		2,465.28		2,465.28	
11.2106 021	Centrifuge, ultra hi speed, explosion proof	EA	11,224.05		11,224.05		11,224.05	
11.2106 031	Centrifuge, ultra hi speed, refrigerated	EA	17,838.24		17,838.24		17,838.24	
11.2107 000	REAGENT RACKS:							
11.2107 011	Rack, metal upright, wall, 1 tier	EA	96.18	43.86	140.04	32.03	128.21	0.4630
11.2107 021	Rack, metal upright center, 1 tier	EA	118.24	43.86	162.10	32.03	150.27	0.4630
11.2107 031	Laboratory storage, wardrobe	LF	269.50	62.19	331.69	45.42	314.92	0.6565
11.2108 000	LABORATORY EQUIPMENT, MISCELLANEOUS:							
11.2108 011	Fume hood	LF	1,202.56	323.03	1,525.59	235.94	1,438.50	3.4100
11.2108 021	Add for stainless steel	LF	601.27		601.27		601.27	
11.2108 031	Water distiller, 10 GPM	EA	7,591.13	404.52	7,995.65	253.60	7,844.73	3.4114
11.2108 041	Water tank, stainless steel, 50 gal	EA	8,284.71	404.52	8,689.23	253.60	8,538.31	3.4114
11.2108 051	Washer	EA	9,870.63	809.01	10,679.64	507.18	10,377.81	6.8225
11.2108 061	Portable water distiller, 18 liters per hour	EA	1,271.99	132.15	1,404.14	96.52	1,368.51	1.3950
11.2108 071	Fume hood laminar flow	LF	1,769.50	323.03	2,092.53	235.94	2,005.44	3.4100
11.2200 000	LIBRARY EQUIPMENT:							
11.2201 000	STUDY CARRELS, HARDWOOD:							
11.2201 011	Carrel, 36"x24"x29", 2 face, hardware	EA	448.21	99.55	547.76	72.71	520.92	1.0509
11.2201 021	Carrel, individual lights, hardware	EA	79.95	59.77	139.72	43.66	123.61	0.6310
11.2201 031	Carrel, power post receptacle, hardware	EA	22.32	59.77	82.09	43.66	65.98	0.6310
11.2202 000	LIBRARY TABLES & CHAIRS:							
11.2202 011	Table, 60" x 36" x 39"	EA	1,430.03		1,430.03		1,430.03	
11.2202 021	Table, 48", round	EA	1,295.56		1,295.56		1,295.56	
11.2202 031	Chairs, wood	EA	241.70		241.70		241.70	
11.2203 000	CARD CATALOG CABINET:							
11.2203 011	Card catalog, wood, 60 tray	EA	1,093.63		1,093.63		1,093.63	
11.2203 021	Card catalog, wood, 30 tray	EA	629.18		629.18		629.18	
11.2203 031	Charging counters, hardwood	LF	159.33	59.77	219.10	43.66	202.99	0.6310
11.2203 041	Charging counter top	SF	14.16	9.96	24.12	7.27	21.43	0.1051
11.2204 000	LIBRARY SHELVING:							
11.2204 011	Shelving, metal, bracket, 3 tier, 3x7	EA	184.92	54.75	239.67	39.99	224.91	0.5780
11.2204 021	Shelving, metal, bracket, 5 tier, 3x7	EA	199.19	59.77	258.96	43.66	242.85	0.6310
11.2204 031	Shelving, metal, bracket, 7 tier, 3x7	EA	215.26	66.12	281.38	48.29	263.55	0.6980
11.2205 011	Detection device, walk thru, expandable	EA	18,465.59	568.38	19,033.97	415.14	18,880.73	6.0000
11.2205 021	Detection device, walk thru, non-expandable	EA	14,765.89	511.54	15,277.43	373.63	15,139.52	5.4000

140

Division 11 CSI #	11 - EQUIPMENT Description	Unit	Material	Union Install	Union Total	Open Install	Open Total	Unit Man-Hrs
11.2300 000	HOSPITAL EQUIPMENT:							
	Note: The following prices do not include costs for mechanical or electrical hookup.							
11.2301 000	NURSES MONITORING EQUIPMENT, CCU/ICU:							
11.2301 011	Cardioscope, 1 channel, bed side	EA	4,725.98		4,725.98		4,725.98	
11.2301 021	Blood pressure monitor, bed side, with readout	EA	7,256.17		7,256.17		7,256.17	
11.2301 031	Coronary care unit bed & nurse display, 8 bed	EA	147,649.63		147,649.63		147,649.63	
11.2301 041	Telemetry, wireless, 8 bed	EA	403,828.78		403,828.78		403,828.78	
11.2302 000	NURSING ACUTE CARE EQUIPMENT:							
11.2302 011	Modular wall unit, 1 bed core, prewire	EA	5,369.72	685.15	6,054.87	500.43	5,870.15	7.2327
11.2302 021	Modular wall unit, 24" nurse treatment	EA	712.44	158.30	870.74	115.62	828.06	1.6711
11.2302 031	Modular wall unit, 24" storage center	EA	771.31	174.12	945.43	127.18	898.49	1.8381
11.2302 041	Patient communication & convenience unit	EA	1,664.65		1,664.65		1,664.65	
11.2302 051	Cubicle track & curtain, to 8' high	LF	13.03	3.86	16.89	2.82	15.85	0.0408
11.2302 061	Mirror, medicine cabinet, stainless steel, recessed light	EA	513.15	115.32	628.47	84.23	597.38	1.2174
11.2303 000	NURSING STATION/CORE EQUIPMENT:							
11.2303 011	Nurse chart desk	EA	1,170.89		1,170.89		1,170.89	
11.2303 021	Nurse call, 40 station, two way	EA	22,068.97	5,833.91	27,902.88	4,261.04	26,330.01	61.5846
11.2303 031	Nourishment station, 84" x 80", stainless steel	EA	20,016.03	352.40	20,368.43	257.39	20,273.42	3.7200
11.2303 041	Medical preparation cabinet, 72"x80", stainless steel, lock	EA	9,238.11	352.40	9,590.51	257.39	9,495.50	3.7200
11.2303 051	Intravenous prep center, 60" x 80", stainless steel	EA	7,955.06	352.40	8,307.46	257.39	8,212.45	3.7200
11.2303 061	Sani-prep maintenance station, stainless steel	EA	5,773.82	1,526.32	7,300.14	1,114.81	6,888.63	16.1123
11.2303 071	Multi-use tote carts, average cost	EA	1,621.58		1,621.58		1,621.58	
11.2303 081	Modular storage systems	LF	368.72		368.72		368.72	
11.2304 000	CORRIDORS:							
11.2304 011	Hospital corner guard, plastic, 8'	EA	144.34	42.91	187.25	31.34	175.68	0.4530
11.2304 021	Hospital corner guard, plastic, 4'	EA	82.49	31.98	114.47	23.36	105.85	0.3376
11.2304 031	Hospital corner guard, stainless steel, 8'	EA	348.38	137.55	485.93	100.46	448.84	1.4520
11.2304 041	Hospital corner guard, stainless steel, 4'	EA	174.18	74.41	248.59	54.35	228.53	0.7855
11.2305 000	SURGERY TABLES & ACCESSORIES:							
11.2305 011	Surgery table, electric, stationary	EA	24,222.25	2,246.52	26,468.77	1,640.84	25,863.09	23.7150
11.2305 021	Surgery service island, complete	EA	8,768.70	1,828.05	10,596.75	1,335.19	10,103.89	19.2975
11.2305 031	Surgical monitor, conduct casters	EA	9,140.24		9,140.24		9,140.24	
11.2305 041	Conductivity meter, current leak detector	EA	1,011.72	254.39	1,266.11	185.80	1,197.52	2.6854
11.2305 051	Surgical clock, stainless steel, auto reset	EA	1,222.02	261.18	1,483.20	190.76	1,412.78	2.7571
11.2306 000	OBSTETRICAL & NURSERY EQUIPMENT:							
11.2306 011	Delivery table	EA	7,014.91	1,763.74	8,778.65	1,288.22	8,303.13	18.6186
11.2306 021	Incubator, isolation servo-care	EA	6,486.55		6,486.55		6,486.55	
11.2306 031	Incubator, warming	EA	2,122.86		2,122.86		2,122.86	
11.2307 000	SURGICAL LIGHTING:							
11.2307 011	Surgery light, 3 arm, surface mounted	EA	27,393.33	2,924.65	30,317.98	2,124.14	29,517.47	26.7997
11.2307 021	Surgery light, 2 arm, surface mounted	EA	19,024.19	2,692.90	21,717.09	1,955.83	20,980.02	24.6761
11.2307 031	Surgery light, 1 arm, surface mounted	EA	13,270.90	1,953.71	15,224.61	1,418.96	14,689.86	17.9026
11.2307 041	Add for auxiliary light head	EA	6,903.95	811.93	7,715.88	589.69	7,493.64	7.4400
11.2307 051	Surgery light intensity control, 600w	EA	767.11	608.95	1,376.06	442.27	1,209.38	5.5800
11.2307 061	Surgery light intensity control, 300w	EA	575.28	352.40	927.68	257.39	832.67	3.7200
11.2308 000	SCRUB & CLEAN ROOM EQUIPMENT:							
11.2308 011	Scrub station, stainless steel, 3 bay, base mounted	EA	9,998.70	1,681.76	11,680.46	1,054.33	11,053.03	14.1825
11.2308 021	Scrub station, stainless steel base mounted, 1 bay	EA	7,141.93	1,102.79	8,244.72	691.36	7,833.29	9.3000
11.2308 031	Solution warm cab, stainless steel, 24"x30"x74"	EA	7,385.06	275.70	7,660.76	172.84	7,557.90	2.3250
11.2308 041	Surgery storage console, stainless steel, 12'	EA	4,918.36	176.20	5,094.56	128.69	5,047.05	1.8600
11.2308 051	Suture & drug cabinet, stainless steel, 36"x18"x81"	EA	1,626.73	132.15	1,758.88	96.52	1,723.25	1.3950
11.2308 061	Instrument cabinet, stainless steel, 48"x18"x60"	EA	2,206.04	132.15	2,338.19	96.52	2,302.56	1.3950
11.2308 071	Sterilizer, 16" x 16" x 26"	EA	22,811.31	440.49	23,251.80	321.73	23,133.04	4.6500
11.2309 000	CARDIAC EMERGENCY EQUIPMENT:							
11.2309 011	Monitor & resuscitator unit with DC defibrillator	EA	17,872.33		17,872.33		17,872.33	
11.2309 021	Mobile emergency utility, crash cart	EA	9,748.47		9,748.47		9,748.47	
11.2309 031	DC defibrillator	EA	5,199.01		5,199.01		5,199.01	
11.2309 041	External cardiac compressor	EA	5,849.15		5,849.15		5,849.15	
11.2310 000	EMERGENCY ACCESSORIES:							
11.2310 011	Treatment cabinet, mobile unit	EA	1,787.24		1,787.24		1,787.24	
11.2310 021	Treatment cabinet, with suction compressor	EA	3,168.37		3,168.37		3,168.37	
11.2310 031	Exam lights, 22", ceiling mounted	EA	3,480.70	685.06	4,165.76	497.55	3,978.25	6.2775

Division 11 CSI #	11 - EQUIPMENT Description	Unit	Material	Union Install	Union Total	Open Install	Open Total	Unit Man-Hrs
11.2310 000	**EMERGENCY ACCESSORIES: (Cont.)**							
11.2310 041	Plaster sink with trap & fittings	EA	1,392.62	557.62	1,950.24	349.58	1,742.20	4.7025
11.2310 051	Splint cabinet with plaster bins	EA	1,214.08	226.10	1,440.18	165.14	1,379.22	2.3868
11.2311 000	**STERILIZERS, RECESSED, WITH AUTOMATIC DOORS:**							
11.2311 011	Sterilizer, 24"x36"x36", 1 door, steam	EA	92,315.83	27,504.87	119,820.70	17,243.31	109,559.14	231.9520
11.2311 021	Sterilizer, 24"x36"x48", 1 door, steam	EA	94,085.51	27,504.87	121,590.38	17,243.31	111,328.82	231.9520
11.2311 031	Sterilizer, gas, 24"x36"x60", 1 door	EA	110,616.64	22,216.35	132,832.99	13,927.84	124,544.48	187.3533
11.2311 041	Sterilizer, gas, 24"x36"x60", pass-thru	EA	116,024.77	22,216.35	138,241.12	13,927.84	129,952.61	187.3533
11.2311 051	Sterilizer, steam, 24"x36"x48", pass-thru	EA	118,134.28	27,504.87	145,639.15	17,243.31	135,377.59	231.9520
11.2311 061	Sterilizer, steam, 24"x36"x60", pass-thru	EA	120,216.98	27,504.87	147,721.85	17,243.31	137,460.29	231.9520
11.2311 071	Sterilizer, gas/cryotherm, 24"x36"x60", pass-thru	EA	99,148.40	23,844.17	122,992.57	14,948.35	114,096.75	201.0809
11.2311 081	Sterilizer, gas/cryotherm, 24"x36"x48", 1 door	EA	84,381.65	10,962.57	95,344.22	6,872.64	91,254.29	92.4487
11.2311 091	Gas aerator, 24" x 36" x 60"	EA	10,547.69	2,965.25	13,512.94	1,858.97	12,406.66	25.0063
11.2311 101	Gas aerator, 24" x 36" x 48"	EA	5,695.74	1,589.61	7,285.35	996.56	6,692.30	13.4054
11.2312 000	**STERILIZER ACCESSORIES:**							
11.2312 011	Loading car & carriage, large	EA	6,961.46		6,961.46		6,961.46	
11.2312 021	Loading car & carriage, medium	EA	5,695.74		5,695.74		5,695.74	
11.2312 031	Steam generator, 10 BHP/110 PSIG/208v, 3ph	EA	5,010.11	1,199.85	6,209.96	752.21	5,762.32	10.1185
11.2313 000	**INSTRUMENT & UTENSIL WASHER/STERILIZER:**							
11.2313 011	Instrument cleaner, sonic, 12x11x24, 1 compartment	EA	16,348.92	5,597.62	21,946.54	3,509.25	19,858.17	47.2054
11.2313 021	Instrument cleaner, sonic, 12x11x24, 2 compartment	EA	22,054.24	5,597.62	27,651.86	3,509.25	25,563.49	47.2054
11.2313 031	Glass washer, steam, 24x20x24, pass-thru	EA	34,692.34	8,078.24	42,770.58	5,064.40	39,756.74	68.1248
11.2313 041	Utensil washer, 27x27x60, free stand	EA	14,766.77	3,187.63	17,954.40	1,998.39	16,765.16	26.8817
11.2313 051	Utensil washer, conveyor, pass-thru	EA	50,101.54	11,877.77	61,979.31	7,446.39	57,547.93	100.1667
11.2313 061	Drying oven, 25"x25"x50", steam	EA	12,235.32	2,705.98	14,941.30	1,696.43	13,931.75	22.8199
11.2313 071	Charging table, 5', stainless steel, 2 sink	EA	2,320.47	668.72	2,989.19	419.23	2,739.70	5.6394
11.2314 000	**HOSPITAL CART WASH, PIT MOUNTED:**							
11.2314 011	Cart washer, 92"x72"x98", pass-thru, pit	EA	96,152.85	23,181.83	119,334.68	14,533.12	110,685.97	195.4953
11.2314 021	Cart washer, 92x72x196, automatic, 2 stage	EA	241,040.78	28,022.00	269,062.78	17,567.51	258,608.29	236.3130
11.2315 000	**CENTRAL PHARMACY EQUIPMENT:**							
11.2315 011	Pharmacy unit with basic modules	LF	592.46		592.46		592.46	
11.2315 021	Medication refrigerator, 115 CF, stainless steel	EA	4,106.59	325.53	4,432.12	204.08	4,310.67	2.7452
11.2315 031	Water purifier, reverse osmosis, 6 liters per minute	EA	3,392.38	812.37	4,204.75	509.29	3,901.67	6.8508
11.2315 041	Lam flow hood, 36" work area	EA	7,713.25	1,550.29	9,263.54	971.91	8,685.16	13.0738
11.2315 051	Hi-density storage, caster/track	EA	3,213.80	254.75	3,468.55	159.70	3,373.50	2.1483
11.2316 000	**CENTRAL LABORATORY EQUIPMENT:**							
11.2316 011	Laboratory work counter, with base units	LF	521.91		521.91		521.91	
11.2316 021	Laboratory sterilizer, 16"x26", 208v, 3ph	EA	6,427.73	815.19	7,242.92	511.06	6,938.79	6.8746
11.2316 031	Liquid nitrogen refrigerator, 30 CF, 190 deg	EA	28,567.75	849.16	29,416.91	532.36	29,100.11	7.1611
11.2316 041	Water distribution, steam, 10 GPH, wall	EA	15,821.49	1,160.52	16,982.01	727.55	16,549.04	9.7868
11.2316 051	Water tank, stainless steel, 50 gal, wall mounted	EA	9,492.93	1,041.64	10,534.57	653.02	10,145.95	8.7843
11.2316 061	Specimen pass-thru box, stainless steel	EA	196.40	137.39	333.79	86.13	282.53	1.1586
11.2317 000	**X-RAY EQUIPMENT:**							
11.2317 011	X-ray, ceiling mounted, telescoping	EA	38,566.50	5,063.99	43,630.49	3,677.93	42,244.43	46.4033
11.2317 021	X-ray, wall mounted, chest	EA	11,427.07	2,500.74	13,927.81	1,816.26	13,243.33	22.9152
11.2317 031	Mobile x-ray unit	EA	47,768.15		47,768.15		47,768.15	
11.2317 041	X-ray control unit	EA	12,641.17	2,766.45	15,407.62	2,009.24	14,650.41	25.3500
11.2317 051	Multix table	EA	24,104.05	5,274.99	29,379.04	3,831.17	27,935.22	48.3368
11.2318 000	**X-RAY PROCESSING EQUIPMENT:**							
11.2318 011	Auto film processor, complete	EA	37,952.53		37,952.53		37,952.53	
11.2318 021	Development tank, 10 gal, stainless steel, 2 compartment, mix valve	EA	2,051.50		2,051.50		2,051.50	
11.2318 031	X-ray pass box, 2 compartment, ro-in frame	EA	1,714.00		1,714.00		1,714.00	
11.2318 041	X-ray film loading bin	EA	696.34		696.34		696.34	
11.2318 051	Revolving door, 36x80, safe hinge	EA	3,535.20		3,535.20		3,535.20	
11.2319 000	**X-RAY VIEWING EQUIPMENT:**							
11.2319 011	X-ray film illuminator, wet, drip tray	EA	341.01		341.01		341.01	
11.2319 021	X-ray film illuminator, 1 panel, 14x17	EA	272.24		272.24		272.24	
11.2319 031	X-ray film illuminator, 2 panel, 30x18	EA	517.76		517.76		517.76	
11.2319 041	X-ray film illuminator, multibank, 4/4	EA	2,467.52		2,467.52		2,467.52	
11.2319 051	X-ray film illuminator, multibank, 6/6	EA	3,285.26		3,285.26		3,285.26	
11.2319 061	X-ray shield, view glass, deluxe	EA	1,124.86		1,124.86		1,124.86	

Division 11 CSI #	11 - EQUIPMENT Description	Unit	Material	Union Install	Union Total	Open Install	Open Total	Unit Man-Hrs
11.2320 000	**NUCLEAR EQUIPMENT:**							
11.2320 011	Gamma camera, 10" view, complete	EA	424,660.34		424,660.34		424,660.34	
11.2320 021	Gamma camera, 15" view, complete	EA	478,225.00		478,225.00		478,225.00	
11.2321 000	**ULTRA SOUND EQUIPMENT:**							
11.2321 011	Ultra sound unit complete	EA	247,557.83		247,557.83		247,557.83	
11.2322 000	**HYDROTHERAPY UNITS:**							
11.2322 011	Hubbard tank, 400 gal, twin eject	EA	28,924.82		28,924.82		28,924.82	
11.2322 021	Treatment/wade tank, 1000 gal	EA	35,352.61		35,352.61		35,352.61	
11.2322 031	Whirlpool, stainless steel, 85 gal, leg & hip	EA	5,463.57		5,463.57		5,463.57	
11.2322 041	Whirlpool, stainless steel, 80 gal, arm, leg & hip	EA	4,713.65		4,713.65		4,713.65	
11.2322 051	Whirlpool, stainless steel, 25 gal, arm	EA	3,481.70		3,481.70		3,481.70	
11.2322 061	Moisture heat therapy unit, table	EA	4,558.14		4,558.14		4,558.14	
11.2322 071	Mobile paraffin bath	EA	1,670.34		1,670.34		1,670.34	
11.2322 081	Mobile sitz bath	EA	455.45		455.45		455.45	
11.2323 000	**INHALATION THERAPY EQUIPMENT:**							
11.2323 011	Ventilator, complete	EA	15,488.65		15,488.65		15,488.65	
11.2323 021	Suction unit, stainless steel cabinet	EA	1,427.52		1,427.52		1,427.52	
11.2323 031	IPPB inhaler	EA	1,882.87		1,882.87		1,882.87	
11.2323 041	Air volume tester, lung	EA	7,592.44		7,592.44		7,592.44	
11.2324 000	**PHYSICAL THERAPY EQUIPMENT:**							
11.2324 011	Exercise unit, complete	EA	7,760.55		7,760.55		7,760.55	
11.2324 021	Exercise chair	EA	2,277.62		2,277.62		2,277.62	
11.2324 031	Treadmill, motorized, 5 speed	EA	4,937.61		4,937.61		4,937.61	
11.2324 041	Treadmill, adjustable angle	EA	1,062.96		1,062.96		1,062.96	
11.2324 051	Rowing machine	EA	987.49		987.49		987.49	
11.2324 061	Rehabilitation loom	EA	1,594.11		1,594.11		1,594.11	
11.2325 000	**LAUNDRY EQUIPMENT:**							
11.2325 011	Unloading washer, 60"x44", 400#	EA	103,651.99	15,036.87	118,688.86	10,982.81	114,634.80	158.7340
11.2325 021	Extractor, 200#, with accessories	EA	83,473.25	12,265.06	95,738.31	8,958.30	92,431.55	129.4739
11.2325 031	Washer/extractor, 600#	EA	151,351.01	21,978.91	173,329.92	16,053.21	167,404.22	232.0164
11.2325 041	Dryer, gas or steam, 200/400#	EA	68,405.05	9,934.67	78,339.72	7,256.20	75,661.25	104.8735
11.2325 051	Flat ironer, 6 roller	EA	153,926.59	22,341.94	176,268.53	16,318.36	170,244.95	235.8486
11.2325 061	Ironer/folder, 2 lane	EA	61,793.61	9,076.10	70,869.71	6,629.11	68,422.72	95.8102
11.2325 071	Folder, 3 lane	EA	38,893.95	5,641.89	44,535.84	4,120.79	43,014.74	59.5576
11.2400 000	**DENTAL EQUIPMENT:**							
	Note: The following prices do not include costs for mechanical or electrical hook-up.							
11.2401 000	**DENTAL CHAIRS & INSTRUMENTATION UNITS:**							
11.2401 011	Dental chair, deluxe, with lift	EA	10,080.86		10,080.86		10,080.86	
11.2401 021	Dental chair, standard, tilt	EA	5,867.07		5,867.07		5,867.07	
11.2401 031	Instrument unit, 4 port, tray, chair mounted	EA	6,584.81		6,584.81		6,584.81	
11.2401 041	Assistant instrument unit, chair mounted	EA	5,013.57		5,013.57		5,013.57	
11.2401 051	Mobile instrument unit, cabinet	EA	7,538.29		7,538.29		7,538.29	
11.2401 061	Mobile assistant's unit, cabinet	EA	6,477.66		6,477.66		6,477.66	
11.2401 071	Instrument unit, cabinet, wall mounted	EA	18,851.16		18,851.16		18,851.16	
11.2402 000	**DENTAL LIGHTING & X-RAY:**							
11.2402 011	Dental light, chair or unit mounted	EA	1,710.47		1,710.47		1,710.47	
11.2402 021	Dental light, ceiling mounted	EA	1,710.47		1,710.47		1,710.47	
11.2402 031	Dental x-ray, wall mounted	EA	13,955.31		13,955.31		13,955.31	
11.2402 041	Dental x-ray, wall, extra remote heavy duty	EA	22,061.44		22,061.44		22,061.44	
11.2403 000	**DENTAL EQUIPMENT, MISCELLANEOUS:**							
11.2403 011	Dental sterilizer, chemiclave	EA	1,965.81		1,965.81		1,965.81	
11.2403 021	Dental sterilizer, vibraclean	EA	1,199.08		1,199.08		1,199.08	
11.2403 031	Dental compressor with dryer	EA	3,557.31		3,557.31		3,557.31	
11.2404 000	**DENTAL EQUIPMENT, LABORATORY, MISCELLANEOUS:**							
11.2404 011	Dust collector, pedestal	EA	2,492.48	484.02	2,976.50	303.44	2,795.92	4.0818
11.2404 021	Waxing unit, 3 compartment	EA	98.71		98.71		98.71	
11.2404 031	Pneumatic curing unit	EA	211.54		211.54		211.54	
11.2404 041	Double pneumatic press	EA	1,481.19		1,481.19		1,481.19	
11.2404 051	Curing tank assembly	EA	1,151.61	219.14	1,370.75	137.38	1,288.99	1.8480
11.2404 061	Boilout assembly	EA	946.31	180.02	1,126.33	112.86	1,059.17	1.5181
11.2404 071	Plaster bin, 4 compartment, 300#	EA	657.01	124.58	781.59	78.10	735.11	1.0506

Division 11 CSI #	11 - EQUIPMENT Description	Unit	Material	Union Install	Union Total	Open Install	Open Total	Unit Man-Hrs
11.2405 000	**DENTAL LABORATORY FURNITURE, METAL:**							
11.2405 011	Dental laboratory tech bench, 5 drawer	EA	1,248.53	189.76	1,438.29	138.60	1,387.13	2.0032
11.2405 021	Dental laboratory, 2 door cab, 36"x24"x36"	EA	1,414.04	244.21	1,658.25	178.37	1,592.41	2.5780
11.2405 031	Dental laboratory, 1 door cab, 24"x24"x36"	EA	1,099.79	189.98	1,289.77	138.76	1,238.55	2.0055
11.2405 041	Dental laboratory, 1 door cabinet, corner	EA	1,728.31	298.48	2,026.79	218.00	1,946.31	3.1508
11.2501 000	**MORTUARY EQUIPMENT:**							
11.2501 011	Mortuary refrigerator, 4 place, 2 tier	EA	27,415.90	1,378.08	28,793.98	1,006.53	28,422.43	14.5474
11.2501 021	Mortuary refrigerator, 6 place, 2 tier	EA	36,060.73	1,722.66	37,783.39	1,258.21	37,318.94	18.1849
11.2501 031	Mortuary refrigerator, 10 place, 2 tier	EA	50,709.78	2,997.36	53,707.14	2,189.25	52,899.03	31.6411
11.2501 041	Autopsy table	EA	10,319.63		10,319.63		10,319.63	
11.2600 000	**PRISON EQUIPMENT:**							
11.2601 000	**CELL & CORRIDOR CONSTRUCTION:**							
11.2601 011	Steel plate wall lining	SF	17.68	15.67	33.35	11.44	29.12	0.1654
11.2601 021	Steel plate ceiling lining	SF	17.68	36.50	54.18	26.66	44.34	0.3853
11.2601 031	Bar walls, normal security	SF	28.37	15.67	44.04	11.44	39.81	0.1654
11.2601 041	Bar door, hinged, key locking device only	SF	106.37	52.17	158.54	38.10	144.47	0.5507
11.2601 051	Bar door, hinged, key locking device only	SF	116.97	57.36	174.33	41.89	158.86	0.6055
11.2601 061	Panel door, hinged, key locking device only	SF	88.63	46.98	135.61	34.31	122.94	0.4959
11.2601 071	Panel door, sliding, key locking device only	SF	92.21	46.98	139.19	34.31	126.52	0.4959
11.2601 081	Cells, average door	EA	6,244.18	2,618.34	8,862.52	1,912.41	8,156.59	27.6400
11.2601 091	Sallyport, average door	EA	5,203.46	2,618.34	7,821.80	1,912.41	7,115.87	27.6400
11.2601 101	Air locking device	EA	6,660.42	2,618.34	9,278.76	1,912.41	8,572.83	27.6400
11.2602 000	**REMOTE ELECTRIC CONTROLS:**							
11.2602 011	Add to total cost, per door	EA	132.64	695.48	828.12	507.97	640.61	7.3417
11.2603 000	**CELL ACCESSORIES, BUILT-INS:**							
11.2603 011	Single bunk, stainless steel	EA	922.44	323.40	1,245.84	236.21	1,158.65	3.4139
11.2603 021	Double bunks, stainless steel	EA	1,578.91	432.97	2,011.88	316.24	1,895.15	4.5706
11.2701 000	**CENTRAL VACUUM SYSTEM:**							
11.2701 011	Vacuum, central residential, 8 outlet max	INLET	294.43		294.43		294.43	
11.2701 021	Vacuum, central commercial, 1 station/1200 SF	STATI	1,137.68		1,137.68		1,137.68	
11.2702 000	**VACUUM, CENTRAL COMMERCIAL, COMPONENTS:**							
11.2702 011	Vacuum, motor closed, 1200 CFM/1200 SF	EA	1,222.00		1,222.00		1,222.00	
11.2702 021	Vacuum, motor closed, 2400 CFM/2500 SF	EA	2,591.30		2,591.30		2,591.30	
11.2702 031	Vacuum, motor closed, 5000 CFM/50,000 SF	EA	5,353.93		5,353.93		5,353.93	
11.2702 041	Filter separator, 10 bag (2:1)	EA	2,743.86		2,743.86		2,743.86	
11.2702 051	Steel tubing, 1-1/2"	LF	8.79		8.79		8.79	
11.2702 061	Steel tubing, 2-1/2"	LF	10.26		10.26		10.26	
11.2702 071	Inlets	EA	33.85		33.85		33.85	
11.2702 081	Portable pickup with wet separator	EA	803.06		803.06		803.06	
11.2800 000	**STAGE EQUIPMENT:**							
11.2801 000	**STAGE EQUIPMENT, IN PLACE:**							
	Note: The following prices include lighting, control, rigging and drops.							
11.2801 011	Large stage, professional/college	GSF	743.38		743.38		743.38	
11.2801 021	Medium stage, college/high school	GSF	446.01		446.01		446.01	
11.2801 031	Medium stage, community theater	GSF	371.65		371.65		371.65	
11.2801 041	Small stage, junior high school	GSF	297.34		297.34		297.34	
11.2801 051	Small stage, elementary school	GSF	208.12		208.12		208.12	
11.2801 061	Minimum equip stage, multipurpose	GSF	118.87		118.87		118.87	
11.2802 000	**CONTROL CENTERS-LIGHTING:**							
11.2802 011	Five scene, 2 sub-scene, 390 pot	LS	178,427.57		178,427.57		178,427.57	
11.2802 021	One scene, 2 sub-scene, 24 pot	LS	92,187.55		92,187.55		92,187.55	
11.2802 031	Patch board, 3 2500w dim, 15 non-dim	LS	22,898.17		22,898.17		22,898.17	
11.2803 000	**LIGHTING INSTRUMENTS:**							
11.2803 011	Footlights, disappearing, reflect	PER 5	906.93		906.93		906.93	
11.2803 021	Add for motorized	PER 5	1,561.16		1,561.16		1,561.16	
11.2803 031	Border lights, 1 row, reflective, 3 color	PER 8	758.27		758.27		758.27	
11.2803 041	Border lights, 1 row, roundel, 3 color	PER 8	1,055.64		1,055.64		1,055.64	
11.2803 051	Border lights, 2 row, roundel, 4 color	PER 8	2,676.34		2,676.34		2,676.34	
11.2803 061	Ball, mirrored, rotating, 30"	EA	2,379.17	1,568.79	3,947.96	1,139.39	3,518.56	14.3754
11.2803 071	Spotlight, follow, carbon arc	EA	6,542.33		6,542.33		6,542.33	
11.2803 081	Spotlight, follow, quartz halogen	EA	2,081.60		2,081.60		2,081.60	
11.2803 091	Quartz spot, elliptical, iodine lamp, 3000w	EA	1,932.89		1,932.89		1,932.89	

Division 11 CSI #	11 - EQUIPMENT Description	Unit	Material	Union Install	Union Total	Open Install	Open Total	Unit Man-Hrs
11.2803 000	**LIGHTING INSTRUMENTS: (Cont.)**							
11.2803 101	Quartz spot, elliptical, iodine lamp, 1500w	EA	669.06		669.06		669.06	
11.2803 111	Quartz spot, elliptical, iodine lamp, 500w	EA	416.28		416.28		416.28	
11.2803 121	Quartz spot, fresnel, iodine lamp, 1000w	EA	475.71		475.71		475.71	
11.2803 131	Quartz spot, fresnel, iodine lamp, 500w	EA	282.45		282.45		282.45	
11.2803 141	Color wheel, motorized, 20"	EA	282.45		282.45		282.45	
11.2803 151	Quartz beam projection, iodine lamp, 1500w	EA	460.82		460.82		460.82	
11.2803 161	Floodlight, utility, incandescent, 1000w	EA	252.70		252.70		252.70	
11.2803 171	Flood, scoop, iodine lamp, 18", 750w	EA	282.45		282.45		282.45	
11.2804 000	**LIGHTING & CONTROL ACCESSORIES:**							
11.2804 011	Light tower, 4' x 6' x 15'	EA	7,434.42		7,434.42		7,434.42	
11.2804 021	Light stand, cast iron base, 24"	EA	341.96		341.96		341.96	
11.2804 031	Plug strip	LF	50.49		50.49		50.49	
11.2804 041	Floor pocket, plug, 4 outlet, 100a	EA	237.83		237.83		237.83	
11.2804 051	Floor pocket, plug, 2 outlet, 50a	EA	208.12		208.12		208.12	
11.2804 061	Wall pocket, surface plug, 3 outlet, 50a	EA	74.31		74.31		74.31	
11.2804 071	Wall pocket, surface plug, 1 outlet, 50a	EA	163.50		163.50		163.50	
11.2804 081	Wall pocket, flush, 2 outlet, 100a	EA	288.40		288.40		288.40	
11.2804 091	Wall pocket, flush, 4 outlet, 50a	EA	252.70		252.70		252.70	
11.2804 101	Catwalk, wood, metal pipe mount rail	LF	20.68	89.18	109.86	65.14	85.82	0.9414
11.2805 000	**STAGE RIGGING, CURTAINS & DROPS:**							
	Note: The price for the scissors lift at the end of this section does not include costs for any structural work.							
11.2805 011	Acoustic cloud, adjust, wood frame	SF	3.84	7.36	11.20	5.38	9.22	0.0777
11.2805 021	Curtain track, heavy duty, straight	LF	15.32	18.95	34.27	13.84	29.16	0.2000
11.2805 031	Curtain track, medium duty, straight	LF	9.64	18.95	28.59	13.84	23.48	0.2000
11.2805 041	Curtain track, heavy duty, curved	LF	61.50	28.47	89.97	20.79	82.29	0.3005
11.2805 051	Curtain track, medium duty, curved	LF	15.86	28.47	44.33	20.79	36.65	0.3005
11.2805 061	Add for electric driven heavy duty	EA	1,365.05	273.12	1,638.17	198.36	1,563.41	2.5027
11.2805 071	Add for electric driven medium duty	EA	1,311.51	273.12	1,584.63	198.36	1,509.87	2.5027
11.2805 081	T bar rigg, counter weight, 4 loft block, 55x35	SET	47,580.63		47,580.63		47,580.63	
11.2805 091	Rigg, wire guard, 4 loft block, 45x30	SET	41,633.09		41,633.09		41,633.09	
11.2805 101	T bar rigg, 4 loft block, caster mounted	SET	50,554.44		50,554.44		50,554.44	
11.2805 111	Add for electric control	LS	47,580.63		47,580.63		47,580.63	
11.2805 121	Curtain, fireproof, straight, lift, 23x47	LS	66,910.27		66,910.27		66,910.27	
11.2805 131	Curtain, trip, 23' x 47'	LS	63,936.50		63,936.50		63,936.50	
11.2805 141	Curtain, main, velour, heavy	SY	23.01		23.01		23.01	
11.2805 151	Curtain, main, velour, medium	SY	16.14		16.14		16.14	
11.2805 161	Curtain, light weight, cyclorama	SY	12.12		12.12		12.12	
11.2805 171	Drops, velour, heavy, 6' x 40'	EA	1,905.86		1,905.86		1,905.86	
11.2805 181	Drops, velour, medium, 6' x 40'	EA	1,784.25		1,784.25		1,784.25	
11.2805 191	Wings, velour, heavy, 10' x 30'	EA	1,338.15		1,338.15		1,338.15	
11.2805 201	Wings, velour, medium, 10' x 30'	EA	1,248.92		1,248.92		1,248.92	
11.2805 211	Scissors lift, 5'x10', 12' lift	SECTI	17,842.69		17,842.69		17,842.69	
11.2805 221	Scissors lift, 15'x40' with 15' lift	EA	187,107.58		187,107.58		187,107.58	
11.2806 000	**TELEVISION STUDIO LIGHTING, INCLUDING LAMPS:**							
11.2806 011	Studio, 8000 SF, very well equipped	PKG	581,427.44	15,688.18	597,115.62	11,394.16	592,821.60	143.7568
11.2806 021	Studio, 6, 60'x72', well equipped	PKG	137,698.66	4,392.67	142,091.33	3,190.35	140,889.01	40.2517
11.2806 031	Studio, medium equipment	PKG	107,065.85	3,137.68	110,203.53	2,278.87	109,344.72	28.7518
11.2806 041	Studios, 2, 20'x30', medium equipped	PKG	24,714.32	1,506.07	26,220.39	1,093.84	25,808.16	13.8007
11.2806 051	Studio, portable, minimum equipment, no control	PKG	3,866.19	627.50	4,493.69	455.75	4,321.94	5.7500
11.2901 000	**GARBAGE COMPACTORS:**							
11.2901 011	Garbage compactor, 1-1/2 CY	EA	13,901.31	1,102.79	15,004.10	691.36	14,592.67	9.3000
11.2901 021	Garbage compactor, 2 CY	EA	20,639.86	1,102.79	21,742.65	691.36	21,331.22	9.3000
11.2901 031	Garbage compactor, 2-1/2" CY	EA	25,322.60	1,323.35	26,645.95	829.63	26,152.23	11.1600
11.3000 000	**WINDOW WASHING EQUIPMENT, POWERED:**							
	Note: The following items constitute a spider staging system.							
11.3000 011	Rolling davit, tilting type	EACH	94,444.79		94,444.79		94,444.79	
11.3000 021	Trackage	LF	94.41		94.41		94.41	
11.3000 031	Rolling unit stepladder, 56' long	EA	94,444.79		94,444.79		94,444.79	
11.3000 041	Modulated platform	EA	66,111.34		66,111.34		66,111.34	
11.3000 051	Turntable	EA	7,555.59		7,555.59		7,555.59	

Division 11 CSI #	11 - EQUIPMENT Description	Unit	Material	Union Install	Union Total	Open Install	Open Total	Unit Man-Hrs
11.3000 000	**WINDOW WASHING EQUIPMENT, POWERED: (Cont.)**							
11.3000 061	Trollies	EA	5,666.68		5,666.68		5,666.68	
11.4001 000	**VOCATIONAL EQUIPMENT:**							
11.4001 011	Drill press, floor, 12", 1/2 hp	EA	1,068.13	183.85	1,251.98	134.28	1,202.41	1.9408
11.4001 021	Grinders, double wheel, 1 hp	EA	847.15	183.85	1,031.00	134.28	981.43	1.9408
11.4001 031	Jointer, 4", 1 hp	EA	2,646.23	183.85	2,830.08	134.28	2,780.51	1.9408
11.4001 041	Lathe, wood, 10", 1/2 hp	EA	1,020.18	183.85	1,204.03	134.28	1,154.46	1.9408
11.4001 051	Planer, 13"x6", 3/4 hp	EA	2,991.98	183.85	3,175.83	134.28	3,126.26	1.9408
11.4001 061	Band saw, woodcutting, 14", 3/4 hp	EA	1,683.98	183.85	1,867.83	134.28	1,818.26	1.9408
11.4001 071	Band saw, metal cutting, 14", 3/4 hp	EA	3,367.91	183.85	3,551.76	134.28	3,502.19	1.9408
11.4001 081	Radial arm saw, 10", 1-1/2 hp	EA	1,568.52	183.85	1,752.37	134.28	1,702.80	1.9408
11.4001 091	Scroll saw, 24", 1/2 hp	EA	2,405.66	183.85	2,589.51	134.28	2,539.94	1.9408
11.4001 101	Table saw, 10", 2 hp	EA	3,079.25	183.85	3,263.10	134.28	3,213.53	1.9408
11.4001 111	Potter's wheel, motorized	EA	1,213.18	183.85	1,397.03	134.28	1,347.46	1.9408
11.4001 121	Kiln, 16 CF to 2000 degrees	EA	3,813.41	183.85	3,997.26	134.28	3,947.69	1.9408

Division 12 CSI #	12 - FURNISHINGS Description	Unit	Material	Union Install	Union Total	Open Install	Open Total	Unit Man-Hrs
12.0000 000	**FURNISHINGS:**							
12.1101 000	**BLINDS & SHADES:**							
12.1101 011	Shades, standard roller	SF	2.50		2.50		2.50	
12.1101 021	Shades, extra quality	SF	2.74		2.74		2.74	
12.1101 031	Shades, decorator	SF	10.03		10.03		10.03	
12.1101 041	Blinds, horizontal	SF	5.72		5.72		5.72	
12.1101 051	Blinds, horizontal, mini	SF	7.19		7.19		7.19	
12.1101 061	Blinds, vertical, PVC	SF	6.88		6.88		6.88	
12.1101 071	Blinds, vertical, fabric	SF	9.17		9.17		9.17	
12.3000 000	**CABINETS & LAMINATED PLASTIC TOPS:**							
	Note: For plastic laminated cabinets, use the prices listed in section 12.3501.							
12.3001 000	**CABINETS, MULTI-UNIT, ECONOMY:**							
12.3001 011	Cabinets, hardwood, economy, base	LF	37.98	20.01	57.99	14.61	52.59	0.2112
12.3001 021	Cabinets, hardwood, economy, wall	LF	24.51	35.35	59.86	25.82	50.33	0.3732
12.3001 031	Cabinets, hardwood, economy, full height	LF	94.67	45.43	140.10	33.18	127.85	0.4796
12.3002 000	**CABINETS, HARDWOOD, CUSTOM:**							
12.3002 011	Cabinets, hardwood, custom, base	LF	54.66	20.01	74.67	14.61	69.27	0.2112
12.3002 021	Cabinets, hardwood, custom, wall	LF	39.61	35.35	74.96	25.82	65.43	0.3732
12.3002 031	Cabinets, hardwood, custom, full height	LF	95.70	45.43	141.13	33.18	128.88	0.4796
12.3003 000	**CABINETS, PREMIUM, INSTITUTIONAL:**							
12.3003 011	Cabinets, birch, premium, base	LF	109.65	39.20	148.85	28.63	138.28	0.4138
12.3003 021	Cabinets, birch, premium, wall	LF	92.01	68.76	160.77	50.22	142.23	0.7258
12.3003 031	Cabinets, birch, premium, full height	LF	155.54	49.49	205.03	36.14	191.68	0.5224
12.3004 000	**ADDERS FOR MILL MADE CABINETS:**							
	Note: For field finishing see section 09.0000.							
12.3004 011	Add for ash	LF	10.02		10.02		10.02	
12.3004 021	Add for walnut	LF	54.52		54.52		54.52	
12.3004 031	Add for overlay	LF	6.70		6.70		6.70	
12.3004 041	Add for flush overlay	LF	10.02		10.02		10.02	
12.3004 051	Add for edge banding	LF	6.70		6.70		6.70	
12.3004 061	Add for pre-finishing, exterior	LF	5.13		5.13		5.13	
12.3004 071	Add for pre-finishing, interior	LF	10.99		10.99		10.99	
12.3004 081	Add for standard hardware	LF	4.55		4.55		4.55	
12.3004 091	Add for institutional hardware	LF	6.70		6.70		6.70	
12.3004 101	Add for roller guides	SET	5.13		5.13		5.13	
12.3004 111	Add for roller guides, full suspension	SET	25.48		25.48		25.48	
12.3005 000	**CABINET UNITS, PREMIUM:**							
12.3005 011	Cabinet, open, with one shelf	LF	68.55		68.55		68.55	
12.3005 021	Cabinet, with door & one shelf	LF	84.98		84.98		84.98	
12.3005 031	Cabinet, door, 1 shelf & 1 drawer	LF	117.98		117.98		117.98	
12.3005 041	Cabinet, sink	LF	75.44		75.44		75.44	
12.3005 051	Cabinet, 4 drawers	LF	135.83		135.83		135.83	
12.3005 061	Add for apron (knee space)	LF	19.17		19.17		19.17	
12.3005 071	Add for backsplash	LF	10.99		10.99		10.99	
12.3006 000	**CABINETS, METAL, COMMERCIAL:**							
	Note: The following prices include hardware and plastic tops.							
12.3006 011	Cabinet, metal, base, with door, shelf	LF	108.97	20.86	129.83	15.24	124.21	0.2202
12.3006 021	Cabinet, metal, wall, with door, 2 shelves	LF	80.25	25.05	105.30	18.29	98.54	0.2644
12.3006 031	Cabinet, metal, full, with door, 5 shelves	LF	189.08	32.73	221.81	23.91	212.99	0.3455
12.3006 041	Cabinet, metal, library shelving	LF	70.18	18.30	88.48	13.37	83.55	0.1932
12.3006 051	Cabinet, metal, wardrobe, 4' wide	EA	458.67	55.27	513.94	40.37	499.04	0.5835
12.3007 000	**CABINETS, WOOD, FORMICA FACED, SCHOOL:**							
	Note: The following prices include hardware and plastic tops.							
12.3007 011	Cabinet, wood, base, with door, 1 shelf	LF	208.72	34.68	243.40	25.33	234.05	0.3661
12.3007 021	Cabinet, wood, wall, with door, 2 shelves	LF	151.56	41.64	193.20	30.42	181.98	0.4396
12.3007 031	Cabinet, wood, full, with doors	LF	247.70	42.85	290.55	31.29	278.99	0.4523
12.3007 041	Add for laboratory cabinets	LF	48.94	23.94	72.88	17.48	66.42	0.2527
12.3008 000	**CABINETS, WOOD & METAL, HOSPITAL:**							
	Note: The following prices include hardware and plastic tops.							
12.3008 011	Cabinet, wood & metal, with door, 1 shelf, 1 drawer	LF	158.26	70.17	228.43	51.25	209.51	0.7407
12.3008 021	Cabinet, wood & metal, wall, with door, 2 shelves	LF	92.75	46.75	139.50	34.15	126.90	0.4935
12.3008 031	Cabinet, wood & metal, full, with doors	LF	191.37	36.52	227.89	26.67	218.04	0.3855

Division 12 CSI #	12 - FURNISHINGS Description	Unit	Material	Union Install	Union Total	Open Install	Open Total	Unit Man-Hrs
12.3009 000	**CABINETS, FURNITURE GRADE, LABORATORY:**							
	Note: The following prices include hardware and plastic tops.							
12.3009 011	Cabinet, furniture, base, laboratory	LF	221.63	123.27	344.90	90.04	311.67	1.3013
12.3009 021	Cabinet, furniture, wall, laboratory	LF	105.58	59.54	165.12	43.49	149.07	0.6285
12.3009 031	Cabinet, furniture, wardrobe, laboratory	LF	237.04	51.01	288.05	37.26	274.30	0.5385
12.3009 041	Cabinet, furniture, laboratory island	LF	316.90	148.77	465.67	108.66	425.56	1.5705
12.3009 051	Cabinet, furniture, fume hood	LF	438.03	331.51	769.54	242.13	680.16	3.4995
12.3009 061	Cabinet, furniture, fume hood, stainless steel	LF	584.92	318.79	903.71	232.85	817.77	3.3653
12.3009 071	Add for premium quality	LF	25.23	22.95	48.18	16.76	41.99	0.2423
12.3500 000	**LAMINATED PLASTIC & SIMULATED MARBLE TOPS:**							
	Note: For ceramic tile tops see section 09.3001. For solid surface color, add 11% to the total costs.							
	For solid core color, add 25% to the total costs.							
12.3501 000	**LAMINATED PLASTIC & SIMULATED MARBLE TOPS:**							
12.3501 011	Laminated plastic top, multires	LF	32.03		32.03		32.03	
12.3501 021	Laminated plastic top, small projects	LF	36.99		36.99		36.99	
12.3501 031	Laminated plastic top, custom jobs	LF	49.38		49.38		49.38	
12.3501 041	Vanity top, cultured marble, no bowl	LF	44.21		44.21		44.21	
12.3501 051	Add to vanity for molded bowl	EA	40.99		40.99		40.99	
12.3501 061	Add to vanity, molded clam shell	EA	71.75		71.75		71.75	
12.3501 071	Acid proof tops	LF	99.18		99.18		99.18	
12.3501 081	Komar simulated marble, molded section	SF	18.51		18.51		18.51	
12.4000 000	**CARPETS:**							
12.4001 000	**CARPETS, WITH 50 OZ PAD:**							
12.4001 011	Carpet, 30 oz polyester, with pad	SY	24.26	10.08	34.34	8.41	32.67	0.1147
12.4001 021	Carpet, 35 oz polyester, with pad	SY	26.93	10.08	37.01	8.41	35.34	0.1147
12.4001 031	Carpet, 40 oz polyester, with pad	SY	28.70	10.08	38.78	8.41	37.11	0.1147
12.4001 041	Carpet, 50 oz polyester, with pad	SY	33.69	10.08	43.77	8.41	42.10	0.1147
12.4001 051	Carpet, 20 oz nylon shag, pad	SY	14.11	10.08	24.19	8.41	22.52	0.1147
12.4001 061	Carpet, 24 oz nylon shag, pad	SY	16.07	10.08	26.15	8.41	24.48	0.1147
12.4001 071	Carpet, 20 oz nylon filament, pad	SY	14.11	10.08	24.19	8.41	22.52	0.1147
12.4001 081	Carpet, 24 oz nylon filament, pad	SY	19.49	10.08	29.57	8.41	27.90	0.1147
12.4001 091	Carpet, 15 oz nylon level loop, rubber back	SY	16.07	8.64	24.71	7.21	23.28	0.0983
12.4001 101	Carpet, 21 oz nylon level loop, rubber back	SY	19.49	8.64	28.13	7.21	26.70	0.0983
12.4001 111	Carpet, 28 oz nylon level loop, rubber back	SY	26.59	8.64	35.23	7.21	33.80	0.0983
12.4001 121	Carpet, 15 oz nylon level loop, pad	SY	16.83	10.08	26.91	8.41	25.24	0.1147
12.4001 131	Carpet, 21 oz nylon level loop, pad	SY	20.45	10.08	30.53	8.41	28.86	0.1147
12.4001 141	Carpet, 28 oz nylon level loop, pad	SY	28.01	10.08	38.09	8.41	36.42	0.1147
12.4001 151	Carpet, 48 oz nylon level loop	SY	33.88	10.08	43.96	8.41	42.29	0.1147
12.4001 161	Carpet, 21 oz antron nylon, anti-static	SY	26.59	10.08	36.67	8.41	35.00	0.1147
12.4001 171	Carpet, wool commercial, pad, standard weight	SY	56.90	10.08	66.98	8.41	65.31	0.1147
12.4001 181	Carpet, exterior, premium, without pad	SY	26.26	11.54	37.80	9.62	35.88	0.1313
12.4002 000	**CARPET PADS:**							
12.4002 011	Carpet pad, 40 oz jute	SY	3.50	2.14	5.64	1.79	5.29	0.0244
12.4002 021	Carpet pad, 50 oz jute/hair	SY	4.92	2.14	7.06	1.79	6.71	0.0244
12.4002 031	Carpet pad, 50 oz hair	SY	6.18	2.14	8.32	1.79	7.97	0.0244
12.4002 041	Carpet pad, rubber waffle, 72 oz	SY	4.50	2.14	6.64	1.79	6.29	0.0244
12.4002 051	Carpet pad, rubber waffle, 100 oz	SY	8.51	2.14	10.65	1.79	10.30	0.0244
12.4002 061	Carpet pad, rubber slab, 72 oz	SY	5.68	2.14	7.82	1.79	7.47	0.0244
12.4002 071	Carpet pad, rubber slab, 88 oz	SY	8.51	2.14	10.65	1.79	10.30	0.0244
12.4002 081	Carpet pad, 15# urethane	SY	2.90	2.14	5.04	1.79	4.69	0.0244
12.4002 091	Carpet pad, 2# urethane	SY	4.68	2.14	6.82	1.79	6.47	0.0244
12.4002 101	Carpet pad, 25# urethane	SY	5.48	2.14	7.62	1.79	7.27	0.0244
12.4002 111	Carpet pad, urethane rebound	SY	5.99	2.14	8.13	1.79	7.78	0.0244
12.4003 000	**CARPET, AVERAGE ALLOWANCES:**							
12.4003 011	Carpet, average, housing	SY	21.68		21.68		21.68	
12.4003 021	Carpet, average, commercial	SY	30.70		30.70		30.70	
12.4003 031	Carpet, average, school	SY	33.46		33.46		33.46	
12.4003 041	Carpet, average, hotel/motel, theater	SY	36.28		36.28		36.28	
12.4003 051	Carpet, average, custom housing	SY	53.03		53.03		53.03	
12.4004 000	**FLOOR MATS:**							
12.4004 011	Floor mat, rubber, 1/4", recessed	SF	6.98	3.01	9.99	2.41	9.39	0.0399
12.4004 021	Floor mat, rubber, 1/2", recessed	SF	11.03	3.79	14.82	3.03	14.06	0.0502

Division 12 CSI #	12 - FURNISHINGS Description	Unit	Material	Union Install	Union Total	Open Install	Open Total	Unit Man-Hrs
12.4004 000	**FLOOR MATS: (Cont.)**							
12.4004 031	Floor mat, vinyl, 1/4", recessed	SF	10.26	3.01	13.27	2.41	12.67	0.0399
12.4004 041	Floor mat, vinyl, 1/2", recessed	SF	13.59	3.79	17.38	3.03	16.62	0.0502
12.4004 051	Pedimat with serrated filler	SF	70.83	5.90	76.73	4.72	75.55	0.0781
12.5001 000	**DRAPERIES & CURTAINS:**							
	Note: The prices in the following items are based on the measurement of window glass only.							
	Allowances have already been made for overlap and pleating.							
12.5001 011	Curtain, lead mesh (soundproof)	SY	54.13		54.13		54.13	
12.5001 021	Curtain, lead mesh, 25#/SF, x-ray	SY	61.85		61.85		61.85	
12.5001 031	Draperies, window, multires	LF	23.12		23.12		23.12	
12.5001 041	Draperies, sliding door	LF	23.12		23.12		23.12	
12.5001 051	Draperies, window, custom residential	LF	61.85		61.85		61.85	
12.5001 061	Draperies, sliding door, custom	LF	50.26		50.26		50.26	
12.5001 071	Draperies, lining	LF	3.84		3.84		3.84	
12.5001 081	Draperies, fiberglass	LF	61.08		61.08		61.08	
12.5001 091	Draperies, filter light control	LF	55.18		55.18		55.18	
12.5001 101	Draperies, flameproof	LF	59.27		59.27		59.27	
12.5001 111	Draperies, velour grand	LF	64.44		64.44		64.44	
12.5001 121	Blinds, vertical	SF	5.54		5.54		5.54	
12.8000 000	**OFFICE LANDSCAPE, FURNITURE BY STATION:**							
	Note: The following prices are based on quantities of 100 or more stations.							
12.8001 000	**OFFICE LANDSCAPE, FURNITURE BY STATION:**							
	Note: The following workstations include:							
	Reception:. . . . . horseshoe counter and secretarial chair.							
	Secretarial:. . . . . desk with return and secretarial chair.							
	Engineering:. . . . . desk, chair, drafting table and 35" x 80" partition with shelving.							
	Managerial:. . . desk, 3 chairs, table, 70" x 80" partition with shelving, and file storage.							
	Executive:. . . . . desk, 5 chairs, table and work table with over/under storage.							
12.8001 011	Furniture, reception station, good	EA	2,796.86		2,796.86		2,796.86	
12.8001 021	Furniture, reception station, better	EA	5,585.88		5,585.88		5,585.88	
12.8001 031	Furniture, reception station, best	EA	13,504.22		13,504.22		13,504.22	
12.8001 051	Furniture, secretarial station, good	EA	746.74		746.74		746.74	
12.8001 061	Furniture, secretarial station, better	EA	1,940.35		1,940.35		1,940.35	
12.8001 071	Furniture, secretarial station, best	EA	4,566.73		4,566.73		4,566.73	
12.8001 101	Furniture, engineering station, good	EA	5,389.90		5,389.90		5,389.90	
12.8001 111	Furniture, engineering station, better	EA	7,155.89		7,155.89		7,155.89	
12.8001 121	Furniture, engineering station, best	EA	8,482.75		8,482.75		8,482.75	
12.8001 151	Furniture, managerial station, good	EA	5,086.14		5,086.14		5,086.14	
12.8001 161	Furniture, managerial station, better	EA	6,509.06		6,509.06		6,509.06	
12.8001 171	Furniture, managerial station, best	EA	10,113.48		10,113.48		10,113.48	
12.8001 201	Furniture, executive station, good	EA	4,057.15		4,057.15		4,057.15	
12.8001 211	Furniture, executive station, better	EA	7,055.87		7,055.87		7,055.87	
12.8001 221	Furniture, executive station, best	EA	11,818.62		11,818.62		11,818.62	
12.8002 000	**ADDERS & DEDUCTORS FOR OFFICE LANDSCAPE:**							
12.8002 011	Partitioning, 5'6" high, good	LF	172.48		172.48		172.48	
12.8002 021	Partitioning system, work surface, good	STA	2,765.70		2,765.70		2,765.70	
12.8002 031	Desk, good	EA	403.75		403.75		403.75	
12.8002 041	Desk, better	EA	1,170.11		1,170.11		1,170.11	
12.8002 051	Desk, best	EA	2,822.38		2,822.38		2,822.38	
12.8002 061	Add for task light per SF cover	SF	93.35		93.35		93.35	
12.8002 071	Secretarial desk with return, good	EA	605.65		605.65		605.65	
12.8002 081	Secretarial desk with return, better	EA	1,615.04		1,615.04		1,615.04	
12.8002 091	Secretarial desk with return, best	EA	4,037.53		4,037.53		4,037.53	
12.8002 101	Drafting table, good	EA	646.80		646.80		646.80	
12.8002 111	Drafting table, better	EA	1,150.49		1,150.49		1,150.49	
12.8002 121	Drafting table, best	EA	1,393.06		1,393.06		1,393.06	
12.8002 131	Desk chair, good	EA	467.58		467.58		467.58	
12.8002 141	Desk chair, better	EA	815.52		815.52		815.52	
12.8002 151	Desk chair, best	EA	1,400.88		1,400.88		1,400.88	
12.8002 161	Secretarial chair, good	EA	232.00		232.00		232.00	
12.8002 171	Secretarial chair, better	EA	467.58		467.58		467.58	
12.8002 181	Secretarial chair, best	EA	815.52		815.52		815.52	

Division 12 CSI #	12 - FURNISHINGS Description	Unit	Material	Union Install	Union Total	Open Install	Open Total	Unit Man-Hrs
12.8002 000	**ADDERS & DEDUCTORS FOR OFFICE LANDSCAPE: (Cont.)**							
12.8002 191	Drafting stool, good	EA	182.23		182.23		182.23	
12.8002 201	Drafting stool, better	EA	362.59		362.59		362.59	
12.8002 211	Drafting stool, best	EA	605.65		605.65		605.65	
12.8002 221	Side chair, good	EA	161.69		161.69		161.69	
12.8002 231	Side chair, better	EA	301.85		301.85		301.85	
12.8002 241	Side chair, best	EA	523.29		523.29		523.29	
12.8002 251	Credenza, 60" long, good	EA	460.59		460.59		460.59	
12.8002 261	Credenza, 60" long, better	EA	1,250.47		1,250.47		1,250.47	
12.8002 271	Credenza, 60" long, best	EA	2,220.64		2,220.64		2,220.64	
12.8002 281	Bookcase, 72" high, 36" wide, good	EA	221.47		221.47		221.47	
12.8002 291	Bookcase, 72" high, 36" wide, better	EA	382.18		382.18		382.18	
12.8002 301	Bookcase, 72" high, 36" wide, best	EA	554.66		554.66		554.66	
12.8002 311	File cabinet, 4 drawer, good	EA	201.88		201.88		201.88	
12.8002 321	File cabinet, 4 drawer, better	EA	262.65		262.65		262.65	
12.8002 331	File cabinet, 4 drawer, best	EA	403.75		403.75		403.75	
12.8002 341	Conference table, 8', good	EA	484.08		484.08		484.08	
12.8002 351	Conference table, 8', better	EA	1,714.97		1,714.97		1,714.97	
12.8002 361	Conference table, 8', best	EA	4,037.53		4,037.53		4,037.53	
12.8002 371	Conference chair, good	EA	182.23		182.23		182.23	
12.8002 381	Conference chair, better	EA	382.18		382.18		382.18	
12.8002 391	Conference chair, best	EA	607.60		607.60		607.60	

Division 13 CSI #	13 - SPECIAL CONSTRUCTION Description	Unit	Material	Union Install	Union Total	Open Install	Open Total	Unit Man-Hrs
13.0000 000	**SPECIAL CONSTRUCTION:**							
13.1001 000	**AUDIOMETRIC ROOMS:**							
13.1001 011	Audiometric rooms, 500 SF & over	SFSA	52.35	16.89	69.24	12.34	64.69	0.1783
13.1001 021	Audiometric masking system, 5000 SF	SFSA	1.76	.58	2.34	.42	2.18	0.0061
13.1002 000	**BOWLING ALLEYS:**							
13.1002 011	Bowling lanes, complete, auto	LANE	64,137.51		64,137.51		64,137.51	
13.1002 021	Automatic scorer, 4 lane	EA	40,066.71		40,066.71		40,066.71	
13.1003 000	**BROADCASTING STUDIOS:**							
13.1003 011	Sound wall, 4" short wall, record	SFSA	48.90	14.43	63.33	10.54	59.44	0.1523
13.1003 021	Sound wall, 4" wall, echo chamber	SFSA	33.59	12.03	45.62	8.79	42.38	0.1270
13.1004 000	**INSULATED ROOMS:**							
	Note: The floating floor item listed below includes jack-up neoprene mounts, 3/4" perimeter board, 6 ml polyethylene, raising floors to operating position and grouting jack-screw holes flush. Concrete, repair & caulking are not included.							
13.1004 011	Blast absorption chamber, 4" perforated metal	SF	61.61		61.61		61.61	
13.1004 021	Sound deadening enclosure, 4"	SF	41.07		41.07		41.07	
13.1004 031	Floating floor sound isolate system	SF	6.46	6.10	12.56	4.46	10.92	0.0644
13.1005 000	**GREENHOUSES:**							
	Note: The following items are 500 sf or less, foundations & stubwalls not included.							
13.1005 011	Greenhouses, to 1000 SF	SF	34.72		34.72		34.72	
13.1005 021	Greenhouses, to 4000 SF	SF	25.89		25.89		25.89	
13.1005 031	Greenhouse, to 10,000 SF	SF	22.59		22.59		22.59	
13.1006 000	**INCINERATORS:**							
13.1006 011	Incinerator, 50#/hour, no scrubber	EA	16,503.20		16,503.20		16,503.20	
13.1006 021	Incinerator, 100#/hour, no scrubber	EA	20,629.01		20,629.01		20,629.01	
13.1006 031	Incinerator, 200#/hour, no scrubber	EA	23,802.72		23,802.72		23,802.72	
13.1006 041	Incinerator, 500#/hour, no scrubber	EA	49,192.33		49,192.33		49,192.33	
13.1006 051	Incinerator, 1000#/hour, no scrubber	EA	63,473.95		63,473.95		63,473.95	
13.1007 000	**INTEGRATED CEILINGS:**							
13.1007 011	Suspended ceiling, T bar, 100 foot candles	SF	16.90		16.90		16.90	
13.1007 021	Suspended ceiling, T bar, 85 foot candles	SF	16.10		16.10		16.10	
13.1007 031	Suspended ceiling, T bar, 70 foot candles	SF	15.27		15.27		15.27	
13.1007 041	Suspended ceiling, T bar, 55 foot candles	SF	13.62		13.62		13.62	
13.1007 051	T bar ceiling, 80% plastic, 100 foot candles	SF	20.62		20.62		20.62	
13.1007 061	T bar ceiling, 70% plastic, 85 foot candles	SF	19.14		19.14		19.14	
13.1007 071	T bar ceiling, 60% plastic, 70 foot candles	SF	18.32		18.32		18.32	
13.1007 081	T bar ceiling, 50% plastic, 55 foot candles	SF	16.87		16.87		16.87	
13.1008 000	**PEDESTAL FLOORS:**							
13.1008 011	Pedestal floor, vinyl tile, gridless	SF	19.95		19.95		19.95	
13.1008 021	Pedestal floor, vinyl tile, grid	SF	23.95		23.95		23.95	
13.1008 031	Pedestal floor, perma kleen, grid	SF	26.10		26.10		26.10	
13.1008 041	Pedestal floor, carpeted system	SF	26.95		26.95		26.95	
13.1008 051	Pedestal floor, ramps	SF	28.47		28.47		28.47	
13.1008 061	Add for cutouts	EA	226.05		226.05		226.05	
13.1008 071	Add for floor grills	EA	100.51		100.51		100.51	
13.1008 081	Add for seismic bracing	SF	.06		.06		.06	
13.1008 091	Add for sheet metal trim & casing	LF	111.55		111.55		111.55	
13.1008 101	Add for CO2 fire system (smoke detector)	SF	6.39		6.39		6.39	
13.1008 111	Add for automatic fire alarm	SF	.42		.42		.42	
13.1100 000	**PREFABRICATED STRUCTURES:**							
	Note: See also section 05.1108.							
13.1101 000	**PREFABRICATED WALL PANELS:**							
13.1101 011	Prefab wall panel, 84" high	LF	73.76	17.62	91.38	12.87	86.63	0.1860
13.1101 021	Prefab wall panel, 96" high	LF	82.78	18.50	101.28	13.51	96.29	0.1953
13.1101 031	Prefab wall panel, 108" high	LF	91.79	19.38	111.17	14.16	105.95	0.2046
13.1101 041	Prefab wall panel, 120" high	LF	101.38	20.26	121.64	14.80	116.18	0.2139
13.1101 051	Prefab wall panel, 132" high	LF	112.16	21.14	133.30	15.44	127.60	0.2232
13.1101 061	Prefab wall panel, 144" high	LF	120.01	22.02	142.03	16.09	136.10	0.2325
13.1102 000	**PREFABRICATED STRUCTURES, CORNER POSTS:**							
13.1102 011	Prefab, corner posts, 96" high	EA	57.58	17.62	75.20	12.87	70.45	0.1860
13.1102 021	Prefab, corner posts, 108" high	EA	70.78	17.62	88.40	12.87	83.65	0.1860
13.1102 031	Prefab, corner posts, 120" high	EA	84.00	17.62	101.62	12.87	96.87	0.1860

Division 13 CSI #	13 - SPECIAL CONSTRUCTION Description	Unit	Material	Union Install	Union Total	Open Install	Open Total	Unit Man-Hrs
13.1102 000	**PREFABRICATED STRUCTURES, CORNER POSTS: (Cont.)**							
13.1102 041	Prefab, corner posts, 132" high	EA	97.16	17.62	114.78	12.87	110.03	0.1860
13.1102 051	Prefab, corner posts, 144" high	EA	110.36	17.62	127.98	12.87	123.23	0.1860
13.1103 000	**PREFABRICATED STRUCTURES, WALL STARTS:**							
13.1103 011	Prefab, wall starts, 96" high	EA	28.78		28.78		28.78	
13.1103 021	Prefab, wall starts, 108" high	EA	32.37		32.37		32.37	
13.1103 031	Prefab, wall starts, 120" high	EA	35.97		35.97		35.97	
13.1103 041	Prefab, wall starts, 132" high	EA	39.59		39.59		39.59	
13.1103 051	Prefab, wall starts, 144" high	EA	43.15		43.15		43.15	
13.1104 000	**PREFABRICATED STRUCTURES, DOORS & WINDOWS:**							
13.1104 011	Prefab, door with threshold	EA	456.07		456.07		456.07	
13.1104 021	Prefab, door closer	EA	143.98		143.98		143.98	
13.1104 031	Door lites, 20x30, 1/8" tempered, fixed	EA	76.77		76.77		76.77	
13.1104 041	Prefab, lock sets	EA	35.97		35.97		35.97	
13.1104 051	Prefab, window 3'-4' fixed lite, 1/8" tempered	EA	191.94		191.94		191.94	
13.1104 061	Prefab, window 3-4' side slide & 1 hung, 1/8"	EA	300.00		300.00		300.00	
13.1104 071	Prefab, window 2' fixed lites, 1/8" tempered	EA	143.98		143.98		143.98	
13.1105 000	**PREFABRICATED STRUCTURES, ROOF PANELS:**							
13.1105 011	Prefab, roof panel	SF	11.83		11.83		11.83	
13.1105 021	Prefab, roof fascia	LF	2.95		2.95		2.95	
13.1105 031	Prefab, ridge beam	LF	14.31		14.31		14.31	
13.1105 041	Angle to attach to each wall	LF	7.16		7.16		7.16	
13.1106 000	**PREFABRICATED STRUCTURES, ELECTRICAL:**							
13.1106 011	Prefab, switch or duplex outlet	EA	35.97		35.97		35.97	
13.1106 021	Prefab, floor fixture, #4 tube	EA	124.80		124.80		124.80	
13.1106 031	Prefab, balance stems, 2 fixture	SET	35.97		35.97		35.97	
13.1106 041	Prefab, circuit breaker, 4 circuit	EA	71.98		71.98		71.98	
13.1106 051	Prefab, circuit breaker, 6 circuit	EA	96.01		96.01		96.01	
13.1106 061	Prefab, circuit breaker, 8 circuit	EA	139.16		139.16		139.16	
13.1106 071	Prefab, circuit breaker, 10 circuit	EA	211.18		211.18		211.18	
13.1107 000	**PREFABRICATED STRUCTURES, HVAC:**							
13.1107 011	Prefab HVAC, heater, 100 watt, baseboard	EA	107.99		107.99		107.99	
13.1107 021	Thermostat for above	EA	45.58		45.58		45.58	
13.1107 031	Prefab HVAC, heater, 3200-5600w, 220v, fan force	EA	384.06		384.06		384.06	
13.1107 041	Prefab, fan, exhaust, 160 CFM	EA	172.76		172.76		172.76	
13.1107 051	Prefab, fan, exhaust, 350 CFM	EA	302.41		302.41		302.41	
13.1107 061	Prefab, air conditioner, panel prepared	EA	71.98		71.98		71.98	
13.1107 071	Caulking, silicone, per tube	EA	11.98		11.98		11.98	
13.1108 000	**PREFABRICATED STRUCTURES, COMPLETE, IN-PLACE:**							
13.1108 011	Prefab, in place, 64-144 SF	SF	93.70		93.70		93.70	
13.1108 021	Prefab, in place, 145-288 SF	SF	52.60		52.60		52.60	
13.1108 031	Prefab, in place, 289-576 SF	SF	50.38		50.38		50.38	
13.1108 041	Prefab, in place, 577-1132 SF	SF	49.15		49.15		49.15	
13.1108 051	Prefab, in place, 1133-2264 SF	SF	48.59		48.59		48.59	
13.1201 000	**RADIATION PROTECTION:**							
13.1201 011	Lead lined lath, 2#	SF	9.04		9.04		9.04	
13.1201 021	Lead lined lath, 4#	SF	13.38		13.38		13.38	
13.1201 031	Lead lined lath, 6#	SF	16.02		16.02		16.02	
13.1201 041	Lead lined lath, 8#	SF	20.64		20.64		20.64	
13.1201 051	Lead glass windows with lead frames	SF	335.87		335.87		335.87	
13.1201 061	Lead lined door, to 4#	SF	34.99		34.99		34.99	
13.1201 071	Lead lined door frames	EA	457.86		457.86		457.86	
13.1201 081	Lead lined window frame	SF	58.33		58.33		58.33	
13.1201 111	Lead lined gypsum wall board, 2#	SF	5.68		5.68		5.68	
13.1201 121	Lead lined gypsum wall board, 2-1/2#	SF	6.35		6.35		6.35	
13.1201 131	Lead lined gypsum wall board, 4#	SF	12.20		12.20		12.20	
13.1201 141	Add for second layer lead lining, 2#	SF	4.42		4.42		4.42	
13.1201 151	Add for corner angle, 2" x 2", 8'	LF	28.00		28.00		28.00	
13.1202 000	**CHIMNEY, INSULATING REFRACTORY, NO FOUNDATIONS:**							
	Note: The following item includes 28 ga aluminized steel jacket, floor support, tee, clean out, straight sections and spark screen. It is 24" deep with a 30' stack.							
13.1202 011	Chimney, insulated 1800 - 2000 degrees F	LF	359.83		359.83		359.83	

Division 13 CSI #	13 - SPECIAL CONSTRUCTION Description	Unit	Material	Union Install	Union Total	Open Install	Open Total	Unit Man-Hrs
13.1203 000	**SWIMMING POOLS:**							
	Note: The following items include filters, chlorinators, heaters, and gunite or concrete. Gunite is listed separately in section 03.8001. For plaster see section 09.1400. Pool deck or flatwork is not included.							
13.1203 011	Pool, residential	SF	65.04		65.04		65.04	
13.1203 021	Pool, multiple residence	SF	73.45		73.45		73.45	
13.1203 031	Pool, community	SF	78.44		78.44		78.44	
13.1203 041	Pool, hotel, resort	SF	84.55		84.55		84.55	
13.1203 051	Pool, school, 42' x 75'	SF	86.63		86.63		86.63	
13.1203 061	Pool, school, 42' x 165'	SF	89.95		89.95		89.95	
13.1203 071	Pool, school, 30' x 30'	SF	93.75		93.75		93.75	
13.1203 081	Pool deck concrete	SF	7.01		7.01		7.01	
13.1203 091	Pool cool deck	SF	10.28		10.28		10.28	
13.1204 000	**SPA:**							
13.1204 011	Spa with pool, 4' diameter	EA	10,387.86		10,387.86		10,387.86	
13.1204 021	Spa, recreational, 8' diameter	EA	24,930.81		24,930.81		24,930.81	
13.1205 000	**DOMES, IN PLACE:**							
	Note: The following prices are for net area covered, including roofing.							
13.1205 011	Dome, corrugated metal, belem truss	SF	24.35		24.35		24.35	
13.1205 021	Dome, steel deck, cable suspended	SF	30.05		30.05		30.05	
13.1205 031	Dome, fabric cover, cable suspended	SF	34.30		34.30		34.30	
13.1205 041	Dome, air floated fabric cover, cable suspended	SF	27.77		27.77		27.77	
13.1205 051	Dome, fink, steel, corrugated cover	SF	30.05		30.05		30.05	
13.1205 061	Dome, aluminum, geodesic	SF	37.94		37.94		37.94	
13.1205 071	Dome, glu-lams, decking, ribbed	SF	26.95		26.95		26.95	
13.1205 081	Dome, glu-lam, decking, tridesic	SF	30.37		30.37		30.37	
13.1205 091	Dome, thin-shell concrete, hyperbolic paraboloid	SF	36.78		36.78		36.78	
13.1205 101	Dome, steel rib frame, skylight cover	SF	55.49		55.49		55.49	
13.1205 111	Dome, steel rib frame, skylight, partial opening	SF	110.96		110.96		110.96	
13.1205 121	Dome, aluminum skin, revolve, 10-40' base	SF	229.21		229.21		229.21	
13.1206 000	**AIR STRUCTURE, FABRIC COMPLETE:**							
13.1206 011	Foundation and floor concrete	SF	3.29	4.12	7.41	2.71	6.00	0.0491
13.1206 021	Fabric structure, 3,000 SF, inflated	SF	17.67	.40	18.07	.26	17.93	0.0048
13.1206 031	Fabric structure, 5,000 SF, inflated	SF	15.53	.40	15.93	.26	15.79	0.0048
13.1206 041	Fabric structure, 10,000 SF, inflated	SF	13.47	.40	13.87	.26	13.73	0.0048
13.1206 051	Air curtain, doorway, 3' x 8'	EA	1,059.55	632.18	1,691.73	387.42	1,446.97	8.0410
13.1206 061	Air curtain, doorway, 5' x 10'	EA	1,558.18	948.28	2,506.46	581.12	2,139.30	12.0615
13.1207 000	**BULLET RESISTANT CONSTRUCTION:**							
	Note: Fiberglass matting is usually built into regular stud walls. See Division 9, for other wall components.							
13.1207 011	Bullet resistant fiberglass matting	SF	30.77	3.61	34.38	2.64	33.41	0.0381
13.1207 021	Bullet resistant service window, voice	EA	2,753.95	153.94	2,907.89	112.43	2,866.38	1.6250
13.1207 031	Bullet resistant service window, speaker	EA	3,689.95	177.62	3,867.57	129.73	3,819.68	1.8750

Division 14 CSI #	14 - CONVEYING SYSTEMS Description	Unit	Material	Union Install	Union Total	Open Install	Open Total	Unit Man-Hrs
14.0000 000	**CONVEYING SYSTEMS:**							
14.1001 000	**DUMBWAITER, TRAY, FOOD OR RECORD:**							
14.1001 011	Dumbwaiter, 2 station, manual, 200#, 24x24x36	EA	9,964.01		9,964.01		9,964.01	
14.1001 021	Add for additional stop	STOP	1,706.65		1,706.65		1,706.65	
14.1001 031	Dumbwaiter, 2 station, electric, 300#, 30x30x36	EA	24,784.56		24,784.56		24,784.56	
14.1001 041	Add for additional stop	STOP	3,438.37		3,438.37		3,438.37	
14.1002 000	**DUMBWAITER, CART, FLOOR LEVEL, ELECTRIC:**							
14.1002 011	Dumbwaiter, 2 station, electric, 500#, 23x56x48	EA	51,991.11		51,991.11		51,991.11	
14.1002 021	Add for additional stop	STOP	4,128.64		4,128.64		4,128.64	
14.1003 000	**ELEVATOR, HOMELIFT, 450#:**							
14.1003 011	Elevator, 450#, 2 stop	EA	21,421.37		21,421.37		21,421.37	
14.1003 021	Elevator, 450#, 3 stop	EA	23,943.75		23,943.75		23,943.75	
14.1003 031	Chairlift	FLOOR	10,164.78		10,164.78		10,164.78	
14.1005 000	**ELEVATOR, HYDRAULIC, 125'/MIN, 2000#, 5'X6' CAB, AUTO EXIT:**							
	Note: For 3 stops or more, elevator must be at least 2500# capacity with a platform at least 7' x 5'.							
14.1005 011	Elevator, 2000#, 2 stop	EA	68,584.65		68,584.65		68,584.65	
14.1005 021	Elevator, 2000#, 4 stop	EA	89,554.62		89,554.62		89,554.62	
14.1005 031	Elevator, 2000#, 5 stop	EA	103,260.08		103,260.08		103,260.08	
14.1005 041	Add for additional stop	STOP	13,893.15		13,893.15		13,893.15	
14.1005 051	Add for premium 2 stop basic	EA	57,726.12		57,726.12		57,726.12	
14.1006 000	**ELEVATOR, HYDRAULIC, 126'/MIN, 2500#, 7' X 5' CAB:**							
14.1006 011	Elevator, 2500#, 2 stop	EA	70,577.94		70,577.94		70,577.94	
14.1006 021	Elevator, 2500#, 3 stop	EA	81,348.30		81,348.30		81,348.30	
14.1006 031	Elevator, 2500#, 4 stop	EA	92,156.66		92,156.66		92,156.66	
14.1006 041	Elevator, 2500#, 5 stop	EA	106,266.57		106,266.57		106,266.57	
14.1006 051	Add for each additional stop	EA	14,296.33		14,296.33		14,296.33	
14.1006 061	Add for premium 2 stop basic	EA	59,408.04		59,408.04		59,408.04	
14.1007 000	**ELEVATOR, HYDRAULIC, 125'-150'/MIN, 4000#, 8'X 6' CAB:**							
14.1007 011	Elevator, 4000#, 3 stop	EA	95,144.21		95,144.21		95,144.21	
14.1008 000	**ELEVATOR, HYDRAULIC, 100'/MIN, 20, 000#, 10X16 CAB, AUTO EXIT:**							
14.1008 011	Elevator, 20,000#, 3 stop	EA	180,774.01		180,774.01		180,774.01	
14.1008 021	Elevator, 20,000#, 4 stop	EA	199,802.84		199,802.84		199,802.84	
14.1009 000	**ELEVATOR, GEAR, 350'/MIN, 3500#, 5' X 8' CAB:**							
14.1009 011	Elevator, 3500#, 10 stop	EA	236,960.43		236,960.43		236,960.43	
14.1009 021	Elevator, 3500#, 15 stop	EA	282,529.76		282,529.76		282,529.76	
14.1009 031	Add for additional stop	STOP	9,113.86		9,113.86		9,113.86	
14.1010 000	**ELEVATOR, GEAR, 350'/MIN, 4000#, 8'X 6' CAB:**							
14.1010 011	Elevator, 4000#, 5 stop	EA	304,461.46		304,461.46		304,461.46	
14.1011 000	**ELEVATOR, GEAR, 200'/MIN, 4000#, 6'X 8' CAB:**							
14.1011 011	Elevator, 4000#, 3 stop	EA	266,403.76		266,403.76		266,403.76	
14.1012 000	**ELEVATOR, GEAR, 350'/MIN, 4500#, 6' X 9' CAB:**							
14.1012 011	Elevator, 4500#, 10 stop	EA	271,357.92		271,357.92		271,357.92	
14.1012 021	Elevator, 4500#, 15 stop	EA	333,979.01		333,979.01		333,979.01	
14.1012 031	Add for additional stop	STOP	13,567.87		13,567.87		13,567.87	
14.1013 000	**ELEVATOR, GEAR, 100'/MIN, 8' X 10' CAB:**							
14.1013 011	Elevator, 6000#, 3 stop	EA	285,432.61		285,432.61		285,432.61	
14.1014 000	**ELEVATOR, GEARLESS, 500'/MIN, 3500#, 6' X 9' CAB:**							
14.1014 011	Elevator, gearless, 3500#, 10 stop	EA	333,248.38		333,248.38		333,248.38	
14.1014 021	Elevator, gearless, 3500#, 15 stop	EA	397,748.12		397,748.12		397,748.12	
14.1014 031	Add for additional stop	STOP	16,124.89		16,124.89		16,124.89	
14.1015 000	**ELEVATOR, GEARLESS, 700'/MIN, 4500#, 6' X 9' CAB:**							
14.1015 011	Elevator, gearless, 4500#, 10 stop	EA	354,651.40		354,651.40		354,651.40	
14.1015 021	Elevator, gearless, 4500#, 15 stop	EA	409,660.82		409,660.82		409,660.82	
14.1015 031	Elevator, gearless, 4500#, 20 stop	EA	464,670.31		464,670.31		464,670.31	
14.1015 041	Add for additional stop	STOP	11,264.71		11,264.71		11,264.71	
14.1016 000	**ELEVATOR, GEARLESS, 1200'/MIN, 4500#, 6'X9' CAB:**							
14.1016 011	Elevator, gearless, 4500#, 20 stop	EA	661,735.00		661,735.00		661,735.00	
14.1016 021	Add for additional stop	STOP	12,465.07		12,465.07		12,465.07	
14.1017 000	**ELEVATOR, GEAR, FREIGHT, 100'/MIN, 4500#, MANUAL DOOR:**							
14.1017 011	Elevator, freight, 2 stop	EA	140,809.16		140,809.16		140,809.16	
14.1017 021	Add for additional stop	STOP	12,109.54		12,109.54		12,109.54	
14.1017 031	Elevator, sidewalk, 2500#, 2 stop	EA	56,094.69		56,094.69		56,094.69	

Division 14 CSI #	14 - CONVEYING SYSTEMS Description	Unit	Material	Union Install	Union Total	Open Install	Open Total	Unit Man-Hrs
14.1018 000	**ELEVATOR CAB, INCLUDED WITH ABOVE PASSENGER ELEVATOR:**							
14.1018 011	Elevator cab, hydraulic, 4' x 5'	CAR	6,571.05		6,571.05		6,571.05	
14.1018 021	Elevator cab, hydraulic, 5' x 6'	CAR	7,697.58		7,697.58		7,697.58	
14.1018 031	Elevator cab, geared, 5' x 8'	CAR	8,636.29		8,636.29		8,636.29	
14.1018 041	Elevator cab, geared, 6' x 9'	CAR	12,203.45		12,203.45		12,203.45	
14.1018 051	Elevator cab, gearless, 6' x 9'	CAR	12,203.45		12,203.45		12,203.45	
14.1018 061	Add for glass finish	EA	38,057.69		38,057.69		38,057.69	
14.1018 071	Add for stainless steel finish	EA	14,271.59		14,271.59		14,271.59	
14.1018 081	Add for grouting sills	STOP	576.43		576.43		576.43	
14.1019 000	**INCLINE ELEVATORS:**							
14.1019 011	Incline elevator, 3 stop, 100 fpm	EA	30,564.94		30,564.94		30,564.94	
14.1019 021	Add for additional stops	EA	15,826.92		15,826.92		15,826.92	
14.1019 031	Incline elevator, 5 stop, 250 fpm	EA	430,876.08		430,876.08		430,876.08	
14.1019 041	Add for additional stops	EA	19,243.95		19,243.95		19,243.95	
14.1020 000	**ESCALATORS:**							
	Note: The following prices are based on 12' floor to floor height.							
14.1020 011	Escalator, 24"	FLOOR	162,510.96		162,510.96		162,510.96	
14.1020 021	Escalator, 32"	FLOOR	165,539.13		165,539.13		165,539.13	
14.1020 031	Escalator, 36"	FLOOR	169,782.42		169,782.42		169,782.42	
14.1020 041	Escalator, 40"	FLOOR	170,296.93		170,296.93		170,296.93	
14.1020 051	Escalator, 44"	FLOOR	174,065.02		174,065.02		174,065.02	
14.1020 061	Escalator, 48"	FLOOR	181,444.29		181,444.29		181,444.29	
14.1020 081	Add for baked enamel sides	FLOOR	6,761.89		6,761.89		6,761.89	
14.1020 091	Add for glass sides	FLOOR	6,964.73		6,964.73		6,964.73	
14.1020 101	Add for stainless steel sides	FLOOR	9,286.35		9,286.35		9,286.35	
14.1021 000	**AIR HOIST:**							
14.1021 011	Air hoist, 2000#, 30' lift, rail	EA	10,084.32	719.11	10,803.43	538.49	10,622.81	8.0204
14.1021 021	Air hoist, 4000#, 30' lift, rail	EA	10,980.63	719.11	11,699.74	538.49	11,519.12	8.0204
14.1022 000	**ELECTRIC HOIST:**							
14.1022 011	Electric hoist, 1000#, 30' lift, rail	EA	6,562.77	719.11	7,281.88	538.49	7,101.26	8.0204
14.1022 021	Electric hoist, 500#, 30' lift, rail	EA	5,698.41	719.11	6,417.52	538.49	6,236.90	8.0204
14.1023 000	**CRANES:**							
14.1023 011	Crane, hydraulic, 2000#, portable	EA	3,594.45		3,594.45		3,594.45	
14.1023 021	Crane, gantry, 4000#, 10-20' range	EA	3,735.86		3,735.86		3,735.86	
14.1024 000	**CRANE, MONORAIL, OVERHEAD:**							
14.1024 011	Crane, monorail, 200#/LF, manual, channel	LF	26.58	28.25	54.83	21.16	47.74	0.3151
14.1024 021	Crane, monorail, 100#/LF, manual, channel	LF	10.92	23.48	34.40	17.58	28.50	0.2619
14.1024 031	Rail system	LF	93.82		93.82		93.82	
14.1024 041	Crane, 1/2 ton	EA	3,754.90		3,754.90		3,754.90	
14.1025 000	**BRIDGE CRANES WITHOUT RAILS:**							
14.1025 011	Crane, bridge, 1 ton	EA	9,387.24		9,387.24		9,387.24	
14.1025 021	Crane, bridge, 3 ton	EA	18,774.54		18,774.54		18,774.54	
14.1025 031	Crane, bridge, 5 ton	EA	28,161.83		28,161.83		28,161.83	
14.1026 000	**MANLIFTS:**							
	Note: Be sure to check local codes about the use of the following items. Their use may be restricted or illegal.							
14.1026 011	Manlift, 2 stop	EA	22,588.43		22,588.43		22,588.43	
14.1026 021	Manlift, 3 stop	EA	24,797.09		24,797.09		24,797.09	
14.1026 031	Manlift, 4 stop	EA	27,005.78		27,005.78		27,005.78	
14.1026 041	Add for additional stop	EA	2,208.61		2,208.61		2,208.61	
14.1027 000	**LIFT, SCISSOR TYPE, PORTABLE:**							
	Note: For garage lift, see section 11.1801.							
14.1027 011	Lift, scissor, 2000#, 4' lift	EA	3,709.47		3,709.47		3,709.47	
14.1027 021	Lift, scissor, 1000#, 3' lift	EA	3,312.94		3,312.94		3,312.94	
14.1028 000	**CONVEYORS, BELT TYPE:**							
14.1028 011	Conveyor, belt, horizontal, 24"	LF	778.01		778.01		778.01	
14.1028 021	Conveyor, belt, elevated & descending, 24"	FLIGH	8,583.59		8,583.59		8,583.59	
14.1028 031	Add for direction changes	EA	7,717.66		7,717.66		7,717.66	
14.1028 041	Add for starter section	EA	3,227.61		3,227.61		3,227.61	
14.1029 000	**CONVEYORS, AUTO/SELECTIVE/COLLECTIVE:**							
14.1029 011	Horizontal	LF	3,200.01		3,200.01		3,200.01	
14.1029 021	Vertical	LF	4,291.80		4,291.80		4,291.80	

Division 14 CSI #	14 - CONVEYING SYSTEMS Description	Unit	Material	Union Install	Union Total	Open Install	Open Total	Unit Man-Hrs
14.1030 000	**MAIL CONVEYORS, AUTOMATIC, ELECTRONIC:**							
14.1030 011	Mail conveyor, horizontal	LF	1,731.71		1,731.71		1,731.71	
14.1030 021	Mail conveyor, vertical, 12' high	FLOOR	23,692.71		23,692.71		23,692.71	
14.1031 000	**MOVING SIDEWALKS:**							
14.1031 011	Moving sidewalk, horizontal, 48"	LF	2,269.57		2,269.57		2,269.57	
14.1031 021	Moving sidewalk, horizontal, 72"	LF	2,701.32		2,701.32		2,701.32	
14.1031 031	Moving sidewalk, elevating, 48"	LF	4,372.11		4,372.11		4,372.11	
14.1032 000	**BAGGAGE CAROUSELS:**							
14.1032 011	Baggage carousel, round, 20'	EA	39,289.71	14,935.77	54,225.48	11,184.34	50,474.05	166.5823
14.1032 021	Baggage carousel, round, 25'	EA	50,683.68	18,669.76	69,353.44	13,980.45	64,664.13	208.2284
14.1032 031	Baggage carousel, rectangular 75' x 30'	EA	172,174.49		172,174.49		172,174.49	
14.1032 041	Baggage carousel, average cost/LF	LF	815.62		815.62		815.62	
14.1033 000	**PNEUMATIC TUBE SYSTEMS:**							
14.1033 011	Pneumatic tube, twin, 3", 2 station	TOTAL	25,048.07		25,048.07		25,048.07	
14.1033 021	Add for additional station	STATION	10,440.85		10,440.85		10,440.85	
14.1033 031	Pneumatic tube, twin, 4", 2 station	TOTAL	25,851.21		25,851.21		25,851.21	
14.1033 041	Add for additional station	STATION	10,842.44		10,842.44		10,842.44	
14.1033 051	Pneumatic tube, twin, 4" x 7", 2 station	TOTAL	40,252.63		40,252.63		40,252.63	
14.1033 061	Add for additional station	STATION	15,179.44		15,179.44		15,179.44	
14.1033 071	Pneumatic tube, twin, electric, 4", 2 station	TOTAL	52,585.97		52,585.97		52,585.97	
14.1033 081	Add for additional station	STATION	20,736.19		20,736.19		20,736.19	
14.1033 091	Pneumatic tube, twin, electric, 6", 2 station	TOTAL	69,391.80		69,391.80		69,391.80	
14.1033 101	Add for additional station	STATION	23,853.41		23,853.41		23,853.41	
14.1033 111	Pneumatic tube, twin, electric, 4"x7", 2 station	TOTAL	76,906.24		76,906.24		76,906.24	
14.1033 121	Add for additional station	STATION	29,816.81		29,816.81		29,816.81	
14.1033 131	Pneumatic tube, twin, electric, 4x12, 2 station	TOTAL	102,092.40		102,092.40		102,092.40	
14.1033 141	Add for additional station	STATION	43,098.78		43,098.78		43,098.78	
14.1033 151	Pneumatic tube, pharmacy, 8", positive interlock	STATION	38,284.93		38,284.93		38,284.93	

SECTION	DESCRIPTION
15.0000	**MECHANICAL WORK**
15.0001	**PLUMBING**
	NOTE: FOR SITEWORK, SEE 02.5000.
.0001	IN-PLACE COSTS
.1000	EQUIPMENT
.1200	FIXTURES
	Fixtures, Economy Grade
	Fixtures, Standard Grade
	Fixtures, Institutional Grade
	Fixtures, Specialty Grade
.1300	PIPING
	Piping, Rough-in For Fixtures
	Piping, Rough-in At Fixtures
	Piping, General
.1400	VALVES AND SPECIALTIES
.1500	INSULATION
.1600	MISCELLANEOUS SPECIALTIES
.1700	MEDICAL/LAB EQUIPMENT & PIPE
.1800	FEES, PERMITS & STERILIZATION
.1900	INDUSTRIAL PIPING
.2000	GATE, GLOBE & CHECK VALVES
.2100	INDUSTRIAL PIPE INSULATION

SEWER SERVICE NOTES:

Cleanouts requirements:
At each building line.
For each 100 feet of pipe run.
At each alignment change exceeding 22.5 degrees.
In building horizontal runs with turns over 5' long.
At runs servicing sinks and urinals.
At aggregate change over 135 degrees.
Manholes are required for each 300 feet of pipe run.
All abandoned sewer lines must be plugged.

WATER SERVICE NOTES:

Plumbing codes require that all service valves 2" and
under must be made of brass.
Gate valves are required at the following locations:
Each water meter or other source.
Each separate building supply line.
Each apartment supply line.
Each storage tank outlet.
Each hot water heater supply.
Control valves are required at these locations:
Immediately ahead of all appliances.
Ahead of metering valves.
Asbestos cement pipe is only used outside the building.
Urinals all require vacuum breakers.

FUEL GAS NOTES:

PERMITS ARE REQUIRED.
Pipe can be steel, yellow brass or pvc.
Pipe under building must be in a vented sleeve.
Separate shut-off valves required for each building.
Shut off cocks are required at appliance connections.

Division 15 CSI #	15 - MECHANICAL Description	Unit	Material	Union Install	Union Total	Open Install	Open Total	Unit Man-Hrs
15.0000 000	**PLUMBING:**							
15.0000 000	**MECHANICAL WORK:**							
15.0001 000	**PLUMBING, IN PLACE COST PER FIXTURE:**							
	Note: The following prices include piping to 5' beyond building line. Gas lines and storm system piping are not included.							
15.0001 011	Plumbing, residential, tract housing	FIX	1,147.25	360.65	1,507.90	190.54	1,337.79	4.4415
15.0001 021	Plumbing, residential, multi, 2 story	FIX	1,261.28	420.75	1,682.03	222.29	1,483.57	5.1816
15.0001 031	Plumbing, residential, multi, 3 story	FIX	1,460.25	526.66	1,986.91	278.25	1,738.50	6.4860
15.0001 041	Plumbing, residential, custom, good to better	FIX	1,556.76	575.33	2,132.09	303.96	1,860.72	7.0853
15.0001 051	Plumbing, custom residential, best	FIX	2,042.39	830.06	2,872.45	438.54	2,480.93	10.2224
15.0001 061	Plumbing, commercial, frame construction	FIX	1,995.38	1,219.32	3,214.70	644.19	2,639.57	15.0162
15.0001 071	Plumbing, commercial, type 1 building	FIX	2,199.17	1,371.02	3,570.19	724.35	2,923.52	16.8845
15.0001 081	Plumbing, commercial, high rise	FIX	2,757.34	1,774.60	4,531.94	937.57	3,694.91	21.8547
15.0001 091	Plumbing, institutional, schools, elementary	FIX	2,622.26	1,665.83	4,288.09	880.10	3,502.36	20.5152
15.0001 101	Plumbing, institutional, high schools	FIX	2,955.93	2,040.78	4,996.71	1,078.20	4,034.13	25.1328
15.0001 111	Plumbing, institutional, public structures	FIX	3,200.36	2,218.24	5,418.60	1,171.95	4,372.31	27.3182
15.0001 121	Plumbing, institutional, hospital, 1 & 2 story	FIX	3,975.44	2,779.25	6,754.69	1,468.35	5,443.79	34.2272
15.0001 131	Plumbing, institutional, hospital, high rise	FIX	4,449.49	3,188.55	7,638.04	1,684.59	6,134.08	39.2678
15.1000 000	**EQUIPMENT:**							
	Note: The following prices do not include valving, auxiliary equipment or supports, unless otherwise noted. For boilers see section "15.3200.							
15.1001 000	**WATER HEATER, GLASS LINED, RESIDENTIAL, ELECTRIC:**							
15.1001 011	Heater, hot water, electric, 30 gallon, 5 year, glass lined	EA	579.13	272.62	851.75	170.91	750.04	2.2990
15.1001 021	Heater, hot water, electric, 40 gallon, 5 year, glass lined	EA	638.49	272.62	911.11	170.91	809.40	2.2990
15.1001 031	Heater, hot water, electric, 82 gallon, 5 year, glass lined	EA	1,054.82	363.48	1,418.30	227.87	1,282.69	3.0653
15.1001 041	Heater, hot water, electric, 119 gallon, 5 year, glass lined	EA	1,573.42	454.35	2,027.77	284.84	1,858.26	3.8316
15.1001 051	Heater, hot water, electric, 30 gallon, 10 year, glass lined	EA	610.18	272.62	882.80	170.91	781.09	2.2990
15.1001 061	Heater, hot water, electric, 40 gallon, 10 year, glass lined	EA	669.63	272.62	942.25	170.91	840.54	2.2990
15.1001 071	Heater, hot water, electric, 82 gallon, 10 year, glass lined	EA	1,085.86	363.48	1,449.34	227.87	1,313.73	3.0653
15.1001 081	Heater, hot water, electric, 119 gallon, 10 year, glass lined	EA	1,605.56	454.35	2,059.91	284.84	1,890.40	3.8316
15.1002 000	**WATER HEATERS, GLASS LINED, RESIDENTIAL:**							
15.1002 011	Heater, hot water, gas, 30 gallon, 5 year, glass lined	EA	548.09	318.06	866.15	199.39	747.48	2.6822
15.1002 021	Heater, hot water, gas, 40 gallon, 5 year, glass lined	EA	617.89	318.06	935.95	199.39	817.28	2.6822
15.1002 031	Heater, hot water, gas, 75 gallon, 5 year, glass lined	EA	1,248.73	408.92	1,657.65	256.36	1,505.09	3.4485
15.1002 041	Heater, hot water, gas, 100 gallon, 5 year, glass lined	EA	2,024.41	499.79	2,524.20	313.33	2,337.74	4.2148
15.1002 051	Heater, hot water, gas, 30 gallon, 10 year, glass lined	EA	615.30	318.06	933.36	199.39	814.69	2.6822
15.1002 061	Heater, hot water, gas, 40 gallon, 10 year, glass lined	EA	651.50	318.06	969.56	199.39	850.89	2.6822
15.1002 071	Heater, hot water, gas, 50 gallon, 10 year, glass lined	EA	793.80	363.48	1,157.28	227.87	1,021.67	3.0653
15.1002 081	Heater, hot water, gas, 100g, 10 year, glass lined	EA	2,091.37	499.81	2,591.18	313.34	2,404.71	4.2150
15.1003 000	**WATER HEATERS, COMMERCIAL, 3 YEAR, WITH CONNECTIONS:**							
15.1003 011	Heater, hot water, electric, 6 gallon, 17 GPM, with connection	EA	651.50	237.16	888.66	148.68	800.18	2.0000
15.1003 021	Heater, hot water, electric, 50 gallon, 100 GPH, with connection	EA	3,392.67	590.66	3,983.33	370.29	3,762.96	4.9811
15.1003 031	Heater, hot water, electric, 85 gallon, 200 GPH, with connection	EA	4,265.15	590.66	4,855.81	370.29	4,635.44	4.9811
15.1003 041	Heater, hot water, electric, 120 gallon, 221 GPH, with connection	EA	4,821.68	726.97	5,548.65	455.75	5,277.43	6.1306
15.1003 051	Heater, hot water, gas, 20 gallon, 100 GPH, with connection	EA	1,465.79	636.10	2,101.89	398.78	1,864.57	5.3643
15.1003 061	Heater, hot water, gas, 50 gallon, 100 GPH, with connection	EA	1,737.67	636.10	2,373.77	398.78	2,136.45	5.3643
15.1003 071	Heater, hot water, gas, 75 gallon, 300 GPH, with connection	EA	4,534.93	681.53	5,216.46	427.26	4,962.19	5.7474
15.1003 081	Heater, hot water, gas, 85 gallon, 168 GPH, with connection	EA	5,878.87	681.53	6,560.40	427.26	6,306.13	5.7474
15.1003 091	Heater, hot water, 100 gallon, 235 GPH, with connection	EA	6,073.27	726.97	6,800.24	455.75	6,529.02	6.1306
15.1004 000	**INTERCEPTORS, CAST IRON:**							
15.1004 011	Grease intercept, cast iron, 4 GPM, 8#	EA	749.49	227.18	976.67	142.42	891.91	1.9158
15.1004 021	Grease intercept, cast iron, 10 GPM, 20#	EA	1,226.25	272.62	1,498.87	170.91	1,397.16	2.2990
15.1004 031	Grease intercept, cast iron, 20 GPM, 40#	EA	2,224.70	363.48	2,588.18	227.87	2,452.57	3.0653
15.1004 041	Grease intercept, cast iron, 50 GPM, 100#	EA	4,089.26	1,090.45	5,179.71	683.62	4,772.88	9.1959
15.1004 051	Hair intercept, cast iron, small	EA	281.06	227.18	508.24	142.42	423.48	1.9158
15.1004 061	Hair intercept, cast iron, large	EA	517.52	318.06	835.58	199.39	716.91	2.6822
15.1004 071	Plaster intercept, cast iron, small	EA	426.44	227.18	653.62	142.42	568.86	1.9158
15.1004 081	Plaster intercept, cast iron, large	EA	1,090.75	318.06	1,408.81	199.39	1,290.14	2.6822
15.1005 000	**PUMPS, CIRCULATING, IN LINE, FLANGED, IRON BODY:**							
15.1005 011	Pump, circulating, iron body, 3/4"-1-1/2", flanged, 1/12 hp	EA	598.23	172.66	770.89	108.25	706.48	1.4561
15.1005 021	Pump, circulating, iron body, to 2", flanged, 1/6 hp	EA	723.92	199.93	923.85	125.34	849.26	1.6860
15.1005 031	Pump, circulating, iron body, to 2-1/2", flanged, 1/4 hp	EA	1,906.01	254.44	2,160.45	159.51	2,065.52	2.1457

Division 15 CSI #	15 - MECHANICAL Description	Unit	Material	Union Install	Union Total	Open Install	Open Total	Unit Man-Hrs
15.1005 000	**PUMPS, CIRCULATING, IN LINE, FLANGED, IRON BODY: (Cont.)**							
15.1005 041	Pump, circulating, iron body, to 3", flanged, 1/3 hp	EA	2,431.17	281.70	2,712.87	176.60	2,607.77	2.3756
15.1006 000	**PUMPS, SEWAGE EJECTOR, WITH TANKS & FITTINGS:**							
15.1006 011	Pump, sewage ejector, single, 1/2 hp, 2", tank	EA	4,369.63	1,017.75	5,387.38	638.05	5,007.68	8.5828
15.1006 021	Pump, sewage ejector, single, 1 hp, 3", tank, fittings	EA	10,543.14	1,226.76	11,769.90	769.08	11,312.22	10.3454
15.1006 031	Pump, sewage ejector, single, 2 hp, 4", tank, fittings	EA	11,670.75	1,408.49	13,079.24	883.01	12,553.76	11.8780
15.1006 041	Pump, sewage ejector, duplex, 2 hp, tank, fittings	EA	17,368.02	1,935.55	19,303.57	1,213.43	18,581.45	16.3227
15.1006 051	Pump, sewage ejector, duplex, 3 hp, tank, fittings	EA	17,534.37	2,344.46	19,878.83	1,469.78	19,004.15	19.7711
15.1006 061	Pump, sewage ejector, duplex, 5 hp, tank, fittings	EA	20,832.43	2,753.37	23,585.80	1,726.14	22,558.57	23.2195
15.1007 000	**PUMPS, SUMP, ELECTRIC, WITH IRON GUARD ACCESSORIES:**							
	Note: For bronze body, add 67% to the material costs.							
15.1007 011	Sump, 1/4 hp, 2' deep, 1-1/4" outlet	EA	1,200.17	181.75	1,381.92	113.94	1,314.11	1.5327
15.1007 021	Sump, 1/3 hp, 3' deep, 1-1/2" outlet	EA	1,942.66	227.18	2,169.84	142.42	2,085.08	1.9158
15.1007 031	Sump, 1/2 hp, 6' deep, 2" outlet	EA	2,448.32	318.06	2,766.38	199.39	2,647.71	2.6822
15.1008 000	**TANKS, SEPTIC, STEEL, INCLUDE BURY:**							
15.1008 011	Septic tank, steel, 200 gallon, buried	EA	1,035.31	308.57	1,343.88	181.43	1,216.74	3.4485
15.1008 021	Septic tank, steel, 500 gallon, buried	EA	1,475.97	514.28	1,990.25	302.37	1,778.34	5.7474
15.1008 031	Septic tank, steel, 1,000 gallon, buried	EA	3,250.69	737.14	3,987.83	433.40	3,684.09	8.2380
15.1008 041	Septic tank, steel, 10,000 gallon, buried	EA	22,192.21	2,811.39	25,003.60	1,652.96	23,845.17	31.4192
15.1009 000	**COMPRESSOR, AIR, TANK MOUNTED, CONTROL PANEL WITH ACCESS:**							
15.1009 011	Compressor, simplex, 5 hp, reciprocating, tank mounted	EA	8,001.08	1,897.28	9,898.36	1,189.44	9,190.52	16.0000
15.1009 021	Compressor, simplex, 7.5 hp, reciprocating, tank mounted	EA	11,088.77	2,134.44	13,223.21	1,338.12	12,426.89	18.0000
15.1009 031	Compressor, simplex, 10 hp, tank mounted	EA	14,504.88	2,371.60	16,876.48	1,486.80	15,991.68	20.0000
15.1009 041	Compressor, simplex, 15 hp, reciprocating, tank mounted	EA	19,906.57	2,490.18	22,396.75	1,561.14	21,467.71	21.0000
15.1009 051	Compressor, simplex, 20 hp, reciprocating, tank mounted	EA	24,148.20	2,845.92	26,994.12	1,784.16	25,932.36	24.0000
15.1010 000	**TANKS, WATER, GLASS LINED, ASME:**							
15.1010 011	Tank, water, glass lined, 140 gallon, ASME	EA	2,257.57	590.66	2,848.23	370.29	2,627.86	4.9811
15.1010 021	Tank, water, glass lined, 200 gallon, ASME	EA	2,724.22	813.29	3,537.51	509.87	3,234.09	6.8586
15.1010 031	Tank, water, glass lined, 350 gallon, ASME	EA	3,689.77	1,158.60	4,848.37	726.35	4,416.12	9.7706
15.1010 041	Tank, water, glass lined, 400 gallon, ASME	EA	3,712.76	1,299.45	5,012.21	814.65	4,527.41	10.9584
15.1011 000	**WATER SOFTENERS, WITH BRINETANK & START-UP:**							
15.1011 011	Water softener, 8 GPM, brinetank & start-up	EA	1,806.46	533.61	2,340.07	334.53	2,140.99	4.5000
15.1011 021	Water softener, 25 GPM, brinetank & start-up	EA	3,448.03	726.97	4,175.00	455.75	3,903.78	6.1306
15.1011 031	Water softener, 50 GPM, brinetank & start-up	EA	6,284.36	1,317.63	7,601.99	826.04	7,110.40	11.1117
15.1012 000	**PUMP, PRESSURE BOOSTER SYSTEM:**							
	Note: The following prices include pumps, valves, controls. All items are pre-piped and skid-mounted.							
15.1012 011	2 pump system, 100 GPM @ 50 PSI	EACH	21,293.98	2,845.92	24,139.90	1,784.16	23,078.14	24.0000
15.1012 021	2 pump system, 320 GPM @ 50 PSI	EACH	30,782.68	2,845.92	33,628.60	1,784.16	32,566.84	24.0000
15.1012 031	3 pump system, 300 GPM @ 100 PSI	EACH	33,079.87	3,794.56	36,874.43	2,378.88	35,458.75	32.0000
15.1012 041	3 pump system, 950 GPM @ 100 PSI	EACH	64,205.53	3,794.56	68,000.09	2,378.88	66,584.41	32.0000
15.1200 000	**FIXTURES:**							
	Note: The following prices include trim with stops, hangars and supports. For rough in at fixtures see section "15.1300000.							
15.1201 000	**FIXTURES, ECONOMY GRADE:**							
15.1201 011	Bath tub, steel, with shower	EA	395.66	318.06	713.72	199.39	595.05	2.6822
15.1201 021	Bath tub, steel, with out shower	EA	338.56	272.62	611.18	170.91	509.47	2.2990
15.1201 031	Tub, fiberglass, integral walls	EA	775.98	318.06	1,094.04	199.39	975.37	2.6822
15.1201 041	Bidets, floor mounted	EA	537.47	181.75	719.22	113.94	651.41	1.5327
15.1201 051	Lavatory, steel, wall hung	EA	221.66	181.75	403.41	113.94	335.60	1.5327
15.1201 061	Lavatory, steel, vanity mounted	EA	173.26	181.75	355.01	113.94	287.20	1.5327
15.1201 071	Service sink	EA	409.79	227.18	636.97	142.42	552.21	1.9158
15.1201 081	Shower & drain receptor, 32" square	EA	319.02	272.62	591.64	170.91	489.93	2.2990
15.1201 091	Shower cabinet, with door, 32" square	EA	678.50	408.92	1,087.42	256.36	934.86	3.4485
15.1201 101	Sink, porcelain on steel, counter, single	EA	151.09	136.31	287.40	85.45	236.54	1.1495
15.1201 111	Sink, porcelain on cast iron, counter, single	EA	214.91	136.31	351.22	85.45	300.36	1.1495
15.1201 121	Sink, stainless steel, counter, single	EA	225.02	136.31	361.33	85.45	310.47	1.1495
15.1201 131	Sink, porcelain on steel, counter, double	EA	166.83	136.31	303.14	85.45	252.28	1.1495
15.1201 141	Sink, porcelain on cast iron, counter, double	EA	228.35	136.31	364.66	85.45	313.80	1.1495
15.1201 151	Sink, stainless steel, counter double	EA	257.90	136.31	394.21	85.45	343.35	1.1495
15.1201 161	Sink, bar	EA	218.67	136.31	354.98	85.45	304.12	1.1495
15.1201 171	Sink, floor	EA	161.16	90.88	252.04	56.97	218.13	0.7664
15.1201 181	Urinal, floor, with flush valve	EA	486.73	181.75	668.48	113.94	600.67	1.5327

Division 15 CSI #	15 - MECHANICAL Description	Unit	Material	Union Install	Union Total	Open Install	Open Total	Unit Man-Hrs
15.1201 000	**FIXTURES, ECONOMY GRADE: (Cont.)**							
15.1201 191	Urinal, wall, with flush valve, carrier	EA	514.14	181.75	695.89	113.94	628.08	1.5327
15.1201 201	Water closet, floor, with tank	EA	500.44	181.75	682.19	113.94	614.38	1.5327
15.1201 211	Water closet, wall, with flush valve, carrier	EA	530.69	181.75	712.44	113.94	644.63	1.5327
15.1202 000	**FIXTURES, STANDARD GRADE:**							
15.1202 011	Bath tub, porcelain enamel on cast iron, with shower	EA	1,319.36	318.06	1,637.42	199.39	1,518.75	2.6822
15.1202 021	Bath tub, porcelain enamel on cast iron, no shower	EA	1,307.36	272.62	1,579.98	170.91	1,478.27	2.2990
15.1202 031	Tub, fiberglass, with integral wall	EA	1,016.12	318.06	1,334.18	199.39	1,215.51	2.6822
15.1202 041	Bidet, floor mounted	EA	846.29	181.75	1,028.04	113.94	960.23	1.5327
15.1202 051	Lavatory, wall hung	EA	627.87	181.75	809.62	113.94	741.81	1.5327
15.1202 061	Lavatory, vanity mounted	EA	447.53	181.75	629.28	113.94	561.47	1.5327
15.1202 071	Service sink	EA	1,104.23	227.18	1,331.41	142.42	1,246.65	1.9158
15.1202 081	Shower & drain receptor, 32" square	EA	811.39	272.62	1,084.01	170.91	982.30	2.2990
15.1202 091	Shower, cabinet with door, 32" square	EA	1,340.38	408.92	1,749.30	256.36	1,596.74	3.4485
15.1202 101	Sink, porcelain on cast iron, counter, single	EA	739.06	136.31	875.37	85.45	824.51	1.1495
15.1202 111	Sink, stainless steel, counter, single	EA	757.70	136.31	894.01	85.45	843.15	1.1495
15.1202 121	Sink, porcelain on cast iron, counter, double	EA	835.20	136.31	971.51	85.45	920.65	1.1495
15.1202 131	Sink, stainless steel, counter, double	EA	1,028.84	136.31	1,165.15	85.45	1,114.29	1.1495
15.1202 141	Sink, bar	EA	527.18	136.31	663.49	85.45	612.63	1.1495
15.1202 151	Sink, floor	EA	223.79	90.88	314.67	56.97	280.76	0.7664
15.1202 161	Urinal, trough, with flush valve	EA	719.81	181.75	901.56	113.94	833.75	1.5327
15.1202 171	Urinal, wall, flush valve & carrier	EA	795.24	181.75	976.99	113.94	909.18	1.5327
15.1202 181	Water closet, floor, with tank	EA	555.27	181.75	737.02	113.94	669.21	1.5327
15.1202 191	Water closet, wall, with flush valve & carrier	EA	582.71	181.75	764.46	113.94	696.65	1.5327
15.1202 201	Water closet, floor, with flush valve, handicap	EA	682.46	181.75	864.21	113.94	796.40	1.5327
15.1203 000	**FIXTURES, INSTITUTIONAL GRADE:**							
15.1203 011	Bath tub, with shower	EA	1,734.68	363.48	2,098.16	227.87	1,962.55	3.0653
15.1203 021	Bath tub, with out shower	EA	1,722.69	318.06	2,040.75	199.39	1,922.08	2.6822
15.1203 031	Bidet, floor mounted	EA	924.08	227.18	1,151.26	142.42	1,066.50	1.9158
15.1203 041	Lavatory, wall hung	EA	821.18	227.18	1,048.36	142.42	963.60	1.9158
15.1203 051	Lavatory, vanity mounted	EA	647.89	227.18	875.07	142.42	790.31	1.9158
15.1203 061	Service sink	EA	1,308.60	227.18	1,535.78	142.42	1,451.02	1.9158
15.1203 071	Shower & drain receptor, 36" square	EA	917.58	318.06	1,235.64	199.39	1,116.97	2.6822
15.1203 081	Shower cabinet, with door, 36" square	EA	1,519.45	454.35	1,973.80	284.84	1,804.29	3.8316
15.1203 091	Shower cabinet, corner, with door & trim	EACH	4,655.12	454.35	5,109.47	284.84	4,939.96	3.8316
15.1203 101	Shower cabinet, handicap, with door, trim	EACH	4,562.66	653.51	5,216.17	409.70	4,972.36	5.5111
15.1203 111	Sink, clinic	EA	1,373.28	227.18	1,600.46	142.42	1,515.70	1.9158
15.1203 121	Sink, counter, single, porcelain on cast iron	EA	847.88	181.75	1,029.63	113.94	961.82	1.5327
15.1203 131	Sink, counter, single, stainless steel	EA	871.95	181.75	1,053.70	113.94	985.89	1.5327
15.1203 141	Sink, counter, double, porcelain on cast iron	EA	954.49	181.75	1,136.24	113.94	1,068.43	1.5327
15.1203 151	Sink, counter, double, stainless steel	EA	1,194.68	181.75	1,376.43	113.94	1,308.62	1.5327
15.1203 161	Sink, bar	EA	555.09	181.75	736.84	113.94	669.03	1.5327
15.1203 171	Sink, floor	EA	441.06	136.31	577.37	85.45	526.51	1.1495
15.1203 181	Sitz bath	EA	1,789.76	318.06	2,107.82	199.39	1,989.15	2.6822
15.1203 191	Urinal, floor, with flush valve	EA	1,017.73	227.18	1,244.91	142.42	1,160.15	1.9158
15.1203 201	Urinal, wall, flush valve & carrier	EA	1,168.17	227.18	1,395.35	142.42	1,310.59	1.9158
15.1203 211	Urinal, trough 4 deg, valve, carrier	EA	481.32	363.48	844.80	227.87	709.19	3.0653
15.1203 221	Water closet, floor, with flush valve	EA	852.43	227.18	1,079.61	142.42	994.85	1.9158
15.1203 231	Water closet, wall, with flush valve & carrier	EA	833.29	227.18	1,060.47	142.42	975.71	1.9158
15.1203 241	Water closet, floor, with bed pan flush	EA	988.48	272.62	1,261.10	170.91	1,159.39	2.2990
15.1203 251	Water closet, wall, bed pan flush, flush valve	EA	1,791.73	272.62	2,064.35	170.91	1,962.64	2.2990
15.1203 261	Water closet lavatory, hospital, standard	EA	2,925.87	399.84	3,325.71	250.67	3,176.54	3.3719
15.1203 271	Water closet lavatory, hospital, deluxe	EA	3,721.51	399.84	4,121.35	250.67	3,972.18	3.3719
15.1204 000	**SPECIALTY FIXTURES:**							
	Note: For stainless steel, add 30% to the material costs. For enameled steel, add 18%.							
15.1204 011	Column showers, 2 head	FIX	828.86	499.79	1,328.65	313.33	1,142.19	4.2148
15.1204 021	Column showers, 3 head	FIX	1,012.84	536.14	1,548.98	336.11	1,348.95	4.5213
15.1204 031	Column showers, 6 head	FIX	1,441.90	590.66	2,032.56	370.29	1,812.19	4.9811
15.1204 041	Drinking fountain, cast iron, wall	FIX	410.33	90.88	501.21	56.97	467.30	0.7664
15.1204 051	Drinking fountain, stainless steel, wall	FIX	531.80	90.88	622.68	56.97	588.77	0.7664
15.1204 061	Water cooler, elec, enamel, semi-recess	FIX	810.45	136.31	946.76	85.45	895.90	1.1495
15.1204 071	Water cooler, elec, stainless steel, semi-recess	FIX	923.12	136.31	1,059.43	85.45	1,008.57	1.1495

Division 15 CSI #	15 - MECHANICAL Description	Unit	Material	Union Install	Union Total	Open Install	Open Total	Unit Man-Hrs
15.1204 000	**SPECIALTY FIXTURES: (Cont.)**							
15.1204 081	Water cooler, elec, enamel, wheel chair	EA	1,104.39	136.31	1,240.70	85.45	1,189.84	1.1495
15.1204 091	Water cooler, elec, stainless steel, wheel chair	EA	1,265.70	136.31	1,402.01	85.45	1,351.15	1.1495
15.1204 101	Water cooler, elec, stainless steel, dual purpose	FIX	1,673.40	136.31	1,809.71	85.45	1,758.85	1.1495
15.1204 111	Water fountain, granite 36" half circle	FIX	3,388.65	454.35	3,843.00	284.84	3,673.49	3.8316
15.1204 121	Water fountain, granite 54" half circle	FIX	4,179.32	499.79	4,679.11	313.33	4,492.65	4.2148
15.1204 131	Water fountain, granite 36" full circle	FIX	3,840.45	454.35	4,294.80	284.84	4,125.29	3.8316
15.1204 141	Water fountain, granite 54" full circle	FIX	4,970.04	499.79	5,469.83	313.33	5,283.37	4.2148
15.1204 171	Eye-wash fountain	FIX	408.32	181.75	590.07	113.94	522.26	1.5327
15.1204 181	Eye-wash & shower	FIX	1,033.48	545.23	1,578.71	341.82	1,375.30	4.5980
15.1204 191	Shower, head drench	FIX	483.84	454.35	938.19	284.84	768.68	3.8316
15.1204 201	Water closet, stainless steel, park & rec	FIX	942.37	318.06	1,260.43	199.39	1,141.76	2.6822
15.1204 251	Urinal, stainless steel, park & rec	FIX	1,216.49	318.06	1,534.55	199.39	1,415.88	2.6822
15.1204 261	Lavatory basin, stainless steel, park & rec	FIX	773.17	272.62	1,045.79	170.91	944.08	2.2990
15.1204 271	Decontamination shower, walk-thru, eye-wash	FIX	4,807.61	1,090.45	5,898.06	683.62	5,491.23	9.1959
15.1204 281	Bathing pool (tub), 5' x 42"	EA	1,801.52	318.06	2,119.58	199.39	2,000.91	2.6822
15.1204 291	Bathing pool (tub), 6' x 36"	EA	2,505.68	318.06	2,823.74	199.39	2,705.07	2.6822
15.1204 301	Recess bath with whirlpool	EA	5,958.02	454.35	6,412.37	284.84	6,242.86	3.8316
15.1204 311	Water closet & lavatory, stainless steel, jail, wall	FIX	2,198.44	318.06	2,516.50	199.39	2,397.83	2.6822
15.1204 321	Water closet & lavatory, stainless steel, jail, floor	FIX	3,870.20	318.06	4,188.26	199.39	4,069.59	2.6822
15.1204 331	Water closet, in floor, stainless steel, jail	FIX	2,798.48	272.62	3,071.10	170.91	2,969.39	2.2990
15.1204 341	Shower, wall mounted unit, h & c	FIX	1,062.60	454.35	1,516.95	284.84	1,347.44	3.8316
15.1204 351	Water closet, stainless steel, wall, jail	FIX	1,179.52	272.62	1,452.14	170.91	1,350.43	2.2990
15.1204 361	Lavatory, stainless steel, oval, wall, jail	FIX	1,048.05	272.62	1,320.67	170.91	1,218.96	2.2990
15.1204 371	Shower stall, jail, 36" x 36"	FIX	6,356.89	545.23	6,902.12	341.82	6,698.71	4.5980
15.1204 401	Add for paddle control for sink	EA	290.11		290.11		290.11	
15.1204 411	Add for flush sensor	EA	248.65		248.65		248.65	
15.1300 000	**PIPING:**							
15.1301 000	**ROUGH-IN FOR FIXTURES:**							
	Note: Use the following prices for schematic and preliminary estimates only, where piping takeoff is not possible. Unit prices include allowances for all piping and valving from fixture to 5' beyond building perimeter. Gas lines, roof drains and off-site work are not included.							
15.1301 011	Tract housing	FIX	330.73	204.82	535.55	128.41	459.14	1.7273
15.1301 021	Custom housing	FIX	633.15	380.36	1,013.51	238.45	871.60	3.2076
15.1301 031	Apartment building	FIX	458.33	284.24	742.57	178.19	636.52	2.3970
15.1301 041	Industrial building	FIX	844.49	489.06	1,333.55	306.60	1,151.09	4.1243
15.1301 051	Commercial building	FIX	1,035.30	530.84	1,566.14	332.79	1,368.09	4.4766
15.1301 061	Institutional structures	FIX	2,313.29	1,818.25	4,131.54	1,139.89	3,453.18	15.3335
15.1301 071	Schools	FIX	2,173.25	1,312.49	3,485.74	822.82	2,996.07	11.0684
15.1301 081	Hospital, 1 or 2 story	FIX	2,811.85	2,202.78	5,014.63	1,380.96	4,192.81	18.5763
15.1301 091	Hospital, high rise	FIX	3,255.39	2,549.73	5,805.12	1,598.47	4,853.86	21.5022
15.1301 101	Office building, high rise	FIX	2,229.92	1,763.90	3,993.82	1,105.82	3,335.74	14.8752
15.1302 000	**ROUGH-IN AT FIXTURES:**							
	Note: The following prices include fittings and valving required to connect fixtures to the waste line, vent riser and water runs. Straight run piping and risers should be taken off separately. Use these prices only when you are not making a detailed takeoff of connecting piping and fittings at fixtures. Do not use for residential work.							
15.1302 011	Rough-in at bath tubs	EA	325.71	318.06	643.77	199.39	525.10	2.6822
15.1302 021	Rough-in at fountains & coolers	EA	190.22	204.47	394.69	128.18	318.40	1.7243
15.1302 031	Rough-in at lavatory	EA	268.72	295.34	564.06	185.15	453.87	2.4906
15.1302 041	Rough-in at shower	EA	299.13	318.06	617.19	199.39	498.52	2.6822
15.1302 051	Rough-in at sinks	EA	269.71	295.34	565.05	185.15	454.86	2.4906
15.1302 061	Rough-in at urinal	EA	211.02	295.34	506.36	185.15	396.17	2.4906
15.1302 071	Rough-in at washing machine	EA	281.47	272.62	554.09	170.91	452.38	2.2990
15.1302 081	Rough-in at water closet	EA	339.33	381.66	720.99	239.27	578.60	3.2186
15.1302 091	Rough-in at wash fountain	EA	613.91	454.35	1,068.26	284.84	898.75	3.8316
15.1303 000	**CAST IRON PIPE, SOIL, SERVICE WEIGHT, SINGLE HUB:**							
15.1303 011	Cast iron pipe, soil, 1 hub, 2", service weight	LF	9.94	21.81	31.75	13.67	23.61	0.1839
15.1303 021	Cast iron pipe, soil, 1 hub, 3", service weight	LF	12.17	23.17	35.34	14.53	26.70	0.1954
15.1303 031	Cast iron pipe, soil, 1 hub, 4", service weight	LF	16.21	25.00	41.21	15.67	31.88	0.2108
15.1303 041	Cast iron pipe, soil, 1 hub, 5", service weight	LF	22.94	28.17	51.11	17.66	40.60	0.2376
15.1303 051	Cast iron pipe, soil, 1 hub, 6", service weight	LF	28.15	32.27	60.42	20.23	48.38	0.2721

Division 15 CSI #	15 - MECHANICAL Description	Unit	Material	Union Install	Union Total	Open Install	Open Total	Unit Man-Hrs
15.1303 000	**CAST IRON PIPE, SOIL, SERVICE WEIGHT, SINGLE HUB: (Cont.)**							
15.1303 061	Cast iron pipe, soil, 1 hub, 8", service weight	LF	54.30	35.44	89.74	22.22	76.52	0.2989
15.1303 071	Cast iron pipe, soil, 1 hub, 10", service weight	LF	71.28	41.03	112.31	25.72	97.00	0.3460
15.1304 000	**CAST IRON PIPE, SOIL, SERVICE WEIGHT, HUBBELL:**							
15.1304 011	Cast iron pipe, soil, 1-1/2", no hub	LF	10.17	20.16	30.33	12.64	22.81	0.1700
15.1304 021	Cast iron pipe, soil, 2", no hub, service weight	LF	10.49	20.16	30.65	12.64	23.13	0.1700
15.1304 031	Cast iron pipe, soil, 3", no hub, service weight	LF	11.84	22.06	33.90	13.83	25.67	0.1860
15.1304 041	Cast iron pipe, soil, 4", no hub, service weight	LF	15.84	23.21	39.05	14.55	30.39	0.1957
15.1304 051	Cast iron pipe, soil, 5", no hub, service weight	LF	24.64	26.62	51.26	16.69	41.33	0.2245
15.1304 061	Cast iron pipe, soil, 6", no hub, service weight	LF	29.04	30.57	59.61	19.16	48.20	0.2578
15.1304 071	Cast iron pipe, soil, 8", no hub, service weight	LF	52.14	34.53	86.67	21.65	73.79	0.2912
15.1304 081	Cast iron pipe, soil, 10", no hub, service weight	LF	75.06	39.17	114.23	24.55	99.61	0.3303
15.1305 000	**CAST IRON PIPE, SOIL, EXTRA HEAVY, SINGLE HUB:**							
15.1305 011	Cast iron pipe, soil, extra heavy, 1 hub, 2"	LF	11.49	21.81	33.30	13.67	25.16	0.1839
15.1305 021	Cast iron pipe, soil, extra heavy, 1 hub, 3"	LF	14.17	23.17	37.34	14.53	28.70	0.1954
15.1305 031	Cast iron pipe, soil, extra heavy, 1 hub, 4"	LF	18.73	25.00	43.73	15.67	34.40	0.2108
15.1305 041	Cast iron pipe, soil, extra heavy, 1 hub, 5"	LF	24.79	28.17	52.96	17.66	42.45	0.2376
15.1305 051	Cast iron pipe, soil, extra heavy, 1 hub, 6"	LF	32.54	32.27	64.81	20.23	52.77	0.2721
15.1305 061	Cast iron pipe, soil, extra heavy, 1 hub, 8"	LF	62.70	35.44	98.14	22.22	84.92	0.2989
15.1305 071	Cast iron pipe, soil, extra heavy, 1 hub, 10"	LF	82.31	41.03	123.34	25.72	108.03	0.3460
15.1305 081	Cast iron pipe, soil, extra heavy, 1 hub, 12"	LF	118.55	46.34	164.89	29.05	147.60	0.3908
15.1306 000	**CAST IRON PIPE, DUR IRON:**							
15.1306 011	Cast iron pipe, dur iron, 2"	LF	53.21	20.91	74.12	13.11	66.32	0.1763
15.1306 021	Cast iron pipe, dur iron, 3"	LF	66.67	23.17	89.84	14.53	81.20	0.1954
15.1306 031	Cast iron pipe, dur iron, 4"	LF	93.02	24.63	117.65	15.44	108.46	0.2077
15.1306 041	Cast iron pipe, dur iron, 6"	LF	147.65	31.82	179.47	19.95	167.60	0.2683
15.1306 051	Cast iron pipe, dur iron, 8"	LF	278.47	34.41	312.88	21.57	300.04	0.2902
15.1307 000	**COPPER PIPE, "K", UNDERGROUND, WITH TRENCHING:**							
15.1307 011	Pipe, copper, 'K', soft, 1/2" coils, underground	LF	5.11	7.49	12.60	4.70	9.81	0.0632
15.1307 021	Pipe, copper, 'K', soft, 3/4" coils, underground	LF	9.08	8.63	17.71	5.41	14.49	0.0728
15.1307 031	Pipe, copper, 'K', soft, 1" coils, underground	LF	12.21	8.63	20.84	5.41	17.62	0.0728
15.1307 041	Pipe, copper, 'K', soft, 1-1/4" coil	LF	16.00	15.44	31.44	9.68	25.68	0.1302
15.1307 051	Pipe, copper, 'K', hard, 1-1/2", underground	LF	20.14	15.91	36.05	9.98	30.12	0.1342
15.1307 061	Pipe, copper, 'K', hard, 2", underground	LF	31.13	19.08	50.21	11.96	43.09	0.1609
15.1307 071	Pipe, copper, 'K, hard, 2-1/2", underground	LF	44.38	19.08	63.46	11.96	56.34	0.1609
15.1307 081	Pipe, copper, 'K', hard, 3", underground	LF	61.82	19.54	81.36	12.25	74.07	0.1648
15.1307 091	Pipe, copper, 'K', hard, 4", underground	LF	102.24	21.76	124.00	13.64	115.88	0.1835
15.1307 101	Pipe, copper, 'K', hard, 5", underground	LF	225.01	28.63	253.64	17.95	242.96	0.2414
15.1307 111	Pipe, copper, 'K', hard, 6", underground	LF	297.85	31.35	329.20	19.66	317.51	0.2644
15.1308 000	**COPPER PIPE, "L", IN BUILDING, WITH FITTINGS & SUPPORTS:**							
15.1308 011	Pipe, copper, 'L', 1/2", in building, with fittings & supports	LF	4.33	9.38	13.71	5.88	10.21	0.0791
15.1308 021	Pipe, copper, 'L', 3/4", in building, with fittings & supports	LF	6.74	11.41	18.15	7.15	13.89	0.0962
15.1308 031	Pipe, copper, 'L', 1", in building, with fittings & supports	LF	9.76	13.54	23.30	8.49	18.25	0.1142
15.1308 041	Pipe, copper, 'L', 1-1/4", in building, with fittings & supports	LF	13.98	14.62	28.60	9.17	23.15	0.1233
15.1308 051	Pipe, copper, 'L', 1-1/2", in building, with fittings & supports	LF	17.41	15.55	32.96	9.75	27.16	0.1311
15.1308 061	Pipe, copper, 'L', 2", in building, with fittings & supports	LF	21.60	18.75	40.35	11.75	33.35	0.1581
15.1308 071	Pipe, copper, 'L', 2-1/2", in building, with fittings & supports	LF	38.08	20.78	58.86	13.02	51.10	0.1752
15.1308 081	Pipe, copper, 'L', 3", in building, with fittings & supports	LF	52.38	23.86	76.24	14.96	67.34	0.2012
15.1308 091	Pipe, copper, 'L', 4", in building, with fittings & supports	LF	87.98	29.08	117.06	18.23	106.21	0.2452
15.1308 101	Pipe, copper, 'L', 5", in building, with fittings & supports	LF	209.76	36.44	246.20	22.84	232.60	0.3073
15.1308 111	Pipe, copper, 'L', 6", in building, with fittings & supports	LF	247.27	44.61	291.88	27.97	275.24	0.3762
15.1309 000	**COPPER PIPE, "M", IN BUILDING, WITH FITTINGS & SUPPORTS:**							
15.1309 011	Pipe, copper, 'M', 1/2", in building, with fittings & supports	LF	3.36	9.38	12.74	5.88	9.24	0.0791
15.1309 021	Pipe, copper, 'M', 3/4", in building, with fittings & supports	LF	5.28	11.41	16.69	7.15	12.43	0.0962
15.1309 031	Pipe, copper, 'M', 1", in building, with fittings & supports	LF	7.87	13.54	21.41	8.49	16.36	0.1142
15.1309 041	Pipe, copper, 'M', 1-1/4", in building, with fittings & supports	LF	11.83	14.62	26.45	9.17	21.00	0.1233
15.1309 051	Pipe, copper, 'M', 1-1/2", in building, with fittings & supports	LF	15.72	15.55	31.27	9.75	25.47	0.1311
15.1309 061	Pipe, copper, 'M', 2", in building, with fittings & supports	LF	24.77	18.75	43.52	11.75	36.52	0.1581
15.1309 071	Pipe, copper, 'M', 3", in building, with fittings & supports	LF	44.33	23.86	68.19	14.96	59.29	0.2012
15.1309 081	Pipe, copper, 'M', 4", in building, with fittings & supports	LF	79.65	29.08	108.73	18.23	97.88	0.2452
15.1309 091	Pipe, copper, 'M', 5", in building, with fittings & supports	LF	188.80	37.26	226.06	23.36	212.16	0.3142
15.1309 101	Pipe, copper, 'M', 6", in building, with fittings & supports	LF	242.52	36.18	278.70	22.68	265.20	0.3051

Division 15 CSI #	15 - MECHANICAL Description	Unit	Material	Union Install	Union Total	Open Install	Open Total	Unit Man-Hrs
15.1310 000	**COPPER 'DWV' DRAINAGE TUBE:**							
15.1310 011	Tube, copper, 'DWV', 1-1/4"	LF	21.58	14.62	36.20	9.17	30.75	0.1233
15.1310 021	Tube, copper, 'DWV', 1-1/2"	LF	23.18	15.55	38.73	9.75	32.93	0.1311
15.1310 031	Tube, copper, 'DWV', 2"	LF	33.59	18.75	52.34	11.75	45.34	0.1581
15.1310 041	Tube, copper, 'DWV', 3"	LF	45.00	23.86	68.86	14.96	59.96	0.2012
15.1310 051	Tube, copper, 'DWV', 4"	LF	97.65	29.08	126.73	18.23	115.88	0.2452
15.1310 061	Tube, copper, 'DWV', 5"	LF	210.48	37.26	247.74	23.36	233.84	0.3142
15.1311 000	**PVC, SCH 40, IN BUILDING, WITH FITTINGS & SUPPORTS:**							
	Note: For schedule 80, add 31% to the material costs.							
15.1311 011	Pipe, PVC, sch 40, 1/2", in building, with fittings & supports	LF	1.33	6.59	7.92	4.13	5.46	0.0556
15.1311 021	Pipe, PVC, sch 40, 3/4", in building, with fittings & supports	LF	1.55	7.36	8.91	4.62	6.17	0.0621
15.1311 031	Pipe, PVC, sch 40, 1", in building, with fittings & supports	LF	2.05	7.36	9.41	4.62	6.67	0.0621
15.1311 041	Pipe, PVC, sch 40, 1-1/4", building, with fittings & supports	LF	2.62	12.72	15.34	7.98	10.60	0.1073
15.1311 051	Pipe, PVC, sch 40, 1-1/2", in building, with fittings & supports	LF	2.81	14.54	17.35	9.11	11.92	0.1226
15.1311 061	Pipe, PVC, sch 40, 2", in building, with fittings & supports	LF	3.63	18.90	22.53	11.85	15.48	0.1594
15.1311 071	Pipe, PVC, sch 40, 3", in building, with fittings & supports	LF	7.05	22.81	29.86	14.30	21.35	0.1924
15.1311 081	Pipe, PVC, sch 40, 4", in building, with fittings & supports	LF	10.83	25.26	36.09	15.83	26.66	0.2130
15.1311 091	Pipe, PVC, sch 40, 5", in building, with fittings & supports	LF	18.24	31.58	49.82	19.80	38.04	0.2663
15.1311 101	Pipe, PVC, sch 40, 6", in building, with fittings & supports	LF	21.53	37.92	59.45	23.77	45.30	0.3198
15.1312 000	**ACID WASTE PIPE, POLYPROPYLENE:**							
15.1312 011	Pipe, polypropylene, 2", acid waste	LF	20.54	5.99	26.53	3.75	24.29	0.0505
15.1312 021	Pipe, polypropylene, 3", acid waste	LF	28.35	8.99	37.34	5.63	33.98	0.0758
15.1312 031	Pipe, polypropylene, 4", acid waste	LF	38.08	10.81	48.89	6.78	44.86	0.0912
15.1312 041	Pipe, polypropylene, 6", acid waste	LF	71.02	15.63	86.65	9.80	80.82	0.1318
15.1313 000	**PLASTIC 'DWV', ABS:**							
15.1313 011	Pipe, plastic, 'DWV', 1-1/2"	LF	8.09	14.54	22.63	9.11	17.20	0.1226
15.1313 021	Pipe, plastic, 'DWV', 2"	LF	10.46	18.90	29.36	11.85	22.31	0.1594
15.1313 031	Pipe, plastic, 'DWV', 3"	LF	15.65	22.81	38.46	14.30	29.95	0.1924
15.1313 041	Pipe, plastic, 'DWV', 4"	LF	26.62	25.26	51.88	15.83	42.45	0.2130
15.1313 051	Pipe, plastic, 'DWV', 6"	LF	100.60	25.90	126.50	16.24	116.84	0.2184
15.1314 000	**PYREX GLASS:**							
15.1314 011	Pipe, Pyrex, 1"	LF	23.21	24.76	47.97	15.52	38.73	0.2088
15.1314 021	Pipe, Pyrex, 1-1/2"	LF	32.81	27.25	60.06	17.08	49.89	0.2298
15.1314 031	Pipe, Pyrex, 2"	LF	40.23	29.74	69.97	18.64	58.87	0.2508
15.1314 041	Pipe, Pyrex, 3"	LF	44.12	38.31	82.43	24.02	68.14	0.3231
15.1314 051	Pipe, Pyrex, 4"	LF	76.91	51.88	128.79	32.52	109.43	0.4375
15.1315 000	**STEEL PIPE, BLACK, WELD, SCH 40, A-120, SCREWED:**							
	Note: The following prices include malleable iron fittings and supports.							
15.1315 011	Black steel pipe, weld, A-120, sch 40, 1/2", screwed	LF	2.06	8.92	10.98	5.59	7.65	0.0752
15.1315 021	Black steel pipe, weld, A-120, sch 40, 3/4", screwed	LF	2.42	11.04	13.46	6.92	9.34	0.0931
15.1315 031	Black steel pipe, weld, A-120, sch 40, 1", screwed	LF	3.11	13.30	16.41	8.34	11.45	0.1122
15.1315 041	Black steel pipe, weld, A-120, sch 40, 1-1/4", screwed	LF	4.33	14.36	18.69	9.00	13.33	0.1211
15.1315 051	Black steel pipe, weld, A-120, sch 40, 1-1/2", screwed	LF	4.88	16.62	21.50	10.42	15.30	0.1402
15.1315 061	Black steel pipe, weld, A-120, sch 40, 2", screwed	LF	6.50	22.63	29.13	14.18	20.68	0.1908
15.1315 071	Black steel pipe, weld, A-120, sch 40, 2-1/2", screwed	LF	9.98	27.17	37.15	17.03	27.01	0.2291
15.1315 081	Black steel pipe, weld, A-120, sch 40, 3", screwed	LF	13.48	31.71	45.19	19.88	33.36	0.2674
15.1315 091	Black steel pipe, weld, A-120, sch 40, 4", screwed	LF	23.51	41.35	64.86	25.92	49.43	0.3487
15.1315 101	Black steel pipe, weld, A-120, sch 40, 5", screwed	LF	30.27	44.72	74.99	28.03	58.30	0.3771
15.1315 111	Black steel pipe, weld, A-120, sch 40, 6", screwed	LF	34.71	49.98	84.69	31.33	66.04	0.4215
15.1316 000	**STEEL PIPE, GALVANIZED, WELD, SCH 40, A-120, SCREWED:**							
	Note: The following prices include gmi fittings and supports.							
15.1316 011	Galvanized steel pipe, A-120, sch 40, 1/2", screwed	LF	2.58	8.92	11.50	5.59	8.17	0.0752
15.1316 021	Galvanized steel pipe, A-120, sch 40, 3/4", screwed	LF	3.04	11.04	14.08	6.92	9.96	0.0931
15.1316 031	Galvanized steel pipe, A-120, sch 40, 1", screwed	LF	3.68	13.30	16.98	8.34	12.02	0.1122
15.1316 041	Galvanized steel pipe, A-120, sch 40, 1-1/4", screwed	LF	5.16	14.36	19.52	9.00	14.16	0.1211
15.1316 051	Galvanized steel pipe, A-120, sch 40, 1-1/2", screwed	LF	5.65	16.62	22.27	10.42	16.07	0.1402
15.1316 061	Galvanized steel pipe, A-120, sch 40, 2", screwed	LF	7.44	22.63	30.07	14.18	21.62	0.1908
15.1316 071	Galvanized steel pipe, A-120, sch 40, 2-1/2", screwed	LF	12.44	27.17	39.61	17.03	29.47	0.2291
15.1316 081	Galvanized steel pipe, A-120, sch 40, 3", screwed	LF	16.71	31.71	48.42	19.88	36.59	0.2674
15.1316 091	Galvanized steel pipe, A-120, sch 40, 4", screwed	LF	26.63	41.33	67.96	25.91	52.54	0.3485
15.1316 101	Galvanized steel pipe, A-120, sch 40, 5", screwed	LF	39.63	44.72	84.35	28.03	67.66	0.3771
15.1316 111	Galvanized steel pipe, A-120, sch 40, 6", screwed	LF	54.59	49.98	104.57	31.33	85.92	0.4215

Division 15 CSI #	15 - MECHANICAL Description	Unit	Material	Union Install	Union Total	Open Install	Open Total	Unit Man-Hrs
15.1317 000	**STEEL PIPE, BLACK, WELDED, SCH 40, A-53:**							
15.1317 011	Black steel pipe, welded, A-53, sch 40, 2"	LF	14.28	22.81	37.09	14.30	28.58	0.1924
15.1317 021	Black steel pipe, welded, A-53, sch 40, 2-1/2"	LF	18.80	29.08	47.88	18.23	37.03	0.2452
15.1317 031	Black steel pipe, welded, A-53, sch 40, 3"	LF	23.34	33.08	56.42	20.74	44.08	0.2790
15.1317 041	Black steel pipe, welded, A-53, sch 40, 4"	LF	32.65	42.49	75.14	26.64	59.29	0.3583
15.1318 000	**STEEL PIPE, SEAMLESS, SCH 40, A-53, WELDED:**							
15.1318 011	Steel pipe, seamless, A-53, sch 40, 2", welded	LF	17.01	22.81	39.82	14.30	31.31	0.1924
15.1318 021	Steel pipe, seamless, A-53, sch 40, 2-1/2", welded	LF	19.11	29.51	48.62	18.50	37.61	0.2489
15.1318 031	Steel pipe, seamless, A-53, sch 40, 3", welded	LF	23.34	33.02	56.36	20.70	44.04	0.2785
15.1318 041	Steel pipe, seamless, A-53, sch 40, 4", welded	LF	33.16	42.49	75.65	26.64	59.80	0.3583
15.1318 051	Steel pipe, seamless, A-53, sch 40, 5", welded	LF	39.88	47.25	87.13	29.62	69.50	0.3985
15.1318 061	Steel pipe, seamless, A-53, sch 40, 6", welded	LF	42.04	52.15	94.19	32.69	74.73	0.4398
15.1318 071	Steel pipe, seamless, A-53, sch 40, 8", welded	LF	64.45	58.15	122.60	36.46	100.91	0.4904
15.1318 081	Steel pipe, seamless, A-53, sch 40, 10", welded	LF	121.50	65.42	186.92	41.01	162.51	0.5517
15.1318 091	Steel pipe, seamless, A-53, sch 40, 12", welded	LF	184.61	85.41	270.02	53.55	238.16	0.7203
15.1319 000	**STEEL PIPE, SEAMLESS, SCH 80, A-53, WELDED:**							
15.1319 011	Steel pipe, seamless, A-53, sch 80, 2", welded	LF	18.23	26.17	44.40	16.41	34.64	0.2207
15.1319 021	Steel pipe, seamless, A-53, sch 80, 2-1/2", welded	LF	21.44	33.94	55.38	21.28	42.72	0.2862
15.1319 031	Steel pipe, seamless, A-53, sch 80, 3", welded	LF	26.39	37.90	64.29	23.76	50.15	0.3196
15.1319 041	Steel pipe, seamless, A-53, sch 80, 4", welded	LF	38.70	48.80	87.50	30.59	69.29	0.4115
15.1319 051	Steel pipe, seamless, A-53, sch 80, 5", welded	LF	47.00	54.35	101.35	34.07	81.07	0.4583
15.1319 061	Steel pipe, seamless, A-53, sch 80, 6", welded	LF	51.81	59.98	111.79	37.60	89.41	0.5058
15.1319 071	Steel pipe, seamless, A-53, sch 80, 8", welded	LF	79.53	66.88	146.41	41.93	121.46	0.5640
15.1319 081	Steel pipe, seamless, A-53, sch 80, 10", welded	LF	157.06	75.24	232.30	47.17	204.23	0.6345
15.1319 091	Steel pipe, seamless, A-53, sch 80, 12", welded	LF	233.97	98.15	332.12	61.53	295.50	0.8277
15.1320 000	**STEEL PIPE, BLACK, WELDED, SCH 40, A-120:**							
	Note: The following prices include victaulic couplings with victaulic fittings.							
15.1320 011	Black steel pipe, weld, A-120, sch 40, 2"	LF	16.80	12.05	28.85	7.55	24.35	0.1016
15.1320 021	Black steel pipe, weld, A-120, sch 40, 2-1/2"	LF	18.80	15.58	34.38	9.77	28.57	0.1314
15.1320 031	Black steel pipe, weld, A-120, sch 40, 3"	LF	23.34	17.44	40.78	10.94	34.28	0.1471
15.1320 041	Black steel pipe, weld, A-120, sch 40, 4"	LF	30.12	22.44	52.56	14.07	44.19	0.1892
15.1320 051	Black steel pipe, weld, A-120, sch 40, 5"	LF	39.26	24.95	64.21	15.64	54.90	0.2104
15.1320 061	Black steel pipe, weld, A-120, sch 40, 6"	LF	41.12	27.53	68.65	17.26	58.38	0.2322
15.1320 071	Black steel pipe, weld, A-120, sch 40, 8"	LF	68.45	30.68	99.13	19.23	87.68	0.2587
15.1320 081	Black steel pipe, weld, A-120, sch 40, 10"	LF	119.56	35.76	155.32	22.42	141.98	0.3016
15.1320 091	Black steel pipe, weld, A-120, sch 40, 12"	LF	182.18	57.84	240.02	36.26	218.44	0.4878
15.1321 000	**FLANGES, CAST IRON, SCREWED, BLACK, 125#:**							
15.1321 011	Cast iron flange, black, screwed, 125#, 1-1/2"	EA	29.43	86.34	115.77	54.13	83.56	0.7281
15.1321 021	Cast iron flange, black, screwed, 125#, 2"	EA	36.76	90.88	127.64	56.97	93.73	0.7664
15.1321 031	Cast iron flange, black, screwed, 125#, 2-1/2"	EA	43.94	99.96	143.90	62.67	106.61	0.8430
15.1321 041	Cast iron flange, black, screwed, 125#, 3"	EA	48.53	111.77	160.30	70.07	118.60	0.9426
15.1321 051	Cast iron flange, black, screwed, 125#, 4"	EA	64.52	136.31	200.83	85.45	149.97	1.1495
15.1321 061	Cast iron flange, black, screwed, 125#, 5"	EA	77.49	152.66	230.15	95.71	173.20	1.2874
15.1321 071	Cast iron flange, black, screwed, 125#, 6"	EA	76.79	179.00	255.79	112.22	189.01	1.5095
15.1321 081	Cast iron flange, black, screwed, 125#, 8"	EA	132.34	190.83	323.17	119.64	251.98	1.6093
15.1321 091	Cast iron flange, black, screwed, 125#, 10"	EA	215.31	214.45	429.76	134.44	349.75	1.8085
15.1322 000	**FLANGES, SLIP-ON, 150#:**							
15.1322 011	Steel flange, slip-on, 150#, 2"	EA	19.14	99.96	119.10	62.67	81.81	0.8430
15.1322 021	Steel flange, slip-on, 150#, 3"	EA	27.54	145.40	172.94	91.16	118.70	1.2262
15.1322 031	Steel flange, slip-on, 150#, 4"	EA	35.01	190.83	225.84	119.64	154.65	1.6093
15.1322 041	Steel flange, slip-on, 150#, 5"	EA	49.46	236.27	285.73	148.12	197.58	1.9925
15.1322 051	Steel flange, slip-on, 150#, 6"	EA	57.48	281.70	339.18	176.60	234.08	2.3756
15.1322 061	Steel flange, slip-on, 150#, 8"	EA	87.40	390.74	478.14	244.97	332.37	3.2952
15.1322 071	Steel flange, slip-on, 150#, 10"	EA	157.99	481.61	639.60	301.93	459.92	4.0615
15.1322 081	Steel flange, slip-on, 150#, 12"	EA	328.36	590.66	919.02	370.29	698.65	4.9811
15.1400 000	**VALVES & SPECIALTIES:**							
15.1401 000	**VACUUM BREAKERS, ANTI-SIPHON:**							
15.1401 011	Vacuum breaker, brass, 1/2", anti-siphon	EA	22.74	30.27	53.01	18.98	41.72	0.2553
15.1401 021	Vacuum breaker, brass, 3/4", anti-siphon	EA	26.86	36.33	63.19	22.78	49.64	0.3064
15.1401 031	Vacuum breaker, brass, 1", anti-siphon	EA	42.09	36.64	78.73	22.97	65.06	0.3090
15.1401 041	Vacuum breaker, brass, 1-1/4", anti-siphon	EA	70.17	45.38	115.55	28.45	98.62	0.3827
15.1401 051	Vacuum breaker, brass, 1-1/2", anti-siphon	EA	82.00	54.42	136.42	34.11	116.11	0.4589

Division 15 CSI #	15 - MECHANICAL Description	Unit	Material	Union Install	Union Total	Open Install	Open Total	Unit Man-Hrs
15.1401 000	**VACUUM BREAKERS, ANTI-SIPHON: (Cont.)**							
15.1401 061	Vacuum breaker, brass, 2", anti-siphon	EA	127.88	65.29	193.17	40.93	168.81	0.5506
15.1401 071	Vacuum breaker, brass, 2-1/2", anti-siphon	EA	367.87	222.35	590.22	139.39	507.26	1.8751
15.1401 081	Vacuum breaker, brass, 3", anti-siphon	EA	489.05	192.08	681.13	120.42	609.47	1.6198
15.1402 000	**STRAINERS, 'Y', WITH STAINLESS SCREENS:**							
15.1402 011	Y strainer, 1/2" screwed, 250# cast iron, stainless steel screen	EA	25.16	29.06	54.22	18.22	43.38	0.2451
15.1402 021	Y strainer, 3/4" screwed, 250# cast iron, stainless steel screen	EA	29.09	34.82	63.91	21.83	50.92	0.2936
15.1402 031	Y strainer, 1" screwed, 250# cast iron, stainless steel screen	EA	36.32	36.29	72.61	22.75	59.07	0.3060
15.1402 041	Y strainer, 1-1/4" screwed, 250# cast iron, screen	EA	55.33	46.46	101.79	29.13	84.46	0.3918
15.1402 051	Y strainer, 1-1/2" screwed, 250# cast iron, screen	EA	62.04	53.69	115.73	33.66	95.70	0.4528
15.1402 061	Y strainer, 2" screwed, 250# cast iron, screen	EA	94.03	64.07	158.10	40.17	134.20	0.5403
15.1402 071	Y strainer, 2-1/2" flange, 150# cast iron, screen	EA	310.33	191.46	501.79	120.03	430.36	1.6146
15.1402 081	Y strainer, 3" flange, 150# cast iron, stainless steel screen	EA	368.78	221.00	589.78	138.55	507.33	1.8637
15.1402 091	Y strainer, 4" flange, 150# cast iron, stainless steel screen	EA	653.69	324.99	978.68	203.74	857.43	2.7407
15.1402 101	Y strainer, 6" flange, 150# cast iron, stainless steel screen	EA	1,348.06	391.80	1,739.86	245.63	1,593.69	3.3041
15.1402 111	Y strainer, 8" flange, 150# cast iron, stainless steel screen	EA	2,149.32	534.27	2,683.59	334.95	2,484.27	4.5056
15.1402 121	Y strainer, 10" flange, 150# cast iron, stainless steel screen	EA	3,744.12	581.04	4,325.16	364.27	4,108.39	4.9000
15.1402 131	Y strainer 12" flange, 150# cast iron, stainless steel screen	EA	5,616.17	640.33	6,256.50	401.44	6,017.61	5.4000
15.1403 000	**GATE, GLOBE & CHECK VALVES, BRASS, 125#, SCREWED:**							
15.1403 011	Valves, brass, 125#, screwed, 1/2"	EA	12.17	30.36	42.53	19.03	31.20	0.2560
15.1403 021	Valves, brass, 125#, screwed, 3/4"	EA	15.82	36.36	52.18	22.79	38.61	0.3066
15.1403 031	Valves, brass, 125#, screwed, 1"	EA	22.61	37.90	60.51	23.76	46.37	0.3196
15.1403 041	Valves, brass, 125#, screwed, 1-1/4"	EA	32.22	48.52	80.74	30.42	62.64	0.4092
15.1403 051	Valves, brass, 125#, screwed, 1-1/2"	EA	42.38	79.79	122.17	50.02	92.40	0.6729
15.1403 061	Valves, brass, 125#, screwed, 2"	EA	64.16	135.18	199.34	84.75	148.91	1.1400
15.1403 071	Valves, brass, 125#, screwed, 2-1/2"	EA	115.44	183.80	299.24	115.23	230.67	1.5500
15.1403 081	Valves, brass, 125#, screwed, 3"	EA	160.92	227.67	388.59	142.73	303.65	1.9200
15.1403 091	Valves, brass, 125#, screwed, 4"	EA	347.47	320.17	667.64	200.72	548.19	2.7000
15.1404 000	**GATE, GLOBE, & CHECK VALVES, PVC:**							
15.1404 011	Valve, gate, globe & check, PVC, 1/2", solvent joint	EA	36.81	23.72	60.53	14.87	51.68	0.2000
15.1404 021	Valve, gate, globe & check, PVC, 3/4", solvent joint	EA	49.32	29.65	78.97	18.59	67.91	0.2500
15.1404 031	Valve, gate, globe & check, PVC, 1", solvent joint	EA	61.75	33.20	94.95	20.82	82.57	0.2800
15.1404 041	Valve, gate, globe & check, PVC, 1-1/4", solvent joint	EA	74.23	39.13	113.36	24.53	98.76	0.3300
15.1404 051	Valve, gate, globe & check, PVC, 1-1/2", solvent joint	EA	86.65	65.22	151.87	40.89	127.54	0.5500
15.1404 061	Valve, gate, globe & check, PVC, 2", solvent joint	EA	170.86	104.35	275.21	65.42	236.28	0.8800
15.1404 071	Valve, gate, globe & check, PVC, 2-1/2", solvent joint	EA	255.14	160.08	415.22	100.36	355.50	1.3500
15.1404 081	Valve, gate, globe & check, PVC, 3", solvent joint	EA	421.96	203.96	625.92	127.86	549.82	1.7200
15.1404 091	Valve, gate, globe & check, PVC, 4", solvent joint	EA	588.78	231.23	820.01	144.96	733.74	1.9500
15.1405 000	**GATE, GLOBE & CHECK VALVES, IRON, FLANGED, 125#:**							
	Note: The following prices do not include companion flanges or bolt and gaskets sets.							
15.1405 011	Valve, gate, globe & check, iron body, flange, 125#, 2"	EA	404.51	167.39	571.90	104.94	509.45	1.4116
15.1405 021	Valve, gate, globe & check, iron body, flange, 125#, 2-1/2"	EA	442.18	199.93	642.11	125.34	567.52	1.6860
15.1405 031	Valve, gate, globe & check, iron body, flange, 125#, 3"	EA	504.59	232.46	737.05	145.74	650.33	1.9604
15.1405 041	Valve, gate, globe & check, iron body, flange, 125#, 4"	EA	740.42	339.35	1,079.77	212.75	953.17	2.8618
15.1405 051	Valve, gate, globe & check, iron body, flange, 125#, 5-6"	EA	1,283.88	450.60	1,734.48	282.49	1,566.37	3.8000
15.1405 061	Valve, gate, globe & check, iron body, flange, 125#, 8"	EA	2,535.83	664.05	3,199.88	416.30	2,952.13	5.6000
15.1405 071	Valve, gate, globe & check, iron body, flange, 125#, 10"	EA	4,190.40	889.35	5,079.75	557.55	4,747.95	7.5000
15.1405 081	Valve, gate, globe & check, iron body, flange, 125#, 12"	EA	5,597.71	1,173.94	6,771.65	735.97	6,333.68	9.9000
15.1405 091	Valve, gate, globe & check, iron body, flange, 125#, 14"	EA	9,167.62	1,458.53	10,626.15	914.38	10,082.00	12.3000
15.1406 000	**GAS SERVICE COCKS, BRASS, SCREWED:**							
15.1406 011	Gas cock, brass, screwed, 1/2"	EA	29.90	41.80	71.70	26.20	56.10	0.3525
15.1406 021	Gas cock, brass, screwed, 3/4"	EA	35.01	44.18	79.19	27.70	62.71	0.3726
15.1406 031	Gas cock, brass, screwed, 1"	EA	50.36	61.86	112.22	38.78	89.14	0.5217
15.1406 041	Gas cock, brass, screwed, 1-1/4"	EA	59.17	72.06	131.23	45.18	104.35	0.6077
15.1406 051	Gas cock, brass, screwed, 1-1/2"	EA	98.22	79.54	177.76	49.87	148.09	0.6708
15.1406 061	Gas cock, brass, screwed, 2"	EA	154.30	114.80	269.10	71.97	226.27	0.9681
15.1406 071	Gas cock, iron, flanged, 2-1/2"	EA	263.25	154.15	417.40	96.64	359.89	1.3000
15.1406 081	Gas cock, iron, flanged, 3"	EA	417.13	201.59	618.72	126.38	543.51	1.7000
15.1406 091	Gas cock, iron, flanged, 4"	EA	646.01	249.02	895.03	156.11	802.12	2.1000
15.1407 000	**HOSE GATE VALVE, WITH BRASS CAP & HOSE BIBB:**							
15.1407 011	Hose gate valve, 1", with cap & bibb	EA	150.79	43.26	194.05	27.12	177.91	0.3648
15.1407 021	Hose gate valve, 1-1/2", cap, bibb	EA	235.57	58.63	294.20	36.75	272.32	0.4944

Division 15 CSI #	15 - MECHANICAL Description	Unit	Material	Union Install	Union Total	Open Install	Open Total	Unit Man-Hrs
15.1407 000	**HOSE GATE VALVE, WITH BRASS CAP & HOSE BIBB: (Cont.)**							
15.1407 031	Hose gate valve, 2", with cap & bibb	EA	335.48	86.59	422.07	54.28	389.76	0.7302
15.1407 041	Hose bibb, brass, 3/4"	EA	21.74	36.12	57.86	22.64	44.38	0.3046
15.1407 051	Hose bibb, with wall box, 3/4"	EA	68.48	60.16	128.64	37.71	106.19	0.5073
15.1407 061	Wall hydrant, auto drain, wall to 14" thick	EA	236.25	88.94	325.19	55.76	292.01	0.7500
15.1407 071	Wall hydrant with box, wall to 14" thick	EACH	417.66	112.65	530.31	70.62	488.28	0.9500
15.1408 000	**PRESSURE REDUCING VALVE, IRON, BRONZE TRIM, 125, 0-100:**							
15.1408 011	Pressure reducing valve, brass, 125#, 0-100, 3/4"	EA	132.89	59.29	192.18	37.17	170.06	0.5000
15.1408 021	Pressure reducing valve, brass, 125#, 0-100, 1"	EA	207.00	71.15	278.15	44.60	251.60	0.6000
15.1408 031	Pressure reducing valve, iron body, bronze trim, 125#, 0-100, 1-1/2"	EA	603.97	145.81	749.78	91.41	695.38	1.2296
15.1408 041	Pressure reducing valve, iron body, bronze trim, 125#, 0-100, 2"	EA	1,242.04	165.00	1,407.04	103.44	1,345.48	1.3915
15.1408 051	Pressure reducing valve, iron body, bronze trim, 125#, 0-100, 3"	EA	1,567.56	194.33	1,761.89	121.83	1,689.39	1.6388
15.1408 061	Pressure reducing valve, iron body, bronze trim, 125#, 0-100, 4"	EA	1,927.07	320.65	2,247.72	201.02	2,128.09	2.7041
15.1408 071	Pressure reducing valve, iron body, bronze trim, 125#, 0-100, 6"	EA	2,879.11	398.42	3,277.53	249.77	3,128.88	3.3599
15.1408 081	Pressure reducing valve, iron body, bronze trim, 125#, 0-100, 8"	EA	4,824.69	524.66	5,349.35	328.92	5,153.61	4.4245
15.1408 091	Pressure reducing valve, iron body, bronze trim, 125#, 0-100, 10"	EA	9,627.41	719.06	10,346.47	450.79	10,078.20	6.0639
15.1409 000	**RELIEF VALVES, BRONZE, SCREWED, HOT WATER:**							
15.1409 011	Valve, relief, hot water, screwed, bronze, 3/4"	EA	53.21	39.87	93.08	24.99	78.20	0.3362
15.1409 021	Valve, relief, hot water, screwed, bronze, 1"	EA	69.97	48.61	118.58	30.47	100.44	0.4099
15.1409 031	Valve, relief, hot water, screwed, bronze, 1-1/2"	EA	226.50	66.03	292.53	41.39	267.89	0.5568
15.1409 041	Valve, relief, hot water, screwed, bronze, 2"	EA	254.98	106.89	361.87	67.01	321.99	0.9014
15.1410 000	**GAS REGULATOR, SCREWED, WITH AUTO SHUTOFF & RELIEF:**							
15.1410 011	Gas regulator valve, screwed, 1", shut off, relief	EA	261.35	48.61	309.96	30.47	291.82	0.4099
15.1410 021	Gas regulator valve, screwed, 1-1/2", shut off, relief	EA	315.80	66.03	381.83	41.39	357.19	0.5568
15.1410 031	Gas regulator valve, screwed, 2", shut off, relief	EA	592.58	106.89	699.47	67.01	659.59	0.9014
15.1410 041	Gas regulator valve, quake, shut off, CA approved, 3/4"	EA	644.19	41.05	685.24	25.74	669.93	0.3462
15.1410 051	Gas regulator valve, quake, shut off, CA approved, 2"	EA	5,897.80	108.07	6,005.87	67.75	5,965.55	0.9114
15.1411 000	**STEAM TRAPS, CAST IRON, SCREWED, WITH STAINLESS STEEL BUCKET:**							
15.1411 011	Steam trap, cast iron, screwed, 1/2", bucket	EA	235.14	38.92	274.06	24.40	259.54	0.3282
15.1411 021	Steam trap, cast iron, screwed, 3/4", bucket	EA	377.17	53.70	430.87	33.67	410.84	0.4529
15.1411 031	Steam trap, cast iron, screwed, 1", stainless steel bucket	EA	749.99	67.97	817.96	42.61	792.60	0.5732
15.1411 041	Steam trap, cast iron, screwed, 1-1/2", bucket	EA	1,163.97	87.44	1,251.41	54.82	1,218.79	0.7374
15.1412 000	**THERMOSTATIC MIXING VALVES:**							
15.1412 011	Thermostatic mix valve, cab, 3/4x3/4	EA	2,249.82	148.23	2,398.05	92.93	2,342.75	1.2500
15.1412 021	Thermostatic mix valve, cab, 3/4 x 1	EA	2,638.91	157.71	2,796.62	98.87	2,737.78	1.3300
15.1413 000	**VALVES, SOLENOID:**							
15.1413 011	Valve, solenoid, water or air, 1/2"	EA	163.83	59.29	223.12	37.17	201.00	0.5000
15.1413 021	Valve, solenoid, water or air, 3/4"	EA	204.04	59.29	263.33	37.17	241.21	0.5000
15.1413 031	Valve, solenoid, water or air, 1"	EA	321.42	71.15	392.57	44.60	366.02	0.6000
15.1413 051	Valve, solenoid, water or air, 1-1/2"	EA	596.47	94.86	691.33	59.47	655.94	0.8000
15.1413 061	Valve, solenoid, water or air, 2"	EA	883.89	118.58	1,002.47	74.34	958.23	1.0000
15.1413 071	Valve, solenoid, gas, 1/2"	EA	157.57	59.29	216.86	37.17	194.74	0.5000
15.1413 081	Valve, solenoid, gas, 3/4"	EA	183.52	59.29	242.81	37.17	220.69	0.5000
15.1413 091	Valve, solenoid, gas, 1"	EA	255.91	71.15	327.06	44.60	300.51	0.6000
15.1414 000	**BACKFLOW PREVENTERS, WITH SUPPORTS:**							
15.1414 011	Backflow preventer, 3/4" screwed	EA	1,141.49	106.38	1,247.87	66.69	1,208.18	0.8971
15.1414 021	Backflow preventer, 1" screwed	EA	1,155.71	119.88	1,275.59	75.16	1,230.87	1.0110
15.1414 031	Backflow preventer, 1-1/2" screwed	EA	1,821.75	223.05	2,044.80	139.83	1,961.58	1.8810
15.1414 041	Backflow preventer, 2" screwed	EA	4,366.48	250.22	4,616.70	156.86	4,523.34	2.1101
15.1414 051	Backflow preventer, 3" flanged	EA	5,710.05	358.23	6,068.28	224.58	5,934.63	3.0210
15.1414 061	Backflow preventer, 4" flanged	EA	6,777.38	696.66	7,474.04	436.75	7,214.13	5.8750
15.1414 071	Backflow preventer, 6" flanged	EA	9,976.92	762.94	10,739.86	478.30	10,455.22	6.4340
15.1414 081	Backflow preventer, 8" flanged	EA	17,013.33	1,003.90	18,017.23	629.36	17,642.69	8.4660
15.1414 091	Backflow preventer, 10" flanged	EA	18,681.16	1,377.19	20,058.35	863.38	19,544.54	11.6140
15.1415 000	**VICTAULIC COUPLINGS:**							
15.1415 011	Victaulic coupling, 2"	EA	36.84	14.54	51.38	9.11	45.95	0.1226
15.1415 021	Victaulic coupling, 3"	EA	49.59	14.54	64.13	9.11	58.70	0.1226
15.1415 031	Victaulic coupling, 4"	EA	70.30	14.54	84.84	9.11	79.41	0.1226
15.1415 041	Victaulic coupling, 6"	EA	122.17	18.18	140.35	11.40	133.57	0.1533
15.1415 051	Victaulic coupling, 8"	EA	192.47	18.18	210.65	11.40	203.87	0.1533
15.1415 061	Victaulic coupling, 10"	EA	294.87	18.18	313.05	11.40	306.27	0.1533
15.1415 071	Victaulic coupling, 12"	EA	330.05	18.18	348.23	11.40	341.45	0.1533

Division 15 CSI #	15 - MECHANICAL Description	Unit	Material	Union Install	Union Total	Open Install	Open Total	Unit Man-Hrs
15.1416 000	**WATER METER, TURBINE, AWWA:**							
	Note: The following prices include flanges and bolt-ups.							
15.1416 011	Water meter, turbine, 3/4"	EA	290.49	110.64	401.13	69.36	359.85	0.9330
15.1416 021	Water meter, turbine, 1-1/4"	EA	593.23	142.53	735.76	89.36	682.59	1.2020
15.1416 031	Water meter, turbine, with 2 bolt & gaskets, 2"	EA	1,300.62	127.14	1,427.76	79.71	1,380.33	1.0722
15.1416 041	Water meter, turbine, with 2 bolt & gaskets, 3"	EA	1,913.50	310.73	2,224.23	194.80	2,108.30	2.6204
15.1416 051	Water meter, turbine, with 2 bolt & gaskets, 4"	EA	3,808.42	482.62	4,291.04	302.56	4,110.98	4.0700
15.1416 061	Water meter, turbine, with 2 bolt & gaskets, 6"	EA	5,715.93	1,332.84	7,048.77	835.58	6,551.51	11.2400
15.1416 071	Water meter, turbine, with 2 bolt & gaskets, 8"	EA	9,317.56	640.33	9,957.89	401.44	9,719.00	5.4000
15.1416 081	Add remote reader	EA	10,055.07	239.53	10,294.60	150.17	10,205.24	2.0200
15.1417 000	**VALVE, EARTHQUAKE ACTUATED, GAS SHUT OFF:**							
15.1417 011	Valve, earthquake actuated, gas shut off, 3/4"	EA	341.87	41.05	382.92	25.74	367.61	0.3462
15.1417 021	Valve, earthquake actuated, gas shut off, 1"	EA	366.95	53.36	420.31	33.45	400.40	0.4500
15.1417 031	Valve, earthquake actuated, gas shut off, 1-1/4"	EA	389.69	73.52	463.21	46.09	435.78	0.6200
15.1417 041	Valve, earthquake actuated, gas shut off, 1-1/2"	EA	414.74	89.65	504.39	56.20	470.94	0.7560
15.1417 051	Valve, earthquake actuated, gas shut off, flanged, 2"	EA	2,734.79	108.07	2,842.86	67.75	2,802.54	0.9114
15.1417 061	Valve, earthquake actuated, gas shut off, flanged, 3"	EA	5,232.61	177.87	5,410.48	111.51	5,344.12	1.5000
15.1417 071	Valve, earthquake actuated, gas shut off, flanged, 4"	EA	6,800.55	237.16	7,037.71	148.68	6,949.23	2.0000
15.1418 000	**EXPANSION JOINTS:**							
15.1418 011	Expansion joints, neoprene, flanged, 6" length, to 1-1/2"	EA	403.02	94.90	497.92	59.49	462.51	0.8003
15.1418 021	Expansion joints, neoprene, flanged, 6" length, to 3"	EA	489.23	176.47	665.70	110.63	599.86	1.4882
15.1418 031	Expansion joints, neoprene, flanged, 6" length, to 4"	EA	514.30	239.45	753.75	150.11	664.41	2.0193
15.1418 041	Expansion joints, neoprene, flanged, 6" length, to 6"	EA	654.33	293.25	947.58	183.84	838.17	2.4730
15.1418 051	Expansion joints, neoprene, flanged, 6" length, to 8"	EA	747.79	372.44	1,120.23	233.49	981.28	3.1408
15.1418 061	Expansion joints, neoprene, flanged, 6" length, to 10"	EA	1,056.18	402.19	1,458.37	252.14	1,308.32	3.3917
15.1418 071	Expansion joints, neoprene, flanged, 6" length, to 12"	EA	1,190.70	437.19	1,627.89	274.08	1,464.78	3.6869
15.1418 111	Expansion joints, neoprene, flanged, 10" length, to 3"	EA	701.75	182.12	883.87	114.17	815.92	1.5358
15.1418 121	Expansion joints, neoprene, flanged, 10" length, to 4"	EA	781.54	250.32	1,031.86	156.93	938.47	2.1110
15.1418 131	Expansion joints, neoprene, flanged, 10" length, to 6"	EA	935.65	333.80	1,269.45	209.27	1,144.92	2.8150
15.1418 141	Expansion joints, neoprene, flanged, 10" length, to 8"	EA	1,105.15	400.52	1,505.67	251.09	1,356.24	3.3776
15.1418 151	Expansion joints, neoprene, flanged, 10" length, to 10"	EA	1,214.17	435.41	1,649.58	272.97	1,487.14	3.6719
15.1418 161	Expansion joints, neoprene, flanged, 10" length, to 12"	EA	1,383.61	502.20	1,885.81	314.84	1,698.45	4.2351
15.1418 171	Expansion joints, neoprene, flanged, 10" length, to 16"	EA	1,990.68	690.54	2,681.22	432.91	2,423.59	5.8234
15.1418 181	Expansion joints, neoprene, flanged, 10" length, to 20"	EA	2,349.56	953.61	3,303.17	597.83	2,947.39	8.0419
15.1418 191	Expansion joints, neoprene, flanged, 10" length, to 24"	EA	2,725.78	1,112.56	3,838.34	697.49	3,423.27	9.3824
15.1418 211	Expansion joints, neoprene, flanged, 10" length, to 30"	EA	3,364.88	1,692.36	5,057.24	1,060.97	4,425.85	14.2710
15.1418 221	Expansion joints, neoprene, flanged, 10" length, to 36"	EA	4,112.28	2,009.07	6,121.35	1,259.52	5,371.80	16.9427
15.1500 000	**INSULATION, PIPING:**							
	Note: Prices include insulation allowance at pipe runs, valves and fittings.							
15.1501 000	**INSULATION, 1-1/2" CALCIUM SILICATE:**							
	Note:							
	For 1" calsil on pipe sizes 1" to 6" .... add 28% to material cost							
	For 2" calsil on sizes 1" to 6" .... add 56%							
	For 2" calsil on sizes 8" to 14" .... add 41%							
	For 2 1/2" calsil on sizes 1" to 6" .... add 94%							
	For 2 1/2" calsil on sizes 8" to 14" .... add 80%							
15.1501 011	Insulation, 1-1/2" calcium silicate, 1/2" pipe	LF	3.96	3.09	7.05	1.94	5.90	0.0261
15.1501 021	Insulation, 1-1/2" calcium silicate, 3/4" pipe	LF	4.03	3.09	7.12	1.94	5.97	0.0261
15.1501 031	Insulation, 1-1/2" calcium silicate, 1" pipe	LF	4.34	3.09	7.43	1.94	6.28	0.0261
15.1501 041	Insulation, 1-1/2" calcium silicate, 1-1/4" pipe	LF	4.50	3.09	7.59	1.94	6.44	0.0261
15.1501 051	Insulation, 1-1/2" calcium silicate, 1-1/2" pipe	LF	4.89	3.09	7.98	1.94	6.83	0.0261
15.1501 061	Insulation, 1-1/2" calcium silicate, 2" pipe	LF	5.41	4.55	9.96	2.85	8.26	0.0384
15.1501 071	Insulation, 1-1/2" calcium silicate, 2-1/2" pipe	LF	5.87	4.55	10.42	2.85	8.72	0.0384
15.1501 081	Insulation, 1-1/2" calcium silicate, 3" pipe	LF	6.18	6.10	12.28	3.82	10.00	0.0514
15.1501 091	Insulation, 1-1/2" calcium silicate, 4" pipe	LF	7.11	6.10	13.21	3.82	10.93	0.0514
15.1501 101	Insulation, 1-1/2" calcium silicate, 5" pipe	LF	8.00	6.10	14.10	3.82	11.82	0.0514
15.1501 111	Insulation, 1-1/2" calcium silicate, 6" pipe	LF	8.24	6.10	14.34	3.82	12.06	0.0514
15.1501 121	Insulation, 1-1/2" calcium silicate, 8" pipe	LF	11.19	7.64	18.83	4.79	15.98	0.0644
15.1501 131	Insulation, 1-1/2" calcium silicate, 10" pipe	LF	14.92	9.10	24.02	5.70	20.62	0.0767
15.1501 141	Insulation, 1-1/2" calcium silicate, 12" pipe	LF	17.61	10.64	28.25	6.67	24.28	0.0897
15.1501 151	Insulation, 1-1/2" calcium silicate, 14" pipe	LF	20.02	10.64	30.66	6.67	26.69	0.0897

Division 15 CSI #	15 - MECHANICAL Description	Unit	Material	Union Install	Union Total	Open Install	Open Total	Unit Man-Hrs
15.1502 000	**INSULATION, 3" CALCIUM SILICATE:**							
15.1502 011	Insulation, 3" calcium silicate, 3" pipe	LF	13.94	9.10	23.04	5.70	19.64	0.0767
15.1502 021	Insulation, 3" calcium silicate, 4" pipe	LF	18.27	9.10	27.37	5.70	23.97	0.0767
15.1502 031	Insulation, 3" calcium silicate, 5" pipe	LF	20.78	9.10	29.88	5.70	26.48	0.0767
15.1502 041	Insulation, 3" calcium silicate, 6" pipe	LF	22.40	9.10	31.50	5.70	28.10	0.0767
15.1502 061	Insulation, 3" calcium silicate, 8" pipe	LF	26.62	12.27	38.89	7.69	34.31	0.1035
15.1502 071	Insulation, 3" calcium silicate, 10" pipe	LF	32.09	13.64	45.73	8.55	40.64	0.1150
15.1502 081	Insulation, 3" calcium silicate, 12" pipe	LF	35.54	16.36	51.90	10.26	45.80	0.1380
15.1502 101	Insulation, 3" calcium silicate, 14" pipe	LF	39.87	18.85	58.72	11.82	51.69	0.1590
15.1503 000	**INSULATION, 1" FIBERGLASS WITH ALUMINUM JACKET:**							
	Note:							
	For 1-1/2" fiberglass, sizes 1/2" to 1-1/2" . . . add 100% to matl							
	For sizes 2" to 3" . . . . add 70%							
	For sizes 4" to 6" . . . . add 45%							
	For sizes 8" to 12" . . . . add 25%							
15.1503 011	Insulation, 1" fiberglass, 1/2" pipe, with aluminum jacket	LF	2.12	4.55	6.67	2.85	4.97	0.0384
15.1503 021	Insulation, 1" fiberglass, 3/4" pipe, with aluminum jacket	LF	2.28	4.55	6.83	2.85	5.13	0.0384
15.1503 031	Insulation, 1" fiberglass, 1" pipe, with aluminum jacket	LF	2.43	4.55	6.98	2.85	5.28	0.0384
15.1503 041	Insulation, 1" fiberglass, 1-1/4" pipe, with aluminum jacket	LF	2.98	4.55	7.53	2.85	5.83	0.0384
15.1503 051	Insulation, 1" fiberglass, 1-1/2" pipe, with aluminum jacket	LF	3.02	4.55	7.57	2.85	5.87	0.0384
15.1503 061	Insulation, 1" fiberglass, 2" pipe, with aluminum jacket	LF	3.27	6.10	9.37	3.82	7.09	0.0514
15.1503 071	Insulation, 1" fiberglass, 2-1/2" pipe, with aluminum jacket	LF	3.62	6.10	9.72	3.82	7.44	0.0514
15.1503 081	Insulation, 1" fiberglass, 3" pipe, with aluminum jacket	LF	4.03	7.64	11.67	4.79	8.82	0.0644
15.1503 091	Insulation, 1" fiberglass, 4" pipe, with aluminum jacket	LF	5.28	7.64	12.92	4.79	10.07	0.0644
15.1503 101	Insulation, 1" fiberglass, 5" pipe, with aluminum jacket	LF	6.01	7.64	13.65	4.79	10.80	0.0644
15.1503 111	Insulation, 1" fiberglass, 6" pipe, with aluminum jacket	LF	6.50	7.64	14.14	4.79	11.29	0.0644
15.1503 121	Insulation, 1" fiberglass, 8" pipe, with aluminum jacket	LF	9.34	12.27	21.61	7.69	17.03	0.1035
15.1503 131	Insulation, 1" fiberglass, 10" pipe, with aluminum jacket	LF	11.00	16.72	27.72	10.48	21.48	0.1410
15.1503 141	Insulation, 1" fiberglass, 12" pipe, with aluminum jacket	LF	12.60	18.18	30.78	11.40	24.00	0.1533
15.1504 000	**INSULATION, 2" FIBERGLASS WITH ALUMINUM JACKET:**							
15.1504 011	Insulation, 2" fiberglass, 1/2" pipe, with aluminum jacket	LF	7.05	6.10	13.15	3.82	10.87	0.0514
15.1504 021	Insulation, 2" fiberglass, 3/4" pipe, with aluminum jacket	LF	7.24	6.10	13.34	3.82	11.06	0.0514
15.1504 031	Insulation, 2" fiberglass, 1" pipe, with aluminum jacket	LF	7.63	6.10	13.73	3.82	11.45	0.0514
15.1504 041	Insulation, 2" fiberglass, 1-1/4" pipe with aluminum jacket	LF	8.09	6.10	14.19	3.82	11.91	0.0514
15.1504 051	Insulation, 2" fiberglass, 1-1/2" pipe, with aluminum jacket	LF	8.53	6.10	14.63	3.82	12.35	0.0514
15.1504 061	Insulation, 2" fiberglass, 2" pipe, with aluminum jacket	LF	8.84	7.64	16.48	4.79	13.63	0.0644
15.1504 071	Insulation, 2" fiberglass, 2-1/2" pipe, with aluminum jacket	LF	9.60	7.64	17.24	4.79	14.39	0.0644
15.1504 081	Insulation, 2" fiberglass, 3" pipe, with aluminum jacket	LF	10.19	9.10	19.29	5.70	15.89	0.0767
15.1504 091	Insulation, 2" fiberglass, 4" pipe, with aluminum jacket	LF	11.92	9.10	21.02	5.70	17.62	0.0767
15.1504 101	Insulation, 2" fiberglass, 5" pipe, with aluminum jacket	LF	13.43	9.10	22.53	5.70	19.13	0.0767
15.1504 111	Insulation, 2" fiberglass, 6" pipe, with aluminum jacket	LF	13.70	9.10	22.80	5.70	19.40	0.0767
15.1504 121	Insulation, 2" fiberglass, 8" pipe, with aluminum jacket	LF	17.01	13.64	30.65	8.55	25.56	0.1150
15.1504 131	Insulation, 2" fiberglass, 10" pipe, with aluminum jacket	LF	20.27	18.18	38.45	11.40	31.67	0.1533
15.1504 141	Insulation, 2" fiberglass, 12" pipe, with aluminum jacket	LF	22.64	19.72	42.36	12.36	35.00	0.1663
15.1505 000	**INSULATION, VALVES, FIBERGLASS WITH ALUMINUM JACKET:**							
15.1505 011	Insulation, fiberglass, 1" valve, with aluminum jacket	EA	8.76	41.80	50.56	26.20	34.96	0.3525
15.1505 021	Insulation, fiberglass, 2" valve, with aluminum jacket	EA	23.46	67.25	90.71	42.16	65.62	0.5671
15.1505 031	Insulation, fiberglass, 3" valve, with aluminum jacket	EA	30.05	86.34	116.39	54.13	84.18	0.7281
15.1505 041	Insulation, fiberglass, 4" valve, with aluminum jacket	EA	35.17	108.13	143.30	67.79	102.96	0.9119
15.1505 051	Insulation, fiberglass, 6" valve, with aluminum jacket	EA	54.92	160.84	215.76	100.83	155.75	1.3564
15.1505 061	Insulation, fiberglass, 8" valve, with aluminum jacket	EA	62.50	210.81	273.31	132.16	194.66	1.7778
15.1505 071	Insulation, fiberglass, 10" valve, with aluminum jacket	EA	70.27	276.24	346.51	173.18	243.45	2.3296
15.1505 081	Insulation, fiberglass, 12" valve, with aluminum jacket	EA	78.15	365.30	443.45	229.01	307.16	3.0806
15.1600 000	**MISCELLANEOUS PLUMBING SPECIALTIES:**							
15.1601 000	**ACCESS DOORS:**							
	Note: For fire rating, add 300% to the material costs. Stainless steel, add 200%.							
15.1601 011	Access door, painted steel, 8" x 8"	EA	68.87	36.36	105.23	22.79	91.66	0.3066
15.1601 021	Access door, painted steel, 12" x 12"	EA	77.03	36.36	113.39	22.79	99.82	0.3066
15.1601 031	Access door, painted steel, 18" x 18"	EA	110.06	45.44	155.50	28.49	138.55	0.3832
15.1601 041	Access door, 24" x 24", painted steel	EA	156.89	45.44	202.33	28.49	185.38	0.3832
15.1601 051	Access door, painted steel, 36" x 36"	EA	305.48	63.62	369.10	39.88	345.36	0.5365

Division 15 CSI #	15 - MECHANICAL Description	Unit	Material	Union Install	Union Total	Open Install	Open Total	Unit Man-Hrs
15.1602 000	**CLEANOUTS, CAST IRON, FLOOR & WALL:**							
15.1602 011	Floor cleanout, cast iron, 2" & 3"	EA	144.01	95.42	239.43	59.82	203.83	0.8047
15.1602 021	Floor cleanout, cast iron, 4"	EA	195.81	97.22	293.03	60.95	256.76	0.8199
15.1602 031	Floor cleanout, cast iron, 6"	EA	341.32	99.96	441.28	62.67	403.99	0.8430
15.1602 041	Floor cleanout, cast iron, 8"	EA	351.34	113.59	464.93	71.21	422.55	0.9579
15.1602 051	Cleanout, cast iron, 4", to grade	EA	304.47	99.96	404.43	62.67	367.14	0.8430
15.1602 061	Cleanout, cast iron, 6", to grade	EA	498.28	113.59	611.87	71.21	569.49	0.9579
15.1602 071	Cleanout, cast iron, 8", to grade	EA	568.72	127.22	695.94	79.76	648.48	1.0729
15.1602 081	Wall cleanout, cast iron, 2"	EA	42.23	90.88	133.11	56.97	99.20	0.7664
15.1602 091	Wall cleanout, cast iron, 4"	EA	53.79	95.42	149.21	59.82	113.61	0.8047
15.1602 101	Wall cleanout, cast iron, 6"	EA	92.71	97.22	189.93	60.95	153.66	0.8199
15.1603 000	**DRAINS, CAST IRON, AREA & FLOOR:**							
15.1603 011	Area drain, 2", cast iron, with 5" x 5" strainer	EA	125.62	136.31	261.93	85.45	211.07	1.1495
15.1603 021	Area drain, 3", cast iron, with 6" x 6" strainer	EA	145.60	136.31	281.91	85.45	231.05	1.1495
15.1603 031	Area drain, 4", cast iron, with 8" x 8" strainer	EA	259.96	136.31	396.27	85.45	345.41	1.1495
15.1603 041	Floor drain, 2"-4", cast iron, with trap	EA	149.14	136.31	285.45	85.45	234.59	1.1495
15.1603 051	Floor drain, 6", cast iron, with trap	EA	378.94	159.03	537.97	99.70	478.64	1.3411
15.1604 000	**DRAINS, ROOF, CAST IRON, WITH ALUMINUM DOMES:**							
	Note: For best quality roof drains, add 75% to the material costs.							
15.1604 011	Roof drain, cast iron, 2"-4", aluminum dome	EA	181.65	172.66	354.31	108.25	289.90	1.4561
15.1604 021	Roof drain, cast iron, 5"-6", aluminum dome	EA	259.20	218.09	477.29	136.73	395.93	1.8392
15.1604 031	Roof drain, cast iron, 8", aluminum dome	EA	336.96	254.44	591.40	159.51	496.47	2.1457
15.1605 000	**DRAINS, SHOWER, WITH NICALOY STRAINER:**							
15.1605 011	Shower drain, 1-1/2", with 4" strainer	EA	101.61	145.40	247.01	91.16	192.77	1.2262
15.1605 021	Shower drain, 2", with 7" strainer	EA	157.76	145.40	303.16	91.16	248.92	1.2262
15.1605 031	Shower drain, 3", with 7" strainer	EA	171.86	163.57	335.43	102.54	274.40	1.3794
15.1605 041	Shower drain, 4", with 8" strainer	EA	192.95	190.83	383.78	119.64	312.59	1.6093
15.1605 051	Shower drain, 2", with 5" x 5" strainer	EA	174.42	145.40	319.82	91.16	265.58	1.2262
15.1605 061	Shower drain, 3", with 6" x 6" strainer	EA	192.87	163.57	356.44	102.54	295.41	1.3794
15.1605 071	Shower drain, 4", with 8" x 8" strainer	EA	270.66	190.83	461.49	119.64	390.30	1.6093
15.1606 000	**MISCELLANEOUS ITEMS:**							
15.1606 011	Roof jacks, galvanized iron, 4"	EA	60.85	36.36	97.21	22.79	83.64	0.3066
15.1606 021	Roof jacks, galvanized iron, 6"	EA	93.94	45.44	139.38	28.49	122.43	0.3832
15.1606 031	Water hammer arrestor, 1-11 FU, 3/4"	EACH	129.67	54.55	184.22	34.20	163.87	0.4600
15.1606 041	Water hammer arrestor, 12-32 FU, 1"	EA	259.76	56.92	316.68	35.68	295.44	0.4800
15.1606 051	Water hammer arrestor, 33-60 FU, 1"	EA	388.74	56.92	445.66	35.68	424.42	0.4800
15.1606 061	Water hammer arrestor, 61-113 FU, 1"	EA	974.89	56.92	1,031.81	35.68	1,010.57	0.4800
15.1607 000	**FIRE BARRIER PENETRATION SYSTEM, PLASTIC PIPE:**							
	Note: The following systems are rated for 4 hours.							
15.1607 011	Fire barrier, water, coupling, fitting with plug, 1/2-1-1/2"	EA	2.16	9.25	11.41	5.80	7.96	0.0780
15.1607 021	Fire barrier, water, coupling, fitting with plug, 2"	EA	5.58	10.71	16.29	6.71	12.29	0.0903
15.1607 031	Fire barrier, water, coupling, fitting with plug, 2-1/2-3"	EA	6.61	13.08	19.69	8.20	14.81	0.1103
15.1607 041	Fire barrier, water, coupling, fitting with plug, 4-5"	EA	9.55	14.79	24.34	9.27	18.82	0.1247
15.1607 051	Fire barrier, water, coupling, fitting with plug, 6"	EA	21.10	16.03	37.13	10.05	31.15	0.1352
15.1607 061	Fire barrier, water, coupling, fitting with plug, 8"	EA	32.22	17.64	49.86	11.06	43.28	0.1488
15.1607 071	Fire barrier, DWV, coupling, fitting with plug, 2"	EA	13.19	11.85	25.04	7.43	20.62	0.0999
15.1607 081	Fire barrier, DWV, coupling, fitting with plug, 3"	EA	18.99	15.40	34.39	9.66	28.65	0.1299
15.1607 091	Fire barrier, DWV, coupling, fitting with plug, 4"	EA	24.15	17.79	41.94	11.15	35.30	0.1500
15.1607 101	Fire barrier, DWV, coupling, fitting with plug, 6"	EA	36.60	21.18	57.78	13.28	49.88	0.1786
15.1607 111	Fire barrier, DWV, coupling, fitting with plug, 8"	EA	41.71	23.86	65.57	14.96	56.67	0.2012
15.1607 121	Fire barrier, caulk, wrap/strip, 1/2" - 1"	EA	1.72	11.85	13.57	7.43	9.15	0.0999
15.1607 131	Fire barrier, caulk, wrap/strip, 2"	EA	2.45	14.23	16.68	8.92	11.37	0.1200
15.1607 141	Fire barrier, caulk, wrap/strip, 3"	EA	4.72	16.58	21.30	10.39	15.11	0.1398
15.1607 151	Fire barrier, caulk, wrap/strip, 4"	EA	6.02	17.78	23.80	11.14	17.16	0.1499
15.1607 161	Fire barrier, caulk, wrap/strip, 5"	EA	6.42	20.16	26.58	12.64	19.06	0.1700
15.1607 171	Fire barrier, caulk, wrap/strip, 6"	EA	10.75	22.52	33.27	14.12	24.87	0.1899
15.1607 181	Fire barrier, caulk, wrap/strip, 8"	EA	19.26	24.89	44.15	15.60	34.86	0.2099
15.1607 191	Fire barrier, batt with smoke seal, 1/2" - 1"	EA	.03	11.04	11.07	6.92	6.95	0.0931
15.1607 201	Fire barrier, batt with smoke seal, 2"	EA	.09	12.93	13.02	8.10	8.19	0.1090
15.1607 211	Fire barrier, batt with smoke seal, 3"	EA	.25	14.62	14.87	9.17	9.42	0.1233
15.1607 221	Fire barrier, batt with smoke seal, 4"	EA	.42	17.19	17.61	10.78	11.20	0.1450
15.1607 231	Fire barrier, batt with smoke seal, 5"	EA	.55	19.06	19.61	11.95	12.50	0.1607

Division 15 CSI #	15 - MECHANICAL Description	Unit	Material	Union Install	Union Total	Open Install	Open Total	Unit Man-Hrs
15.1607 000	**FIRE BARRIER PENETRATION SYSTEM, PLASTIC PIPE: (Cont.)**							
15.1607 241	Fire barrier, batt with smoke seal, 6"	EA	1.03	21.96	22.99	13.77	14.80	0.1852
15.1607 251	Fire barrier, batt with smoke seal, 8"	EA	1.77	24.05	25.82	15.08	16.85	0.2028
15.1700 000	**MEDICAL & LABORATORY EQUIPMENT & PIPE:**							
15.1701 000	**MANIFOLDS, OXYGEN OR NITROUS OXIDE:**							
15.1701 011	Manifold, 4 cylinder	EA	8,918.06	581.58	9,499.64	364.60	9,282.66	4.9045
15.1701 021	Manifold, 6 cylinder	EA	9,377.72	817.83	10,195.55	512.72	9,890.44	6.8969
15.1701 031	Manifold, 12 cylinder	EA	10,325.43	1,090.45	11,415.88	683.62	11,009.05	9.1959
15.1701 041	Manifold, 24 cylinder	EA	13,578.48	1,897.28	15,475.76	1,189.44	14,767.92	16.0000
15.1701 051	Zone valve, with box, 1 @ 1/2"	EA	431.30	68.16	499.46	42.73	474.03	0.5748
15.1701 061	Zone valve, with box, 2 @ 1/2"	EA	613.65	109.05	722.70	68.36	682.01	0.9196
15.1701 071	Zone valve, with box 3 @ 1/2"	EA	870.05	179.19	1,049.24	112.34	982.39	1.5111
15.1701 081	Zone valve, with box 5 @ 1/2	EA	1,593.47	249.02	1,842.49	156.11	1,749.58	2.1000
15.1701 091	Shut-off valve, with out box, 1"	EA	165.51	40.90	206.41	25.64	191.15	0.3449
15.1701 101	Shut-off valve, with out box, 1-1/4"	EA	241.93	54.52	296.45	34.18	276.11	0.4598
15.1701 111	Shut-off valve, with out box, 1-1/2"	EA	338.46	63.62	402.08	39.88	378.34	0.5365
15.1701 121	Gas outlet, wall	EA	114.88	56.33	171.21	35.31	150.19	0.4750
15.1702 000	**ALARMS:**							
15.1702 011	Alarm, line press, local, 1 gas	EA	3,136.92	69.82	3,206.74	43.77	3,180.69	0.5888
15.1702 021	Alarm, line press, local, 2 gas	EA	3,887.39	90.88	3,978.27	56.97	3,944.36	0.7664
15.1702 031	Alarm, line press, local, 3 gas, liquid	EA	4,870.69	136.31	5,007.00	85.45	4,956.14	1.1495
15.1702 041	Alarm, line press, local, 5 gas	EA	5,745.89	230.73	5,976.62	144.65	5,890.54	1.9458
15.1702 051	Emergency inlet connection, liquid	EA	2,199.90	238.46	2,438.36	149.50	2,349.40	2.0110
15.1702 061	Alarm, master, 15 signal	EA	4,231.55	297.64	4,529.19	186.59	4,418.14	2.5100
15.1702 071	Switch, vacuum	EA	543.48	90.88	634.36	56.97	600.45	0.7664
15.1702 081	Switch, nitrogen	EA	452.88	90.88	543.76	56.97	509.85	0.7664
15.1702 091	Alarm, pressure switch, liquid	EA	452.88	90.88	543.76	56.97	509.85	0.7664
15.1703 000	**MEDICAL VACUUM PUMPS WITH ALL RELATED ACCESSORIES:**							
15.1703 011	Vacuum pump, duplex, 30 CFM, 5 hp	EA	30,021.42	2,726.11	32,747.53	1,709.05	31,730.47	22.9896
15.1703 021	Vacuum pump, duplex, 60 CFM, 10 hp	EA	35,612.66	3,271.34	38,884.00	2,050.86	37,663.52	27.5876
15.1703 031	Vacuum pump, duplex, 210 CFM, 15 hp	EA	38,567.91	3,634.81	42,202.72	2,278.73	40,846.64	30.6528
15.1704 000	**MEDICAL AIR COMPRESSOR WITH ACCESSORIES:**							
15.1704 011	Air compressor, duplex, 2 @ 3 hp	EA	16,371.27	1,453.93	17,825.20	911.50	17,282.77	12.2612
15.1704 021	Air compressor, duplex, 2 @ 5 hp	EA	41,852.44	1,909.14	43,761.58	1,196.87	43,049.31	16.1000
15.1704 031	Air compressor, duplex, 2 @ 10 hp	EA	66,256.36	2,726.11	68,982.47	1,709.05	67,965.41	22.9896
15.1705 000	**MEDICAL GAS PIPE, COPPER, 'L':**							
	Note: The following prices include purging, sterilizing, etc.							
15.1705 011	Medical gas pipe, 1/2", copper, 'L'	LF	10.97	18.76	29.73	11.76	22.73	0.1582
15.1705 021	Medical gas pipe, 3/4", copper, 'L'	LF	14.91	22.79	37.70	14.29	29.20	0.1922
15.1705 031	Medical gas pipe, 1", copper, 'L'	LF	19.50	27.06	46.56	16.96	36.46	0.2282
15.1705 041	Medical gas pipe, 1-1/4", copper, 'L'	LF	25.91	29.22	55.13	18.32	44.23	0.2464
15.1705 051	Medical gas pipe, 1-1/2", copper, 'L'	LF	31.07	31.08	62.15	19.48	50.55	0.2621
15.1705 061	Medical gas pipe, 2", copper, 'L'	LF	46.19	37.49	83.68	23.51	69.70	0.3162
15.1705 071	Medical gas pipe, 2-1/2", copper, 'L'	LF	68.76	41.54	110.30	26.04	94.80	0.3503
15.1705 081	Medical gas pipe, 3", copper, 'L'	LF	87.72	47.72	135.44	29.91	117.63	0.4024
15.1706 000	**STAINLESS STEEL PIPE, NON-SPOOLED, '304', SCH 10, SEAMLESS:**							
	Note: The following items are normally used in labs, manufacturing or chemical plants. Note that all pricing by user should be P.O.A. from suppliers.							
15.1706 011	Stainless steel pipe, seamless, '304', sch 10, 1/2", non-spooled	LF	9.98	9.85	19.83	7.16	17.14	0.0903
15.1706 021	Stainless steel pipe, seamless, '304', sch 10, 3/4", non-spooled	LF	11.37	12.20	23.57	8.86	20.23	0.1118
15.1706 031	Stainless steel pipe, seamless, '304', sch 10, 1", non-spooled	LF	15.86	14.69	30.55	10.67	26.53	0.1346
15.1706 041	Stainless steel pipe, seamless, '304', sch 10, 1-1/4", non-spooled	LF	19.48	15.87	35.35	11.52	31.00	0.1454
15.1706 051	Stainless steel pipe, seamless, '304', sch 10, 1-1/2", non-spooled	LF	21.85	18.37	40.22	13.34	35.19	0.1683
15.1706 061	Stainless steel pipe, seamless, '304', sch 10, 2", non-spooled	LF	24.77	24.99	49.76	18.15	42.92	0.2290
15.1706 071	Stainless steel pipe, seamless, '304', sch 10, 2-1/2", non-spooled	LF	33.90	30.02	63.92	21.80	55.70	0.2751
15.1706 081	Stainless steel pipe, seamless, '304', sch 10, 3", non-spooled	LF	42.32	35.03	77.35	25.44	67.76	0.3210
15.1706 091	Stainless steel pipe, seamless, '304', sch 10, 4", non-spooled	LF	52.52	45.67	98.19	33.17	85.69	0.4185
15.1707 000	**STAINLESS STEEL PIPE, '304', SCH 40, SEAMLESS:**							
15.1707 011	Stainless steel pipe, seamless, '304', sch 40, 1/2"	LF	11.91	10.33	22.24	7.51	19.42	0.0947
15.1707 021	Stainless steel pipe, seamless, '304', sch 40, 3/4"	LF	14.06	13.91	27.97	8.72	22.78	0.1173
15.1707 031	Stainless steel pipe, seamless, '304', sch 40, 1"	LF	17.69	16.77	34.46	10.51	28.20	0.1414
15.1707 041	Stainless steel pipe, seamless, '304', sch 40, 1-1/4"	LF	21.27	18.11	39.38	11.35	32.62	0.1527

Division 15 CSI #	15 - MECHANICAL Description	Unit	Material	Union Install	Union Total	Open Install	Open Total	Unit Man-Hrs
15.1707 000	STAINLESS STEEL PIPE, '304', SCH 40, SEAMLESS: (Cont.							
15.1707 051	Stainless steel pipe, seamless, '304', sch 40, 1-1/2"	LF	24.83	20.95	45.78	13.14	37.97	0.1767
15.1707 061	Stainless steel pipe, seamless, '304', sch 40, 2"	LF	31.60	28.52	60.12	17.88	49.48	0.2405
15.1707 071	Stainless steel pipe, seamless, '304', sch 40, 2-1/2"	LF	46.37	34.23	80.60	21.46	67.83	0.2887
15.1707 081	Stainless steel pipe, seamless, '304', sch 40, 3"	LF	59.64	39.96	99.60	25.05	84.69	0.3370
15.1707 091	Stainless steel pipe, seamless, '304', sch 40, 4"	LF	79.10	52.10	131.20	32.66	111.76	0.4394
15.1707 101	Stainless steel pipe, seamless, '304', sch 40, 6"	LF	135.73	62.98	198.71	39.48	175.21	0.5311
15.1707 111	Stainless steel pipe, seamless, '304', sch 40, 8"	LF	219.04	67.99	287.03	42.63	261.67	0.5734
15.1708 000	STAINLESS STEEL PIPE, '304', SCH 80, SEAMLESS:							
15.1708 011	Stainless steel pipe, seamless, '304', sch 80, 1/2"	LF	15.61	11.81	27.42	7.40	23.01	0.0996
15.1708 021	Stainless steel pipe, seamless, '304', sch 80, 3/4"	LF	19.70	14.62	34.32	9.17	28.87	0.1233
15.1708 031	Stainless steel pipe, seamless, '304', sch 80, 1"	LF	25.87	17.60	43.47	11.03	36.90	0.1484
15.1708 041	Stainless steel pipe, seamless, '304', sch 80, 1-1/4"	LF	32.85	19.02	51.87	11.92	44.77	0.1604
15.1708 051	Stainless steel pipe, seamless, '304', sch 80, 1-1/2"	LF	37.64	20.95	58.59	13.14	50.78	0.1767
15.1708 061	Stainless steel pipe, seamless, '304', sch 80, 2"	LF	46.34	31.40	77.74	19.69	66.03	0.2648
15.1708 071	Stainless steel pipe, seamless, '304', sch 80, 2-1/2"	LF	94.78	40.73	135.51	25.54	120.32	0.3435
15.1708 081	Stainless steel pipe, seamless, '304', sch 80, 3"	LF	118.52	45.49	164.01	28.52	147.04	0.3836
15.1708 091	Stainless steel pipe, seamless, '304', sch 80, 4"	LF	176.63	58.57	235.20	36.72	213.35	0.4939
15.1708 101	Stainless steel pipe, seamless, '304', sch 80, 6"	LF	412.78	65.22	478.00	40.89	453.67	0.5500
15.1708 111	Stainless steel pipe, seamless, '304', sch 80, 8"	LF	690.70	71.98	762.68	45.12	735.82	0.6070
15.1709 000	STAINLESS STEEL PIPE, '316' EXTRA LOW CARBON, SCH 10, SEAMLESS:							
15.1709 011	Stainless steel pipe, seamless, '316', extra low carbon, sch 10, 1/2"	LF	11.40	10.71	22.11	6.71	18.11	0.0903
15.1709 021	Stainless steel pipe, seamless, '316', extra low carbon, sch 10, 3/4"	LF	13.18	13.26	26.44	8.31	21.49	0.1118
15.1709 031	Stainless steel pipe, seamless, '316', extra low carbon, sch 10, 1"	LF	18.80	15.96	34.76	10.01	28.81	0.1346
15.1709 041	Stainless steel pipe, seamless, '316', extra low carbon, sch 10, 1-1/4"	LF	22.49	17.24	39.73	10.81	33.30	0.1454
15.1709 051	Stainless steel pipe, seamless, '316', extra low carbon, sch 10, 1-1/2"	LF	25.45	19.96	45.41	12.51	37.96	0.1683
15.1709 061	Stainless steel pipe, seamless, '316', extra low carbon, sch 10, 2"	LF	32.20	27.15	59.35	17.02	49.22	0.2290
15.1709 071	Stainless steel pipe, seamless, '316', extra low carbon, sch 10 2-1/2"	LF	39.96	32.62	72.58	20.45	60.41	0.2751
15.1709 081	Stainless steel pipe, seamless, '316', extra low carbon, sch 10, 3"	LF	52.08	38.06	90.14	23.86	75.94	0.3210
15.1709 091	Stainless steel pipe, seamless, '316', extra low carbon, sch 10, 4"	LF	63.64	49.63	113.27	31.11	94.75	0.4185
15.1710 000	STAINLESS STEEL PIPE, '316' EXTRA LOW CARBON, SCH 40, SEAMLESS:							
15.1710 011	Stainless steel pipe, seamless, '316', extra low carbon, sch 40, 1/2"	LF	16.13	11.23	27.36	7.04	23.17	0.0947
15.1710 021	Stainless steel pipe, seamless, '316', extra low carbon, sch 40, 3/4"	LF	18.57	13.91	32.48	8.72	27.29	0.1173
15.1710 031	Stainless steel pipe, seamless, '316', extra low carbon, sch 40, 1"	LF	25.08	16.77	41.85	10.51	35.59	0.1414
15.1710 041	Stainless steel pipe, seamless, '316', extra low carbon, sch 40, 1-1/4"	LF	30.10	18.11	48.21	11.35	41.45	0.1527
15.1710 051	Stainless steel pipe, seamless, '316', extra low carbon, sch 40, 1-1/2"	LF	35.48	20.95	56.43	13.14	48.62	0.1767
15.1710 061	Stainless steel pipe, seamless, '316', extra low carbon, sch 40, 2"	LF	46.03	28.52	74.55	17.88	63.91	0.2405
15.1710 071	Stainless steel pipe, seamless, '316', extra low carbon, sch 40, 2-1/2"	LF	73.36	34.23	107.59	21.46	94.82	0.2887
15.1710 081	Stainless steel pipe, seamless, '316', extra low carbon, sch 40, 3"	LF	98.24	39.96	138.20	25.05	123.29	0.3370
15.1710 091	Stainless steel pipe, seamless, '316', extra low carbon, sch 40, 4"	LF	130.55	52.10	182.65	32.66	163.21	0.4394
15.1710 101	Stainless steel pipe, seamless, '316', extra low carbon, sch 40, 6"	LF	241.33	62.98	304.31	39.48	280.81	0.5311
15.1710 111	Stainless steel pipe, seamless, '316', extra low carbon, sch 40, 8"	LF	431.75	67.99	499.74	42.63	474.38	0.5734
15.1711 000	STAINLESS STEEL PIPE, '316', SCH 80, SEAMLESS:							
15.1711 011	Stainless steel pipe, seamless, '316', extra low carbon, sch 80, 1/2"	LF	20.52	11.81	32.33	7.40	27.92	0.0996
15.1711 021	Stainless steel pipe, seamless, '316', extra low carbon, sch 80, 3/4"	LF	23.91	14.62	38.53	9.17	33.08	0.1233
15.1711 031	Stainless steel pipe, seamless, '316', extra low carbon, sch 80, 1"	LF	31.40	17.60	49.00	11.03	42.43	0.1484
15.1711 041	Stainless steel pipe, seamless, '316', extra low carbon, sch 80, 1-1/4"	LF	42.15	19.02	61.17	11.92	54.07	0.1604
15.1711 051	Stainless steel pipe, seamless, '316', extra low carbon, sch 80, 1-1/2"	LF	47.14	20.95	68.09	13.14	60.28	0.1767
15.1711 061	Stainless steel pipe, seamless, '316', extra low carbon, sch 80, 2"	LF	59.45	31.40	90.85	19.69	79.14	0.2648
15.1711 071	Stainless steel pipe, seamless, '316', extra low carbon, sch 80, 2-1/2"	LF	145.86	40.73	186.59	25.54	171.40	0.3435
15.1711 081	Stainless steel pipe, seamless, '316', extra low carbon, sch 80, 3"	LF	165.91	45.49	211.40	28.52	194.43	0.3836
15.1711 091	Stainless steel pipe, seamless, '316', extra low carbon, sch 80, 4"	LF	220.63	58.57	279.20	36.72	257.35	0.4939
15.1711 101	Stainless steel pipe, seamless, '316', extra low carbon, sch 80, 6"	LF	417.82	65.22	483.04	40.89	458.71	0.5500
15.1711 111	Stainless steel pipe, seamless, '316', extra low carbon, sch 80, 8"	LF	729.93	71.98	801.91	45.12	775.05	0.6070
15.1800 000	FEES, PERMITS & STERILIZATION:							

Note: The fees listed below represent typical installation costs for Contra Costa County, California. It is recommended that you contact the local utility district for charges in your area.

Permits:
Under $2,000 . . . . 2.00%
$2,000 to 10,000 . . . . 1.00%
$10,000 to 50,000 . . . . 0.50%
$50,000 to 100,000 . . . . 0.25%

Division 15 CSI #	15 - MECHANICAL Description	Unit	Material	Union Install	Union Total	Open Install	Open Total	Unit Man-Hrs
15.1801 000	**FEES, WATER METER (WHERE APPLICABLE):**							
15.1801 011	Water meter fee, 3/4" connection	EA	1,314.36		1,314.36		1,314.36	
15.1801 021	Water meter fee, 1" connection	EA	2,022.55		2,022.55		2,022.55	
15.1801 031	Water meter fee, 1-1/2" connect	EA	3,895.60		3,895.60		3,895.60	
15.1801 041	Water meter fee, 2" connection	EA	6,035.21		6,035.21		6,035.21	
15.1801 051	Water meter fee, 3" connection	EA	9,993.39		9,993.39		9,993.39	
15.1801 061	Water meter fee, 4" connection	EA	15,855.92		15,855.92		15,855.92	
15.1801 071	Water meter fee, 6" connection	EA	31,607.53		31,607.53		31,607.53	
15.1802 000	**SEWER CONNECTION FEE, NO PLANT OR LINE CHARGE:**							
15.1802 011	Fee, sewer connection, average	FIX	350.00		350.00		350.00	
15.1803 000	**STERILIZATION, TESTING & CLEANING:**							
15.1803 021	Testing & cleaning, per fixture	FIX	100.00		100.00		100.00	
15.1900 000	**INDUSTRIAL PIPING:**							
	Note: This section deals with piping and related specialties for general industrial applications. It is presented with two different approaches - complex systems and straight run pipe. All prices include equipment time, small tools, plumber's assistant and equipment operators. Prices are complete unless otherwise noted.							
15.1901 000	**PIPE, CHROME-MOLY, SCH 120, 2-1/2" INSULATED, ALUMINUM SHEATH:**							
	Note: The following prices are for complex flanged prefabricated spoolpieces, and include all hangers, fittings, pre-heating, stress- relieving testing and site insulation.							
15.1901 011	Pipe, chrome-moly, '120', 1", with insulation	LF	54.05	211.27	265.32	132.45	186.50	1.7817
15.1901 021	Pipe, chrome-moly, '120', 2", insulation, aluminum sheath	LF	116.13	264.67	380.80	165.93	282.06	2.2320
15.1901 031	Pipe, chrome-moly, '120', 4", insulation, aluminum sheath	LF	194.08	382.80	576.88	239.98	434.06	3.2282
15.1901 041	Pipe, chrome-moly, '120', 6", insulation, aluminum sheath	LF	321.34	428.23	749.57	268.46	589.80	3.6113
15.1901 051	Pipe, chrome-moly, '120', 10", insulation, aluminum sheath	LF	848.07	527.05	1,375.12	330.42	1,178.49	4.4447
15.1901 061	Pipe, chrome-moly, '120', 12", insulation, aluminum sheath	LF	1,317.81	725.83	2,043.64	455.04	1,772.85	6.1210
15.1902 000	**PIPE, CHROME-MOLY, SCH 80, 2-1/2" INSULATED, ALUMINUM SHEATH:**							
	Note: The following prices are for complex flanged prefabricated spoolpieces and include all hangers, fittings, pre-heating, stress- relieving testing and site insulation.							
15.1902 011	Pipe, chrome-moly, '80', 1", insulation, aluminum sheath	LF	20.44	178.34	198.78	111.81	132.25	1.5040
15.1902 021	Pipe, chrome-moly, '80', 2", insulation, aluminum sheath	LF	42.67	224.91	267.58	141.00	183.67	1.8967
15.1902 031	Pipe, chrome-moly, '80', 3", insulation, aluminum sheath	LF	71.37	249.90	321.27	156.66	228.03	2.1074
15.1902 041	Pipe, chrome-moly, '80', 4", insulation, aluminum sheath	LF	127.48	329.42	456.90	206.52	334.00	2.7780
15.1902 051	Pipe, chrome-moly, '80', 6", insulation, aluminum sheath	LF	201.74	348.72	550.46	218.62	420.36	2.9408
15.1902 061	Pipe, chrome-moly, '80', 8", insulation, aluminum sheath	LF	310.34	395.29	705.63	247.81	558.15	3.3335
15.1902 071	Pipe, chrome-moly, '80', 10", insulation, aluminum sheath	LF	445.25	515.69	960.94	323.30	768.55	4.3489
15.1902 081	Pipe, chrome-moly, '80', 12", insulation, aluminum sheath	LF	600.74	638.36	1,239.10	400.20	1,000.94	5.3834
15.1903 000	**STEEL PIPE, A-53 GRADE-B ELECTRIC RESISTANCE WELDED, STD WALL THICKNESS:**							
	Note: The following prices are for straight run pipe (simply supported). Prices do not include fittings, insulation or painting.							
15.1903 011	Steel pipe, weld, A-53, '40', grade-B, electric resistance welded, 2"	LF	5.05	35.74	40.79	22.41	27.46	0.3014
15.1903 021	Steel pipe, weld, A-53, '40', grade-B, electric resistance welded, 3"	LF	8.93	37.57	46.50	23.55	32.48	0.3168
15.1903 031	Steel pipe, weld, A-53, '40', grade-B, electric resistance welded, 4"	LF	15.27	54.36	69.63	34.08	49.35	0.4584
15.1903 041	Steel pipe, weld, A-53, '40', grade-B, electric resistance welded, 6"	LF	31.72	64.91	96.63	40.69	72.41	0.5474
15.1903 051	Steel pipe, weld, A-53, '40', grade-B, electric resistance welded, 8"	LF	36.35	85.02	121.37	53.30	89.65	0.7170
15.1903 061	Steel pipe, weld, A-53, '40', grade-B, electric resistance welded, 10"	LF	59.92	96.10	156.02	60.25	120.17	0.8104
15.1903 071	Steel pipe, weld, A-53, .375, grade-B, electric resistance welded, 12"	LF	62.13	105.35	167.48	66.04	128.17	0.8884
15.1903 081	Steel pipe, weld, A-53, '30', grade-B, electric resistance welded, 14"	LF	81.21	130.91	212.12	82.07	163.28	1.1040
15.1903 091	Steel pipe, weld, A-53, '30', grade-B, electric resistance welded, 16"	LF	89.43	143.26	232.69	89.81	179.24	1.2081
15.1903 101	Steel pipe, weld, A-53, .375, grade-B, electric resistance welded, 18"	LF	115.15	153.00	268.15	95.92	211.07	1.2903
15.1903 111	Steel pipe, weld, A-53, '20', grade-B, electric resistance welded, 20"	LF	141.13	169.45	310.58	106.23	247.36	1.4290
15.1903 121	Steel pipe, weld, A-53, '20', grade-B, electric resistance welded, 24"	LF	181.74	188.35	370.09	118.08	299.82	1.5884
15.1904 000	**STEEL PIPE, A-53 GRADE-B ELECTRIC RESISTANCE WELDED, STD WALL THICKNESS:**							
	Note: The following prices are for complex field installations and include fittings and simple supports. Prices do not include insulation or painting. Prices are based on 500 feet of 20 foot random pipe lengths and include 13 bends, 2 tee pieces and 11 S.O. flanges. Make allowance for the complexity of your own job when using these prices. For weld neck flanges, add 3% to the material costs.							
15.1904 011	Steel pipe, weld, A-53, '40', grade-B, electric resistance welded, 2"	LF	7.34	50.66	58.00	31.76	39.10	0.4272
15.1904 021	Steel pipe, weld, A-53, '40', grade-B, electric resistance welded, 4"	LF	16.65	73.05	89.70	45.79	62.44	0.6160
15.1904 031	Steel pipe, weld, A-53, '40', grade-B, electric resistance welded, 6"	LF	34.00	96.09	130.09	60.24	94.24	0.8103
15.1904 041	Steel pipe, weld, A-53, '40', grade-B, electric resistance welded, 8"	LF	41.36	139.24	180.60	87.29	128.65	1.1742
15.1904 051	Steel pipe, weld, A-53, '40', grade-B, electric resistance welded, 10"	LF	67.73	156.55	224.28	98.14	165.87	1.3202

Division 15 CSI #	15 - MECHANICAL Description	Unit	Material	Union Install	Union Total	Open Install	Open Total	Unit Man-Hrs
15.1904 000	**STEEL PIPE, A-53 GRADE-B ELECTRIC RESISTANCE WELDED, STD WALL THICKNESS: (Cont.)**							
15.1904 061	Steel pipe, weld, A-53, .0375, grade-B, electric resistance welded, 12"	LF	73.41	186.40	259.81	116.86	190.27	1.5719
15.1904 071	Steel pipe, weld, A-53, '30', grade-B, electric resistance welded, 16"	LF	109.83	284.01	393.84	178.05	287.88	2.3951
15.1904 081	Steel pipe, weld, A-53, '20', grade-B, electric resistance welded, 20"	LF	178.24	372.46	550.70	233.50	411.74	3.1410
15.1905 000	**STEEL PIPE, A-53 GRADE-B, SEAMLESS:**							
	Note: The following prices are for straight run field erected pipe. Prices do not include insulation or painting.							
15.1905 011	Steel pipe, seamless, A-53, sch 40, grade-B, 2"	LF	9.76	35.74	45.50	22.41	32.17	0.3014
15.1905 021	Steel pipe, seamless, A-53, sch 40, grade-B, 3"	LF	15.64	37.57	53.21	23.55	39.19	0.3168
15.1905 031	Steel pipe, seamless, A-53, sch 40, grade-B, 4"	LF	21.27	54.36	75.63	34.08	55.35	0.4584
15.1905 041	Steel pipe, seamless, A-53, sch 40, grade-B, 6"	LF	41.24	64.91	106.15	40.69	81.93	0.5474
15.1905 051	Steel pipe, seamless, A-53, sch 40, grade-B, 8"	LF	53.98	85.02	139.00	53.30	107.28	0.7170
15.1905 061	Steel pipe, seamless, A-53, sch 40, grade-B, 10"	LF	80.18	96.10	176.28	60.25	140.43	0.8104
15.1905 071	Steel pipe, seamless, A-53, .375, grade-B, 12"	LF	93.57	105.35	198.92	66.04	159.61	0.8884
15.1905 081	Steel pipe, seamless, A-53, sch 30, grade-B, 14"	LF	120.03	130.91	250.94	82.07	202.10	1.1040
15.1905 091	Steel pipe, seamless, A-53, sch 30, grade-B, 16"	LF	129.68	143.26	272.94	89.81	219.49	1.2081
15.1905 101	Steel pipe, seamless, A-53, .375, grade-B, 18"	LF	147.65	153.00	300.65	95.92	243.57	1.2903
15.1905 111	Steel pipe, seamless, A-53, sch 20, grade-B, 20"	LF	162.16	169.45	331.61	106.23	268.39	1.4290
15.1905 121	Steel pipe, seamless, A-53, sch 20, grade-B, 24"	LF	198.93	188.35	387.28	118.08	317.01	1.5884
15.1906 000	**STEEL PIPE, A-53 GRADE-B, SEAMLESS:**							
	Note: The following prices are for complex fabricated and field erected piping. Prices include all fittings and simple support. For weld neck flanges, add 3% to the material costs.							
15.1906 011	Steel pipe, seamless, A-53, sch 40, grade-B, 2"	LF	14.71	50.66	65.37	31.76	46.47	0.4272
15.1906 021	Steel pipe, seamless, A-53, sch 40, grade-B, 3"	LF	21.14	68.22	89.36	42.77	63.91	0.5753
15.1906 031	Steel pipe, seamless, A-53, sch 40, grade-B, 4"	LF	27.36	73.05	100.41	45.79	73.15	0.6160
15.1906 041	Steel pipe, seamless, A-53, sch 40, grade-B, 6"	LF	50.64	96.09	146.73	60.24	110.88	0.8103
15.1906 051	Steel pipe, seamless, A-53, sch 40, grade-B, 8"	LF	67.69	139.24	206.93	87.29	154.98	1.1742
15.1906 061	Steel pipe, seamless, A-53, sch 40, grade-B, 10"	LF	100.49	156.55	257.04	98.14	198.63	1.3202
15.1906 071	Steel pipe, seamless, A-53, .375, grade-B, 12"	LF	121.34	186.40	307.74	116.86	238.20	1.5719
15.1906 081	Steel pipe, seamless, A-53, sch 30, grade-B, 14"	LF	171.10	235.23	406.33	147.47	318.57	1.9837
15.1906 091	Steel pipe, seamless, A-53, sch 30, grade-B, 16"	LF	198.35	284.06	482.41	178.08	376.43	2.3955
15.1906 101	Steel pipe, seamless, A-53, .375, grade-B, 18"	LF	225.84	328.28	554.12	205.80	431.64	2.7684
15.1906 111	Steel pipe, seamless, A-53, sch 20, grade-B, 20"	LF	246.03	372.46	618.49	233.50	479.53	3.1410
15.1906 121	Steel pipe, seamless, A-53, sch 20, grade-B, 24"	LF	304.33	416.76	721.09	261.28	565.61	3.5146
15.1907 000	**STAINLESS STEEL PIPE, '316', SCH 10, SEAMLESS, STRAIGHT RUNS:**							
15.1907 011	Stainless steel pipe, seamless, '316', '10', 1/2", straight run	LF	14.35	28.58	42.93	17.92	32.27	0.2410
15.1907 021	Stainless steel pipe, seamless, '316', '10', 3/4", straight run	LF	16.53	28.58	45.11	17.92	34.45	0.2410
15.1907 031	Stainless steel pipe, seamless, '316', '10', 1", straight run	LF	25.79	29.85	55.64	18.71	44.50	0.2517
15.1907 041	Stainless steel pipe, seamless, '316', '10', 1-1/4", straight run	LF	31.32	30.52	61.84	19.14	50.46	0.2574
15.1907 051	Stainless steel pipe, seamless, '316', '10', 1-1/2", straight run	LF	35.22	31.14	66.36	19.52	54.74	0.2626
15.1907 061	Stainless steel pipe, seamless, '316', '10', 2", straight run	LF	40.61	31.86	72.47	19.98	60.59	0.2687
15.1907 071	Stainless steel pipe, seamless, '316', '10', 2-1/2", straight run	LF	50.47	33.08	83.55	20.74	71.21	0.2790
15.1907 081	Stainless steel pipe, seamless, '316', '10', 3", straight run	LF	57.13	35.10	92.23	22.00	79.13	0.2960
15.1907 091	Stainless steel pipe, seamless, '316', '10', 4", straight run	LF	79.64	38.92	118.56	24.40	104.04	0.3282
15.1908 000	**STAINLESS STEEL PIPE, '316', SCH 10, SEAMLESS, COMPLEX SYSTEM:**							
15.1908 011	Stainless steel pipe, seamless, '316', '10', 1/2", complex	LF	21.47	95.27	116.74	59.72	81.19	0.8034
15.1908 021	Stainless steel pipe, seamless, '316', '10', 3/4", complex	LF	24.83	95.27	120.10	59.72	84.55	0.8034
15.1908 031	Stainless steel pipe, seamless, '316', '10', 1", complex	LF	38.71	99.50	138.21	62.38	101.09	0.8391
15.1908 041	Stainless steel pipe, seamless, '316', '10', 1-1/4", complex	LF	47.07	101.74	148.81	63.78	110.85	0.8580
15.1908 051	Stainless steel pipe, seamless, '316', '10', 1-1/2", complex	LF	52.87	103.79	156.66	65.07	117.94	0.8753
15.1908 061	Stainless steel pipe, seamless, '316', '10', 2", complex	LF	60.99	106.20	167.19	66.58	127.57	0.8956
15.1908 071	Stainless steel pipe, seamless, '316', '10', 2-1/2", complex	LF	75.68	110.27	185.95	69.13	144.81	0.9299
15.1908 081	Stainless steel pipe, seamless, '316', '10', 3", complex	LF	85.72	117.00	202.72	73.35	159.07	0.9867
15.1908 091	Stainless steel pipe, seamless, '316', '10', 4", complex	LF	119.43	129.85	249.28	81.40	200.83	1.0950
15.1909 000	**STAINLESS STEEL PIPE, '316', SCH 40, SEAMLESS, STRAIGHT RUNS:**							
15.1909 011	Stainless steel pipe, seamless, '316', '40', 1/2", straight run	LF	17.95	58.92	76.87	36.94	54.89	0.4969
15.1909 021	Stainless steel pipe, seamless, '316', '40', 3/4", straight run	LF	23.47	58.92	82.39	36.94	60.41	0.4969
15.1909 031	Stainless steel pipe, seamless, '316', '40', 1", straight run	LF	30.00	62.61	92.61	39.25	69.25	0.5280
15.1909 041	Stainless steel pipe, seamless, '316', '40', 1-1/4", straight run	LF	39.88	64.48	104.36	40.43	80.31	0.5438
15.1909 051	Stainless steel pipe, seamless, '316', '40', 1-1/2", straight run	LF	45.51	66.36	111.87	41.60	87.11	0.5596
15.1909 061	Stainless steel pipe, seamless, '316', '40', 2", straight run	LF	55.54	70.33	125.87	44.09	99.63	0.5931
15.1909 071	Stainless steel pipe, seamless, '316', '40', 2-1/2", straight run	LF	79.74	74.08	153.82	46.44	126.18	0.6247

Division 15 CSI #	15 - MECHANICAL Description	Unit	Material	Union Install	Union Total	Open Install	Open Total	Unit Man-Hrs
15.1909 000	STAINLESS STEEL PIPE, '316', SCH 40, SEAMLESS, STRAIGHT RUNS: (Cont.)							
15.1909 081	Stainless steel pipe, seamless, '316', '40', 3", straight run	LF	96.12	81.45	177.57	51.06	147.18	0.6869
15.1909 091	Stainless steel pipe, seamless, '316', '40', 4", straight run	LF	136.94	96.38	233.32	60.42	197.36	0.8128
15.1909 101	Stainless steel pipe, seamless, '316', '40', 6", straight run	LF	240.74	114.38	355.12	71.71	312.45	0.9646
15.1909 111	Stainless steel pipe, seamless, '316', '40', 8", straight run	LF	411.95	141.66	553.61	88.81	500.76	1.1946
15.1910 000	STAINLESS STEEL PIPE, '316', SCH 40, SEAMLESS, COMPLEX SYSTEM:							
15.1910 011	Stainless steel pipe, seamless, '316', '40', 1/2", complex	LF	26.94	196.39	223.33	123.12	150.06	1.6562
15.1910 021	Stainless steel pipe, seamless, '316', '40', 3/4", complex	LF	35.22	196.39	231.61	123.12	158.34	1.6562
15.1910 031	Stainless steel pipe, seamless, '316', '40', 1", complex	LF	45.01	208.70	253.71	130.84	175.85	1.7600
15.1910 041	Stainless steel pipe, seamless, '316', '40', 1-1/4", complex	LF	59.87	214.94	274.81	134.75	194.62	1.8126
15.1910 051	Stainless steel pipe, seamless, '316', '40', 1-1/2", complex	LF	68.27	221.20	289.47	138.67	206.94	1.8654
15.1910 061	Stainless steel pipe, seamless, '316', '40', 2", complex	LF	83.28	234.44	317.72	146.98	230.26	1.9771
15.1910 071	Stainless steel pipe, seamless, '316', '40', 2-1/2", complex	LF	119.66	246.94	366.60	154.81	274.47	2.0825
15.1910 081	Stainless steel pipe, seamless, '316', '40', 3", complex	LF	144.23	271.48	415.71	170.19	314.42	2.2894
15.1910 091	Stainless steel pipe, seamless, '316', '40', 4", complex	LF	205.42	321.26	526.68	201.40	406.82	2.7092
15.1910 101	Stainless steel pipe, seamless, '316', '40', 6", complex	LF	361.17	381.23	742.40	239.00	600.17	3.2150
15.1910 111	Stainless steel pipe, seamless, '316', '40', 8", complex	LF	617.99	472.19	1,090.18	296.02	914.01	3.9820
15.1911 000	CRYOGENIC PIPING, VACUUM JACKETED:							
	Note: The following prices are for inbar schedule 5 internal pipe and 304 stainless steel external pipe. The pipe diameter shown below is for the internal pipe. The external pipe is 2" larger in diameter. For complex systems, add 25% to the material costs.							
15.1911 011	Vacuum jacket inbar/304 stainless steel, 1"	LF	95.10	48.72	143.82	30.55	125.65	0.4109
15.1911 021	Vacuum jacket inbar/304 stainless steel, 1-1/2"	LF	103.01	53.16	156.17	33.33	136.34	0.4483
15.1911 031	Vacuum jacket inbar/304 stainless steel, 2"	LF	106.31	57.59	163.90	36.11	142.42	0.4857
15.1911 041	Vacuum jacket inbar/304 stainless steel, 2-1/2"	LF	118.58	60.54	179.12	37.95	156.53	0.5105
15.1911 051	Vacuum jacket inbar/304 stainless steel, 3"	LF	128.81	64.97	193.78	40.73	169.54	0.5479
15.1911 061	Vacuum jacket inbar/304 stainless steel, 4"	LF	142.11	69.40	211.51	43.51	185.62	0.5853
15.2000 000	GATE, GLOBE & CHECK VALVES, CAST STEEL:							
	Note: The following prices include site handling and bolt-ups. Prices do not include insulation.							
15.2001 000	VALVES, CAST STEEL, CLASS 150:							
15.2001 011	Valve, steel, 150#, flanged, 2"	EA	525.01	237.29	762.30	148.76	673.77	2.0011
15.2001 021	Valve, steel, 150#, flanged, 2-1/2"	EA	705.86	274.83	980.69	172.30	878.16	2.3177
15.2001 031	Valve, steel, 150#, flanged, 3"	EA	625.13	297.64	922.77	186.59	811.72	2.5100
15.2001 041	Valve, steel, 150#, flanged, 4"	EA	918.81	403.31	1,322.12	252.85	1,171.66	3.4012
15.2001 051	Valve, steel, 150#, flanged, 6"	EA	1,440.50	498.04	1,938.54	312.23	1,752.73	4.2000
15.2001 061	Valve, steel, 150#, flanged, 8"	EA	2,443.61	581.04	3,024.65	364.27	2,807.88	4.9000
15.2001 071	Valve, steel, 150#, flanged, 10"	EA	4,555.78	699.62	5,255.40	438.61	4,994.39	5.9000
15.2001 081	Valve, steel, 150#, flanged, 12"	EA	6,028.87	782.63	6,811.50	490.64	6,519.51	6.6000
15.2002 000	VALVES, CAST STEEL, CLASS 300:							
	Note: For motorized valves man-hours remain as listed for valve items. Use the adders at the end of the section to increase the material prices.							
15.2002 011	Valve, steel, 300#, flanged, 2"	EA	724.31	355.74	1,080.05	223.02	947.33	3.0000
15.2002 021	Valve, steel, 300#, flanged, 2-1/2"	EA	890.71	403.17	1,293.88	252.76	1,143.47	3.4000
15.2002 031	Valve, steel, 300#, flanged, 3"	EA	951.46	450.60	1,402.06	282.49	1,233.95	3.8000
15.2002 041	Valve, steel, 300#, flanged, 4"	EA	1,264.64	498.04	1,762.68	312.23	1,576.87	4.2000
15.2002 051	Valve, steel, 300#, flanged, 6"	EA	2,085.85	640.33	2,726.18	401.44	2,487.29	5.4000
15.2002 061	Valve, steel, 300#, flanged, 8"	EA	3,444.62	806.34	4,250.96	505.51	3,950.13	6.8000
15.2002 071	Valve, steel, 300#, flanged, 10"	EA	7,341.35	984.21	8,325.56	617.02	7,958.37	8.3000
15.2002 081	Valve, steel, 300#, flanged, 12"	EA	9,906.83	1,126.51	11,033.34	706.23	10,613.06	9.5000
15.2002 091	Add for motorized valve, 1"-3"	EA	999.14	237.16	1,236.30	148.68	1,147.82	2.0000
15.2002 101	Add for motorized valve, 4"-6"	EA	3,996.57	474.32	4,470.89	297.36	4,293.93	4.0000
15.2002 111	Add for motorized valve, 8"-10"	EA	7,193.81	711.48	7,905.29	446.04	7,639.85	6.0000
15.2003 000	GLOBE VALVES, CRYOGENIC, VACUUM JACKETED, FLANGED:							
15.2003 011	Globe valve, cryogenic, vacuum jacket , flange, 1"	EA	2,881.43	224.45	3,105.88	140.71	3,022.14	1.8928
15.2003 021	Globe valve, cryogenic, vacuum jacket , flange, 1-1/2"	EA	3,921.13	224.45	4,145.58	140.71	4,061.84	1.8928
15.2003 031	Globe valve, cryogenic, vacuum jacket , flange, 2"	EA	4,663.75	375.07	5,038.82	235.14	4,898.89	3.1630
15.2003 041	Globe valve, cryogenic, vacuum jacket , flange, 3"	EA	11,288.20	456.28	11,744.48	286.05	11,574.25	3.8479
15.2003 051	Globe valve, cryogenic, vacuum jacket , flange, 4"	EA	13,664.67	606.89	14,271.56	380.47	14,045.14	5.1180

Division 15 CSI #	15 - MECHANICAL Description	Unit	Material	Union Install	Union Total	Open Install	Open Total	Unit Man-Hrs
15.2100 000	**INDUSTRIAL PIPING INSULATION:**							
15.2101 000	**PIPE INSULATION, 1-1/2" FIBERGLASS, ALUMINUM SHEATH:**							
	Note: The following prices are for straight run pipe. For insulation without sheath, deduct 38% from the							
	material costs. For complex piping, add 30% to the material costs.							
15.2101 011	1-1/2" insulation with aluminum sheath, 1" pipe	LF	5.93	5.85	11.78	3.66	9.59	0.0493
15.2101 021	1-1/2" insulation with aluminum sheath, 2" pipe	LF	7.32	6.53	13.85	4.10	11.42	0.0551
15.2101 031	1-1/2" insulation with aluminum sheath, 3" pipe	LF	8.13	7.42	15.55	4.65	12.78	0.0626
15.2101 041	1-1/2" insulation with aluminum sheath, 4" pipe	LF	9.39	8.79	18.18	5.51	14.90	0.0741
15.2101 051	1-1/2" insulation with aluminum sheath, 6" pipe	LF	11.15	9.91	21.06	6.21	17.36	0.0836
15.2101 061	1-1/2" insulation with aluminum sheath, 8" pipe	LF	14.05	11.49	25.54	7.20	21.25	0.0969
15.2101 071	1-1/2" insulation with aluminum sheath, 10" pipe	LF	16.35	12.61	28.96	7.90	24.25	0.1063
15.2101 081	1-1/2" insulation with aluminum sheath, 12" pipe	LF	19.46	14.41	33.87	9.03	28.49	0.1215
15.2101 091	1-1/2" insulation with aluminum sheath, 14" pipe	LF	21.60	16.21	37.81	10.16	31.76	0.1367
15.2101 101	1-1/2" insulation with aluminum sheath, 16" pipe	LF	25.94	17.34	43.28	10.87	36.81	0.1462
15.2101 111	1-1/2" insulation with aluminum sheath, 20" pipe	LF	29.11	19.58	48.69	12.27	41.38	0.1651
15.2101 121	1-1/2" insulation with aluminum sheath, 24" pipe	LF	34.91	22.28	57.19	13.97	48.88	0.1879
15.2102 000	**PIPE INSULATION, 3" FIBERGLASS, ALUMINUM SHEATH:**							
	Note: For insulation without sheath, deduct 38% from the material costs. For complex piping, add 30%							
	to the material costs.							
15.2102 011	3" fiberglass insulation, aluminum sheath, 1" pipe	LF	13.51	5.85	19.36	3.66	17.17	0.0493
15.2102 021	3" fiberglass insulation, aluminum sheath, 2" pipe	LF	14.65	6.53	21.18	4.10	18.75	0.0551
15.2102 031	3" fiberglass insulation, aluminum sheath, 3" pipe	LF	16.77	7.42	24.19	4.65	21.42	0.0626
15.2102 041	3" fiberglass insulation, aluminum sheath, 4" pipe	LF	19.41	8.79	28.20	5.51	24.92	0.0741
15.2102 051	3" fiberglass insulation, aluminum sheath, 6" pipe	LF	23.42	9.91	33.33	6.21	29.63	0.0836
15.2102 061	3" fiberglass insulation, aluminum sheath, 8" pipe	LF	28.61	11.49	40.10	7.20	35.81	0.0969
15.2102 071	3" fiberglass insulation, aluminum sheath, 10" pipe	LF	33.00	12.61	45.61	7.90	40.90	0.1063
15.2102 081	3" fiberglass insulation, aluminum sheath, 12" pipe	LF	36.96	14.41	51.37	9.03	45.99	0.1215
15.2102 091	3" fiberglass insulation, aluminum sheath, 14" pipe	LF	40.95	16.21	57.16	10.16	51.11	0.1367
15.2102 101	3" fiberglass insulation, aluminum sheath, 16" pipe	LF	49.69	17.34	67.03	10.87	60.56	0.1462
15.2102 111	3" fiberglass insulation, aluminum sheath, 20" pipe	LF	53.29	19.58	72.87	12.27	65.56	0.1651
15.2102 121	3" fiberglass insulation, aluminum sheath, 24" pipe	LF	62.91	22.28	85.19	13.97	76.88	0.1879
15.2103 000	**VALVE INSULATION, 3" FIBERGLASS, ALUMINUM BOX:**							
15.2103 011	3" insulation, fiberglass, aluminum box, 1"-2" valve	EA	21.89	.84	22.73	.53	22.42	0.0071
15.2103 021	3" insulation, fiberglass, aluminum box, 3"-4" valve	EA	32.79	135.18	167.97	84.75	117.54	1.1400
15.2103 031	3" insulation, aluminum box, 1" to 2" valve	EA	21.89	.84	22.73	.53	22.42	0.0071
15.2103 041	3" insulation, fiberglass, aluminum box, 6" valve	EA	51.24	201.05	252.29	126.04	177.28	1.6955
15.2103 051	3" insulation, aluminum box, 3" to 4" valve	EA	32.79	135.18	167.97	84.75	117.54	1.1400
15.2103 061	3" insulation, fiberglass, aluminum box, 8" valve	EA	58.31	263.53	321.84	165.21	223.52	2.2224
15.2103 071	3" insulation, aluminum box, 6" valve	EA	51.24	201.05	252.29	126.04	177.28	1.6955
15.2103 081	3" insulation, fiberglass, aluminum box, 10" valve	EA	65.57	345.32	410.89	216.49	282.06	2.9121
15.2103 091	3" insulation, aluminum box, 8" valve	EA	58.31	263.53	321.84	165.21	223.52	2.2224
15.2103 101	3" insulation, fiberglass, aluminum box, 12" valve	EA	72.90	456.63	529.53	286.27	359.17	3.8508
15.2103 111	3" insulation, aluminum box, 10" valve	EA	65.57	345.32	410.89	216.49	282.06	2.9121
15.2103 121	3" insulation, fiberglass, aluminum box, 14"-16" valve	EA	135.36	683.80	819.16	428.69	564.05	5.7666
15.2103 131	3" insulation, aluminum box, 12" valve	EA	72.90	456.63	529.53	286.27	359.17	3.8508
15.2103 141	3" insulation, fiberglass, aluminum box, 18" valve	EA	147.61	805.35	952.96	504.89	652.50	6.7916
15.2103 151	3" insulation, aluminum box, 14" to 16" valve	EA	135.36	683.80	819.16	428.69	564.05	5.7666
15.2103 161	3" insulation, fiberglass, aluminum box, 20" valve	EA	164.01	925.74	1,089.75	580.36	744.37	7.8069
15.2103 171	3" insulation, aluminum box, 18" valve	EA	147.61	805.35	952.96	504.89	652.50	6.7916
15.2103 181	3" insulation, fiberglass, aluminum sheath, 16" pipe	LF	49.69	17.34	67.03	10.87	60.56	0.1462
15.2103 191	3" insulation, aluminum box, 20" valve	EA	164.01	925.74	1,089.75	580.36	744.37	7.8069
15.2103 201	3" insulation, fiberglass, aluminum sheath, 20" pipe	LF	53.29	19.58	72.87	12.27	65.56	0.1651
15.2103 211	3" insulation, fiberglass, aluminum sheath, 24" pipe	LF	62.91	22.28	85.19	13.97	76.88	0.1879

HEATING, VENTILATING AND AIR CONDITIONING
TABLE OF CONTENTS

SECTION	DESCRIPTION
15.0000	**MECHANICAL WORK**
15.3000	**HVAC**
.3001	IN-PLACE COSTS
.3100	FURNACES
	Gas Fired Furnaces, Residential Gas
	Fired Furnaces, Commercial Unit Heaters
	Duct Heaters
	Electric Furnaces
.3200	HOT WATER AND STEAM EQUIPMENT
.3300	COOLING EQUIPMENT
	Chillers
	Cooling Towers
	Direct Expansion (d-x) Units
	Electric Heaters
	Direct Expansion (d-x) Split Systems
	Computer Room Units
.3400	HEATING AND COOLING COMBINATIONS
	D-X Cooling, Gas Fired Heating, Packaged Units
	Heat Pumps
	D-x Cooling And Electric Heat
	Hydronic Heating And Cooling
	Infrared Heaters
	Radiant Heat Panels
.3500	AUXILIARY HEATING & COOLING EQUIP
	Humidifiers
	Condensate Pumps
	Water Service Pumps
	Fuel Oil Pumps
.3600	AIR HANDLING EQUIPMENT, PRIMARY
	Package, With Coil
	Package, Without Coils
	Chilled Water Coils
	Hot Water Coils
	Filters And Frames
	Low Pressure Fans
	High Pressure Fans
.3700	DISTRIBUTION, TERMINAL EQUIPMENT
	Exhausts, Ceiling And Wall
	Exhausts, Roof
	Exhausts, Utility
	Return Fans
	Centrifugal Fans
	Cabinet Blowers
	Fan Coil Units, Duct
	Fan Coil Units With Cabinet
	Induction Units
	Mixing Boxes, Constant & Variable Volume
	Terminal Units With Reheat Coils
	Terminal Units With Constant Volume Reheat Coils
.3800	MISCELLANEOUS EQUIPMENT
.3900	CONTROLS
.4000	DUCTWORK
.4100	PIPING AND INSULATION
.4200	FITTINGS
.4300	VALVES AND SPECIALTIES
.4400	INSULATION
.4406	PERMITS, TEST AND BALANCE
.5500	FIRE PROTECTION

Division 15 CSI #	15 - MECHANICAL Description	Unit	Material	Union Install	Union Total	Open Install	Open Total	Unit Man-Hrs
15.3000 000	**HVAC:**							
15.3001 000	**HVAC, IN PLACE COSTS:**							
15.3001 011	HVAC, auditoriums and theaters	SF	13.54	16.92	30.46	10.74	24.28	0.1479
15.3001 021	HVAC, banks	SF	10.50	12.85	23.35	8.15	18.65	0.1123
15.3001 031	HVAC, colleges, classroom & administration	SF	15.11	17.63	32.74	11.19	26.30	0.1541
15.3001 041	HVAC, dormitories	SF	5.83	7.05	12.88	4.47	10.30	0.0616
15.3001 051	Ventilation, parking garages	SF	.54	.46	1.00	.29	.83	0.0040
15.3001 061	Heating & ventilating, tract residential	SF	1.71	2.17	3.88	1.38	3.09	0.0190
15.3001 071	HVAC, tract housing	SF	2.66	3.88	6.54	2.46	5.12	0.0339
15.3001 081	HVAC, custom housing	SF	2.92	4.86	7.78	3.09	6.01	0.0425
15.3001 091	Heating & ventilating, multi residential	SF	1.91	2.32	4.23	1.47	3.38	0.0203
15.3001 101	HVAC, multiple residence	SF	2.55	3.62	6.17	2.29	4.84	0.0316
15.3001 111	HVAC, hospitals	SF	27.32	30.40	57.72	19.29	46.61	0.2657
15.3001 121	HVAC, institutional	SF	23.42	14.34	37.76	9.10	32.52	0.1253
15.3001 131	Heating and ventilating, manufacturing	SF	11.07	1.97	13.04	1.25	12.32	0.0172
15.3001 141	HVAC, medical clinics	SF	16.34	19.98	36.32	12.68	29.02	0.1746
15.3001 151	Heating, small office building	SF	7.61	7.55	15.16	4.79	12.40	0.0660
15.3001 161	HVAC, small office building	SF	8.49	10.86	19.35	6.89	15.38	0.0949
15.3001 171	HVAC, high rise office building	SF	15.30	13.84	29.14	8.79	24.09	0.1210
15.3001 181	HVAC, schools	SF	14.30	13.83	28.13	8.78	23.08	0.1209
15.3001 191	HVAC, wet laboratories	SF	39.02	45.61	84.63	28.94	67.96	0.3986
15.3100 000	**EQUIPMENT, FURNACES:**							
15.3101 000	**FURNACES, GAS FIRED, RESIDENTIAL, WITH FLUE & VALVING:**							
15.3101 011	Wall furnace, single, 25 MBTU, manual	EA	376.73	301.58	678.31	189.07	565.80	2.5433
15.3101 021	Wall furnace, single, 35 MBTU, manual	EA	426.98	333.61	760.59	209.15	636.13	2.8134
15.3101 031	Wall furnace, single, 25 MBTU, thermostat	EA	450.00	410.69	860.69	257.47	707.47	3.4634
15.3101 041	Wall furnace, single, 35 MBTU, thermostat	EA	500.25	449.13	949.38	281.57	781.82	3.7876
15.3101 051	Wall furnace, dual, 25 MBTU, manual	EA	420.71	327.20	747.91	205.13	625.84	2.7593
15.3101 061	Wall furnace, dual, 35 MBTU, manual	EA	450.00	340.04	790.04	213.18	663.18	2.8676
15.3101 071	Wall furnace, dual, 25 MBTU, thermostat	EA	494.00	436.28	930.28	273.51	767.51	3.6792
15.3101 081	Wall furnace, dual, 35 MBTU, thermostat	EA	510.70	455.55	966.25	285.59	796.29	3.8417
15.3101 091	Wall furnace, dual, 50 MBTU, thermostat	EA	642.60	558.22	1,200.82	349.96	992.56	4.7075
15.3101 101	Wall furnace, dual, 60 MBTU, thermostat	EA	711.68	596.77	1,308.45	374.12	1,085.80	5.0326
15.3101 111	Floor furnace, 32 MBTU, thermostat	EA	1,325.01	538.96	1,863.97	337.88	1,662.89	4.5451
15.3101 121	Floor furnace, 45 MBTU, thermostat	EA	1,400.14	603.07	2,003.21	378.08	1,778.22	5.0858
15.3101 131	Floor furnace, 65 MBTU, thermostat	EA	1,630.06	673.64	2,303.70	422.32	2,052.38	5.6809
15.3102 000	**FURNACE, FORCED AIR, GAS FIRE, FLUE, VALVE, THERMO:**							
	Note: For A/C preparation, add 12% to the material costs.							
15.3102 011	Furnace, up flow, 50 MBTU, gas fired	EA	653.03	404.16	1,057.19	253.37	906.40	3.4083
15.3102 021	Furnace, up flow, 80 MBTU, gas fired	EA	703.29	436.28	1,139.57	273.51	976.80	3.6792
15.3102 031	Furnace, up flow, 100 MBTU, gas fired	EA	774.41	481.25	1,255.66	301.70	1,076.11	4.0584
15.3102 041	Furnace, up flow, 120 MBTU, gas fired	EA	828.88	590.24	1,419.12	370.03	1,198.91	4.9776
15.3102 051	Furnace, up flow, 150 MBTU, gas fired	EA	1,230.79	725.01	1,955.80	454.52	1,685.31	6.1141
15.3102 061	Furnace, horizontal flow, 80 MBTU, gas fired	EA	815.05	538.96	1,354.01	337.88	1,152.93	4.5451
15.3102 071	Furnace, horizontal flow, 100 MBTU, gas fired	EA	895.28	609.50	1,504.78	382.11	1,277.39	5.1400
15.3102 081	Furnace, counter flow, 80 MBTU, gas fired	EA	1,444.87	436.28	1,881.15	273.51	1,718.38	3.6792
15.3102 091	Furnace, counter flow, 100 MBTU, gas fired	EA	1,494.22	481.25	1,975.47	301.70	1,795.92	4.0584
15.3102 101	Furnace, counter flow, 120 MBTU, gas fired	EA	1,605.42	590.24	2,195.66	370.03	1,975.45	4.9776
15.3102 111	Furnace, counter flow, 160 MBTU, gas fired	EA	1,679.48	725.01	2,404.49	454.52	2,134.00	6.1141
15.3103 000	**UNIT HEATERS, GAS FIRED, WITH FLUE & VALVE:**							
15.3103 011	Unit heater, suspended, 50 MBTU, gas fired	EA	943.05	449.13	1,392.18	281.57	1,224.62	3.7876
15.3103 021	Unit heater, suspended, 75 MBTU, gas fired	EA	1,022.94	486.60	1,509.54	305.06	1,328.00	4.1036
15.3103 031	Unit heater, suspended, 125 MBTU, gas fired	EA	1,225.80	588.12	1,813.92	368.70	1,594.50	4.9597
15.3103 041	Unit heater, suspended, 175 MBTU, gas fired	EA	1,635.86	780.58	2,416.44	489.36	2,125.22	6.5827
15.3103 051	Unit heater, suspended, 225 MBTU, gas fired	EA	1,761.03	839.45	2,600.48	526.27	2,287.30	7.0792
15.3103 061	Unit heater, suspended, 300 MBTU, gas fired	EA	2,244.44	951.69	3,196.13	596.63	2,841.07	8.0257
15.3103 071	Unit heater, suspended, 400 MBTU, gas fired	EA	2,781.75	1,117.45	3,899.20	700.55	3,482.30	9.4236
15.3104 000	**DUCT HEATERS, GAS FIRED, WITH FLUE & VALVE:**							
15.3104 011	Duct heater, indoor, 100 MBTU, gas fired	EA	1,392.60	470.53	1,863.13	294.98	1,687.58	3.9680
15.3104 021	Duct heater, indoor, 125 MBTU, gas fired	EA	1,501.21	514.61	2,015.82	322.62	1,823.83	4.3398
15.3104 031	Duct heater, indoor, 175 MBTU, gas fired	EA	1,755.38	563.02	2,318.40	352.97	2,108.35	4.7480
15.3104 041	Duct heater, indoor, 225 MBTU, gas fired	EA	2,076.96	611.93	2,688.89	383.63	2,460.59	5.1605

Division 15 CSI #	15 - MECHANICAL Description	Unit	Material	Union Install	Union Total	Open Install	Open Total	Unit Man-Hrs
15.3104 000	**DUCT HEATERS, GAS FIRED, WITH FLUE & VALVE: (Cont.)**							
15.3104 051	Duct heater, indoor, 250 MBTU, gas fired	EA	2,372.36	635.77	3,008.13	398.57	2,770.93	5.3615
15.3104 061	Duct heater, indoor, 300 MBTU, gas fired	EA	2,535.32	720.16	3,255.48	451.48	2,986.80	6.0732
15.3104 071	Duct heater, indoor, 350 MBTU, gas fired	EA	2,856.87	775.76	3,632.63	486.34	3,343.21	6.5421
15.3104 081	Duct heater, indoor, 400 MBTU, gas fired	EA	3,121.95	831.36	3,953.31	521.20	3,643.15	7.0110
15.3104 091	Duct heater, roof, 100 MBTU, gas fired	EA	2,087.78	444.79	2,532.57	278.85	2,366.63	3.7510
15.3104 101	Duct heater, roof, 125 MBTU, gas fired	EA	2,292.01	526.87	2,818.88	330.31	2,622.32	4.4432
15.3104 111	Duct heater, roof, 175 MBTU, gas fired	EA	2,622.25	691.01	3,313.26	433.21	3,055.46	5.8274
15.3104 121	Duct heater, roof, 225 MBTU, gas fired	EA	2,885.14	841.95	3,727.09	527.84	3,412.98	7.1003
15.3104 131	Duct heater, roof, 250 MBTU, gas fired	EA	3,321.78	910.81	4,232.59	571.01	3,892.79	7.6810
15.3104 141	Duct heater, roof, 300 MBTU, gas fired	EA	3,523.82	969.02	4,492.84	607.50	4,131.32	8.1719
15.3104 151	Duct heater, roof, 350 MBTU, gas fired	EA	3,784.50	1,093.45	4,877.95	685.50	4,470.00	9.2212
15.3104 161	Duct heater, roof, 400 MBTU, gas fired	EA	4,323.34	1,217.88	5,541.22	763.51	5,086.85	10.2705
15.3105 000	**ELECTRIC FURNACES, UNIT, DUCT, BASEBOARD HEATERS:**							
	Note: The following prices include supports, relays & thermostats.							
15.3105 011	Furnace, up flow, 68 MBTU/Hr	EA	1,050.71	363.58	1,414.29	227.93	1,278.64	3.0661
15.3105 021	Furnace, up flow, 85 MBTU/Hr	EA	1,300.85	390.33	1,691.18	244.70	1,545.55	3.2917
15.3105 031	Furnace, up flow, 102 MBTU/Hr	EA	1,547.47	422.37	1,969.84	264.79	1,812.26	3.5619
15.3105 041	Unit heater, 10 MBTU/Hr, 3kw, 240v	EA	470.49	224.58	695.07	140.79	611.28	1.8939
15.3105 051	Unit heater, 18 MBTU/Hr, 5kw, 240v	EA	492.58	251.32	743.90	157.56	650.14	2.1194
15.3105 061	Unit heater, 34 MBTU/Hr, 10kw, 240v	EA	694.71	336.80	1,031.51	211.15	905.86	2.8403
15.3105 071	Unit heater, 40 MBTU/Hr, 12kw, 240v	EA	801.38	390.33	1,191.71	244.70	1,046.08	3.2917
15.3105 081	Duct heater, 3.4 MBTU/Hr, 1kw, no enclosure	EA	186.15	92.54	278.69	58.01	244.16	0.7804
15.3105 091	Duct heater, 10 MBTU/Hr, 3kw, no enclosure	EA	235.50	113.09	348.59	70.90	306.40	0.9537
15.3105 101	Duct heater, 18 MBTU/Hr, 5kw, no enclosure	EA	278.36	128.56	406.92	80.60	358.96	1.0842
15.3105 111	Duct heater, 25 MBTU/Hr, 75kw, no enclosure	EA	363.15	176.48	539.63	110.64	473.79	1.4883
15.3105 121	Duct heater, 34 MBTU/Hr, 10kw, no enclosure	EA	416.15	213.86	630.01	134.07	550.22	1.8035
15.3105 131	Duct heater, 40 MBTU/Hr, 12kw, no enclosure	EA	518.22	256.68	774.90	160.92	679.14	2.1646
15.3105 151	Baseboard heater, hot water, 1030 BTU	LF	32.65	13.72	46.37	8.60	41.25	0.1157
15.3105 161	Baseboard heater, hot water, 2 row	LF	46.71	17.63	64.34	11.05	57.76	0.1487
15.3105 171	Baseboard heater, elec, 240/160w, aluminum fin	LF	47.45	12.32	59.77	7.72	55.17	0.1039
15.3105 181	Baseboard heater, elec, 240/140w	LF	29.62	12.32	41.94	7.72	37.34	0.1039
15.3200 000	**EQUIPMENT, HOT WATER & STEAM BOILERS:**							
	Note: The following prices do not include stack and breeching.							
	For oil firing . . . . add 2% to the material costs							
	For gas, oil firing . . . . . . add 8%							
15.3201 000	**BOILERS, GAS FIRED, CAST IRON, 15# STEAM, 30# WATER:**							
	Note: The following prices include burner, fire control and trim.							
	For copper water tube to 200 MBH . . . . . . deduct 4% from material							
	For copper water tube over 200 MBH . . . . deduct 30%							
	For forced draft 335 MBH and above . . . . add 50% to material costs							
15.3201 011	Boiler, cast iron, gas, 4hp, 134 MBTU/Hr, 15#/30#	EA	3,591.49	2,180.89	5,772.38	1,367.24	4,958.73	18.3917
15.3201 021	Boiler, cast iron, gas, 6hp, 200 MBTU/Hr, 15#/30#	EA	4,377.05	2,180.89	6,557.94	1,367.24	5,744.29	18.3917
15.3201 031	Boiler, cast iron, gas, 8hp, 268 MBTU/Hr, 15#/30#	EA	5,167.21	2,271.76	7,438.97	1,424.21	6,591.42	19.1580
15.3201 041	Boiler, cast iron, gas, 10hp, 335 MBTU/Hr, 15#/30#	EA	7,615.27	2,544.37	10,159.64	1,595.11	9,210.38	21.4570
15.3201 051	Boiler, cast iron, gas, 12hp, 402 MBTU/Hr, 15#/30#	EA	8,398.77	2,907.85	11,306.62	1,822.99	10,221.76	24.5223
15.3201 061	Boiler, cast iron, gas, 15hp, 502 MBTU/Hr, 15#/30#	EA	9,178.04	3,453.07	12,631.11	2,164.80	11,342.84	29.1202
15.3201 071	Boiler, cast iron, gas, 20hp, 670 MBTU/Hr, 15#/30#	EA	12,249.56	3,725.69	15,975.25	2,335.70	14,585.26	31.4192
15.3201 081	Boiler, cast iron, gas, 25hp, 838 MBTU/Hr, 15#/30#	EA	13,877.56	5,452.21	19,329.77	3,418.09	17,295.65	45.9792
15.3201 091	Boiler, cast iron, gas, 30hp, 1000 MBTU/Hr, 15#/30#	EA	15,507.98	5,906.56	21,414.54	3,702.93	19,210.91	49.8108
15.3201 101	Boiler, cast iron, gas, 35hp, 1170 MBTU/Hr, 15#/30#	EA	18,143.72	6,360.92	24,504.64	3,987.78	22,131.50	53.6424
15.3202 000	**BOILERS, GAS FIRED, STEEL WATER TUBE, 15# STEAM, 30# WATER:**							
	Note: The following prices include burner, fire control and trim.							
	For steel fire tube 35 HP to 100 HP . . . add 50% to material cost.							
15.3202 011	Boiler, steel, gas, 10hp, 335 MBTU/Hr, 15#/30#	EA	12,383.22	1,317.63	13,700.85	826.04	13,209.26	11.1117
15.3202 021	Boiler, steel, gas, 20hp, 670 MBTU/Hr, 15#/30#	EA	14,458.21	1,408.49	15,866.70	883.01	15,341.22	11.8780
15.3202 031	Boiler, steel, gas, 40hp, 1340 MBTU/Hr, 15#/30#	EA	17,840.07	1,635.67	19,475.74	1,025.43	18,865.50	13.7938
15.3202 041	Boiler, steel, gas, 60hp, 2010 MBTU/Hr, 15#/30#	EA	19,712.99	1,999.15	21,712.14	1,253.31	20,966.30	16.8591
15.3202 051	Boiler, steel, gas, 100hp, 3350 MBTU/Hr, 15/30#	EA	29,132.99	3,271.34	32,404.33	2,050.86	31,183.85	27.5876
15.3202 061	Add for forced draft	EA	5,358.99		5,358.99		5,358.99	

Division 15 CSI #	15 - MECHANICAL Description	Unit	Material	Union Install	Union Total	Open Install	Open Total	Unit Man-Hrs
15.3203 000	**BOILERS, GAS, STEEL TUBE, 15# STEAM 30# WATER, FORCED DRAFT:**							
	Note: The following prices include burner, fire control and trim.							
15.3203 011	Boiler, steel, 150hp, 5020 MBTU/Hr, 15#/30#	EA	66,389.74	3,998.29	70,388.03	2,506.60	68,896.34	33.7181
15.3203 021	Boiler, steel, 200hp, 6700 MBTU/Hr, 15#/30#	EA	88,029.69	4,543.51	92,573.20	2,848.41	90,878.10	38.3160
15.3203 031	Boiler, steel, 300hp, 10050 MBTU/Hr, 15#/30#	EA	109,117.82	6,997.01	116,114.83	4,386.56	113,504.38	59.0067
15.3203 041	Boiler, steel, 400hp, 13400 MBTU/Hr, 15#/30#	EA	127,758.79	7,196.62	134,955.41	4,511.69	132,270.48	60.6900
15.3203 051	Boiler, steel, 600hp, 20100 MBTU/Hr, 15#/30#	EA	171,755.33	9,087.02	180,842.35	5,696.82	177,452.15	76.6320
15.3204 000	**BOILERS, STEEL TUBE, GAS FIRED, 150# STEAM:**							
	Note: The following prices include burner, fire control and trim.							
15.3204 011	Boiler, steel, 10hp, 335 MBTU/Hr, 150# steam	EA	16,866.65	1,317.63	18,184.28	826.04	17,692.69	11.1117
15.3204 021	Boiler, steel, 20hp, 670 MBTU/Hr, 150# steam	EA	23,351.43	1,408.49	24,759.92	883.01	24,234.44	11.8780
15.3204 031	Boiler, steel, 40hp, 1340 MBTU/Hr, 150# steam	EA	35,903.19	1,635.67	37,538.86	1,025.43	36,928.62	13.7938
15.3204 041	Boiler, steel, 70hp, 2345 MBTU/Hr, 150# steam	EA	47,674.72	1,999.15	49,673.87	1,253.31	48,928.03	16.8591
15.3204 051	Boiler, steel, 100hp, 3350 MBTU/Hr, 150# steam	EA	57,172.31	3,271.34	60,443.65	2,050.86	59,223.17	27.5876
15.3204 061	Boiler, steel, 150hp, 5020 MBTU/Hr, 150# steam	EA	70,600.34	3,998.29	74,598.63	2,506.60	73,106.94	33.7181
15.3204 071	Boiler, steel, 200hp, 6700 MBTU/Hr, 150# steam	EA	85,315.99	4,543.51	89,859.50	2,848.41	88,164.40	38.3160
15.3204 081	Boiler, steel, 300hp, 10,050 MBTU/Hr, 150# steam	EA	122,473.13	6,997.01	129,470.14	4,386.56	126,859.69	59.0067
15.3204 091	Boiler, steel, 400hp, 13,400 MBTU/Hr, 150# steam	EA	141,862.80	7,723.97	149,586.77	4,842.30	146,705.10	65.1372
15.3204 101	Boiler, steel, 500hp, 16,740 MBTU/Hr, 150# steam	EA	165,228.31	9,087.02	174,315.33	5,696.82	170,925.13	76.6320
15.3204 111	Boiler, steel, 600hp, 20,100 MBTU/Hr, 150# steam	EA	198,069.58	10,904.43	208,974.01	6,836.19	204,905.77	91.9584
15.3205 000	**BLACK IRON FOR STACKS & BREECHING:**							
15.3205 011	Black iron, rectangular, 10 ga - 3/16"	#	2.32	1.66	3.98	1.07	3.39	0.0151
15.3205 021	Black iron, rectangular, 1/4" & over	#	2.13	1.43	3.56	.92	3.05	0.0130
15.3205 031	Black iron, round, 10 ga - 3/16"	#	2.23	1.66	3.89	1.07	3.30	0.0151
15.3205 041	Black iron, round, 1/4" & over	#	1.99	1.43	3.42	.92	2.91	0.0130
15.3206 000	**STACKS & BREECHING, INSULATED, 2000 DEGREE:**							
15.3206 011	Stack, 12" dia, insulated, 2,000 degree	LF	56.63	46.76	103.39	30.06	86.69	0.4241
15.3206 021	Stack, 18" dia, insulated, 2,000 degree	LF	87.96	67.54	155.50	43.42	131.38	0.6126
15.3206 031	Stack, 24" dia, insulated, 2,000 degree	LF	134.85	103.97	238.82	66.84	201.69	0.9430
15.3206 041	Stack, 30" dia, insulated, 2,000 degree	LF	175.82	135.09	310.91	86.85	262.67	1.2253
15.3206 051	Stack, 36" dia, insulated, 2,000 degree	LF	197.92	171.42	369.34	110.20	308.12	1.5548
15.3206 061	Breeching, exhaust duct, insulated	SF	4.95	10.89	15.84	7.00	11.95	0.0988
15.3300 000	**EQUIPMENT, COOLING:**							
15.3301 000	**CHILLERS, WITH STARTER & TRIM, ELECTRIC DRIVEN:**							
	Note: The hot water absorption chiller prices for chillers above 300 tons include duct coil section, remote condenser, controls and accessories. For steam absorption, add 9% to the material costs.							
15.3301 011	Chiller, reciprocating, air cool, 20 ton	EA	21,223.19	4,579.87	25,803.06	2,871.20	24,094.39	38.6226
15.3301 021	Chiller, reciprocating, air cool, 50 ton	EA	44,662.25	6,542.65	51,204.90	4,101.71	48,763.96	55.1750
15.3301 031	Chiller, reciprocating, air cool, 100 ton	EA	73,057.52	11,449.65	84,507.17	7,178.00	80,235.52	96.5563
15.3301 041	Chiller, reciprocating, air cool, 150 ton	EA	98,615.40	13,085.31	111,700.71	8,203.43	106,818.83	110.3501
15.3301 051	Chiller, reciprocating, water cool, 20 ton	EA	20,944.36	4,579.87	25,524.23	2,871.20	23,815.56	38.6226
15.3301 061	Chiller, reciprocating, water cool, 40 ton	EA	33,924.43	5,452.21	39,376.64	3,418.09	37,342.52	45.9792
15.3301 071	Chiller, reciprocating, water cool, 70 ton	EA	53,245.29	8,178.32	61,423.61	5,127.14	58,372.43	68.9688
15.3301 081	Chiller, reciprocating, water cool, 100 ton	EA	61,615.44	11,449.65	73,065.09	7,178.00	68,793.44	96.5563
15.3301 091	Chiller, reciprocating, water cool, 150 ton	EA	98,362.54	13,085.31	111,447.85	8,203.43	106,565.97	110.3501
15.3301 101	Chiller, reciprocating, water cool, 200 ton	EA	124,362.62	21,808.85	146,171.47	13,672.37	138,034.99	183.9168
15.3301 111	Chiller, centrifugal, water cool, 40 ton	EA	39,935.11	4,361.78	44,296.89	2,734.48	42,669.59	36.7834
15.3301 121	Chiller, centrifugal, water cool, 60 ton	EA	52,205.09	5,452.21	57,657.30	3,418.09	55,623.18	45.9792
15.3301 131	Chiller, centrifugal, water cool, 80 ton	EA	63,178.60	7,633.10	70,811.70	4,785.33	67,963.93	64.3709
15.3301 141	Chiller, centrifugal, water cool, 100 ton	EA	72,253.24	9,268.76	81,522.00	5,810.76	78,064.00	78.1646
15.3301 151	Chiller, centrifugal, water cool, 150 ton	EA	97,789.29	12,540.10	110,329.39	7,861.62	105,650.91	105.7522
15.3301 161	Chiller, centrifugal, water cool, 200 ton	EA	126,325.20	16,356.64	142,681.84	10,254.28	136,579.48	137.9376
15.3301 171	Chiller, centrifugal, water cool, 250 ton	EA	129,708.46	19,082.75	148,791.21	11,963.33	141,671.79	160.9272
15.3301 181	Chiller, centrifugal, water cool, 300 ton	EA	155,650.54	21,808.85	177,459.39	13,672.37	169,322.91	183.9168
15.3301 191	Chiller, centrifugal, water cool, 400 ton	EA	198,927.73	26,579.54	225,507.27	16,663.21	215,590.94	224.1486
15.3301 201	Chiller, centrifugal, water cool, 600 ton	EA	271,846.40	29,532.82	301,379.22	18,514.67	290,361.07	249.0540
15.3301 211	Chiller, centrifugal, water cool, 1000 ton	EA	375,707.24	41,345.95	417,053.19	25,920.54	401,627.78	348.6756
15.3301 221	Chiller, absorption, hot water, 50 ton	EA	67,674.55	6,542.65	74,217.20	4,101.71	71,776.26	55.1750
15.3301 231	Chiller, absorption, hot water, 100 ton	EA	135,347.21	9,268.76	144,615.97	5,810.76	141,157.97	78.1646
15.3301 241	Chiller, absorption, hot water, 150 ton	EA	203,021.80	12,540.10	215,561.90	7,861.62	210,883.42	105.7522
15.3301 251	Chiller, absorption, hot water, 200 ton	EA	248,137.48	16,356.64	264,494.12	10,254.28	258,391.76	137.9376
15.3301 261	Chiller, absorption, hot water, 250 ton	EA	310,173.29	19,082.75	329,256.04	11,963.33	322,136.62	160.9272

Division 15 CSI #	15 - MECHANICAL Description	Unit	Material	Union Install	Union Total	Open Install	Open Total	Unit Man-Hrs
15.3301 000	**CHILLERS, WITH STARTER & TRIM, ELECTRIC DRIVEN: (Cont.)**							
15.3301 271	Chiller, absorption, hot water, 300 ton	EA	338,370.83	21,808.85	360,179.68	13,672.37	352,043.20	183.9168
15.3301 281	Chiller, absorption, hot water, 350 ton	EA	394,766.02	22,899.29	417,665.31	14,355.99	409,122.01	193.1126
15.3301 291	Chiller, absorption, hot water, 400 ton	EA	451,161.16	24,534.96	475,696.12	15,381.42	466,542.58	206.9064
15.3301 301	Chiller, absorption, hot water, 650 ton	EA	703,956.28	28,896.74	732,853.02	18,115.90	722,072.18	243.6898
15.3301 311	Chiller, absorption hot water, 1000 ton	EA	902,322.27	38,165.49	940,487.76	23,926.66	926,248.93	321.8544
15.3302 000	**COOLING TOWERS:**							
15.3302 011	Cooling tower, 20 ton, compressor chiller	EA	7,896.13	1,090.44	8,986.57	683.62	8,579.75	9.1958
15.3302 021	Cooling tower, 40 ton, compressor chiller	EA	15,790.45	1,635.67	17,426.12	1,025.43	16,815.88	13.7938
15.3302 031	Cooling tower, 60 ton, compressor chiller	EA	23,686.57	2,180.89	25,867.46	1,367.24	25,053.81	18.3917
15.3302 041	Cooling tower, 80 ton, compressor chiller	EA	27,067.96	2,726.11	29,794.07	1,709.05	28,777.01	22.9896
15.3302 051	Cooling tower, 100 ton, compressor chiller	EA	33,836.29	3,271.33	37,107.62	2,050.85	35,887.14	27.5875
15.3302 061	Cooling tower, 150 ton, compressor chiller	EA	50,754.52	4,034.65	54,789.17	2,529.40	53,283.92	34.0247
15.3302 071	Cooling tower, 200 ton, compressor chiller	EA	56,846.25	4,797.95	61,644.20	3,007.92	59,854.17	40.4617
15.3302 081	Cooling tower, 250 ton, compressor chiller	EA	71,057.78	5,561.27	76,619.05	3,486.46	74,544.24	46.8989
15.3302 091	Cooling tower, 300 ton, compressor chiller	EA	85,269.38	6,542.65	91,812.03	4,101.71	89,371.09	55.1750
15.3302 101	Cooling tower, 400 ton, compressor chiller	EA	112,968.84	8,178.32	121,147.16	5,127.14	118,095.98	68.9688
15.3302 111	Cooling tower, 600 ton, compressor chiller	EA	170,540.62	10,904.43	181,445.05	6,836.19	177,376.81	91.9584
15.3302 121	Cooling tower, 1000 ton, compressor chiller	EA	259,416.91	15,266.20	274,683.11	9,570.67	268,987.58	128.7418
15.3302 131	Cooling tower, 1600 ton, compressor chiller	EA	378,975.58	19,627.97	398,603.55	12,305.14	391,280.72	165.5251
15.3302 141	Cooling tower, 50 ton, absorption chiller	EA	15,575.10	2,180.89	17,755.99	1,367.24	16,942.34	18.3917
15.3302 151	Cooling tower, 100 ton, absorption chiller	EA	18,731.71	3,162.29	21,894.00	1,982.50	20,714.21	26.6680
15.3302 161	Cooling tower, 150 ton, absorption chiller	EA	27,462.50	4,252.73	31,715.23	2,666.11	30,128.61	35.8638
15.3302 171	Cooling tower, 200 ton, absorption chiller	EA	34,976.02	5,125.09	40,101.11	3,213.01	38,189.03	43.2205
15.3302 181	Cooling tower, 250 ton, absorption chiller	EA	38,274.43	5,888.40	44,162.83	3,691.53	41,965.98	49.6576
15.3302 191	Cooling tower, 300 ton, absorption chiller	EA	39,347.73	7,087.88	46,435.61	4,443.52	43,791.25	59.7730
15.3302 201	Cooling tower, 350 ton, absorption chiller	EA	43,282.53	7,960.24	51,242.77	4,990.42	48,272.95	67.1297
15.3302 211	Cooling tower, 400 ton, absorption chiller	EA	48,092.01	8,505.46	56,597.47	5,332.23	53,424.24	71.7276
15.3302 221	Cooling tower, 600 ton, absorption chiller	EA	70,277.98	12,212.97	82,490.95	7,656.54	77,934.52	102.9935
15.3302 231	Cooling tower, 1000 ton, absorption chiller	EA	116,996.28	16,792.83	133,789.11	10,527.73	127,524.01	141.6160
15.3302 241	Cooling tower, 1600 ton, absorption chiller	EA	177,580.69	23,771.66	201,352.35	14,902.90	192,483.59	200.4694
15.3302 251	Cooling tower, 100 ton, closed circuit unit	EA	32,789.81	3,543.94	36,333.75	2,221.76	35,011.57	29.8865
15.3302 261	Cooling tower, 200 ton, closed circuit unit	EA	62,300.62	5,452.21	67,752.83	3,418.09	65,718.71	45.9792
15.3303 000	**AIR CONDITIONERS (D-X), PACKAGE UNIT:**							
15.3303 011	Air conditioner, 8 ton, roof mounted, D-X	EA	12,393.65	1,090.45	13,484.10	683.62	13,077.27	9.1959
15.3303 021	Air conditioner, 10 ton, roof mounted, D-X	EA	16,184.03	1,272.19	17,456.22	797.56	16,981.59	10.7285
15.3303 031	Air conditioner, 15 ton, roof mounted, D-X	EA	19,661.34	1,453.93	21,115.27	911.50	20,572.84	12.2612
15.3303 041	Air conditioner, 20 ton, roof mounted, D-X	EA	22,772.09	1,635.67	24,407.76	1,025.43	23,797.52	13.7938
15.3303 051	Air conditioner, 2 ton, thru-wall, D-X	EA	2,046.76	545.23	2,591.99	341.82	2,388.58	4.5980
15.3303 061	Air conditioner, 3 ton, thru-wall, D-X	EA	2,946.81	636.10	3,582.91	398.78	3,345.59	5.3643
15.3303 071	Air conditioner, 4 ton, thru-wall, D-X	EA	4,068.91	726.97	4,795.88	455.75	4,524.66	6.1306
15.3303 081	Air conditioner, 5 ton, thru-wall, D-X	EA	5,028.22	908.70	5,936.92	569.68	5,597.90	7.6632
15.3304 000	**ELECTRIC HEATERS, FOR USE WITH ABOVE D-X UNITS:**							
15.3304 011	Electric heater, 9.6 kw, 327 MBTU/Hr	EA	512.42	90.88	603.30	56.97	569.39	0.7664
15.3304 021	Electric heater, 19.2 kw, 655 MBTU/Hr	EA	861.06	99.96	961.02	62.67	923.73	0.8430
15.3304 031	Electric heater, 28.8 kw, 983 MBTU/Hr	EA	1,051.08	122.68	1,173.76	76.91	1,127.99	1.0346
15.3305 000	**SPLIT SYSTEM, FOR USE WITH FORCED AIR FURNACE:**							
15.3305 011	Air conditioner, residential, 2 ton, split system	EA	2,867.50	408.92	3,276.42	256.36	3,123.86	3.4485
15.3305 021	Air conditioner, residential, 3 ton, split system	EA	3,632.46	431.64	4,064.10	270.61	3,903.07	3.6401
15.3305 031	Air conditioner, residential, 4 ton, split system	EA	4,807.31	636.10	5,443.41	398.78	5,206.09	5.3643
15.3305 041	Air conditioner, residential, 5 ton, split system	EA	5,592.90	772.41	6,365.31	484.24	6,077.14	6.5138
15.3305 101	Air conditioner, commercial, standard, (Title-24), 3 ton, split system	EA	4,182.04	645.08	4,827.12	404.41	4,586.45	5.4400
15.3305 111	Air conditioner, commercial, standard, (Title-24), 4 ton, split system	EA	4,641.89	813.46	5,455.35	509.97	5,151.86	6.8600
15.3305 121	Air conditioner, commercial, standard, (Title-24), 5 ton, split system	EA	5,189.25	949.83	6,139.08	595.46	5,784.71	8.0100
15.3305 131	Air conditioner, commercial, standard, (Title-24), 6 ton, split system	EA	6,012.54	1,052.99	7,065.53	660.14	6,672.68	8.8800
15.3305 141	Air conditioner, commercial, standard, (Title-24), 7-1/2 ton, split system	EA	7,737.89	1,181.06	8,918.95	740.43	8,478.32	9.9600
15.3305 151	Air conditioner, commercial, standard, (Title-24), 8-1/2 ton, split system	EA	9,349.44	1,332.84	10,682.28	835.58	10,185.02	11.2400
15.3305 161	Air conditioner, commercial, standard, (Title-24), 10 ton, split system	EA	9,912.16	1,522.57	11,434.73	954.53	10,866.69	12.8400
15.3305 171	Air conditioner, commercial, standard, (Title-24), 12-1/2 ton, split system	EA	11,289.35	1,662.49	12,951.84	1,042.25	12,331.60	14.0200
15.3305 181	Air conditioner, commercial, standard, (Title-24), 20 ton, split system	EA	16,709.61	1,499.36	18,208.97	939.98	17,649.59	12.6443
15.3305 191	Air conditioner, commercial, standard, (Title-24), 30 ton, split system	EA	25,102.19	2,907.85	28,010.04	1,822.99	26,925.18	24.5223
15.3305 193	Air conditioner, commercial, standard, (Title-24), 50 ton, split system	EA	36,182.92	3,543.94	39,726.86	2,221.76	38,404.68	29.8865

Division 15 CSI #	15 - MECHANICAL Description	Unit	Material	Union Install	Union Total	Open Install	Open Total	Unit Man-Hrs
15.3305 000	**SPLIT SYSTEM, FOR USE WITH FORCED AIR FURNACE: (Cont.)**							
15.3305 195	Air conditioner, commercial, standard, (Title-24), 70 ton, split system	EA	45,026.25	4,543.51	49,569.76	2,848.41	47,874.66	38.3160
15.3305 201	Air conditioner, commercial, high efficiency, 3 ton, split system	EA	6,174.58	645.08	6,819.66	404.41	6,578.99	5.4400
15.3305 211	Air conditioner, commercial, high efficiency, 4 ton, split system	EA	7,313.09	813.46	8,126.55	509.97	7,823.06	6.8600
15.3305 221	Air conditioner, commercial, high efficiency, 5 ton, split system	EA	7,926.20	949.83	8,876.03	595.46	8,521.66	8.0100
15.3305 231	Air conditioner, commercial, high efficiency, 6 ton, split system	EA	8,731.96	1,052.99	9,784.95	660.14	9,392.10	8.8800
15.3305 241	Air conditioner, commercial, high efficiency, 7-1/2 ton, split system	EA	10,680.68	1,181.06	11,861.74	740.43	11,421.11	9.9600
15.3305 251	Air conditioner, commercial, high efficiency, 8-1/2 ton, split system	EA	12,020.69	1,332.84	13,353.53	835.58	12,856.27	11.2400
15.3305 261	Air conditioner, commercial, high efficiency, 10 ton, split system	EA	13,469.06	1,522.57	14,991.63	954.53	14,423.59	12.8400
15.3305 271	Air conditioner, commercial, high efficiency, 12-1/2 ton, split system	EA	14,917.49	1,662.49	16,579.98	1,042.25	15,959.74	14.0200
15.3305 401	Economizer, add to above, 3 ton to 6 ton unit	EA	1,655.33		1,655.33		1,655.33	
15.3305 411	Economizer, add to above, 7-1/2 ton to 12-1/2 ton unit	EA	2,317.43		2,317.43		2,317.43	
15.3306 000	**COMPUTER ROOM AIR CONDITIONING UNITS:**							
15.3306 011	Air cooled, computer room, air conditioning unit, 5 ton	EA	16,199.35	2,907.85	19,107.20	1,822.99	18,022.34	24.5223
15.3306 021	Air cooled, computer room, air conditioning unit, 8 ton	EA	23,456.41	3,089.59	26,546.00	1,936.92	25,393.33	26.0549
15.3306 031	Air cooled, computer room, air conditioning unit, 10 ton	EA	29,634.49	5,815.70	35,450.19	3,645.97	33,280.46	49.0445
15.3306 041	Air cooled, computer room, air conditioning unit, 15 ton	EA	38,139.13	8,178.32	46,317.45	5,127.14	43,266.27	68.9688
15.3306 051	Air cooled, computer room, air conditioning unit, 20 ton	EA	48,303.78	8,723.55	57,027.33	5,468.96	53,772.74	73.5668
15.3306 061	Water cooled, computer room, air conditioning unit, 5 ton	EA	11,976.16	2,726.11	14,702.27	1,709.05	13,685.21	22.9896
15.3306 071	Water cooled, computer room, air conditioning unit, 8 ton	EA	17,548.65	2,907.85	20,456.50	1,822.99	19,371.64	24.5223
15.3306 081	Water cooled, computer room, air conditioning unit, 10 ton	EA	21,633.14	5,452.21	27,085.35	3,418.09	25,051.23	45.9792
15.3306 091	Water cooled, computer room, air conditioning unit, 15 ton	EA	29,792.92	7,814.85	37,607.77	4,899.27	34,692.19	65.9036
15.3306 101	Water cooled, computer room, air conditioning unit, 20 ton	EA	35,701.75	8,360.07	44,061.82	5,241.08	40,942.83	70.5015
15.3400 000	**EQUIPMENT, HEATING & COOLING COMBINATIONS:**							
15.3401 000	**GAS HEAT AND D-X COOLING:**							
	Note: The following items are roof mounted, single zone, with disposable filters, isolation dampers, curbs, controls and valving.							
	For multi-zoned units, 2nd zone . . . add 8% to material costs							
	For 3rd to 8th zones . . . . add 4% to material costs							
15.3401 011	Air conditioner, 2 ton, 80 MBTU/Hr	EA	4,431.62	1,181.32	5,612.94	740.59	5,172.21	9.9622
15.3401 021	Air conditioner, 3 ton, 100 MBTU/Hr	EA	6,517.71	1,272.19	7,789.90	797.56	7,315.27	10.7285
15.3401 031	Air conditioner, 4 ton, 140 MBTU/Hr	EA	8,732.94	1,363.05	10,095.99	854.52	9,587.46	11.4948
15.3401 041	Air conditioner, 5 ton, 140 MBTU/Hr	EA	9,306.45	1,544.80	10,851.25	968.46	10,274.91	13.0275
15.3401 051	Air conditioner, 8 ton, 200 MBTU/Hr	EA	14,911.17	1,817.40	16,728.57	1,139.36	16,050.53	15.3264
15.3401 061	Air conditioner, 10 ton, 260 MBTU/Hr	EA	17,987.31	2,362.64	20,349.95	1,481.18	19,468.49	19.9244
15.3401 071	Air conditioner, 15 ton, 300 MBTU/Hr	EA	23,461.88	2,726.11	26,187.99	1,709.05	25,170.93	22.9896
15.3401 081	Air conditioner, 20 ton, 400 MBTU/Hr	EA	41,711.22	3,634.81	45,346.03	2,278.73	43,989.95	30.6528
15.3401 091	Air conditioner, 30 ton, 550 MBTU/Hr	EA	58,654.38	5,452.21	64,106.59	3,418.09	62,072.47	45.9792
15.3401 101	Air conditioner, 40 ton, 760 MBTU/Hr	EA	75,598.93	7,723.97	83,322.90	4,842.30	80,441.23	65.1372
15.3401 111	Air conditioner, 60 ton, 1000 MBTU/Hr	EA	106,880.97	9,995.72	116,876.69	6,266.51	113,147.48	84.2952
15.3402 000	**HEAT PUMPS:**							
15.3402 011	Heat pump, 2 ton, 26,000 BTU, thru-wall	EA	2,023.09	726.97	2,750.06	455.75	2,478.84	6.1306
15.3402 021	Heat pump, 3 ton, 37,000 BTU, thru-wall	EA	2,997.58	908.70	3,906.28	569.68	3,567.26	7.6632
15.3402 031	Heat pump, 4 ton, 52,000 BTU, thru-wall	EA	4,120.33	1,090.45	5,210.78	683.62	4,803.95	9.1959
15.3402 041	Heat pump, 5 ton, 61,000 BTU, thru-wall	EA	4,959.64	1,272.19	6,231.83	797.56	5,757.20	10.7285
15.3402 051	Heat pump, 8 ton, 90,000 BTU, roof, duct	EA	12,043.64	1,817.40	13,861.04	1,139.36	13,183.00	15.3264
15.3402 061	Heat pump, 10 ton, 120,000 BTU, roof, duct	EA	15,121.30	2,362.64	17,483.94	1,481.18	16,602.48	19.9244
15.3402 071	Heat pump, 15 ton, 180,000 BTU, roof, duct	EA	22,158.21	2,726.11	24,884.32	1,709.05	23,867.26	22.9896
15.3402 081	Heat pump, 20 ton, 240,000 BTU, roof, duct	EA	28,675.36	3,634.81	32,310.17	2,278.73	30,954.09	30.6528
15.3402 091	Heat pump, 1 ton, 13,000 BTU, plenum	EA	2,612.68	545.23	3,157.91	341.82	2,954.50	4.5980
15.3402 101	Heat pump, 2 ton, 26,000 BTU, plenum	EA	3,388.90	636.10	4,025.00	398.78	3,787.68	5.3643
15.3402 111	Heat pump, 3 ton, 37,000 BTU, plenum	EA	4,431.76	681.53	5,113.29	427.26	4,859.02	5.7474
15.3402 121	Heat pump, 4 ton, 52,000 BTU, plenum	EA	5,735.31	726.97	6,462.28	455.75	6,191.06	6.1306
15.3403 000	**D-X COOLING & ELECTRIC HEAT AIR CONDITIONER:**							
	Note: The following items are packaged units, electric heat, including controls and mounting.							
	Skid-mounted, pre-piped, and prewired.							
15.3403 011	Air conditioner, 8 ton D-X, 58 MBTU/Hr electric	EA	15,544.70	908.70	16,453.40	569.68	16,114.38	7.6632
15.3403 021	Air conditioner, 10 ton D-X, 50 MBTU/Hr electric	EA	20,568.04	1,090.45	21,658.49	683.62	21,251.66	9.1959
15.3404 000	**PACKAGED HYDRONIC HEATING & COOLING UNIT, BOILER CLOSED:**							
	Note: The following items include boiler, closed circuit evaporative cooler, pumps, controls, and are skid mounted, pre-piped and pre-wired.							
15.3404 011	Hydronic unit, 50 ton, 300 MBTU/Hr	EA	34,113.63	1,897.28	36,010.91	1,189.44	35,303.07	16.0000

Division 15 CSI #	15 - MECHANICAL Description	Unit	Material	Union Install	Union Total	Open Install	Open Total	Unit Man-Hrs
15.3404 000	**PACKAGED HYDRONIC HEATING & COOLING UNIT, BOILER CLOSED: (Cont.)**							
15.3404 021	Hydronic unit, 100 ton, 600 MBTU/Hr	EA	60,879.71	2,845.92	63,725.63	1,784.16	62,663.87	24.0000
15.3404 031	Hydronic unit, 150 ton, 900 MBTU/Hr	EA	77,675.61	3,557.40	81,233.01	2,230.20	79,905.81	30.0000
15.3404 041	Hydronic unit, 200 ton, 1200 MBTU/Hr	EA	94,468.36	3,794.56	98,262.92	2,378.88	96,847.24	32.0000
15.3405 000	**INFRA-RED HEATERS, GAS FIRED:**							
15.3405 011	Infra-red heater, 30,000 BTU, gas fired	EA	1,032.07	266.12	1,298.19	166.83	1,198.90	2.2442
15.3405 021	Infra-red heater, 45,000 BTU, gas fired	EA	1,637.60	319.87	1,957.47	200.53	1,838.13	2.6975
15.3405 031	Infra-red heater, 60,000 BTU, gas fired	EA	1,862.19	399.83	2,262.02	250.66	2,112.85	3.3718
15.3405 041	Infra-red heater, 80,000 BTU, gas fired	EA	1,997.48	473.23	2,470.71	296.68	2,294.16	3.9908
15.3406 000	**RADIANT HEAT PANELS, CEILING:**							
15.3406 011	Radiant heat panel, 24x24, 357 w	EA	326.04	90.88	416.92	56.97	383.01	0.7664
15.3406 021	Radiant heat panel, 24x48, 500 w	EA	363.58	90.88	454.46	56.97	420.55	0.7664
15.3500 000	**AUXILIARY HEATING & COOLING EQUIPMENT:**							
15.3501 000	**HUMIDIFIERS, STEAM OR ELECTRIC:**							
15.3501 011	Humidifier, steam, 50#/hr	EA	906.19	726.97	1,633.16	455.75	1,361.94	6.1306
15.3501 021	Humidifier, steam, 100#/hr	EA	1,345.52	1,090.45	2,435.97	683.62	2,029.14	9.1959
15.3501 031	Humidifier, steam, 150#/hr	EA	1,601.77	1,272.19	2,873.96	797.56	2,399.33	10.7285
15.3501 041	Humidifier, steam, 300#/hr	EA	2,480.49	1,703.82	4,184.31	1,068.15	3,548.64	14.3685
15.3501 051	Humidifier, electric, 50#/hr	EA	4,486.84	545.23	5,032.07	341.82	4,828.66	4.5980
15.3501 061	Humidifier, electric, 100#/hr	EA	6,139.91	817.83	6,957.74	512.72	6,652.63	6.8969
15.3501 071	Humidifier, electric, 150#/hr	EA	7,792.93	1,090.45	8,883.38	683.62	8,476.55	9.1959
15.3502 000	**PUMPS, CONDENSATE, DUPLEX:**							
15.3502 011	Pump, condensate, duplex, 15 GPM	EA	4,287.27	1,090.45	5,377.72	683.62	4,970.89	9.1959
15.3502 021	Pump, condensate, duplex, 25 GPM	EA	5,257.47	1,272.19	6,529.66	797.56	6,055.03	10.7285
15.3502 031	Pump, condensate, duplex, 40 GPM	EA	6,529.27	1,817.40	8,346.67	1,139.36	7,668.63	15.3264
15.3502 041	Pump, condensate, duplex, 50 GPM	EA	7,158.59	1,999.15	9,157.74	1,253.31	8,411.90	16.8591
15.3502 051	Pump, condensate, duplex, 60 GPM	EA	7,394.62	2,362.64	9,757.26	1,481.18	8,875.80	19.9244
15.3502 061	Pump, condensate, duplex, 75 GPM	EA	7,656.80	2,726.11	10,382.91	1,709.05	9,365.85	22.9896
15.3502 071	Pump, condensate, duplex, 100 GPM	EA	9,702.15	3,089.59	12,791.74	1,936.92	11,639.07	26.0549
15.3502 081	Pump, condensate, duplex, 120 GPM	EA	9,998.31	3,362.21	13,360.52	2,107.83	12,106.14	28.3539
15.3503 000	**PUMPS, WATER SERVICE:**							
	Note: For 100 foot head, add 30% to the material costs. For 150 foot head, add 40%. For 200 foot head, add 70%.							
15.3503 011	Pump, 7-1/2 GPM, 50' head	EA	1,056.57	363.48	1,420.05	227.87	1,284.44	3.0653
15.3503 021	Pump, 20 GPM, 50' head	EA	1,231.88	408.92	1,640.80	256.36	1,488.24	3.4485
15.3503 031	Pump, 30 GPM, 50' head	EA	1,673.75	545.23	2,218.98	341.82	2,015.57	4.5980
15.3503 041	Pump, 45 GPM, 50' head	EA	1,713.93	636.10	2,350.03	398.78	2,112.71	5.3643
15.3503 051	Pump, 60 GPM, 50' head	EA	1,752.87	908.70	2,661.57	569.68	2,322.55	7.6632
15.3503 061	Pump, 90 GPM, 50' head	EA	1,834.48	999.58	2,834.06	626.66	2,461.14	8.4296
15.3503 071	Pump, 120 GPM, 50' head	EA	2,035.26	1,181.32	3,216.58	740.59	2,775.85	9.9622
15.3503 081	Pump, 150 GPM, 50' head	EA	2,541.12	1,272.19	3,813.31	797.56	3,338.68	10.7285
15.3503 091	Pump, 200 GPM, 50' head	EA	2,964.19	1,544.80	4,508.99	968.46	3,932.65	13.0275
15.3503 101	Pump, 250 GPM, 50' head	EA	3,705.21	1,726.54	5,431.75	1,082.40	4,787.61	14.5601
15.3503 111	Pump, 300 GPM, 50' head	EA	4,000.02	2,090.02	6,090.04	1,310.27	5,310.29	17.6254
15.3503 121	Pump, 400 GPM, 50' head	EA	4,342.75	2,271.76	6,614.51	1,424.21	5,766.96	19.1580
15.3503 131	Pump, 600 GPM, 50' head	EA	5,540.33	2,544.37	8,084.70	1,595.11	7,135.44	21.4570
15.3503 141	Pump, 800 GPM, 50' head	EA	5,714.17	2,907.85	8,622.02	1,822.99	7,537.16	24.5223
15.3503 151	Pump, 1000 GPM, 50' head	EA	5,927.48	3,271.34	9,198.82	2,050.86	7,978.34	27.5876
15.3503 161	Pump, 1500 GPM, 50' head	EA	6,861.82	3,407.63	10,269.45	2,136.31	8,998.13	28.7370
15.3503 171	Pump, 2000 GPM, 50' head	EA	13,242.68	3,998.29	17,240.97	2,506.60	15,749.28	33.7181
15.3503 181	Pump, 2500 GPM, 50' head	EA	13,489.04	4,180.04	17,669.08	2,620.54	16,109.58	35.2508
15.3503 191	Pump, 3000 GPM, 50' head	EA	13,958.23	4,452.64	18,410.87	2,791.44	16,749.67	37.5497
15.3503 201	Pump, 3500 GPM, 50' head	EA	17,453.83	4,725.26	22,179.09	2,962.35	20,416.18	39.8487
15.3503 211	Pump, 4000 GPM, 50' head	EA	17,714.28	4,997.86	22,712.14	3,133.25	20,847.53	42.1476
15.3504 000	**PUMPS, FUEL OIL:**							
	Note: The following prices are based on #2 oil at 100 pounds pressure, with explosion-proof motor. Without explosion-proof motor, deduct 35% from the material costs.							
15.3504 011	Pump, fuel oil, 1 GPM, 1/4 hp	EA	1,048.29	590.66	1,638.95	370.29	1,418.58	4.9811
15.3504 021	Pump, fuel oil, 5 GPM, 1/4 hp	EA	1,212.64	908.70	2,121.34	569.68	1,782.32	7.6632
15.3504 031	Pump, fuel oil, 10 GPM, 1/4 hp	EA	1,342.57	999.58	2,342.15	626.66	1,969.23	8.4296
15.3504 041	Pump, fuel oil, 20 GPM, 1/4 hp	EA	1,496.96	1,181.32	2,678.28	740.59	2,237.55	9.9622
15.3504 051	Pump, fuel oil, 50 GPM, 5 hp	EA	3,420.38	1,817.40	5,237.78	1,139.36	4,559.74	15.3264

Division 15 CSI #	15 - MECHANICAL Description	Unit	Material	Union Install	Union Total	Open Install	Open Total	Unit Man-Hrs
15.3600 000	**AIR HANDLING EQUIPMENT, PRIMARY:**							
	Note: The following prices include attachments and accessories.							
15.3601 000	**AIR HANDLERS, CENTRAL STATION:**							
	Note: The following items have 2 rows heating, 6 rows cooling coils, with disposable filter and isolation package. For multi-zone use, add 5% to the material costs For exterior weather tight, add 15%.							
15.3601 011	Air handler, 1600 CFM, 3 ton	EA	6,216.66	675.90	6,892.56	434.54	6,651.20	6.1306
15.3601 021	Air handler, 2000 CFM, 5 ton	EA	6,987.80	802.63	7,790.43	516.01	7,503.81	7.2801
15.3601 031	Air handler, 2500 CFM, 8 ton	EA	8,734.81	1,056.08	9,790.89	678.96	9,413.77	9.5790
15.3601 041	Air handler, 4000 CFM, 10 ton	EA	15,126.67	1,140.58	16,267.25	733.28	15,859.95	10.3454
15.3601 051	Air handler, 5200 CFM, 12 ton	EA	19,664.68	1,351.80	21,016.48	869.07	20,533.75	12.2612
15.3601 061	Air handler, 6250 CFM, 15 ton	EA	23,635.41	1,605.25	25,240.66	1,032.02	24,667.43	14.5601
15.3601 071	Air handler, 7500 CFM, 20 ton	EA	28,362.50	1,858.72	30,221.22	1,194.97	29,557.47	16.8591
15.3601 081	Air handler, 10,000 CFM, 25 ton	EA	37,215.63	2,196.67	39,412.30	1,412.24	38,627.87	19.9244
15.3601 091	Air handler, 15,000 CFM, 30 ton	EA	60,460.00	2,534.60	62,994.60	1,629.50	62,089.50	22.9896
15.3601 101	Air handler, 18,000 CFM, 35 ton	EA	67,635.30	3,379.47	71,014.77	2,172.67	69,807.97	30.6528
15.3601 111	Air handler, 22,000 CFM, 50 ton	EA	82,459.90	4,224.34	86,684.24	2,715.84	85,175.74	38.3160
15.3601 121	Air handler, 28,000 CFM, 75 ton	EA	104,949.62	5,491.64	110,441.26	3,530.59	108,480.21	49.8108
15.3601 131	Air handler, 32,000 CFM, 100 ton	EA	119,874.87	6,336.51	126,211.38	4,073.76	123,948.63	57.4740
15.3602 000	**AIR HANDLERS, CENTRAL STATION:**							
	Note: The following items are single zone, without coils. Prices include disposable filters and isolation package. See following sections for components. For multi-zone use, add 3% to the material.							
15.3602 011	Air handler, 1600 CFM, 3 ton	EA	4,132.60	506.93	4,639.53	325.91	4,458.51	4.5980
15.3602 021	Air handler, 2000 CFM, 5 ton	EA	4,696.20	591.41	5,287.61	380.22	5,076.42	5.3643
15.3602 031	Air handler, 2500 CFM, 8 ton	EA	5,164.94	675.90	5,840.84	434.54	5,599.48	6.1306
15.3602 041	Air handler, 4000 CFM, 10 ton	EA	8,832.08	760.38	9,592.46	488.85	9,320.93	6.8969
15.3602 051	Air handler, 5200 CFM, 12 ton	EA	10,228.99	844.87	11,073.86	543.17	10,772.16	7.6632
15.3602 061	Air handler, 6250 CFM, 15 ton	EA	12,087.91	1,013.85	13,101.76	651.81	12,739.72	9.1959
15.3602 071	Air handler, 7500 CFM, 20 ton	EA	16,273.08	1,351.80	17,624.88	869.07	17,142.15	12.2612
15.3602 081	Air handler, 10,000 CFM, 25 ton	EA	19,524.44	1,605.25	21,129.69	1,032.02	20,556.46	14.5601
15.3602 091	Air handler, 15,000 CFM, 30 ton	EA	26,034.54	1,858.72	27,893.26	1,194.97	27,229.51	16.8591
15.3602 101	Air handler, 18,000 CFM, 35 ton	EA	37,188.58	2,703.58	39,892.16	1,738.14	38,926.72	24.5223
15.3602 111	Air handler, 22,000 CFM, 50 ton	EA	46,487.43	3,379.47	49,866.90	2,172.67	48,660.10	30.6528
15.3602 121	Air handler, 28,000 CFM, 75 ton	EA	60,431.91	4,055.37	64,487.28	2,607.21	63,039.12	36.7834
15.3602 131	Air handler, 32,000 CFM, 100 ton	EA	74,379.16	4,731.27	79,110.43	3,041.74	77,420.90	42.9140
15.3603 000	**COILS, CHILLED WATER, 6 ROW, VALVE, TRAP & DRAIN PAN:**							
	Note: The following items are for use with the air handlers listed above. Costs for exterior weather tight, add 15%.							
15.3603 011	Coils, chilled water, 44 SF, 22,000 CFM	EA	14,113.87	1,599.32	15,713.19	1,002.65	15,116.52	13.4873
15.3603 021	Coils, chilled water, 48 SF, 24,000 CFM	EA	15,121.62	1,744.71	16,866.33	1,093.79	16,215.41	14.7134
15.3603 031	Coils, chilled water, 56 SF, 28,000 CFM	EA	18,205.38	2,035.50	20,240.88	1,276.09	19,481.47	17.1656
15.3603 041	Coils, chilled water, 64 SF, 32,000 CFM	EA	20,221.93	2,180.89	22,402.82	1,367.24	21,589.17	18.3917
15.3603 051	Use 1 SF of coil at each 500 CFM	SF	310.98	36.36	347.34	22.79	333.77	0.3066
15.3604 000	**COILS, HOT WATER, 2 ROW, VALVE, TRAP & DRAIN PAN:**							
	Note: The following items are for use with the air handlers listed above.							
15.3604 011	Coils, hot water, 4 SF, 4000 CFM	EA	963.61	145.40	1,109.01	91.16	1,054.77	1.2262
15.3604 021	Coils, hot water, 6 SF, 6000 CFM	EA	1,232.41	218.09	1,450.50	136.73	1,369.14	1.8392
15.3604 031	Coils, hot water, 8 SF, 8000 CFM	EA	1,484.43	290.79	1,775.22	182.30	1,666.73	2.4523
15.3604 041	Coils, hot water, 10 SF, 10,000 CFM	EA	1,686.11	363.48	2,049.59	227.87	1,913.98	3.0653
15.3604 051	Coils, hot water, 12 SF, 12,000 CFM	EA	1,921.36	436.18	2,357.54	273.45	2,194.81	3.6784
15.3604 061	Coils, hot water, 14 SF, 14,000 CFM	EA	2,117.04	508.87	2,625.91	319.02	2,436.06	4.2914
15.3604 071	Coils, hot water, 16 SF, 16,000 CFM	EA	2,330.54	581.58	2,912.12	364.60	2,695.14	4.9045
15.3604 081	Coils, hot water, 18 SF, 18,000 CFM	EA	2,486.62	654.28	3,140.90	410.18	2,896.80	5.5176
15.3604 091	Coils, hot water, 20 SF, 20,000 CFM	EA	2,678.15	726.97	3,405.12	455.75	3,133.90	6.1306
15.3604 101	Coils, hot water, 22 SF, 22,000 CFM	EA	2,770.47	799.67	3,570.14	501.33	3,271.80	6.7437
15.3604 111	Coils, hot water, 24 SF, 24,000 CFM	EA	2,990.73	872.36	3,863.09	546.90	3,537.63	7.3567
15.3604 121	Coils, hot water, 28 SF, 28,000 CFM	EA	4,024.63	1,017.75	5,042.38	638.05	4,662.68	8.5828
15.3604 131	Coils, hot water, 32 SF, 32,000 CFM	EA	4,637.28	1,163.14	5,800.42	729.19	5,366.47	9.8089
15.3605 000	**FILTERS & FRAMES, 32,000 CFM:**							
15.3605 011	Filter & frame, throw away	M/CFM	16.70	6.76	23.46	4.34	21.04	0.0613
15.3605 021	High pressure filter frame, up to 90%, roll & bag	M/CFM	525.16	143.63	668.79	92.34	617.50	1.3028
15.3605 031	Active carbon, filter unit, complete	M/CFM	829.52	185.88	1,015.40	119.50	949.02	1.6860
15.3605 041	High efficiency ceiling lay-in	EA	919.50	101.39	1,020.89	65.18	984.68	0.9196

Division 15 CSI #	15 - MECHANICAL Description	Unit	Material	Union Install	Union Total	Open Install	Open Total	Unit Man-Hrs
15.3606 000	**FANS, SUPPLY, LOW PRESSURE, 1-1/2" UTILITY SET:**							
	Note: The following items include vibration mounts.							
15.3606 011	Fan, low pressure, 600 CFM, 1-1/2" utility	EA	1,776.81	314.63	2,091.44	202.28	1,979.09	2.8538
15.3606 021	Fan, low pressure, 1000 CFM, 1-1/2" utility	EA	2,237.43	455.22	2,692.65	292.66	2,530.09	4.1290
15.3606 031	Fan, low pressure, 2000 CFM, 1-1/2" utility	EA	2,762.79	642.71	3,405.50	413.20	3,175.99	5.8296
15.3606 041	Fan, low pressure, 4000 CFM, 1-1/2" utility	EA	2,879.69	736.48	3,616.17	473.49	3,353.18	6.6801
15.3606 051	Fan, low pressure, 6000 CFM, 1-1/2" utility	EA	3,816.71	1,064.07	4,880.78	684.09	4,500.80	9.6514
15.3606 061	Fan, low pressure, 10,000 CFM, 1-1/2" utility	EA	4,474.01	1,169.20	5,643.21	751.68	5,225.69	10.6050
15.3606 071	Fan, low pressure, 16,000 CFM, 1-1/2" utility	EA	5,791.04	1,543.62	7,334.66	992.40	6,783.44	14.0011
15.3606 081	Fan, low pressure, 20,000 CFM, 1-1/2" utility	EA	7,633.75	1,786.69	9,420.44	1,148.67	8,782.42	16.2058
15.3606 091	Fan, low pressure, 30,000 CFM, 1-1/2" utility	EA	9,477.06	2,193.83	11,670.89	1,410.42	10,887.48	19.8987
15.3606 101	Fan, low pressure, 40,000 CFM, 1-1/2" utility	EA	13,029.51	2,949.23	15,978.74	1,896.07	14,925.58	26.7504
15.3606 111	Fan, low pressure, 60,000 CFM, 1-1/2" utility	EA	21,847.94	3,980.51	25,828.45	2,559.08	24,407.02	36.1044
15.3606 121	Fan, low pressure, 80,000 CFM, 1-1/2" utility	EA	25,843.38	5,077.48	30,920.86	3,264.32	29,107.70	46.0542
15.3607 000	**FANS, SUPPLY, HIGH PRESSURE, 3-1/2" UTILITY SET:**							
	Note: The following items include vibration mounts.							
15.3607 011	Fan, high pressure, 2000 CFM, 3-1/2" utility	EA	3,191.48	650.30	3,841.78	418.08	3,609.56	5.8984
15.3607 021	Fan, high pressure, 4000 CFM, 3-1/2" utility	EA	4,351.37	755.32	5,106.69	485.60	4,836.97	6.8510
15.3607 031	Fan, high pressure, 10,000 CFM, 3-1/2" utility	EA	6,418.42	1,234.90	7,653.32	793.92	7,212.34	11.2009
15.3607 041	Fan, high pressure, 16,000 CFM, 3-1/2" utility	EA	8,054.35	1,648.67	9,703.02	1,059.93	9,114.28	14.9539
15.3607 051	Fan, high pressure, 20,000 CFM, 3-1/2" utility	EA	9,997.80	1,924.62	11,922.42	1,237.35	11,235.15	17.4569
15.3607 061	Fan, high pressure, 30,000 CFM, 3-1/2" utility	EA	11,327.33	2,318.67	13,646.00	1,490.68	12,818.01	21.0310
15.3607 071	Fan, high pressure, 40,000 CFM, 3-1/2" utility	EA	16,276.65	3,087.25	19,363.90	1,984.80	18,261.45	28.0023
15.3607 081	Fan, high pressure, 60,000 CFM, 3-1/2" utility	EA	27,247.10	4,118.44	31,365.54	2,647.76	29,894.86	37.3555
15.3607 091	Fan, high pressure, 80,000 CFM, 3-1/2" utility	EA	40,125.76	5,215.40	45,341.16	3,352.99	43,478.75	47.3052
15.3700 000	**DISTRIBUTION, TERMINAL EQUIPMENT:**							
15.3701 000	**FAN, EXHAUST, CEILING AND WALL, RESIDENTIAL:**							
15.3701 011	Exhaust fan, wall, 60 CFM	EA	88.34	71.19	159.53	45.77	134.11	0.6457
15.3701 021	Exhaust fan, wall, 100 CFM	EA	103.81	71.19	175.00	45.77	149.58	0.6457
15.3701 031	Exhaust fan, wall, 200 CFM	EA	112.57	147.80	260.37	95.02	207.59	1.3406
15.3701 041	Exhaust fan, wall, 300 CFM	EA	176.69	197.02	373.71	126.66	303.35	1.7870
15.3702 000	**FAN, EXHAUST, ROOF MOUNTED, BELT DRIVE:**							
	Note: The following prices include curb, hood and bird screen.							
15.3702 011	Exhaust fan, roof, 600 CFM, 1/2" static pressure	EA	1,182.82	388.66	1,571.48	249.87	1,432.69	3.5253
15.3702 021	Exhaust fan, roof, 1600 CFM, 1/2" static pressure	EA	1,311.49	426.98	1,738.47	274.50	1,585.99	3.8728
15.3702 031	Exhaust fan, roof, 2000 CFM, 1/2" static pressure	EA	2,001.11	684.26	2,685.37	439.91	2,441.02	6.2064
15.3702 041	Exhaust fan, roof, 4000 CFM, 1/2" static pressure	EA	2,940.04	974.33	3,914.37	626.40	3,566.44	8.8375
15.3702 051	Exhaust fan, roof, 6000 CFM, 1/2" static pressure	EA	5,026.33	1,603.86	6,630.19	1,031.13	6,057.46	14.5475
15.3702 061	Exhaust fan, roof, 10,000 CFM, 1/2" static pressure	EA	5,299.73	1,718.78	7,018.51	1,105.01	6,404.74	15.5898
15.3702 071	Exhaust fan, roof, 16,000 CFM, 1/2" static pressure	EA	5,642.60	1,888.46	7,531.06	1,214.10	6,856.70	17.1289
15.3703 000	**FAN, EXHAUST, UTILITY SET, WITH VIBRATION MOUNTS:**							
15.3703 011	Exhaust fan, 600 CFM, 3/4" static pressure, vibration mounts	EA	963.11	229.89	1,193.00	147.80	1,110.91	2.0852
15.3703 021	Exhaust fan, 1000 CFM, 3/4" static pressure, vibration mounts	EA	1,408.82	344.82	1,753.64	221.68	1,630.50	3.1276
15.3703 031	Exhaust fan, 2000 CFM, 3/4" static pressure, vibration mounts	EA	2,040.65	487.17	2,527.82	313.20	2,353.85	4.4188
15.3703 041	Exhaust fan, 4000 CFM, 3/4" static pressure, vibration mounts	EA	2,221.81	541.91	2,763.72	348.40	2,570.21	4.9153
15.3703 051	Exhaust fan, 10,000 CFM, 3/4" static pressure, vibration mounts	EA	3,780.93	914.14	4,695.07	587.70	4,368.63	8.2915
15.3703 061	Exhaust fan, 16,000 CFM, 3/4" static pressure, vibration mounts	EA	4,078.93	974.33	5,053.26	626.40	4,705.33	8.8375
15.3703 071	Exhaust fan, 20,000 CFM, 3/4" static pressure, vibration mounts	EA	5,115.95	1,198.76	6,314.71	770.69	5,886.64	10.8731
15.3703 081	Exhaust fan, 30,000 CFM, 3/4" static pressure, vibration mounts	EA	7,785.98	1,718.78	9,504.76	1,105.01	8,890.99	15.5898
15.3703 091	Exhaust fan, 40,000 CFM, 3/4" static pressure, vibration mounts	EA	10,379.67	2,288.02	12,667.69	1,470.97	11,850.64	20.7530
15.3703 101	Exhaust fan, 60,000 CFM, 3/4" static pressure, vibration mounts	EA	15,569.60	3,147.42	18,717.02	2,023.48	17,593.08	28.5480
15.3703 111	Exhaust fan, 80,000 CFM, 3/4" static pressure, vibration mounts	EA	20,389.95	4,006.80	24,396.75	2,575.98	22,965.93	36.3429
15.3704 000	**FANS, EXHAUST, PROPELLER BELT DRIVEN, WALL SHUTTER:**							
15.3704 011	Fan, exhaust, propeller belt driven, 5,000 CFM	EA	1,080.53	617.40	1,697.93	396.93	1,477.46	5.6000
15.3704 021	Fan, exhaust, propeller belt driven, 6,000 CFM	EA	1,155.06	672.53	1,827.59	432.37	1,587.43	6.1000
15.3704 031	Fan, exhaust, propeller belt driven, 8,000 CFM	EA	1,366.18	749.70	2,115.88	481.98	1,848.16	6.8000
15.3704 041	Fan, exhaust, propeller belt driven, 10,000 CFM	EA	1,669.22	782.78	2,452.00	503.25	2,172.47	7.1000
15.3704 051	Fan, exhaust, propeller belt driven, 15,000 CFM	EA	2,359.78	915.08	3,274.86	588.30	2,948.08	8.3000
15.3705 000	**RETURN FANS, VANE AXIAL, WITH VIBRATION MOUNTS, ADJUSTABLE PITCH:**							
	Note: For controllable pitch, add 60% to the material costs.							
15.3705 011	Return fan, 10,000 CFM, 5 hp, vibration mounts	EA	7,578.73	912.46	8,491.19	586.62	8,165.35	8.2763
15.3705 021	Return fan, 12,500 CFM, 5 hp, vibration mounts	EA	7,948.41	912.46	8,860.87	586.62	8,535.03	8.2763

Division 15 CSI #	15 - MECHANICAL Description	Unit	Material	Union Install	Union Total	Open Install	Open Total	Unit Man-Hrs
15.3705 000	**RETURN FANS, VANE AXIAL, WITH VIBRATION MOUNTS, ADJUSTABLE PITCH: (Cont.)**							
15.3705 031	Return fan, 17,500 CFM, 5 hp, vibration mounts	EA	8,429.06	971.60	9,400.66	624.64	9,053.70	8.8127
15.3705 041	Return fan, 21,000 CFM, 7.5 hp, vibration mounts	EA	13,586.28	1,182.82	14,769.10	760.44	14,346.72	10.7285
15.3705 051	Return fan, 31,000 CFM, 10 hp, vibration mounts	EA	17,190.81	1,689.74	18,880.55	1,086.34	18,277.15	15.3264
15.3705 061	Return fan, 115,000 CFM, 50 hp, vibration mounts	EA	25,122.09	4,224.34	29,346.43	2,715.84	27,837.93	38.3160
15.3705 071	Return fan, 150,000 CFM, 75 hp, vibration mounts	EA	32,829.99	5,069.21	37,899.20	3,259.01	36,089.00	45.9792
15.3705 081	Return fan, 178,000 CFM, 200 hp, vibration mounts	EA	48,531.30	5,745.11	54,276.41	3,693.54	52,224.84	52.1098
15.3706 000	**FAN, CENTRIFUGAL IN-LINE WITH VIBRATION ISOLATOR:**							
15.3706 011	Fan, centrifugal in-line, 3,000 CFM	EA	3,013.03	532.31	3,545.34	333.71	3,346.74	4.4890
15.3706 021	Fan, centrifugal in-line, 4,000 CFM	EA	3,518.59	581.04	4,099.63	364.27	3,882.86	4.9000
15.3706 031	Fan, centrifugal in-line, 6,000 CFM	EA	5,119.56	732.82	5,852.38	459.42	5,578.98	6.1800
15.3706 041	Fan, centrifugal in-line, 10,000 CFM	EA	6,354.35	983.15	7,337.50	616.35	6,970.70	8.2910
15.3706 051	Fan, centrifugal in-line, 15,000 CFM	EA	8,637.15	1,045.01	9,682.16	655.14	9,292.29	8.8127
15.3706 061	Fan, centrifugal in-line, 20,000 CFM	EA	10,323.64	1,198.97	11,522.61	751.66	11,075.30	10.1111
15.3706 071	Fan, centrifugal in-line, 30,000 CFM	EA	12,504.52	1,848.64	14,353.16	1,158.95	13,663.47	15.5898
15.3706 081	Fan, centrifugal in-line, 35,000 CFM	EA	15,204.46	2,146.42	17,350.88	1,345.63	16,550.09	18.1010
15.3706 091	Fan, centrifugal, in-line, 45,000 CFM	EA	18,302.84	2,695.93	20,998.77	1,690.13	19,992.97	22.7351
15.3707 000	**CABINET BLOWERS:**							
15.3707 011	Cabinet blower, 8,000 CFM, 1" static pressure	EA	2,434.52	914.14	3,348.66	587.70	3,022.22	8.2915
15.3707 021	Cabinet blower, 10,000 CFM, 1" static pressure	EA	4,059.77	1,373.88	5,433.65	883.27	4,943.04	12.4615
15.3707 031	Cabinet blower, 20,000 CFM, 1" static pressure	EA	8,119.49	2,517.90	10,637.39	1,618.76	9,738.25	22.8381
15.3708 000	**FAN COIL UNITS, DUCT MOUNTED, 2 PIPE, SINGLE COIL:**							
15.3708 011	Fan coil unit, duct mounted, 400 CFM, 2 pipe, 1 coil	EA	1,228.76	178.94	1,407.70	115.04	1,343.80	1.6230
15.3708 021	Fan coil unit, duct mounted, 600 CFM, 2 pipe, 1 coil	EA	1,347.09	208.80	1,555.89	134.24	1,481.33	1.8939
15.3708 031	Fan coil unit, duct mounted, 1000 CFM, 2 pipe, 1 coil	EA	1,963.73	313.14	2,276.87	201.32	2,165.05	2.8403
15.3708 041	Fan coil unit, duct mounted, 1500 CFM, 2 pipe, 1 coil	EA	2,369.71	387.72	2,757.43	249.26	2,618.97	3.5167
15.3709 000	**FAN COIL UNITS, WITH CABINETS, 2 PIPE, SINGLE COIL:**							
	Note: For 3 pipe, 2 coil, add 25% to the total costs. For 4 pipe, 2 coil, add 35%.							
15.3709 011	Fan coil unit, with cabinet, 400 CFM, 2 pipe, 1 coil	EA	1,301.80	208.80	1,510.60	134.24	1,436.04	1.8939
15.3709 021	Fan coil unit, with cabinet, 600 CFM, 2 pipe, 1 coil	EA	1,420.16	258.48	1,678.64	166.18	1,586.34	2.3445
15.3709 031	Fan coil unit, with cabinet, 1000 CFM, 2 pipe, 1 coil	EA	2,603.60	352.95	2,956.55	226.92	2,830.52	3.2014
15.3709 041	Fan coil unit, with cabinet, 1500 CFM, 2 pipe, 1 coil	EA	2,925.56	417.58	3,343.14	268.47	3,194.03	3.7876
15.3710 000	**INDUCTION UNITS:**							
15.3710 011	Induction unit, 250 CFM @ outlet	EA	581.59	288.35	869.94	185.38	766.97	2.6154
15.3710 021	Induction unit, 500 CFM @ outlet	EA	623.83	338.04	961.87	217.33	841.16	3.0661
15.3710 031	Induction unit, 800 CFM @ outlet	EA	663.74	347.98	1,011.72	223.72	887.46	3.1563
15.3710 041	Induction unit, 1000 CFM @ outlet	EA	754.74	372.87	1,127.61	239.72	994.46	3.3820
15.3710 051	Induction unit, 1200 CFM @ outlet	EA	810.26	397.67	1,207.93	255.66	1,065.92	3.6070
15.3711 000	**MIXING BOXES, CONSTANT VOLUME:**							
	Note: For variable volume, add 14% to the total costs.							
15.3711 011	Mixing box, constant volume, 200 CFM #4	EA	849.01	218.75	1,067.76	140.63	989.64	1.9841
15.3711 021	Mixing box, constant volume, 550 CFM #6	EA	916.50	278.38	1,194.88	178.97	1,095.47	2.5250
15.3711 031	Mixing box, constant volume, 850 CFM #8	EA	1,051.49	313.14	1,364.63	201.32	1,252.81	2.8403
15.3711 041	Mixing box, constant volume, 1400 CFM #10	EA	1,208.25	362.91	1,571.16	233.32	1,441.57	3.2917
15.3711 051	Mixing box, constant volume, 2500 CFM #12	EA	1,547.84	417.58	1,965.42	268.47	1,816.31	3.7876
15.3711 061	Mixing box, constant volume, 3200 CFM #14	EA	1,815.64	457.32	2,272.96	294.01	2,109.65	4.1480
15.3711 071	Mixing box, constant volume, 5000 CFM #16	EA	2,020.29	492.16	2,512.45	316.41	2,336.70	4.4640
15.3712 000	**AIR TERMINAL UNITS, WITH RE-HEAT COILS:**							
15.3712 011	Air terminal unit, #7, 4-650 CFM, 1" static pressure, 1.1 SF coil	EA	722.56	228.70	951.26	147.03	869.59	2.0744
15.3712 021	Air terminal unit, #8, 6-850 CFM, 1" static pressure, 1.6 SF coil	EA	782.35	258.48	1,040.83	166.18	948.53	2.3445
15.3712 031	Air terminal unit, #9, 8-1050 CFM, 1"static pressure, 2.8 SF coil	EA	806.63	293.32	1,099.95	188.58	995.21	2.6605
15.3712 041	Air terminal unit, #10, 6-1000 CFM, 1" static pressure, 2 SF coil	EA	862.59	293.32	1,155.91	188.58	1,051.17	2.6605
15.3712 051	Air terminal unit, #12, 12-1800 CFM, 1" static pressure, 2.1 SF coil	EA	944.75	313.14	1,257.89	201.32	1,146.07	2.8403
15.3712 061	Air terminal unit, #14, 2-2800 CFM, 1" static pressure, 3.4 SF coil	EA	1,060.56	387.72	1,448.28	249.26	1,309.82	3.5167
15.3713 000	**AIR TERMINAL UNITS, CONSTANT VOLUME:**							
	Note: The following items are single duct, without coils.							
15.3713 011	Air terminal unit, constant volume, 350 CFM	EA	313.06	197.02	510.08	126.66	439.72	1.7870
15.3713 021	Air terminal unit, constant volume, 500 CFM	EA	349.09	208.00	557.09	133.72	482.81	1.8866
15.3713 031	Air terminal unit, constant volume, 800 CFM	EA	385.09	251.78	636.87	161.87	546.96	2.2837
15.3713 041	Air terminal unit, constant volume, 1600 CFM	EA	495.94	295.60	791.54	190.04	685.98	2.6812
15.3713 051	Air terminal unit, constant volume, 2400 CFM	EA	595.68	344.82	940.50	221.68	817.36	3.1276
15.3713 061	Air terminal unit, constant volume, 3000 CFM	EA	725.90	437.88	1,163.78	281.51	1,007.41	3.9717

Division 15 CSI #	15 - MECHANICAL Description	Unit	Material	Union Install	Union Total	Open Install	Open Total	Unit Man-Hrs
15.3714 000	**AIR TERMINAL UNITS, VARIABLE VOLUME:**							
15.3714 011	Air terminal unit, variable volume, 150 CFM	EA	403.52	164.23	567.75	105.58	509.10	1.4896
15.3714 021	Air terminal unit, variable volume, 350 CFM	EA	603.27	213.62	816.89	137.34	740.61	1.9376
15.3714 031	Air terminal unit, variable volume, 500 CFM	EA	702.51	247.48	949.99	159.10	861.61	2.2447
15.3714 041	Air terminal unit, variable volume, 800 CFM	EA	833.47	293.61	1,127.08	188.76	1,022.23	2.6631
15.3714 051	Air terminal unit, variable volume, 1000 CFM	EA	915.47	322.51	1,237.98	207.35	1,122.82	2.9253
15.3714 061	Air terminal unit, variable volume, 1600 CFM	EA	1,119.20	394.29	1,513.49	253.49	1,372.69	3.5763
15.3714 071	Air terminal unit, variable volume, 2400 CFM	EA	1,254.14	441.83	1,695.97	284.05	1,538.19	4.0075
15.3714 081	Air terminal unit, variable volume, 3200 CFM	EA	1,644.40	557.27	2,201.67	358.27	2,002.67	5.0546
15.3715 000	**RE-HEAT COILS, 2 ROW:**							
15.3715 011	Re-heat coil, 2 row, 1/2 SF	EA	241.49	77.42	318.91	49.77	291.26	0.7022
15.3715 021	Re-heat coil, 2 row, 1 SF	EA	301.91	81.99	383.90	52.71	354.62	0.7437
15.3715 031	Re-heat coil, 2 row, 1-1/2 SF	EA	539.11	86.51	625.62	55.62	594.73	0.7847
15.3715 041	Re-heat coil, 2 row, 2 SF	EA	582.24	91.09	673.33	58.56	640.80	0.8262
15.3715 051	Re-heat coil, 2 row, 2-1/2 SF	EA	614.56	95.60	710.16	61.46	676.02	0.8671
15.3715 061	Re-heat coil, 2 row, 3 SF	EA	789.24	100.17	889.41	64.40	853.64	0.9086
15.3715 071	Re-heat coil, 2 row, 3-1/2 SF	EA	847.50	104.75	952.25	67.34	914.84	0.9501
15.3715 081	Re-heat coil, 2 row, 4 SF	EA	920.78	109.27	1,030.05	70.25	991.03	0.9911
15.3800 000	**MISCELLANEOUS EQUIPMENT:**							
15.3801 000	**EXPANSION TANKS:**							
15.3801 011	Expansion tank, 16 gallon, chilled water	EA	877.61	161.61	1,039.22	101.32	978.93	1.3629
15.3801 021	Expansion tank, 44 gallon, chilled water	EA	1,243.78	186.08	1,429.86	116.65	1,360.43	1.5692
15.3801 031	Expansion tank, 55 gallon, ASME code	EA	2,537.33	665.01	3,202.34	416.91	2,954.24	5.6081
15.3801 041	Expansion tank, 88 gallon, ASME code	EA	3,763.24	813.46	4,576.70	509.97	4,273.21	6.8600
15.3801 051	Expansion tank, 132 gallon, ASME code	EA	4,835.88	1,081.45	5,917.33	677.98	5,513.86	9.1200
15.3801 061	Expansion tank, 150 gallon, ASME code	EA	5,508.50	1,379.09	6,887.59	864.57	6,373.07	11.6300
15.3801 071	Expansion tank, 250 gallon, ASME code	EA	7,251.83	1,607.94	8,859.77	1,008.05	8,259.88	13.5600
15.3801 081	Expansion tank, 375 gallon, ASME code	EA	10,344.37	1,899.65	12,244.02	1,190.93	11,535.30	16.0200
15.3802 000	**SEPARATORS-AIR ELIMINATION, 150#, WITH STRAINER:**							
	Note: The following prices do not include companion flanges or bolt and gasket sets.							
15.3802 011	Air separator, steel, 150#, 2", strainer	EA	1,033.29	179.17	1,212.46	112.33	1,145.62	1.5110
15.3802 021	Air separator, steel, 150#, 2-1/2", strainer	EA	1,221.83	204.25	1,426.08	128.05	1,349.88	1.7225
15.3802 031	Air separator, steel, 150#, 3", strainer	EA	1,788.71	233.60	2,022.31	146.45	1,935.16	1.9700
15.3802 041	Air separator, steel, 150#, 4", strainer	EA	2,577.56	284.59	2,862.15	178.42	2,755.98	2.4000
15.3802 051	Air separator, steel, 150#, 5", strainer	EA	3,266.38	385.39	3,651.77	241.61	3,507.99	3.2500
15.3802 061	Air separator, steel, 150#, 6", strainer	EA	3,921.92	492.11	4,414.03	308.51	4,230.43	4.1500
15.3802 071	Air separator, steel, 150#, 8", strainer	EA	5,855.12	664.05	6,519.17	416.30	6,271.42	5.6000
15.3802 081	Air separator, steel, 150#, 10", strainer	EA	9,221.54	735.20	9,956.74	460.91	9,682.45	6.2000
15.3802 091	Air separator, steel, 150#, 12", strainer	EA	13,221.27	902.63	14,123.90	565.88	13,787.15	7.6120
15.3803 000	**WATER PURIFICATION & TREATMENT:**							
15.3803 011	Water purification, organic, 5m grain, 1 GPM	EA	961.94	817.79	1,779.73	512.69	1,474.63	6.8965
15.3804 000	**RELIEF VENT:**							
15.3804 011	Relief vent, 750 CFM, aluminum	EA	1,178.12	281.20	1,459.32	176.29	1,354.41	2.3714
15.3804 021	Relief vent, 1, 500 CFM, aluminum	EA	1,527.95	349.94	1,877.89	219.38	1,747.33	2.9511
15.3804 031	Relief vent, 3,000 CFM, aluminum	EA	2,120.82	507.43	2,628.25	318.12	2,438.94	4.2792
15.3804 041	Relief vent, 6,000 CFM, aluminum	EA	3,314.52	780.58	4,095.10	489.36	3,803.88	6.5827
15.3804 051	Relief vent, 12,000 CFM, aluminum	EA	5,444.83	1,259.81	6,704.64	789.80	6,234.63	10.6241
15.3804 061	Relief vent, 20,000 CFM, aluminum	EA	7,249.13	1,693.86	8,942.99	1,061.91	8,311.04	14.2845
15.3804 071	Relief vent, 30,000 CFM, aluminum	EA	12,658.78	2,900.22	15,559.00	1,818.20	14,476.98	24.4579
15.3804 081	Relief vent, 40,000 CFM, aluminum	EA	16,094.73	3,430.69	19,525.42	2,150.76	18,245.49	28.9314
15.3804 091	Relief vent, 50,000 CFM, aluminum	EA	17,118.38	3,901.45	21,019.83	2,445.89	19,564.27	32.9014
15.3805 000	**VIBRATION ISOLATORS:**							
15.3805 011	Vibration isolator, pad mounted, neoprene, to 400 lbs	EA	58.61		58.61		58.61	
15.3805 021	Vibration isolator, pad mounted, neoprene, to 1, 200 lbs	EA	139.26		139.26		139.26	
15.3805 031	Vibration isolator, pad mounted, neoprene, to 4,000 lbs	EA	314.62		314.62		314.62	
15.3805 111	Vibration isolator, pad mounted, spring, to 300 lbs	EA	192.20		192.20		192.20	
15.3805 121	Vibration isolator, pad mounted, spring, to 1,000 lbs	EA	271.78		271.78		271.78	
15.3805 131	Vibration isolator, pad mounted, spring, to 1, 300 lbs	EA	305.12		305.12		305.12	
15.3805 141	Vibration isolator, pad mounted, spring, to 1, 800 lbs	EA	436.13		436.13		436.13	
15.3805 151	Vibration isolator, pad mounted, spring, to 2, 600 lbs	EA	486.29		486.29		486.29	
15.3805 161	Vibration isolator, pad mounted, spring, to 4,000 lbs	EA	559.35		559.35		559.35	

Division 15 CSI #	15 - MECHANICAL Description	Unit	Material	Union Install	Union Total	Open Install	Open Total	Unit Man-Hrs
15.3900 000	CONTROLS:							
	Note: Controls are expressed as a percentage of equipment, since it is impossible to classify all							
	possible control systems available for HVAC.							
	Controls for built-up systems:							
	$100,000 or Less 28.00%							
	$100,000 to 200,000 . . . . .26.00%							
	$200,000 to 500,000 . . . . .24.00%							
	$500,000 to 1,000,000 . . . . 22.00%							
	$1,000,000 and Up 20.00%							
	Controls for package systems:							
	$100,000 or Less 11.00%							
	$100,000 to 200,000 . . . . 9.00%							
	$200,000 to 500,000 . . . . 7.00%							
15.3901 000	COMPUTERIZED ENERGY MANAGEMENT SYSTEM ONLY:							
15.3901 011	Control computer, under 300 points	EA	50,507.08		50,507.08		50,507.08	
15.3901 021	Control computer, 500-1,000 data control points	EA	153,325.07		153,325.07		153,325.07	
15.3901 031	Add for each point up to 100	EA	1,803.80		1,803.80		1,803.80	
15.3901 041	Add per point, 100-200	EA	1,352.86		1,352.86		1,352.86	
15.3901 051	Add per point, 200-500	EA	1,082.27		1,082.27		1,082.27	
15.3901 061	Add per point over 500	EA	901.91		901.91		901.91	
15.3902 000	PNEUMATIC CONTROLS:							
15.3902 011	Air compressor station, complete	EA	26,732.47	2,726.11	29,458.58	1,709.05	28,441.52	22.9896
15.3903 000	PNEUMATIC ZONE CONTROLS:							
	Note: The two variable air volume items listed below include thermostat and tubing, with motor by box							
	manufacturer.							
15.3903 011	Reheat zone control, complete	EA	598.51		598.51		598.51	
15.3903 021	Variable air volume zone	EA	538.66		538.66		538.66	
15.3903 031	Variable air volume, complete	EA	748.05		748.05		748.05	
15.3904 000	MISCELLANEOUS ELECTRICAL CONTROLS:							
15.3904 011	Thermostat with fan switch, heat only	EA	96.19	85.20	181.39	53.41	149.60	0.7185
15.3904 021	Thermostat with fan switch, cool only	EA	96.19	85.20	181.39	53.41	149.60	0.7185
15.3904 031	Thermostat with fan switch, heat & cool	EA	96.33	141.99	238.32	89.01	185.34	1.1974
15.4000 000	DUCT WORK, GRILLS & REGISTERS:							
	Note: The following prices include supports, joints, fittings and duct tape. Insulation is not included.							
15.4001 000	ALUMINUM DUCTWORK, WITH SUPPORTS & ACCESSORIES:							
15.4001 011	Duct, aluminum, rectangular, under 4,000#	#	14.92	9.70	24.62	6.24	21.16	0.0880
15.4001 021	Duct, aluminum, rectangular, 4,000-8,000#	#	14.07	9.04	23.11	5.81	19.88	0.0820
15.4001 031	Duct, aluminum, rectangular, over 8,000#	#	12.84	8.37	21.21	5.38	18.22	0.0759
15.4001 041	Duct, aluminum, round, under 4,000#	#	15.94	10.30	26.24	6.62	22.56	0.0934
15.4001 051	Duct, aluminum, round, over 4,000#	#	13.71	9.85	23.56	6.33	20.04	0.0893
15.4002 000	FIBERGLASS DUCT WITH SUPPORTS & ACCESSORIES:							
	Note: The following items do not require insulation.							
15.4002 011	Duct, fiberglass, rectangular	SF	6.46	6.01	12.47	3.86	10.32	0.0545
15.4002 021	Duct, fiberglass, round	SF	7.67	1.79	9.46	1.15	8.82	0.0162
15.4003 000	GALVANIZED IRON DUCT WITH SUPPORTS & ACCESSORIES:							
	Note: The following prices are based on medium pressure, to 3.5# Static pressure. The following is a							
	list of nominal weights by largest side dimension with waste and laps:							
	To 12" 26 GA . . . . MINIMUM 1.0#/SF							
	13"-30" 24 GA . . . . .1.3#/SF							
	31"-54" 22 GA . . . . .1.6#/SF							
	55"-84" 20 GA . . . . .2.0#/SF							
	85" + 18 GA . . . . .2.4#/SF							
15.4003 021	Duct, galvanized iron, rectangular, under 10,000 #, shop fab	#	6.12	5.23	11.35	3.36	9.48	0.0474
15.4003 031	Duct, galvanized iron, rectangular, 10,000-20,000 #, shop fab	#	5.69	4.40	10.09	2.83	8.52	0.0399
15.4003 041	Duct, galvanized iron, rectangular, over 20,000 #, shop fab	#	5.05	3.86	8.91	2.48	7.53	0.0350
15.4003 051	Duct, galvanized iron, round, under 10,000 #, shop fab	#	5.77	4.38	10.15	2.81	8.58	0.0397
15.4003 061	Duct, galvanized iron, round, 10,000-20,000 #, shop fab	#	5.49	3.92	9.41	2.52	8.01	0.0356
15.4003 071	Duct, galvanized iron, round, over 20,000 #, shop fab	#	4.75	3.67	8.42	2.36	7.11	0.0333
15.4003 081	Duct, galvanized iron, spiral, 3", 26 ga, with fittings & supports	LF	3.47	1.32	4.79	.85	4.32	0.0120
15.4003 091	Duct, galvanized iron, spiral, 4", 26 ga, with fittings & supports	LF	4.23	1.57	5.80	1.01	5.24	0.0142
15.4003 101	Duct, galvanized iron, spiral, 6", 26 ga, with fittings & supports	LF	5.76	2.16	7.92	1.39	7.15	0.0196
15.4003 111	Duct, galvanized iron, spiral, 8", 26 ga, with fittings & supports	LF	8.18	2.90	11.08	1.86	10.04	0.0263

Division 15 CSI #	15 - MECHANICAL Description	Unit	Material	Union Install	Union Total	Open Install	Open Total	Unit Man-Hrs
15.4003 000	**GALVANIZED IRON DUCT WITH SUPPORTS & ACCESSORIES: (Cont.)**							
15.4003 121	Duct, galvanized iron, spiral, 10", 24 ga, with fittings & supports	LF	12.56	4.60	17.16	2.96	15.52	0.0417
15.4003 131	Duct, galvanized iron, spiral, 12", 24 ga, with fittings & supports	LF	14.44	5.42	19.86	3.49	17.93	0.0492
15.4003 141	Duct, galvanized iron, spiral, 16", 24 ga, with fittings & supports	LF	19.50	6.97	26.47	4.48	23.98	0.0632
15.4003 151	Duct, galvanized iron, spiral, 20", 24 ga, with fittings & supports	LF	24.66	8.60	33.26	5.53	30.19	0.0780
15.4003 161	Duct, galvanized iron, spiral, 24", 22 ga, with fittings & supports	LF	32.58	10.23	42.81	6.58	39.16	0.0928
15.4003 171	Duct, galvanized iron, spiral, 30", 22 ga, with fittings & supports	LF	45.65	14.00	59.65	9.00	54.65	0.1270
15.4003 181	Duct, galvanized iron, spiral, 36", 22 ga, with fittings & supports	LF	54.19	18.82	73.01	12.10	66.29	0.1707
15.4003 191	Duct, galvanized iron, spiral, 42", 20 ga, with fittings & supports	LF	70.65	26.29	96.94	16.90	87.55	0.2385
15.4003 201	Duct, galvanized iron, spiral, 48", 20 ga, with fittings & supports	LF	81.17	30.01	111.18	19.29	100.46	0.2722
15.4004 000	**STAINLESS STEEL DUCT (304) WITH SUPPORTS & ACCESSORIES:**							
15.4004 011	Duct, stainless steel, rectangular	#	26.64	4.82	31.46	3.10	29.74	0.0437
15.4004 021	Duct, stainless steel, round	#	27.84	5.13	32.97	3.30	31.14	0.0465
15.4005 000	**FLEXIBLE DUCT, WITH CLAMPS:**							
15.4005 011	Duct, flexible, 4", clamps	LF	3.73	5.63	9.36	3.62	7.35	0.0511
15.4005 021	Duct, flexible, 6", clamps	LF	5.01	6.97	11.98	4.48	9.49	0.0632
15.4005 031	Duct, flexible, 8", clamps	LF	7.13	10.07	17.20	6.47	13.60	0.0913
15.4005 041	Duct, flexible, 10", clamps	LF	7.44	13.24	20.68	8.51	15.95	0.1201
15.4005 051	Duct, flexible, 12", clamps	LF	9.13	18.61	27.74	11.96	21.09	0.1688
15.4005 061	Duct, flexible, 14", clamps	LF	10.09	22.84	32.93	14.69	24.78	0.2072
15.4005 071	Duct, flexible, 16", clamps	LF	12.84	28.46	41.30	17.84	30.68	0.2400
15.4005 081	Duct, flexible, 18", clamps	LF	15.64	34.49	50.13	21.63	37.27	0.2909
15.4005 091	Duct, flexible, 20", clamps	LF	16.75	40.66	57.41	25.49	42.24	0.3429
15.4006 000	**FIBERGLASS REINFORCED PLASTIC DUCT, BURIED BELOW BUILDING:**							
15.4006 011	Fiberglass reinforced plastic duct, 8", buried	LF	35.18	15.10	50.28	9.71	44.89	0.1370
15.4006 021	Fiberglass reinforced plastic duct, 10", buried	LF	42.16	18.07	60.23	11.62	53.78	0.1639
15.4006 031	Fiberglass reinforced plastic duct, 12", buried	LF	45.08	19.34	64.42	12.43	57.51	0.1754
15.4006 041	Fiberglass reinforced plastic duct, 14", buried	LF	55.08	23.64	78.72	15.20	70.28	0.2144
15.4006 051	Fiberglass reinforced plastic duct, 16", buried	LF	63.24	27.11	90.35	17.43	80.67	0.2459
15.4006 061	Fiberglass reinforced plastic duct, 18", buried	LF	73.21	31.36	104.57	20.16	93.37	0.2844
15.4006 071	Fiberglass reinforced plastic duct, 20", buried	LF	76.96	32.99	109.95	21.21	98.17	0.2992
15.4006 081	1-1/4" PVC terminal adapters	EA	3.49		3.49		3.49	
15.4007 000	**FIRE DAMPERS:**							
15.4007 011	Fire damper, in wall, sleeve to 1 SF	EA	202.26	93.06	295.32	59.83	262.09	0.8441
15.4007 021	Fire damper, in wall, sleeve 1-2 SF	EA	267.01	114.95	381.96	73.90	340.91	1.0426
15.4007 031	Fire damper, in wall, sleeve 2-4 SF	EA	341.61	169.70	511.31	109.10	450.71	1.5392
15.4007 041	Fire damper, in wall, sleeve 4-6 SF	EA	649.12	197.02	846.14	126.66	775.78	1.7870
15.4007 051	Fire damper, in wall, sleeve 6-10 SF	EA	701.18	284.63	985.81	182.99	884.17	2.5817
15.4007 061	Fire damper, in wall, sleeve 10-16 SF	EA	865.97	344.82	1,210.79	221.68	1,087.65	3.1276
15.4007 071	Fire damper, in wall, sleeve 16-25 SF	EA	1,054.55	483.72	1,538.27	310.99	1,365.54	4.3875
15.4007 081	Fire damper, in wall, sleeve 25-30 SF	EA	1,691.07	580.47	2,271.54	373.18	2,064.25	5.2650
15.4007 091	Fire damper, in wall, sleeve 30-35 SF	EA	2,327.30	600.04	2,927.34	385.76	2,713.06	5.4425
15.4007 101	Fire damper, in wall, sleeve 35-40 SF	EA	2,468.84	685.76	3,154.60	440.87	2,909.71	6.2200
15.4007 111	Fire damper, in wall, sleeve 40-45 SF	EA	2,951.81	721.86	3,673.67	464.09	3,415.90	6.5475
15.4007 121	Fire damper, in wall, sleeve 45-55 SF	EA	3,821.70	882.28	4,703.98	567.22	4,388.92	8.0025
15.4007 131	Fire damper, in duct, to 1 SF	EA	111.49	43.77	155.26	28.14	139.63	0.3970
15.4007 141	Fire damper, in duct, 1-2 SF	EA	146.79	60.21	207.00	38.71	185.50	0.5461
15.4007 151	Fire damper, in duct, 2-4 SF	EA	192.32	82.08	274.40	52.77	245.09	0.7445
15.4007 161	Fire damper, in duct, 4-6 SF	EA	268.29	93.06	361.35	59.83	328.12	0.8441
15.4007 171	Fire damper, in duct, 6-10 SF	EA	394.85	147.80	542.65	95.02	489.87	1.3406
15.4007 181	Fire damper, in duct, 10-16 SF	EA	541.69	169.70	711.39	109.10	650.79	1.5392
15.4008 000	**CEILING RETURN OR EXHAUST REGISTER:**							
15.4008 011	Ceiling return, to 10" large dimension	EA	58.31	60.21	118.52	38.71	97.02	0.5461
15.4008 021	Ceiling return, 12-18" large dimension	EA	81.75	71.19	152.94	45.77	127.52	0.6457
15.4008 031	Ceiling return, 20-30" large dimension	EA	113.14	93.06	206.20	59.83	172.97	0.8441
15.4009 000	**CEILING EXHAUST GRILL:**							
15.4009 011	Ceiling exhaust grill, to 10" large dimension	EA	51.05	54.75	105.80	35.20	86.25	0.4966
15.4009 021	Ceiling exhaust grill, 12-18" large dimension	EA	70.10	65.73	135.83	42.26	112.36	0.5962
15.4009 031	Ceiling exhaust grill, 20-30" large dimension	EA	94.73	87.60	182.33	56.32	151.05	0.7946
15.4010 000	**WALL EXHAUST REGISTER:**							
15.4010 011	Wall exhaust, to 10" large dimension	EA	59.74	54.75	114.49	35.20	94.94	0.4966
15.4010 021	Wall exhaust, 12-18" large dimension	EA	83.73	71.19	154.92	45.77	129.50	0.6457

Division 15 CSI #	15 - MECHANICAL Description	Unit	Material	Union Install	Union Total	Open Install	Open Total	Unit Man-Hrs
15.4010 000	WALL EXHAUST REGISTER: (Cont.)							
15.4010 031	Wall exhaust, 20-30" large dimension	EA	115.90	87.60	203.50	56.32	172.22	0.7946
15.4011 000	WALL EXHAUST GRILL:							
15.4011 011	Wall exhaust grill, to 10" large dimension	EA	51.05	43.77	94.82	28.14	79.19	0.3970
15.4011 021	Wall exhaust grill, 12-18" large dimension	EA	70.10	60.21	130.31	38.71	108.81	0.5461
15.4011 031	Wall exhaust grill, 20-30" large dimension	EA	94.73	82.08	176.81	52.77	147.50	0.7445
15.4012 000	CEILING DIFFUSER, RECTANGULAR, TWO WAY:							
15.4012 011	Ceiling diffuser, to 12", louver, rectangular, 2 way	EA	81.75	65.73	147.48	42.26	124.01	0.5962
15.4012 021	Ceiling diffuser, 14-20", louver, rectangular, 2 way	EA	117.69	82.08	199.77	52.77	170.46	0.7445
15.4012 031	Ceiling diffuser, 25-32", louver, rectangular, 2 way	EA	177.58	103.97	281.55	66.84	244.42	0.9430
15.4012 041	Ceiling diffuser, to 12", perforated, rectangular, 2 way	EA	71.84	65.73	137.57	42.26	114.10	0.5962
15.4012 051	Ceiling diffuser, 14-20", perforated, rectangular, 2 way	EA	99.04	82.08	181.12	52.77	151.81	0.7445
15.4012 061	Ceiling diffuser, 24-30", perforated, rectangular, 2 way	EA	144.15	103.97	248.12	66.84	210.99	0.9430
15.4013 000	LINEAR DIFFUSER, ALUMINUM:							
15.4013 011	Linear diffuser, aluminum, ceiling or wall 2" wide	EA	52.94	29.15	82.09	18.74	71.68	0.2644
15.4013 021	Linear diffuser, aluminum, ceiling or wall 3" wide	EA	63.79	31.66	95.45	20.36	84.15	0.2872
15.4013 031	Linear diffuser, aluminum, ceiling or wall 4" wide	EA	74.58	35.49	110.07	22.82	97.40	0.3219
15.4013 041	Linear diffuser, aluminum, ceiling or wall 6" wide	EA	96.49	38.85	135.34	24.98	121.47	0.3524
15.4013 051	Linear diffuser, aluminum, ceiling or wall 8" wide	EA	112.71	42.45	155.16	27.29	140.00	0.3850
15.4013 061	Linear diffuser, aluminum, ceiling or wall 10" wide	EA	125.49	46.65	172.14	29.99	155.48	0.4231
15.4013 071	Linear diffuser, aluminum, ceiling or wall 12" wide	EA	140.35	51.67	192.02	33.22	173.57	0.4687
15.4014 000	WALL SUPPLY REGISTERS:							
15.4014 011	Wall supply register, to 10" large dimension	EA	56.04	54.75	110.79	35.20	91.24	0.4966
15.4014 021	Wall supply register, 12-15" large dimension	EA	78.73	71.19	149.92	45.77	124.50	0.6457
15.4014 031	Wall supply register, 18-24" large dimension	EA	102.71	82.08	184.79	52.77	155.48	0.7445
15.4014 041	Wall supply register, 30-36" large dimension	EA	129.30	93.06	222.36	59.83	189.13	0.8441
15.4015 000	MISCELLANEOUS DUCT ITEMS, INSULATION:							
15.4015 011	Insulation, duct, internal, 1"	SFCA	2.16	2.54	4.70	1.63	3.79	0.0230
15.4015 021	Insulation, duct, external, 1", plain	SFCA	1.04	.85	1.89	.55	1.59	0.0077
15.4015 031	Insulation, duct, exterior, 1", vapor barrier	SFCA	1.58	1.69	3.27	1.08	2.66	0.0153
15.4015 041	Insulation, duct, exterior, 1", rigid board	SFCA	2.81	4.23	7.04	2.72	5.53	0.0384
15.4016 000	SOUND ATTENUATORS:							
15.4016 011	Attenuator, 3' l x 24" w x 24" h	EA	1,584.53	253.46	1,837.99	162.95	1,747.48	2.2990
15.4016 021	Attenuator, 3' l x 36" w x 24" h	EA	1,747.71	295.71	2,043.42	190.11	1,937.82	2.6822
15.4016 031	Attenuator, 3' l x 48" w x 28" h	EA	2,922.94	295.71	3,218.65	190.11	3,113.05	2.6822
15.4016 041	Attenuator, 5' l x 36" w x 24" h	EA	2,609.12	337.95	2,947.07	217.27	2,826.39	3.0653
15.4016 051	Attenuator, 5' l x 48" w x 24" h	EA	3,442.80	380.20	3,823.00	244.43	3,687.23	3.4485
15.4016 061	Attenuator, 5' l x 72" w x 28" h	EA	4,715.87	422.43	5,138.30	271.58	4,987.45	3.8316
15.4016 071	Attenuator, 7' l x 20" w x 18" h	EA	2,440.83	506.93	2,947.76	325.91	2,766.74	4.5980
15.4016 081	Attenuator, 7' l x 32" w x 20" h	EA	3,148.95	528.04	3,676.99	339.48	3,488.43	4.7895
15.4016 091	Attenuator, 7' l x 48" w x 20" h	EA	4,715.87	549.17	5,265.04	353.06	5,068.93	4.9811
15.4100 000	PIPING & INSULATION:							
15.4101 000	COPPER "L" IN BUILDING, WITH FITTINGS & SUPPORTS:							
	Note: The following prices include fittings, hangers and supports. Prices do not include valves or insulation. For piping not covered here, see section "15.2100.							
15.4101 011	Pipe, copper, 'L', 1/2", in building, with fittings & supports	LF	4.11	9.38	13.49	5.88	9.99	0.0791
15.4101 021	Pipe, copper 'L', 3/4", in building, with fittings & supports	LF	6.40	11.41	17.81	7.15	13.55	0.0962
15.4101 031	Pipe, copper 'L', 1", in building, with fittings & supports	LF	9.32	13.54	22.86	8.49	17.81	0.1142
15.4101 041	Pipe, copper 'L', 1-1/4", in building, with fittings & supports	LF	13.27	14.62	27.89	9.17	22.44	0.1233
15.4101 051	Pipe, copper 'L', 1-1/2", in building, with fittings & supports	LF	16.58	15.55	32.13	9.75	26.33	0.1311
15.4101 061	Pipe, copper 'L', 2", in building, with fittings & supports	LF	20.61	18.75	39.36	11.75	32.36	0.1581
15.4102 000	STEEL PIPE, BLACK, WELDED, SCH 40, A-120, SCREWED:							
	Note: The following prices include malleable iron fittings & supports.							
15.4102 011	Black steel pipe, weld, A-120, '40', 1/2", screwed	LF	1.93	8.92	10.85	5.59	7.52	0.0752
15.4102 021	Black steel pipe, weld, A-120, '40', 3/4", screwed	LF	2.31	11.04	13.35	6.92	9.23	0.0931
15.4102 031	Black steel pipe, weld, A-120, '40', 1", screwed	LF	2.95	13.30	16.25	8.34	11.29	0.1122
15.4102 041	Black steel pipe, weld, A-120, '40', 1-1/4", screwed	LF	4.05	14.36	18.41	9.00	13.05	0.1211
15.4102 051	Black steel pipe, weld, A-120, '40', 1-1/2", screwed	LF	4.60	16.62	21.22	10.42	15.02	0.1402
15.4102 061	Black steel pipe, weld, A-120, '40', 2", screwed	LF	6.17	22.63	28.80	14.18	20.35	0.1908
15.4102 071	Black steel pipe, weld, A-120, '40', 2-1/2", screwed	LF	9.50	27.17	36.67	17.03	26.53	0.2291
15.4102 081	Black steel pipe, weld, A-120, '40', 3", screwed	LF	12.80	31.71	44.51	19.88	32.68	0.2674
15.4102 091	Black steel pipe, weld, A-120, '40', 4", screwed	LF	22.34	41.35	63.69	25.92	48.26	0.3487

Division 15 CSI #	15 - MECHANICAL Description	Unit	Material	Union Install	Union Total	Open Install	Open Total	Unit Man-Hrs
15.4102 000	**STEEL PIPE, BLACK, WELDED, SCH 40, A-120, SCREWED: (Cont.)**							
15.4102 101	Black steel pipe, weld, A-120, '40', 5", screwed	LF	31.80	44.72	76.52	28.03	59.83	0.3771
15.4102 111	Black steel pipe, weld, A-120, '40', 6", screwed	LF	40.70	49.98	90.68	31.33	72.03	0.4215
15.4103 000	**STEEL PIPE, BLACK, WELDED, SCH 40, A-53, WELD CONSTRUCTION:**							
	Note: The following prices include black welded fittings & supports.							
15.4103 011	Black steel pipe, weld, A-53, '40', 2", welded	LF	13.55	22.81	36.36	14.30	27.85	0.1924
15.4103 021	Black steel pipe, weld, A-53, '40', 2-1/2", welded	LF	17.87	29.08	46.95	18.23	36.10	0.2452
15.4103 031	Black steel pipe, weld, A-53, '40', 3", welded	LF	22.15	33.08	55.23	20.74	42.89	0.2790
15.4103 041	Black steel pipe, weld, A-53, '40', 4", welded	LF	31.04	42.49	73.53	26.64	57.68	0.3583
15.4103 051	Black steel pipe, weld, A-53, '40', 5", welded	LF	37.22	47.25	84.47	29.62	66.84	0.3985
15.4103 061	Black steel pipe, weld, A-53, '40', 6", welded	LF	39.12	52.15	91.27	32.69	71.81	0.4398
15.4103 071	Black steel pipe, weld, A-53, '40', 8", welded	LF	65.07	58.15	123.22	36.46	101.53	0.4904
15.4104 000	**STEEL PIPE, SEAMLESS, SCH 40, A-53, WELDED CONSTRUCTION:**							
	Note: The following prices include black welded fittings & supports.							
15.4104 011	Steel pipe, seamless, A-53, '40', 2", welded	LF	16.13	22.81	38.94	14.30	30.43	0.1924
15.4104 021	Steel pipe, seamless, A-53, '40', 2-1/2", welded	LF	18.15	29.51	47.66	18.50	36.65	0.2489
15.4104 031	Steel pipe, seamless, A-53, '40', 3", welded	LF	22.17	33.02	55.19	20.70	42.87	0.2785
15.4104 041	Steel pipe, seamless, A-53, '40', 4", welded	LF	31.50	42.49	73.99	26.64	58.14	0.3583
15.4104 051	Steel pipe, seamless, A-53, '40', 5", welded	LF	37.92	47.25	85.17	29.62	67.54	0.3985
15.4104 061	Steel pipe, seamless, A-53, '40', 6", welded	LF	39.96	52.15	92.11	32.69	72.65	0.4398
15.4104 071	Steel pipe, seamless, A-53, '40', 8", welded	LF	61.24	58.15	119.39	36.46	97.70	0.4904
15.4104 081	Steel pipe, seamless, A-53, '40', 10", welded	LF	115.45	65.42	180.87	41.01	156.46	0.5517
15.4105 000	**STEEL PIPE, SEAMLESS, SCH 80:**							
	Note: The following prices include black welded fittings & supports.							
15.4105 011	Steel pipe, seamless, A-53, '80', 2"	LF	17.36	26.17	43.53	16.41	33.77	0.2207
15.4105 021	Steel pipe, seamless, A-53, '80', 2-1/2"	LF	20.33	33.94	54.27	21.28	41.61	0.2862
15.4105 031	Steel pipe, seamless, A-53, '80', 3"	LF	25.08	37.90	62.98	23.76	48.84	0.3196
15.4105 041	Steel pipe, seamless, A-53, '80', 4"	LF	36.80	48.80	85.60	30.59	67.39	0.4115
15.4105 051	Steel pipe, seamless, A-53, '80', 5"	LF	44.68	54.35	99.03	34.07	78.75	0.4583
15.4105 061	Steel pipe, seamless, A-53, '80', 6"	LF	49.20	59.98	109.18	37.60	86.80	0.5058
15.4105 071	Steel pipe, seamless, A-53, '80', 8"	LF	75.57	66.88	142.45	41.93	117.50	0.5640
15.4105 081	Steel pipe, seamless, A-53, '80', 10"	LF	149.28	75.24	224.52	47.17	196.45	0.6345
15.4106 000	**STEEL PIPE, BLACK, WELDED, SCH 40, A-120, VICTAULIC COUPLINGS:**							
	Note: The following prices include victaulic fittings and supports.							
15.4106 011	Black steel pipe, weld, A-120, '40', 2", victaulic	LF	16.00	12.05	28.05	7.55	23.55	0.1016
15.4106 021	Black steel pipe, weld, A-120, '40', 2-1/2", victaulic	LF	17.87	15.58	33.45	9.77	27.64	0.1314
15.4106 031	Black steel pipe, weld, A-120, '40', 3", victaulic	LF	22.15	17.44	39.59	10.94	33.09	0.1471
15.4106 041	Black steel pipe, weld, A-120, '40', 4", victaulic	LF	28.65	22.44	51.09	14.07	42.72	0.1892
15.4106 051	Black steel pipe, weld, A-120, '40', 5", victaulic	LF	37.22	24.95	62.17	15.64	52.86	0.2104
15.4106 061	Black steel pipe, weld, A-120, '40', 6", victaulic	LF	39.12	27.53	66.65	17.26	56.38	0.2322
15.4106 071	Black steel pipe, weld, A-120, '40', 8", victaulic	LF	65.07	30.70	95.77	19.25	84.32	0.2589
15.4106 081	Black steel pipe, weld, A-120, '40', 10", victaulic	LF	82.94	35.76	118.70	22.42	105.36	0.3016
15.4106 091	Black steel pipe, weld, A-120, '40', 12", victaulic	LF	95.24	57.84	153.08	36.26	131.50	0.4878
15.4106 101	Black steel pipe, weld, A-120, '40', 14', victaulic	LF	108.65	59.37	168.02	37.22	145.87	0.5007
15.4106 111	Black steel pipe, weld, A-120, '40', 16", victaulic	LF	129.91	63.26	193.17	39.66	169.57	0.5335
15.4106 121	Black steel pipe, weld, A-120, '40', 18", victaulic	LF	173.09	77.86	250.95	48.81	221.90	0.6566
15.4106 131	Black steel pipe, weld, A-120, '40', 20", victaulic	LF	224.23	88.48	312.71	55.47	279.70	0.7462
15.4106 141	Black steel pipe, weld, A-120, '40', 24", victaulic	LF	281.92	104.49	386.41	65.51	347.43	0.8812
15.4200 000	**FITTINGS:**							
15.4201 000	**FLANGES, CAST IRON., SCREWED, BLACK, 125#:**							
15.4201 011	Cast iron flange, black, screwed, 125#, 1-1/2"	EA	29.43	64.95	94.38	40.72	70.15	0.5477
15.4201 021	Cast iron flange, black, screwed, 125#, 2"	EA	36.76	77.63	114.39	48.67	85.43	0.6547
15.4201 031	Cast iron flange, black, screwed, 125#, 2-1/2"	EA	41.61	84.50	126.11	52.97	94.58	0.7126
15.4201 041	Cast iron flange, black, screwed, 125#, 3"	EA	43.94	111.77	155.71	70.07	114.01	0.9426
15.4201 051	Cast iron flange, black, screwed, 125#, 4"	EA	48.53	136.31	184.84	85.45	133.98	1.1495
15.4201 061	Cast iron flange, black, screwed, 125#, 5"	EA	64.52	152.66	217.18	95.71	160.23	1.2874
15.4201 071	Cast iron flange, black, screwed, 125#, 6"	EA	76.79	179.01	255.80	112.22	189.01	1.5096
15.4201 081	Cast iron flange, black, screwed, 125#, 8"	EA	132.34	190.83	323.17	119.64	251.98	1.6093
15.4201 091	Cast iron flange, black, screwed, 125#, 10"	EA	215.31	214.45	429.76	134.44	349.75	1.8085
15.4202 000	**FLANGES, STEEL, SLIP-ON, FORGED STEEL 150#:**							
	Note: For weld neck flange, add 20% to the material costs.							
15.4202 011	Steel flange, slip-on, 2", forged steel 150#	EA	19.14	67.90	87.04	42.57	61.71	0.5726

Division 15 CSI #	15 - MECHANICAL Description	Unit	Material	Union Install	Union Total	Open Install	Open Total	Unit Man-Hrs
15.4202 000	**FLANGES, STEEL, SLIP-ON, FORGED STEEL 150#: (Cont.)**							
15.4202 021	Steel flange, slip-on, 2-1/2", forged steel 150	EA	27.20	80.47	107.67	50.45	77.65	0.6786
15.4202 031	Steel flange, slip-on, 3", forged steel 150#	EA	27.54	99.07	126.61	62.11	89.65	0.8355
15.4202 041	Steel flange, slip-on, 4", forged steel 150#	EA	35.01	130.17	165.18	81.60	116.61	1.0977
15.4202 051	Steel flange, slip-on, 5", forged steel 150#	EA	49.46	158.03	207.49	99.07	148.53	1.3327
15.4202 061	Steel flange, slip-on, 6", forged steel 150#	EA	57.48	191.51	248.99	120.06	177.54	1.6150
15.4202 071	Steel flange, slip-on, 8", forged steel 150#	EA	87.40	265.00	352.40	166.14	253.54	2.2348
15.4202 081	Steel flange, slip-on, 10", forged steel 150#	EA	157.99	325.42	483.41	204.01	362.00	2.7443
15.4202 091	Steel flange, slip-on, 12", forged steel 150#	EA	328.36	401.63	729.99	251.79	580.15	3.3870
15.4202 101	Steel flange, slip-on, 14", forged steel 150#	EA	380.37	464.92	845.29	291.46	671.83	3.9207
15.4202 111	Steel flange, slip-on, 16", forged steel 150#	EA	426.90	548.63	975.53	343.95	770.85	4.6267
15.4202 121	Steel flange, slip-on, 18", forged steel 150#	EA	565.44	636.91	1,202.35	399.29	964.73	5.3711
15.4202 131	Steel flange, slip-on, 20", forged steel 150#	EA	673.17	767.06	1,440.23	480.88	1,154.05	6.4687
15.4202 141	Steel flange, slip-on, 24", forged steel 150#	EA	883.68	957.71	1,841.39	600.41	1,484.09	8.0765
15.4203 000	**VICTAULIC COUPLINGS, WITH GROOVING:**							
15.4203 011	Victaulic coupling, 2", grooving	EA	35.26	95.26	130.52	59.72	94.98	0.8033
15.4203 021	Victaulic coupling, 3", grooving	EA	48.45	106.89	155.34	67.01	115.46	0.9014
15.4203 031	Victaulic coupling, 4", grooving	EA	100.98	115.64	216.62	72.50	173.48	0.9752
15.4203 041	Victaulic coupling, 6", grooving	EA	132.02	131.19	263.21	82.24	214.26	1.1063
15.4203 051	Victaulic coupling, 8", grooving	EA	215.89	194.33	410.22	121.83	337.72	1.6388
15.4203 061	Victaulic coupling, 10", grooving	EA	304.80	242.92	547.72	152.29	457.09	2.0486
15.4203 071	Victaulic coupling, 12", grooving	EA	346.52	286.68	633.20	179.72	526.24	2.4176
15.4203 081	Victaulic coupling, 14", grooving	EA	406.98	330.35	737.33	207.10	614.08	2.7859
15.4203 091	Victaulic coupling, 16", grooving	EA	523.78	369.26	893.04	231.49	755.27	3.1140
15.4300 000	**VALVES & SPECIALTIES:**							
	Note: The following prices include 2 appropriate connections to pipe or equipment.							
15.4301 000	**GATE, GLOBE & CHECK VALVES, BRASS, 125#, SCREWED:**							
15.4301 011	Valve, gate, globe & check, brass, 125#, screwed, 1/2"	EA	10.04	33.39	43.43	20.93	30.97	0.2816
15.4301 021	Valve, gate, globe & check, brass, 125#, screwed, 3/4"	EA	13.11	40.00	53.11	25.07	38.18	0.3373
15.4301 031	Valve, gate, globe & check, brass, 125#, screwed, 1"	EA	18.65	41.69	60.34	26.14	44.79	0.3516
15.4301 041	Valve, gate, globe & check, brass, 125#, screwed, 1-1/4"	EA	26.63	53.37	80.00	33.46	60.09	0.4501
15.4301 051	Valve, gate, globe & check, brass, 125#, screwed, 1-1/2"	EA	35.03	79.79	114.82	50.02	85.05	0.6729
15.4301 061	Valve, gate, globe & check, brass, 125#, screwed, 2"	EA	52.97	148.70	201.67	93.22	146.19	1.2540
15.4301 071	Valve, gate, globe & check, brass, 125#, screwed, 2-1/2"	EA	95.36	195.66	291.02	122.66	218.02	1.6500
15.4301 081	Valve, gate, globe & check, brass, 125#, screwed, 3"	EA	132.93	227.67	360.60	142.73	275.66	1.9200
15.4301 091	Valve, gate, globe & check, brass, 125#, screwed, 4"	EA	287.21	320.17	607.38	200.72	487.93	2.7000
15.4302 000	**GATE, GLOBE & CHECK VALVES, BRONZE, 200#, SCREW:**							
15.4302 011	Valve, gate, globe & check, bronze, 200#, screwed, 1/2"	EA	66.94	33.39	100.33	20.93	87.87	0.2816
15.4302 021	Valve, gate, globe & check, bronze, 200#, screwed, 3/4"	EA	86.55	40.00	126.55	25.07	111.62	0.3373
15.4302 031	Valve, gate, globe & check, bronze, 200#, screwed, 1"	EA	120.70	41.69	162.39	26.14	146.84	0.3516
15.4302 041	Valve, gate, globe & check, bronze, 200#, screwed, 1-1/4"	EA	180.45	53.37	233.82	33.46	213.91	0.4501
15.4302 051	Valve, gate, globe & check, bronze, 200#, screwed, 1-1/2"	EA	207.71	4.77	212.48	2.99	210.70	0.0402
15.4302 061	Valve, gate, globe & check, bronze, 200#, screwed, 2"	EA	315.89	148.70	464.59	93.22	409.11	1.2540
15.4302 071	Valve, gate, globe & check, bronze, 200#, screwed, 2-1/2"	EA	689.41	195.66	885.07	122.66	812.07	1.6500
15.4303 000	**GATE, GLOBE & CHECK VALVES, IRON, FLANGE, 125#, BOLT & GASKET:**							
	Note: The following prices do not include companion flanges.							
15.4303 011	Valve, gate, globe & check, iron body, flange, 125#, 2", bolt & gaskets	EA	334.29	143.48	477.77	89.95	424.24	1.2100
15.4303 021	Valve, gate, globe & check, iron body, flange, 125#, 2-1/2", bolt & gaskets	EA	365.44	160.08	525.52	100.36	465.80	1.3500
15.4303 031	Valve, gate, globe & check, iron body, flange, 125#, 3", bolt & gaskets	EA	417.02	177.87	594.89	111.51	528.53	1.5000
15.4303 041	Valve, gate, globe & check, iron body, flange, 125#, 4", bolt & gaskets	EA	611.94	284.59	896.53	178.42	790.36	2.4000
15.4303 051	Valve, gate, globe & check, iron body, flange, 125#, 5-6", bolt & gaskets	EA	1,061.11	415.03	1,476.14	260.19	1,321.30	3.5000
15.4303 061	Valve, gate, globe & check, iron body, flange, 125#, 8", bolt & gaskets	EA	2,095.75	545.47	2,641.22	341.96	2,437.71	4.6000
15.4303 071	Valve, gate, globe & check, iron body, flange, 125#, 10", bolt & gaskets	EA	3,463.11	782.63	4,245.74	490.64	3,953.75	6.6000
15.4303 081	Valve, gate, globe & check, iron body, flange, 125#, 12", bolt & gaskets	EA	4,626.19	889.35	5,515.54	557.55	5,183.74	7.5000
15.4303 091	Valve, gate, globe & check, iron body, flange, 125#, 14", bolt & gaskets	EA	7,576.59	1,458.53	9,035.12	914.38	8,490.97	12.3000
15.4303 101	Valve, gate, globe & check, iron body, flange, 125#, 16", bolt & gaskets	EA	14,949.59	1,909.14	16,858.73	1,196.87	16,146.46	16.1000
15.4303 111	Valve, gate, globe & check, iron body, flange, 125#, 18", bolt & gaskets	EA	18,162.47	2,336.03	20,498.50	1,464.50	19,626.97	19.7000
15.4304 000	**VALVE, TRIPLE DUTY, IRON, FLANGE, WITH BOLT & GASKET SET:**							
	Note: The following prices do not include companion flanges.							
15.4304 011	Valve, 3 duty, iron body, flange .3", bolt & gaskets	EA	667.33	201.59	868.92	126.38	793.71	1.7000
15.4304 021	Valve, 3 duty, iron body, flange, 4", bolt & gaskets	EA	1,415.10	343.88	1,758.98	215.59	1,630.69	2.9000
15.4304 031	Valve, 3 duty, iron body, flange, 5", bolt & gaskets	EA	1,664.38	450.60	2,114.98	282.49	1,946.87	3.8000

Division 15 CSI #	15 - MECHANICAL Description	Unit	Material	Union Install	Union Total	Open Install	Open Total	Unit Man-Hrs
15.4304 000	**VALVE, TRIPLE DUTY, IRON, FLANGE, WITH BOLT & GASKET SET: (Cont.)**							
15.4304 041	Valve, 3 duty, iron body, flange, 6", bolt & gaskets	EA	2,283.50	486.18	2,769.68	304.79	2,588.29	4.1000
15.4304 051	Valve, 3 duty, iron body, flange, 8", bolt & gaskets	EA	3,095.59	664.05	3,759.64	416.30	3,511.89	5.6000
15.4305 000	**PRESSURE RED VALVES, IRON, BRONZE TRIM, 125, 9-100:**							
15.4305 011	Pressure reducing valve, iron body, bronze trim, 125#, 1-1/2", 9-100	EA	730.08	145.81	875.89	91.41	821.49	1.2296
15.4305 021	Pressure reducing valve, iron body, bronze trim, 125#, 2", 9-100	EA	825.81	165.00	990.81	103.44	929.25	1.3915
15.4305 031	Pressure reducing valve, iron body, bronze trim, 125#, 3", 9-100	EA	1,169.16	226.72	1,395.88	142.14	1,311.30	1.9120
15.4305 041	Pressure reducing valve, iron body, bronze trim, 125#, 4", 9-100	EA	1,658.86	337.95	1,996.81	211.87	1,870.73	2.8500
15.4305 051	Pressure reducing valve, iron body, bronze trim, 125#, 6", 9-100	EA	2,632.85	450.60	3,083.45	282.49	2,915.34	3.8000
15.4305 061	Pressure reducing valve, iron body, bronze trim, 125#, 8", 9-100	EA	4,418.18	664.05	5,082.23	416.30	4,834.48	5.6000
15.4305 071	Pressure reducing valve, iron body, bronze trim, 125#, 10", 9-100	EA	6,059.00	889.35	6,948.35	557.55	6,616.55	7.5000
15.4306 000	**VALVES, PRESSURE RELIEF, ASME:**							
15.4306 011	Valve, pressure relief, bronze, 3/4"	EA	48.80	40.06	88.86	25.11	73.91	0.3378
15.4306 021	Valve, pressure relief, bronze, 1"	EA	91.81	41.69	133.50	26.14	117.95	0.3516
15.4306 031	Valve, pressure relief, bronze, 1-1/2"	EA	344.57	73.86	418.43	46.31	390.88	0.6229
15.4306 041	Valve, pressure relief, bronze, 2"	EA	383.57	148.70	532.27	93.22	476.79	1.2540
15.4307 000	**STEAM TRAPS, CAST IRON, SCREWED, WITH STAINLESS STEEL BUCKET:**							
15.4307 011	Steam trap, cast iron, 1/2", screwed, bucket	EA	152.10	38.92	191.02	24.40	176.50	0.3282
15.4307 021	Steam trap, cast iron, 3/4", screwed, bucket	EA	216.85	53.70	270.55	33.67	250.52	0.4529
15.4307 031	Steam trap, cast iron, 1", screwed, bucket	EA	365.04	67.97	433.01	42.61	407.65	0.5732
15.4307 041	Steam trap, cast iron, 1-1/2", screwed, bucket	EA	659.55	87.44	746.99	54.82	714.37	0.7374
15.4308 000	**VALVES, BUTTERFLY, IRON BODY & DISCONNECT, NYLON COAT, WAFER:**							
	Note: The following prices include buna seat, handles and wafer body.							
15.4308 011	Butterfly valve, iron body, nylon, 2", wafer body	EA	153.44	125.54	278.98	78.70	232.14	1.0587
15.4308 021	Butterfly valve, iron body, nylon, 2-1/2", wafer	EA	161.87	149.94	311.81	94.00	255.87	1.2645
15.4308 031	Butterfly valve, iron body, nylon, 3", wafer body	EA	174.45	174.35	348.80	109.30	283.75	1.4703
15.4308 041	Butterfly valve, iron body, nylon, 4", wafer body	EA	218.65	254.52	473.17	159.56	378.21	2.1464
15.4308 051	Butterfly valve, iron body, nylon, 5", wafer body	EA	313.22	337.95	651.17	211.87	525.09	2.8500
15.4308 061	Butterfly valve, iron body, nylon, 6", wafer body	EA	382.55	337.95	720.50	211.87	594.42	2.8500
15.4308 071	Butterfly valve, iron body, nylon, 8", wafer, chain	EA	571.81	498.04	1,069.85	312.23	884.04	4.2000
15.4308 081	Butterfly valve, iron body, nylon, 10", wafer, chain	EA	792.49	667.01	1,459.50	418.16	1,210.65	5.6250
15.4308 091	Butterfly valve, iron body, nylon, 12", wafer, chain	EA	1,219.26	880.46	2,099.72	551.97	1,771.23	7.4250
15.4309 000	**VALVES, BUTTERFLY, IRON BODY & DISCONNECT, NYLON COAT, LUG TYPE:**							
	Note: The following prices include buna seat and handles.							
15.4309 011	Butterfly valve, iron body, nylon, 2", lug type	EA	182.87	125.54	308.41	78.70	261.57	1.0587
15.4309 021	Butterfly valve, iron body, nylon, 2-1/2", lug type	EA	187.10	149.94	337.04	94.00	281.10	1.2645
15.4309 031	Butterfly valve, iron body, nylon, 3", lug type	EA	208.12	174.35	382.47	109.30	317.42	1.4703
15.4309 041	Butterfly valve, iron body, nylon, 4", lug type	EA	260.67	254.52	515.19	159.56	420.23	2.1464
15.4309 051	Butterfly valve, iron body, nylon, 5", lug type	EA	397.27	337.95	735.22	211.87	609.14	2.8500
15.4309 061	Butterfly valve, iron body, nylon, 6", lug type	EA	443.57	337.95	781.52	211.87	655.44	2.8500
15.4309 071	Butterfly valve, iron body, nylon, 8", lug, chain	EA	615.91	498.04	1,113.95	312.23	928.14	4.2000
15.4309 081	Butterfly valve, iron body, nylon, 10", lug, chain	EA	866.09	667.01	1,533.10	418.16	1,284.25	5.6250
15.4309 091	Butterfly valve, iron body, nylon, 12", lug, chain	EA	1,370.58	880.46	2,251.04	551.97	1,922.55	7.4250
15.4310 000	**VALVES, FLOW CONTROL:**							
15.4310 011	Valve, flow control, straight angle, 3/4"	EA		36.36	36.36	22.79	22.79	0.3066
15.4310 021	Valve, flow control, straight angle, 1"	EA		37.90	37.90	23.76	23.76	0.3196
15.4310 031	Valve, flow control, straight angle, 1-1/4"	EA		48.52	48.52	30.42	30.42	0.4092
15.4310 041	Valve, flow control, straight angle, 1-1/2"	EA		79.79	79.79	50.02	50.02	0.6729
15.4310 051	Valve, flow control, straight angle, 2"	EA		135.18	135.18	84.75	84.75	1.1400
15.4310 061	Valve, flow control, straight, 2-1/2"	EA		183.80	183.80	115.23	115.23	1.5500
15.4310 071	Valve, flow control, straight, 3"	EA		227.67	227.67	142.73	142.73	1.9200
15.4310 081	Valve, flow control, straight, 4"	EA		320.17	320.17	200.72	200.72	2.7000
15.4311 000	**SUCTION DIFFUSER, ANGLE BODY:**							
	Note: The following prices include inlet, vanes, strainer and permanent magnet.							
15.4311 011	Suction diffuser, angle body, 3 x 3	EA	578.38	207.52	785.90	130.10	708.48	1.7500
15.4311 021	Suction diffuser, angle body, 4 x 3	EA	682.86	304.75	987.61	191.05	873.91	2.5700
15.4311 031	Suction diffuser, angle body, 4 x 4	EA	794.43	304.75	1,099.18	191.05	985.48	2.5700
15.4311 041	Suction diffuser, angle body, 6 x 4	EA	940.72	409.10	1,349.82	256.47	1,197.19	3.4500
15.4311 051	Suction diffuser, angle body, 6 x 6	EA	1,170.66	409.10	1,579.76	256.47	1,427.13	3.4500
15.4311 061	Suction diffuser, angle body, 8 x 6	EA	1,261.31	604.76	1,866.07	379.13	1,640.44	5.1000
15.4311 071	Suction diffuser, angle body, 8 x 8	EA	2,181.11	610.81	2,791.92	382.93	2,564.04	5.1510
15.4311 081	Suction diffuser, angle body, 10 x 10	EA	2,954.62	838.36	3,792.98	525.58	3,480.20	7.0700

Division 15 CSI #	15 - MECHANICAL Description	Unit	Material	Union Install	Union Total	Open Install	Open Total	Unit Man-Hrs
15.4312 000	**VALVES, BALANCING, CIRCUIT SETTER:**							
15.4312 011	Valve, balancing, circuit setter, 1/2"	EA	82.25	30.36	112.61	19.03	101.28	0.2560
15.4312 013	Valve, balancing, circuit setter, 3/4"	EA	100.33	36.36	136.69	22.79	123.12	0.3066
15.4312 021	Valve, balancing, circuit setter, 1"	EA	116.09	37.90	153.99	23.76	139.85	0.3196
15.4312 041	Valve, balancing, circuit setter, 1-1/4"	EA	143.09	48.52	191.61	30.42	173.51	0.4092
15.4312 051	Valve, balancing, circuit setter, 1-1/2"	EA	154.20	79.79	233.99	50.02	204.22	0.6729
15.4312 061	Valve, balancing, circuit setter, 2"	EA	253.59	135.18	388.77	84.75	338.34	1.1400
15.4312 071	Valve, balancing, circuit setter, 2-1/2"	EA	432.91	183.80	616.71	115.23	548.14	1.5500
15.4312 081	Valve, balancing, circuit setter, 3"	EA	643.08	227.67	870.75	142.73	785.81	1.9200
15.4312 091	Valve, balancing, circuit setter, 4"	EA	914.06	320.17	1,234.23	200.72	1,114.78	2.7000
15.4313 000	**FLEXIBLE CONNECTOR, WITH NEOPRENE COVER, BELLOWS, 125#, FLANGE:**							
	Note: The following prices do not include companion flanges or bolt and gasket sets.							
15.4313 011	Flexible connector, flange, 125#, 2", cover, bellows	EA	152.77	80.63	233.40	50.55	203.32	0.6800
15.4313 021	Flexible connector, flange, 125#, 2-1/2", cover, bellows	EA	188.00	88.94	276.94	55.76	243.76	0.7500
15.4313 031	Flexible connector, flange, 125#, 3", cover, bellows	EA	202.73	130.44	333.17	81.77	284.50	1.1000
15.4313 041	Flexible connector, flange, 125#, 4", cover, bellows	EA	273.15	183.80	456.95	115.23	388.38	1.5500
15.4313 051	Flexible connector, flange, 125#, 5", cover, bellows	EA	299.68	235.97	535.65	147.94	447.62	1.9900
15.4313 061	Flexible connector, flange, 125#, 6", cover, bellows	EA	376.05	297.64	673.69	186.59	562.64	2.5100
15.4314 000	**METER, FLOW, CIRCUIT SENSOR:**							
15.4314 011	Meter, flow, circuit sensor, 6"	EA	307.55	415.03	722.58	260.19	567.74	3.5000
15.4314 021	Meter, flow, circuit sensor, 8"	EA	449.81	545.47	995.28	341.96	791.77	4.6000
15.4314 031	Meter, flow, circuit sensor, 10"	EA	518.06	718.59	1,236.65	450.50	968.56	6.0600
15.4314 041	Meter, flow, circuit sensor, 12"	EA	863.41	889.35	1,752.76	557.55	1,420.96	7.5000
15.4400 000	**INSULATION, PIPING:**							
	Note: The following prices include insulation allowance at pipe runs, valves and fittings.							
15.4401 000	**INSULATION, 1-1/2" CALCIUM SILICATE:**							
	Note:							
	For 1" calsil on pipe sizes 1" to 6" . . . deduct 28% from material							
	For 2" calsil on pipe sizes 1" to 6" . . . add 56%							
	For 2" calsil on sizes 8" to 14" . . . . . . add 41%							
	For 2 1/2" calsil on sizes 1" to 6" . . . . add 94%							
	For 2 1/2" calsil on sizes 8" to 14" . . . add 80%							
15.4401 011	Insulation, 1-1/2" calcium silicate, 1/2" pipe	LF	3.68	3.09	6.77	1.94	5.62	0.0261
15.4401 021	Insulation, 1-1/2" calcium silicate, 3/4" pipe	LF	3.76	3.09	6.85	1.94	5.70	0.0261
15.4401 031	Insulation, 1-1/2" calcium silicate, 1" pipe	LF	4.07	3.09	7.16	1.94	6.01	0.0261
15.4401 041	Insulation, 1-1/2" calcium silicate, 1-1/4" pipe	LF	4.24	3.09	7.33	1.94	6.18	0.0261
15.4401 051	Insulation, 1-1/2" calcium silicate, 1-1/2" pipe	LF	4.56	3.09	7.65	1.94	6.50	0.0261
15.4401 061	Insulation, 1-1/2" calcium silicate, 2" pipe	LF	5.04	4.55	9.59	2.85	7.89	0.0384
15.4401 071	Insulation, 1-1/2" calcium silicate, 2-1/2" pipe	LF	5.50	4.55	10.05	2.85	8.35	0.0384
15.4401 081	Insulation, 1-1/2" calcium silicate, 3" pipe	LF	5.78	6.10	11.88	3.82	9.60	0.0514
15.4401 091	Insulation, 1-1/2" calcium silicate, 4" pipe	LF	6.66	6.10	12.76	3.82	10.48	0.0514
15.4401 101	Insulation, 1-1/2" calcium silicate, 5" pipe	LF	7.49	6.10	13.59	3.82	11.31	0.0514
15.4401 111	Insulation, 1-1/2" calcium silicate, 6" pipe	LF	7.77	6.10	13.87	3.82	11.59	0.0514
15.4401 121	Insulation, 1-1/2" calcium silicate, 8" pipe	LF	10.49	7.64	18.13	4.79	15.28	0.0644
15.4401 131	Insulation, 1-1/2" calcium silicate, 10" pipe	LF	13.99	9.10	23.09	5.70	19.69	0.0767
15.4401 141	Insulation, 1-1/2" calcium silicate, 12" pipe	LF	16.51	10.64	27.15	6.67	23.18	0.0897
15.4401 151	Insulation, 1-1/2" calcium silicate, 14" pipe	LF	18.75	10.64	29.39	6.67	25.42	0.0897
15.4402 000	**INSULATION, 3" CALCIUM SILICATE:**							
15.4402 011	Insulation, 3" calcium silicate, 1" pipe	LF	9.66		9.66		9.66	0.0510
15.4402 021	Insulation, 3" calcium silicate, 2" pipe	LF	11.32		11.32		11.32	0.0610
15.4402 031	Insulation, 3" calcium silicate, 3" pipe	LF	13.04		13.04		13.04	0.0767
15.4402 041	Insulation, 3" calcium silicate, 4" pipe	LF	17.16		17.16		17.16	0.0767
15.4402 051	Insulation, 3" calcium silicate, 5" pipe	LF	19.51		19.51		19.51	0.0926
15.4402 061	Insulation, 3" calcium silicate, 6" pipe	LF	20.96		20.96		20.96	0.0926
15.4402 071	Insulation, 3" calcium silicate, 8" pipe	LF	24.92		24.92		24.92	0.1035
15.4402 081	Insulation, 3" calcium silicate, 10" pipe	LF	30.07		30.07		30.07	0.1150
15.4402 091	Insulation, 3" calcium silicate, 12" pipe	LF	33.32		33.32		33.32	0.1380
15.4402 101	Insulation, 3" calcium silicate, 14" pipe	LF	37.38		37.38		37.38	0.1590

Division 15 CSI #	15 - MECHANICAL Description	Unit	Material	Union Install	Union Total	Open Install	Open Total	Unit Man-Hrs
15.4403 000	**INSULATION, 1" FIBERGLASS WITH ALUMINUM JACKET:**							
	Note:							
	For 1-1/2" fiberglass on sizes 1/2" to 1-1/2" . . . add 100% to material							
	For sizes 2" to 3" . . . . add 70%							
	For sizes 4" to 6" . . . . add 45%							
	For sizes 8" to 12" . . . . add 25%							
15.4403 011	Insulation, 1" fiberglass, 1/2" pipe, with aluminum jacket	LF	1.94	4.55	6.49	2.85	4.79	0.0384
15.4403 021	Insulation, 1" fiberglass, 3/4" pipe, with aluminum jacket	LF	2.13	4.55	6.68	2.85	4.98	0.0384
15.4403 031	Insulation, 1" fiberglass, 1" pipe, with aluminum jacket	LF	2.28	4.55	6.83	2.85	5.13	0.0384
15.4403 041	Insulation, 1" fiberglass, 1-1/4" pipe, with aluminum jacket	LF	2.76	4.55	7.31	2.85	5.61	0.0384
15.4403 051	Insulation, 1" fiberglass, 1-1/2" pipe, with aluminum jacket	LF	2.79	4.55	7.34	2.85	5.64	0.0384
15.4403 061	Insulation, 1" fiberglass, 2" pipe, with aluminum jacket	LF	3.04	6.10	9.14	3.82	6.86	0.0514
15.4403 071	Insulation, 1" fiberglass, 2-1/2" pipe, with aluminum jacket	LF	3.42	6.10	9.52	3.82	7.24	0.0514
15.4403 081	Insulation, 1" fiberglass, 3" pipe, with aluminum jacket	LF	3.76	7.64	11.40	4.79	8.55	0.0644
15.4403 091	Insulation, 1" fiberglass, 4" pipe, with aluminum jacket	LF	4.93	7.64	12.57	4.79	9.72	0.0644
15.4403 101	Insulation, 1" fiberglass, 5" pipe, with aluminum jacket	LF	5.68	9.62	15.30	6.03	11.71	0.0811
15.4403 111	Insulation, 1" fiberglass, 6" pipe, with aluminum jacket	LF	6.09	9.62	15.71	6.03	12.12	0.0811
15.4403 121	Insulation, 1" fiberglass, 8" pipe, with aluminum jacket	LF	8.78	12.27	21.05	7.69	16.47	0.1035
15.4403 131	Insulation, 1" fiberglass, 10" pipe, with aluminum jacket	LF	10.34	16.72	27.06	10.48	20.82	0.1410
15.4403 141	Insulation, 1" fiberglass, 12" pipe, with aluminum jacket	LF	11.82	18.18	30.00	11.40	23.22	0.1533
15.4404 000	**INSULATION, 2" FIBERGLASS WITH ALUMINUM JACKET:**							
15.4404 011	Insulation, 2" fiberglass, 1/2" pipe, with aluminum jacket	LF	6.63	6.10	12.73	3.82	10.45	0.0514
15.4404 021	Insulation, 2" fiberglass, 3/4" pipe, with aluminum jacket	LF	6.79	6.10	12.89	3.82	10.61	0.0514
15.4404 031	Insulation, 2" fiberglass, 1" pipe, with aluminum jacket	LF	7.16	6.10	13.26	3.82	10.98	0.0514
15.4404 041	Insulation, 2" fiberglass, 1-1/4" pipe, with aluminum jacket	LF	7.58	6.10	13.68	3.82	11.40	0.0514
15.4404 051	Insulation, 2" fiberglass, 1-1/2" pipe, with aluminum jacket	LF	7.99	6.10	14.09	3.82	11.81	0.0514
15.4404 061	Insulation, 2" fiberglass, 2" pipe, with aluminum jacket	LF	8.28	7.64	15.92	4.79	13.07	0.0644
15.4404 071	Insulation, 2" fiberglass, 2-1/2" pipe, with aluminum jacket	LF	9.00	7.64	16.64	4.79	13.79	0.0644
15.4404 081	Insulation, 2" fiberglass, 3" pipe, with aluminum jacket	LF	9.58	9.10	18.68	5.70	15.28	0.0767
15.4404 091	Insulation, 2" fiberglass, 4" pipe, with aluminum jacket	LF	11.16	9.10	20.26	5.70	16.86	0.0767
15.4404 101	Insulation, 2" fiberglass, 5" pipe, with aluminum jacket	LF	12.61	9.10	21.71	5.70	18.31	0.0767
15.4404 111	Insulation, 2" fiberglass, 6" pipe, with aluminum jacket	LF	12.85	9.10	21.95	5.70	18.55	0.0767
15.4404 121	Insulation, 2" fiberglass, 8" pipe, with aluminum jacket	LF	15.94	13.64	29.58	8.55	24.49	0.1150
15.4404 131	Insulation, 2" fiberglass, 10" pipe, with aluminum jacket	LF	19.06	18.18	37.24	11.40	30.46	0.1533
15.4404 141	Insulation, 2" fiberglass, 12" pipe, with aluminum jacket	LF	21.24	19.72	40.96	12.36	33.60	0.1663
15.4405 000	**INSULATION, VALVES, FIBERGLASS WITH ALUMINUM JACKET:**							
15.4405 011	Insulation, fiberglass, 1" valve, aluminum jacket	EA	8.22	41.80	50.02	26.20	34.42	0.3525
15.4405 021	Insulation, fiberglass, 2" valve, aluminum jacket	EA	21.97	67.25	89.22	42.16	64.13	0.5671
15.4405 031	Insulation, fiberglass, 3" valve, aluminum jacket	EA	28.17	86.34	114.51	54.13	82.30	0.7281
15.4405 041	Insulation, fiberglass, 4" valve, aluminum jacket	EA	32.95	108.13	141.08	67.79	100.74	0.9119
15.4405 051	Insulation, fiberglass, 6" valve, aluminum jacket	EA	51.48	160.84	212.32	100.83	152.31	1.3564
15.4405 061	Insulation, fiberglass, 8" valve, aluminum jacket	EA	58.57	210.81	269.38	132.16	190.73	1.7778
15.4405 071	Insulation, fiberglass, 10" valve, aluminum jacket	EA	65.88	276.24	342.12	173.18	239.06	2.3296
15.4405 081	Insulation, fiberglass, 12" valve, aluminum jacket	EA	73.23	365.30	438.53	229.01	302.24	3.0806
15.4406 000	**PERMITS, TEST AND BALANCE:**							
	Note: Permits will equal approximately 3% of the HVAC. Testing will be approximately 5% of the equipment costs.							
15.4406 031	Balance	REG		90.88	90.88	56.97	56.97	0.7664
15.5500 000	**FIRE PROTECTION SYSTEMS:**							
	Note: Remember to add alarm and valve riser for each fire sprinkler system.							
15.5501 000	**FIRE PROTECTION, EXPOSED SYSTEM, WET, PLACED, NORMAL HAZARD:**							
15.5501 011	Fire protection sprinklers, exposed, wet, 5,000 SF, normal hazard	SF	2.35	2.42	4.77	1.60	3.95	0.0261
15.5501 021	Fire protection sprinklers, exposed, wet, 6,000-15,000 SF, normal hazard	SF	1.96	1.76	3.72	1.16	3.12	0.0190
15.5501 031	Fire protection sprinklers, exposed, wet, over 15,000 SF, normal hazard	SF	1.88	1.67	3.55	1.10	2.98	0.0180
15.5502 000	**FIRE PROTECTION,, CONCEALED SYSTEM, WET, PLACED, NORMAL HAZARD:**							
	Note:							
	For high hazard, add 30% to the material costs and 15% to the labor costs							
	For light hazard deduct 15% from the material costs							
	For concealed systems in rooms less than 2,500 SF, add 40% to the total costs							
15.5502 011	Fire protection sprinklers, concealed, wet, 5,000 SF, normal hazard	SF	3.64	2.62	6.26	1.73	5.37	0.0283
15.5502 021	Fire protection sprinklers, concealed, wet, 6,000-15,000 SF, normal hazard	SF	3.20	1.95	5.15	1.29	4.49	0.0210
15.5502 031	Fire protection sprinklers, concealed, wet, over 15,000 SF, normal hazard	SF	3.00	1.83	4.83	1.21	4.21	0.0197

Division 15 CSI #	15 - MECHANICAL Description	Unit	Material	Union Install	Union Total	Open Install	Open Total	Unit Man-Hrs
15.5502 000	**FIRE PROTECTION,, CONCEALED SYSTEM, WET, PLACED, NORMAL HAZARD: (Cont.)**							
15.5502 041	Add for testing systems	HEAD	3.08	2.42	5.50	1.60	4.68	0.0261
15.5503 000	**FIRE PROTECTION, EXPOSED SYSTEM, WET, PER HEAD:**							
15.5503 011	Fire protection sprinklers, exposed, wet, small	HEAD	164.20	193.42	357.62	127.89	292.09	2.0863
15.5503 021	Fire protection sprinklers, exposed, wet, medium	HEAD	152.02	181.34	333.36	119.90	271.92	1.9560
15.5503 031	Fire protection sprinklers, exposed, wet, large	HEAD	138.21	164.83	303.04	108.99	247.20	1.7779
15.5504 000	**FIRE PROTECTION, CONCEALED SYSTEM, WET, PER HEAD:**							
15.5504 011	Fire protection sprinklers, concealed, wet, small	HEAD	182.50	217.60	400.10	143.88	326.38	2.3471
15.5504 021	Fire protection sprinklers, concealed, wet, medium	HEAD	172.29	205.51	377.80	135.88	308.17	2.2167
15.5504 031	Fire protection sprinklers, concealed, wet, large	HEAD	158.52	189.04	347.56	124.99	283.51	2.0390
15.5505 000	**FIRE WATER CONNECTION FEES (WHERE APPLICABLE):**							
15.5505 011	Fire water, 4" connection	EA	3,639.89	4,934.27	8,574.16	3,262.55	6,902.44	53.2226
15.5505 021	Fire water, 6" connection	EA	4,216.24	5,714.52	9,930.76	3,778.45	7,994.69	61.6387
15.5505 031	Fire water, 8" connection	EA	5,439.05	7,374.06	12,813.11	4,875.74	10,314.79	79.5390
15.5506 000	**STANDPIPE, DRY, 6" DIAMETER, HOOK UP:**							
15.5506 011	Standpipe connection, pumper, 6"	EA	1,734.93	492.35	2,227.28	325.54	2,060.47	5.3106
15.5506 021	Standpipe connection, pumper, 4"	EA	1,652.59	479.45	2,132.04	317.01	1,969.60	5.1715
15.5506 031	Gate valve, 3 x 2-1/2 PB	EA	286.75	99.26	386.01	65.63	352.38	1.0706
15.5506 041	Roof manifold, with valves	EA	1,059.14	639.27	1,698.41	422.69	1,481.83	6.8954
15.5507 000	**STANDPIPE, WET, HOSE RACK STATION:**							
	Note: The following prices include 75' hose, cabinet, angle valves, flow switch and pipe.							
15.5507 011	Standpipe, wet, 2-1/2", per floor	EA	2,282.73	711.17	2,993.90	470.23	2,752.96	7.6709
15.5507 021	Standpipe, 4", wet, per floor	EA	2,445.65	787.36	3,233.01	520.60	2,966.25	8.4927
15.5507 031	Standpipe, 6", wet, per floor	EA	2,805.01	843.04	3,648.05	557.42	3,362.43	9.0933
15.5508 000	**ALARM & VALVE RISERS:**							
	Note: The following items should be added to each fire sprinkler system.							
15.5508 011	Alarm & valve riser, 4"	EA	2,613.36	2,002.60	4,615.96	1,324.12	3,937.48	21.6007
15.5508 021	Alarm & valve riser, 6"	EA	3,100.41	2,051.44	5,151.85	1,356.42	4,456.83	22.1275
15.5508 031	Alarm & valve riser, 8"	EA	3,738.03	2,197.98	5,936.01	1,453.31	5,191.34	23.7081
15.5509 000	**FIRE PUMPS, ELECTRIC:**							
15.5509 011	Fire pump, electric, 250 GPM @ 40 PSI	EA	18,102.58	4,171.95	22,274.53	2,758.50	20,861.08	45.0000
15.5509 021	Fire pump, electric, 500 GPM @ 100 PSI	EA	24,404.24	4,450.08	28,854.32	2,942.40	27,346.64	48.0000
15.5509 031	Fire pump, electric, 750 GPM @ 100 PSI	EA	26,367.52	5,006.34	31,373.86	3,310.20	29,677.72	54.0000
15.5509 041	Fire pump, electric, 1000 GPM @ 150 PSI	EA	50,243.98	5,562.60	55,806.58	3,678.00	53,921.98	60.0000
15.5509 051	Fire pump, electric, 1500 GPM @ 150 PSI	EA	52,587.32	7,416.80	60,004.12	4,904.00	57,491.32	80.0000
15.5509 061	Fire pump, electric, 2000 GPM @ 150 PSI	EA	55,553.35	9,641.84	65,195.19	6,375.20	61,928.55	104.0000
15.5509 071	Fire pump, electric, 3000 GPM @ 150 PSI	EA	73,845.95	11,496.04	85,341.99	7,601.20	81,447.15	124.0000
15.5509 081	Jockey pump, 10 hp	EA	2,501.66	741.68	3,243.34	490.40	2,992.06	8.0000
15.5510 000	**FIRE PUMPS, DIESEL:**							
15.5510 011	Fire pump, diesel, 500 GPM @ 100 PSI	EA	50,476.16	4,635.50	55,111.66	3,065.00	53,541.16	50.0000
15.5510 021	Fire pump, diesel, 750 GPM @ 100 PSI	EA	57,432.19	5,191.76	62,623.95	3,432.80	60,864.99	56.0000
15.5510 031	Fire pump, diesel, 1000 GPM @ 150 PSI	EA	82,279.79	6,118.86	88,398.65	4,045.80	86,325.59	66.0000
15.5510 041	Fire pump, diesel, 1500 GPM @ 150 PSI	EA	93,014.65	7,602.22	100,616.87	5,026.60	98,041.25	82.0000
15.5510 051	Fire pump, diesel, 2000 GPM @ 150 PSI	EA	97,355.06	10,012.68	107,367.74	6,620.40	103,975.46	108.0000
15.5510 061	Fire pump, diesel, 3000 GPM @ 150 PSI	EA	177,120.51	13,164.82	190,285.33	8,704.60	185,825.11	142.0000
15.5511 000	**BACKFLOW PREVENTER, OUTSIDE STEM & YOKE, UL APPROVED:**							
15.5511 011	Back flow preventer, outside stem & yoke, UL approved, 2-1/2"	EA	4,539.84	574.90	5,114.74	380.13	4,919.97	6.2011
15.5511 021	Back flow preventer, outside stem & yoke, UL approved, 3"	EA	4,821.66	693.12	5,514.78	458.29	5,279.95	7.4762
15.5511 031	Back flow preventer, outside stem & yoke, UL approved, 4"	EA	6,250.67	1,095.68	7,346.35	724.47	6,975.14	11.8184
15.5511 041	Back flow preventer, outside stem & yoke, UL approved, 6"	EA	8,485.31	1,285.99	9,771.30	850.30	9,335.61	13.8711
15.5511 051	Back flow preventer, outside stem & yoke, UL approved, 8"	EA	13,305.17	1,484.40	14,789.57	981.49	14,286.66	16.0112
15.5511 061	Back flow preventer, outside stem & yoke, UL approved, 10"	EA	15,340.23	2,237.21	17,577.44	1,479.25	16,819.48	24.1313
15.5512 000	**FIRE PROTECTION, HALON SYSTEM, 8' CEILING & 1" RAISED FLOOR:**							
15.5512 011	Fire protection, halon, 200 SF, 8' ceiling, 1" floor	SF	103.67		103.67		103.67	
15.5512 021	Fire protection, halon, 500 SF, 8' ceiling, 1" floor	SF	38.35		38.35		38.35	
15.5512 031	Fire protection, halon, 600 SF, 8' ceiling, 1" floor	SF	37.34		37.34		37.34	
15.5512 041	Fire protection, halon, 700 SF, 8' ceiling, 1" floor	SF	35.27		35.27		35.27	
15.5512 051	Fire protection, halon, 1,000 SF, 8' ceiling, 1" floor	SF	31.08		31.08		31.08	
15.5512 061	Fire protection, halon, 2,000 SF, 8' ceiling, 1" floor	SF	23.81		23.81		23.81	
15.5512 071	Fire protection, halon, 2,500 SF, 8' ceiling, 1" floor	SF	21.23		21.23		21.23	
15.5512 081	Fire protection, halon, 3,000 SF, 8' ceiling, 1" floor	SF	19.17		19.17		19.17	
15.5512 091	Fire protection, halon, 4,000 SF, 8' ceiling, 1" floor	SF	17.64		17.64		17.64	

Division 15 CSI #	15 - MECHANICAL Description	Unit	Material	Union Install	Union Total	Open Install	Open Total	Unit Man-Hrs
15.5512 000	**FIRE PROTECTION, HALON SYSTEM, 8' CEILING & 1" RAISED FLOOR: (Cont.)**							
15.5512 101	Fire protection, halon, 5,000 SF, 8' ceiling, 1" floor	SF	16.06		16.06		16.06	
15.5512 111	Fire protection, halon, 10,000 SF, 8' ceiling, 1" floor	SF	14.53		14.53		14.53	
15.5512 121	Fire protection, halon, 20,000 SF, 8' ceiling, 1" floor	SF	12.46		12.46		12.46	
15.5513 000	**FIRE PROTECTION, CHEMETRON SYSTEM, FM-200:**							
15.5513 011	Fire protection, chemetron, raised floor, to 5,000 SF	CF	6.38		6.38		6.38	
15.5513 021	Fire protection, chemetron, raised floor, to 10,000 SF	CF	5.49		5.49		5.49	
15.5513 031	Fire protection, chemetron, non raised floor, to 10,000 SF	CF	4.58		4.58		4.58	
15.5515 000	**FIRE PROTECTION, IN PLACE, TYPICAL PER SQUARE FOOT:**							
15.5515 011	Fire protection, housing high rise	SF	1.88	1.57	3.45	1.04	2.92	0.0169
15.5515 021	Fire protection, auditorium/theater	SF	2.82	2.42	5.24	1.60	4.42	0.0261
15.5515 031	Fire protection, college/school	SF	2.02	1.75	3.77	1.16	3.18	0.0189
15.5515 041	Fire protection, garage, underground	SF	1.38	1.17	2.55	.77	2.15	0.0126
15.5515 051	Fire protection, hospital	SF	2.97	2.53	5.50	1.67	4.64	0.0273
15.5515 061	Fire protection, government building	SF	2.46	2.07	4.53	1.37	3.83	0.0223
15.5515 071	Fire protection, manufacturing	SF	1.49	1.32	2.81	.87	2.36	0.0142
15.5515 081	Fire protection, medical clinic	SF	2.02	1.72	3.74	1.13	3.15	0.0185
15.5515 091	Fire protection, office, low rise	SF	1.98	1.67	3.65	1.10	3.08	0.0180
15.5515 111	Fire protection, office, high rise	SF	2.17	1.84	4.01	1.22	3.39	0.0199
15.5515 121	Fire protection, warehouse	SF	1.38	1.17	2.55	.77	2.15	0.0126
15.5515 131	Fire protection, shopping center, 1 story	SF	1.75	1.52	3.27	1.01	2.76	0.0164
15.5515 141	Fire protection, shopping center, quality	SF	2.02	1.72	3.74	1.13	3.15	0.0185
15.5515 151	Fire protection, hotel, low rise	SF	2.11	1.82	3.93	1.20	3.31	0.0196
15.5515 161	Fire protection, hotel, mid rise	SF	2.25	1.91	4.16	1.26	3.51	0.0206
15.5515 171	Fire protection, hotel, high rise	SF	2.22	1.90	4.12	1.26	3.48	0.0205
15.5515 181	Fire protection, hotel, high, deluxe	SF	2.30	2.00	4.30	1.32	3.62	0.0216
15.5515 191	Fire protection, hotel, high, luxury	SF	2.46	2.10	4.56	1.39	3.85	0.0227

SAYLOR
Publications, Inc.

2010

residential square foot building costs

18th ANNUAL EDITION SAYLOR PUBLICATIONS, INC.

18th Annual Edition

$44.95

over 200 pages!

Square Foot Costs by:
- Building Class
- Size
- Exterior Wall
- Number of Stories

Six Building Classes:

- Economy
- Fair
- Standard
- Custom
- Estate
- Luxury

Location Multipliers
Special Landscape Cost Section
Special Features with extra items

FUNCTIONAL ASSEMBLIES SECTION:
Use this section to "build-up" the cost of unique dwellings or buildings that have special structural requirements or non-standard design.

ELECTRICAL
TABLE OF CONTENTS

SECTION	DESCRIPTION
16.0000	ELECTRICAL
16.0100	TOTAL ELECTRICAL WORK, BUILDINGS
16.1000	ELECTRICAL COST, IN-PLACE
.1100	Main Switchboards
.1200	Distribution Panels
.1300	Transformers
.1400	Raceway & Wire, Combined
.1500	Underfloor Distribution Systems
.1600	Lighting Fixtures, In-place
.1700	Branch Circuit Runs, Special Purpose
.1800	Signal & Communications Systems
.1900	Branch Circuit Outlets & Devices
.1950	Fees, Permits & Testing
16.2000	EQUIPMENT, UNIT SUBSTATIONS
16.2100	EQUIPMENT, SWITCHGEAR & TRANSFORMERS
.2200	High Voltage Transformers
.2300	Service Sections
.2400	Combination Service & Distribution Swbds
.3000	Motor Control Centers
.4000	Panelboards, 600v Max.
.4100	Transformers, Dry, Low Voltage
.4200	Panelboards, 120/240v
.4300	Load Centers
.4400	Plug-in Circuit Breakers
16.4500	SPECIAL GEAR
.4501	Emergency Generators
.4502	Transfer Switches
.4504	Uninterrupted power
16.5000	PVC, RSC, IMC & AL RACEWAY
.5100	Pvc, Rsc, Imc & Al Conduit Term, Elbows
16.5200	EMT RACEWAY, TERMINATIONS & ELBOWS
16.5300	ENT, MI CABLE & TERMINATIONS
16.5400	SPECIALTY FITTINGS, EXPLOSION-PROOF
16.5500	UNDERFLOOR & FLUSH TRENCH DUCT, CABLE TRAY
16.5600	STEEL GUTTERS-PULL BOXES & HANGERS
16.5700	SPECIAL RACEWAY ASSEMBLY SYSTEMS
16.5800	CONDUCTOR ONLY
16.5900	BUSWAYS
16.5950	RACEWAY & WIRE COMBINED
16.6000	LIGHTING FIXTURES
16.7000	ELECTRIC & SIGNAL DEVICES
16.7100	COMMUNICATION, INTERCOM, PA
16.7200	SPECIAL HOSPITAL SYSTEMS
16.7500	SOFT WIRE SYSTEMS, 3 WIRE
16.7600	ENERGY & BUILDING MANAGEMENT SYSTEMS
16.7700	TESTING

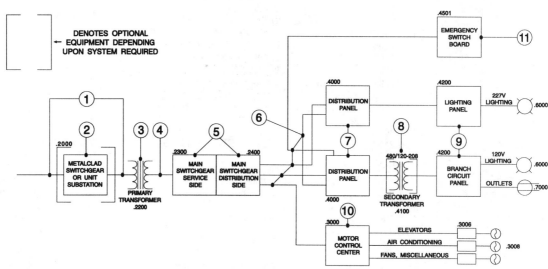

1. CONDUIT BY CONTRACTOR - WIRE BY UTILITY COMPANY
2. MAIN SWITCHGEAR FOR HIGH VOLTAGE DELIVERY
3. PRIMARY TRANSFORMER BY UTILITY UNLESS INCLUDED IN OWNER'S UNIT SUBSTATION
4. SECONDARY CONDUIT AND WIRE BY CONTRACTOR
5. MAIN SWITCHGEAR FOR SECTION BREAKDOWN, SEE DIAGRAM #2
6. CONDUIT AND WIRE OR BUSS DUCT (FEEDERS)
7. DISTRIBUTION PANELS FROM MAIN SWITCHGEAR FOR DISTRIBUTION DIRECT TO POWER AND/OR LIGHTING OR TO BRANCH CIRCUIT AND/OR LIGHTING PANELS
8. SECONDARY TRANSFORMERS - AS REQUIRED
9. LIGHTING OR BRANCH CIRCUIT PANELS
10. MOTOR CONTROL CENTER - IF REQUIRED
11. EMERGENCY GENERATOR WITH TRANSFER SWITCH

NOTE: FOR SMALL STRUCTURES THE MAIN SWITCHGEAR MAY SERVE AS THE MAIN DISTRIBUTION PANEL, BRANCH CIRCUIT PANEL, AND MOTOR CONTROL CENTER. IN SUCH CASES, THE CURRENT IS BROUGHT FROM THE UTILITY AT USEABLE VOLTAGES ALREADY TRANSFORMED.

DIAGRAM NUMBER ONE

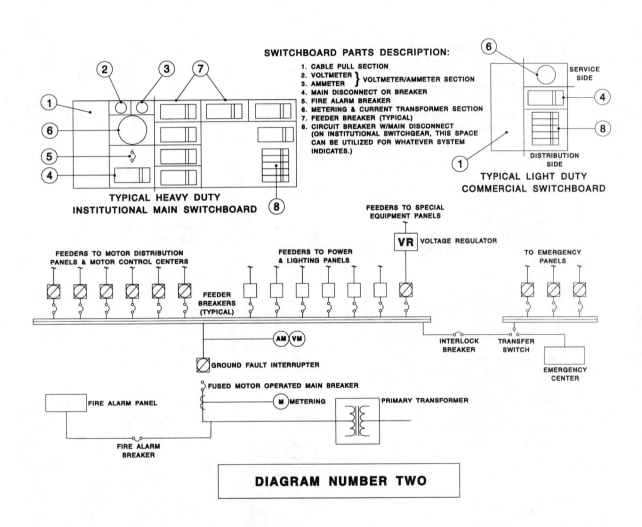

SWITCHBOARD PARTS DESCRIPTION:

1. CABLE PULL SECTION
2. VOLTMETER } VOLTMETER/AMMETER SECTION
3. AMMETER
4. MAIN DISCONNECT OR BREAKER
5. FIRE ALARM BREAKER
6. METERING & CURRENT TRANSFORMER SECTION
7. FEEDER BREAKER (TYPICAL)
8. CIRCUIT BREAKER W/MAIN DISCONNECT
   (ON INSTITUTIONAL SWITCHGEAR, THIS SPACE
   CAN BE UTILIZED FOR WHATEVER SYSTEM
   INDICATES.)

TYPICAL HEAVY DUTY
INSTITUTIONAL MAIN SWITCHBOARD

SERVICE SIDE

DISTRIBUTION SIDE

TYPICAL LIGHT DUTY
COMMERCIAL SWITCHBOARD

FEEDERS TO SPECIAL
EQUIPMENT PANELS

VR VOLTAGE REGULATOR

FEEDERS TO MOTOR DISTRIBUTION
PANELS & MOTOR CONTROL CENTERS

FEEDERS TO POWER
& LIGHTING PANELS

TO EMERGENCY
PANELS

FEEDER
BREAKERS
(TYPICAL)

AM VM

GROUND FAULT INTERRUPTER

INTERLOCK
BREAKER

TRANSFER
SWITCH

EMERGENCY
CENTER

FUSED MOTOR OPERATED MAIN BREAKER

FIRE ALARM PANEL

M METERING

PRIMARY TRANSFORMER

FIRE ALARM
BREAKER

DIAGRAM NUMBER TWO

Division 16 CSI #	16 - ELECTRICAL Description	Unit	Material	Union Install	Union Total	Open Install	Open Total	Unit Man-Hrs
16.0000 000	ELECTRICAL WORK:							
16.0101 000	TOTAL ELECTRICAL WORK, BUILDINGS:							
16.0101 011	Electrical work, Commercial stores	SF	3.80	8.71	12.51	6.32	10.12	0.0798
16.0101 015	Electrical work, Commercial stores, quality retail	SF	8.11	13.94	22.05	10.12	18.23	0.1277
16.0101 021	Electrical work, Market buildings	SF	4.02	9.05	13.07	6.57	10.59	0.0829
16.0101 031	Electrical work, Recreational buildings	SF	13.40	10.17	23.57	7.39	20.79	0.0932
16.0101 041	Electrical work, Schools, elementary & high	SF	11.02	23.86	34.88	17.33	28.35	0.2186
16.0101 051	Electrical work, College buildings	SF	12.55	15.04	27.59	10.92	23.47	0.1378
16.0101 055	Electrical work, College dormitory	SF	6.66	9.55	16.21	6.94	13.60	0.0875
16.0101 061	Electrical work, Clinical-mob	SF	11.26	24.66	35.92	17.91	29.17	0.2260
16.0101 071	Electrical work, Hospitals, full service	SF	18.97	34.82	53.79	25.29	44.26	0.3191
16.0101 081	Electrical work, Office buildings, high rise, 4 - 7 story	SF	6.63	14.89	21.52	10.81	17.44	0.1364
16.0101 085	Electrical work, Office buildings, high rise, 8 - 30 story	SF	5.86	12.00	17.86	8.72	14.58	0.1100
16.0101 091	Electrical work, Warehouses	SF	2.13	4.71	6.84	3.42	5.55	0.0432
16.0101 101	Electrical work, Parking lots, 2.5 foot candles	SF	1.32	1.40	2.72	1.01	2.33	0.0128
16.0101 111	Electrical work, Garages, 5 foot candles	SF	1.85	2.11	3.96	1.53	3.38	0.0193
16.0101 121	Electrical work, Assembly buildings, light industrial	SF	7.40	9.21	16.61	6.69	14.09	0.0844
16.0101 131	Electrical work, Laboratory buildings, wet science	SF	23.63	26.94	50.57	19.57	43.20	0.2469
16.0101 141	Electrical work, City hall	SF	15.48	21.38	36.86	15.53	31.01	0.1959
16.0101 151	Electrical work, Hotel, low rise	SF	3.96	8.00	11.96	5.81	9.77	0.0733
16.0101 161	Electrical work, Hotel, mid rise	SF	5.26	9.72	14.98	7.06	12.32	0.0891
16.0101 171	Electrical work, Hotel, high rise, first class	SF	7.10	10.74	17.84	7.80	14.90	0.0984
16.0101 181	Electrical work, Hotel, high rise, deluxe	SF	8.11	11.94	20.05	8.67	16.78	0.1094
16.0101 191	Electrical work, Hotel, high rise, luxury	SF	11.03	13.97	25.00	10.15	21.18	0.1280
16.0101 201	Electrical work, Housing, low rise	SF	2.15	4.88	7.03	3.54	5.69	0.0447
16.0101 211	Electrical work, Housing, high rise	SF	4.04	6.97	11.01	5.06	9.10	0.0639
16.1000 000	ELECTRICAL COST, IN-PLACE, PRELIMINARY ESTIMATES:							
16.1001 000	SELECTOR SWITCHES:							
16.1001 011	Selector switch, 3-way, high voltage	EA	7,398.03	1,741.58	9,139.61	1,264.89	8,662.92	15.9588
16.1001 021	Selector switch, 4-way, high voltage	EA	7,942.04	1,912.33	9,854.37	1,388.90	9,330.94	17.5234
16.1002 000	HIGH VOLTAGE UNIT SUBSTATIONS:							
16.1002 011	Unit substation, high voltage, 150kva	EA	47,532.67	5,715.97	53,248.64	4,151.45	51,684.12	52.3776
16.1002 021	Unit substation, high voltage, 225kva	EA	55,982.90	7,144.96	63,127.86	5,189.31	61,172.21	65.4720
16.1002 031	Unit substation, high voltage, 300kva	EA	66,545.69	8,038.08	74,583.77	5,837.97	72,383.66	73.6560
16.1002 041	Unit substation, high voltage, 500kva	EA	80,277.37	10,717.44	90,994.81	7,783.97	88,061.34	98.2080
16.1002 051	Unit substation, high voltage, 750kva	EA	95,065.30	14,289.92	109,355.22	10,378.62	105,443.92	130.9440
16.1002 061	Unit substation, high voltage, 1000kva	EA	105,628.15	17,862.40	123,490.55	12,973.28	118,601.43	163.6800
16.1002 071	Unit substation, high voltage, 1500kva	EA	121,472.34	21,434.88	142,907.22	15,567.93	137,040.27	196.4160
16.1002 081	Unit substation, high voltage, 2000kva	EA	137,316.56	28,579.84	165,896.40	20,757.24	158,073.80	261.8880
16.1003 000	DISTRIBUTION TRANSFORMERS, PRIMARY:							
16.1003 011	Transformer, high voltage, 112.5kva	EA	17,378.76	2,857.98	20,236.74	2,075.72	19,454.48	26.1888
16.1003 021	Transformer, high voltage, 150kva	EA	20,275.11	3,215.23	23,490.34	2,335.19	22,610.30	29.4624
16.1003 031	Transformer, high voltage, 225kva	EA	29,580.12	4,822.85	34,402.97	3,502.78	33,082.90	44.1936
16.1003 041	Transformer, high voltage, 300kva	EA	37,178.88	5,358.72	42,537.60	3,891.98	41,070.86	49.1040
16.1003 051	Transformer, high voltage, 500kva	EA	47,869.30	6,251.84	54,121.14	4,540.65	52,409.95	57.2880
16.1003 061	Transformer, high voltage, 750kva	EA	55,365.31	7,144.96	62,510.27	5,189.31	60,554.62	65.4720
16.1003 071	Transformer, high voltage, 1000kva	EA	68,503.20	8,931.20	77,434.40	6,486.64	74,989.84	81.8400
16.1003 081	Transformer, high voltage, 1500kva	EA	78,820.14	10,717.44	89,537.58	7,783.97	86,604.11	98.2080
16.1003 091	Transformer, high voltage, 2000kva	EA	88,199.23	12,503.68	100,702.91	9,081.29	97,280.52	114.5760
16.1003 101	Transformer, high voltage, 2500kva	EA	101,798.93	14,289.92	116,088.85	10,378.62	112,177.55	130.9440
16.1003 111	Transformer, high voltage, 3000kva	EA	121,025.99	16,076.16	137,102.15	11,675.95	132,701.94	147.3120
16.1004 000	MAIN SWITCHGEAR, TO 600V, LIGHT COMMERCIAL:							
	Note: The following prices are based on average service amps.							
16.1004 011	Service enclosure with metering	AMP	1.11	.63	1.74	.46	1.57	0.0058
16.1004 021	Pull section	AMP	.50	.28	.78	.21	.71	0.0026
16.1004 031	Fire alarm circuit breaker	AMP	.23	.16	.39	.12	.35	0.0015
16.1004 041	Main disconnect	AMP	1.10	.59	1.69	.43	1.53	0.0054
16.1004 051	Distribution circuit breaker to 150% service	AMP	3.48	1.89	5.37	1.37	4.85	0.0173
16.1004 061	Total average	AMP	6.58	3.51	10.09	2.55	9.13	0.0322

Division 16 CSI #	16 - ELECTRICAL Description	Unit	Material	Union Install	Union Total	Open Install	Open Total	Unit Man-Hrs
16.1005 000	**MAIN SWITCHGEAR, TO 600V, COMMERCIAL & SMALL INSTITUTIONAL:**							
	Note: The following prices are based on average service amps.							
16.1005 011	Service enclosure with metering	AMP	4.43	2.38	6.81	1.73	6.16	0.0218
16.1005 021	Pull section	AMP	1.11	.59	1.70	.43	1.54	0.0054
16.1005 031	Fire alarm circuit breaker	AMP	.32	.26	.58	.19	.51	0.0024
16.1005 041	Main disconnect	AMP	1.67	.89	2.56	.65	2.32	0.0082
16.1005 051	Distribution circuit breaker to 150% service	AMP	3.93	2.50	6.43	1.82	5.75	0.0229
16.1005 061	Total average	AMP	11.93	6.41	18.34	4.65	16.58	0.0587
16.1006 000	**MAIN SWITCHGEAR, TO 600V, LARGE COMMERCIAL & INSTITUTIONAL:**							
	Note: The following prices are based on average service amps.							
16.1006 011	Service enclosure with metering	AMP	3.90	2.01	5.91	1.46	5.36	0.0184
16.1006 021	Pull section	AMP	.73	.38	1.11	.28	1.01	0.0035
16.1006 031	Fire alarm circuit breaker	AMP	.06	.10	.16	.07	.13	0.0009
16.1006 041	Main disconnect	AMP	8.24	4.17	12.41	3.03	11.27	0.0382
16.1006 051	Distribution circuit breaker to 150% service	AMP	8.11	2.68	10.79	1.95	10.06	0.0246
16.1006 061	Ground fault system	AMP	.61	.28	.89	.21	.82	0.0026
16.1006 071	Customer option metering	AMP	.23	.26	.49	.19	.42	0.0024
16.1006 081	Total average	AMP	19.55	11.17	30.72	8.12	27.67	0.1024
16.1100 000	**MAIN SWITCHBOARDS, 600V, SERVICE & DISTRIBUTION:**							
16.1101 000	**MAIN SWITCHBOARDS, 600V, COMMERCIAL & LIGHT INSTITUTIONAL:**							
	Note: The following prices include service & distribution sides with average distribution and feeder breakers.							
16.1101 011	Main switchboard, 600v, 400a	EA	1,709.36	3,572.48	5,281.84	2,594.66	4,304.02	32.7360
16.1101 021	Main switchboard, 600v, 600a	EA	2,848.97	4,286.98	7,135.95	3,113.59	5,962.56	39.2832
16.1101 031	Main switchboard, 600v, 800a	EA	5,697.89	5,715.97	11,413.86	4,151.45	9,849.34	52.3776
16.1101 041	Main switchboard, 600v, 1200a	EA	7,977.08	6,430.46	14,407.54	4,670.38	12,647.46	58.9248
16.1101 051	Main switchboard, 600v, 1600a	EA	9,971.38	7,859.46	17,830.84	5,708.24	15,679.62	72.0192
16.1101 061	Main switchboard, 600v, 2000a	EA	11,395.88	9,824.32	21,220.20	7,135.30	18,531.18	90.0240
16.1101 071	Main switchboard, 600v, 2500a	EA	12,820.38	12,503.68	25,324.06	9,081.29	21,901.67	114.5760
16.1101 081	Main switchboard, 600v, 3000a	EA	15,669.39	17,862.40	33,531.79	12,973.28	28,642.67	163.6800
16.1102 000	**MAIN PANELS, 250V, LIGHT COMMERCIAL:**							
16.1102 011	Main panel. 250v, 100a	EA	482.14	1,250.37	1,732.51	908.13	1,390.27	11.4576
16.1102 021	Main panel, 250v, 150a	EA	723.26	1,607.62	2,330.88	1,167.59	1,890.85	14.7312
16.1102 031	Main panel, 250v, 225a	EA	964.41	2,143.49	3,107.90	1,556.79	2,521.20	19.6416
16.1102 041	Main panel, 250v, 400a	EA	1,446.54	3,215.23	4,661.77	2,335.19	3,781.73	29.4624
16.1102 051	Main panel, 250v, 600a	EA	2,410.92	3,751.10	6,162.02	2,724.39	5,135.31	34.3728
16.1102 061	Main panel, 250v, 800a	EA	3,616.42	4,286.98	7,903.40	3,113.59	6,730.01	39.2832
16.1102 071	Main panel, 250v, 1000a	EA	4,821.90	5,358.72	10,180.62	3,891.98	8,713.88	49.1040
16.1200 000	**DISTRIBUTION PANELS TO 600V:**							
16.1201 000	**DISTRIBUTION, POWER PANELS, TO 600V, WITHOUT MAINS:**							
	Note: The following prices include breakers installed in typical distribution by connected breaker load.							
16.1201 011	Power panel, 600v, 100a & circuit breaker	EA	1,257.88	1,107.51	2,365.39	804.37	2,062.25	10.1485
16.1201 021	Power panel, 600v, 225a & circuit breaker	EA	2,012.58	1,339.68	3,352.26	973.00	2,985.58	12.2760
16.1201 031	Power panel, 600v, 400a & circuit breaker	EA	3,018.91	1,786.24	4,805.15	1,297.33	4,316.24	16.3680
16.1201 041	Power panel, 600v, 800a & circuit breaker	EA	4,025.21	2,857.98	6,883.19	2,075.72	6,100.93	26.1888
16.1201 051	Power panel, 600v, 1200a & circuit breaker	EA	5,031.56	4,286.98	9,318.54	3,113.59	8,145.15	39.2832
16.1201 061	Power panel, 600v, 1600a & circuit breaker	EA	6,289.42	5,715.97	12,005.39	4,151.45	10,440.87	52.3776
16.1201 071	Power panel, 600v, 2000a & circuit breaker	EA	7,547.30	7,144.96	14,692.26	5,189.31	12,736.61	65.4720
16.1201 081	Power panel, 600v, 3000a & circuit breaker	EA	11,320.99	9,824.32	21,145.31	7,135.30	18,456.29	90.0240
16.1201 091	Power panel, 600v, 4000a & circuit breaker	EA	13,836.81	12,503.68	26,340.49	9,081.29	22,918.10	114.5760
16.1202 000	**BRANCH CIRCUIT PANELS, TO 600V, COMMERCIAL:**							
16.1202 011	Panelboard, 600v, 100a & circuit breaker	EA	733.69	893.12	1,626.81	648.66	1,382.35	8.1840
16.1202 021	Panelboard, 600v, 150a & circuit breaker	EA	1,027.20	1,071.74	2,098.94	778.40	1,805.60	9.8208
16.1202 031	Panelboard, 600v, 225a & circuit breaker	EA	1,247.38	1,250.37	2,497.75	908.13	2,155.51	11.4576
16.1202 041	Panelboard, 600v, 400a & circuit breaker	EA	1,761.02	1,428.99	3,190.01	1,037.86	2,798.88	13.0944
16.1203 000	**BRANCH CIRCUIT PANELS, TO 600V, INSTITUTIONAL:**							
16.1203 011	Panelboard, 600v, 100a & circuit breaker	EA	1,352.93	1,071.74	2,424.67	778.40	2,131.33	9.8208
16.1203 021	Panelboard, 600v, 150a & circuit breaker	EA	1,758.89	1,250.37	3,009.26	908.13	2,667.02	11.4576
16.1203 031	Panelboard, 600v, 225a & circuit breaker	EA	2,074.56	1,518.30	3,592.86	1,102.73	3,177.29	13.9128
16.1203 041	Panelboard, 600v, 400a & circuit breaker	EA	2,976.58	1,786.24	4,762.82	1,297.33	4,273.91	16.3680

Division 16 CSI #	16 - ELECTRICAL Description	Unit	Material	Union Install	Union Total	Open Install	Open Total	Unit Man-Hrs
16.1300 000	TRANSFORMERS:							
16.1301 000	DISTRIBUTION TRANSFORMERS, LIGHT/POWER TO 600V:							
16.1301 011	Transformer, 600v, 9kva	EA	2,007.16	535.87	2,543.03	389.20	2,396.36	4.9104
16.1301 021	Transformer, 600v, 15kva	EA	2,716.78	803.81	3,520.59	583.80	3,300.58	7.3656
16.1301 031	Transformer, 600v, 30kva	EA	3,474.43	1,571.47	5,045.90	1,141.34	4,615.77	14.4000
16.1301 041	Transformer, 600v, 45 kva	EA	3,718.10	1,746.08	5,464.18	1,268.16	4,986.26	16.0000
16.1301 051	Transformer, 600v, 75kva	EA	5,116.13	2,500.74	7,616.87	1,816.26	6,932.39	22.9152
16.1301 061	Transformer, 600v, 112.5kva	EA	6,808.06	2,857.98	9,666.04	2,075.72	8,883.78	26.1888
16.1301 071	Transformer, 600v, 150kva	EA	8,893.52	3,036.61	11,930.13	2,205.46	11,098.98	27.8256
16.1301 081	Transformer, 600v, 225kva	EA	11,858.07	4,465.60	16,323.67	3,243.32	15,101.39	40.9200
16.1301 091	Transformer, 600v, 300kva	EA	15,205.06	5,715.97	20,921.03	4,151.45	19,356.51	52.3776
16.1301 101	Transformer, 600v, 500kva	EA	24,098.65	6,877.02	30,975.67	4,994.71	29,093.36	63.0168
16.1301 111	Transformer, 600v, 750kva	EA	39,160.36	7,144.96	46,305.32	5,189.31	44,349.67	65.4720
16.1301 121	Transformer, 600v, 1000kva	EA	47,241.07	8,931.20	56,172.27	6,486.64	53,727.71	81.8400
16.1301 131	Transformer, 600v, 1500kva	EA	72,068.27	10,717.44	82,785.71	7,783.97	79,852.24	98.2080
16.1301 141	Transformer, 600v, 2000kva	EA	83,840.42	12,503.68	96,344.10	9,081.29	92,921.71	114.5760
16.1301 151	Transformer, 600v, 2500kva	EA	99,632.26	14,289.92	113,922.18	10,378.62	110,010.88	130.9440
16.1301 161	Transformer, 600v, 3000kva	EA	113,988.49	16,076.16	130,064.65	11,675.95	125,664.44	147.3120
16.1302 000	MOTOR CONTROL CENTERS, 600V, 22,000 AMPERE INTERRUPT CAPACITY:							
16.1302 011	Motor control center, 100a section	EA	1,455.44	535.87	1,991.31	389.20	1,844.64	4.9104
16.1302 021	Motor control center, 225a section	EA	1,940.59	803.81	2,744.40	583.80	2,524.39	7.3656
16.1302 031	Motor control center, 400a section	EA	2,425.76	893.12	3,318.88	648.66	3,074.42	8.1840
16.1302 041	Motor control center, 800a section	EA	2,910.96	1,071.74	3,982.70	778.40	3,689.36	9.8208
16.1302 051	Motor control center, 1200a section	EA	3,881.27	1,428.99	5,310.26	1,037.86	4,919.13	13.0944
16.1302 061	Motor control center, 1600a section	EA	4,829.02	1,786.24	6,615.26	1,297.33	6,126.35	16.3680
16.1302 071	Combination starter, size 1	EA	1,160.49	468.89	1,629.38	340.55	1,501.04	4.2966
16.1302 081	Combination starter, size 2	EA	1,437.27	669.84	2,107.11	486.50	1,923.77	6.1380
16.1302 091	Combination starter, size 3	EA	1,939.62	1,116.40	3,056.02	810.83	2,750.45	10.2300
16.1302 101	Combination starter, size 4	EA	3,546.61	1,786.24	5,332.85	1,297.33	4,843.94	16.3680
16.1302 111	Combination starter, size 5	EA	12,479.26	2,857.98	15,337.24	2,075.72	14,554.98	26.1888
16.1302 112	Combination starter, size 6	EA	4,151.57	3,990.24	8,141.81	2,898.07	7,049.64	36.5641
16.1302 113	Combination starter, size 7	EA	5,411.83	5,201.50	10,613.33	3,777.79	9,189.62	47.6633
16.1303 000	EMERGENCY GENERATORS:							
16.1303 011	Emergency generator, to 30kw	EA	29,800.45	3,572.48	33,372.93	2,594.66	32,395.11	32.7360
16.1303 021	Emergency generator, to 60kw	EA	35,564.33	5,358.72	40,923.05	3,891.98	39,456.31	49.1040
16.1303 031	Emergency generator, to 100kw	EA	50,806.23	7,144.96	57,951.19	5,189.31	55,995.54	65.4720
16.1303 041	Emergency generator, to 150kw	EA	60,967.51	8,931.20	69,898.71	6,486.64	67,454.15	81.8400
16.1303 051	Emergency generator, to 200kw	EA	71,128.71	10,717.44	81,846.15	7,783.97	78,912.68	98.2080
16.1303 061	Emergency generator, to 400kw	EA	147,338.04	12,503.68	159,841.72	9,081.29	156,419.33	114.5760
16.1303 071	Emergency generator, to 600kw	EA	228,628.09	14,289.92	242,918.01	10,378.62	239,006.71	130.9440
16.1303 081	Emergency generator, to 750kw	EA	320,079.28	17,862.40	337,941.68	12,973.28	333,052.56	163.6800
16.1303 091	Emergency generator, to 1000kw	EA	367,989.06	21,434.88	389,423.94	15,567.93	383,556.99	196.4160
16.1304 000	AUTO TRANSFER SWITCHES:							
16.1304 011	Auto transfer switch, to 30a	EA	7,002.56	357.25	7,359.81	259.47	7,262.03	3.2736
16.1304 021	Auto transfer switch, to 70a	EA	7,083.14	535.87	7,619.01	389.20	7,472.34	4.9104
16.1304 031	Auto transfer switch, to 100a	EA	7,745.80	714.50	8,460.30	518.93	8,264.73	6.5472
16.1304 041	Auto transfer switch, to 150a	EA	8,249.78	893.12	9,142.90	648.66	8,898.44	8.1840
16.1304 051	Auto transfer switch, to 225a	EA	13,410.02	1,071.74	14,481.76	778.40	14,188.42	9.8208
16.1304 061	Auto transfer switch, to 400a	EA	15,042.86	1,428.99	16,471.85	1,037.86	16,080.72	13.0944
16.1304 071	Auto transfer switch, to 800a	EA	27,605.52	1,786.24	29,391.76	1,297.33	28,902.85	16.3680
16.1304 081	Auto transfer switch, to 1200a	EA	47,342.11	2,322.11	49,664.22	1,686.53	49,028.64	21.2784
16.1304 091	Auto transfer switch, to 1600a	EA	58,771.95	2,857.98	61,629.93	2,075.72	60,847.67	26.1888
16.1304 101	Auto transfer switch to 2000a	EA	61,216.30	3,214.97	64,431.27	2,335.00	63,551.30	29.4600
16.1400 000	RACEWAY & WIRE, COMBINED:							
16.1401 000	PVC & COPPER WIRE:							
16.1401 011	PVC & copper wire, to 30a	LF	3.53	3.76	7.29	2.73	6.26	0.0345
16.1401 021	PVC & copper wire, to 60a	LF	7.27	5.01	12.28	3.64	10.91	0.0459
16.1401 031	PVC & copper wire, to 100a	LF	13.75	10.73	24.48	7.79	21.54	0.0983
16.1401 041	PVC & copper wire, to 150a	LF	21.85	11.61	33.46	8.43	30.28	0.1064
16.1401 051	PVC & copper wire, to 225a	LF	44.16	14.30	58.46	10.38	54.54	0.1310
16.1401 061	PVC & copper wire, to 400a	LF	91.20	19.53	110.73	14.19	105.39	0.1790
16.1401 071	PVC & copper wire to 800a	LF	203.46	21.58	225.04	15.67	219.13	0.1977

Division 16 CSI #	16 - ELECTRICAL Description	Unit	Material	Union Install	Union Total	Open Install	Open Total	Unit Man-Hrs
16.1402 000	**EMT & COPPER WIRE:**							
16.1402 011	EMT & copper wire, to 30a	LF	3.05	7.15	10.20	5.19	8.24	0.0655
16.1402 021	EMT & copper wire, to 60a	LF	9.07	8.94	18.01	6.49	15.56	0.0819
16.1402 031	EMT & copper wire, to 100a	LF	21.38	10.28	31.66	7.47	28.85	0.0942
16.1402 041	EMT & copper wire, to 150a	LF	29.26	11.82	41.08	8.58	37.84	0.1083
16.1402 051	EMT & copper wire, to 225a	LF	56.46	14.86	71.32	10.80	67.26	0.1362
16.1403 000	**RSC & COPPER WIRE:**							
16.1403 011	RSC & copper wire, to 30a	LF	5.84	8.81	14.65	6.40	12.24	0.0807
16.1403 021	RSC & copper wire, to 60a	LF	11.16	10.80	21.96	7.85	19.01	0.0990
16.1403 031	RSC & copper wire, to 100a	LF	26.59	13.37	39.96	9.71	36.30	0.1225
16.1403 041	RSC & copper wire, to 150a	LF	36.93	15.19	52.12	11.03	47.96	0.1392
16.1403 051	RSC & copper wire, to 225a	LF	70.68	19.65	90.33	14.27	84.95	0.1801
16.1403 061	RSC & copper wire, to 400a	LF	141.96	30.31	172.27	22.01	163.97	0.2777
16.1403 071	RSC & copper wire to 800a	LF	318.10	38.52	356.62	27.98	346.08	0.3530
16.1404 000	**PVC & ALUMINUM WIRE:**							
	Note: Aluminum wire not recommended for under 100 amps.							
16.1404 011	PVC & aluminum wire, to 100a	LF	13.52	9.83	23.35	7.14	20.66	0.0901
16.1404 021	PVC & aluminum wire, to 150a	LF	19.21	11.17	30.38	8.12	27.33	0.1024
16.1404 031	PVC & aluminum wire, to 225a	LF	26.95	13.40	40.35	9.73	36.68	0.1228
16.1404 041	PVC & aluminum wire, to 400a	LF	34.66	16.09	50.75	11.68	46.34	0.1474
16.1405 000	**EMT & ALUMINUM WIRE:**							
16.1405 011	EMT & aluminum wire, to 100a	LF	16.06	8.04	24.10	5.84	21.90	0.0737
16.1405 021	EMT & aluminum wire, to 150a	LF	23.46	9.83	33.29	7.14	30.60	0.0901
16.1405 031	EMT & aluminum wire, to 225a	LF	32.24	11.61	43.85	8.43	40.67	0.1064
16.1405 041	EMT & aluminum wire, to 400a	LF	39.08	14.30	53.38	10.38	49.46	0.1310
16.1406 000	**RSC & ALUMINUM WIRE:**							
16.1406 011	RSC & aluminum wire, to 100a	LF	23.00	10.73	33.73	7.79	30.79	0.0983
16.1406 021	RSC & aluminum wire, to 150a	LF	32.61	14.30	46.91	10.38	42.99	0.1310
16.1406 031	RSC & aluminum wire, to 225a	LF	42.23	17.86	60.09	12.97	55.20	0.1637
16.1406 041	RSC & aluminum wire, to 400a	LF	56.03	26.80	82.83	19.47	75.50	0.2456
16.1500 000	**UNDERFLOOR DISTRIBUTION SYSTEMS:**							
16.1501 000	**UNDERFLOOR DUCT & ACCESSORIES:**							
16.1501 011	Underfloor duct, blank standard	LF	5.37	6.71	12.08	4.87	10.24	0.0615
16.1501 021	Underfloor duct, blank jumbo	LF	11.92	9.83	21.75	7.14	19.06	0.0901
16.1501 031	Underfloor duct, insert standard	LF	7.54	6.71	14.25	4.87	12.41	0.0615
16.1501 041	Underfloor duct, insert jumbo	LF	19.00	9.83	28.83	7.14	26.14	0.0901
16.1501 051	Underfloor duct, J-box, 1 way	EA	223.69	223.28	446.97	162.17	385.86	2.0460
16.1501 061	Underfloor duct, J-box, 2 way	EA	337.76	312.59	650.35	227.03	564.79	2.8644
16.1501 071	Underfloor duct, J-box, 3 way	EA	567.53	446.56	1,014.09	324.33	891.86	4.0920
16.1501 081	Underfloor duct, panel riser, standard	EA	104.02	357.25	461.27	259.47	363.49	3.2736
16.1501 091	Underfloor duct, panel riser, jumbo	EA	167.52	446.56	614.08	324.33	491.85	4.0920
16.1502 000	**CELLULAR FLOOR SYSTEMS:**							
16.1502 011	Bond-seal floor cell joints	SF						
16.1502 021	Flush trench duct, to 12"	LF	102.23	71.46	173.69	51.90	154.13	0.6548
16.1502 031	Flush trench duct, to 24"	LF	143.63	98.25	241.88	71.36	214.99	0.9003
16.1502 041	Flush trench duct, to 36"	LF	218.31	178.62	396.93	129.73	348.04	1.6368
16.1502 051	Flush trench ell, to 12"	EA	339.92	89.31	429.23	64.87	404.79	0.8184
16.1502 061	Flush trench ell, to 24"	EA	552.76	156.30	709.06	113.52	666.28	1.4322
16.1502 071	Flush trench ell, to 36"	EA	912.01	223.28	1,135.29	162.17	1,074.18	2.0460
16.1502 081	Flush trench tee, to 12"	EA	339.92	133.97	473.89	97.30	437.22	1.2276
16.1502 091	Flush trench tee, to 24"	EA	552.76	200.95	753.71	145.95	698.71	1.8414
16.1502 101	Flush trench tee, to 36"	EA	912.01	312.59	1,224.60	227.03	1,139.04	2.8644
16.1502 111	Flush trench riser, to 12"	EA	386.91	178.62	565.53	129.73	516.64	1.6368
16.1502 121	Flush trench riser, to 24"	EA	450.50	267.94	718.44	194.60	645.10	2.4552
16.1502 131	Flush trench riser, to 36"	EA	580.39	357.25	937.64	259.47	839.86	3.2736
16.1502 141	Flush trench duct, 3" grommet	EA	5.47	.14	5.61	.10	5.57	0.0013
16.1502 151	Flush trench duct, 6" grommet	EA	8.26	.33	8.59	.24	8.50	0.0030
16.1503 000	**FLOOR SYSTEM OUTLETS:**							
16.1503 011	Core drill, add afterset insert	EA	11.02	31.27	42.29	22.71	33.73	0.2865
16.1503 021	Flush outlet at insert, power	EA	51.05	31.27	82.32	22.71	73.76	0.2865
16.1503 031	Flush outlet at insert, signal	EA	44.18	17.86	62.04	12.97	57.15	0.1637
16.1503 041	Surface outlet at insert, power	EA	84.28	44.66	128.94	32.43	116.71	0.4092

Division 16 CSI #	16 - ELECTRICAL Description	Unit	Material	Union Install	Union Total	Open Install	Open Total	Unit Man-Hrs
16.1503 000	**FLOOR SYSTEM OUTLETS: (Cont.)**							
16.1503 051	Surface outlet at insert, signal	EA	75.95	35.73	111.68	25.95	101.90	0.3274
16.1503 061	Preset power/signal access box	EA	45.83	22.33	68.16	16.22	62.05	0.2046
16.1503 071	Add 110v duplex at access box	EA	15.11	22.33	37.44	16.22	31.33	0.2046
16.1600 000	**LIGHTING FIXTURES, IN-PLACE:**							
16.1601 000	**FIXTURES BY BUILDING TYPE:**							
16.1601 011	Fixtures, college, classroom, 70 foot candles	SF	3.63	1.70	5.33	1.24	4.87	0.0156
16.1601 021	Fixtures, store, commercial	SF	2.75	2.11	4.86	1.53	4.28	0.0193
16.1601 031	Fixtures, garage, commercial, 5 foot candles	SF	.04	.14	.18	.10	.14	0.0013
16.1601 041	Fixtures, hospital, general space 70 foot candles	SF	3.63	1.70	5.33	1.24	4.87	0.0156
16.1601 051	Fixtures, hospital, wards & rooms 50 foot candles	SF	1.62	1.08	2.70	.78	2.40	0.0099
16.1601 061	Fixtures, market, 70 foot candles	SF	2.42	1.70	4.12	1.24	3.66	0.0156
16.1601 071	Fixtures, light manufacturing, 100 foot candles	SF	2.75	1.67	4.42	1.21	3.96	0.0153
16.1601 081	Fixtures, office, general & high rise	SF	3.63	1.70	5.33	1.24	4.87	0.0156
16.1601 091	Fixtures, office, drafting, 100 foot candles	SF	5.61	2.25	7.86	1.63	7.24	0.0206
16.1601 101	Fixtures, elementary & high school, 70 foot candles	SF	3.04	1.48	4.52	1.08	4.12	0.0136
16.1601 111	Fixtures, recreational facility, 40 foot candles	SF	2.89	1.35	4.24	.98	3.87	0.0124
16.1601 121	Fixtures, warehouse, 20 foot candles	SF	.17	.27	.44	.20	.37	0.0025
16.1601 131	Fixtures, churches	SF	5.09	1.66	6.75	1.20	6.29	0.0152
16.1601 141	Fixtures, banks, 50 foot candles	SF	3.04	2.18	5.22	1.59	4.63	0.0200
16.1601 151	Fixtures, libraries, 70 foot candles	SF	4.77	2.12	6.89	1.54	6.31	0.0194
16.1601 161	Fixtures, motels & hotels	SF	.95	1.04	1.99	.75	1.70	0.0095
16.1602 000	**FIXTURES, COMMERCIAL, AVERAGE:**							
16.1602 011	Incandescent, surface, 100w	EA	102.53	75.92	178.45	55.14	157.67	0.6957
16.1602 021	Incandescent, surface, 150w	EA	108.24	84.85	193.09	61.62	169.86	0.7775
16.1602 031	Incandescent, surface, 200w	EA	125.31	98.25	223.56	71.36	196.67	0.9003
16.1602 041	Incandescent, recessed, 100w	EA	136.68	111.64	248.32	81.08	217.76	1.0230
16.1602 051	Incandescent, recessed, 150w	EA	148.08	116.11	264.19	84.33	232.41	1.0640
16.1602 061	Incandescent, recessed, 200w	EA	170.93	133.97	304.90	97.30	268.23	1.2276
16.1602 071	Mercury vapor, 100w fixture	EA	240.36	125.04	365.40	90.82	331.18	1.1458
16.1602 081	Mercury vapor, 175w fixture	EA	293.23	142.91	436.14	103.79	397.02	1.3095
16.1602 091	Mercury vapor, 250w fixture	EA	370.96	178.62	549.58	129.73	500.69	1.6368
16.1602 101	Mercury vapor, 400w fixture	EA	455.86	267.94	723.80	194.60	650.46	2.4552
16.1602 111	High pressure sodium/lucalux fixture, 100w	EA	319.09	133.97	453.06	97.30	416.39	1.2276
16.1602 121	High pressure sodium/lucalux fixture, 250w	EA	569.80	223.28	793.08	162.17	731.97	2.0460
16.1602 131	High pressure sodium/lucalux fixture, 400w	EA	740.79	357.25	1,098.04	259.47	1,000.26	3.2736
16.1602 141	Fluorescent strip, surface, 2 lamp, 4'	EA	63.80	66.98	130.78	48.65	112.45	0.6138
16.1602 151	Fluorescent strip, surface, 2 lamp, 8'	EA	77.43	98.25	175.68	71.36	148.79	0.9003
16.1602 161	Fluorescent, lens, surface, 2 lamp, 4'	EA	86.56	89.31	175.87	64.87	151.43	0.8184
16.1602 171	Fluorescent, lens, surface, 2 lamp, 8'	LF	170.93	125.04	295.97	90.82	261.75	1.1458
16.1602 181	Fluorescent, lens, recessed, 2'x2', 2 lamp	EA	132.15	89.31	221.46	64.87	197.02	0.8184
16.1602 191	Fluorescent, lens, recessed, 2'x4', 2 lamp	EA	141.34	89.31	230.65	64.87	206.21	0.8184
16.1602 201	Fluorescent, lens, recessed, 2'x4', 3 lamp	EA	148.08	89.31	237.39	64.87	212.95	0.8184
16.1602 211	Fluorescent, lens, recessed, 2'x4', 4 lamp	EA	182.32	89.31	271.63	64.87	247.19	0.8184
16.1602 221	Fluorescent, industrial, suspended, 2 lamp, 4'	EA	182.32	133.97	316.29	97.30	279.62	1.2276
16.1602 231	Fluorescent, industrial, suspended, 2 lamp, 8'	EA	296.27	178.62	474.89	129.73	426.00	1.6368
16.1602 241	Exit signs, surface mounted	EA	136.68	89.31	225.99	64.87	201.55	0.8184
16.1602 251	Exit signs, recessed	EA	182.32	133.97	316.29	97.30	279.62	1.2276
16.1700 000	**BRANCH CIRCUIT RUNS, SPECIAL PURPOSE CONDUIT & WIRE:**							
16.1701 000	**LIGHTING OUTLETS & DEVICES WITHOUT WIRE & CONDUIT:**							
16.1701 011	Fixture outlets	EA	7.55	22.33	29.88	16.22	23.77	0.2046
16.1701 021	Fixture junction boxes	EA	7.55	17.86	25.41	12.97	20.52	0.1637
16.1701 031	Fixture flex assemblies	EA	10.24	8.94	19.18	6.49	16.73	0.0819
16.1701 041	Fixture switch outlets	EA	26.09	69.84	95.93	50.73	76.82	0.6400
16.1701 051	Fixture switch & pilot lights	EA	17.92	86.21	104.13	62.62	80.54	0.7900
16.1701 061	Fixture switch outlets, waterproof	EA	42.46	86.21	128.67	62.62	105.08	0.7900
16.1701 071	Fixture switch, two gang	EA	31.04	86.21	117.25	62.62	93.66	0.7900
16.1702 000	**LIGHTING CIRCUITS:**							
16.1702 011	Lighting circuits, EMT & wire	LF	2.69	5.37	8.06	3.90	6.59	0.0492
16.1702 021	Lighting circuits, RSC & wire	LF	6.06	6.71	12.77	4.87	10.93	0.0615

Division 16 CSI #	16 - ELECTRICAL Description	Unit	Material	Union Install	Union Total	Open Install	Open Total	Unit Man-Hrs
16.1800 000	SIGNAL & COMMUNICATIONS SYSTEMS:							
16.1801 000	TELEPHONE SYSTEMS:							
16.1801 011	Telephone main terminal	EA	113.42	267.94	381.36	194.60	308.02	2.4552
16.1801 021	Telephone auxiliary terminal	EA	80.99	178.62	259.61	129.73	210.72	1.6368
16.1801 031	Telephone riser raceway	LF	14.05	12.96	27.01	9.42	23.47	0.1188
16.1801 041	Telephone riser sleeve	EA	21.02	44.66	65.68	32.43	53.45	0.4092
16.1801 051	Telephone outlet, wall	EA	17.73	26.80	44.53	19.47	37.20	0.2456
16.1801 061	Telephone outlet, floor box	EA	133.28	44.66	177.94	32.43	165.71	0.4092
16.1801 071	Telephone outlet raceway	LF	1.80	4.80	6.60	3.49	5.29	0.0440
16.1802 000	FIRE ALARM SYSTEMS:							
16.1802 011	Fire alarm main panel	EA	3,346.47	1,071.74	4,418.21	778.40	4,124.87	9.8208
16.1802 021	Fire alarm annunciator	EA	2,455.37	893.12	3,348.49	648.66	3,104.03	8.1840
16.1802 031	Fire alarm power supply	EA	1,938.44	535.87	2,474.31	389.20	2,327.64	4.9104
16.1802 041	Fire alarm terminal cabinet	EA	387.64	267.94	655.58	194.60	582.24	2.4552
16.1802 051	Fire alarm stations	EA	142.09	111.64	253.73	81.08	223.17	1.0230
16.1802 061	Fire alarm horns	EA	129.22	89.31	218.53	64.87	194.09	0.8184
16.1802 071	Fire alarm bells	EA	116.26	89.31	205.57	64.87	181.13	0.8184
16.1802 081	Fire alarm chimes	EA	142.09	89.31	231.40	64.87	206.96	0.8184
16.1802 091	Fire alarm smoke detector, ceiling	EA	186.92	133.97	320.89	97.30	284.22	1.2276
16.1802 101	Fire alarm smoke detector, duct	EA	542.76	223.28	766.04	162.17	704.93	2.0460
16.1802 111	Fire alarm ionization detector	EA	317.23	111.64	428.87	81.08	398.31	1.0230
16.1802 121	Fire alarm heat detector	EA	180.64	66.98	247.62	48.65	229.29	0.6138
16.1802 131	Fire alarm flow switch connect	EA	180.64	111.64	292.28	81.08	261.72	1.0230
16.1802 141	Fire alarm door hold assembly	EA	170.53	178.62	349.15	129.73	300.26	1.6368
16.1802 151	Fire alarm door release assembly	EA	170.53	178.62	349.15	129.73	300.26	1.6368
16.1802 161	Fire alarm distribution feeders	LF	9.22	19.65	28.87	14.27	23.49	0.1801
16.1802 171	Fire alarm device circuits	LF	3.14	6.25	9.39	4.54	7.68	0.0573
16.1803 000	COMMUNICATION, INTERCOM, PUBLIC ADDRESS:							
16.1803 011	Main amplifier panel power supply	EA	3,466.84	714.50	4,181.34	518.93	3,985.77	6.5472
16.1803 021	Auxiliary terminal cabinet	EA	346.68	357.25	703.93	259.47	606.15	3.2736
16.1803 031	Speaker enclosure, surface	EA	14.76	31.27	46.03	22.71	37.47	0.2865
16.1803 041	Speaker enclosure, flush	EA	34.48	44.66	79.14	32.43	66.91	0.4092
16.1803 051	Microphone outlet, wall	EA	15.01	31.27	46.28	22.71	37.72	0.2865
16.1803 061	Microphone outlet, floor	EA	43.85	44.66	88.51	32.43	76.28	0.4092
16.1803 071	Intercom outlet, wall	EA	15.01	31.27	46.28	22.71	37.72	0.2865
16.1803 081	Intercom outlet, floor	EA	43.85	44.66	88.51	32.43	76.28	0.4092
16.1803 091	System feeder raceway	LF	2.83	12.96	15.79	9.42	12.25	0.1188
16.1803 101	System feeder cable	LF	7.74	1.79	9.53	1.30	9.04	0.0164
16.1803 111	System device raceway	LF	2.07	3.13	5.20	2.27	4.34	0.0287
16.1803 121	System device cable	LF	2.58	.72	3.30	.52	3.10	0.0066
16.1900 000	BRANCH CIRCUIT OUTLETS & DEVICES:							
16.1901 000	POWER OUTLETS, AVERAGE, WITH CONDUIT & WIRE:							
16.1901 011	Duplex outlet	EA	21.89	82.94	104.83	60.24	82.13	0.7600
16.1901 021	Duplex outlet, waterproof	EA	50.59	88.40	138.99	64.20	114.79	0.8100
16.1901 031	Duplex outlet, ground fault interrupter	EA	45.48	100.40	145.88	72.92	118.40	0.9200
16.1901 041	Duplex outlet, ground fault interrupter, waterproof	EA	85.73	128.77	214.50	93.53	179.26	1.1800
16.1901 051	Double duplex outlet	EA	132.73	57.95	190.68	42.09	174.82	0.5310
16.1901 061	Outlet, 30 amp	EA	28.55	100.40	128.95	72.92	101.47	0.9200
16.1901 071	Outlet, 50 amp	EA	36.85	110.88	147.73	80.53	117.38	1.0160
16.1901 081	Outlet, 60 amp, welding receptacle	EA	283.30	152.78	436.08	110.96	394.26	1.4000
16.1901 091	Outlet, 100 amp, welding receptacle	EA	426.25	190.98	617.23	138.71	564.96	1.7500
16.1901 101	Motor connect, 1 ph, fractional hp	EA	27.29	165.88	193.17	120.48	147.77	1.5200
16.1901 111	Motor connection, 3 ph	EA	34.18	196.43	230.61	142.67	176.85	1.8000
16.1901 121	Clock outlet	EA	50.59	100.40	150.99	72.92	123.51	0.9200
16.1901 131	J-box outlet	EA	13.30	34.92	48.22	25.36	38.66	0.3200
16.1901 141	J-box outlet & equipment connection	EA	27.29	103.67	130.96	75.30	102.59	0.9500
16.1901 151	Floor box with flush 110v outlet	EA	93.08	66.98	160.06	48.65	141.73	0.6138
16.1901 161	Floor box with surface 110v outlet	EA	105.85	111.64	217.49	81.08	186.93	1.0230
16.1901 171	Floor box with equipment connection	EA	105.85	156.30	262.15	113.52	219.37	1.4322
16.1901 181	Outlet circuit, EMT/wire to 20a	LF	1.28	5.01	6.29	3.64	4.92	0.0459
16.1901 191	Outlet circuit, RSC/wire to 20a	LF	3.06	7.15	10.21	5.19	8.25	0.0655
16.1901 201	Outlet circuit, PVC/wire to 20a	LF	2.22	4.03	6.25	2.92	5.14	0.0369

Division 16 CSI #	16 - ELECTRICAL Description	Unit	Material	Union Install	Union Total	Open Install	Open Total	Unit Man-Hrs
16.1950 000	**FEES, PERMITS, TESTING:**							
16.1951 000	**FEES, INSPECTION:**							
16.1951 011	Fee, inspection, per fixture	EA	3.64		3.64		3.64	
16.1951 021	Fee, inspection, per outlet	EA	1.18		1.18		1.18	
16.1951 031	Fee, inspection, per amp	EA	.20		.20		.20	
16.1951 041	Fee, inspection, per horsepower	EA	7.32		7.32		7.32	
16.1952 000	**TESTING:**							
16.1952 011	Testing, per fixture	EA	8.50		8.50		8.50	
16.1952 021	Testing, per outlet	EA	4.84		4.84		4.84	
16.1952 031	Testing, per amp, service switchgear	EA	.58		.58		.58	
16.1952 041	Testing, per horsepower	EA	36.46		36.46		36.46	
16.2000 000	**EQUIPMENT, UNIT SUBSTATIONS:**							
16.2001 000	**UNIT SUB-STATION, HIGH VOLTAGE, CUSTOMER OWNED:**							
16.2001 011	Substation, 4.16kv, 75,000 va, 1200a	EA	18,571.68	3,925.01	22,496.69	2,850.70	21,422.38	35.9664
16.2001 021	Substation, 4.16kv, 250,000 va, 2000a	EA	28,685.54	7,604.41	36,289.95	5,523.00	34,208.54	69.6821
16.2001 031	Substation, 4.16kv, 350,000 va, 1200a	EA	30,164.76	6,259.55	36,424.31	4,546.25	34,711.01	57.3587
16.2001 041	Substation, 4.16kv, 350,000 va, 3000a	EA	54,400.21	11,196.87	65,597.08	8,132.17	62,532.38	102.6012
16.2001 051	Substation, 138kv, 500,000 va, 1200a	EA	31,530.11	6,731.71	38,261.82	4,889.17	36,419.28	61.6852
16.2001 061	Substation, 13.8kv, 500,000 va, 2000a	EA	34,817.16	9,738.76	44,555.92	7,073.16	41,890.32	89.2400
16.2001 071	Substation, 13.8kv, 750,000 va, 1200a	EA	39,102.87	10,607.56	49,710.43	7,704.16	46,807.03	97.2011
16.2001 081	Substation, 13.8kv, 1,000,000 va, 1200a	EA	53,982.99	13,055.51	67,038.50	9,482.08	63,465.07	119.6326
16.2001 091	Substation, 138kv, 1,000,000 va, 3000a	EA	83,060.59	16,156.94	99,217.53	11,734.62	94,795.21	148.0522
16.2002 000	**UNIT SUB-STATION, 2400V OR 4160V, 3 PH, 120/208-240, 4 WIRE:**							
16.2002 011	Substation, 112.5kva, 5kv, 120/208v, 3ph, 4 wire	EA	33,228.75	3,131.52	36,360.27	2,274.39	35,503.14	28.6953
16.2002 021	Substation, 150kva, 5kv, 120/208v, 3ph, 4 wire	EA	36,127.87	3,278.88	39,406.75	2,381.41	38,509.28	30.0456
16.2002 031	Substation, 225kva, 5kv, 120/208v, 3ph, 4 wire	EA	42,037.70	4,605.17	46,642.87	3,344.68	45,382.38	42.1989
16.2002 041	Substation, 300kva, 5kv, 120/208v, 3ph, 4 wire	EA	49,831.99	4,936.74	54,768.73	3,585.50	53,417.49	45.2372
16.2002 051	Substation, 500kva, 5kv, 120/208v, 3ph, 4 wire	EA	71,531.09	5,489.35	77,020.44	3,986.86	75,517.95	50.3010
16.2003 000	**UNIT SUB-STATION, 2400V OR 4160V, 3 PH, 277/480, 4 WIRE:**							
16.2003 011	Substation, 112.5kva, 5kv, 277/480v, 3ph, 4 wire	EA	30,796.85	3,131.52	33,928.37	2,274.39	33,071.24	28.6953
16.2003 021	Substation, 150kva, 5kv, 277/480v, 3ph, 4 wire	EA	33,239.31	3,278.88	36,518.19	2,381.41	35,620.72	30.0456
16.2003 031	Substation, 225kva, 5kv, 277/480v, 3ph, 4 wire	EA	38,018.18	4,605.17	42,623.35	3,344.68	41,362.86	42.1989
16.2003 041	Substation, 300kva, 5kv, 277/480v, 3ph, 4 wire	EA	44,942.15	4,936.74	49,878.89	3,585.50	48,527.65	45.2372
16.2003 051	Substation, 500kva, 5kv, 277/480v, 3ph, 4 wire	EA	64,471.68	5,489.35	69,961.03	3,986.86	68,458.54	50.3010
16.2004 000	**UNIT SUB-STATION, 12000-13800V, 3 PH, 120/208-240, 4 WIRE:**							
16.2004 011	Substation, 112.5kva, 15kv, 120/208, 3ph, 4 wire	EA	43,253.08	3,109.41	46,362.49	2,258.33	45,511.41	28.4927
16.2004 021	Substation, 150kva, 15kv, 120/208v, 3ph, 4 wire	EA	48,064.60	3,256.77	51,321.37	2,365.36	50,429.96	29.8430
16.2004 031	Substation, 225kva, 15kv, 120/208v, 3ph, 4 wire	EA	57,598.40	4,605.17	62,203.57	3,344.68	60,943.08	42.1989
16.2004 041	Substation, 300kva, 15kv, 120/208v, 3ph, 4 wire	EA	69,997.86	4,944.09	74,941.95	3,590.84	73,588.70	45.3046
16.2004 051	Substation, 500kva, 15kv, 120/208v, 3ph, 4 wire	EA	86,589.94	5,341.99	91,931.93	3,879.83	90,469.77	48.9507
16.2005 000	**UNIT SUB-STATION, 12000V-13800V, 3 PH, 277/408, 4 WIRE:**							
16.2005 011	Substation, 112.5kva, 15kv, 277/480, 3ph, 4 wire	EA	42,388.97	3,109.41	45,498.38	2,258.33	44,647.30	28.4927
16.2005 021	Substation, 150kva, 15kv, 277/480v, 3ph, 4 wire	EA	47,451.36	3,256.77	50,708.13	2,365.36	49,816.72	29.8430
16.2005 031	Substation, 225kva, 15kv, 277/480v, 3ph, 4 wire	EA	55,702.73	4,605.17	60,307.90	3,344.68	59,047.41	42.1989
16.2005 041	Substation, 300kva, 15kv, 277/480v, 3ph, 4 wire	EA	68,470.20	4,944.09	73,414.29	3,590.84	72,061.04	45.3046
16.2005 051	Substation, 500kva, 15kv, 277/480v, 3ph, 4 wire	EA	84,638.60	5,341.99	89,980.59	3,879.83	88,518.43	48.9507
16.2006 000	**UNIT SUB-STATION, HIGH VOLTAGE SECTION OPTIONS:**							
16.2006 011	Single feed, 3 conductors pothead	EA	1,512.86	442.10	1,954.96	321.09	1,833.95	4.0511
16.2006 021	Lightning arrest, 3-3 kv	EA	803.94	184.22	988.16	133.80	937.74	1.6881
16.2006 031	Lightning arrest, 3-4.5 kv	EA	1,148.50	184.22	1,332.72	133.80	1,282.30	1.6881
16.2006 041	Lightning arrest, 3-6 kv	EA	1,148.50	184.22	1,332.72	133.80	1,282.30	1.6881
16.2006 051	Lightning arrest, 3-9 kv	EA	1,435.58	184.22	1,619.80	133.80	1,569.38	1.6881
16.2006 061	Lightning arrest, 3-15 kv	EA	2,165.17	184.22	2,349.39	133.80	2,298.97	1.6881
16.2006 101	Switch, ram, oil, 15kv, 400a, 3ph, 4 wire	EA	38,696.15	5,238.24	43,934.39	3,804.48	42,500.63	48.0000
16.2006 111	Switch, fused, oil, 15kv, 100a	EA	12,855.71	3,219.34	16,075.05	2,338.17	15,193.88	29.5000
16.2006 121	Switch, fused, oil, 15kv, 600a	EA	24,421.58	4,256.07	28,677.65	3,091.14	27,512.72	39.0000
16.2006 131	Switch, interrupt, gas, 15kv, 4 pole	EA	27,162.98	4,692.59	31,855.57	3,408.18	30,571.16	43.0000
16.2007 000	**UNIT SUB-STATION, LOW VOLTAGE SECTION OPTIONS:**							
16.2007 011	Kirk key interlock	EA	386.55		386.55		386.55	
16.2007 021	Indicating watt meter	EA	2,795.24		2,795.24		2,795.24	
16.2007 031	One phase indicating ammeter	EA	921.84		921.84		921.84	
16.2007 041	One phase indicating voltmeter	EA	921.84		921.84		921.84	

Division 16 CSI #	16 - ELECTRICAL Description	Unit	Material	Union Install	Union Total	Open Install	Open Total	Unit Man-Hrs
16.2007 000	**UNIT SUB-STATION, LOW VOLTAGE SECTION OPTIONS: (Cont.)**							
16.2007 051	Indicating watt-hour meter	EA	1,709.79		1,709.79		1,709.79	
16.2007 061	Demand watt-hour meter	EA	416.21		416.21		416.21	
16.2007 071	Selector switch with volt or ammeter	EA	208.08		208.08		208.08	
16.2007 081	Potential transformer	EA	892.07		892.07		892.07	
16.2007 091	Current transformer, 5-800a	EA	669.01		669.01		669.01	
16.2007 101	Current transformer, to 1500a	EA	1,100.23		1,100.23		1,100.23	
16.2100 000	**EQUIPMENT, SWITCHGEAR & TRANSFORMERS:**							
	Note: Main switchgear consists of two sides service & distribution. Both sides must be listed to							
	complete the switchgear. These are the component parts:							
	SERVICE SIDE:DISTRIBUTION SIDE:							
	Equipment Enclosure . . . Switchboard Enclosures							
	Current Transformers . . . . Feeder Breakers							
	Volt Meter . . . . Fused Switches							
	Amp Meter							
	Main Breaker							
	Fire Alarm Breaker							
	Pull Section							
	Light commercial applications, a volt meter, amp meter, fire alarm breaker or current transformers							
	may not be required. See diagram at beginning of this section.							
16.2200 000	**EQUIPMENT, HIGH VOLTAGE TRANSFORMERS:**							
	Note: Items are based on 150 degree rise. Primary voltages are 2400 delta, 4160 delta, and 4160/2400							
	delta. Secondary voltages are 120/208, 277/480, 240 delta and 600 delta.							
16.2201 000	**TRANSFORMERS, DRY, 150 DEGREE RISE, HIGH VOLTAGE, 3PH, 2.4KV & 5KV:**							
16.2201 011	Transformer, to 5kv(p)/norm(s) 45kva	EA	5,846.47	1,952.60	7,799.07	1,418.15	7,264.62	17.8924
16.2201 021	Transformer, to 5kv(p)/norm(s) 75kva	EA	7,281.29	2,173.64	9,454.93	1,578.69	8,859.98	19.9179
16.2201 031	Transformer, to 5kv(p)/norm(s) 112.5kva	EA	8,686.24	3,020.99	11,707.23	2,194.11	10,880.35	27.6825
16.2201 041	Transformer, to 5kv(p)/norm(s) 150kva	EA	10,514.93	3,168.35	13,683.28	2,301.14	12,816.07	29.0328
16.2201 051	Transformer, to 5kv(p)/norm(s) 225kva	EA	24,012.97	4,936.74	28,949.71	3,585.50	27,598.47	45.2372
16.2201 061	Transformer, to 5kv(p)/norm(s) 300kva	EA	28,560.90	5,378.82	33,939.72	3,906.58	32,467.48	49.2882
16.2201 071	Transformer, to 5kv(p)/norm(s) 500kva	EA	37,656.77	6,189.33	43,846.10	4,495.25	42,152.02	56.7152
16.2201 081	Transformer, to 5kv(p)/norm(s) 750kva	EA	49,481.35	6,631.42	56,112.77	4,816.33	54,297.68	60.7662
16.2201 091	Transformer, to 5kv(p)/norm(s) 1000kva	EA	58,122.45	6,926.15	65,048.60	5,030.39	63,152.84	63.4670
16.2201 101	Transformer, to 5kv(p)/norm(s) 1500kva	EA	67,673.09	7,368.24	75,041.33	5,351.48	73,024.57	67.5180
16.2201 111	Transformer, to 5kv(p)/norm(s) 2000kva	EA	79,497.70	9,210.31	88,708.01	6,689.35	86,187.05	84.3976
16.2201 121	Transformer, to 5kv(p)/norm(s) 2500kva	EA	90,412.68	10,978.69	101,391.37	7,973.71	98,386.39	100.6019
16.2201 131	Transformer, to 5kv(p)/norm(s) 3000kva	EA	108,221.34	11,789.18	120,010.52	8,562.36	116,783.70	108.0288
16.2202 000	**TRANSFORMERS, DRY, 150 DEGREE RISE, HIGH VOLTAGE, 3PH, 15KV, 480/277V:**							
16.2202 011	Transformer, 15kv/277-480, 3ph, 4 wire, 45kva	EA	8,842.29	1,915.74	10,758.03	1,391.39	10,233.68	17.5547
16.2202 021	Transformer, 15kv/277-480, 3ph, 4 wire, 75kva	EA	11,369.79	2,173.64	13,543.43	1,578.69	12,948.48	19.9179
16.2202 031	Transformer, 15kv/277-480, 3ph, 112.5kva	EA	13,079.54	3,020.99	16,100.53	2,194.11	15,273.65	27.6825
16.2202 041	Transformer, 15kv/277-480, 3ph, 4 wire, 150kva	EA	15,380.30	3,168.35	18,548.65	2,301.14	17,681.44	29.0328
16.2202 051	Transformer, 15kv/277-480, 3ph, 4 wire, 225kva	EA	28,686.89	4,936.74	33,623.63	3,585.50	32,272.39	45.2372
16.2202 061	Transformer, 15kv/277-480, 3ph, 4 wire, 300kva	EA	36,056.23	5,378.82	41,435.05	3,906.58	39,962.81	49.2882
16.2202 071	Transformer, 15kv/277-480, 3ph, 4 wire, 500kva	EA	46,423.79	6,189.33	52,613.12	4,495.25	50,919.04	56.7152
16.2202 081	Transformer, 15kv/277-480, 3ph, 4 wire, 750kva	EA	58,248.40	6,631.42	64,879.82	4,816.33	63,064.73	60.7662
16.2202 091	Transformer, 15kv/277-480, 3ph, 4 wire, 1000kva	EA	66,434.67	6,926.15	73,360.82	5,030.39	71,465.06	63.4670
16.2202 101	Transformer, 15kv/277-480, 3ph, 4 wire, 1500kva	EA	76,440.12	7,368.24	83,808.36	5,351.48	81,791.60	67.5180
16.2202 111	Transformer, 15kv/277/480, 3ph, 4 wire, 2000kva	EA	85,535.90	9,210.31	94,746.21	6,689.35	92,225.25	84.3976
16.2202 121	Transformer, 15kv/277-480, 3ph, 4 wire, 2500kva	EA	98,724.92	10,978.69	109,703.61	7,973.71	106,698.63	100.6019
16.2202 131	Transformer, 15kv/277-480, 3ph, 4 wire, 3000kva	EA	117,371.41	11,789.18	129,160.59	8,562.36	125,933.77	108.0288
16.2300 000	**SERVICE SECTIONS:**							
16.2301 000	**SERVICE SECTION, AIR CIRCUIT BREAKER MAIN, 480V:**							
	Note: The following prices include air circuit main breaker, horizontal bus, underground pull section							
	and Class I gear to 600 volts.							
16.2301 011	Service section, 1200a, 3ph, 480v, 3 wire, air circuit breaker	EA	18,055.55	2,147.85	20,203.40	1,559.96	19,615.51	19.6816
16.2301 021	Service section, 1600a, 3ph, 480v, 3 wire, air circuit breaker	EA	19,123.23	2,652.57	21,775.80	1,926.53	21,049.76	24.3065
16.2301 031	Service section, 2000a, 3ph, 480v, 3 wire, air circuit breaker	EA	44,028.05	3,757.82	47,785.87	2,729.26	46,757.31	34.4343
16.2301 041	Service section, 3000a, 3ph, 480v, 3 wire, air circuit breaker	EA	51,972.86	5,157.77	57,130.63	3,746.03	55,718.89	47.2626
16.2301 051	Service section, 4000a, 3ph, 480v, 3 wire, air circuit breaker	EA	73,209.22	6,115.65	79,324.87	4,441.73	77,650.95	56.0400

Division 16 CSI #	16 - ELECTRICAL Description	Unit	Material	Union Install	Union Total	Open Install	Open Total	Unit Man-Hrs
16.2302 000	**SERVICE SECTION, AIR CIRCUIT BREAKER MAIN, 120/208V:**							
	Note: The following prices include air circuit main breaker, horizontal bus, underground pull section							
	and Class I gear to 600 volts.							
16.2302 011	Service section, 1200a, 3ph, 120/208v, air circuit breaker	EA	19,337.84	2,332.06	21,669.90	1,693.75	21,031.59	21.3696
16.2302 021	Service section, 1600a, 3ph, 120/208v, air circuit breaker	EA	20,801.37	2,873.62	23,674.99	2,087.08	22,888.45	26.3321
16.2302 031	Service section, 2000a, 3ph, 120/208v, air circuit breaker	EA	46,400.35	4,015.70	50,416.05	2,916.56	49,316.91	36.7974
16.2302 041	Service section, 3000a, 3ph, 120/208v, air circuit breaker	EA	53,954.91	5,526.19	59,481.10	4,013.62	57,968.53	50.6386
16.2302 051	Service section, 4000a, 3ph, 120/208v, air circuit breaker	EA	75,260.90	6,557.74	81,818.64	4,762.82	80,023.72	60.0911
16.2303 000	**SERVICE SECTION, AIR CIRCUIT BREAKER MAIN, 277/480V:**							
	Note: The following prices include air circuit main breaker, horizontal bus, underground pull section							
	and Class I gear to 600 volts.							
16.2303 011	Service section, 1200a, 3ph, 277/480v, air circuit breaker	EA	18,981.01	2,332.06	21,313.07	1,693.75	20,674.76	21.3696
16.2303 021	Service section, 1600a, 3ph, 277/480v, air circuit breaker	EA	20,447.35	2,873.62	23,320.97	2,087.08	22,534.43	26.3321
16.2303 031	Service section, 2000a, 3ph, 277/480v, air circuit breaker	EA	46,046.37	4,015.70	50,062.07	2,916.56	48,962.93	36.7974
16.2303 041	Service section, 3000a, 3ph, 277/480v, air circuit breaker	EA	53,600.90	5,526.19	59,127.09	4,013.62	57,614.52	50.6386
16.2303 051	Service section, 4000a, 3ph, 277/480v, air circuit breaker	EA	75,046.30	6,557.74	81,604.04	4,762.82	79,809.12	60.0911
16.2304 000	**SERVICE SECTION, AIR CIRCUIT BREAKER MAIN, OPTIONS:**							
16.2304 011	Add for ground fault protection	EA	5,354.39	1,549.52	6,903.91	1,125.40	6,479.79	14.1988
16.2305 000	**SERVICE SECTION, BOLTED PRESSURE SWITCH MAIN, 480V:**							
	Note: The following prices include horizontal bus, underground pull section and Class I gear to							
	600 volts.							
16.2305 011	Service section, 1200a, 3ph, 480v, 3 wire, bolted pressure switch	EA	13,425.22	2,221.54	15,646.76	1,613.48	15,038.70	20.3568
16.2305 021	Service section, 1600a, 3ph, 480v, 3 wire, bolted pressure switch	EA	15,089.46	2,799.94	17,889.40	2,033.57	17,123.03	25.6569
16.2305 031	Service section, 2000a, 3ph, 480v, 3 wire, bolted pressure switch	EA	17,138.40	3,463.09	20,601.49	2,515.21	19,653.61	31.7336
16.2305 041	Service section, 2500a, 3ph, 480v, 3 wire, bolted pressure switch	EA	21,135.88	3,978.86	25,114.74	2,889.80	24,025.68	36.4598
16.2305 051	Service section, 3000a, 3ph, 480v, 3 wire, bolted pressure switch	EA	28,629.08	4,494.64	33,123.72	3,264.41	31,893.49	41.1861
16.2305 061	Service section, 4000a, 3ph, 480v, 3 wire, bolted pressure switch	EA	37,557.92	5,378.82	42,936.74	3,906.58	41,464.50	49.2882
16.2306 000	**SERVICE SECTION, BOLTED PRESSURE SWITCH MAIN, 277/480V:**							
	Note: The following prices include horizontal bus, underground pull section and Class I gear to							
	600 volts.							
16.2306 011	Service section, 1200a, 3ph, 277/480v, bolted pressure switch	EA	14,203.04	2,468.37	16,671.41	1,792.75	15,995.79	22.6186
16.2306 021	Service section, 1600a, 3ph, 277/480v, bolted pressure switch	EA	15,976.00	3,094.66	19,070.66	2,247.62	18,223.62	28.3576
16.2306 031	Service section, 2000a, 3ph, 277/480v, bolted pressure switch	EA	18,161.49	3,794.65	21,956.14	2,756.01	20,917.50	34.7718
16.2306 041	Service section, 2500a, 3ph, 277/480v, bolted pressure switch	EA	22,273.25	4,347.27	26,620.52	3,157.38	25,430.63	39.8357
16.2306 051	Service section, 3000a, 3ph, 277/480v, bolted pressure switch	EA	29,590.85	4,936.74	34,527.59	3,585.50	33,176.35	45.2372
16.2306 061	Service section, 4000a, 3ph, 277/480v, bolted pressure switch	EA	39,107.83	5,820.92	44,928.75	4,227.67	43,335.50	53.3393
16.2307 000	**SERVICE SECTION, BOLTED PRESSURE SWITCH MAIN, OPTIONS:**							
16.2307 011	Add for ground fault protection	EA	5,004.06		5,004.06		5,004.06	
16.2308 000	**SERVICE SECTION, MOLDED CASE MAIN CIRCUIT BREAKER, 120/240V:**							
	Note: The following prices include molded case main circuit breaker, horizontal bus, underground pull							
	section and Class I gear to 600 volts.							
16.2308 011	Service section, 225a, 1ph, 120/240v, molded case main breaker	EA	2,606.41	1,352.09	3,958.50	982.01	3,588.42	12.3897
16.2308 021	Service section, 400a, 1ph, 120/240v, molded case main breaker	EA	3,997.43	1,506.82	5,504.25	1,094.39	5,091.82	13.8076
16.2308 031	Service section, 800a, 1ph, 120/240v, molded case main breaker	EA	7,688.22	1,864.18	9,552.40	1,353.94	9,042.16	17.0822
16.2308 041	Service section, 1000a, 1ph, 120/240v, molded case main breaker	EA	9,249.34	2,203.12	11,452.46	1,600.10	10,849.44	20.1880
16.2308 051	Service section, 1200a, 1ph, 120/240v, molded case main breaker	EA	10,958.20	2,258.38	13,216.58	1,640.24	12,598.44	20.6944
16.2309 000	**SERVICE SECTION, MOLDED CASE MAIN CIRCUIT BREAKER, 277/480V:**							
	Note: The following prices include molded case main circuit breaker, horizontal bus, underground pull							
	section and Class I gear to 600 volts.							
16.2309 011	Service section, 225a, 3ph, 277/480v, molded case main breaker	EA	3,098.25	1,407.34	4,505.59	1,022.14	4,120.39	12.8960
16.2309 021	Service section, 400a, 3ph, 277/480v, molded case main breaker	EA	4,555.75	1,595.24	6,150.99	1,158.61	5,714.36	14.6178
16.2309 031	Service section, 600a, 3ph, 277/480v, molded case main breaker	EA	6,950.46	1,901.01	8,851.47	1,380.69	8,331.15	17.4197
16.2309 041	Service section, 800a, 3ph, 277/480v, molded case main breaker	EA	7,128.41	2,011.54	9,139.95	1,460.96	8,589.37	18.4325
16.2309 051	Service section, 1000a, 3ph, 277/480v, molded case main breaker	EA	10,853.19	2,442.58	13,295.77	1,774.02	12,627.21	22.3823
16.2309 061	Service section, 1200a, 3ph, 277/480v, molded case main breaker	EA	12,132.85	2,461.00	14,593.85	1,787.40	13,920.25	22.5511
16.2309 071	Service section, 1600a, 3ph, 277/480v, molded case main breaker	EA	15,265.61	2,873.62	18,139.23	2,087.08	17,352.69	26.3321
16.2309 081	Service section, 2000a, 3ph, 277/480v, molded case main breaker	EA	19,062.18	4,015.70	23,077.88	2,916.56	21,978.74	36.7974
16.2309 091	Service section, 2500a, 3ph, 277/480v, molded case main breaker	EA	26,692.33	4,863.04	31,555.37	3,531.98	30,224.31	44.5619
16.2310 000	**SERVICE SECTION, MOLDED CASE MAIN CIRCUIT BREAKER, OPTIONS:**							
16.2310 011	Add for ground fault protection	EA	5,004.06	1,549.52	6,553.58	1,125.40	6,129.46	14.1988

Division 16 CSI #	16 - ELECTRICAL Description	Unit	Material	Union Install	Union Total	Open Install	Open Total	Unit Man-Hrs
16.2311 000	**SERVICE SECTION, FUSIBLE SWITCH, 1 PH, 120/240V:**							
	Note: The following prices include fusible switch, horizontal bus, underground pull section and Class I							
	gear to 600 volts.							
16.2311 011	Service section, 225a, 1ph, 120/240v, fusible switch	EA	1,254.34	1,090.50	2,344.84	792.02	2,046.36	9.9927
16.2311 021	Service section, 400a, 1ph, 120/240v, fusible switch	EA	3,124.87	1,333.67	4,458.54	968.63	4,093.50	12.2209
16.2311 031	Service section, 600a, 1ph, 120/240v, fusible switch	EA	3,869.23	1,661.56	5,530.79	1,206.77	5,076.00	15.2255
16.2311 041	Service section, 800a, 1ph, 120/240v, fusible switch	EA	5,976.65	1,772.07	7,748.72	1,287.04	7,263.69	16.2382
16.2311 051	Service section, 1200a, 1ph, 120/240v, fusible switch	EA	7,412.31	2,055.75	9,468.06	1,493.07	8,905.38	18.8376
16.2312 000	**SERVICE SECTION, FUSIBLE SWITCH, 3 PH, 600V:**							
	Note: The following prices include fusible switch, horizontal bus, underground pull section and Class I							
	gear to 600 volts.							
16.2312 011	Service section, 225a, 3ph, 600v, 3 wire, fusible switch	EA	3,183.45	1,090.50	4,273.95	792.02	3,975.47	9.9927
16.2312 021	Service section, 400a, 3ph, 600v, 3 wire, fusible switch	EA	4,050.39	1,333.67	5,384.06	968.63	5,019.02	12.2209
16.2312 031	Service section, 600a, 3ph, 600v, 3 wire, fusible switch	EA	5,906.94	1,661.56	7,568.50	1,206.77	7,113.71	15.2255
16.2312 041	Service section, 800a, 3ph, 600v, 3 wire, fusible switch	EA	7,097.29	1,772.07	8,869.36	1,287.04	8,384.33	16.2382
16.2312 051	Service section, 1200a, 3ph, 600v, 3 wire, fusible switch	EA	8,293.20	2,055.75	10,348.95	1,493.07	9,786.27	18.8376
16.2313 000	**SERVICE SECTION, FUSIBLE SWITCH, 3 PH, 120/240V:**							
	Note: The following prices include fusible switch, horizontal bus, underground pull section and Class I							
	gear to 600 volts.							
16.2313 011	Service section, 225a, 3ph, 120/208v, fusible switch	EA	3,127.38	1,370.50	4,497.88	995.38	4,122.76	12.5584
16.2313 021	Service section, 400a, 3ph, 120/208v, fusible switch	EA	3,753.97	1,665.24	5,419.21	1,209.44	4,963.41	15.2592
16.2313 031	Service section, 600a, 3ph, 120/208v, fusible switch	EA	5,989.38	1,915.74	7,905.12	1,391.39	7,380.77	17.5547
16.2313 041	Service section, 800a, 3ph, 120/208v, fusible switch	EA	7,117.73	2,111.01	9,228.74	1,533.21	8,650.94	19.3440
16.2313 051	Service section, 1200a, 3ph, 120/208v, fusible switch	EA	8,524.79	2,438.89	10,963.68	1,771.34	10,296.13	22.3485
16.2314 000	**SERVICE SECTION, FUSIBLE SWITCH, 3 PH, 277/480V:**							
	Note: The following prices include fusible switch, horizontal bus, underground pull section and Class I							
	gear to 600 volts.							
16.2314 011	Service section, 225a, 3ph, 277/480v, fusible switch	EA	3,437.05	1,370.50	4,807.55	995.38	4,432.43	12.5584
16.2314 021	Service section, 400a, 3ph, 277/480v, fusible switch	EA	4,248.28	1,665.24	5,913.52	1,209.44	5,457.72	15.2592
16.2314 031	Service section, 600a, 3ph, 277/480v, fusible switch	EA	6,428.23	1,915.74	8,343.97	1,391.39	7,819.62	17.5547
16.2314 041	Service section, 800a, 3ph, 277/480v, fusible switch	EA	7,755.12	2,111.01	9,866.13	1,533.21	9,288.33	19.3440
16.2314 051	Service section, 1200a, 3ph, 277/480v, fusible switch	EA	15,900.68	2,438.89	18,339.57	1,771.34	17,672.02	22.3485
16.2315 000	**SERVICE SECTION, FUSIBLE SWITCH, OPTIONS:**							
16.2315 011	Add for ground fault protection	EA	5,004.06	1,549.52	6,553.58	1,125.40	6,129.46	14.1988
16.2400 000	**COMBINATION SERVICE & DISTRIBUTION SWITCHBOARDS:**							
	Note: The following prices include main switch and distribution circuit breakers.							
16.2401 000	**COMBINATION SWITCHBOARDS WITH FUSIBLE MAIN:**							
16.2401 011	Switchboard, 225a, 1ph, 120/240v, fusible	EA	2,603.58	799.48	3,403.06	580.65	3,184.23	7.3259
16.2401 021	Switchboard, 400a, 1ph, 120/240v, fusible	EA	3,476.16	954.20	4,430.36	693.03	4,169.19	8.7437
16.2401 031	Switchboard, 600a, 1ph, 120/240v, fusible	EA	4,482.50	1,108.94	5,591.44	805.41	5,287.91	10.1616
16.2401 041	Switchboard, 225a, 3ph, 480v, fusible, 3 wide	EA	4,147.49	799.48	4,946.97	580.65	4,728.14	7.3259
16.2401 051	Switchboard, 400a, 3ph, 480v, fusible, 3 wide	EA	6,298.96	954.20	7,253.16	693.03	6,991.99	8.7437
16.2401 061	Switchboard, 600a, 3ph, 480v, fusible, 3 wide	EA	8,040.49	1,108.94	9,149.43	805.41	8,845.90	10.1616
16.2401 071	Switchboard, 200a, 3ph, 120/208v, fusible	EA	3,647.02	854.72	4,501.74	620.77	4,267.79	7.8321
16.2401 081	Switchboard, 400a, 3ph, 120/208v, fusible	EA	5,210.05	1,042.62	6,252.67	757.24	5,967.29	9.5539
16.2401 091	Switchboard, 600a, 3ph, 120/208v, fusible	EA	7,004.32	1,219.46	8,223.78	885.68	7,890.00	11.1744
16.2401 101	Switchboard, 225a, 3ph, 277/480v, fusible	EA	3,825.53	854.72	4,680.25	620.77	4,446.30	7.8321
16.2401 111	Switchboard, 400a, 3ph, 277/480v, fusible	EA	4,674.89	1,031.56	5,706.45	749.21	5,424.10	9.4526
16.2401 121	Switchboard, 600a, 3ph, 277/480v, fusible	EA	6,564.87	1,219.46	7,784.33	885.68	7,450.55	11.1744
16.2402 000	**COMBINATION SWITCHBOARD WITH CIRCUIT BREAKER MAIN:**							
16.2402 011	Switchboard, 225a, 1ph, 120/240v, circuit breaker main	EA	2,997.20	799.48	3,796.68	580.65	3,577.85	7.3259
16.2402 021	Switchboard, 400a, 1ph, 120/240v, circuit breaker main	EA	4,794.36	954.20	5,748.56	693.03	5,487.39	8.7437
16.2402 031	Switchboard, 600a, 1ph, 120/240v, circuit breaker main	EA	5,681.26	1,108.94	6,790.20	805.41	6,486.67	10.1616
16.2402 041	Switchboard, 800a, 1ph, 120/240v, circuit breaker main	EA	7,979.05	1,145.78	9,124.83	832.17	8,811.22	10.4992
16.2402 051	Switchboard, 1000a, 1ph, 120/240v, circuit breaker main	EA	9,913.86	1,326.29	11,240.15	963.27	10,877.13	12.1533
16.2402 061	Switchboard, 1200a, 1ph, 120/240v, circuit breaker main	EA	12,211.50	1,466.29	13,677.79	1,064.95	13,276.45	13.4362
16.2402 071	Switchboard, 225a, 3ph, 480v, circuit breaker main, 3 wire	EA	4,122.88	799.48	4,922.36	580.65	4,703.53	7.3259
16.2402 081	Switchboard, 400a, 3ph, 480v, circuit breaker main, 3 wire	EA	6,757.16	954.20	7,711.36	693.03	7,450.19	8.7437
16.2402 091	Switchboard, 600a, 3ph, 480v, circuit breaker main, 3 wire	EA	8,541.29	1,108.94	9,650.23	805.41	9,346.70	10.1616
16.2402 101	Switchboard, 800a, 3ph, 480v, circuit breaker main, 3 wire	EA	11,303.84	1,145.78	12,449.62	832.17	12,136.01	10.4992
16.2402 111	Switchboard, 1000a, 3ph, 480v, circuit breaker main, 3 wire	EA	14,099.87	1,326.29	15,426.16	963.27	15,063.14	12.1533
16.2402 121	Switchboard, 1200a, 3ph, 480v, circuit breaker main, 3 wire	EA	16,684.06	1,466.29	18,150.35	1,064.95	17,749.01	13.4362

Division 16 CSI #	16 - ELECTRICAL Description	Unit	Material	Union Install	Union Total	Open Install	Open Total	Unit Man-Hrs
16.2402 000	**COMBINATION SWITCHBOARD WITH CIRCUIT BREAKER MAIN: (Cont.)**							
16.2402 131	Switchboard, 225a, 3ph, 120/208v, circuit breaker main	EA	3,849.69	854.72	4,704.41	620.77	4,470.46	7.8321
16.2402 141	Switchboard, 400a, 3ph, 120/208v, circuit breaker main	EA	6,054.74	1,042.62	7,097.36	757.24	6,811.98	9.5539
16.2402 151	Switchboard, 600a, 3ph, 120/208v, circuit breaker main	EA	7,613.03	1,219.46	8,832.49	885.68	8,498.71	11.1744
16.2402 161	Switchboard, 800a, 3ph, 120/208v, circuit breaker main	EA	10,041.05	1,293.14	11,334.19	939.19	10,980.24	11.8495
16.2402 171	Switchboard, 1000a, 3ph, 120/208v, circuit breaker main	EA	12,697.65	1,481.03	14,178.68	1,075.65	13,773.30	13.5712
16.2402 181	Switchboard, 1200a, 3ph, 120/208v, circuit breaker main	EA	14,320.08	1,558.40	15,878.48	1,131.85	15,451.93	14.2802
16.2402 191	Switchboard, 225a, 3ph, 277/480v, circuit breaker main	EA	3,849.69	854.72	4,704.41	620.77	4,470.46	7.8321
16.2402 201	Switchboard, 400a, 3ph, 277/480v, circuit breaker main	EA	6,054.74	1,042.62	7,097.36	757.24	6,811.98	9.5539
16.2402 211	Switchboard, 600a, 3ph, 277/480v, circuit breaker main	EA	7,613.03	1,219.46	8,832.49	885.68	8,498.71	11.1744
16.2402 221	Switchboard, 800a, 3ph, 277/480v, circuit breaker main	EA	10,041.05	1,293.14	11,334.19	939.19	10,980.24	11.8495
16.2402 231	Switchboard, 1000a, 3ph, 277/480v, circuit breaker main	EA	19,449.34	1,481.03	20,930.37	1,075.65	20,524.99	13.5712
16.2402 241	Switchboard, 1200a, 3ph, 277/480v, circuit breaker main	EA	21,088.49	1,558.40	22,646.89	1,131.85	22,220.34	14.2802
16.2403 000	**COMBINATION SERVICE & DISTRIBUTION SWITCHBOARD OPTIONS:**							
16.2403 011	Add for underground pull section	EA	326.08	350.00	676.08	254.20	580.28	3.2072
16.2403 021	Add for ground fault protection	EA	5,354.39	1,549.52	6,903.91	1,125.40	6,479.79	14.1988
16.2404 000	**DISTRIBUTION SWITCHBOARD, 36", ENCLOSURE ONLY:**							
16.2404 011	Switchboard enclosure, 36", 225a, 1ph, 120/240v	EA	900.32	497.37	1,397.69	361.24	1,261.56	4.5576
16.2404 021	Switchboard enclosure, 36", 400a, 1ph, 120/240v	EA	981.17	497.37	1,478.54	361.24	1,342.41	4.5576
16.2404 031	Switchboard enclosure, 36", 600a, 1ph, 120/240v	EA	1,123.31	497.37	1,620.68	361.24	1,484.55	4.5576
16.2404 041	Switchboard enclosure, 36", 800a, 1ph, 120/240v	EA	1,237.62	534.21	1,771.83	387.99	1,625.61	4.8952
16.2404 051	Switchboard enclosure, 36", 1200a, 1ph, 120/240v	EA	1,544.25	626.31	2,170.56	454.88	1,999.13	5.7391
16.2404 061	Switchboard enclosure, 36", 1600a, 1ph, 120/240v	EA	1,825.87	810.52	2,636.39	588.67	2,414.54	7.4271
16.2404 071	Switchboard enclosure, 36", 2000a, 1ph, 120/240v	EA	2,104.66	1,252.62	3,357.28	909.76	3,014.42	11.4782
16.2404 081	Switchboard enclosure, 36", 225a, 3ph, 120/208v	EA	1,011.84	515.79	1,527.63	374.61	1,386.45	4.7264
16.2404 091	Switchboard enclosure, 36", 400a, 3ph, 120/208v	EA	1,095.46	515.79	1,611.25	374.61	1,470.07	4.7264
16.2404 101	Switchboard enclosure, 36", 600a, 3ph, 120/208v	EA	1,262.70	515.79	1,778.49	374.61	1,637.31	4.7264
16.2404 111	Switchboard enclosure, 36", 800a, 3ph, 120/208v	EA	1,446.71	515.79	1,962.50	374.61	1,821.32	4.7264
16.2404 121	Switchboard enclosure, 36", 1200a, 3ph, 120/208v	EA	1,839.79	663.15	2,502.94	481.64	2,321.43	6.0767
16.2404 131	Switchboard enclosure, 36", 1600a, 3ph, 120/208v	EA	2,163.19	957.88	3,121.07	695.70	2,858.89	8.7774
16.2404 141	Switchboard enclosure, 36", 2000a, 3ph, 120/208v	EA	2,525.54	957.88	3,483.42	695.70	3,221.24	8.7774
16.2404 151	Switchboard enclosure, 36", 2500a, 3ph, 120/208v	EA	3,732.57	1,621.02	5,353.59	1,177.33	4,909.90	14.8540
16.2404 161	Switchboard enclosure, 36", 3000a, 3ph, 120/208v	EA	4,351.43	1,768.39	6,119.82	1,284.36	5,635.79	16.2044
16.2404 171	Switchboard enclosure, 36", 4000a, 3ph, 120/208v	EA	5,251.88	2,284.17	7,536.05	1,658.97	6,910.85	20.9307
16.2404 181	Switchboard enclosure, 36", 225a, 3ph, 277/480v	EA	910.58	497.37	1,407.95	361.24	1,271.82	4.5576
16.2404 191	Switchboard enclosure, 36", 400a, 3ph, 277/480v	EA	1,039.67	497.37	1,537.04	361.24	1,400.91	4.5576
16.2404 201	Switchboard enclosure, 36", 600a, 3ph, 277/480v	EA	1,181.95	497.37	1,679.32	361.24	1,543.19	4.5576
16.2404 211	Switchboard enclosure, 36", 800a, 3ph, 277/480v	EA	1,293.40	534.21	1,827.61	387.99	1,681.39	4.8952
16.2404 221	Switchboard enclosure, 36", 1200a, 3ph, 277/480v	EA	1,602.83	626.31	2,229.14	454.88	2,057.71	5.7391
16.2404 231	Switchboard enclosure, 36", 1600a, 3ph, 277/480v	EA	1,881.60	810.52	2,692.12	588.67	2,470.27	7.4271
16.2404 241	Switchboard enclosure, 36", 2000a, 3ph, 277/480v	EA	2,177.10	1,252.62	3,429.72	909.76	3,086.86	11.4782
16.2404 251	Switchboard enclosure, 36", 2500a, 3ph, 277/480v	EA	3,370.22	1,547.34	4,917.56	1,123.82	4,494.04	14.1789
16.2404 261	Switchboard enclosure, 36", 3000a, 3ph, 277/480v	EA	4,000.20	1,621.02	5,621.22	1,177.33	5,177.53	14.8540
16.2404 271	Switchboard enclosure, 36", 4000a, 3ph, 277/480v	EA	4,351.43	1,989.44	6,340.87	1,444.91	5,796.34	18.2300
16.2405 000	**CIRCUIT BREAKER FOR DISTRIBUTION SWITCHBOARDS, BOLT-ON, 240/480V:**							
16.2405 011	Circuit breaker, 15/1-50/1, 240v, 10k ampere interrupt capacity, bolt on	EA	18.55	20.65	39.20	15.00	33.55	0.1892
16.2405 021	Circuit breaker, 15/2-50/2, 240v, 10k ampere interrupt capacity, bolt on	EA	36.63	36.85	73.48	26.77	63.40	0.3377
16.2405 031	Circuit breaker, 15/3-50/3, 240v, 10k, ampere interrupt capacity, bolt on	EA	125.94	44.22	170.16	32.12	158.06	0.4052
16.2405 041	Circuit breaker, 70/3-100/3, 240v, 10k ampere interrupt capacity, bolt on	EA	183.23	51.59	234.82	37.47	220.70	0.4727
16.2405 051	Circuit breaker, 15/1-50/1, 240v, 20k ampere interrupt capacity, bolt on	EA	38.97	20.65	59.62	15.00	53.97	0.1892
16.2405 061	Circuit breaker, 15/2-50/2, 240v, 20k ampere interrupt capacity, bolt on	EA	81.30	41.27	122.57	29.98	111.28	0.3782
16.2405 071	Circuit breaker, 15/3-50/3, 240v, 20k ampere interrupt capacity, bolt on	EA	153.46	61.90	215.36	44.96	198.42	0.5672
16.2405 081	Circuit breaker, 70/1-100/1, 240v, 20k ampere interrupt capacity, bolt on	EA	50.41	56.75	107.16	41.22	91.63	0.5200
16.2405 091	Circuit breaker, 70/2-100/2, 240v, 20k ampere interrupt capacity, bolt on	EA	180.94	78.57	259.51	57.07	238.01	0.7200
16.2405 101	Circuit breaker, 70/3-100/3, 240v, 20k ampere interrupt capacity, bolt on	EA	231.90	110.53	342.43	80.27	312.17	1.0128
16.2405 111	Circuit breaker, 125/2-225/2, 240v, 10k ampere interrupt capacity, bolt on	EA	242.80	136.33	379.13	99.01	341.81	1.2492
16.2405 121	Circuit breaker, 125/3-225/3, 240v, 10k ampere interrupt capacity, bolt on	EA	625.31	218.26	843.57	158.52	783.83	2.0000
16.2405 131	Circuit breaker, 15/1-50/1, 480v, 20k ampere interrupt capacity, bolt on	EA	81.33	20.65	101.98	15.00	96.33	0.1892
16.2405 141	Circuit breaker, 15/2-50/2, 480v, 20k ampere interrupt capacity, bolt on	EA	284.03	41.27	325.30	29.98	314.01	0.3782
16.2405 151	Circuit breaker, 15/3-50/3, 480v, 20k ampere interrupt capacity, bolt on	EA	366.16	61.90	428.06	44.96	411.12	0.5672
16.2405 161	Circuit breaker, 70/2-100/2, 480v, 20k ampere interrupt capacity, bolt on	EA	370.97	78.57	449.54	57.07	428.04	0.7200
16.2405 171	Circuit breaker, 70/3-100/3, 480v, 20k ampere interrupt capacity, bolt on	EA	435.18	110.53	545.71	80.27	515.45	1.0128

Division 16 CSI #	16 - ELECTRICAL Description	Unit	Material	Union Install	Union Total	Open Install	Open Total	Unit Man-Hrs
16.2405 000	**CIRCUIT BREAKER FOR DISTRIBUTION SWITCHBOARDS, BOLT-ON, 240/480V: (Cont.)**							
16.2405 181	Circuit breaker, 70/2-225/2 600v, 25k ampere interrupt capacity, bolt on	EA	702.95	139.69	842.64	101.45	804.40	1.2800
16.2405 191	Circuit breaker, 70/3-225/3, 600v, 25k ampere interrupt capacity, bolt on	EA	869.51	218.26	1,087.77	158.52	1,028.03	2.0000
16.2405 201	Circuit breaker, 125/2-400/2, 600v, 50k ampere interrupt capacity, bolt on	EA	1,250.74	205.16	1,455.90	149.01	1,399.75	1.8800
16.2405 211	Circuit breaker, 125/3-400/3, 600v, 50k ampere interrupt capacity, bolt on	EA	1,493.51	305.56	1,799.07	221.93	1,715.44	2.8000
16.2405 221	Circuit breaker, 500/2-600/2, 600v, 50k ampere interrupt capacity, bolt on	EA	2,075.16	302.12	2,377.28	219.42	2,294.58	2.7684
16.2405 231	Circuit breaker, 500/3-600/3, 600v, 50k ampere interrupt capacity, bolt on	EA	2,631.34	453.16	3,084.50	329.13	2,960.47	4.1525
16.2405 241	Circuit breaker, 700/2-800/2, 600v, 50k ampere interrupt capacity, bolt on	EA	2,730.23	302.12	3,032.35	219.42	2,949.65	2.7684
16.2405 251	Circuit breaker, 700/3-800/3, 600v, 50k ampere interrupt capacity, bolt on	EA	3,458.67	453.16	3,911.83	329.13	3,787.80	4.1525
16.2405 261	Circuit breaker, 1000/2, 600v, 50k ampere interrupt capacity, bolt-on	EA	3,656.30	412.63	4,068.93	299.69	3,955.99	3.7811
16.2405 271	Circuit breaker, 1000/3, 600v, 50k ampere interrupt capacity, bolt-on	EA	4,379.12	618.94	4,998.06	449.53	4,828.65	5.6716
16.2405 281	Circuit breaker, 1200/2, 600v, 50k ampere interrupt capacity, bolt-on	EA	5,302.35	427.36	5,729.71	310.39	5,612.74	3.9161
16.2405 291	Circuit breaker, 1220/3, 600v, 50k ampere interrupt capacity, bolt-on	EA	6,056.28	641.04	6,697.32	465.58	6,521.86	5.8741
16.2405 301	Circuit breaker, 2000/3, 600v, 50k ampere interrupt capacity, bolt-on	EA	8,758.30	773.68	9,531.98	561.91	9,320.21	7.0895
16.2406 000	**MAIN/BRANCH FUSED SWITCH FOR DISTRIBUTION SWITCHBOARD, 240/480V:**							
16.2406 011	Fused switch, 30/30 twin, 240v, 2p	EA	335.24	73.70	408.94	53.52	388.76	0.6753
16.2406 021	Fused switch, 60/60 twin, 240v, 2p	EA	335.24	117.89	453.13	85.62	420.86	1.0803
16.2406 031	Fused switch, 100a, 240v, 2p	EA	259.75	81.06	340.81	58.87	318.62	0.7428
16.2406 041	Fused switch, 200a, 240v, 2p	EA	564.84	184.22	749.06	133.80	698.64	1.6881
16.2406 051	Fused switch, 400a, 240v, 2p	EA	1,262.80	294.74	1,557.54	214.07	1,476.87	2.7008
16.2406 061	Fused switch, 600a, 240v, 2p	EA	1,643.34	383.16	2,026.50	278.28	1,921.62	3.5110
16.2406 071	Fused switch, 30/30 twin, 480v, 3p	EA	428.89	110.53	539.42	80.27	509.16	1.0128
16.2406 081	Fused switch, 60/60 twin, 480v, 3p	EA	453.11	176.85	629.96	128.44	581.55	1.6205
16.2406 091	Fused switch, 100a, 480v, 3p	EA	350.38	121.59	471.97	88.31	438.69	1.1142
16.2406 101	Fused switch, 200a, 480v, 3p	EA	776.31	276.33	1,052.64	200.69	977.00	2.5321
16.2406 111	Fused switch, 400a, 480v, 3p	EA	1,797.49	442.10	2,239.59	321.09	2,118.58	4.0511
16.2406 121	Fused switch, 600a, 480v, 3p	EA	2,175.14	574.73	2,749.87	417.42	2,592.56	5.2665
16.2407 000	**DISTRIBUTION SWITCHBOARDS FOR CURRENT LIMITING BREAKERS, 240/480V:**							
	Note: The following prices are based on 36" wide enclosures only. Components must be added.							
16.2407 011	Distribution switchboard, 225a, 120/240v, 1ph	EA	1,099.94	497.37	1,597.31	361.24	1,461.18	4.5576
16.2407 021	Distribution switchboard, 400a, 120/240v, 1ph	EA	1,188.43	497.37	1,685.80	361.24	1,549.67	4.5576
16.2407 031	Distribution switchboard, 600a, 120/240v, 1ph	EA	1,335.86	497.37	1,833.23	361.24	1,697.10	4.5576
16.2407 041	Distribution switchboard, 800a, 120/240v, 1ph	EA	1,515.77	534.21	2,049.98	387.99	1,903.76	4.8952
16.2407 051	Distribution switchboard, 1200a, 120/240v, 1ph	EA	1,872.69	626.31	2,499.00	454.88	2,327.57	5.7391
16.2407 061	Distribution switchboard, 1600a, 120/240v, 1ph	EA	2,226.57	810.52	3,037.09	588.67	2,815.24	7.4271
16.2407 071	Distribution switchboard, 2000a, 120/240v, 1ph	EA	2,568.65	1,252.62	3,821.27	909.76	3,478.41	11.4782
16.2407 081	Distribution switchboard, 225a, 277/480v, 3ph	EA	1,890.42	497.37	2,387.79	361.24	2,251.66	4.5576
16.2407 091	Distribution switchboard, 400a, 277/480v, 3ph	EA	2,009.41	497.37	2,506.78	361.24	2,370.65	4.5576
16.2407 101	Distribution switchboard, 600a, 277/480v, 3ph	EA	2,462.14	497.37	2,959.51	361.24	2,823.38	4.5576
16.2407 111	Distribution switchboard, 800a, 277/480v, 3ph	EA	2,789.44	534.21	3,323.65	387.99	3,177.43	4.8952
16.2407 121	Distribution switchboard, 1200a, 277/480v, 3ph	EA	3,423.76	626.31	4,050.07	454.88	3,878.64	5.7391
16.2407 131	Distribution switchboard, 1600a, 277/480v, 3ph	EA	4,058.23	810.52	4,868.75	588.67	4,646.90	7.4271
16.2407 141	Distribution switchboard, 2000a, 277/480v, 3ph	EA	4,717.80	1,252.62	5,970.42	909.76	5,627.56	11.4782
16.2407 151	Distribution switchboard, 3000a, 277/480v, 3ph	EA	7,507.23	1,621.02	9,128.25	1,177.33	8,684.56	14.8540
16.2407 161	Distribution switchboard, 4000a, 277/480v, 3ph	EA	10,548.47	1,989.44	12,537.91	1,444.91	11,993.38	18.2300
16.2408 000	**MAIN/BRANCH CURRENT LIMITING BREAKERS, 240 OR 480V:**							
16.2408 011	Current limiting circuit breaker, 15-100a, 2p, 600v	EA	1,557.98	53.06	1,611.04	38.54	1,596.52	0.4862
16.2408 021	Current limiting circuit breaker, 15-100a, 3p, 600v	EA	1,878.34	79.59	1,957.93	57.80	1,936.14	0.7293
16.2408 031	Current limiting circuit breaker, 125-225a, 2p, 600v	EA	2,902.42	82.54	2,984.96	59.94	2,962.36	0.7563
16.2408 041	Current limiting circuit breaker, 125-225a, 3p, 600v	EA	3,642.64	123.80	3,766.44	89.91	3,732.55	1.1344
16.2408 051	Current limiting circuit breaker, 250-400a, 2p, 600v	EA	3,289.31	151.80	3,441.11	110.25	3,399.56	1.3910
16.2408 061	Current limiting circuit breaker, 250-400a, 3p, 600v	EA	4,186.82	227.69	4,414.51	165.37	4,352.19	2.0864
16.2408 071	Current limiting circuit breaker, 600-800a, 2p, 600v	EA	4,717.88	257.90	4,975.78	187.31	4,905.19	2.3632
16.2408 081	Current limiting circuit breaker, 600-800a, 3p, 600v	EA	5,895.52	386.85	6,282.37	280.97	6,176.49	3.5449
16.2408 091	Current limiting circuit breaker, 800-1600a, 2p, 600v	EA	12,065.14	346.31	12,411.45	251.52	12,316.66	3.1734
16.2408 101	Current limiting circuit breaker, 800-1600a, 3p, 600v	EA	14,665.56	519.47	15,185.03	377.29	15,042.85	4.7601
16.2408 111	Current limiting circuit breaker, 1800-2000a, 2p, 600v	EA	14,665.56	515.79	15,181.35	374.61	15,040.17	4.7264
16.2408 121	Current limiting circuit breaker, 1800-2000a, 3p, 600v	EA	15,572.37	773.68	16,346.05	561.91	16,134.28	7.0895
16.2409 000	**ENCLOSED CIRCUIT BREAKERS:**							
16.2409 011	Circuit breaker to 30/3, 600v, with enclosure	EA	678.75	218.26	897.01	158.52	837.27	2.0000
16.2409 021	Circuit breaker to 60/3, 600v, with enclosure	EA	678.75	240.09	918.84	174.37	853.12	2.2000
16.2409 031	Circuit breaker to 100/3, 600v, with enclosure	EA	760.14	283.74	1,043.88	206.08	966.22	2.6000

Division 16 CSI #	16 - ELECTRICAL Description	Unit	Material	Union Install	Union Total	Open Install	Open Total	Unit Man-Hrs
16.2409 000	**ENCLOSED CIRCUIT BREAKERS: (Cont.)**							
16.2409 041	Circuit breaker to 225/3, 600v, with enclosure	EA	2,682.03	611.13	3,293.16	443.86	3,125.89	5.6000
16.2409 051	Circuit breaker to 400/3, 600v, with enclosure	EA	3,489.13	1,047.65	4,536.78	760.90	4,250.03	9.6000
16.2409 061	Circuit breaker to 600/3, 600v, with enclosure	EA	4,421.77	1,222.26	5,644.03	887.71	5,309.48	11.2000
16.2409 071	Circuit breaker to 800/3, 600v, with enclosure	EA	5,490.99	1,396.86	6,887.85	1,014.53	6,505.52	12.8000
16.2501 000	**ENCLOSED CIRCUIT BREAKERS, EXPLOSION PROOF:**							
16.2501 011	Circuit breaker to 30/3, 600v, explosion proof	EA	1,082.58	398.32	1,480.90	289.30	1,371.88	3.6500
16.2501 021	Circuit breaker to 60/3, 600v, explosion proof	EA	1,160.30	463.80	1,624.10	336.86	1,497.16	4.2500
16.2501 031	Circuit breaker to 100/3, 600v, explosion proof	EA	1,341.00	614.40	1,955.40	446.23	1,787.23	5.6300
16.2501 041	Circuit breaker to 225/3, 600v, explosion proof	EA	2,703.69	1,173.15	3,876.84	852.05	3,555.74	10.7500
16.2501 051	Circuit breaker to 400/3, 600v, explosion proof	EA	5,430.91	1,966.52	7,397.43	1,428.27	6,859.18	18.0200
16.2501 061	Circuit breaker to 600/3, 600v, explosion proof	EA	9,453.98	2,723.88	12,177.86	1,978.33	11,432.31	24.9600
16.2501 071	Circuit breaker to 800/3, 600v, explosion proof	EA	12,605.89	3,158.22	15,764.11	2,293.78	14,899.67	28.9400
16.3000 000	**MOTOR CONTROL CENTERS:**							
16.3001 000	**MOTOR CONTROL CENTER ENCLOSURE, ADD COMPONENTS:**							
16.3001 011	Motor control center enclosure only, 600v, 225a section	EA	1,387.61	783.43	2,171.04	569.00	1,956.61	7.1789
16.3001 021	Motor control center enclosure only, 600v, 400a section	EA	2,312.68	783.43	3,096.11	569.00	2,881.68	7.1789
16.3001 031	Motor control center enclosure only, 600v, 600a section	EA	2,415.75	783.43	3,199.18	569.00	2,984.75	7.1789
16.3001 041	Motor control center enclosure only, 600v, 800a section	EA	2,497.72	783.43	3,281.15	569.00	3,066.72	7.1789
16.3001 051	Motor control center enclosure only, 600v, 1200a section	EA	4,625.45	1,093.16	5,718.61	793.95	5,419.40	10.0170
16.3001 061	Motor control center enclosure only, 600v, 1600a section	EA	6,955.51	1,093.16	8,048.67	793.95	7,749.46	10.0170
16.3002 000	**COMPONENTS FOR MOTOR CONTROL CENTERS:**							
16.3002 011	Start-stop push button	EA	148.50	44.22	192.72	32.12	180.62	0.4052
16.3002 021	HOA selector switch	EA	148.50	58.95	207.45	42.82	191.32	0.5402
16.3002 031	Pilot light	EA	185.02	29.48	214.50	21.41	206.43	0.2701
16.3002 041	Electric interlock	EA	108.90	29.48	138.38	21.41	130.31	0.2701
16.3002 051	Ammeter in cover	EA	399.27	58.95	458.22	42.82	442.09	0.5402
16.3002 061	Ammeter & switch	EA	1,711.53	88.43	1,799.96	64.22	1,775.75	0.8103
16.3002 071	Voltmeter	EA	1,128.97	29.48	1,158.45	21.41	1,150.38	0.2701
16.3002 081	Voltmeter & switch	EA	1,711.53	58.95	1,770.48	42.82	1,754.35	0.5402
16.3002 091	Control transformers for starters, standard	EA	126.09	58.95	185.04	42.82	168.91	0.5402
16.3002 101	Combination starter, size 00, full voltage non reversing, to fractional hp	EA	853.13	468.89	1,322.02	340.55	1,193.68	4.2966
16.3002 111	Combination starter, size 0, full voltage non reversing, to 5hp	EA	912.84	468.89	1,381.73	340.55	1,253.39	4.2966
16.3002 121	Combination starter, size 1, full voltage non reversing, to 10hp	EA	1,140.13	468.89	1,609.02	340.55	1,480.68	4.2966
16.3002 131	Combination starter, size 2, full voltage non reversing, to 25hp	EA	1,412.08	669.84	2,081.92	486.50	1,898.58	6.1380
16.3002 141	Combination starter, size 3, full voltage non reversing, to 50hp	EA	1,905.58	1,116.40	3,021.98	810.83	2,716.41	10.2300
16.3002 151	Combination starter, size 4, full voltage non reversing, to 100hp	EA	3,484.48	1,786.24	5,270.72	1,297.33	4,781.81	16.3680
16.3002 161	Combination starter, size 5, full voltage non reversing, to 200hp	EA	12,260.55	2,857.98	15,118.53	2,075.72	14,336.27	26.1888
16.3002 171	Combination starter, size 6, full voltage non reversing, to 400hp	EA	30,236.09	3,990.24	34,226.33	2,898.07	33,134.16	36.5641
16.3002 181	Combination starter, size 7, full voltage non reversing, to 600hp	EA	46,855.02	5,201.50	52,056.52	3,777.79	50,632.81	47.6633
16.3002 191	Combination starter, size 8, full voltage non reversing, to 900hp	EA	70,416.16	6,241.79	76,657.95	4,533.35	74,949.51	57.1959
16.3002 201	Machine tool control transformer, 100va	EA	110.20	29.48	139.68	21.41	131.61	0.2701
16.3002 211	Machine tool control transformer, 300va	EA	191.76	29.48	221.24	21.41	213.17	0.2701
16.3002 221	Machine tool control transformer, 500va	EA	207.51	29.48	236.99	21.41	228.92	0.2701
16.3002 231	Machine tool control transformer, 1000va	EA	321.79	36.85	358.64	26.77	348.56	0.3377
16.3003 000	**AC CONTROL RELAYS:**							
16.3003 011	Relay, 20a, 2 pole, 600v	EA	105.23	29.48	134.71	21.41	126.64	0.2701
16.3003 021	Relay, 20a, 3 pole, 600v	EA	122.78	44.22	167.00	32.12	154.90	0.4052
16.3003 031	Relay, 20a, 6 pole, 600v	EA	175.37	88.43	263.80	64.22	239.59	0.8103
16.3003 041	Relay, 20a, 8 pole, 600v	EA	210.51	117.89	328.40	85.62	296.13	1.0803
16.3003 051	Relay, 20a, 10 pole, 600v	EA	245.56	147.37	392.93	107.03	352.59	1.3504
16.3003 061	Relay, 20a, 12 pole, 600v	EA	280.68	176.85	457.53	128.44	409.12	1.6205
16.3004 000	**MOTOR STARTERS, 600V, WITH ENCLOSURE:**							
16.3004 011	Fractional hp manual starter	EA	57.45	64.16	121.61	46.60	104.05	0.5879
16.3004 021	Manual starter, 1ph, to 5hp, with enclosure	EA	162.24	152.78	315.02	110.96	273.20	1.4000
16.3004 031	Magnetic starter, 3ph, to 10hp, with enclosure	EA	315.79	305.56	621.35	221.93	537.72	2.8000
16.3004 041	Magnetic starter, 3ph, to 25hp, with enclosure	EA	631.60	611.13	1,242.73	443.86	1,075.46	5.6000
16.3004 051	Magnetic starter, 3ph, to 50hp, with enclosure	EA	1,052.60	785.74	1,838.34	570.67	1,623.27	7.2000
16.3004 061	Magnetic starter, 3ph, to 100hp, with enclosure	EA	2,473.63	1,309.56	3,783.19	951.12	3,424.75	12.0000
16.3005 000	**COMBINATION MOTOR STARTERS, 600V, WITH ENCLOSURE:**							
16.3005 011	Combination starter, to size 0, full voltage non reversing to 5hp	EA	1,263.85	190.98	1,454.83	138.71	1,402.56	1.7500
16.3005 021	Combination starter, size 1, full voltage non reversing to 10hp	EA	1,314.77	245.54	1,560.31	178.34	1,493.11	2.2500

Division 16 CSI #	16 - ELECTRICAL Description	Unit	Material	Union Install	Union Total	Open Install	Open Total	Unit Man-Hrs
16.3005 000	COMBINATION MOTOR STARTERS, 600V, WITH ENCLOSURE: (Cont.)							
16.3005 031	Combination starter, size 2, full voltage non reversing, 25hp	EA	1,860.96	381.96	2,242.92	277.41	2,138.37	3.5000
16.3005 041	Combination starter, size 3, full voltage non reversing to 50hp	EA	2,706.88	491.09	3,197.97	356.67	3,063.55	4.5000
16.3005 051	Combination starter, size 4, full voltage non reversing to 100hp	EA	5,941.15	627.50	6,568.65	455.75	6,396.90	5.7500
16.3005 061	Combination starter, size 5, full voltage non reversing, to 200hp	EA	13,778.15	873.04	14,651.19	634.08	14,412.23	8.0000
16.3005 071	Combination starter, size 6, full voltage non reversing, to 400hp	EA	34,359.09	1,364.13	35,723.22	990.75	35,349.84	12.5000
16.3005 081	Combination starter, size 7, full voltage non reversing, to 600hp	EA	53,244.30	1,636.95	54,881.25	1,188.90	54,433.20	15.0000
16.3006 000	SWITCHES, FUSIBLE DISCONNECT, 240/480V:							
16.3006 011	Switch, fusible disconnect, single pole, 30a, 240/480v	EA	249.37	218.26	467.63	158.52	407.89	2.0000
16.3006 021	Switch, fusible disconnect, 3 pole, 30a, 240/480v	EA	291.22	240.09	531.31	174.37	465.59	2.2000
16.3006 031	Switch, fusible disconnect, 3 pole, 60a, 240/480v	EA	334.35	305.56	639.91	221.93	556.28	2.8000
16.3006 041	Switch, fusible disconnect, 3 pole, 100a, 240/480v	EA	603.25	349.22	952.47	253.63	856.88	3.2000
16.3006 051	Switch, fusible disconnect, 3 pole, 200a, 240/480v	EA	880.48	545.65	1,426.13	396.30	1,276.78	5.0000
16.3006 061	Switch, fusible disconnect, 3 pole, 400a, 240/480v	EA	2,258.41	873.04	3,131.45	634.08	2,892.49	8.0000
16.3006 071	Switch, fusible disconnect, 3 pole, 600a, 240/480v	EA	3,697.63	1,222.26	4,919.89	887.71	4,585.34	11.2000
16.3007 000	SWITCHES, NONFUSED DISCONNECT, 240/480V:							
16.3007 011	Switch, nonfuse disconnect, single pole, 30a, 240/480v	EA	70.23	147.33	217.56	107.00	177.23	1.3500
16.3007 021	Switch, nonfuse disconnect, 3 pole, 30a, 240/480v	EA	118.39	163.70	282.09	118.89	237.28	1.5000
16.3007 031	Switch, nonfuse disconnect, 3 pole, 60a, 240/480v	EA	224.72	218.26	442.98	158.52	383.24	2.0000
16.3007 041	Switch, nonfuse disconnect, 3 pole, 100a, 240/480v	EA	382.47	272.83	655.30	198.15	580.62	2.5000
16.3007 051	Switch, nonfuse disconnect, 3 pole, 200a, 240/480v	EA	590.30	491.09	1,081.39	356.67	946.97	4.5000
16.3007 061	Switch, nonfuse disconnect, 3 pole, 400a, 240/480v	EA	1,223.43	829.39	2,052.82	602.38	1,825.81	7.6000
16.3007 071	Switch, nonfuse disconnect, 3 pole, 600a, 240/480v	EA	2,177.94	1,134.95	3,312.89	824.30	3,002.24	10.4000
16.3007 081	Switch, nonfuse, explosion proof, single pole, 30a, 240/480v	EA	442.92	357.18	800.10	259.42	702.34	3.2730
16.3007 091	Switch, nonfuse, explosion proof, 3 pole, 30a, 240/480v	EA	921.95	420.26	1,342.21	305.23	1,227.18	3.8510
16.3007 101	Switch, nonfuse, explosion proof, 3 pole, 60a, 240/480v	EA	979.01	493.49	1,472.50	358.41	1,337.42	4.5220
16.3007 111	Switch, nonfuse, explosion proof, 3 pole, 100a, 240/480v	EA	1,222.39	638.85	1,861.24	463.99	1,686.38	5.8540
16.3007 121	Switch, nonfuse, explosion proof, 3 pole, 200a, 240/480v	EA	2,575.04	1,141.83	3,716.87	829.30	3,404.34	10.4630
16.3007 131	Switch, nonfuse, explosion proof, 3 pole, 400a, 240/480v	EA	5,121.67	1,846.59	6,968.26	1,341.16	6,462.83	16.9210
16.3007 141	Switch, nonfuse, explosion proof, 3 pole, 600a, 240/480v	EA	9,084.77	2,569.47	11,654.24	1,866.18	10,950.95	23.5450
16.3008 000	MOTOR CONNECTIONS:							
16.3008 011	Motor connection, 1 ph, to 5hp	EA	34.93	165.88	200.81	120.48	155.41	1.5200
16.3008 021	Motor connection, 3 ph, to 5hp	EA	41.95	174.61	216.56	126.82	168.77	1.6000
16.3008 031	Motor connection, 3 ph, to 15hp	EA	69.92	245.54	315.46	178.34	248.26	2.2500
16.3008 041	Motor connection, 3 ph, to 40hp	EA	128.27	600.22	728.49	435.93	564.20	5.5000
16.3008 051	Motor connection, 3 ph, to 75hp	EA	186.58	1,091.30	1,277.88	792.60	979.18	10.0000
16.3008 061	Motor connection, 3 ph, to 100hp	EA	221.49	1,636.95	1,858.44	1,188.90	1,410.39	15.0000
16.3008 071	Motor connection, 3 ph, to 150hp	EA	291.51	2,291.73	2,583.24	1,664.46	1,955.97	21.0000
16.3008 081	Motor connection, 3 ph, to 250hp	EA	583.04	2,728.25	3,311.29	1,981.50	2,564.54	25.0000
16.3008 091	Motor connection, 3 ph, to 500hp	EA	932.86	4,365.20	5,298.06	3,170.40	4,103.26	40.0000
16.3008 101	Start/stop panelboard station, NEMA 1	EA	62.63	43.65	106.28	31.70	94.33	0.4000
16.3008 111	On/off pilot light, panelboard station, NEMA 1	EA	153.16	49.11	202.27	35.67	188.83	0.4500
16.3008 121	3 position panelboard station NEMA 1	EA	95.69	43.65	139.34	31.70	127.39	0.4000
16.3008 131	Start/stop panelboard explosion proof	EA	279.03	251.00	530.03	182.30	461.33	2.3000
16.3008 141	On/off pilot, panelboard, explosion proof	EA	588.40	251.00	839.40	182.30	770.70	2.3000
16.3008 151	3 position panelboard station explosion proof	EA	569.43	283.74	853.17	206.08	775.51	2.6000
16.3009 000	CAPACITORS:							
16.3009 011	Capacitor, 240v, 3ph to 5kvar	EA	1,237.21	357.25	1,594.46	259.47	1,496.68	3.2736
16.3009 021	Capacitor, 240v, 3ph to 15kvar	EA	3,028.88	446.56	3,475.44	324.33	3,353.21	4.0920
16.3009 031	Capacitor, 240v, 3ph to 25kvar	EA	3,862.09	580.53	4,442.62	421.63	4,283.72	5.3196
16.3009 041	Capacitor, 480v, 3ph to 5kvar	EA	1,524.22	357.25	1,881.47	259.47	1,783.69	3.2736
16.3009 051	Capacitor, 480v, 3ph to 15kvar	EA	1,738.75	446.56	2,185.31	324.33	2,063.08	4.0920
16.3009 061	Capacitor, 480v, 3ph to 40kvar	EA	3,034.46	535.87	3,570.33	389.20	3,423.66	4.9104
16.3009 071	Capacitor, 480v, 3ph to 50kvar	EA	3,497.02	669.84	4,166.86	486.50	3,983.52	6.1380
16.4000 000	PANELBOARDS, 600V MAX, BOLT-ON BREAKERS:							
	Note: The following prices include circuit breakers for branch circuits.							
16.4001 000	PANELBOARDS, BOLT-ON CIRCUIT BREAKERS, 277/480V, 3 PH, 4 WIRE, MAIN CIRCUIT BREAKER:							
	Note: The following items include main circuit breaker.							
16.4001 011	Panel, 18 circuit, 100a, 277/480v, main circuit breaker	EA	2,094.25	486.32	2,580.57	353.21	2,447.46	4.4563
16.4001 021	Panel, 24 circuit, 100a, 277/480v, main circuit breaker	EA	3,100.73	486.32	3,587.05	353.21	3,453.94	4.4563
16.4001 031	Panel, 30 circuit, 225a, 277/480v, main circuit breaker	EA	3,289.00	1,134.95	4,423.95	824.30	4,113.30	10.4000
16.4001 041	Panel, 42 circuit, 225a, 277/480v, main circuit breaker	EA	4,298.21	1,623.85	5,922.06	1,179.39	5,477.60	14.8800

Division 16 CSI #	16 - ELECTRICAL Description	Unit	Material	Union Install	Union Total	Open Install	Open Total	Unit Man-Hrs
16.4001 000	**PANELBOARDS, BOLT-ON CIRCUIT BREAKERS, 277/480V, 3 PH, 4 WIRE, MAIN CIRCUIT BREAKER: (Cont.)**							
16.4001 051	Panel, 30 circuit, 400a, 277/480v, main circuit breaker	EA	3,526.41	1,440.52	4,966.93	1,046.23	4,572.64	13.2000
16.4001 061	Panel, 42 circuit, 400a, 277/480v, main circuit breaker	EA	4,507.00	1,798.46	6,305.46	1,306.20	5,813.20	16.4800
16.4001 071	Panel, 42 circuit, 600a, 277/480v, main circuit breaker	EA	4,697.92	1,973.07	6,670.99	1,433.02	6,130.94	18.0800
16.4002 000	**PANELBOARDS, BOLT-ON BREAKERS, 277/480V, 3 PH, 4 WIRE, MAIN LUG ONLY:**							
	Note: The following prices are main lug only.							
16.4002 011	Panel, 18 circuit, 100a, 277/480v, main lug only	EA	1,944.55	467.08	2,411.63	339.23	2,283.78	4.2800
16.4002 021	Panel, 24 circuit, 100a, 277/480v, main lug only	EA	2,455.78	692.63	3,148.41	503.05	2,958.83	6.3468
16.4002 031	Panel, 30 circuit, 100a, 277/480v, main lug only	EA	3,455.97	1,134.95	4,590.92	824.30	4,280.27	10.4000
16.4002 041	Panel, 30 circuit, 400a, 277/480v, main lug only	EA	5,488.28	1,527.82	7,016.10	1,109.64	6,597.92	14.0000
16.4002 051	Panel, 30 circuit, 225a, 277/480v, main lug only	EA	4,378.11	1,222.26	5,600.37	887.71	5,265.82	11.2000
16.4002 061	Panel, 42 circuit, 225a, 277/480v, main lug only	EA	5,330.02	1,711.16	7,041.18	1,242.80	6,572.82	15.6800
16.4002 071	Panel, 42 circuit, 400a, 277/480v, main lug only	EA	6,459.82	1,885.77	8,345.59	1,369.61	7,829.43	17.2800
16.4100 000	**TRANSFORMERS, DRY, LOW VOLTAGE:**							
16.4101 000	**TRANSFORMERS, LOW VOLTAGE, 1 PH, 240/480V PRIMARY, 120/240V SECOND:**							
16.4101 011	Transformer, 0.5kva, 240-480/120-240v, 1ph	EA	164.31	261.91	426.22	190.22	354.53	2.4000
16.4101 021	Transformer, 1 kva, 240-480/120-240v, 1ph	EA	255.06	305.56	560.62	221.93	476.99	2.8000
16.4101 031	Transformer, 1.5kva, 240-480/120-240v, 1ph	EA	305.12	305.56	610.68	221.93	527.05	2.8000
16.4101 041	Transformer, 2kva, 240-480/120-240v, 1ph	EA	380.04	349.22	729.26	253.63	633.67	3.2000
16.4101 051	Transformer, 3kva, 240-480/120-240v, 1ph	EA	486.17	371.04	857.21	269.48	755.65	3.4000
16.4101 061	Transformer, 5kva, 240-480/120-240v, 1ph	EA	659.04	458.35	1,117.39	332.89	991.93	4.2000
16.4101 071	Transformer, 7.5kva, 240-480/120-240v, 1ph	EA	926.13	698.43	1,624.56	507.26	1,433.39	6.4000
16.4101 081	Transformer, 10kva, 240-480/120-240v, 1ph	EA	1,148.65	785.74	1,934.39	570.67	1,719.32	7.2000
16.4101 091	Transformer, 15kva, 240-480/120-240v, 1ph	EA	1,540.65	1,047.65	2,588.30	760.90	2,301.55	9.6000
16.4101 101	Transformer, 25kva, 240-480/120-240v, 1ph	EA	2,002.89	1,309.56	3,312.45	951.12	2,954.01	12.0000
16.4101 111	Transformer, 38kva, 240-480/120-240v, 1ph	EA	2,670.49	1,527.82	4,198.31	1,109.64	3,780.13	14.0000
16.4101 121	Transformer, 50kva, 240-480/120-240v, 1ph	EA	3,249.10	1,746.08	4,995.18	1,268.16	4,517.26	16.0000
16.4101 131	Transformer, 75kva, 240-480/120-240v, 1ph	EA	4,406.35	1,964.34	6,370.69	1,426.68	5,833.03	18.0000
16.4101 141	Transformer, 100kva, 240-480/120-240v, 1ph	EA	5,697.07	2,182.60	7,879.67	1,585.20	7,282.27	20.0000
16.4102 000	**TRANSFORMERS, LOW VOLTAGE, 3 PH, 480V PRIME, 4 WIRE, 120/208V SECOND:**							
16.4102 011	Transformer, 3kva, 480/120-208v, 3ph	EA	1,000.71	698.43	1,699.14	507.26	1,507.97	6.4000
16.4102 021	Transformer, 6kva, 480/120-208v, 3ph	EA	1,147.08	873.04	2,020.12	634.08	1,781.16	8.0000
16.4102 031	Transformer, 9kva, 480/120-208v, 3ph	EA	1,532.17	1,047.65	2,579.82	760.90	2,293.07	9.6000
16.4102 041	Transformer, 15kva, 480/120-208v, 3ph	EA	2,304.29	1,222.26	3,526.55	887.71	3,192.00	11.2000
16.4102 051	Transformer, 30kva, 480/120-208v, 3ph	EA	3,459.37	1,571.47	5,030.84	1,141.34	4,600.71	14.4000
16.4102 061	Transformer, 45kva, 480/120-208v, 3ph	EA	3,702.04	1,746.08	5,448.12	1,268.16	4,970.20	16.0000
16.4102 071	Transformer, 75kva, 480/120-208v, 3ph	EA	5,579.15	1,964.34	7,543.49	1,426.68	7,005.83	18.0000
16.4102 081	Transformer, 112.5kva, 480/120-208v, 3ph	EA	7,424.19	2,182.60	9,606.79	1,585.20	9,009.39	20.0000
16.4102 091	Transformer, 150kva, 480/120-208v, 3ph	EA	9,698.41	2,357.21	12,055.62	1,712.02	11,410.43	21.6000
16.4102 101	Transformer, 225kva, 480/120-208v, 3ph	EA	12,931.17	3,055.64	15,986.81	2,219.28	15,150.45	28.0000
16.4102 111	Transformer, 300kva, 480/120-208v, 3ph	EA	16,581.12	3,492.16	20,073.28	2,536.32	19,117.44	32.0000
16.4102 121	Transformer, 500kva, 480/120-208v, 3ph	EA	26,279.60	4,365.20	30,644.80	3,170.40	29,450.00	40.0000
16.4102 131	Transformer, 750kva, 480/120-208v, 3ph	EA	42,704.30	5,238.24	47,942.54	3,804.48	46,508.78	48.0000
16.4102 141	Transformer, 1000kva, 480/120-208v, 3ph	EA	51,516.30	5,674.76	57,191.06	4,121.52	55,637.82	52.0000
16.4103 000	**TRANSFORMERS, LOW VOLTAGE, 3 PH, 480V PRIME, 240V SECOND:**							
16.4103 011	Transformer, 6kva, 480/240v, 3ph	EA	1,042.85	873.04	1,915.89	634.08	1,676.93	8.0000
16.4103 021	Transformer, 9kva, 480/240v, 3ph	EA	1,392.89	1,047.65	2,440.54	760.90	2,153.79	9.6000
16.4103 031	Transformer, 15kva, 480/240v, 3ph	EA	2,094.81	1,222.26	3,317.07	887.71	2,982.52	11.2000
16.4103 041	Transformer, 30kva, 480/240v, 3ph	EA	2,796.69	1,571.47	4,368.16	1,141.34	3,938.03	14.4000
16.4103 051	Transformer, 45kva, 480/240v, 3ph	EA	3,365.49	1,746.08	5,111.57	1,268.16	4,633.65	16.0000
16.4103 061	Transformer, 75kva, 480/240v, 3ph	EA	5,071.96	1,964.34	7,036.30	1,426.68	6,498.64	18.0000
16.4103 071	Transformer, 112.5kva, 480/240v, 3ph	EA	6,749.28	2,182.60	8,931.88	1,585.20	8,334.48	20.0000
16.4103 081	Transformer, 150kva, 480/240v, 3ph	EA	8,816.72	2,357.21	11,173.93	1,712.02	10,528.74	21.6000
16.4103 091	Transformer, 225kva, 480/240v, 3ph	EA	11,755.09	3,055.64	14,810.73	2,219.28	13,974.37	28.0000
16.4103 101	Transformer, 300kva, 480/240v, 3ph	EA	15,073.75	3,492.16	18,565.91	2,536.32	17,610.07	32.0000
16.4200 000	**PANELBOARDS FOR BOLT-ON BREAKERS, 1240/240V, 1PH, 3 WIRE:**							
	Note: The following prices include circuit breakers for branch circuits.							
16.4201 000	**PANELBOARDS, BOLT-ON BEAKERS, 120/240V, 1 PH, 3 WIRE, MAIN LUG ONLY:**							
	Note: The following items are main lug only.							
16.4201 011	Panel, 12 circuit, 100a, 120/240v, main lug only	EA	714.49	467.08	1,181.57	339.23	1,053.72	4.2800
16.4201 021	Panel, 24 circuit, 100a, 120/240v, main lug only	EA	951.66	742.08	1,693.74	538.97	1,490.63	6.8000
16.4201 031	Panel, 30 circuit, 225a, 120/240v, main lug only	EA	1,249.49	1,134.95	2,384.44	824.30	2,073.79	10.4000

Division 16 CSI #	16 - ELECTRICAL Description	Unit	Material	Union Install	Union Total	Open Install	Open Total	Unit Man-Hrs
16.4201 000	**PANELBOARDS, BOLT-ON BEAKERS, 120/240V, 1 PH, 3 WIRE, MAIN LUG ONLY: (Cont.)**							
16.4201 041	Panel, 42 circuit, 225a, 120/240v, main lug only	EA	1,580.33	1,623.85	3,204.18	1,179.39	2,759.72	14.8800
16.4201 051	Panel, 30 circuit, 400a, 120/240v, main lug only	EA	1,514.13	1,440.52	2,954.65	1,046.23	2,560.36	13.2000
16.4201 061	Panel, 42 circuit, 400a, 120/240v, main lug only	EA	1,843.51	1,798.46	3,641.97	1,306.20	3,149.71	16.4800
16.4202 000	**PANELBOARDS, BOLT-ON BREAKERS, 120/240V, 1 PH, 3 WIRE, MAIN CIRCUIT BREAKER:**							
	Note: The following prices include main circuit breaker.							
16.4202 011	Panel, 12 circuit, 100a, 120/240v, main circuit breaker	EA	973.62	467.08	1,440.70	339.23	1,312.85	4.2800
16.4202 021	Panel, 24 circuit, 100a, 120/240v, main circuit breaker	EA	1,209.34	785.74	1,995.08	570.67	1,780.01	7.2000
16.4202 031	Panel, 30 circuit, 225a, 120/240v, main circuit breaker	EA	2,314.81	1,222.26	3,537.07	887.71	3,202.52	11.2000
16.4202 041	Panel, 42 circuit, 225a, 120/240v, main circuit breaker	EA	2,642.82	1,711.16	4,353.98	1,242.80	3,885.62	15.6800
16.4202 051	Panel, 30 circuit, 400a, 120/240v, main circuit breaker	EA	3,414.74	1,527.82	4,942.56	1,109.64	4,524.38	14.0000
16.4202 061	Panel, 42 circuit, 400a, 120/240v, main circuit breaker	EA	3,749.72	1,885.77	5,635.49	1,369.61	5,119.33	17.2800
16.4203 000	**PANELBOARDS, BOLT-ON BREAKERS, 120/208V, 3 PH, 4 WIRE, MAIN LUG ONLY:**							
	Note: The following items are main lug only.							
16.4203 011	Panel, 12 circuit, 100a, 120/208v, main lug only	EA	768.60	467.08	1,235.68	339.23	1,107.83	4.2800
16.4203 021	Panel, 24 circuit, 100a, 120/208v, main lug only	EA	1,115.98	742.08	1,858.06	538.97	1,654.95	6.8000
16.4203 031	Panel, 30 circuit, 100a, 120/208v, main lug only	EA	1,280.00	1,069.47	2,349.47	776.75	2,056.75	9.8000
16.4203 041	Panel, 30 circuit, 225a, 120/208v, main lug only	EA	1,325.67	1,134.95	2,460.62	824.30	2,149.97	10.4000
16.4203 051	Panel, 30 circuit, 400a, 120/208v, main lug only	EA	1,615.25	1,440.52	3,055.77	1,046.23	2,661.48	13.2000
16.4203 061	Panel, 42 circuit, 225a, 120/208v, main lug only	EA	1,767.64	1,569.29	3,336.93	1,139.76	2,907.40	14.3800
16.4203 071	Panel, 42 circuit, 400a, 120/208v, main lug only	EA	1,944.68	1,798.46	3,743.14	1,306.20	3,250.88	16.4800
16.4204 000	**PANELBOARDS, BOLT-ON BREAKERS, 120/208V, 3 PH, 4 WIRE, MAIN CIRCUIT BREAKER:**							
	Note: The following prices include main circuit breaker.							
16.4204 011	Panel, 12 circuit, 100a, 120/208v, main circuit breaker	EA	1,121.80	423.69	1,545.49	307.72	1,429.52	3.8824
16.4204 021	Panel, 24 circuit, 100a, 120/208v, main circuit breaker	EA	1,469.25	977.80	2,447.05	710.17	2,179.42	8.9600
16.4204 031	Panel, 30 circuit, 100a, 120/208v, main circuit breaker	EA	1,633.49	1,156.78	2,790.27	840.16	2,473.65	10.6000
16.4204 041	Panel, 42 circuit, 225a, 120/208v, main circuit breaker	EA	2,946.22	1,711.16	4,657.38	1,242.80	4,189.02	15.6800
16.4204 051	Panel, 30 circuit, 400a, 120/208v, main circuit breaker	EA	3,774.94	1,505.99	5,280.93	1,093.79	4,868.73	13.8000
16.4204 061	Panel, 42 circuit, 400a, 120/208v, main circuit breaker	EA	4,108.52	1,885.77	5,994.29	1,369.61	5,478.13	17.2800
16.4300 000	**LOAD CENTERS, MAIN LUG & CIRCUIT BREAKER TYPES, 240V MAX**							
	Note: The following items are for plug-in breakers and include ground bus and cover with door. Prices do not include breakers.							
16.4301 000	**LOAD CENTERS, 120/240V, 1 PH, 3W, NEMA 1, INDOOR:**							
	Note: The following items are main lug only.							
16.4301 011	Panel, 12 circuit, 100a, 120/240, NEMA 1	EA	80.78	245.54	326.32	178.34	259.12	2.2500
16.4301 021	Panel, 16 circuit, 125a, 120/240, NEMA 1	EA	94.49	272.64	367.13	198.02	292.51	2.4983
16.4301 031	Panel, 24 circuit, 125a, 120/240, NEMA 1	EA	115.02	438.42	553.44	318.42	433.44	4.0174
16.4301 041	Panel, 24 circuit, 150a, 120/240, NEMA 1	EA	204.17	438.42	642.59	318.42	522.59	4.0174
16.4301 051	Panel, 30 circuit, 150a, 120/240, NEMA 1	EA	220.92	438.42	659.34	318.42	539.34	4.0174
16.4301 061	Panel, 16 circuit, 225a, 120/240, NEMA 1	EA	205.65	272.64	478.29	198.02	403.67	2.4983
16.4301 071	Panel, 24 circuit, 225a, 120/240, NEMA 1	EA	230.03	438.42	668.45	318.42	548.45	4.0174
16.4301 081	Panel, 30 circuit, 225a, 120/240, NEMA 1	EA	252.92	600.22	853.14	435.93	688.85	5.5000
16.4301 091	Panel, 42 circuit, 225a, 120/240, NEMA 1	EA	425.15	709.35	1,134.50	515.19	940.34	6.5000
16.4302 000	**LOAD CENTER, 120/240V, 1 PH, 3 WIRE, SOLID NEUTRAL , NEMA 3R, OUTDOOR, MAIN LUG ONLY:**							
	Note: The following items are main lug only.							
16.4302 011	Panel, 3 circuit, 60a, 120/208v, NEMA 3R	EA	53.28	163.70	216.98	118.89	172.17	1.5000
16.4302 021	Panel, 12 circuit, 125a, 120/208v, NEMA 3R	EA	184.36	381.96	566.32	277.41	461.77	3.5000
16.4302 031	Panel, 12 circuit, 200a, 120/208v, NEMA 3R	EA	249.75	436.52	686.27	317.04	566.79	4.0000
16.4302 041	Panel, 20 circuit, 125a, 120/208v, NEMA 3R	EA	261.91	491.09	753.00	356.67	618.58	4.5000
16.4302 051	Panel, 30 circuit, 225a, 120/208v, NEMA 3R	EA	364.13	480.17	844.30	348.74	712.87	4.4000
16.4302 061	Panel, 42 circuit, 225a, 120/208v, NEMA 3R	EA	498.27	567.48	1,065.75	412.15	910.42	5.2000
16.4303 000	**LOAD CENTER, 120/240V, 1 PH, 3 WIRE, SOLID NEUTRAL, NEMA 1, INDOOR:**							
	Note: The following prices include main circuit breaker.							
16.4303 011	Panel, 16 circuit, 100a, 120/240v, main circuit breaker	EA	181.36	323.02	504.38	234.61	415.97	2.9600
16.4303 021	Panel, 20 circuit, 100a, 120/240v, main circuit breaker	EA	218.66	366.68	585.34	266.31	484.97	3.3600
16.4303 031	Panel, 24 circuit, 125a, 120/240v, main circuit breaker	EA	415.27	464.46	879.73	337.33	752.60	4.2560
16.4303 041	Panel, 30 circuit, 150a, 120/240v, main circuit breaker	EA	432.75	464.46	897.21	337.33	770.08	4.2560
16.4303 051	Panel, 30 circuit, 225a, 120/240v, main circuit breaker	EA	534.82	545.65	1,080.47	396.30	931.12	5.0000
16.4303 061	Panel, 42 circuit, 225a, 120/240v, main circuit breaker	EA	627.87	567.37	1,195.24	412.07	1,039.94	5.1990
16.4304 000	**LOAD CENTER, 120/208V, 3 PH, 4 WIRE, NEMA 1, INDOOR:**							
	Note: The following prices include main circuit breaker.							
16.4304 011	Panel, 30 circuit, 125a, 120/208v, main circuit breaker	EA	1,031.59	535.87	1,567.46	389.20	1,420.79	4.9104

Division 16 CSI #	16 - ELECTRICAL Description	Unit	Material	Union Install	Union Total	Open Install	Open Total	Unit Man-Hrs
16.4304 000	**LOAD CENTER, 120/208V, 3 PH, 4 WIRE, NEMA 1, INDOOR: (Cont.)**							
16.4304 021	Panel, 30 circuit, 150a, 120/208v, main circuit breaker	EA	1,031.59	535.87	1,567.46	389.20	1,420.79	4.9104
16.4304 031	Panel, 30 circuit, 225a, 120/208v, main circuit breaker	EA	1,031.59	535.87	1,567.46	389.20	1,420.79	4.9104
16.4304 041	Panel, 42 circuit, 150a, 120/208v, main circuit breaker	EA	1,132.16	535.87	1,668.03	389.20	1,521.36	4.9104
16.4304 051	Panel, 42 circuit, 225a, 120/208v, main circuit breaker	EA	1,132.16	535.87	1,668.03	389.20	1,521.36	4.9104
16.4400 000	**PLUG-IN CIRCUIT BREAKERS, TYPE QO:**							
16.4401 000	**PLUG-IN CIRCUIT BREAKER, MAX 240V:**							
16.4401 011	Plug-in circuit breaker, to 30/1, 10k ampere interrupt capacity	EA	16.42	30.56	46.98	22.19	38.61	0.2800
16.4401 021	Plug-in circuit breaker, to 40/1, 10k ampere interrupt capacity	EA	16.42	32.74	49.16	23.78	40.20	0.3000
16.4401 031	Plug-in circuit breaker, to 50/1, 10k ampere interrupt capacity	EA	16.42	34.92	51.34	25.36	41.78	0.3200
16.4401 041	Plug-in circuit breaker, to 30/1, with ground fault interrupter	EA	128.61	30.56	159.17	22.19	150.80	0.2800
16.4401 051	Plug-in circuit breaker, to 30/2, 10k ampere interrupt capacity	EA	37.35	48.02	85.37	34.87	72.22	0.4400
16.4401 061	Plug-in circuit breaker, to 40/2, 10k ampere interrupt capacity	EA	37.35	50.20	87.55	36.46	73.81	0.4600
16.4401 071	Plug-in circuit breaker, to 50/2, 10k ampere interrupt capacity	EA	37.35	52.38	89.73	38.04	75.39	0.4800
16.4401 081	Plug-in circuit breaker, to 60/2, 10k ampere interrupt capacity	EA	37.35	65.48	102.83	47.56	84.91	0.6000
16.4401 091	Plug-in circuit breaker, to 70/2, 10k ampere interrupt capacity	EA	75.92	65.48	141.40	47.56	123.48	0.6000
16.4401 101	Plug-in circuit breaker, to 100/2, 10k ampere interrupt capacity	EA	106.97	78.57	185.54	57.07	164.04	0.7200
16.4401 111	Plug-in circuit breaker, to 125/2, 10k ampere interrupt capacity	EA	227.80	87.30	315.10	63.41	291.21	0.8000
16.4401 121	Plug-in circuit breaker, to 150/2, 10k ampere interrupt capacity	EA	227.80	96.03	323.83	69.75	297.55	0.8800
16.4401 131	Plug-in circuit breaker, to 30/3, 10k ampere interrupt capacity	EA	128.61	48.02	176.63	34.87	163.48	0.4400
16.4401 141	Plug-in circuit breaker, to 40/3, 10k ampere interrupt capacity	EA	128.61	50.20	178.81	36.46	165.07	0.4600
16.4401 151	Plug-in circuit breaker, to 50/3, 10k ampere interrupt capacity	EA	128.61	52.38	180.99	38.04	166.65	0.4800
16.4401 161	Plug-in circuit breaker, to 60/3, 10k ampere interrupt capacity	EA	128.61	66.33	194.94	48.17	176.78	0.6078
16.4401 171	Plug-in circuit breaker, to 70/3, 10k ampere interrupt capacity	EA	165.84	66.33	232.17	48.17	214.01	0.6078
16.4401 181	Plug-in circuit breaker, to 90/3, 10k ampere interrupt capacity	EA	272.30	74.21	346.51	53.90	326.20	0.6800
16.4401 191	Plug-in circuit breaker, to 100/3, 10k ampere interrupt capacity	EA	254.47	78.57	333.04	57.07	311.54	0.7200
16.4402 000	**PLUG-IN CIRCUIT BREAKER, MAX 240V, 65K AMPERE INTERRUPT CAPACITY:**							
16.4402 011	Plug-in circuit breaker, to 30/1, 65k ampere interrupt capacity	EA	59.68	30.56	90.24	22.19	81.87	0.2800
16.4402 021	Plug-in circuit breaker, to 30/2, 65k ampere interrupt capacity	EA	147.73	48.02	195.75	34.87	182.60	0.4400
16.4402 031	Plug-in circuit breaker, to 30/3, 65k ampere interrupt capacity	EA	258.09	48.02	306.11	34.87	292.96	0.4400
16.4500 000	**SPECIAL GEAR:**							
16.4501 000	**EMERGENCY GENERATORS WITH ACCESSORIES:**							
16.4501 011	Emergency generator to 30 kw	EA	29,453.74	3,572.48	33,026.22	2,594.66	32,048.40	32.7360
16.4501 021	Emergency generator to 60 kw	EA	35,150.58	5,358.72	40,509.30	3,891.98	39,042.56	49.1040
16.4501 031	Emergency generator to 100 kw	EA	50,215.15	7,144.96	57,360.11	5,189.31	55,404.46	65.4720
16.4501 041	Emergency generator to 150 kw	EA	60,258.21	8,931.20	69,189.41	6,486.64	66,744.85	81.8400
16.4501 051	Emergency generator to 200 kw	EA	70,301.21	10,717.44	81,018.65	7,783.97	78,085.18	98.2080
16.4501 061	Emergency generator to 400 kw	EA	145,623.92	12,503.68	158,127.60	9,081.29	154,705.21	114.5760
16.4501 071	Emergency generator to 600 kw	EA	225,968.22	14,289.92	240,258.14	10,378.62	236,346.84	130.9440
16.4501 081	Emergency generator to 750 kw	EA	316,355.46	17,862.40	334,217.86	12,973.28	329,328.74	163.6800
16.4501 091	Emergency generator to 1000 kw	EA	363,707.88	21,434.88	385,142.76	15,567.93	379,275.81	196.4160
16.4502 000	**TRANSFER SWITCHES, AUTOMATIC:**							
16.4502 011	Auto transfer switch to 30a	EA	7,222.00	357.25	7,579.25	259.47	7,481.47	3.2736
16.4502 021	Auto transfer switch to 70a	EA	7,317.74	535.87	7,853.61	389.20	7,706.94	4.9104
16.4502 031	Auto transfer switch to 100a	EA	7,988.55	714.50	8,703.05	518.93	8,507.48	6.5472
16.4502 041	Auto transfer switch to 150a	EA	8,508.32	893.12	9,401.44	648.66	9,156.98	8.1840
16.4502 051	Auto transfer switch to 225a	EA	13,830.27	1,071.74	14,902.01	778.40	14,608.67	9.8208
16.4502 061	Auto transfer switch to 260a	EA	13,830.27	1,250.37	15,080.64	908.13	14,738.40	11.4576
16.4502 071	Auto transfer switch to 400a	EA	15,514.27	1,428.99	16,943.26	1,037.86	16,552.13	13.0944
16.4502 081	Auto transfer switch to 600a	EA	23,821.27	1,607.62	25,428.89	1,167.59	24,988.86	14.7312
16.4502 091	Auto transfer switch to 800a	EA	28,470.65	1,786.24	30,256.89	1,297.33	29,767.98	16.3680
16.4502 101	Auto transfer switch to 1000a	EA	47,102.50	1,964.86	49,067.36	1,427.06	48,529.56	18.0048
16.4502 111	Auto transfer switch to 1200a	EA	48,825.75	2,143.49	50,969.24	1,556.79	50,382.54	19.6416
16.4502 121	Auto transfer switch to 1600a	EA	60,613.66	2,679.36	63,293.02	1,945.99	62,559.65	24.5520
16.4502 131	Auto transfer switch to 2000a	EA	63,134.73	3,215.23	66,349.96	2,335.19	65,469.92	29.4624
16.4503 000	**TRANSFER SWITCHES, AUTOMATIC WITH BYPASS:**							
16.4503 011	Auto transfer switch to 150a, bypass	EA	28,215.35	892.68	29,108.03	648.35	28,863.70	8.1800
16.4503 021	Auto transfer switch to 260a, bypass	EA	31,278.93	1,249.54	32,528.47	907.53	32,186.46	11.4500
16.4503 031	Auto transfer switch to 400a, bypass	EA	42,573.44	1,428.51	44,001.95	1,037.51	43,610.95	13.0900
16.4503 041	Auto transfer switch to 600a, bypass	EA	58,706.27	1,607.48	60,313.75	1,167.50	59,873.77	14.7300
16.4503 051	Auto transfer switch to 800a, bypass	EA	69,551.53	1,785.37	71,336.90	1,296.69	70,848.22	16.3600
16.4503 061	Auto transfer switch to 1000a, bypass	EA	106,410.23	1,964.34	108,374.57	1,426.68	107,836.91	18.0000

Division 16 CSI #	16 - ELECTRICAL Description	Unit	Material	Union Install	Union Total	Open Install	Open Total	Unit Man-Hrs
16.4503 000	**TRANSFER SWITCHES, AUTOMATIC WITH BYPASS: (Cont.)**							
16.4503 071	Auto transfer switch to 1200a, bypass	EA	119,914.00	2,143.31	122,057.31	1,556.67	121,470.67	19.6400
16.4503 081	Auto transfer switch to 1600a, bypass	EA	154,950.97	2,679.14	157,630.11	1,945.83	156,896.80	24.5500
16.4503 091	Auto transfer switch to 2000a, bypass	EA	173,268.87	3,214.97	176,483.84	2,335.00	175,603.87	29.4600
16.4504 000	**UNINTERRUPTED POWER SYSTEMS:**							
16.4504 011	Uninterrupted power supply with battery bank, 37.5kva	EA	127,714.82	14,035.38	141,750.20	10,193.76	137,908.58	128.6116
16.4504 021	Uninterrupted power supply with battery bank, 50kva	EA	141,976.22	18,713.55	160,689.77	13,591.46	155,567.68	171.4794
16.4504 031	Uninterrupted power supply with battery bank, 75kva	EA	157,906.65	21,265.19	179,171.84	15,444.69	173,351.34	194.8611
16.4504 041	Uninterrupted power supply with battery bank, 100kva	EA	192,901.70	26,793.60	219,695.30	19,459.92	212,361.62	245.5200
16.4504 051	Uninterrupted power supply with battery bank, 125kva	EA	198,391.15	31,211.18	229,602.33	22,668.36	221,059.51	286.0000
16.4504 061	Uninterrupted power supply with battery bank, 225 kva	EA	237,188.82	37,758.98	274,947.80	27,423.96	264,612.78	346.0000
16.5000 000	**PVC, RSC, IMC & ALUMINUM RACEWAY:**							
16.5001 000	**PVC CONDUIT, SCHEDULE 40, CONCRETE ENCASED, TRENCH & BURIED:**							
16.5001 011	PVC conduit, '40', trench & buried in concrete, 1-2"	LF	17.87	4.32	22.19	2.80	20.67	0.0504
16.5001 021	PVC conduit, '40', trench & buried in concrete, 2-2"	LF	21.96	5.30	27.26	3.43	25.39	0.0619
16.5001 031	PVC conduit, '40', trench & buried in concrete, 3-2"	LF	22.76	6.15	28.91	3.98	26.74	0.0718
16.5001 041	PVC conduit, '40', trench & buried in concrete, 4-2"	LF	23.59	7.10	30.69	4.60	28.19	0.0829
16.5001 051	PVC conduit, '40', trench & buried in concrete, 1-3"	LF	19.10	5.69	24.79	3.68	22.78	0.0664
16.5001 061	PVC conduit, '40', trench & buried in concrete, 2-3"	LF	23.13	7.11	30.24	4.61	27.74	0.0830
16.5001 071	PVC conduit, '40', trench & buried in concrete, 3-3"	LF	27.61	8.52	36.13	5.52	33.13	0.0995
16.5001 081	PVC conduit, '40', trench & buried in concrete, 4-3"	LF	29.21	9.46	38.67	6.13	35.34	0.1105
16.5001 091	PVC conduit, '40', trench & buried in concrete, 1-4"	LF	22.88	9.46	32.34	6.13	29.01	0.1105
16.5001 101	PVC conduit, '40', trench & buried in concrete, 2-4"	LF	27.79	12.30	40.09	7.97	35.76	0.1436
16.5001 111	PVC conduit, '40', trench & buried in concrete, 3-4"	LF	33.35	14.20	47.55	9.21	42.56	0.1659
16.5001 121	PVC conduit, '40', trench & buried in concrete, 4-4"	LF	35.91	15.62	51.53	10.12	46.03	0.1824
16.5001 131	PVC conduit, '40', trench & buried in concrete, 1-5"	LF	29.59	10.88	40.47	7.05	36.64	0.1271
16.5001 141	PVC conduit, '40', trench & buried in concrete, 2-5"	LF	35.22	15.15	50.37	9.82	45.04	0.1769
16.5001 151	PVC conduit, '40', trench & buried in concrete, 3-5"	LF	37.72	17.52	55.24	11.35	49.07	0.2046
16.5001 161	PVC conduit, '40', trench & buried in concrete, 4-5"	LF	39.83	19.89	59.72	12.89	52.72	0.2323
16.5001 171	PVC conduit, '40', trench & buried in concrete, 1-6"	LF	34.19	11.37	45.56	7.37	41.56	0.1328
16.5001 181	PVC conduit, '40', trench & buried in concrete, 2-6"	LF	39.84	15.73	55.57	10.19	50.03	0.1837
16.5001 191	PVC conduit, '40', trench & buried in concrete, 4-6"	LF	61.19	24.13	85.32	15.64	76.83	0.2818
16.5001 201	PVC conduit, '40', trench & buried in concrete, 6-6"	LF	81.81	32.24	114.05	20.89	102.70	0.3765
16.5001 211	PVC conduit, '40', trench & buried in concrete, 8-6"	LF	112.63	44.40	157.03	28.78	141.41	0.5186
16.5001 221	PVC conduit, '40', trench & buried in concrete, 10-6"	LF	131.44	51.83	183.27	33.59	165.03	0.6053
16.5001 231	PVC conduit, '40', trench & buried in concrete, 12-6"	LF	150.88	59.48	210.36	38.55	189.43	0.6947
16.5002 000	**PVC CONDUIT, SCHEDULE 40, EMBEDDED:**							
16.5002 011	PVC conduit, 1/2", underground embed in slab	LF	.90	3.49	4.39	2.54	3.44	0.0320
16.5002 021	PVC conduit, 3/4", underground embed in slab	LF	1.18	3.49	4.67	2.54	3.72	0.0320
16.5002 031	PVC conduit, 1", underground embed in slab	LF	1.81	3.49	5.30	2.54	4.35	0.0320
16.5002 041	PVC conduit, 1-1/4", underground embed in slab	LF	2.49	3.49	5.98	2.54	5.03	0.0320
16.5002 051	PVC conduit, 1-1/2", underground embed in slab	LF	3.03	4.37	7.40	3.17	6.20	0.0400
16.5002 061	PVC conduit, 2", underground embed in slab	LF	3.80	5.24	9.04	3.80	7.60	0.0480
16.5002 071	PVC conduit, 2-1/2", underground embed in slab	LF	6.09	7.86	13.95	5.71	11.80	0.0720
16.5002 081	PVC conduit, 3", underground embed in slab	LF	7.68	10.48	18.16	7.61	15.29	0.0960
16.5002 091	PVC conduit, 3-1/2", underground embed in slab	LF	9.69	12.22	21.91	8.88	18.57	0.1120
16.5002 101	PVC conduit, 4", underground embed in slab	LF	10.90	13.97	24.87	10.15	21.05	0.1280
16.5002 111	PVC conduit, 5", underground embed in slab	LF	15.53	19.21	34.74	13.95	29.48	0.1760
16.5002 121	PVC conduit, 6", underground embed in slab	LF	20.15	26.19	46.34	19.02	39.17	0.2400
16.5003 000	**PVC CONDUIT TERMINATIONS & ELBOWS:**							
16.5003 011	1/2" PVC terminal adapters	EA	.87	10.91	11.78	7.93	8.80	0.1000
16.5003 021	3/4" PVC terminal adapters	EA	1.60	13.10	14.70	9.51	11.11	0.1200
16.5003 031	1" PVC terminal adapters	EA	2.00	16.37	18.37	11.89	13.89	0.1500
16.5003 041	1-1/4" PVC terminal adapters	EA	2.60	18.55	21.15	13.47	16.07	0.1700
16.5003 051	1-1/2" PVC terminal adapters	EA	3.10	21.83	24.93	15.85	18.95	0.2000
16.5003 061	2" PVC terminal adapters	EA	4.52	27.28	31.80	19.82	24.34	0.2500
16.5003 071	2-1/2" terminal adapters	EA	7.71	32.74	40.45	23.78	31.49	0.3000
16.5003 081	3" PVC terminal adapters	EA	11.17	38.20	49.37	27.74	38.91	0.3500
16.5003 091	3-1/2" PVC terminal adapters	EA	14.65	43.65	58.30	31.70	46.35	0.4000
16.5003 101	4" PVC terminal adapters	EA	19.14	49.11	68.25	35.67	54.81	0.4500
16.5003 111	5" PVC terminal adapters	EA	37.80	52.87	90.67	38.40	76.20	0.4845
16.5003 121	6" PVC terminal adapters	EA	45.53	63.46	108.99	46.09	91.62	0.5815

Division 16 CSI #	16 - ELECTRICAL Description	Unit	Material	Union Install	Union Total	Open Install	Open Total	Unit Man-Hrs
16.5003 000	PVC CONDUIT TERMINATIONS & ELBOWS: (Cont.)							
16.5003 131	5" PVC elbow with 1 coupling	EA	143.23	190.38	333.61	138.27	281.50	1.7445
16.5003 141	6" PVC elbow with 1 coupling	EA	227.20	222.10	449.30	161.31	388.51	2.0352
16.5003 151	1/2" PVC elbow with 1 coupling	EA	3.02	19.64	22.66	14.27	17.29	0.1800
16.5003 161	3/4" PVC elbow with 1 coupling	EA	3.41	24.01	27.42	17.44	20.85	0.2200
16.5003 171	1" PVC elbow with 1 coupling	EA	5.33	28.37	33.70	20.61	25.94	0.2600
16.5003 181	1-1/4" PVC elbow with 1 coupling	EA	7.40	36.01	43.41	26.16	33.56	0.3300
16.5003 191	1-1/2" PVC elbow with 1 coupling	EA	10.01	49.11	59.12	35.67	45.68	0.4500
16.5003 201	2" PVC elbow with 1 coupling	EA	14.30	61.11	75.41	44.39	58.69	0.5600
16.5003 211	2-1/2" PVC elbow with 1 coupling	EA	25.95	89.49	115.44	64.99	90.94	0.8200
16.5003 221	3" PVC elbow with 1 coupling	EA	44.51	130.96	175.47	95.11	139.62	1.2000
16.5003 231	3-1/2" PVC elbow with 1 coupling	EA	59.06	163.70	222.76	118.89	177.95	1.5000
16.5003 241	4" PVC elbow with 1 coupling	EA	75.26	182.98	258.24	132.90	208.16	1.6767
16.5004 000	RIGID STEEL CONDUIT, EMBEDDED:							
16.5004 011	RSC, 1/2", embedded	LF	2.05	3.49	5.54	2.54	4.59	0.0320
16.5004 021	RSC, 3/4", embedded	LF	2.56	4.37	6.93	3.17	5.73	0.0400
16.5004 031	RSC, 1", embedded	LF	3.54	5.24	8.78	3.80	7.34	0.0480
16.5004 041	RSC, 1-1/4", embedded	LF	4.56	6.55	11.11	4.76	9.32	0.0600
16.5004 051	RSC, 1-1/2", embedded	LF	5.76	7.86	13.62	5.71	11.47	0.0720
16.5004 061	RSC, 2", embedded	LF	7.44	9.60	17.04	6.97	14.41	0.0880
16.5004 071	RSC, 2-1/2", embedded	LF	12.57	10.48	23.05	7.61	20.18	0.0960
16.5004 081	RSC, 3", embedded	LF	15.34	13.10	28.44	9.51	24.85	0.1200
16.5004 091	RSC, 3-1/2", embedded	LF	19.16	15.71	34.87	11.41	30.57	0.1440
16.5004 101	RSC, 4", embedded	LF	22.63	18.33	40.96	13.32	35.95	0.1680
16.5004 111	RSC, 5", embedded	LF	51.70	24.45	76.15	17.75	69.45	0.2240
16.5004 121	RSC, 6", embedded	LF	65.06	31.43	96.49	22.83	87.89	0.2880
16.5005 000	RIGID STEEL CONDUIT, CONCEALED:							
16.5005 011	RSC, 1/2", concealed	LF	2.12	4.80	6.92	3.49	5.61	0.0440
16.5005 021	RSC, 3/4", concealed	LF	2.68	5.67	8.35	4.12	6.80	0.0520
16.5005 031	RSC, 1", concealed	LF	3.71	6.98	10.69	5.07	8.78	0.0640
16.5005 041	RSC, 1-1/4", concealed	LF	4.79	8.73	13.52	6.34	11.13	0.0800
16.5005 051	RSC, 1-1/2", concealed	LF	6.02	10.48	16.50	7.61	13.63	0.0960
16.5005 061	RSC, 2", concealed	LF	7.83	12.22	20.05	8.88	16.71	0.1120
16.5005 071	RSC, 2-1/2", concealed	LF	13.15	13.97	27.12	10.15	23.30	0.1280
16.5005 081	RSC, 3", concealed	LF	16.05	17.46	33.51	12.68	28.73	0.1600
16.5005 091	RSC, 3-1/2", concealed	LF	20.14	20.95	41.09	15.22	35.36	0.1920
16.5005 101	RSC, 4", concealed	LF	23.76	24.45	48.21	17.75	41.51	0.2240
16.5005 111	RSC, 5", concealed	LF	54.82	33.18	88.00	24.10	78.92	0.3040
16.5005 121	RSC, 6", concealed	LF	68.32	41.91	110.23	30.44	98.76	0.3840
16.5006 000	RIGID STEEL CONDUIT, EXPOSED:							
16.5006 011	RSC, 1/2", exposed	LF	2.20	5.90	8.10	4.29	6.49	0.0541
16.5006 021	RSC, 3/4", exposed	LF	2.72	7.20	9.92	5.23	7.95	0.0660
16.5006 031	RSC, 1", exposed	LF	3.79	8.73	12.52	6.34	10.13	0.0800
16.5006 041	RSC, 1-1/4", exposed	LF	4.95	10.91	15.86	7.93	12.88	0.1000
16.5006 051	RSC, 1-1/2", exposed	LF	6.19	13.10	19.29	9.51	15.70	0.1200
16.5006 061	RSC, 2", exposed	LF	8.06	15.71	23.77	11.41	19.47	0.1440
16.5006 071	RSC, 2-1/2", exposed	LF	13.60	17.46	31.06	12.68	26.28	0.1600
16.5006 081	RSC, 3", exposed	LF	16.54	21.83	38.37	15.85	32.39	0.2000
16.5006 091	RSC, 3-1/2", exposed	LF	20.72	26.19	46.91	19.02	39.74	0.2400
16.5006 101	RSC, 4", exposed	LF	25.63	30.56	56.19	22.19	47.82	0.2800
16.5006 111	RSC, 5", exposed	LF	59.22	41.03	100.25	29.80	89.02	0.3760
16.5006 121	RSC, 6", exposed	LF	73.79	52.38	126.17	38.04	111.83	0.4800
16.5007 000	INTERMEDIATE METAL CONDUIT, EMBEDDED:							
16.5007 011	Intermediate metal conduit, 1/2", embedded	LF	1.59	3.44	5.03	2.50	4.09	0.0315
16.5007 021	Intermediate metal conduit, 3/4", embedded	LF	1.88	4.52	6.40	3.28	5.16	0.0414
16.5007 031	Intermediate metal conduit, 1", embedded	LF	2.63	5.83	8.46	4.23	6.86	0.0534
16.5007 041	Intermediate metal conduit, 1-1/4", embedded	LF	3.36	5.83	9.19	4.23	7.59	0.0534
16.5007 051	Intermediate metal conduit, 1-1/2", embedded	LF	3.89	7.12	11.01	5.17	9.06	0.0652
16.5007 061	Intermediate metal conduit, 2", embedded	LF	5.35	7.86	13.21	5.71	11.06	0.0720
16.5007 071	Intermediate metal conduit, 2-1/2", embedded	LF	11.00	8.73	19.73	6.34	17.34	0.0800
16.5007 081	Intermediate metal conduit, 3", embedded	LF	13.79	13.90	27.69	10.10	23.89	0.1274
16.5007 091	Intermediate metal conduit, 3-1/2", embedded	LF	16.08	17.46	33.54	12.68	28.76	0.1600

Division 16 CSI #	16 - ELECTRICAL Description	Unit	Material	Union Install	Union Total	Open Install	Open Total	Unit Man-Hrs
16.5007 000	**INTERMEDIATE METAL CONDUIT, EMBEDDED: (Cont.)**							
16.5007 101	Intermediate metal conduit, 4", embedded	LF	19.04	18.41	37.45	13.37	32.41	0.1687
16.5008 000	**INTERMEDIATE METAL CONDUIT, CONCEALED:**							
16.5008 011	Intermediate metal conduit, 1/2", concealed	LF	1.67	4.25	5.92	3.08	4.75	0.0389
16.5008 021	Intermediate metal conduit, 3/4", concealed	LF	1.92	6.13	8.05	4.45	6.37	0.0562
16.5008 031	Intermediate metal conduit, 1", concealed	LF	2.72	6.80	9.52	4.94	7.66	0.0623
16.5008 041	Intermediate metal conduit, 1-1/4", concealed	LF	3.49	6.80	10.29	4.94	8.43	0.0623
16.5008 051	Intermediate metal conduit, 1-1/2", concealed	LF	4.08	8.32	12.40	6.04	10.12	0.0762
16.5008 061	Intermediate metal conduit, 2", concealed	LF	5.67	10.48	16.15	7.61	13.28	0.0960
16.5008 071	Intermediate metal conduit, 2-1/2", concealed	LF	11.58	11.35	22.93	8.24	19.82	0.1040
16.5008 081	Intermediate metal conduit, 3", concealed	LF	14.48	13.97	28.45	10.15	24.63	0.1280
16.5008 091	Intermediate metal conduit, 3-1/2", concealed	LF	16.90	15.71	32.61	11.41	28.31	0.1440
16.5008 101	Intermediate metal conduit, 4", concealed	LF	19.98	21.58	41.56	15.67	35.65	0.1977
16.5009 000	**INTERMEDIATE METAL CONDUIT, EXPOSED:**							
16.5009 011	Intermediate metal conduit, 1/2", exposed	LF	1.73	5.67	7.40	4.12	5.85	0.0520
16.5009 021	Intermediate metal conduit, 3/4", exposed	LF	1.96	7.64	9.60	5.55	7.51	0.0700
16.5009 031	Intermediate metal conduit, 1", exposed	LF	2.79	8.23	11.02	5.98	8.77	0.0754
16.5009 041	Intermediate metal conduit, 1-1/4", exposed	LF	3.62	8.23	11.85	5.98	9.60	0.0754
16.5009 051	Intermediate metal conduit, 1-1/2", exposed	LF	4.16	10.91	15.07	7.93	12.09	0.1000
16.5009 061	Intermediate metal conduit, 2", exposed	LF	5.78	13.10	18.88	9.51	15.29	0.1200
16.5009 071	Intermediate metal conduit, 2-1/2", exposed	LF	11.89	13.97	25.86	10.15	22.04	0.1280
16.5009 081	Intermediate metal conduit, 3", exposed	LF	14.88	17.46	32.34	12.68	27.56	0.1600
16.5009 091	Intermediate metal conduit, 3-1/2", exposed	LF	17.39	19.64	37.03	14.27	31.66	0.1800
16.5009 101	Intermediate metal conduit, 4", exposed	LF	20.56	24.65	45.21	17.90	38.46	0.2259
16.5010 000	**ALUMINUM CONDUIT, CONCEALED:**							
16.5010 011	Aluminum conduit, 1/2", concealed	LF	1.82	4.19	6.01	3.04	4.86	0.0384
16.5010 021	Aluminum conduit, 3/4", concealed	LF	2.42	5.67	8.09	4.12	6.54	0.0520
16.5010 031	Aluminum conduit, 1", concealed	LF	3.45	6.55	10.00	4.76	8.21	0.0600
16.5010 041	Aluminum conduit, 1-1/4" concealed	LF	4.52	7.86	12.38	5.71	10.23	0.0720
16.5010 051	Aluminum conduit, 1-1/2", concealed	LF	5.68	9.60	15.28	6.97	12.65	0.0880
16.5010 061	Aluminum conduit, 2", concealed	LF	7.55	6.98	14.53	5.07	12.62	0.0640
16.5010 071	Aluminum conduit, 2-1/2", concealed	LF	11.93	9.60	21.53	6.97	18.90	0.0880
16.5010 081	Aluminum conduit, 3", concealed	LF	15.68	12.22	27.90	8.88	24.56	0.1120
16.5010 091	Aluminum conduit, 3-1/2", concealed	LF	18.67	13.97	32.64	10.15	28.82	0.1280
16.5010 101	Aluminum conduit, 4", concealed	LF	22.29	16.59	38.88	12.05	34.34	0.1520
16.5010 111	Aluminum conduit, 5", concealed	LF	31.90	20.95	52.85	15.22	47.12	0.1920
16.5010 121	Aluminum conduit, 6", concealed	LF	42.05	26.19	68.24	19.02	61.07	0.2400
16.5011 000	**ALUMINUM CONDUIT, EXPOSED:**							
16.5011 011	Aluminum conduit, 1/2", exposed	LF	1.95	5.67	7.62	4.12	6.07	0.0520
16.5011 021	Aluminum conduit, 3/4", exposed	LF	2.63	6.55	9.18	4.76	7.39	0.0600
16.5011 031	Aluminum conduit, 1", exposed	LF	3.66	8.08	11.74	5.87	9.53	0.0740
16.5011 041	Aluminum conduit, 1-1/4", exposed	LF	4.86	10.04	14.90	7.29	12.15	0.0920
16.5011 051	Aluminum conduit, 1-1/2", exposed	LF	6.02	12.22	18.24	8.88	14.90	0.1120
16.5011 061	Aluminum conduit, 2", exposed	LF	8.06	8.73	16.79	6.34	14.40	0.0800
16.5011 071	Aluminum conduit, 2-1/2", exposed	LF	12.78	11.79	24.57	8.56	21.34	0.1080
16.5011 081	Aluminum conduit, 3", exposed	LF	16.79	15.28	32.07	11.10	27.89	0.1400
16.5011 091	Aluminum conduit, 3-1/2" exposed	LF	19.98	17.46	37.44	12.68	32.66	0.1600
16.5011 101	Aluminum conduit, 4", exposed	LF	23.84	20.95	44.79	15.22	39.06	0.1920
16.5011 111	Aluminum conduit, 5", exposed	LF	34.14	26.19	60.33	19.02	53.16	0.2400
16.5011 121	Aluminum conduit, 6", exposed	LF	44.98	32.30	77.28	23.46	68.44	0.2960
16.5100 000	**PVC, RSC, IMC & ALUMINUM CONDUIT TERMINALS, ELBOWS & FITTINGS:**							
16.5101 000	**CONDUIT TERMINATION FOR RSC, IMC & ALUMINUM:**							
16.5101 011	1/2" double locknut & ground bushing	EA	4.56	21.83	26.39	15.85	20.41	0.2000
16.5101 021	3/4" double locknut & ground bushing	EA	5.29	27.28	32.57	19.82	25.11	0.2500
16.5101 031	1" double locknut & ground bushing	EA	7.84	32.74	40.58	23.78	31.62	0.3000
16.5101 041	1-1/4" double locknut & ground bushing	EA	9.35	38.20	47.55	27.74	37.09	0.3500
16.5101 051	1-1/2" double locknut & ground bushing	EA	11.59	54.57	66.16	39.63	51.22	0.5000
16.5101 061	2" double locknut & ground bushing	EA	16.32	65.48	81.80	47.56	63.88	0.6000
16.5101 071	2-1/2" double locknut & ground bushing	EA	28.32	109.13	137.45	79.26	107.58	1.0000
16.5101 081	3" double locknut & ground bushing	EA	36.32	141.87	178.19	103.04	139.36	1.3000
16.5101 091	3-1/2" double locknut & ground bushing	EA	53.33	163.70	217.03	118.89	172.22	1.5000
16.5101 101	4" double locknut & ground bushing	EA	68.17	196.43	264.60	142.67	210.84	1.8000

221

Division 16 CSI #	16 - ELECTRICAL Description	Unit	Material	Union Install	Union Total	Open Install	Open Total	Unit Man-Hrs
16.5101 000	**CONDUIT TERMINATION FOR RSC, IMC & ALUMINUM: (Cont.)**							
16.5101 111	5" double locknut & ground busing	EA	78.40	305.56	383.96	221.93	300.33	2.8000
16.5101 121	6" double locknut & ground bushing	EA	123.07	436.52	559.59	317.04	440.11	4.0000
16.5102 000	**CONDUIT HUBS:**							
16.5102 011	1/2" conduit hub	EA	6.72	27.28	34.00	19.82	26.54	0.2500
16.5102 021	3/4" conduit hub	EA	7.71	32.74	40.45	23.78	31.49	0.3000
16.5102 031	1" conduit hub	EA	9.71	38.20	47.91	27.74	37.45	0.3500
16.5102 041	1-1/4" conduit hub	EA	11.10	43.65	54.75	31.70	42.80	0.4000
16.5102 051	1-1/2" conduit hub	EA	11.60	54.57	66.17	39.63	51.23	0.5000
16.5102 061	2" conduit hub	EA	15.87	81.85	97.72	59.45	75.32	0.7500
16.5102 071	2-1/2" conduit hub	EA	31.35	109.13	140.48	79.26	110.61	1.0000
16.5102 081	3" conduit hub	EA	44.32	163.70	208.02	118.89	163.21	1.5000
16.5102 091	3-1/2" conduit hub	EA	58.48	218.26	276.74	158.52	217.00	2.0000
16.5102 101	4" conduit hub	EA	73.09	305.56	378.65	221.93	295.02	2.8000
16.5102 111	5" conduit hub	EA	134.82	436.52	571.34	317.04	451.86	4.0000
16.5102 121	6" conduit hub	EA	180.80	545.65	726.45	396.30	577.10	5.0000
16.5103 000	**RIGID CONDUIT ELBOWS:**							
16.5103 011	1/2" galvanized rigid conduit elbow with 1 coupling	EA	7.80	27.28	35.08	19.82	27.62	0.2500
16.5103 021	3/4" galvanized rigid conduit elbow with 1 coupling	EA	9.45	32.74	42.19	23.78	33.23	0.3000
16.5103 031	1" galvanized rigid conduit elbow with 1 coupling	EA	13.83	38.20	52.03	27.74	41.57	0.3500
16.5103 041	1-1/4" galvanized rigid conduit elbow with 1 coupling	EA	19.32	60.02	79.34	43.59	62.91	0.5500
16.5103 051	1-1/2" galvanized rigid conduit elbow with 1 coupling	EA	24.19	76.39	100.58	55.48	79.67	0.7000
16.5103 061	2" galvanized rigid conduit elbow with 1 coupling	EA	34.78	98.22	133.00	71.33	106.11	0.9000
16.5103 071	2-1/2" galvanized rigid conduit elbow with 1 coupling	EA	62.27	152.78	215.05	110.96	173.23	1.4000
16.5103 081	3" galvanized rigid conduit elbow with 1 coupling	EA	91.12	218.26	309.38	158.52	249.64	2.0000
16.5103 091	3-1/2" galvanized rigid conduit elbow with 1 coupling	EA	149.30	272.83	422.13	198.15	347.45	2.5000
16.5103 101	4" galvanized rigid conduit elbow with 1 coupling	EA	170.11	355.55	525.66	258.23	428.34	3.2580
16.5103 111	5" galvanized rigid conduit elbow with 1 coupling	EA	369.95	436.52	806.47	317.04	686.99	4.0000
16.5103 121	6" galvanized rigid conduit elbow with 1 coupling	EA	584.63	545.65	1,130.28	396.30	980.93	5.0000
16.5104 000	**INTERMEDIATE METAL CONDUIT ELBOWS:**							
16.5104 011	1/2" intermediate metal conduit elbow	EA	4.87	21.83	26.70	15.85	20.72	0.2000
16.5104 021	3/4" intermediate metal conduit elbow	EA	6.39	27.28	33.67	19.82	26.21	0.2500
16.5104 031	1" intermediate metal conduit elbow	EA	9.19	32.74	41.93	23.78	32.97	0.3000
16.5104 041	1-1/4" intermediate metal conduit elbow	EA	12.88	54.57	67.45	39.63	52.51	0.5000
16.5104 051	1-1/2" intermediate metal conduit elbow	EA	16.31	70.93	87.24	51.52	67.83	0.6500
16.5104 061	2" intermediate metal conduit elbow	EA	23.53	92.76	116.29	67.37	90.90	0.8500
16.5104 071	2-1/2" intermediate metal conduit elbow	EA	40.66	136.41	177.07	99.08	139.74	1.2500
16.5104 081	3" intermediate metal conduit elbow	EA	62.23	190.98	253.21	138.71	200.94	1.7500
16.5104 091	3-1/2" intermediate metal conduit elbow	EA	109.88	218.26	328.14	158.52	268.40	2.0000
16.5104 101	4 " intermediate metal conduit elbow	EA	127.47	300.11	427.58	217.97	345.44	2.7500
16.5105 000	**ALUMINUM ELBOWS:**							
16.5105 011	1/2" aluminum elbow	EA	5.15	16.37	21.52	11.89	17.04	0.1500
16.5105 021	3/4" aluminum elbow	EA	7.03	21.83	28.86	15.85	22.88	0.2000
16.5105 031	1" aluminum elbow	EA	9.77	28.16	37.93	20.45	30.22	0.2580
16.5105 041	1-1/4" aluminum elbow	EA	15.52	49.11	64.63	35.67	51.19	0.4500
16.5105 051	1-1/2" aluminum elbow	EA	20.67	65.48	86.15	47.56	68.23	0.6000
16.5105 061	2" aluminum elbow	EA	30.42	87.30	117.72	63.41	93.83	0.8000
16.5105 071	2-1/2" aluminum elbow	EA	51.35	130.96	182.31	95.11	146.46	1.2000
16.5105 081	3" aluminum elbow	EA	79.28	163.70	242.98	118.89	198.17	1.5000
16.5105 091	3-1/2" aluminum elbow	EA	123.64	190.98	314.62	138.71	262.35	1.7500
16.5105 101	4" aluminum elbow	EA	146.64	272.83	419.47	198.15	344.79	2.5000
16.5105 111	5" aluminum elbow	EA	400.25	354.67	754.92	257.60	657.85	3.2500
16.5105 121	6" aluminum elbow	EA	554.01	436.52	990.53	317.04	871.05	4.0000
16.5200 000	**EMT RACEWAY, TERMINATIONS & ELBOWS:**							
16.5201 000	**EMT CONDUIT, CONCEALED:**							
16.5201 011	1/2" EMT conduit, concealed	LF	.82	3.82	4.64	2.77	3.59	0.0350
16.5201 021	3/4" EMT conduit, concealed	LF	1.02	4.37	5.39	3.17	4.19	0.0400
16.5201 031	1" EMT conduit, concealed	LF	1.62	4.91	6.53	3.57	5.19	0.0450
16.5201 041	1-1/4" EMT conduit, concealed	LF	2.57	6.00	8.57	4.36	6.93	0.0550
16.5201 051	1-1/2" EMT conduit, concealed	LF	3.08	7.09	10.17	5.15	8.23	0.0650
16.5201 061	2" EMT conduit, concealed	LF	3.55	8.18	11.73	5.94	9.49	0.0750
16.5201 071	2-1/2" EMT conduit, concealed	LF	9.97	9.82	19.79	7.13	17.10	0.0900

Division 16 CSI #	16 - ELECTRICAL Description	Unit	Material	Union Install	Union Total	Open Install	Open Total	Unit Man-Hrs
16.5201 000	**EMT CONDUIT, CONCEALED: (Cont.)**							
16.5201 081	3" EMT conduit, concealed	LF	12.47	12.00	24.47	8.72	21.19	0.1100
16.5201 091	4" EMT conduit, concealed	LF	19.16	15.28	34.44	11.10	30.26	0.1400
16.5202 000	**EMT CONDUIT, EXPOSED:**							
16.5202 011	1/2" EMT conduit, exposed	LF	.87	4.37	5.24	3.17	4.04	0.0400
16.5202 021	3/4" EMT conduit, exposed	LF	1.08	4.91	5.99	3.57	4.65	0.0450
16.5202 031	1" EMT conduit, exposed	LF	1.75	5.46	7.21	3.96	5.71	0.0500
16.5202 041	1-1/4" EMT conduit, exposed	LF	2.83	7.09	9.92	5.15	7.98	0.0650
16.5202 051	1-1/2" EMT conduit, exposed	LF	3.25	8.18	11.43	5.94	9.19	0.0750
16.5202 061	2" EMT conduit, exposed	LF	4.16	9.28	13.44	6.74	10.90	0.0850
16.5202 071	2-1/2" EMT conduit, exposed	LF	11.10	10.91	22.01	7.93	19.03	0.1000
16.5202 081	3" EMT conduit, exposed	LF	12.47	13.10	25.57	9.51	21.98	0.1200
16.5202 091	4" EMT conduit, exposed	LF	21.40	17.46	38.86	12.68	34.08	0.1600
16.5203 000	**EMT CONDUIT TERMINATIONS:**							
16.5203 011	1/2" EMT set-screw connectors	EA	1.23	10.91	12.14	7.93	9.16	0.1000
16.5203 021	3/4" EMT set-screw connectors	EA	2.03	10.91	12.94	7.93	9.96	0.1000
16.5203 031	1" EMT set-screw connectors	EA	3.31	16.37	19.68	11.89	15.20	0.1500
16.5203 041	1-1/4" EMT set-screw connectors	EA	6.01	16.37	22.38	11.89	17.90	0.1500
16.5203 051	1-1/2" EMT set-screw connectors	EA	8.74	21.83	30.57	15.85	24.59	0.2000
16.5203 061	2" EMT set-screw connectors	EA	12.64	27.28	39.92	19.82	32.46	0.2500
16.5203 071	2-1/2" EMT set-screw connectors	EA	56.20	38.20	94.40	27.74	83.94	0.3500
16.5203 081	3" EMT set-screw connectors	EA	66.41	54.57	120.98	39.63	106.04	0.5000
16.5203 091	3-1/2" EMT set-screw connectors	EA	89.03	65.48	154.51	47.56	136.59	0.6000
16.5203 101	4" EMT set-screw connectors	EA	97.16	65.48	162.64	47.56	144.72	0.6000
16.5204 000	**EMT ELBOWS:**							
16.5204 011	1" EMT elbow with 2 couplings	EA	10.17	16.37	26.54	11.89	22.06	0.1500
16.5204 021	1-1/4" elbow with 2 couplings	EA	17.61	21.83	39.44	15.85	33.46	0.2000
16.5204 031	1-1/2" EMT elbow with 2 couplings	EA	24.46	32.74	57.20	23.78	48.24	0.3000
16.5204 041	2" EMT elbow with 2 couplings	EA	34.88	38.20	73.08	27.74	62.62	0.3500
16.5204 051	2-1/2" EMT elbow with 2 couplings	EA	85.50	65.48	150.98	47.56	133.06	0.6000
16.5204 061	3" EMT elbow with 2 couplings	EA	111.15	98.22	209.37	71.33	182.48	0.9000
16.5204 071	3-1/2" EMT elbow with 2 couplings	EA	139.22	152.78	292.00	110.96	250.18	1.4000
16.5204 081	4" EMT elbow with 2 couplings	EA	161.72	152.78	314.50	110.96	272.68	1.4000
16.5205 000	**CONDUIT BODIES WITH COVER & GASKET:**							
16.5205 011	1/2" LB form 8, cover, gasket	EA	11.21	43.65	54.86	31.70	42.91	0.4000
16.5205 021	3/4" LB form 8, cover, gasket	EA	13.45	43.65	57.10	31.70	45.15	0.4000
16.5205 031	1" LB form 8, cover, gasket	EA	19.04	54.57	73.61	39.63	58.67	0.5000
16.5205 041	1-1/4" LB form 8, cover, gasket	EA	26.67	87.30	113.97	63.41	90.08	0.8000
16.5205 051	1-1/2" LB form 8, cover, gasket	EA	32.28	109.13	141.41	79.26	111.54	1.0000
16.5205 061	2" LB form 8, cover, gasket	EA	51.88	130.96	182.84	95.11	146.99	1.2000
16.5205 071	2-1/2" LB form 8, cover, gasket	EA	106.68	218.26	324.94	158.52	265.20	2.0000
16.5205 081	3" LB form 8, cover, gasket	EA	134.82	283.74	418.56	206.08	340.90	2.6000
16.5205 091	3-1/2" LB form 8, cover, gasket	EA	213.40	327.39	540.79	237.78	451.18	3.0000
16.5205 101	4" LB form 8, cover, gasket	EA	239.06	392.87	631.93	285.34	524.40	3.6000
16.5205 111	1/2" T form 8, cover, gasket	EA	12.69	65.48	78.17	47.56	60.25	0.6000
16.5205 121	3/4" T form 8, cover, gasket	EA	15.64	65.48	81.12	47.56	63.20	0.6000
16.5205 131	1" T form 8, cover, gasket	EA	21.29	81.85	103.14	59.45	80.74	0.7500
16.5205 141	1-1/4" T form 8, cover, gasket	EA	30.79	130.96	161.75	95.11	125.90	1.2000
16.5205 151	1-1/2" T form 8, cover, gasket	EA	38.42	163.70	202.12	118.89	157.31	1.5000
16.5205 161	2" T form 8, cover, gasket	EA	59.22	196.43	255.65	142.67	201.89	1.8000
16.5205 171	2-1/2" T form 8, cover, gasket	EA	106.92	327.39	434.31	237.78	344.70	3.0000
16.5205 181	3" T form 8, cover, gasket	EA	146.79	425.61	572.40	309.11	455.90	3.9000
16.5205 191	3-1/2" T form 8, cover, gasket	EA	254.95	491.09	746.04	356.67	611.62	4.5000
16.5205 201	4" T form 8, cover, gasket	EA	278.20	589.30	867.50	428.00	706.20	5.4000
16.5205 211	1/2" X form 8, cover, gasket	EA	16.08	81.85	97.93	59.45	75.53	0.7500
16.5205 221	3/4" X form 8, cover, gasket	EA	19.04	81.85	100.89	59.45	78.49	0.7500
16.5205 231	1" X form 8, cover, gasket	EA	25.63	98.22	123.85	71.33	96.96	0.9000
16.5205 241	1-1/4" X form 8, cover, gasket	EA	36.43	163.70	200.13	118.89	155.32	1.5000
16.5205 251	1-1/2" X form 8, cover, gasket	EA	44.36	196.43	240.79	142.67	187.03	1.8000
16.5205 261	2" X form 8, cover, gasket	EA	74.59	218.26	292.85	158.52	233.11	2.0000
16.5206 000	**HIGH VOLTAGE CONDUIT FITTINGS:**							
16.5206 011	2" LBD condulet	EA	88.43	130.96	219.39	95.11	183.54	1.2000

Division 16 CSI #	16 - ELECTRICAL Description	Unit	Material	Union Install	Union Total	Open Install	Open Total	Unit Man-Hrs
16.5206 000	HIGH VOLTAGE CONDUIT FITTINGS: (Cont.)							
16.5206 021	2-1/2" LBD condulet	EA	261.80	218.26	480.06	158.52	420.32	2.0000
16.5206 031	3" LBD condulet	EA	261.80	283.74	545.54	206.08	467.88	2.6000
16.5206 041	3-1/2" LBD condulet	EA	485.86	327.39	813.25	237.78	723.64	3.0000
16.5206 051	4" LBD condulet	EA	482.52	392.87	875.39	285.34	767.86	3.6000
16.5300 000	ENT, MI CABLE & TERMINATIONS:							
16.5301 000	ENT CONDUIT:							
16.5301 011	1/2" ENT conduit, concealed	LF	.51	2.42	2.93	1.76	2.27	0.0222
16.5301 021	3/4" ENT conduit, concealed	LF	.74	2.66	3.40	1.93	2.67	0.0244
16.5301 031	1" ENT conduit, concealed	LF	1.15	2.91	4.06	2.12	3.27	0.0267
16.5302 000	ENT TERMINATIONS:							
16.5302 011	1/2" ENT quick connect term	EA	.55	6.36	6.91	4.62	5.17	0.0583
16.5302 021	3/4" ENT quick connect term	EA	1.28	7.27	8.55	5.28	6.56	0.0666
16.5302 031	1" ENT quick connect terminator	EA	1.21	8.18	9.39	5.94	7.15	0.0750
16.5303 000	MI CABLE							
16.5303 011	MI cable with 3 #12 solid copper wire	LF	5.71	8.47	14.18	6.15	11.86	0.0776
16.5303 021	MI cable with 4 #12 solid copper wire	LF	6.69	8.47	15.16	6.15	12.84	0.0776
16.5304 011	3 #12 termination	EA	10.56	80.82	91.38	58.70	69.26	0.7406
16.5304 021	4 #12 termination	EA	15.81	96.99	112.80	70.45	86.26	0.8888
16.5400 000	SPECIALTY FITTINGS, EXPLOSION PROOF:							
16.5401 000	CONDUIT BODIES, EXPLOSION PROOF:							
16.5401 011	1/2" EYS, explosion proof	EA	13.85	109.13	122.98	79.26	93.11	1.0000
16.5401 021	3/4" EYS, explosion proof	EA	16.80	130.96	147.76	95.11	111.91	1.2000
16.5401 031	1" EYS, explosion proof	EA	22.00	163.70	185.70	118.89	140.89	1.5000
16.5401 041	1-1/4" EYS, explosion proof	EA	26.69	261.91	288.60	190.22	216.91	2.4000
16.5401 051	1-1/2" EYS, explosion proof	EA	39.60	272.83	312.43	198.15	237.75	2.5000
16.5401 061	2" EYS, explosion proof	EA	51.24	283.74	334.98	206.08	257.32	2.6000
16.5401 071	2-1/2" EYS, explosion proof	EA	79.94	294.65	374.59	214.00	293.94	2.7000
16.5401 081	3" EYS, explosion proof	EA	100.71	305.56	406.27	221.93	322.64	2.8000
16.5401 091	1/2" UNY, explosion proof	EA	9.40	21.83	31.23	15.85	25.25	0.2000
16.5401 101	3/4" UNY, explosion proof	EA	13.37	27.28	40.65	19.82	33.19	0.2500
16.5401 111	1" UNY, explosion proof	EA	22.72	32.74	55.46	23.78	46.50	0.3000
16.5401 121	1-1/4" UNY, explosion proof	EA	34.91	38.20	73.11	27.74	62.65	0.3500
16.5401 131	1-1/2" UNY, explosion proof	EA	45.27	49.11	94.38	35.67	80.94	0.4500
16.5401 141	2" UNY, explosion proof	EA	58.42	60.02	118.44	43.59	102.01	0.5500
16.5401 151	2-1/2" UNY, explosion proof	EA	94.78	65.48	160.26	47.56	142.34	0.6000
16.5401 161	3" UNY, explosion proof	EA	128.68	70.93	199.61	51.52	180.20	0.6500
16.5401 171	1/2" 2-hub GUA, explosion proof	EA	30.05	43.65	73.70	31.70	61.75	0.4000
16.5401 181	3/4" 2-hub GUA, explosion proof	EA	31.46	43.65	75.11	31.70	63.16	0.4000
16.5401 191	1" 2-hub GUA, explosion proof	EA	40.08	54.57	94.65	39.63	79.71	0.5000
16.5401 201	1-1/4" 2-hub GUA, explosion proof	EA	67.72	87.30	155.02	63.41	131.13	0.8000
16.5401 211	1-1/2" 2-hub GUA, explosion proof	EA	134.77	109.13	243.90	79.26	214.03	1.0000
16.5401 221	2" 2-hub GUA, explosion proof	EA	143.14	130.96	274.10	95.11	238.25	1.2000
16.5401 231	1/2" 3-hub GUA, explosion proof	EA	31.46	65.48	96.94	47.56	79.02	0.6000
16.5401 241	3/4" 3-hub GUA, explosion proof	EA	34.35	65.48	99.83	47.56	81.91	0.6000
16.5401 251	1" 3-hub GUA, explosion proof	EA	42.20	81.85	124.05	59.45	101.65	0.7500
16.5401 261	1-1/4" 3-hub GUA, explosion proof	EA	72.03	130.96	202.99	95.11	167.14	1.2000
16.5401 271	1-1/2" 3-hub GUA, explosion proof	EA	147.87	163.70	311.57	118.89	266.76	1.5000
16.5401 281	2" 3-hub GUA, explosion proof	EA	152.67	196.43	349.10	142.67	295.34	1.8000
16.5401 291	1/2" 4-hub GUA, explosion proof	EA	33.61	87.30	120.91	63.41	97.02	0.8000
16.5401 301	3/4" 4-hub GUA, explosion proof	EA	37.19	87.30	124.49	63.41	100.60	0.8000
16.5401 311	1" 4-hub GUA, explosion proof	EA	46.98	109.13	156.11	79.26	126.24	1.0000
16.5401 321	1-1/4" 4-hub GUA, explosion proof	EA	76.57	174.61	251.18	126.82	203.39	1.6000
16.5401 331	1-1/2" 4-hub GUA, explosion proof	EA	152.67	218.26	370.93	158.52	311.19	2.0000
16.5401 341	2" 4-hub GUA, explosion proof	EA	161.01	261.91	422.92	190.22	351.23	2.4000
16.5403 000	FLEXIBLE COUPLINGS, EXPLOSION PROOF:							
16.5403 011	Flex coupling, 1/2", to 15", explosion proof	EA	90.17	61.11	151.28	44.39	134.56	0.5600
16.5403 021	Flex coupling, 3/4", to 15", explosion proof	EA	114.13	69.84	183.97	50.73	164.86	0.6400
16.5403 031	Flex coupling, 1", to 15", explosion proof	EA	192.38	87.30	279.68	63.41	255.79	0.8000
16.5403 041	Flex coupling, 1-1/4", to 15", explosion proof	EA	295.42	104.76	400.18	76.09	371.51	0.9600
16.5403 051	Flex coupling, 1-1/2", to 15", explosion proof	EA	387.15	122.23	509.38	88.77	475.92	1.1200
16.5403 061	Flex coupling, 2", to 15", explosion proof	EA	498.11	148.42	646.53	107.79	605.90	1.3600

Division 16 CSI #	16 - ELECTRICAL Description	Unit	Material	Union Install	Union Total	Open Install	Open Total	Unit Man-Hrs
16.5403 000	**FLEXIBLE COUPLINGS, EXPLOSION PROOF: (Cont.)**							
16.5403 071	Flex coupling, 2-1/2", to 15", explosion proof	EA	1,059.34	200.95	1,260.29	145.95	1,205.29	1.8414
16.5403 081	Flex coupling, 3", to 15", explosion proof	EA	1,412.43	232.22	1,644.65	168.66	1,581.09	2.1279
16.5403 091	Flex coupling, 4", to 15", explosion proof	EA	1,684.82	312.59	1,997.41	227.03	1,911.85	2.8644
16.5404 000	**CONDUIT UNIONS, EXPLOSION PROOF**							
16.5404 011	Conduit union, explosion proof, 1/2"	EA	9.43	49.11	58.54	35.67	45.10	0.4500
16.5404 021	Conduit union, explosion proof, 3/4"	EA	12.67	49.11	61.78	35.67	48.34	0.4500
16.5404 031	Conduit union, explosion proof, 1"	EA	23.20	49.11	72.31	35.67	58.87	0.4500
16.5404 041	Conduit union, explosion proof, 1-1/4"	EA	34.68	49.11	83.79	35.67	70.35	0.4500
16.5404 051	Conduit union, explosion proof, 1-1/2"	EA	44.54	49.11	93.65	35.67	80.21	0.4500
16.5404 061	Conduit union, explosion proof, 2"	EA	58.17	49.11	107.28	35.67	93.84	0.4500
16.5404 071	Conduit union, explosion proof, 2-1/2"	EA	84.06	49.11	133.17	35.67	119.73	0.4500
16.5404 081	Conduit union, explosion proof, 3"	EA	120.11	49.11	169.22	35.67	155.78	0.4500
16.5404 091	Conduit union, explosion proof, 3-1/2"	EA	178.54	49.11	227.65	35.67	214.21	0.4500
16.5404 101	Conduit union, explosion proof, 4"	EA	202.20	49.11	251.31	35.67	237.87	0.4500
16.5500 000	**UNDERFLOOR & FLUSH TRENCH DUCT, CABLE TRAY:**							
16.5501 000	**STEEL UNDERFLOOR DUCT:**							
16.5501 011	Underfloor duct, blank, standard	LF	8.54	6.65	15.19	4.83	13.37	0.0609
16.5501 021	Underfloor duct, blank, jumbo	LF	15.86	9.59	25.45	6.97	22.83	0.0879
16.5501 031	Underfloor duct, junction box, 1 duct	EA	217.41	223.28	440.69	162.17	379.58	2.0460
16.5501 041	Underfloor duct, junction box, 2 duct	EA	303.06	312.59	615.65	227.03	530.09	2.8644
16.5501 051	Underfloor duct, junction box, 3 duct	EA	329.39	446.56	775.95	324.33	653.72	4.0920
16.5501 061	Underfloor duct, panel riser, standard	EA	92.13	357.25	449.38	259.47	351.60	3.2736
16.5501 071	Underfloor duct, panel riser, jumbo	EA	148.32	446.56	594.88	324.33	472.65	4.0920
16.5502 000	**FLUSH TRENCH DUCT:**							
16.5502 011	Flush trench duct, to 12"	LF	92.52	71.46	163.98	51.90	144.42	0.6548
16.5502 021	Flush trench duct, to 24"	LF	131.63	98.25	229.88	71.36	202.99	0.9003
16.5502 031	Flush trench duct, to 36"	LF	199.59	178.62	378.21	129.73	329.32	1.6368
16.5502 041	Flush trench duct, ell, to 12"	EA	311.10	392.87	703.97	285.34	596.44	3.6000
16.5502 051	Flush trench duct, ell, to 24"	EA	507.85	523.82	1,031.67	380.45	888.30	4.8000
16.5502 061	Flush trench duct, ell, to 36"	EA	838.37	698.43	1,536.80	507.26	1,345.63	6.4000
16.5502 071	Flush trench duct, tee, to 12"	EA	311.10	523.82	834.92	380.45	691.55	4.8000
16.5502 081	Flush trench duct, tee, to 24"	EA	507.85	654.78	1,162.63	475.56	983.41	6.0000
16.5502 091	Flush trench duct, tee, to 36"	EA	838.37	829.39	1,667.76	602.38	1,440.75	7.6000
16.5502 101	Flush trench duct, riser, to 12"	EA	357.27	384.14	741.41	279.00	636.27	3.5200
16.5502 111	Flush trench duct, riser, t0 24"	EA	413.14	523.82	936.96	380.45	793.59	4.8000
16.5502 121	Flush trench duct, riser, to 36"	EA	532.17	676.61	1,208.78	491.41	1,023.58	6.2000
16.5502 131	Flush trench duct, 3" grommet	EA	5.04	.14	5.18	.10	5.14	0.0013
16.5502 141	Flush trench duct, 6" grommet	EA	7.56	.33	7.89	.24	7.80	0.0030
16.5502 151	Flush trench duct, add barrier	LF	2.77	8.94	11.71	6.49	9.26	0.0819
16.5502 161	Core drill, add afterset insert	EA	5.04	22.33	27.37	16.22	21.26	0.2046
16.5502 171	Flush outlet @ insert, 110v	EA	46.80	31.27	78.07	22.71	69.51	0.2865
16.5502 181	Flush outlet @ insert, phone	EA	40.49	17.86	58.35	12.97	53.46	0.1637
16.5502 191	Surface outlet @ insert, 110v	EA	69.60	44.66	114.26	32.43	102.03	0.4092
16.5502 201	Surface outlet @ insert, phone	EA	69.60	35.73	105.33	25.95	95.55	0.3274
16.5502 211	Preset power/signal access box	EA	42.02	22.33	64.35	16.22	58.24	0.2046
16.5502 221	Add 110v duplex @ access box	EA	13.85	22.33	36.18	16.22	30.07	0.2046
16.5503 000	**CABLE TRAY:**							
16.5503 011	Cable tray, ladder, to 12"	LF	16.75	12.22	28.97	8.88	25.63	0.1120
16.5503 021	Cable tray, ladder, to 24"	LF	18.33	13.97	32.30	10.15	28.48	0.1280
16.5503 031	Cable tray trough to 12"	LF	20.58	15.01	35.59	10.90	31.48	0.1375
16.5503 041	Cable tray trough to 24"	LF	23.71	17.20	40.91	12.49	36.20	0.1576
16.5503 051	Cable tray horizontal, 90 elbow 12"	LF	195.13	261.91	457.04	190.22	385.35	2.4000
16.5503 061	Cable tray horizontal 90 elbow 24"	EA	232.52	349.22	581.74	253.63	486.15	3.2000
16.5503 071	Cable tray vertical outside ell-12"	EA	205.52	201.89	407.41	146.63	352.15	1.8500
16.5503 081	Cable tray vertical outside ell-24"	EA	224.20	269.18	493.38	195.50	419.70	2.4666
16.5503 091	Cable tray inside ell-12"	EA	205.52	207.35	412.87	150.59	356.11	1.9000
16.5503 101	Cable tray vertical inside ell-24"	EA	224.20	276.46	500.66	200.79	424.99	2.5333
16.5503 111	Cable tray tee fitting-to 12"	EA	361.22	392.87	754.09	285.34	646.56	3.6000
16.5503 121	Cable tray tee fitting-to 24"	LF	458.78	480.17	938.95	348.74	807.52	4.4000
16.5503 131	Cable tray end plate to 12"	LF	25.72	234.63	260.35	170.41	196.13	2.1500
16.5503 141	Cable tray end plate to 24"	LF	33.61	312.06	345.67	226.64	260.25	2.8595

Division 16 CSI #	16 - ELECTRICAL Description	Unit	Material	Union Install	Union Total	Open Install	Open Total	Unit Man-Hrs
16.5503 000	CABLE TRAY: (Cont.)							
16.5503 151	Cable tray drop out to 12"	EA	17.64	278.28	295.92	202.11	219.75	2.5500
16.5503 161	Cable tray drop out to 24"	EA	21.37	365.59	386.96	265.52	286.89	3.3500
16.5503 171	Cable tray/cover, ell, to 36"	EA	458.99	506.36	965.35	367.77	826.76	4.6400
16.5503 181	Cable tray/cover, tee, to 12"	EA	327.03	410.33	737.36	298.02	625.05	3.7600
16.5503 191	Cable tray/cover, tee, to 24"	EA	458.99	593.67	1,052.66	431.17	890.16	5.4400
16.5503 201	Cable tray/cover, tee, to 36"	EA	628.57	829.39	1,457.96	602.38	1,230.95	7.6000
16.5503 211	Cable tray/cover, drop, to 12"	EA	284.81	323.02	607.83	234.61	519.42	2.9600
16.5503 221	Cable tray/cover, drop, to 24"	EA	362.24	550.02	912.26	399.47	761.71	5.0400
16.5503 231	Cable tray/cover, drop, to 36"	EA	506.93	742.08	1,249.01	538.97	1,045.90	6.8000
16.5600 000	STEEL GUTTERS, PULL BOXES & UNISTRUT HANGERS:							
16.5601 000	STEEL GUTTERS:							
16.5601 011	Steel gutter, 4" x 4"	LF	13.20	17.86	31.06	12.97	26.17	0.1637
16.5601 021	Steel gutter, 6" x 6"	LF	26.99	26.80	53.79	19.47	46.46	0.2456
16.5601 031	Steel gutter, 8" x 8"	LF	45.08	31.27	76.35	22.71	67.79	0.2865
16.5601 041	Steel gutter, 10" x 10"	LF	53.01	35.73	88.74	25.95	78.96	0.3274
16.5601 051	Steel gutter, 12" x 12"	LF	61.24	44.66	105.90	32.43	93.67	0.4092
16.5602 000	PULL BOXES:							
16.5602 011	Pull box, 6" x 6" x 6"	EA	21.76	87.30	109.06	63.41	85.17	0.8000
16.5602 021	Pull box, 8" x 8" x 6"	EA	29.65	96.03	125.68	69.75	99.40	0.8800
16.5602 031	Pull box, 12" x 12" x 8"	EA	66.82	152.78	219.60	110.96	177.78	1.4000
16.5602 041	Pull box, 18" x 18" x 8"	EA	158.23	196.43	354.66	142.67	300.90	1.8000
16.5602 051	Pull box, 24" x 24" x 8"	EA	177.84	261.91	439.75	190.22	368.06	2.4000
16.5602 061	Pull box, 24" x 24" x 12"	EA	365.56	305.56	671.12	221.93	587.49	2.8000
16.5603 000	UNISTRUT CONDUIT HANGERS:							
16.5603 011	Unistrut hangers, 12" x 24"	EA	14.03	44.66	58.69	32.43	46.46	0.4092
16.5603 021	Unistrut hangers, 18" x 24"	EA	15.91	53.59	69.50	38.92	54.83	0.4911
16.5603 031	Unistrut hangers, 24" x 24"	EA	15.91	53.59	69.50	38.92	54.83	0.4911
16.5603 041	Unistrut hangers, 36" x 24"	EA	21.48	89.31	110.79	64.87	86.35	0.8184
16.5700 000	SPECIAL RACEWAY ASSEMBLY SYSTEMS:							
16.5701 000	WIREMOLD SURFACE RACEWAY:							
16.5701 011	Wiremold, to size 1000	LF	11.25	8.94	20.19	6.49	17.74	0.0819
16.5701 021	Wiremold, to size 2000	LF	14.44	11.17	25.61	8.12	22.56	0.1024
16.5701 031	Wiremold, to size 3000	LF	19.54	15.64	35.18	11.36	30.90	0.1433
16.5701 041	Wiremold, to size 4000	LF	21.65	20.10	41.75	14.60	36.25	0.1842
16.5701 051	Wiremold, to size 5000	LF	30.91	26.80	57.71	19.47	50.38	0.2456
16.5701 061	Wiremold, to size 6000	LF	46.42	35.73	82.15	25.95	72.37	0.3274
16.5702 000	PLUGMOLD:							
16.5702 011	Plugmold, 2000, 1 ft with 4 outlets	EA	45.73	44.66	90.39	32.43	78.16	0.4092
16.5702 021	Plugmold, 2000, 3 ft with 6 outlets	EA	48.04	89.31	137.35	64.87	112.91	0.8184
16.5702 031	Plugmold, 2000, 5 ft with 10 outlets	EA	72.34	133.97	206.31	97.30	169.64	1.2276
16.5702 041	Plugmold, 2000, 6 ft with 12 outlets	EA	73.48	156.30	229.78	113.52	187.00	1.4322
16.5702 051	Telephone-power pole, hangar assembly 10'8"	EA	460.09	96.03	556.12	69.75	529.84	0.8800
16.5703 000	FLAT WIRE UNDER-CARPET POWER SYSTEMS:							
16.5703 011	Under-carpet system, 3 wire, low density	SF	2.93		2.93		2.93	
16.5703 021	Under-carpet system, 3 wire, high density	SF	6.03		6.03		6.03	
16.5704 000	WIREMOLD OVERHEAD DISTRIBUTION SYSTEMS (ODS):							
16.5704 011	Wiremold overhead distribution system	SF	3.05		3.05		3.05	
16.5704 021	Add for light fixture	EA	155.98	75.92	231.90	55.14	211.12	0.6957
16.5704 031	Add for power & telephone pole	EA	200.77	107.18	307.95	77.84	278.61	0.9821
16.5705 000	FLEXIBLE STEEL CONDUIT:							
16.5705 011	Flex conduit, 1/2", wood	LF	1.45	3.49	4.94	2.54	3.99	0.0320
16.5705 021	Flex conduit, 1/2", in ceiling	LF	1.45	4.37	5.82	3.17	4.62	0.0400
16.5705 031	Flex conduit, 3/4", wood	LF	1.72	4.37	6.09	3.17	4.89	0.0400
16.5705 041	Flex conduit, 3/4", in ceiling	LF	1.72	5.67	7.39	4.12	5.84	0.0520
16.5705 051	Flex conduit, 1", wood	LF	4.10	6.98	11.08	5.07	9.17	0.0640
16.5705 061	Flex conduit, 1", in ceiling	LF	4.10	8.73	12.83	6.34	10.44	0.0800
16.5705 071	Flex conduit, 1-1/4", wood	LF	4.58	9.60	14.18	6.97	11.55	0.0880
16.5705 081	Flex conduit, 1-1/4", in ceiling	LF	5.24	11.79	17.03	8.56	13.80	0.1080
16.5705 091	Flex conduit, 1-1/2", wood	LF	6.34	13.10	19.44	9.51	15.85	0.1200
16.5705 101	Flex conduit, 1-1/2", in ceiling	LF	7.22	16.59	23.81	12.05	19.27	0.1520
16.5705 111	Flex conduit, 2", wood	LF	8.30	17.46	25.76	12.68	20.98	0.1600

Division 16 CSI #	16 - ELECTRICAL Description	Unit	Material	Union Install	Union Total	Open Install	Open Total	Unit Man-Hrs
16.5705 000	**FLEXIBLE STEEL CONDUIT: (Cont.)**							
16.5705 121	Flex conduit, 2", in ceiling	LF	9.24	21.83	31.07	15.85	25.09	0.2000
16.5705 131	Flex conduit, 3", in ceiling	LF	13.72	43.65	57.37	31.70	45.42	0.4000
16.5706 000	**ARMORED CABLE, COPPER, BX, 600V, WITH CONNECTORS:**							
16.5706 011	Copper BX, 14/2 solid, 600v, wood frame, connector	LF	1.63	3.06	4.69	2.22	3.85	0.0280
16.5706 021	Copper BX, 12/2 solid, 600v, wood frame, connector	LF	1.77	3.49	5.26	2.54	4.31	0.0320
16.5706 031	Copper BX, 10/2 solid, 600v, wood frame, connector	LF	2.99	3.93	6.92	2.85	5.84	0.0360
16.5706 041	Copper BX, 8/2 solid, 600v, wood frame, connector	LF	4.33	5.24	9.57	3.80	8.13	0.0480
16.5706 051	Copper BX, 14/3 solid, 600v, wood frame, connector	LF	2.00	3.49	5.49	2.54	4.54	0.0320
16.5706 061	Copper BX, 12/3 solid, 600v, wood frame, connector	LF	2.52	3.93	6.45	2.85	5.37	0.0360
16.5706 071	Copper BX, 10/3 solid, 600v, wood frame, connector	LF	3.64	4.37	8.01	3.17	6.81	0.0400
16.5706 081	Copper BX, 8/3 solid, 600v, wood frame, connector	LF	5.32	6.11	11.43	4.44	9.76	0.0560
16.5706 091	Copper BX, 14/4 solid, 600v, wood frame, connector	LF	2.56	3.93	6.49	2.85	5.41	0.0360
16.5706 101	Copper BX, 12/4 solid, 600v, wood frame, connector	LF	3.23	4.37	7.60	3.17	6.40	0.0400
16.5706 111	Copper BX, 10/4 solid, 600v, wood frame, connector	LF	5.24	4.80	10.04	3.49	8.73	0.0440
16.5706 121	Copper BX, 8/4 solid, 600v, wood frame, connector	LF	8.55	6.98	15.53	5.07	13.62	0.0640
16.5800 000	**CONDUCTOR ONLY:**							
16.5801 000	**COPPER WIRE, THW, THHN, 600V:**							
16.5801 011	Copper wire, solid, 600v, THW #14	LF	.16	.55	.71	.40	.56	0.0050
16.5801 021	Copper wire, solid, 600v, THW #12	LF	.26	.64	.90	.47	.73	0.0059
16.5801 031	Copper wire, solid, 600v, THW #10	LF	.35	.83	1.18	.60	.95	0.0076
16.5801 041	Copper wire, solid, 600v, THHN #14	LF	.16	.55	.71	.40	.56	0.0050
16.5801 051	Copper wire, solid, 600v, THHN #12	LF	.26	.64	.90	.47	.73	0.0059
16.5801 061	Copper wire, solid, 600v, THHN #10	LF	.35	.83	1.18	.60	.95	0.0076
16.5801 071	Copper wire, stranded, 600v, THHN #12	LF	.28	.64	.92	.47	.75	0.0059
16.5801 081	Copper wire, stranded, 600v, THHN #10	LF	.47	.83	1.30	.60	1.07	0.0076
16.5801 091	Copper wire, stranded, 600v, THHN #8	LF	.74	1.03	1.77	.75	1.49	0.0094
16.5801 101	Copper wire, stranded, 600v, THHN #6	LF	.97	1.07	2.04	.78	1.75	0.0098
16.5801 111	Copper wire, stranded, 600v, THHN #4	LF	1.46	1.29	2.75	.94	2.40	0.0118
16.5801 121	Copper wire, stranded, 600v, THHN #3	LF	1.92	1.40	3.32	1.01	2.93	0.0128
16.5801 131	Copper wire, stranded, 600v, THHN #2	LF	2.50	1.57	4.07	1.14	3.64	0.0144
16.5801 141	Copper wire, stranded, 600v, THHN #1	LF	3.19	1.75	4.94	1.27	4.46	0.0160
16.5801 151	Copper wire, stranded, 600v, THW with THHN 1/0	LF	3.92	1.96	5.88	1.43	5.35	0.0180
16.5801 161	Copper wire, stranded, 600v, THW with THHN 2/0	LF	4.61	2.18	6.79	1.59	6.20	0.0200
16.5801 171	Copper wire, stranded, 600v, THW with THHN 3/0	LF	5.68	2.44	8.12	1.78	7.46	0.0224
16.5801 181	Copper wire, stranded, 600v, THHN 4/0	LF	7.07	2.71	9.78	1.97	9.04	0.0248
16.5801 191	Copper wire, stranded, 600v, THW with THHN 250	LF	8.73	2.97	11.70	2.16	10.89	0.0272
16.5801 201	Copper wire, stranded, 600v, THW with THHN 300	LF	10.16	3.23	13.39	2.35	12.51	0.0296
16.5801 211	Copper wire, stranded, 600v, THW with THHN 350	LF	11.85	3.49	15.34	2.54	14.39	0.0320
16.5801 221	Copper wire, stranded, 600v, THW with THHN 400	LF	14.10	3.84	17.94	2.79	16.89	0.0352
16.5801 231	Copper wire, stranded, 600v, THW with THHN 500	LF	16.81	4.28	21.09	3.11	19.92	0.0392
16.5801 241	Copper wire, stranded, 600v, THW with THHN 600	LF	23.30	4.71	28.01	3.42	26.72	0.0432
16.5801 251	Copper wire, stranded, 600v, THW with THHN 750	LF	28.62	5.24	33.86	3.80	32.42	0.0480
16.5801 261	Copper wire, stranded, 600v, THHN 1000	LF	43.81	6.11	49.92	4.44	48.25	0.0560
16.5802 000	**ALUMINUM WIRE, THHN, 600V:**							
16.5802 011	Aluminum wire, stranded, 600v, THHN #8	LF	.50	.79	1.29	.57	1.07	0.0072
16.5802 021	Aluminum wire, stranded, 600v, THHN #6	LF	.60	.87	1.47	.63	1.23	0.0080
16.5802 031	Aluminum wire, stranded, 600v, THHN #4	LF	.85	1.00	1.85	.73	1.58	0.0092
16.5802 041	Aluminum wire, stranded, 600v, THHN #2	LF	1.14	1.31	2.45	.95	2.09	0.0120
16.5802 051	Aluminum wire, stranded, 600v, THHN #1	LF	1.66	1.48	3.14	1.08	2.74	0.0136
16.5802 061	Aluminum wire, stranded, 600v, THHN 1/0	LF	1.88	1.66	3.54	1.20	3.08	0.0152
16.5802 071	Aluminum wire, stranded, 600v, THHN 2/0	LF	2.24	1.83	4.07	1.33	3.57	0.0168
16.5802 081	Aluminum wire, stranded, 600v, THHN 3/0	LF	2.69	2.01	4.70	1.46	4.15	0.0184
16.5802 091	Aluminum wire, stranded, 600v, THHN 4/0	LF	3.10	2.18	5.28	1.59	4.69	0.0200
16.5802 101	Aluminum wire, stranded, 600v, THHN 250	LF	3.72	2.36	6.08	1.71	5.43	0.0216
16.5802 111	Aluminum wire, stranded, 600v, THHN 300	LF	4.80	2.62	7.42	1.90	6.70	0.0240
16.5802 121	Aluminum wire, stranded, 600v, THHN 350	LF	5.32	2.88	8.20	2.09	7.41	0.0264
16.5802 131	Aluminum wire, stranded, 600v, THHN 400	LF	5.72	3.14	8.86	2.28	8.00	0.0288
16.5802 141	Aluminum wire, stranded, 600v, THHN 500	LF	6.73	3.40	10.13	2.47	9.20	0.0312
16.5802 151	Aluminum wire, stranded, 600v, THHN 600	LF	8.02	3.75	11.77	2.73	10.75	0.0344
16.5802 161	Aluminum wire, stranded, 600v, THHN 750	LF	9.42	4.19	13.61	3.04	12.46	0.0384
16.5802 171	Aluminum wire, stranded, 600v, THHN 1000	LF	14.28	4.71	18.99	3.42	17.70	0.0432

Division 16 CSI #	16 - ELECTRICAL Description	Unit	Material	Union Install	Union Total	Open Install	Open Total	Unit Man-Hrs
16.5803 000	**COPPER WIRE, RHH-RHW; AERIAL-DIRECT BURIAL, 600V:**							
	Note: The following prices do not include trenching.							
16.5803 011	Copper wire, buried, solid, 600v, #12	LF	.47	.51	.98	.37	.84	0.0047
16.5803 021	Copper wire, buried, solid, 600v, #10	LF	.60	.62	1.22	.45	1.05	0.0057
16.5803 031	Copper wire, buried, solid, 600v, #8	LF	.97	.70	1.67	.51	1.48	0.0064
16.5803 041	Copper wire, buried, stranded, 600v, #14	LF	.49	.44	.93	.32	.81	0.0040
16.5803 051	Copper wire, buried, stranded, 600v, #12	LF	.50	.51	1.01	.37	.87	0.0047
16.5803 061	Copper wire, buried, stranded, 600v, #10	LF	.62	.65	1.27	.48	1.10	0.0060
16.5803 071	Copper wire, buried, stranded, 600v, #8	LF	.93	.70	1.63	.51	1.44	0.0064
16.5803 081	Copper wire, buried, stranded, 600v, #6	LF	1.12	.83	1.95	.60	1.72	0.0076
16.5803 091	Copper wire, buried, stranded, 600v, #4	LF	1.78	.97	2.75	.71	2.49	0.0089
16.5803 101	Copper wire, buried, stranded, 600v, #2	LF	2.69	1.25	3.94	.91	3.60	0.0115
16.5803 111	Copper wire, buried, stranded, 600v, #1	LF	3.53	1.40	4.93	1.01	4.54	0.0128
16.5803 121	Copper wire, buried, stranded, 600v, 1/0	LF	4.26	1.57	5.83	1.14	5.40	0.0144
16.5803 131	Copper wire, buried, stranded, 600v, 2/0	LF	5.04	1.75	6.79	1.27	6.31	0.0160
16.5803 141	Copper wire, buried, stranded, 600v, 3/0	LF	6.24	1.95	8.19	1.42	7.66	0.0179
16.5803 151	Copper wire, buried, stranded, 600v, 4/0	LF	7.58	2.16	9.74	1.57	9.15	0.0198
16.5803 161	Copper wire, buried, stranded, 600v, 250	LF	9.43	2.37	11.80	1.72	11.15	0.0217
16.5803 171	Copper wire, buried, stranded, 600v, 300	LF	10.96	2.58	13.54	1.87	12.83	0.0236
16.5803 181	Copper wire, buried, stranded, 600v, 350	LF	12.62	2.79	15.41	2.03	14.65	0.0256
16.5803 191	Copper wire, buried, stranded, 600v, 400	LF	15.03	3.07	18.10	2.23	17.26	0.0281
16.5803 201	Copper wire, buried, stranded, 600v, 500	LF	17.46	3.42	20.88	2.48	19.94	0.0313
16.5803 211	Copper wire, buried, stranded, 600v, 600	LF	25.37	3.76	29.13	2.73	28.10	0.0345
16.5803 221	Copper wire, buried, stranded, 600v, 750	LF	30.48	4.19	34.67	3.04	33.52	0.0384
16.5803 231	Trench, 1" w x 2' d, backfill, tamp	LF	1.34	1.13	2.47	.82	2.16	0.0104
16.5804 000	**COPPER WIRE, BARE, GROUNDING:**							
16.5804 011	Copper wire, bare, ground, soft #14 solid	LF	.16	.43	.59	.31	.47	0.0039
16.5804 021	Copper wire, bare, ground soft #12 solid	LF	.26	.51	.77	.37	.63	0.0047
16.5804 031	Copper wire, bare, ground soft #10 solid	LF	.35	.62	.97	.45	.80	0.0057
16.5804 041	Copper wire, bare, ground, soft #8 stranded	LF	.69	.70	1.39	.51	1.20	0.0064
16.5804 051	Copper wire, bare, ground soft #6 stranded	LF	.93	.83	1.76	.60	1.53	0.0076
16.5804 061	Copper wire, bare, ground soft #4 stranded	LF	1.46	.97	2.43	.71	2.17	0.0089
16.5804 071	Copper wire, bare, ground #2 stranded	LF	2.48	.16	2.64	.12	2.60	0.0015
16.5804 081	Copper wire, bare, ground, soft #1 stranded	LF	3.16	1.40	4.56	1.01	4.17	0.0128
16.5804 091	Copper wire, bare, ground soft #1/0 stranded	LF	3.82	1.57	5.39	1.14	4.96	0.0144
16.5804 101	Copper wire, bare, ground soft #2/0 stranded	LF	4.50	1.75	6.25	1.27	5.77	0.0160
16.5804 111	Copper wire, bare, ground soft #3/0 stranded	LF	5.60	1.95	7.55	1.42	7.02	0.0179
16.5804 121	Copper wire, bare, ground soft #4/0 stranded	LF	6.95	2.16	9.11	1.57	8.52	0.0198
16.5805 000	**COPPER CONTROL CABLE, MULTICONDUCTOR, #14:**							
16.5805 011	Copper control cable, #14, 2 conductors	LF	.52	.97	1.49	.71	1.23	0.0089
16.5805 021	Copper control cable, #14, 3 conductors	LF	.85	1.42	2.27	1.03	1.88	0.0130
16.5805 031	Copper control cable, #14, 4 conductors	LF	1.06	1.92	2.98	1.39	2.45	0.0176
16.5805 041	Copper control cable, #14, 8 conductors	LF	2.26	3.40	5.66	2.47	4.73	0.0312
16.5805 051	Copper control cable, #14, 10 conductors	LF	2.81	4.22	7.03	3.07	5.88	0.0387
16.5805 061	Copper control cable, #14, 12 conductors	LF	3.38	5.11	8.49	3.71	7.09	0.0468
16.5805 071	Copper control cable, #14, 16 conductors	LF	4.43	6.13	10.56	4.45	8.88	0.0562
16.5805 081	Copper control cable, #14, 20 conductors	LF	5.68	7.67	13.35	5.57	11.25	0.0703
16.5805 091	Copper control cable, #14, 24 conductors	LF	6.95	8.64	15.59	6.28	13.23	0.0792
16.5805 101	Copper control cable, #14, 36 conductors	LF	10.53	12.17	22.70	8.84	19.37	0.1115
16.5806 000	**COPPER POWER CABLE, 5 KV, SHIELDED, PULLED AND SPLICED:**							
16.5806 011	Copper wire cable, 5kv, #8, shielded, pulled & spliced	LF	3.35	1.51	4.86	1.09	4.44	0.0138
16.5806 021	Copper power cable, 5kv, #6, shielded, pulled & spliced	LF	3.63	1.56	5.19	1.13	4.76	0.0143
16.5806 031	Copper power cable, 5kv, #4, shielded, pulled & spliced	LF	4.15	1.99	6.14	1.44	5.59	0.0182
16.5806 041	Copper power cable, 5kv, #2, shielded, pulled & spliced	LF	5.07	2.24	7.31	1.62	6.69	0.0205
16.5806 051	Copper power cable, 5kv, #1, shielded, pulled & spliced	LF	6.86	2.55	9.41	1.85	8.71	0.0234
16.5806 061	Copper power cable, 5kv, 1/0, shielded, pulled & spliced	LF	8.66	2.80	11.46	2.04	10.70	0.0257
16.5806 071	Copper power cable, 5kv, 2/0, shielded, pulled & spliced	LF	11.20	3.12	14.32	2.27	13.47	0.0286
16.5806 081	Copper power cable, 5kv, 4/0, shielded, pulled & spliced	LF	11.72	3.36	15.08	2.44	14.16	0.0308
16.5806 091	Copper power cable, 5kv, 250, shielded, pulled & spliced	LF	17.17	4.21	21.38	3.06	20.23	0.0386
16.5806 101	Copper power cable, 5kv, 350, shielded, pulled & spliced	LF	21.21	5.00	26.21	3.63	24.84	0.0458
16.5806 111	Copper power cable, 5kv, 500, shielded, pulled & spliced	LF	27.18	6.09	33.27	4.42	31.60	0.0558
16.5806 121	Copper power cable, 5kv, 750, shielded, pulled & spliced	LF	41.92	7.49	49.41	5.44	47.36	0.0686

Division 16 CSI #	16 - ELECTRICAL Description	Unit	Material	Union Install	Union Total	Open Install	Open Total	Unit Man-Hrs
16.5807 000	**ALUMINUM POWER CABLE, 5 KV, SHIELDED, PULLED AND SPLICED:**							
16.5807 011	Aluminum power cable, 5kv, #8, shielded, pulled & spliced	LF	1.10	1.17	2.27	.85	1.95	0.0107
16.5807 021	Aluminum power cable, 5kv, #6, shielded, pulled & spliced	LF	2.17	1.27	3.44	.92	3.09	0.0116
16.5807 031	Aluminum power cable, 5kv, #4, shielded, pulled & spliced	LF	2.50	1.59	4.09	1.16	3.66	0.0146
16.5807 041	Aluminum power cable, 5kv, #2, shielded, pulled & spliced	LF	3.32	1.79	5.11	1.30	4.62	0.0164
16.5807 051	Aluminum power cable, 5kv, #1, shielded, pulled & spliced	LF	3.99	2.03	6.02	1.47	5.46	0.0186
16.5807 061	Aluminum power cable, 5kv, 1/0, shielded, pulled & spliced	LF	4.90	2.24	7.14	1.62	6.52	0.0205
16.5807 071	Aluminum power cable, 5kv, 2/0, shielded, pulled & spliced	LF	5.50	2.41	7.91	1.75	7.25	0.0221
16.5807 081	Aluminum power cable, 5kv, 4/0, shielded, pulled & spliced	LF	7.42	2.95	10.37	2.14	9.56	0.0270
16.5807 091	Aluminum power cable, 5kv, 250, shielded, pulled & spliced	LF	8.66	3.36	12.02	2.44	11.10	0.0308
16.5807 101	Aluminum power cable, 5kv, 350, shielded, pulled & spliced	LF	11.02	4.01	15.03	2.91	13.93	0.0367
16.5807 111	Aluminum power cable, 5kv, 500, shielded, pulled & spliced	LF	14.01	4.87	18.88	3.53	17.54	0.0446
16.5807 121	Aluminum power cable, 5kv, 750, shielded, pulled & spliced	LF	20.91	5.90	26.81	4.29	25.20	0.0541
16.5808 000	**COPPER POWER CABLE, 15 KV, SHIELD, GROUND, PULLED:**							
16.5808 011	Copper power cable, 15kv, #4, ground, shielded & pulled	LF	3.07	1.53	4.60	1.11	4.18	0.0140
16.5808 021	Copper power cable, 15kv, #2, ground, shielded & pulled	LF	5.16	1.72	6.88	1.25	6.41	0.0158
16.5808 031	Copper power cable, 15 kv, 1/0, ground, shielded & pulled	LF	6.43	2.16	8.59	1.57	8.00	0.0198
16.5808 041	Copper power cable, 15kv, 2/0, ground, shielded & pulled	LF	6.43	2.40	8.83	1.74	8.17	0.0220
16.5808 051	Copper power cable, 15kv, 4/0, ground, shielded & pulled	LF	9.56	2.84	12.40	2.06	11.62	0.0260
16.5808 061	Copper power cable, 15kv, 250, ground, shielded & pulled	LF	11.37	2.59	13.96	1.88	13.25	0.0237
16.5808 071	Copper power cable, 15kv, ground, 350, shielded & pulled	LF	13.55	3.08	16.63	2.24	15.79	0.0282
16.5808 081	Copper power cable, 15kv, 500, ground, shielded & pulled	LF	16.74	3.73	20.47	2.71	19.45	0.0342
16.5808 091	Copper power cable, 15kv, 750, ground, shielded & pulled	LF	21.33	4.54	25.87	3.30	24.63	0.0416
16.5809 000	**ALUMINUM POWER CABLE, 15 KV, SHIELD, GROUND, PULLED:**							
16.5809 011	Aluminum power cable, 15kv, #4, ground, shielded & pulled	LF	2.61	1.22	3.83	.89	3.50	0.0112
16.5809 021	Aluminum power cable, 15kv, #2, ground, shielded & pulled	LF	3.25	1.38	4.63	1.00	4.25	0.0126
16.5809 031	Aluminum power cable, 15kv, 1/0, ground, shielded & pulled	LF	4.65	1.72	6.37	1.25	5.90	0.0158
16.5809 041	Aluminum power cable, 15kv, 2/0, ground, shielded & pulled	LF	5.35	1.92	7.27	1.39	6.74	0.0176
16.5809 051	Aluminum power cable, 15kv, 4/0, ground, shielded & pulled	LF	6.84	2.27	9.11	1.65	8.49	0.0208
16.5809 061	Aluminum power cable, 15kv, 250, ground, shielded & pulled	LF	7.61	2.59	10.20	1.88	9.49	0.0237
16.5809 071	Aluminum power cable, 15kv, 350, ground, shielded & pulled	LF	9.56	3.08	12.64	2.24	11.80	0.0282
16.5809 081	Aluminum power cable, 15kv, 500, ground, shielded & pulled	LF	12.51	3.73	16.24	2.71	15.22	0.0342
16.5809 091	Aluminum power cable, 15kv, 750, ground, shielded & pulled	LF	16.92	4.54	21.46	3.30	20.22	0.0416
16.5900 000	**BUSWAYS:**							
16.5901 000	**ALUMINUM BUSWAY, PLUG-IN, 600V, 3 P, PLUG-INS:**							
16.5901 011	Aluminum busway, plug-in, 600v, 3 pole, 400a	LF	163.07	26.19	189.26	19.02	182.09	0.2400
16.5901 021	Aluminum busway, plug-in, 600v, 3 pole, 600a	LF	188.20	30.56	218.76	22.19	210.39	0.2800
16.5901 031	Aluminum busway, plug-in, 600v, 3 pole, 800a	LF	205.09	34.92	240.01	25.36	230.45	0.3200
16.5901 041	Aluminum busway, plug-in, 600v, 3 pole, 1000a	LF	230.27	39.29	269.56	28.53	258.80	0.3600
16.5901 051	Aluminum busway, plug-in, 600v, 3 pole, 1350a	LF	339.55	43.65	383.20	31.70	371.25	0.4000
16.5901 061	Aluminum busway, plug-in, 600v, 3 pole, 1600a	LF	415.18	48.02	463.20	34.87	450.05	0.4400
16.5901 071	Aluminum busway, plug-in, 600v, 3 pole, 2000a	LF	492.48	52.38	544.86	38.04	530.52	0.4800
16.5901 081	Aluminum busway, plug-in, 600v, 3 pole, 2500a	LF	593.35	61.11	654.46	44.39	637.74	0.5600
16.5901 091	Aluminum busway, plug-in, 600v, 3 pole, 3000a	LF	679.09	78.57	757.66	57.07	736.16	0.7200
16.5902 000	**ALUMINUM BUSWAY, PLUG-IN, 600V, 4 POLE:**							
16.5902 011	Aluminum busway, plug-in, 600v, 4 pole, 400a	LF	186.51	27.50	214.01	19.97	206.48	0.2520
16.5902 021	Aluminum busway, plug-in, 600v, 4 pole, 600a	LF	235.34	32.08	267.42	23.30	258.64	0.2940
16.5902 031	Aluminum busway, plug-in, 600v, 4 pole, 800a	LF	243.75	36.67	280.42	26.63	270.38	0.3360
16.5902 041	Aluminum busway, plug-in, 600v, 4 pole, 1000a	LF	290.76	41.25	332.01	29.96	320.72	0.3780
16.5902 051	Aluminum busway, plug-in, 600v, 4 pole, 1350a	LF	410.14	45.83	455.97	33.29	443.43	0.4200
16.5902 061	Aluminum busway, plug-in, 600v, 4 pole, 1600a	LF	484.05	50.42	534.47	36.62	520.67	0.4620
16.5902 071	Aluminum busway, plug-in, 600v, 4 pole, 2000a	LF	593.35	55.00	648.35	39.95	633.30	0.5040
16.5902 081	Aluminum busway, plug-in, 600v, 4 pole, 2500a	LF	709.30	64.17	773.47	46.60	755.90	0.5880
16.5902 091	Aluminum busway, plug-in, 600v, 4 pole, 3000a	LF	838.76	82.50	921.26	59.92	898.68	0.7560
16.5903 000	**COPPER BUSWAYS, PLUG-IN, 600V, 3 POLE:**							
16.5903 011	Copper busway, plug-in, 600v, 3 pole, 400a	LF	230.27	34.92	265.19	25.36	255.63	0.3200
16.5903 021	Copper busway, plug-in, 600v, 3 pole, 600a	LF	277.35	39.29	316.64	28.53	305.88	0.3600
16.5903 031	Copper busway, plug-in, 600v, 3 pole, 800a	LF	327.73	43.65	371.38	31.70	359.43	0.4000
16.5903 041	Copper busway, plug-in, 600v, 3 pole, 1000a	LF	341.22	48.02	389.24	34.87	376.09	0.4400
16.5903 051	Copper busway, plug-in, 600v, 3 pole, 1350a	LF	504.29	52.38	556.67	38.04	542.33	0.4800
16.5903 061	Copper busway, plug-in, 600v, 3 pole, 1600a	LF	593.35	61.11	654.46	44.39	637.74	0.5600
16.5903 071	Copper busway, plug-in, 600v, 3 pole, 2000a	LF	737.92	69.84	807.76	50.73	788.65	0.6400

Division 16 CSI #	16 - ELECTRICAL Description	Unit	Material	Union Install	Union Total	Open Install	Open Total	Unit Man-Hrs
16.5903 000	**COPPER BUSWAYS, PLUG-IN, 600V, 3 POLE: (Cont.)**							
16.5903 081	Copper busway, plug-in, 600v, 3 pole, 2500a	LF	914.44	78.57	993.01	57.07	971.51	0.7200
16.5903 091	Copper busway, plug-in, 600v, 3 pole, 3000a	LF	1,164.78	96.03	1,260.81	69.75	1,234.53	0.8800
16.5904 000	**COPPER BUSWAYS, PLUG-IN, 600V, 4 POLE:**							
16.5904 011	Copper busway, plug-in, 600v, 4 pole, 400a	LF	333.27	36.67	369.94	26.63	359.90	0.3360
16.5904 021	Copper busway, plug-in, 600v, 4 pole, 600a	LF	360.15	41.25	401.40	29.96	390.11	0.3780
16.5904 031	Copper busway, plug-in, 600v, 4 pole, 800a	LF	453.32	45.83	499.15	33.29	486.61	0.4200
16.5904 041	Copper busway, plug-in, 600v, 4 pole, 1000a	LF	516.09	50.42	566.51	36.62	552.71	0.4620
16.5904 051	Copper busway, plug-in, 600v, 4 pole, 1350a	LF	688.09	55.00	743.09	39.95	728.04	0.5040
16.5904 061	Copper busway, plug-in, 600v, 4 pole, 1600a	LF	827.84	64.17	892.01	46.60	874.44	0.5880
16.5904 071	Copper busway, plug-in, 600v, 4 pole, 2000a	LF	998.08	73.34	1,071.42	53.26	1,051.34	0.6720
16.5904 081	Copper busway, plug-in, 600v, 4 pole, 2500a	LF	1,223.92	82.50	1,306.42	59.92	1,283.84	0.7560
16.5904 091	Copper busway, plug-in, 600v, 4 pole, 3000a	LF	1,542.85	100.84	1,643.69	73.24	1,616.09	0.9240
16.5905 000	**ALUMINUM BUSWAY, TAP BOX, 600V, 3 POLE:**							
16.5905 011	Aluminum busway tap box, 600v, 400a, 3 pole	EA	2,858.89	580.53	3,439.42	421.63	3,280.52	5.3196
16.5905 021	Aluminum busway tap box, 600v, 600a, 3 pole	EA	2,858.89	714.50	3,573.39	518.93	3,377.82	6.5472
16.5905 031	Aluminum busway tap box, 600v, 800a, 3 pole	EA	2,986.83	848.46	3,835.29	616.23	3,603.06	7.7748
16.5905 041	Aluminum busway tap box, 600v, 1000a, 3 pole	EA	3,098.83	1,071.74	4,170.57	778.40	3,877.23	9.8208
16.5905 051	Aluminum busway tap box, 600v, 1350a, 3 pole	EA	3,888.03	1,250.37	5,138.40	908.13	4,796.16	11.4576
16.5905 061	Aluminum busway tap box, 600v, 1600a, 3 pole	EA	4,282.99	1,428.99	5,711.98	1,037.86	5,320.85	13.0944
16.5905 071	Aluminum busway tap box, 600v, 2000a, 3 pole	EA	4,632.35	1,607.62	6,239.97	1,167.59	5,799.94	14.7312
16.5905 081	Aluminum busway tap box, 600v, 2500a, 3 pole	EA	8,144.98	2,054.18	10,199.16	1,491.93	9,636.91	18.8232
16.5905 091	Aluminum busway tap box, 600v, 3000a, 3 pole	EA	9,209.64	2,322.11	11,531.75	1,686.53	10,896.17	21.2784
16.5906 000	**ALUMINUM BUSWAY, TAP BOX, 600V, 4 POLE:**							
16.5906 011	Aluminum busway tap box, 600v, 400a, 4 pole	EA	2,858.89	669.84	3,528.73	486.50	3,345.39	6.1380
16.5906 021	Aluminum busway tap box, 600v, 600a, 4 pole	EA	2,858.89	803.81	3,662.70	583.80	3,442.69	7.3656
16.5906 031	Aluminum busway tap box, 600v, 800a, 4 pole	EA	3,992.84	982.43	4,975.27	713.53	4,706.37	9.0024
16.5906 041	Aluminum busway tap box, 600v, 1000a, 4 pole	EA	4,229.28	1,250.37	5,479.65	908.13	5,137.41	11.4576
16.5906 051	Aluminum busway tap box, 600v, 1350a, 4 pole	EA	4,481.87	1,428.99	5,910.86	1,037.86	5,519.73	13.0944
16.5906 061	Aluminum busway tap box, 600v, 1600a, 4 pole	EA	4,946.73	1,607.62	6,554.35	1,167.59	6,114.32	14.7312
16.5906 071	Aluminum busway tap box, 600v, 2000a, 4 pole	EA	5,484.11	1,875.55	7,359.66	1,362.19	6,846.30	17.1864
16.5906 081	Aluminum busway tap box, 600v, 2500a, 4 pole	EA	8,500.93	2,143.49	10,644.42	1,556.79	10,057.72	19.6416
16.5906 091	Aluminum busway tap box, 600v, 3000a, 4 pole	EA	10,623.72	2,679.36	13,303.08	1,945.99	12,569.71	24.5520
16.5907 000	**COPPER BUSWAY, TAP BOX, 600V, 3 POLE:**							
16.5907 011	Copper busway tap box, 600v, 400a, 3 pole	EA	3,047.67	535.83	3,583.50	389.17	3,436.84	4.9100
16.5907 021	Copper busway tap box, 600v, 600a, 3 pole	EA	3,047.67	668.97	3,716.64	485.86	3,533.53	6.1300
16.5907 031	Copper busway tap box, 600v, 800a, 3 pole	EA	3,184.08	758.45	3,942.53	550.86	3,734.94	6.9500
16.5907 041	Copper busway tap box, 600v, 1000a, 3 pole	EA	3,303.46	937.43	4,240.89	680.84	3,984.30	8.5900
16.5907 051	Copper busway tap box, 600v, 1350a, 3 pole	EA	4,144.77	1,116.40	5,261.17	810.83	4,955.60	10.2300
16.5907 061	Copper busway tap box, 600v, 1600a, 3 pole	EA	4,565.90	1,339.03	5,904.93	972.52	5,538.42	12.2700
16.5907 071	Copper busway tap box, 600v, 2000a, 3 pole	EA	4,938.26	1,607.48	6,545.74	1,167.50	6,105.76	14.7300
16.5907 081	Copper busway tap box, 600v, 2500a, 3 pole	EA	8,682.85	1,874.85	10,557.70	1,361.69	10,044.54	17.1800
16.5907 091	Copper busway tap box, 600v, 3000a, 3 pole	EA	88.44	2,143.31	2,231.75	1,556.67	1,645.11	19.6400
16.5908 000	**COPPER BUSWAY, TAP BOX, 600V, 4 POLE:**							
16.5908 011	Copper busway tap box, 600v, 400a, 4 pole	EA	3,047.67	625.18	3,672.85	454.06	3,501.73	5.7288
16.5908 021	Copper busway tap box, 600v, 600a, 4 pole	EA	3,047.67	759.15	3,806.82	551.36	3,599.03	6.9564
16.5908 031	Copper busway tap box, 600v, 800a, 4 pole	EA	4,256.56	937.78	5,194.34	681.10	4,937.66	8.5932
16.5908 041	Copper busway tap box, 600v, 1000a, 4 pole	EA	4,508.53	1,116.40	5,624.93	810.83	5,319.36	10.2300
16.5908 051	Copper busway tap box, 600v, 1350a, 4 pole	EA	4,777.85	1,339.68	6,117.53	973.00	5,750.85	12.2760
16.5908 061	Copper busway tap box, 600v, 1600a, 4 pole	EA	5,273.40	1,607.62	6,881.02	1,167.59	6,440.99	14.7312
16.5908 071	Copper busway tap box, 600v, 2000a, 4 pole	EA	5,846.27	1,875.55	7,721.82	1,362.19	7,208.46	17.1864
16.5908 081	Copper busway tap box, 600v, 2500a, 4 pole	EA	9,062.34	2,143.49	11,205.83	1,556.79	10,619.13	19.6416
16.5908 091	Copper busway tap box, 600v, 3000a, 4 pole	EA	9,062.34	2,411.42	11,473.76	1,751.39	10,813.73	22.0968
16.5909 000	**PLUG-IN UNIT, CIRCUIT BREAKER:**							
16.5909 011	Plug-in circuit breaker, to 60a, 3 pole, 600v	EA	1,106.69	152.78	1,259.47	110.96	1,217.65	1.4000
16.5909 021	Plug-in circuit breaker, 100a, 3 pole, 600v	EA	1,221.41	196.43	1,417.84	142.67	1,364.08	1.8000
16.5909 031	Plug-in circuit breaker, 225a, 3 pole, 600v	EA	2,647.34	458.35	3,105.69	332.89	2,980.23	4.2000
16.5909 041	Plug-in circuit breaker, 400a, 3 pole, 600v	EA	5,386.43	1,004.00	6,390.43	729.19	6,115.62	9.2000
16.5909 051	Plug-in circuit breaker, 600a, 3 pole, 600v	EA	8,800.21	1,396.86	10,197.07	1,014.53	9,814.74	12.8000
16.5909 061	Plug-in circuit breaker, 800a, 3 pole, 600v	EA	10,367.62	2,226.25	12,593.87	1,616.90	11,984.52	20.4000
16.5909 071	Plug-in circuit breaker, 1000a, 3 pole, 600v	EA	11,783.96	2,793.73	14,577.69	2,029.06	13,813.02	25.6000
16.5909 081	Plug-in circuit breaker, 1200a, 3 pole, 600v	EA	19,314.09	3,055.64	22,369.73	2,219.28	21,533.37	28.0000

Division 16 CSI #	16 - ELECTRICAL Description	Unit	Material	Union Install	Union Total	Open Install	Open Total	Unit Man-Hrs
16.5909 000	**PLUG-IN UNIT, CIRCUIT BREAKER: (Cont.)**							
16.5909 091	Plug-in circuit breaker, 1400a, 3 pole, 600v	EA	19,314.09	3,055.64	22,369.73	2,219.28	21,533.37	28.0000
16.5909 101	Plug-in circuit breaker, 1600a, 3 pole, 600v	EA	19,314.09	3,754.07	23,068.16	2,726.54	22,040.63	34.4000
16.5909 111	Plug-in circuit breaker, to 60a, 3 pole, 240v	EA	835.26	152.78	988.04	110.96	946.22	1.4000
16.5909 121	Plug-in circuit breaker, 100a, 3 pole, 240v	EA	978.61	196.43	1,175.04	142.67	1,121.28	1.8000
16.5909 131	Plug-in circuit breaker, to 60a, 3 pole, 480v	EA	1,018.79	152.78	1,171.57	110.96	1,129.75	1.4000
16.5909 141	Plug-in circuit breaker, 100a, 3 pole, 480v	EA	1,112.44	196.43	1,308.87	142.67	1,255.11	1.8000
16.5909 151	Plug-in circuit breaker, to 60a, 4 pole, 277/480v	EA	1,133.47	152.78	1,286.25	110.96	1,244.43	1.4000
16.5909 161	Plug-in circuit breaker, 100a, 4 pole, 277/480v	EA	1,217.47	196.43	1,413.90	142.67	1,360.14	1.8000
16.5909 171	Plug-in circuit breaker, 225a, 4 pole, 277/480v	EA	2,836.59	458.35	3,294.94	332.89	3,169.48	4.2000
16.5909 181	Plug-in circuit breaker, 400a, 4 pole, 277/480v	EA	5,667.33	1,004.00	6,671.33	729.19	6,396.52	9.2000
16.5909 191	Plug-in circuit breaker, 600a, 4 pole, 277/480v	EA	7,997.53	1,396.86	9,394.39	1,014.53	9,012.06	12.8000
16.5909 201	Plug-in circuit breaker, 800a, 4 pole, 277/480v	EA	11,244.98	2,226.25	13,471.23	1,616.90	12,861.88	20.4000
16.5909 211	Plug-in circuit breaker, 1000a, 4 pole, 277/480v	EA	11,244.98	2,793.73	14,038.71	2,029.06	13,274.04	25.6000
16.5909 221	Plug-in circuit breaker, 1200a, 4 pole, 277/480v	EA	17,457.16	3,055.64	20,512.80	2,219.28	19,676.44	28.0000
16.5909 231	Plug-in circuit breaker, 1400a, 4 pole, 277/480v	EA	17,457.16	3,055.64	20,512.80	2,219.28	19,676.44	28.0000
16.5909 241	Plug-in circuit breaker, 1600a, 4 pole, 277/480v	EA	5,672.46	3,754.07	9,426.53	2,726.54	8,399.00	34.4000
16.5910 000	**BUSWAY PLUG-IN, 600V, 3 POLE, FUSED:**							
16.5910 011	Bus plug, 600v, fused, 30a, 3 pole	EA	602.04	106.85	708.89	77.60	679.64	0.9791
16.5910 021	Bus plug, 600v, fused, 60a, 3 pole	EA	640.64	106.85	747.49	77.60	718.24	0.9791
16.5910 031	Bus plug, 600v, fused, 100a, 3 pole	EA	876.11	125.27	1,001.38	90.98	967.09	1.1479
16.5910 041	Bus plug, 600v, fused, 200a, 3 pole	EA	1,484.01	309.47	1,793.48	224.77	1,708.78	2.8358
16.5910 051	Bus plug, 600v, fused, 400a, 3 pole	EA	3,763.11	604.21	4,367.32	438.83	4,201.94	5.5366
16.5910 061	Bus plug, 600v, fused, 600a, 3 pole	EA	5,388.01	898.94	6,286.95	652.89	6,040.90	8.2373
16.5911 000	**BUSWAY PLUG-IN, 600V, 4 POLE, FUSED:**							
16.5911 011	Bus plug, 600v, fused, 30a, 4 pole	EA	685.02	114.22	799.24	82.95	767.97	1.0466
16.5911 021	Bus plug, 600v, fused, 60a, 4 pole	EA	712.08	114.22	826.30	82.95	795.03	1.0466
16.5911 031	Bus plug, 600v, fused, 100a, 4 pole	EA	1,003.50	132.64	1,136.14	96.33	1,099.83	1.2154
16.5911 041	Bus plug, 600v, fused, 200a, 4 pole	EA	1,657.67	316.84	1,974.51	230.12	1,887.79	2.9033
16.5911 051	Bus plug, 600v, fused, 400a, 4 pole	EA	4,048.75	611.58	4,660.33	444.18	4,492.93	5.6041
16.5911 061	Bus plug, 600v, fused, 600a, 4 pole	EA	5,893.66	906.30	6,799.96	658.24	6,551.90	8.3048
16.5912 000	**BUSWAY PLUG-IN, 600V, BOLTED FUSE:**							
16.5912 011	Bus plug, 800a, 3 pole, hi-cap fuse	EA	9,284.59	1,267.34	10,551.93	920.45	10,205.04	11.6131
16.5912 021	Bus plug, 1000a, 3 pole, hi-cap fuse	EA	11,009.33	1,709.43	12,718.76	1,241.54	12,250.87	15.6642
16.5912 031	Bus plug, 1200a, 3 pole, hi-cap fuse	EA	17,416.90	2,372.58	19,789.48	1,723.18	19,140.08	21.7409
16.5912 041	Bus plug, 1600a, 3 pole, hi-cap fuse	EA	17,416.90	2,814.68	20,231.58	2,044.27	19,461.17	25.7920
16.5912 051	Bus plug, 800a, 4 pole, hi-cap fuse	EA	9,646.17	1,274.71	10,920.88	925.81	10,571.98	11.6807
16.5912 061	Bus plug, 1000a, 4 pole, hi-cap fuse	EA	11,374.75	1,716.81	13,091.56	1,246.90	12,621.65	15.7318
16.5912 071	Bus plug, 1200a, 4 pole, hi-cap fuse	EA	17,658.63	2,379.95	20,038.58	1,728.53	19,387.16	21.8084
16.5912 081	Bus plug, 1600a, 4 pole, hi-cap fuse	EA	17,658.63	2,822.08	20,480.71	2,049.65	19,708.28	25.8598
16.5913 000	**BUSWAY PLUG-IN, 600V, HI-CAP CIRCUIT BREAKER:**							
16.5913 011	Bus plug, 30a, 3 pole, hi-cap circuit breaker	EA	1,284.44	92.12	1,376.56	66.90	1,351.34	0.8441
16.5913 021	Bus plug, 60a, 3 pole, hi-cap circuit breaker	EA	1,284.44	92.12	1,376.56	66.90	1,351.34	0.8441
16.5913 031	Bus plug, 100a, 3 pole, hi-cap circuit breaker	EA	471.58	36.56	508.14	26.55	498.13	0.3350
16.5913 041	Bus plug, 225a, 3 pole, hi-cap circuit breaker	EA	1,444.90	110.53	1,555.43	80.27	1,525.17	1.0128
16.5913 051	Bus plug, 400a, 3 pole, hi-cap circuit breaker	EA	6,628.66	589.47	7,218.13	428.12	7,056.78	5.4015
16.5913 061	Bus plug, 600a, 3 pole, hi-cap circuit breaker	EA	9,503.50	884.19	10,387.69	642.18	10,145.68	8.1022
16.5913 071	Bus plug, 800a, 3 pole, hi-cap circuit breaker	EA	11,504.60	895.37	12,399.97	650.30	12,154.90	8.2046
16.5913 081	Bus plug, 1200a, 3 pole, hi-cap circuit breaker	EA	13,703.76	1,694.70	15,398.46	1,230.84	14,934.60	15.5292
16.5913 091	Bus plug, 1400a, 3 pole, hi-cap circuit breaker	EA	18,036.15	2,357.84	20,393.99	1,712.48	19,748.63	21.6058
16.5913 101	Bus plug, 1600a, 3 pole, hi-cap circuit breaker	EA	20,286.42	2,578.89	22,865.31	1,873.02	22,159.44	23.6314
16.5950 000	**RACEWAY & WIRE COMBINED:**							
16.5951 000	**PVC & COPPER WIRE:**							
16.5951 011	PVC & copper wire to 30a	LF	3.36	3.76	7.12	2.73	6.09	0.0345
16.5951 021	PVC & copper wire to 60a	LF	6.95	5.01	11.96	3.64	10.59	0.0459
16.5951 031	PVC & copper wire to 100a	LF	13.20	10.73	23.93	7.79	20.99	0.0983
16.5951 041	PVC & copper wire to 150a	LF	20.95	11.61	32.56	8.43	29.38	0.1064
16.5951 051	PVC & copper wire to 200a	LF	33.85	12.95	46.80	9.41	43.26	0.1187
16.5951 061	PVC & copper wire to 225a	LF	42.35	14.30	56.65	10.38	52.73	0.1310
16.5951 071	PVC & copper wire to 250a	LF	47.83	15.47	63.30	11.24	59.07	0.1418
16.5951 081	PVC & copper wire to 300a	LF	68.09	16.36	84.45	11.88	79.97	0.1499
16.5951 091	PVC & copper wire to 400a	LF	87.43	19.53	106.96	14.19	101.62	0.1790

231

Division 16 CSI #	16 - ELECTRICAL Description	Unit	Material	Union Install	Union Total	Open Install	Open Total	Unit Man-Hrs
16.5951 000	PVC & COPPER WIRE: (Cont.)							
16.5951 101	PVC & copper wire to 600a	LF	153.70	20.55	174.25	14.92	168.62	0.1883
16.5951 111	PVC & copper wire to 800a	LF	195.09	21.58	216.67	15.67	210.76	0.1977
16.5951 121	PVC & copper wire to 1000a	LF	215.12	30.89	246.01	22.44	237.56	0.2831
16.5951 131	PVC & copper wire to 1200a	LF	309.17	40.21	349.38	29.21	338.38	0.3685
16.5951 141	PVC & copper wire to 1600a	LF	439.69	51.37	491.06	37.31	477.00	0.4707
16.5951 151	PVC & copper wire to 2000a	LF	538.70	59.06	597.76	42.90	581.60	0.5412
16.5952 000	EMT & COPPER WIRE:							
16.5952 011	EMT & copper wire to 30a	LF	2.94	7.15	10.09	5.19	8.13	0.0655
16.5952 021	EMT & copper wire to 60a	LF	8.67	8.94	17.61	6.49	15.16	0.0819
16.5952 031	EMT & copper wire to 100a	LF	20.51	10.28	30.79	7.47	27.98	0.0942
16.5952 041	EMT & copper wire to 150a	LF	28.04	11.82	39.86	8.58	36.62	0.1083
16.5952 051	EMT & copper wire to 200a	LF	38.34	13.37	51.71	9.71	48.05	0.1225
16.5952 061	EMT & copper wire to 225a	LF	54.14	14.86	69.00	10.80	64.94	0.1362
16.5952 071	EMT & copper wire to 250a	LF	64.25	17.20	81.45	12.49	76.74	0.1576
16.5952 081	EMT & copper wire to 300a	LF	85.65	18.37	104.02	13.34	98.99	0.1683
16.5952 091	EMT & copper wire to 400a	LF	108.75	19.53	128.28	14.19	122.94	0.1790
16.5952 101	EMT & copper wire to 600a	LF	194.73	20.30	215.03	14.74	209.47	0.1860
16.5952 111	EMT & copper wire to 800a	LF	243.28	21.06	264.34	15.30	258.58	0.1930
16.5952 121	EMT & copper wire to 1000a	LF	284.89	28.50	313.39	20.70	305.59	0.2612
16.5952 131	EMT & copper wire to 1200a	LF	404.18	35.96	440.14	26.12	430.30	0.3295
16.5952 141	EMT & copper wire to 1600a	LF	560.77	45.20	605.97	32.83	593.60	0.4142
16.5952 151	EMT & copper wire to 2000a	LF	671.54	60.46	732.00	43.91	715.45	0.5540
16.5953 000	IMC & COPPER WIRE							
16.5953 011	Intermediate metal conduit & copper wire to 30a	LF	3.93	8.08	12.01	5.87	9.80	0.0740
16.5953 021	Intermediate metal conduit & copper wire to 60a	LF	9.49	10.09	19.58	7.33	16.82	0.0925
16.5953 031	Intermediate metal conduit & copper wire to 100a	LF	24.17	11.61	35.78	8.43	32.60	0.1064
16.5953 041	Intermediate metal conduit & copper wire to 150a	LF	33.83	13.35	47.18	9.69	43.52	0.1223
16.5953 051	Intermediate metal conduit & copper wire to 200a	LF	47.65	15.10	62.75	10.97	58.62	0.1384
16.5953 061	Intermediate metal conduit & copper wire to 225a	LF	61.00	16.80	77.80	12.20	73.20	0.1539
16.5953 071	Intermediate metal conduit & copper wire to 250a	LF	75.70	19.43	95.13	14.11	89.81	0.1780
16.5953 081	Intermediate metal conduit & copper wire to 300a	LF	97.60	20.75	118.35	15.07	112.67	0.1901
16.5953 091	Intermediate metal conduit & copper wire to 400a	LF	131.40	22.07	153.47	16.03	147.43	0.2022
16.5953 101	Intermediate metal conduit & copper wire to 600a	LF	221.74	22.93	244.67	16.65	238.39	0.2101
16.5953 111	Intermediate metal conduit & copper wire to 800a	LF	291.82	23.79	315.61	17.28	309.10	0.2180
16.5953 121	Intermediate metal conduit & copper wire to 1000a	LF	325.86	32.20	358.06	23.39	349.25	0.2951
16.5953 131	Intermediate metal conduit & copper wire to 1200a	LF	459.07	40.63	499.70	29.51	488.58	0.3723
16.5953 141	Intermediate metal conduit & copper wire to 1600a	LF	629.40	51.07	680.47	37.09	666.49	0.4680
16.5953 151	Intermediate metal conduit & copper wire to 2000a	LF	763.03	61.12	824.15	44.39	807.42	0.5601
16.5954 000	RSC & COPPER WIRE							
16.5954 011	RSC & copper wire to 30a	LF	5.56	8.81	14.37	6.40	11.96	0.0807
16.5954 021	RSC & copper wire to 60a	LF	10.70	10.80	21.50	7.85	18.55	0.0990
16.5954 031	RSC & copper wire to 100a	LF	25.51	13.37	38.88	9.71	35.22	0.1225
16.5954 041	RSC & copper wire to 150a	LF	35.40	15.19	50.59	11.03	46.43	0.1392
16.5954 051	RSC & copper wire to 200a	LF	50.48	16.54	67.02	12.02	62.50	0.1516
16.5954 061	RSC & copper wire to 225a	LF	67.78	19.65	87.43	14.27	82.05	0.1801
16.5954 071	RSC & copper wire to 250a	LF	78.60	24.98	103.58	18.14	96.74	0.2289
16.5954 081	RSC & copper wire to 300a	LF	111.85	27.64	139.49	20.08	131.93	0.2533
16.5954 091	RSC & copper wire to 400a	LF	136.12	30.31	166.43	22.01	158.13	0.2777
16.5954 101	RSC & copper wire to 600a	LF	254.69	34.41	289.10	24.99	279.68	0.3153
16.5954 111	RSC & copper wire to 800a	LF	305.03	38.52	343.55	27.98	333.01	0.3530
16.5954 121	RSC & copper wire to 1000a	LF	361.33	42.27	403.60	30.70	392.03	0.3873
16.5954 131	RSC & copper wire to 1200a	LF	519.67	46.02	565.69	33.42	553.09	0.4217
16.5954 141	RSC & copper wire to 1600a	LF	714.27	53.10	767.37	38.57	752.84	0.4866
16.5954 151	RSC & copper wire to 2000a	LF	867.44	62.18	929.62	45.16	912.60	0.5698
16.6000 000	LIGHTING FIXTURES:							
16.6001 000	INCANDESCENT FIXTURES, COMMERCIAL:							
16.6001 011	Incandescent fixture, surface, with lens, 100w	EA	50.78	44.66	95.44	32.43	83.21	0.4092
16.6001 021	Incandescent fixture, surface, with lens, 150w	EA	59.46	46.90	106.36	34.07	93.53	0.4298
16.6001 031	Incandescent fixture, surface, with lens, 200w	EA	70.59	49.13	119.72	35.68	106.27	0.4502
16.6001 041	Incandescent fixture, surface, with lens, 300w	EA	80.66	53.59	134.25	38.92	119.58	0.4911
16.6001 051	Incandescent fixture, recessed, open, 100w	EA	61.12	89.31	150.43	64.87	125.99	0.8184

Division 16 CSI #	16 - ELECTRICAL Description	Unit	Material	Union Install	Union Total	Open Install	Open Total	Unit Man-Hrs
16.6001 000	INCANDESCENT FIXTURES, COMMERCIAL: (Cont.)							
16.6001 061	Incandescent fixture, recessed, open, 150w	EA	68.43	98.25	166.68	71.36	139.79	0.9003
16.6001 071	Incandescent fixture, recessed, open, 200w	EA	78.52	111.64	190.16	81.08	159.60	1.0230
16.6001 081	Incandescent fixture, recessed, open, 300w	EA	88.82	133.97	222.79	97.30	186.12	1.2276
16.6001 091	Incandescent fixture, recessed, with reflector, 100w	EA	75.47	111.64	187.11	81.08	156.55	1.0230
16.6001 101	Incandescent fixture, recessed, with reflector, 150w	EA	84.73	120.58	205.31	87.57	172.30	1.1049
16.6001 111	Incandescent fixture, recessed, with reflector, 200w	EA	97.20	133.97	231.17	97.30	194.50	1.2276
16.6001 121	Incandescent fixture, recessed, with reflector, 300w	EA	109.96	156.30	266.26	113.52	223.48	1.4322
16.6001 131	Incandescent fixture, recessed, with lens, 100w	EA	85.84	116.11	201.95	84.33	170.17	1.0640
16.6001 141	Incandescent fixture, recessed, with lens, 150w	EA	98.61	125.04	223.65	90.82	189.43	1.1458
16.6001 151	Incandescent fixture, recessed, with lens, 200w	EA	111.65	147.37	259.02	107.03	218.68	1.3504
16.6001 161	Incandescent fixture, recessed, with lens, 300w	EA	124.72	178.62	303.34	129.73	254.45	1.6368
16.6001 171	Keyless light fixture, utility	EA	10.03	30.56	40.59	22.19	32.22	0.2800
16.6001 181	Recessed shower light, 60w	EA	23.60	44.10	67.70	32.03	55.63	0.4041
16.6002 000	FLUORESCENT FIXTURES, COMMERCIAL							
16.6002 011	Fluorescent fixture, surface, 2-9w lamps	EA	226.52	44.66	271.18	32.43	258.95	0.4092
16.6002 021	Fluorescent fixture surface, 2-13w lamps	EA	261.37	49.13	310.50	35.68	297.05	0.4502
16.6002 031	Fluorescent fixture, recessed, 2-9w lamps	EA	124.45	89.31	213.76	64.87	189.32	0.8184
16.6002 041	Fluorescent fixture, recessed, 2-13w lamps	EA	142.79	111.64	254.43	81.08	223.87	1.0230
16.6002 051	Fluorescent fixture recessed, quad tube	EA	364.64	133.97	498.61	97.30	461.94	1.2276
16.6002 061	Fluorescent, recessed 7" shower light, 1-13w lamp	EA	89.39	112.29	201.68	81.56	170.95	1.0290
16.6002 071	Fluorescent drum light, surf, 2-13w lamps	EA	261.37	99.32	360.69	72.13	333.50	0.9101
16.6002 081	Fluorescent drum light, pendant, 2-13w lamps	EA	289.38	99.32	388.70	72.13	361.51	0.9101
16.6002 091	Emergency ballast for above	EA	227.39	54.57	281.96	39.63	267.02	0.5000
16.6003 000	ELECTRIC DISCHARGE LIGHTING FIXTURES:							
16.6003 011	Mercury vapor fixture, indoor, 75w	EA	266.26	133.97	400.23	97.30	363.56	1.2276
16.6003 021	Mercury vapor fixture, indoor, 100w	EA	266.26	156.30	422.56	113.52	379.78	1.4322
16.6003 031	Mercury vapor fixture, indoor, 175w	EA	274.83	169.70	444.53	123.25	398.08	1.5550
16.6003 041	Mercury vapor fixture, indoor, 250w	EA	277.21	200.95	478.16	145.95	423.16	1.8414
16.6003 051	Mercury vapor fixture, indoor, 400w	EA	378.58	223.28	601.86	162.17	540.75	2.0460
16.6003 061	Mercury vapor fixture, outdoor, 75w	EA	284.61	156.30	440.91	113.52	398.13	1.4322
16.6003 071	Mercury vapor fixture, outdoor, 100w	EA	284.61	169.70	454.31	123.25	407.86	1.5550
16.6003 081	Mercury vapor fixture, outdoor, 175w	EA	383.44	187.56	571.00	136.22	519.66	1.7187
16.6003 091	Mercury vapor fixture, outdoor, 250w	EA	391.98	223.28	615.26	162.17	554.15	2.0460
16.6003 101	Mercury vapor fixture, outdoor, 400w	EA	533.19	267.94	801.13	194.60	727.79	2.4552
16.6003 111	High pressure sodium/lucalux fixture, indoor, 75w	EA	328.62	133.97	462.59	97.30	425.92	1.2276
16.6003 121	High pressure sodium/lucalux fixture, indoor, 100w	EA	335.86	156.30	492.16	113.52	449.38	1.4322
16.6003 131	High pressure sodium/lucalux fixture, indoor, 175w	EA	365.23	169.70	534.93	123.25	488.48	1.5550
16.6003 141	High pressure sodium/lucalux fixture, indoor, 250w	EA	483.63	200.95	684.58	145.95	629.58	1.8414
16.6003 151	High pressure sodium/lucalux fixture, indoor, 400w	EA	525.13	223.28	748.41	162.17	687.30	2.0460
16.6003 161	High pressure sodium/lucalux fixture, outdoor, 75w	EA	437.15	156.30	593.45	113.52	550.67	1.4322
16.6003 171	High pressure sodium/lucalux fixture, outdoor, 100w	EA	437.15	169.70	606.85	123.25	560.40	1.5550
16.6003 181	High pressure sodium/lucalux fixture, outdoor, 175w	EA	464.11	187.56	651.67	136.22	600.33	1.7187
16.6003 191	High pressure sodium/lucalux fixture, outdoor, 250w	EA	493.35	223.28	716.63	162.17	655.52	2.0460
16.6003 201	High pressure sodium/lucalux fixture, outdoor, 400w	EA	522.72	267.94	790.66	194.60	717.32	2.4552
16.6003 211	High pressure sodium/lucalux fixture, outdoor, 1000w	EA	694.03	300.11	994.14	217.97	912.00	2.7500
16.6004 000	FLUORESCENT FIXTURES, COMMERCIAL:							
16.6004 011	Fluorescent strip, 1 lamp, to 4'	EA	51.88	82.07	133.95	59.60	111.48	0.7520
16.6004 021	Fluorescent strip, 2 lamp, to 4'	EA	64.73	87.30	152.03	63.41	128.14	0.8000
16.6004 031	Fluorescent strip, 4 lamp, to 4'	EA	124.55	98.22	222.77	71.33	195.88	0.9000
16.6004 041	Fluorescent strip, 1 lamp, to 8'	EA	79.83	103.89	183.72	75.46	155.29	0.9520
16.6004 051	Fluorescent strip, 2 lamp, to 8'	EA	92.58	112.62	205.20	81.80	174.38	1.0320
16.6004 061	Fluorescent strip, 4 lamp, to 8'	EA	211.96	163.70	375.66	118.89	330.85	1.5000
16.6004 071	Fluorescent, with reflector, 2 lamp, to 4'	EA	101.35	71.46	172.81	51.90	153.25	0.6548
16.6004 081	Fluorescent, with reflector, 4 lamp, to 4'	EA	175.38	89.31	264.69	64.87	240.25	0.8184
16.6004 091	Fluorescent, with reflector, 2 lamp, to 8'	EA	172.69	93.79	266.48	68.12	240.81	0.8594
16.6004 101	Fluorescent, with reflector, 4 lamp, to 8'	EA	280.89	120.58	401.47	87.57	368.46	1.1049
16.6004 111	Fluorescent, baffle type, 2 lamp, to 4'	EA	126.49	75.92	202.41	55.14	181.63	0.6957
16.6004 121	Fluorescent, baffle type, 4 lamp, to 4'	EA	230.08	98.25	328.33	71.36	301.44	0.9003
16.6004 131	Fluorescent, baffle type, 2 lamp, to 8'	EA	250.85	102.71	353.56	74.60	325.45	0.9412
16.6004 141	Fluorescent, RLM reflector, 4 lamp, to 8'	EA	278.21	133.97	412.18	97.30	375.51	1.2276
16.6004 151	Fluorescent, 1 piece lens, 1 lamp, to 4'	EA	123.57	87.30	210.87	63.41	186.98	0.8000

Division 16 CSI #	16 - ELECTRICAL Description	Unit	Material	Union Install	Union Total	Open Install	Open Total	Unit Man-Hrs
16.6004 000	**FLUORESCENT FIXTURES, COMMERCIAL: (Cont.)**							
16.6004 161	Fluorescent, 1 piece lens, 2 lamp, to 4'	EA	135.25	99.31	234.56	72.13	207.38	0.9100
16.6004 171	Fluorescent, 1 piece lens, 1 lamp, to 8'	EA	198.05	152.78	350.83	110.96	309.01	1.4000
16.6004 181	Fluorescent, 1 piece lens, 2 lamp, to 8'	EA	216.66	174.61	391.27	126.82	343.48	1.6000
16.6004 191	Fluorescent, surface, lens, 2 lamp, 4'	EA	119.07	99.31	218.38	72.13	191.20	0.9100
16.6004 201	Fluorescent, surface, lens, 4 lamp, 4'	EA	209.44	120.04	329.48	87.19	296.63	1.1000
16.6004 211	Fluorescent, surface, lens, 2 lamp, 8'	EA	219.09	196.43	415.52	142.67	361.76	1.8000
16.6004 221	Fluorescent, surface, lens, 4 lamp, 8'	EA	313.00	207.35	520.35	150.59	463.59	1.9000
16.6005 000	**FLUORESCENT FIXTURES, RECESSED, COMMERCIAL:**							
16.6005 011	2' x 2' lay-in, recessed, 2 lamp, economy	EA	120.28	70.93	191.21	51.52	171.80	0.6500
16.6005 021	2' x 2' lay-in, recessed, 3 lamp, medium	EA	138.32	76.39	214.71	55.48	193.80	0.7000
16.6005 031	2' x 2' lay-in, recessed, 4 lamp, custom	EA	159.05	81.85	240.90	59.45	218.50	0.7500
16.6005 041	1' x 4' lay-in, recessed, 2 lamp, economy	EA	134.32	76.39	210.71	55.48	189.80	0.7000
16.6005 051	1' x 4' lay-in, recessed, 3 lamp, medium	EA	177.65	81.85	259.50	59.45	237.10	0.7500
16.6005 061	1' x 4' lay-in, recessed, 4 lamp, custom	EA	187.45	87.30	274.75	63.41	250.86	0.8000
16.6005 071	2' x 4' lay-in, recessed, 2 lamp, economy	EA	152.68	87.30	239.98	63.41	216.09	0.8000
16.6005 081	2' x 4' lay-in, recessed, 3 lamp, medium	EA	175.50	92.76	268.26	67.37	242.87	0.8500
16.6005 091	2' x 4' lay-in, recessed, 4 lamp, custom	EA	197.26	98.22	295.48	71.33	268.59	0.9000
16.6005 101	2' x 2' spline, recessed, 2 lamp, economy	EA	157.61	81.85	239.46	59.45	217.06	0.7500
16.6005 111	2' x 2' spline, recessed, 3 lamp, medium	EA	181.24	87.30	268.54	63.41	244.65	0.8000
16.6005 121	2' x 2' spline, recessed, 4 lamp, custom	EA	208.42	92.76	301.18	67.37	275.79	0.8500
16.6005 131	1' x 4' spline, recessed, 2 lamp, economy	EA	157.32	87.30	244.62	63.41	220.73	0.8000
16.6005 141	1' x 4' spline, recessed, 3 lamp, medium	EA	200.61	92.76	293.37	67.37	267.98	0.8500
16.6005 151	1' x 4' spline, recessed, 4 lamp, custom	EA	230.72	98.22	328.94	71.33	302.05	0.9000
16.6005 161	2' x 4' spline, recessed, 2 lamp, economy	EA	175.92	98.22	274.14	71.33	247.25	0.9000
16.6005 171	2' x 4' spline, recessed, 3 lamp, medium	EA	202.30	103.67	305.97	75.30	277.60	0.9500
16.6005 181	2' x 4' spline, recessed, 4 lamp, custom	EA	220.41	109.13	329.54	79.26	299.67	1.0000
16.6005 191	4' x 4' lay-in, recessed, 4 lamp, economy	EA	390.80	163.70	554.50	118.89	509.69	1.5000
16.6005 201	4' x 4' lay-in, recessed, 6 lamp, medium	EA	444.53	174.61	619.14	126.82	571.35	1.6000
16.6005 211	4' x 4' lay-in, recessed, 8 lamp, custom	EA	530.65	185.52	716.17	134.74	665.39	1.7000
16.6005 221	4' x 4' spline, recessed, 4 lamp, economy	EA	426.28	218.26	644.54	158.52	584.80	2.0000
16.6005 231	4' x 4' spline, recessed, 6 lamp, medium	EA	479.98	223.72	703.70	162.48	642.46	2.0500
16.6005 241	4' x 4' spline, recessed, 8 lamp, custom	EA	566.06	229.17	795.23	166.45	732.51	2.1000
16.6005 251	1x4 lay-in, recessed, 3 lamp, master-slave	EA	248.30	183.20	431.50	133.05	381.35	1.6787
16.6005 261	2x4 lay-in, recessed, 3 lamp, master-slave	EA	258.35	183.20	441.55	133.05	391.40	1.6787
16.6006 000	**FLUORESCENT FIXTURES, RECESSED, INSTITUTIONAL:**							
16.6006 011	2' x 2' lay-in, recessed, 2 lamp, economy	EA	124.88	76.39	201.27	55.48	180.36	0.7000
16.6006 021	2' x 2' lay-in, recessed, 3 lamp, medium	EA	138.32	81.85	220.17	59.45	197.77	0.7500
16.6006 031	2' x 2' lay-in, recessed, 4 lamp, custom	EA	166.57	87.30	253.87	63.41	229.98	0.8000
16.6006 041	1' x 4' lay-in, recessed, 2 lamp, economy	EA	134.32	81.85	216.17	59.45	193.77	0.7500
16.6006 051	1' x 4' lay-in, recessed, 3 lamp, medium	EA	177.65	87.30	264.95	63.41	241.06	0.8000
16.6006 061	1' x 4' lay-in, recessed, 4 lamp, custom	EA	187.45	92.76	280.21	67.37	254.82	0.8500
16.6006 071	2' x 4' lay-in, recessed, 2 lamp, economy	EA	152.68	92.76	245.44	67.37	220.05	0.8500
16.6006 081	2' x 4' lay-in, recessed, 3 lamp, medium	EA	175.50	98.22	273.72	71.33	246.83	0.9000
16.6006 091	2' x 4' lay-in, recessed, 4 lamp, custom	EA	197.26	103.67	300.93	75.30	272.56	0.9500
16.6006 101	2' x 2' spline, recessed, 2 lamp, economy	EA	157.61	87.30	244.91	63.41	221.02	0.8000
16.6006 111	2' x 2' spline, recessed, 3 lamp, medium	EA	187.40	92.76	280.16	67.37	254.77	0.8500
16.6006 121	2' x 2' spline, recessed, 4 lamp, custom	EA	218.64	98.22	316.86	71.33	289.97	0.9000
16.6006 131	1' x 4' spline, recessed, 2 lamp, economy	EA	157.32	92.76	250.08	67.37	224.69	0.8500
16.6006 141	1' x 4' spline, recessed, 3 lamp, medium	EA	200.61	98.22	298.83	71.33	271.94	0.9000
16.6006 151	1' x 4' spline, recessed, 4 lamp, custom	EA	230.72	103.67	334.39	75.30	306.02	0.9500
16.6006 161	2' x 4' spline, recessed, 2 lamp, economy	EA	177.02	103.67	280.69	75.30	252.32	0.9500
16.6006 171	2' x 4' spline, recessed, 3 lamp, medium	EA	218.64	109.13	327.77	79.26	297.90	1.0000
16.6006 181	2' x 4' spline, recessed, 4 lamp, custom	EA	249.86	114.59	364.45	83.22	333.08	1.0500
16.6006 191	4' x 4' lay-in, recessed, 4 lamp, economy	EA	390.80	174.61	565.41	126.82	517.62	1.6000
16.6006 201	4' x 4' lay-in, recessed, 6 lamp, medium	EA	444.53	185.52	630.05	134.74	579.27	1.7000
16.6006 211	4' x 4' lay-in, recessed, 8 lamp, custom	EA	530.65	196.43	727.08	142.67	673.32	1.8000
16.6006 221	4' x 4' spline, recessed, 4 lamp, economy	EA	426.28	241.18	667.46	175.16	601.44	2.2100
16.6006 231	4' x 4' spline, recessed, 6 lamp, medium	EA	479.98	240.09	720.07	174.37	654.35	2.2000
16.6006 241	4' x 4' spline, recessed, 8 lamp, custom	EA	562.21	251.00	813.21	182.30	744.51	2.3000
16.6006 251	Add for fluorescent battery unit	EA	504.07		504.07		504.07	
16.6006 261	Add for 1 x 4 parabolic louvers	EA	43.16		43.16		43.16	

Division 16 CSI #	16 - ELECTRICAL Description	Unit	Material	Union Install	Union Total	Open Install	Open Total	Unit Man-Hrs
16.6006 000	FLUORESCENT FIXTURES, RECESSED, INSTITUTIONAL: (Cont.)							
16.6006 271	Add for 2 x 4 parabolic louvers	EA	84.23		84.23		84.23	
16.6007 000	FLOODLIGHT FIXTURES, INDUSTRIAL:							
16.6007 011	Fluorescent hi-bay, reflector, 4', 2 lamp, high output	EA	156.15	139.69	295.84	101.45	257.60	1.2800
16.6007 021	Fluorescent hi-bay, reflector, 4', 4 lamp, high output	EA	199.87	161.51	361.38	117.30	317.17	1.4800
16.6007 031	Fluorescent hi-bay, reflector, 8', 4 lamp, high output	EA	333.16	223.28	556.44	162.17	495.33	2.0460
16.6007 041	Mercury vapor hi-bay, 250w	EA	364.37	226.99	591.36	164.86	529.23	2.0800
16.6007 051	Mercury vapor hi-bay, 400w	EA	416.44	261.91	678.35	190.22	606.66	2.4000
16.6007 061	Mercury vapor hi-bay, 750w	EA	676.76	261.91	938.67	190.22	866.98	2.4000
16.6007 071	Mercury vapor hi-bay, 1000w	EA	937.03	261.91	1,198.94	190.22	1,127.25	2.4000
16.6007 081	Mercury vapor hi-bay, 1500w	EA	989.10	305.56	1,294.66	221.93	1,211.03	2.8000
16.6007 091	High pressure sodium hi-bay, 250w	EA	409.11	226.99	636.10	164.86	573.97	2.0800
16.6007 101	High pressure sodium hi-bay, 400w	EA	451.90	261.91	713.81	190.22	642.12	2.4000
16.6007 111	High pressure sodium hi-bay, 750w	EA	745.78	305.56	1,051.34	221.93	967.71	2.8000
16.6007 121	High pressure sodium hi-bay, 1000w	EA	768.14	305.56	1,073.70	221.93	990.07	2.8000
16.6007 131	High pressure sodium hi-bay, 1500w	EA	1,082.80	305.56	1,388.36	221.93	1,304.73	2.8000
16.6007 141	Metal halide hi-bay, 250w, economy	EA	268.20	225.90	494.10	164.07	432.27	2.0700
16.6007 151	Metal halide hi-bay, 250w, custom	EA	411.69	225.90	637.59	164.07	575.76	2.0700
16.6007 161	Metal halide hi-bay, 400w, custom	EA	588.18	260.65	848.83	189.30	777.48	2.3884
16.6007 171	Metal halide hi-bay, 400w complete assembly	EA	570.81	481.07	1,051.88	349.39	920.20	4.4082
16.6007 181	Metal halide hi-bay, 400w with stand by	EA	694.34	481.07	1,175.41	349.39	1,043.73	4.4082
16.6008 000	OUTDOOR WALL PACK FIXTURES:							
16.6008 011	Wall pack, 250w high pressure sodium	EA	463.68	199.99	663.67	145.25	608.93	1.8326
16.6008 021	Wall pack, 400w high pressure sodium	EA	500.74	199.99	700.73	145.25	645.99	1.8326
16.6008 031	Wall pack, 1000w high pressure sodium	EA	683.87	199.99	883.86	145.25	829.12	1.8326
16.6009 000	SPECIALTY LIGHTING:							
16.6009 011	Neon tubing baked enamel finish	LF	19.38	10.37	29.75	7.53	26.91	0.0950
16.6009 021	Cold cathode transformer	EA	38.94	25.69	64.63	18.66	57.60	0.2354
16.6009 031	Tivoli lighting	LF	55.03	10.37	65.40	7.53	62.56	0.0950
16.6009 041	Transformer 120vp, 24vs @ 24' (3" OC)	EA	23.52	25.69	49.21	18.66	42.18	0.2354
16.6009 051	Fluorescent aisle fixture, louvered, faceplate	EA	75.37	92.76	168.13	67.37	142.74	0.8500
16.6009 061	Incandescent aisle fixture, louver, faceplate	EA	67.16	92.76	159.92	67.37	134.53	0.8500
16.6009 071	Perimeter lighting, flour strip 1-lamp	LF	52.92	27.28	80.20	19.82	72.74	0.2500
16.6009 081	Cove lighting, indirect fluorescent, 1-lamp	LF	102.82	27.28	130.10	19.82	122.64	0.2500
16.6009 091	Valance lighting, indirect fluorescent, 1-l	LF	175.15	27.28	202.43	19.82	194.97	0.2500
16.6009 101	Architectural custom perimeter lighting	LF	411.69	27.28	438.97	19.82	431.51	0.2500
16.6009 111	Surface track, single circuit	LF	13.77	26.80	40.57	19.47	33.24	0.2456
16.6009 121	Surface track, 2-circuit	LF	14.83	26.80	41.63	19.47	34.30	0.2456
16.6009 131	Track cylinder, 50w R-20	EA	69.75	17.46	87.21	12.68	82.43	0.1600
16.6009 141	Track sphere, 6" dia, 50w	EA	59.27	17.46	76.73	12.68	71.95	0.1600
16.6009 151	Track spot, 200w, par-46	EA	125.49	17.46	142.95	12.68	138.17	0.1600
16.6009 161	Recessed shower light, 60w	EA	41.32	44.65	85.97	32.43	73.75	0.4091
16.6009 171	6" dia tube light fixture, pendulum mounted	EA	144.37	81.51	225.88	59.20	203.57	0.7469
16.6009 181	Linear lighting, uplight, pendant mounted	EA	68.22	32.74	100.96	23.78	92.00	0.3000
16.6009 191	Linear lighting, up-down light, pendant mounted	EA	83.39	38.20	121.59	27.74	111.13	0.3500
16.6009 201	Linear lighting, custom, pendant mounted	EA	90.95	38.20	129.15	27.74	118.69	0.3500
16.6009 211	Linear lighting, uplight, wall mounted	EA	60.63	21.83	82.46	15.85	76.48	0.2000
16.6009 221	Linear lighting, custom, wall mounted	EA	83.39	21.83	105.22	15.85	99.24	0.2000
16.6009 311	Dock light, dual arm, 300w flood	EA	388.17	223.28	611.45	162.17	550.34	2.0460
16.6010 000	EXIT SIGNS, FLUORESCENT & INCANDESCENT:							
16.6010 011	Exit sign, incandescent, surface, 1 circuit	EA	114.69	66.98	181.67	48.65	163.34	0.6138
16.6010 021	Exit sign, incandescent, surface, 2 circuit	EA	160.96	80.39	241.35	58.38	219.34	0.7366
16.6010 031	Exit sign, incandescent, recessed, 1 circuit	EA	104.81	111.64	216.45	81.08	185.89	1.0230
16.6010 041	Exit sign, incandescent, recessed, 2 circuit	EA	151.23	120.58	271.81	87.57	238.80	1.1049
16.6010 051	Exit sign, fluorescent, surface, 1 circuit	EA	114.69	66.98	181.67	48.65	163.34	0.6138
16.6010 061	Exit sign, fluorescent, surface, 2 circuit	EA	126.91	80.39	207.30	58.38	185.29	0.7366
16.6010 071	Exit sign, fluorescent, recessed, 1 circuit	EA	115.04	111.64	226.68	81.08	196.12	1.0230
16.6010 081	Exit sign, fluorescent, recessed, 2 circuit	EA	135.96	120.04	256.00	87.19	223.15	1.1000
16.6010 091	Add for emergency battery unit	EA	229.10		229.10		229.10	
16.6010 101	Exit sign, self luminous, 1 side	EA	508.37	32.74	541.11	23.78	532.15	0.3000
16.6010 111	Exit sign, self luminous, 2 sides	EA	893.05	32.74	925.79	23.78	916.83	0.3000

Division 16 CSI #	16 - ELECTRICAL Description	Unit	Material	Union Install	Union Total	Open Install	Open Total	Unit Man-Hrs
16.6011 000	EMERGENCY LIGHT FIXTURES:							
16.6011 011	Emergency light, economy, 1 head	EA	168.55	178.62	347.17	129.73	298.28	1.6368
16.6011 021	Emergency light, economy, 2 head	EA	195.00	178.62	373.62	129.73	324.73	1.6368
16.6011 031	Emergency light, lead acid battery, custom	EA	696.11	178.62	874.73	129.73	825.84	1.6368
16.6011 041	Emergency light, nickel cadmium battery, custom	EA	1,042.50	178.62	1,221.12	129.73	1,172.23	1.6368
16.6011 051	Remote emergency light, 1 head	EA	55.27	66.98	122.25	48.65	103.92	0.6138
16.6011 061	Remote emergency light, 2 head	EA	113.82	80.39	194.21	58.38	172.20	0.7366
16.6011 071	Emergency light, square, battery, commercial	EA	255.30	99.31	354.61	72.13	327.43	0.9100
16.6012 000	CHANDELIERS, INCANDESCENT							
16.6012 011	Chandelier, incandescent, 6 lamp, 15 lbs.	EA	618.56	1,159.16	1,777.72	841.88	1,460.44	10.6218
16.6012 021	Chandelier, incandescent, 8 lamp, 25 lbs.	EA	818.69	1,429.72	2,248.41	1,038.39	1,857.08	13.1011
16.6012 031	Chandelier, incandescent, 12 lamp, 50 lbs.	EA	1,019.97	1,805.18	2,825.15	1,311.09	2,331.06	16.5416
16.6012 041	Chandelier, incandescent, 16 lamp, 75 lbs.	EA	1,421.50	2,143.25	3,564.75	1,556.62	2,978.12	19.6394
16.6012 051	Chandelier, incandescent, 20 lamp, 100 lbs.	EA	2,028.68	2,664.37	4,693.05	1,935.10	3,963.78	24.4146
16.6012 061	Chandelier, incandescent, 24 lamp, 150 lbs.	EA	2,659.54	3,155.08	5,814.62	2,291.50	4,951.04	28.9112
16.6012 071	Chandelier, incandescent, 30 lamp, 200 lbs.	EA	3,911.25	3,760.10	7,671.35	2,730.92	6,642.17	34.4552
16.6012 081	Chandelier, incandescent, 36 lamp, 300 lbs.	EA	4,560.72	4,222.79	8,783.51	3,066.97	7,627.69	38.6950
16.6013 000	EXPLOSION PROOF FIXTURES							
16.6013 011	Explosion proof, incandescent, 100 watt	EA	302.63	185.24	487.87	134.54	437.17	1.6974
16.6013 021	Explosion proof, incandescent, 200 watt	EA	495.10	218.43	713.53	158.65	653.75	2.0016
16.6013 031	Explosion proof, incandescent, 300 watt	EA	665.10	263.71	928.81	191.53	856.63	2.4165
16.6013 041	Explosion proof, fluorescent, 1' x 4'	EA	2,540.08	323.14	2,863.22	234.70	2,774.78	2.9611
16.6013 051	Explosion proof, fluorescent, 2' x 2'	EA	2,802.04	334.93	3,136.97	243.26	3,045.30	3.0691
16.6013 061	Explosion proof, fluorescent, 2' x 4'	EA	3,286.05	445.95	3,732.00	323.89	3,609.94	4.0864
16.6013 071	Explosion proof, H. I. D. 175 watt	EA	1,242.80	294.41	1,537.21	213.83	1,456.63	2.6978
16.6013 081	Explosion proof, H. I. D. 250 watt	EA	1,346.10	329.61	1,675.71	239.39	1,585.49	3.0203
16.6013 091	Explosion proof, H. I. D. 400 watt	EA	1,786.40	401.45	2,187.85	291.57	2,077.97	3.6786
16.6013 101	Explosion proof, H. I. D. 1,000 watt	EA	2,372.22	482.50	2,854.72	350.43	2,722.65	4.4213
16.6013 111	Explosion proof, exit sign, 1 face	EA	517.30	192.30	709.60	139.66	656.96	1.7621
16.6013 121	Explosion proof, exit sign, 2 face	EA	586.15	217.45	803.60	157.93	744.08	1.9926
16.6014 000	VANDAL PROOF FIXTURES							
16.6014 011	Vandal proof, max security, fluorescent, 1'x4', 2 tube	EA	399.36	229.64	629.00	166.79	566.15	2.1043
16.6014 021	Vandal proof, max security, fluorescent, 2'x4', 2 tube	EA	461.91	274.66	736.57	199.48	661.39	2.5168
16.6014 031	Vandal proof, max security, fluorescent, 2'x4', 3 tube	EA	520.59	319.79	840.38	232.26	752.85	2.9304
16.6014 041	Vandal proof, max security, fluorescent, 2'x4', 4 tube	EA	577.73	364.95	942.68	265.06	842.79	3.3442
16.6014 051	Vandal proof, max security, fluorescent, 2' strip, 1 tube	EA	367.30	193.44	560.74	140.50	507.80	1.7726
16.6014 061	Vandal proof, max security, fluorescent, 4' strip, 2 tube	EA	390.49	232.43	622.92	168.81	559.30	2.1298
16.6014 071	Vandal proof, med security, fluorescent, 1'x4', 2 tube	EA	354.43	201.74	556.17	146.52	500.95	1.8486
16.6014 081	Vandal proof, med security, fluorescent, 2'x4', 2 tube	EA	380.31	241.62	621.93	175.49	555.80	2.2141
16.6014 091	Vandal proof, med security, fluorescent, 2'x4', 3 tube	EA	435.03	281.35	716.38	204.34	639.37	2.5781
16.6014 101	Vandal proof, med security, fluorescent, 2'x4', 4 tube	EA	482.48	321.16	803.64	233.25	715.73	2.9429
16.6014 111	Vandal proof, med security, fluorescent, 2' strip, 1 tube	EA	337.26	180.38	517.64	131.01	468.27	1.6529
16.6014 121	Vandal proof, med security, fluorescent, 4' strip, 2 tube	EA	351.37	204.47	555.84	148.50	499.87	1.8736
16.7000 000	ELECTRIC & SIGNAL DEVICES:							
16.7001 000	LIGHTING DEVICES & OUTLETS:							
16.7001 011	Fixture outlet, commercial	EA	7.05	22.33	29.38	16.22	23.27	0.2046
16.7001 021	Fixture junction box, commercial	EA	7.05	17.86	24.91	12.97	20.02	0.1637
16.7001 031	Fixture flex conduit/wire assembly	EA	12.08	16.16	28.24	11.74	23.82	0.1481
16.7001 041	Switch/pilot light outlet	EA	20.21	88.40	108.61	64.20	84.41	0.8100
16.7001 051	Switch, 20a, 1 pole, commercial	EA	23.94	69.84	93.78	50.73	74.67	0.6400
16.7001 061	Switch, 20a, 2-gang, commercial	EA	27.73	86.21	113.94	62.62	90.35	0.7900
16.7001 071	Switch 20a, 3-gang, commercial	EA	67.26	98.21	165.47	71.33	138.59	0.8999
16.7001 081	Switch, 20a, 4-gang, commercial	EA	89.14	114.56	203.70	83.21	172.35	1.0498
16.7001 091	Switch, 20a, 5-gang, commercial	EA	130.79	130.96	261.75	95.11	225.90	1.2000
16.7001 101	Switch, 20a, 3-way, commercial	EA	26.74	88.40	115.14	64.20	90.94	0.8100
16.7001 111	Switch, 20a, 4-way, commercial	EA	57.38	97.13	154.51	70.54	127.92	0.8900
16.7001 121	Switch, 20a, waterproof, commercial	EA	40.03	86.21	126.24	62.62	102.65	0.7900
16.7001 131	Incandescent dimmer, 600w	EA	46.34	91.67	138.01	66.58	112.92	0.8400
16.7001 141	Incandescent dimmer, 1000w	EA	87.43	102.58	190.01	74.50	161.93	0.9400
16.7001 151	Incandescent dimmer, 1500w	EA	165.61	113.50	279.11	82.43	248.04	1.0400
16.7001 161	Incandescent dimmer, 2000w	EA	213.08	113.50	326.58	82.43	295.51	1.0400
16.7001 171	Switch 20a, tamperproof keyed, 1 pole	EA	43.13	69.84	112.97	50.73	93.86	0.6400

236

Division 16 CSI #	16 - ELECTRICAL Description	Unit	Material	Union Install	Union Total	Open Install	Open Total	Unit Man-Hrs
16.7001 000	**LIGHTING DEVICES & OUTLETS: (Cont.)**							
16.7001 181	Switch 20a, explosion proof, 1 pole	EA	195.89	97.70	293.59	70.96	266.85	0.8953
16.7001 191	Fluorescent dimmer, 2-12 lamps	EA	123.36	69.84	193.20	50.73	174.09	0.6400
16.7001 201	Fluorescent dimmer, 4-220 lamps	EA	154.18	86.21	240.39	62.62	216.80	0.7900
16.7001 211	Fluorescent dimmer, 6-30 lamps	EA	307.47	88.40	395.87	64.20	371.67	0.8100
16.7001 221	Fluorescent dimmer, 8-40 lamps	EA	399.24	88.40	487.64	64.20	463.44	0.8100
16.7001 231	Time switch, 7 day calendar	EA	157.15	240.09	397.24	174.37	331.52	2.2000
16.7001 241	Time switch, 1 pole, 24 hr, dial	EA	108.83	196.43	305.26	142.67	251.50	1.8000
16.7001 251	Time switch, 24 hr, with reserve power	EA	522.03	218.26	740.29	158.52	680.55	2.0000
16.7001 261	Time switch, photoelectric cell, k-1100	EA	66.52	87.30	153.82	63.41	129.93	0.8000
16.7001 271	Time switch, photoelectric cell, k-1900	EA	116.07	87.30	203.37	63.41	179.48	0.8000
16.7001 281	Lighting circuits, EMT/wire	LF	1.26	5.01	6.27	3.64	4.90	0.0459
16.7001 291	Lighting circuits, RSC/wire	LF	2.82	6.25	9.07	4.54	7.36	0.0573
16.7001 301	Lighting circuits, modular boxes	EA	34.35	7.15	41.50	5.19	39.54	0.0655
16.7001 311	Lighting circuits, modular flex	LF	1.22	1.35	2.57	.98	2.20	0.0124
16.7002 000	**OCCUPANCY SENSOR SYSTEM**							
16.7002 011	Wall switch, 120v or 277v	EA	143.10	69.84	212.94	50.73	193.83	0.6400
16.7002 021	Sensor, 1-way, relay & transformer or switch pack	EA	198.12	133.97	332.09	97.30	295.42	1.2276
16.7002 031	Sensor, room, 2-way, relay & transformer or switchpack	EA	291.99	141.87	433.86	103.04	395.03	1.3000
16.7002 041	Sensor, warehouse, relay & transformer or switchpack	EA	296.13	141.87	438.00	103.04	399.17	1.3000
16.7002 051	Remote control relay	EA	41.71	29.48	71.19	21.41	63.12	0.2701
16.7002 061	Transformer, 120v	EA	23.15	25.69	48.84	18.66	41.81	0.2354
16.7002 071	Transformer, 277v	EA	33.37	25.69	59.06	18.66	52.03	0.2354
16.7002 081	Switchpack, 120/277v	EA	45.85	1.09	46.94	.79	46.64	0.0100
16.7002 091	Circuit timer, 120/277v	EA	46.36	87.30	133.66	63.41	109.77	0.8000
16.7003 000	**CONTACTOR, LIGHTING:**							
16.7003 011	Contactor, lighting to 30a, 4 pole, enclosed	EA	298.26	267.94	566.20	194.60	492.86	2.4552
16.7003 021	Contactor, lighting, to 60a, 4 pole, enclosed	EA	610.11	334.92	945.03	243.25	853.36	3.0690
16.7003 031	Contactor, lighting, to 100a, 4 pole, enclosed	EA	1,003.21	401.90	1,405.11	291.90	1,295.11	3.6828
16.7003 041	Contactor, lighting, to 200a, 4 pole, enclosed	EA	2,548.72	579.48	3,128.20	420.87	2,969.59	5.3100
16.7004 000	**BRANCH CIRCUIT DEVICES/OUTLETS:**							
16.7004 011	Duplex receptacle, commercial	EA	18.68	82.94	101.62	60.24	78.92	0.7600
16.7004 021	Double duplex receptacle, commercial	EA	32.09	100.40	132.49	72.92	105.01	0.9200
16.7004 031	Duplex receptacle, waterproof	EA	43.18	88.40	131.58	64.20	107.38	0.8100
16.7004 041	Duplex receptacle, ground fault interrupter	EA	33.66	100.40	134.06	72.92	106.58	0.9200
16.7004 051	Duplex receptacle, ground fault interrupter, waterproof, enclosed	EA	58.16	88.40	146.56	64.20	122.36	0.8100
16.7004 061	Receptacle, 30a, commercial	EA	24.38	100.40	124.78	72.92	97.30	0.9200
16.7004 071	Receptacle, 50a, commercial	EA	27.56	110.88	138.44	80.53	108.09	1.0160
16.7004 081	Tamperproof receptacle, 20a	EA	28.04	82.94	110.98	60.24	88.28	0.7600
16.7004 091	Isolated ground duplex receptacle	EA	23.91	100.40	124.31	72.92	96.83	0.9200
16.7004 093	Surge suppression duplex receptacle	EA	76.31	97.13	173.44	70.54	146.85	0.8900
16.7004 101	60a welding receptacle	EA	241.66	152.78	394.44	110.96	352.62	1.4000
16.7004 111	100a welding receptacle	EA	367.24	190.98	558.22	138.71	505.95	1.7500
16.7004 121	Duplex receptacle, hospital grade	EA	43.18	100.40	143.58	72.92	116.10	0.9200
16.7004 131	Single receptacle, commercial	EA	16.42	72.75	89.17	52.83	69.25	0.6666
16.7004 135	Single receptacle, explosion proof, 20a	EA	260.50	121.13	381.63	87.98	348.48	1.1100
16.7004 136	Single receptacle, explosion proof, 30a	EA	439.35	136.41	575.76	99.08	538.43	1.2500
16.7004 137	Single receptacle, explosion proof, 60a	EA	625.14	208.44	833.58	151.39	776.53	1.9100
16.7004 141	Power cord reel, 10" dia, 50' cord	EA	331.58	54.57	386.15	39.63	371.21	0.5000
16.7004 151	Branch circuit junction box, indoor	EA	10.45	34.92	45.37	25.36	35.81	0.3200
16.7004 161	Branch circuit junction box, water proof	EA	19.81	61.11	80.92	44.39	64.20	0.5600
16.7004 171	Branch circuit junction box, equipment connector	EA	23.35	103.67	127.02	75.30	98.65	0.9500
16.7004 181	Branch circuit junction box, equipment connector, water proof	EA	29.18	148.42	177.60	107.79	136.97	1.3600
16.7004 191	Motor-rated toggle switch	EA	29.37	69.84	99.21	50.73	80.10	0.6400
16.7004 201	Motor connection, 20a, 1 ph	EA	23.35	165.88	189.23	120.48	143.83	1.5200
16.7004 211	Motor connection, 20a, 3 ph	EA	29.18	196.43	225.61	142.67	171.85	1.8000
16.7004 221	Floor box & flush outlet	EA	79.42	66.98	146.40	48.65	128.07	0.6138
16.7004 231	Floor box & surface outlet/enclosure	EA	90.33	111.64	201.97	81.08	171.41	1.0230
16.7004 241	Floor box & equipment flex connector	EA	90.33	156.30	246.63	113.52	203.85	1.4322
16.7004 251	Outlet circuits, EMT/wire	LF	1.07	5.01	6.08	3.64	4.71	0.0459
16.7004 261	Outlet circuits, RSC/wire	LF	2.56	7.15	9.71	5.19	7.75	0.0655
16.7004 271	Outlet circuits, PVC/wire	LF	1.90	2.68	4.58	1.95	3.85	0.0246

Division 16 CSI #	16 - ELECTRICAL Description	Unit	Material	Union Install	Union Total	Open Install	Open Total	Unit Man-Hrs
16.7005 000	**TELEPHONE SYSTEMS:**							
16.7005 011	Phone backboards, 4' x 8' ply	EA	71.39	178.62	250.01	129.73	201.12	1.6368
16.7005 021	Phone cabinets, average	EA	204.21	223.28	427.49	162.17	366.38	2.0460
16.7005 031	Phone cabinets, large	EA	367.56	357.25	724.81	259.47	627.03	3.2736
16.7005 041	Phone raceway, 2" EMT, average	LF	3.77	10.73	14.50	7.79	11.56	0.0983
16.7005 051	Phone raceway, 3" EMT, average	LF	10.52	12.96	23.48	9.42	19.94	0.1188
16.7005 061	Phone raceway, 4" EMT average	LF	17.67	19.65	37.32	14.27	31.94	0.1801
16.7005 071	Phone riser sleeves, to 4"	EA	41.08	44.66	85.74	32.43	73.51	0.4092
16.7005 081	Phone outlet, wall	EA	15.53	26.80	42.33	19.47	35.00	0.2456
16.7005 091	Phone outlet, floor box	EA	116.95	44.66	161.61	32.43	149.38	0.4092
16.7005 101	Phone/data outlet, wall	EA	26.86	33.83	60.69	24.57	51.43	0.3100
16.7005 111	Phone raceway, 3/4" EMT, average	LF	1.29	5.21	6.50	3.78	5.07	0.0477
16.7005 121	Phone raceway, 1" EMT, average	LF	1.48	6.25	7.73	4.54	6.02	0.0573
16.7005 131	Phone raceway, 1" RSC, average	LF	3.19	7.15	10.34	5.19	8.38	0.0655
16.7005 141	Phone raceway, 1" PVC, average	LF	1.20	3.22	4.42	2.34	3.54	0.0295
16.7005 151	Phone raceway, 1" PVC, average	LF	1.20	3.22	4.42	2.34	3.54	0.0295
16.7006 000	**TELEPHONE SYSTEM:**							
16.7006 011	Telephone cable, 2 pair	LF	.08	.86	.94	.63	.71	0.0079
16.7006 021	Telephone cable, 4 pair	LF	.16	1.07	1.23	.78	.94	0.0098
16.7006 031	Telephone cable, 25 pair	LF	1.33	2.15	3.48	1.56	2.89	0.0197
16.7007 000	**FIRE ALARM SYSTEMS, LIFE SAFETY:**							
16.7007 011	Fire alarm main panel, 10 zone	EA	3,064.24	1,178.60	4,242.84	856.01	3,920.25	10.8000
16.7007 021	Fire alarm, main panel, 30 zone	EA	5,942.87	1,571.47	7,514.34	1,141.34	7,084.21	14.4000
16.7007 031	Fire alarm, main panel, 50 zone	EA	9,285.74	1,964.34	11,250.08	1,426.68	10,712.42	18.0000
16.7007 041	Fire alarm annunciator, 10 zone	EA	1,276.76	535.87	1,812.63	389.20	1,665.96	4.9104
16.7007 051	Fire alarm annunciator, 30 zone	EA	2,205.35	893.12	3,098.47	648.66	2,854.01	8.1840
16.7007 061	Fire alarm annunciator, 50 zone	EA	3,598.27	1,428.99	5,027.26	1,037.86	4,636.13	13.0944
16.7007 071	Fire alarm power supply, 10 zone	EA	1,392.83	357.25	1,750.08	259.47	1,652.30	3.2736
16.7007 081	Fire alarm power supply, 30 zone	EA	2,611.53	535.87	3,147.40	389.20	3,000.73	4.9104
16.7007 091	Fire alarm power supply, 50 zone	EA	4,004.42	714.50	4,718.92	518.93	4,523.35	6.5472
16.7007 101	Fire alarm, terminal cabinet, average	EA	232.12	223.28	455.40	162.17	394.29	2.0460
16.7007 111	Fire alarm, 4 zone, with battery backup	EA	1,953.26	392.87	2,346.13	285.34	2,238.60	3.6000
16.7007 121	Fire alarm, manual stations	EA	134.47	111.64	246.11	81.08	215.55	1.0230
16.7007 131	Fire alarm horn	EA	89.15	89.31	178.46	64.87	154.02	0.8184
16.7007 141	Fire alarm bells	EA	123.87	89.31	213.18	64.87	188.74	0.8184
16.7007 151	Fire alarm chimes	EA	117.07	89.31	206.38	64.87	181.94	0.8184
16.7007 161	Fire alarm visual alarm/horn	EA	161.85	141.87	303.72	103.04	264.89	1.3000
16.7007 171	Fire alarm visual alarm/signal	EA	161.43	141.87	303.30	103.04	264.47	1.3000
16.7007 181	Fire alarm, smoke detect, ceiling	EA	172.29	133.97	306.26	97.30	269.59	1.2276
16.7007 191	Fire alarm, smoke detector, duct	EA	498.89	223.28	722.17	162.17	661.06	2.0460
16.7007 201	Fire alarm, ionization detector	EA	313.97	111.64	425.61	81.08	395.05	1.0230
16.7007 211	Fire alarm, heat detector	EA	71.95	66.98	138.93	48.65	120.60	0.6138
16.7007 221	Fire alarm, flow switch connector	EA	101.83	111.64	213.47	81.08	182.91	1.0230
16.7007 231	Fire alarm, door hold assembly	EA	138.57	178.62	317.19	129.73	268.30	1.6368
16.7007 241	Fire alarm, door release assembly	EA	138.57	178.62	317.19	129.73	268.30	1.6368
16.7007 251	Fire alarm, phone jacks	EA	69.69	53.88	123.57	39.13	108.82	0.4937
16.7007 261	Handsets for phone jack	EA	99.58		99.58		99.58	
16.7007 271	Fire alarm, distribution circuits, 10 zone	LF	4.26	8.94	13.20	6.49	10.75	0.0819
16.7007 281	Fire alarm, distribution circuits, 30 zone	LF	8.36	19.65	28.01	14.27	22.63	0.1801
16.7007 291	Fire alarm, distribution circuits, 50 zone	LF	15.28	29.93	45.21	21.74	37.02	0.2743
16.7007 301	Fire alarm circuits, EMT/wire	LF	2.76	6.25	9.01	4.54	7.30	0.0573
16.7101 000	**COMMUNICATION, INTERCOM, PUBLIC ADDRESS:**							
16.7101 011	Public address/intercom, main amp, power supply	EA	3,027.95	714.50	3,742.45	518.93	3,546.88	6.5472
16.7101 021	Public address/intercom, auxilliary terminal cabinet	EA	302.75	357.25	660.00	259.47	562.22	3.2736
16.7101 031	Public address/intercom, speaker enclosure, surface	EA	12.89	31.27	44.16	22.71	35.60	0.2865
16.7101 041	Public address/intercom, speaker enclosures, flush	EA	30.12	44.66	74.78	32.43	62.55	0.4092
16.7101 051	Public address/intercom, microphone outlet, wall	EA	12.89	31.27	44.16	22.71	35.60	0.2865
16.7101 061	Public address/intercom, microphone outlet, floor	EA	38.23	44.66	82.89	32.43	70.66	0.4092
16.7101 071	Public address/intercom, intercom outlet, wall	EA	12.89	31.27	44.16	22.71	35.60	0.2865
16.7101 081	Public address/intercom, intercom outlet, floor	EA	38.23	44.66	82.89	32.43	70.66	0.4092
16.7101 091	Public address/intercom, television outlet, wall	EA	12.89	31.27	44.16	22.71	35.60	0.2865
16.7101 101	Public address/intercom, television outlet, floor	EA	38.23	44.66	82.89	32.43	70.66	0.4092

Division 16 CSI #	16 - ELECTRICAL Description	Unit	Material	Union Install	Union Total	Open Install	Open Total	Unit Man-Hrs
16.7101 000	COMMUNICATION, INTERCOM, PUBLIC ADDRESS: (Cont.)							
16.7101 111	Public address/intercom, speakers, flush	EA	47.85	44.66	92.51	32.43	80.28	0.4092
16.7101 121	Public address/intercom, speakers, horn	EA	83.77	44.66	128.43	32.43	116.20	0.4092
16.7101 131	Volume control	EA	90.55	54.57	145.12	39.63	130.18	0.5000
16.7101 141	Public address/intercom, distribution raceway	LF	2.51	12.96	15.47	9.42	11.93	0.1188
16.7101 151	Public address/intercom device raceway	LF	1.86	3.13	4.99	2.27	4.13	0.0287
16.7101 161	Public address/intercom device cable	LF	.79	.72	1.51	.52	1.31	0.0066
16.7101 171	Intercom station - all master desk	EA	508.45	72.03	580.48	52.31	560.76	0.6600
16.7101 181	Intercom power supply, 1 for 3 master station	EA	196.59	21.83	218.42	15.85	212.44	0.2000
16.7101 191	Intercom 1 station master, wall mounted, flush	EA	674.20	52.38	726.58	38.04	712.24	0.4800
16.7101 201	Intercom 1 station remote, wall mounted flush	EA	181.15	52.38	233.53	38.04	219.19	0.4800
16.7102 000	TELEPHONE TIE-IN FOR PAGING:							
16.7102 011	6 line tie-in module	EA	2,160.52	425.61	2,586.13	309.11	2,469.63	3.9000
16.7102 021	19" relay rack, 84" high	EA	880.45	130.96	1,011.41	95.11	975.56	1.2000
16.7103 000	TELEVISION ANTENNA SYSTEMS:							
16.7103 011	TV antenna mast, lead-in box	EA	154.85	714.50	869.35	518.93	673.78	6.5472
16.7103 021	TV main control cabinet, average	EA	1,620.56	357.25	1,977.81	259.47	1,880.03	3.2736
16.7103 031	TV main control cabinet, large	EA	2,812.20	580.53	3,392.73	421.63	3,233.83	5.3196
16.7103 041	TV auxiliary terminal cabinets	EA	238.33	357.25	595.58	259.47	497.80	3.2736
16.7103 051	TV distribution raceway	LF	3.13	8.94	12.07	6.49	9.62	0.0819
16.7103 061	TV outlet	EA	12.86	22.33	35.19	16.22	29.08	0.2046
16.7103 071	TV outlet & jack assembly	EA	22.89	44.66	67.55	32.43	55.32	0.4092
16.7103 081	TV outlet raceway	LF	1.04	5.37	6.41	3.90	4.94	0.0492
16.7103 091	TV outlet coax cable	LF	.10	.72	.82	.52	.62	0.0066
16.7104 000	CLOSED-CIRCUIT TELEVISION SYSTEM:							
16.7104 011	Commercial camera & monitor	EA	1,790.89	357.25	2,148.14	259.47	2,050.36	3.2736
16.7104 021	Commercial camera station only	EA	1,016.14	174.61	1,190.75	126.82	1,142.96	1.6000
16.7104 031	Industrial camera & monitor	EA	7,932.38	625.18	8,557.56	454.06	8,386.44	5.7288
16.7104 041	Industrial camera station only	EA	4,545.07	178.62	4,723.69	129.73	4,674.80	1.6368
16.7104 051	Add for low light	EA	2,544.70	156.30	2,701.00	113.52	2,658.22	1.4322
16.7104 061	Add for weatherproof station	EA	1,395.49	66.98	1,462.47	48.65	1,444.14	0.6138
16.7104 071	Add for pan & tilt	EA	2,754.64	261.91	3,016.55	190.22	2,944.86	2.4000
16.7104 081	Add for zoom - remote control	EA	3,181.50	138.44	3,319.94	100.55	3,282.05	1.2686
16.7104 091	Closed circuit TV monitor with rack	EA	1,389.56	218.26	1,607.82	158.52	1,548.08	2.0000
16.7104 101	Closed circuit TV switcher	EA	816.76	218.26	1,035.02	158.52	975.28	2.0000
16.7104 111	Add for automatic iris	EA	2,884.06	138.44	3,022.50	100.55	2,984.61	1.2686
16.7104 121	Video cable	LF	5.99	.97	6.96	.71	6.70	0.0089
16.7104 131	EMT & video cable, 3/4" average	LF	6.75	4.55	11.30	3.31	10.06	0.0417
16.7104 141	RSC & video cable, 3/4" average	LF	8.34	6.49	14.83	4.72	13.06	0.0595
16.7105 000	SECURITY SYSTEM:							
16.7105 011	Master control panel	EA	627.44	1,309.56	1,937.00	951.12	1,578.56	12.0000
16.7105 021	Intruder alarm panel	EA	260.51	654.78	915.29	475.56	736.07	6.0000
16.7105 031	Security starter kit	EA	631.13	654.78	1,285.91	475.56	1,106.69	6.0000
16.7105 041	Passive infrared motion detector	EA	308.78	76.39	385.17	55.48	364.26	0.7000
16.7105 051	Sound discriminator detector	EA	217.23	76.39	293.62	55.48	272.71	0.7000
16.7105 061	Security conduit/wire	EA	2.77	3.82	6.59	2.77	5.54	0.0350
16.7106 000	MISCELLANEOUS ALARMS:							
16.7106 011	Alarm panel, 4 zone	EA	1,130.63	306.66	1,437.29	222.72	1,353.35	2.8100
16.7106 021	Alarm panel, 20 zone	EA	6,402.36	982.17	7,384.53	713.34	7,115.70	9.0000
16.7106 031	20 zone annunciator	EA	569.79	491.09	1,060.88	356.67	926.46	4.5000
16.7106 041	Door switch	EA	19.42	36.12	55.54	26.24	45.66	0.3310
16.7106 051	Hold up button	EA	229.70	45.83	275.53	33.29	262.99	0.4200
16.7106 061	Foot switch	EA	450.46	52.93	503.39	38.44	488.90	0.4850
16.7108 000	SEISMIC MONITORING SYSTEMS							
16.7108 011	Accelerograph, seismic monitor, digital	EA	7,263.78	1,036.74	8,300.52	752.97	8,016.75	9.5000
16.7108 021	Accelerograph, seismic monitor, analog	EA	8,171.77	1,287.73	9,459.50	935.27	9,107.04	11.8000
16.7200 000	SPECIAL HOSPITAL SYSTEMS:							
16.7201 000	NURSE CALL SYSTEMS-AUDIO VISUAL:							
16.7201 011	Nurse call, audio visual station, single	EA	310.60	89.31	399.91	64.87	375.47	0.8184
16.7201 021	Nurse call, 20 station desk master	EA	2,168.48	714.50	2,882.98	518.93	2,687.41	6.5472
16.7201 031	Nurse call, 30 station desk master	EA	2,593.27	1,071.74	3,665.01	778.40	3,371.67	9.8208
16.7201 041	Nurse call, 40 station desk master	EA	3,025.47	1,428.99	4,454.46	1,037.86	4,063.33	13.0944

239

Division 16 CSI #	16 - ELECTRICAL Description	Unit	Material	Union Install	Union Total	Open Install	Open Total	Unit Man-Hrs
16.7201 000	**NURSE CALL SYSTEMS-AUDIO VISUAL: (Cont.)**							
16.7201 051	Nurse call, master control panel with power supply	EA	2,772.11	1,555.10	4,327.21	1,129.46	3,901.57	14.2500
16.7201 061	Staff locator station	EA	274.20	89.31	363.51	64.87	339.07	0.8184
16.7201 071	Pillow speaker	EA	201.17	21.83	223.00	15.85	217.02	0.2000
16.7201 081	Code blue panel, 50 lights	EA	581.25	1,036.74	1,617.99	752.97	1,334.22	9.5000
16.7201 091	Code blue control panel	EA	1,128.90	1,036.74	2,165.64	752.97	1,881.87	9.5000
16.7201 101	Code blue push button	EA	143.08	89.31	232.39	64.87	207.95	0.8184
16.7201 111	Emergency pull cord or push button	EA	76.22	89.31	165.53	64.87	141.09	0.8184
16.7201 121	Dome light, single	EA	76.22	66.98	143.20	48.65	124.87	0.6138
16.7201 131	Dome light, double	EA	88.85	75.92	164.77	55.14	143.99	0.6957
16.7201 141	Dome light, quad	EA	111.11	81.17	192.28	58.95	170.06	0.7438
16.7201 151	Nurse call system junction box	EA	10.12	44.66	54.78	32.43	42.55	0.4092
16.7201 161	Nurse call system feeder	LF	9.35	22.33	31.68	16.22	25.57	0.2046
16.7201 171	Nurse call system device circuit	LF	3.14	6.25	9.39	4.54	7.68	0.0573
16.7202 000	**RADIO PAGING SYSTEMS:**							
16.7202 011	Master station & power supply	EA	3,176.38	714.50	3,890.88	518.93	3,695.31	6.5472
16.7202 021	Personal call pocket receiver	EA	317.63	89.31	406.94	64.87	382.50	0.8184
16.7203 000	**DOCTORS REGISTRY SYSTEMS:**							
16.7203 011	Doctors registry display, to 50	EA	3,893.78	1,071.74	4,965.52	778.40	4,672.18	9.8208
16.7203 021	Doctors registry display, to 100	EA	5,652.28	1,786.24	7,438.52	1,297.33	6,949.61	16.3680
16.7203 031	Doctors registry display, to 200	EA	12,560.73	2,857.98	15,418.71	2,075.72	14,636.45	26.1888
16.7204 000	**ROOM OCCUPANCY SYSTEMS:**							
16.7204 011	Room occupancy display, to 50	EA	3,014.52	1,071.74	4,086.26	778.40	3,792.92	9.8208
16.7204 021	Room occupancy display, to 100	EA	4,521.82	1,786.24	6,308.06	1,297.33	5,819.15	16.3680
16.7204 031	Room occupancy display, to 200	EA	6,280.34	2,857.98	9,138.32	2,075.72	8,356.06	26.1888
16.7205 000	**MEDICAL CARE SYSTEMS:**							
16.7205 011	Bedside patient consoles, normal	EA	3,140.14	714.50	3,854.64	518.93	3,659.07	6.5472
16.7205 021	Bedside patient consoles, intensive care unit	EA	5,652.28	1,071.74	6,724.02	778.40	6,430.68	9.8208
16.7206 000	**EQUIPOTENTIAL GROUNDING SYSTEMS:**							
16.7206 011	Equipotential ground, operating room	SF	4.99	4.47	9.46	3.25	8.24	0.0410
16.7206 021	Equipotential ground, ward area	SF	2.70	2.25	4.95	1.63	4.33	0.0206
16.7206 031	Equipotential ground, private room	SF	3.31	2.68	5.99	1.95	5.26	0.0246
16.7206 041	Equipotential ground, intensive care unit ward	SF	3.09	3.13	6.22	2.27	5.36	0.0287
16.7206 051	Equipotential ground, intensive care unit room	SF	3.70	4.03	7.73	2.92	6.62	0.0369
16.7206 061	Ground modules, wall outlet	EA	163.26	178.62	341.88	129.73	292.99	1.6368
16.7206 071	Master ground module	EA	678.30	714.50	1,392.80	518.93	1,197.23	6.5472
16.7206 081	Equipotential circuits, RSC/wire	LF	5.53	7.15	12.68	5.19	10.72	0.0655
16.7207 000	**HOSPITAL ISOLATING PANELS:**							
16.7207 011	Power/light panel, 8 circuit, 3kva, operating room	EA	6,976.57	1,205.71	8,182.28	875.70	7,852.27	11.0484
16.7207 021	Power/light panel, 8 circuit, 5kva, operating room	EA	7,214.20	1,339.68	8,553.88	973.00	8,187.20	12.2760
16.7207 031	Power/light panel, 8 circuit, 75kva, operating room	EA	7,647.10	1,428.99	9,076.09	1,037.86	8,684.96	13.0944
16.7207 041	Power/light panel, 8 circuit, 10kva, operating room	EA	8,411.14	1,607.62	10,018.76	1,167.59	9,578.73	14.7312
16.7207 051	Intensive care unit/coronary care unit area panel, 8 circuit, 3 kva	EA	8,345.29	1,205.71	9,551.00	875.70	9,220.99	11.0484
16.7207 061	Intensive care unit/coronary care unit area panel, 8 circuit, 5 kva	EA	8,524.26	1,339.68	9,863.94	973.00	9,497.26	12.2760
16.7207 071	Intensive care unit/coronary care unit area panel, 8 circuit, 75 kva	EA	9,291.29	1,428.99	10,720.28	1,037.86	10,329.15	13.0944
16.7207 081	Intensive care unit/coronary care unit area panel, 8 circuit, 10 kva	EA	10,155.28	1,607.62	11,762.90	1,167.59	11,322.87	14.7312
16.7207 091	X-ray panel, 15 kva, 277/208v	EA	16,900.79	1,607.62	18,508.41	1,167.59	18,068.38	14.7312
16.7207 101	X-ray panel, 25 kva, 277/208v	EA	17,307.36	1,964.86	19,272.22	1,427.06	18,734.42	18.0048
16.7207 111	X-ray outlets, 60 a	EA	1,007.79	65.48	1,073.27	47.56	1,055.35	0.6000
16.7208 000	**CLOCK AND PROGRAM SYSTEMS:**							
16.7208 011	Clock main panel/generator	EA	2,780.42	714.50	3,494.92	518.93	3,299.35	6.5472
16.7208 021	Clock terminal cabinet	EA	241.71	223.28	464.99	162.17	403.88	2.0460
16.7208 031	Clock distribution raceway	LF	3.13	8.94	12.07	6.49	9.62	0.0819
16.7208 041	Clock distribution cable	LF	5.54	.72	6.26	.52	6.06	0.0066
16.7208 051	Clock outlets	EA	12.86	22.33	35.19	16.22	29.08	0.2046
16.7208 061	Elapsed timer, 15 seconds to 2 hour	EA	160.61	89.31	249.92	64.87	225.48	0.8184
16.7208 071	Clock, standard, wall mounted	EA	39.52	89.31	128.83	64.87	104.39	0.8184
16.7208 081	Clock, standard, flush mounted	EA	135.82	178.62	314.44	129.73	265.55	1.6368
16.7208 091	Clock circuits, EMT/wire	LF	2.57	6.25	8.82	4.54	7.11	0.0573
16.7209 000	**LOW VOLTAGE SWITCHING SYSTEMS:**							
16.7209 011	Low voltage relays, one pole	EA	42.26	8.94	51.20	6.49	48.75	0.0819
16.7209 021	Low voltage relays, multi-pole	EA	107.24	40.19	147.43	29.19	136.43	0.3683

Division 16 CSI #	16 - ELECTRICAL Description	Unit	Material	Union Install	Union Total	Open Install	Open Total	Unit Man-Hrs
16.7209 000	**LOW VOLTAGE SWITCHING SYSTEMS: (Cont.)**							
16.7209 031	Low voltage relay cabinet, 18 pole	EA	200.53	312.59	513.12	227.03	427.56	2.8644
16.7209 041	Low voltage switch, single	EA	33.03	35.73	68.76	25.95	58.98	0.3274
16.7209 051	Low voltage switch, master	EA	376.51	133.97	510.48	97.30	473.81	1.2276
16.7209 061	Low voltage transformer	EA	39.52	22.33	61.85	16.22	55.74	0.2046
16.7209 071	Low voltage push-button	EA	9.02	22.33	31.35	16.22	25.24	0.2046
16.7209 081	Low voltage door switch	EA	27.34	44.66	72.00	32.43	59.77	0.4092
16.7209 091	Low voltage raceway, EMT	LF	1.04	5.37	6.41	3.90	4.94	0.0492
16.7209 101	Low voltage conductor #14	LF	.06	.55	.61	.40	.46	0.0050
16.7300 000	**PRISON CELL DOOR CONTROL SYSTEMS:**							
16.7300 011	Door, prison cell, locking relay cabinet	EA	1,137.56	1,153.21	2,290.77	837.56	1,975.12	10.5673
16.7300 021	Door, prison cell, gang control cabinet	EA	175.35	463.81	639.16	336.86	512.21	4.2501
16.7300 031	Door, prison cell, gang control panel	EA	542.06	821.11	1,363.17	596.36	1,138.42	7.5241
16.7300 041	Door, prison cell, cable gutter	LF	22.20	19.80	42.00	14.38	36.58	0.1814
16.7300 051	Door, prison cell, junction box	EA	7.11	13.90	21.01	10.10	17.21	0.1274
16.7300 061	Door, prison cell, door connections	EA	12.81	27.42	40.23	19.92	32.73	0.2513
16.7300 071	Door, prison cell, 2-2" concealed, RSG conduit	LF	16.79	23.24	40.03	16.88	33.67	0.2130
16.7300 081	Door, prison cell, 2-2" concealed, RSG conduit	LF	25.18	30.86	56.04	22.41	47.59	0.2828
16.7300 091	Door, prison cell, 2-2" concealed, RSG conduit	LF	4.34	7.12	11.46	5.17	9.51	0.0652
16.7300 101	Door, prison cell, #14 wire	LF	.09	.34	.43	.25	.34	0.0031
16.7300 111	Door, prison cell, #16 wire	LF	.04	.21	.25	.15	.19	0.0019
16.7500 000	**SOFT WIRE SYSTEMS, 3 WIRE:**							
16.7501 000	**LIGHTING, 15 FIXTURE GROUP:**							
	Note: The following prices include wiring only. Fixtures must be added separately.							
16.7501 011	Fixtures on 6' centers	GR	50.80	129.50	180.30	94.06	144.86	1.1867
16.7501 021	Fixtures on 8' centers	GR	53.81	129.50	183.31	94.06	147.87	1.1867
16.7501 031	Fixtures on 10' centers	GR	56.73	129.50	186.23	94.06	150.79	1.1867
16.7501 041	Fixtures on 12' centers	GR	59.19	129.50	188.69	94.06	153.25	1.1867
16.7501 051	Fixtures on 16' centers	GR	66.11	129.50	195.61	94.06	160.17	1.1867
16.7501 061	Fixtures on 20' centers	GR	71.81	129.50	201.31	94.06	165.87	1.1867
16.7502 000	**SWITCHING:**							
16.7502 011	Single pole - single level	EA	92.11	44.66	136.77	32.43	124.54	0.4092
16.7502 021	Single pole - double level	EA	126.98	44.66	171.64	32.43	159.41	0.4092
16.7502 031	Three-way, per pair of switches	EA	148.46	98.25	246.71	71.36	219.82	0.9003
16.7502 041	Four-way, per switch drop	EA	109.66	44.66	154.32	32.43	142.09	0.4092
16.7503 000	**OUTLETS, 9 OUTLET GROUP:**							
16.7503 011	Outlets on 4' centers	GR	404.87	361.72	766.59	262.72	667.59	3.3146
16.7503 021	Outlets on 8' centers	GR	410.82	361.72	772.54	262.72	673.54	3.3146
16.7503 031	Outlets on 10' centers	GR	413.50	36.18	449.68	26.27	439.77	0.3315
16.7503 041	Outlets on 12' centers	GR	416.02	36.18	452.20	26.27	442.29	0.3315
16.7503 051	Outlets on 16' centers	GR	422.81	36.18	458.99	26.27	449.08	0.3315
16.7504 000	**POWER COLUMNS, 9 COLUMN GROUP:**							
16.7504 011	Power columns on 10' centers	GR	1,598.90	1,607.62	3,206.52	1,167.59	2,766.49	14.7312
16.7504 021	Power columns on 12' centers	GR	1,601.64	1,607.62	3,209.26	1,167.59	2,769.23	14.7312
16.7504 031	Power columns on 16' centers	GR	1,604.52	1,607.62	3,212.14	1,167.59	2,772.11	14.7312
16.7504 041	Power columns on 20' centers	GR	1,611.24	1,607.62	3,218.86	1,167.59	2,778.83	14.7312
16.7504 051	Power columns on 24' centers	GR	1,623.34	1,607.62	3,230.96	1,167.59	2,790.93	14.7312
16.7504 061	Soft wire poke-thru receptacle	EA	160.22	130.40	290.62	94.71	254.93	1.1949
16.7601 000	**ENERGY & BUILDING MANAGEMENT SYSTEM:**							
16.7601 011	Relay panel	EA	366.51	123.25	489.76	89.52	456.03	1.1294
16.7601 021	Monitor point, 3" pipe	EA	169.79	105.68	275.47	76.76	246.55	0.9684
16.7601 031	Monitor point, 4" pipe	EA	229.29	107.18	336.47	77.84	307.13	0.9821
16.7601 041	Monitor point, 5" pipe	EA	337.69	108.66	446.35	78.92	416.61	0.9957
16.7601 051	Monitor point, 6" pipe	EA	409.43	110.14	519.57	80.00	489.43	1.0093
16.7601 061	Monitor point, 8" pipe	EA	493.33	111.64	604.97	81.08	574.41	1.0230
16.7601 071	Monitor point, 10" pipe	EA	516.18	113.12	629.30	82.16	598.34	1.0366
16.7601 081	Monitor point, 12" pipe	LF	711.70	114.61	826.31	83.24	794.94	1.0502
16.7601 091	Monitor EMT & wire, 3/4" average	LF	1.14	5.01	6.15	3.64	4.78	0.0459
16.7601 101	Monitor RSC & wire, 3/4" average	LF	2.44	6.25	8.69	4.54	6.98	0.0573
16.7601 111	Monitor point termination	EA	.10	14.89	14.99	10.81	10.91	0.1364
16.7601 121	Master control panel	EA	2,138.14	763.63	2,901.77	554.61	2,692.75	6.9974

Division 16 CSI #	16 - ELECTRICAL Description	Unit	Material	Union Install	Union Total	Open Install	Open Total	Unit Man-Hrs
16.7701 000	**TESTING:**							
16.7701 011	Testing, light fixtures	EA	7.79		7.79		7.79	
16.7701 021	Testing, wiring devices	EA	5.51		5.51		5.51	
16.7701 031	Testing, motors & control by hp	EA	32.34		32.34		32.34	

1.1   DEMOLITION   **245**
1.1105 Building   245
1.1110 Wall   245
1.1115 Roof   245
1.1120 Ceiling   245
1.1200 Foundation   245
1.1305 Paving, Curbs and Walks   246
1.1400 Utilities   246

1.2   SITE WORK   **247**
1.2100 Clear & Grub   247
1.2200 Mass Excavation   247
1.2300 Site Fill   247
1.2400 Site Paving, Asphalt   247
1.2500 Site Paving, Concrete   247
1.2600 Site Other, Surface   247
1.2700 Site Utilities   248
1.2800 Site Lighting   249

2.1   SUBSTRUCTURE   **250**
2.1100 Excavation for Buildings   250
2.1200 Piles   250
2.1300 Foundations & Pile Caps   251
2.1400 Walls Below Grade   251
2.1500 Waterproofing   251
2.1600 Substructure drainage   252
2.1700 Slabs on Grade   252

3.0   STRUCTURE   **253**
3.0105 Columns, Cast in Place   253
3.0110 Columns, Precast   253
3.0115 Columns, Steel   253
3.0120 Columns, Wood   254
3.0205 Beams & Girders, Cast in Place   254
3.0210 Beams & Girders, Precast   254
3.0215 Beams & Girders, Steel   254
3.0220 Beams & Girders, Wood   254
3.0305 Floors, Cast in Place   255
3.0310 Floors, Precast   255
3.0315 Floors, Concrete on Steel Joists   255
3.0320 Floors, Wood   255
3.0325 Roofs, Metal Deck on Steel Joists   256
3.0330 Roofs, Wood   256
3.0400 Floor, Topping   256
3.0500 Fireproofing   256

4.1   ENCLOSURE, VERTICAL   **258**
4.1105 Walls, Cast in Place   258
4.1110 Walls, Tilt-up Concrete Panel   259
4.1115 Walls, Precast Concrete Panels   259

4.1120 Walls, Concrete Block   259
4.1125 Walls, Brick Veneer with Block Back-up   260
4.1130 Walls, Brick   260
4.1135 Walls, Stone Veneer with Block Back-up   260
4.1140 Walls, Brick Veneer on Stud Frame   261
4.1145 Walls, Siding on Stud Frame   262
4.1150 Walls, Stone Veneer on Stud Frame   263
4.1155 Walls, Stucco on Stud Frame   263
4.1160 Walls, Metal Siding   263
4.1165 Walls, Curtain Walls   264
4.1170 Walls, Exterior Coating   265
4.1175 Interior Surface of Exterior Wall   265
4.1200 Fenestration   266
4.1300 Exterior Doors   268
4.1400 Store Front Systems   268
4.1500 Special Doors   268

4.2   ENCLOSURE, HORIZONTAL   **269**
4.2100 Roof & Roof Material   269
4.2200 Rigid Insulation   269

4.3   SUPPORT ITEMS   **271**
4.3100 Miscellaneous Iron   271
4.3200 Sheetmetal   271
4.3300 Skylights   272
4.3400 Insulation   273
4.3500 Caulking & Sealants   273

5.1   INTERNALS, VERTICAL   **275**
5.1105 Gypsum Board on Stud   275
5.1110 Lath and Plaster on Stud   277
5.1115 Concrete Block   278
5.1120 Structural Tile   279
5.1125 Wall Finishes   279
5.1200 Doors, Including Hardware   281
5.1300 Internal Fenestration   282

5.2   INTERNALS, HORIZONTAL   **283**
5.2100 Ceiling   283
5.2200 Floor, Resilient   283

5.3   FINISHES, SPECIAL   **285**
5.3100 Tile   285
5.3200 Terrazzo   285
5.3300 Hardwood Floors   285
5.3400 Wall Covering   285
5.3500 Wood   285

ASSEMBLY COSTS
TABLE OF CONTENTS

5.4 INTERIORS — 286
5.4100 Cabinets & Tops — 286
5.4300 Carpet — 287

6.0 SPECIALTIES — 289
6.0100 Chalk & Tack Board — 289
6.0200 Toilet Partitions — 289
6.0300 Demountable Partitions — 290
6.0400 Toilet Accessories — 290

7.0 EQUIPMENT — 292
7.0100 Bank Equipment — 292
7.0200 Educational Equipment — 292
7.0300 Food Service Equipment — 293
7.0400 Gymnasium & Playground Equipment — 295
7.0500 Industrial Equipment — 297
7.0600 Parking Lot Equipment — 297
7.0700 Material Handling Equipment — 297
7.0800 Laboratory Equipment — 297
7.0900 Library Equipment — 298
7.1000 Hospital Equipment — 299
7.1100 Dental Equipment — 302
7.1200 Stage Equipment — 303
7.1300 Garbage Compactors — 304

8.0 SPECIAL CONSTRUCTION — 305
8.0100 Raised Floors — 305
8.0200 X-ray Room Construction — 305
8.0300 Pools — 305

9.0 CONVEYING — 306
9.0100 Stairs — 306
9.0205 Elevators, Hydraulic — 306
9.0210 Elevators, Electric Gear — 306
9.0215 Elevators, Electric Gearless — 306
9.0220 Hoists and Cranes — 307
9.0225 Manlift — 307
9.0300 Dumb-Waiters — 307
9.0400 Escalators — 307
9.0500 Pneumatic Systems — 307

10.1 PLUMBING & FIRE PROTECTION — 308
10.1100 Equipment — 308
10.1205 Fixtures, Economy Grade — 308
10.1210 Fixtures, Standard Grade — 309
10.1215 Fixtures, Institutional Grade — 309
10.1305 Rough-Ins — 309
10 1310 Pipe, Cast Iron — 310
10.1315 Pipe, Copper — 311
10.1320 Pipe, PVC — 311

10.1325 Pipe, Polypropylene — 312
10.1330 Pipe, Plastic — 312
10.1335 Pipe, Pyrex — 312
10.1340 Pipe, Steel — 312
10.1400 Miscellaneous Plumbing Specialties — 312
10.1500 Medical Gases, Accessories — 312
10.1515 Medical Gas Piping — 313
10.1600 Fees, Permits, Sterilization — 314
10.1700 Fire Protection System — 314

10.2 HEAT, VENT & AIR CONDITIONING — 315
10.2105 Furnaces — 315
10.2110 Boilers — 315
10.2115 Chillers — 315
10.2120 Cooling Towers — 315
10.2125 Air Conditioners — 316
10.2130 Split Systems — 316
10.2135 Computer Room Air Conditioning — 316
10.2140 Roof Mounted Units — 316
10.2145 Heat Pumps — 316
10.2150 Hydronic Systems — 316
10.2155 Infra-Read and Radiant Systems — 316
10.2160 Humidifiers — 317
10.2165 Pumps — 317
10.2170 Air Handlers — 317
10.2175 Coils — 317
10.2180 Fans — 317
10.2185 Tanks — 318
10.2200 Controls — 318
10.2300 Ductwork — 318
10.2400 Piping — 319

11.0 ELECTRICAL — 320
11.0100 Switchgear — 320
11.0200 Emergency Systems — 320
11.0300 Feeder Conduit & Wire — 321
11.0400 Fixtures — 322
11.0500 Signal & Communications — 323
11.0600 Devices — 323

CSI #	1.1 DEMOLITION Description	Unit	Material	Union Install	Union Total	Open Install	Open Total
	The demolition costs, in this section, includes disposal.						
	However, no allowances are included for dumping charges or						
	special handling of toxic or hazardous waste. Other						
	conditions, such as excessive haul distances, unusual work						
	hours, high voltage lines, or limited access must also be						
	accounted for by increased costs or additional allowances.						
	Consult local authorities for special conditions and						
	legislation which may affect the demolition and disposal						
	costs.						
01.1105	DEMOLITION, BUILDING						
01.1105 100	Demolition, frame building, one story	SF	.16	3.93	4.09	1.80	1.96
01.1105 105	Demolition, frame building, two story	SF	.16	3.81	3.97	1.74	1.90
01.1105 110	Demolition, frame building, three story	SF	.16	3.73	3.89	1.71	1.87
01.1105 115	Demolition, concrete block building, two story	SF	.76	7.74	8.50	3.55	4.31
01.1105 120	Demolition, concrete block building, three story	SF	.70	7.48	8.18	3.43	4.13
01.1105 125	Demolition, concrete building, monolithic, large	SF	3.44	8.73	12.17	4.00	7.44
01.1105 130	Demolition, concrete building, precast panel, frame roof	SF	2.64	8.01	10.65	3.67	6.31
01.1105 135	Demolition, steel frame building, no fireproofing	SF	1.50	9.30	10.80	4.26	5.76
01.1105 140	Demolition, steel frame building, with fireproofing	SF	1.95	12.09	14.04	5.54	7.49
01.1105 145	Demolition, steel frame building, salvage steel	SF	2.25	13.95	16.20	6.39	8.64
01.1110	DEMOLITION, WALL						
01.1110 105	Demolition, remove wall, concrete to 10" thick, reinforced	SF	2.53	3.77	6.30	2.37	4.90
01.1110 110	Demolition, remove wall, concrete block, reinforced	SF	1.35	2.71	4.06	1.71	3.06
01.1110 115	Demolition, remove wall, stucco/plaster, metal stud	SF	.06	1.00	1.06	.63	.69
01.1110 120	Demolition, remove wall, gypsum board, metal stud	SF	.02	.73	.75	.46	.48
01.1110 125	Demolition, remove wall, brick veneer, overlaid	SF	.23	6.81	7.04	4.29	4.52
01.1110 130	Demolition, remove wall, 8" solid brick, 10" cavity	SF	.39	6.48	6.87	4.08	4.47
01.1110 135	Demolition, remove wall, 10"-12" solid brick, reinforced, grout	SF	.78	8.93	9.71	5.62	6.40
01.1110 140	Demolition, remove wall, metal siding, no save	SF	.29	4.42	4.71	2.78	3.07
01.1110 145	Demolition, remove curtain wall, save glass	SF	.53	5.74	6.27	3.62	4.15
01.1115	DEMOLITION, ROOF						
01.1115 100	Demolition, remove built-up roof, on plywood	SQ	1.87	57.96	59.83	26.56	28.43
01.1115 105	Demolition, remove built-up roof, on metal deck	SQ	2.75	43.14	45.89	19.77	22.52
01.1115 110	Demolition, remove built-up roof, on gypsum plank	SQ	1.87	44.12	45.99	20.21	22.08
01.1115 115	Demolition, remove built-up roof, on concrete	SQ	1.87	50.67	52.54	23.21	25.08
01.1115 120	Demolition, remove roof, asphalt shingles	SQ	1.87	37.56	39.43	17.21	19.08
01.1115 125	Demolition, remove roof, wood shingles	SQ	1.87	35.57	37.44	16.30	18.17
01.1120	DEMOLITION, CEILING						
01.1120 100	Demolition, remove ceiling, plaster/lath/frame	SF	.03	1.98	2.01	.91	.94
01.1120 105	Demolition, remove ceiling, plaster suspended grid	SF	.03	1.49	1.52	.68	.71
01.1120 110	Demolition, remove ceiling, acoustic suspended grid	SF	.03	.46	.49	.21	.24
01.1120 115	Demolition, remove ceiling, acoustic salvage	SF	.03	.86	.89	.39	.42
01.1120 120	Demolition, remove ceiling, area light, salvage	SF	.03	1.60	1.63	.73	.76
01.1200	DEMOLITION, FOUNDATION						
01.1200 100	Demolition, remove concrete foundation, no rebar	CY	43.71	67.01	110.72	42.20	85.91

CSI #	1.1 DEMOLITION Description	Unit	Material	Union Install	Union Total	Open Install	Open Total
01.1200	**DEMOLITION, FOUNDATION (Cont.)**						
01.1200 105	Demolition, remove concrete foundation, with rebar	CY	51.10	98.99	150.09	62.34	113.44
01.1305	**DEMOLITION, PAVING, CURBS & WALKS**						
01.1305 100	Demolition, remove pavement, asphaltic concrete, short haul, 5,000 to 25,000 SF	SF	.55	.29	.84	.21	.76
01.1305 105	Demolition, remove pavement, asphaltic concrete, short haul, 25,000 to 50,000 SF	SF	.35	.29	.64	.21	.56
01.1305 110	Demolition, remove pavement, asphaltic concrete, short haul, over 50,000 SF	SF	.24	.18	.42	.13	.37
01.1305 115	Demolition, remove pavement, concrete slab, 5" thick, no rebar	SF	.51	.79	1.30	.36	.87
01.1305 120	Demolition, remove pavement, concrete slab, 5" thick, with rebar	SF	.57	1.02	1.59	.47	1.04
01.1305 125	Demolition, remove pavement, concrete slab, 9" - 12" thick, with rebar	SF	2.75	4.43	7.18	2.03	4.78
01.1305 130	Demolition, remove pavement, concrete slab, 13" - 18" thick, with rebar	SF	3.98	7.98	11.96	3.66	7.64
01.1305 135	Demolition, remove pavement, concrete curb and gutter, no sawing	LF	.95	1.75	2.70	.80	1.75
01.1305 140	Demolition, remove pavement, concrete curb-planter & batt	LF	1.18	2.46	3.64	1.13	2.31
01.1305 145	Demolition, remove pavement, concrete drive with curb & retaining wall	LF	.55	1.03	1.58	.47	1.02
01.1305 150	Demolition, remove pavement, concrete sidewalk	SF	.42	.91	1.33	.42	.84
01.1305 155	Demolition, remove pavement, concrete catch basin, sump and dry well	EACH	108.26	186.88	295.14	85.62	193.88
01.1400	**DEMOLITION, UTILITIES**						
01.1400 100	Demolition, remove hydrant, with reset thrust blocks	EACH	118.33	418.38	536.71	191.69	310.02
01.1400 105	Demolition, remove storm drain line, dispose	LF	2.81	6.67	9.48	3.05	5.86
01.1400 110	Demolition, remove sanitary line, dispose	LF	3.26	6.56	9.82	3.01	6.27

CSI #	1.21 SITEWORK Description	Unit	Material	Union Install	Union Total	Open Install	Open Total
	The sitework costs, in this section, are typical of costs associated with the construction of a building. They include allowances for materials, labor, overhead and profit for the subcontractor. There are no allowances for the markup or profit for the general contractor. The costs include all costs associated with completion of the installation. For example, the costs for underground utilities and site lighting have allowances for trenching and backfill included. However, there are no built-in allowances for adverse weather conditions nor are there any allowances for unusual soil or rock conditions or local legislation.						
01.2100	**CLEAR & GRUB**						
01.2100 100	Clear & grub, brush, turf, roots, with disposal	SF	.05	.09	.14	.06	.11
01.2100 105	Clear & grub, large area, without disposal	SF	.03	.09	.12	.06	.09
01.2100 110	Clear & grub, large products	CY	1.19	1.25	2.44	.88	2.07
01.2100 115	Strip and stockpile 6" deep	CY	1.57	1.49	3.06	1.05	2.62
01.2100 120	Scarify and compact 6" topping	SF	.06	.20	.26	.14	.20
01.2100 125	Rough grade machine	SF	.03	.09	.12	.06	.09
01.2100 130	Fine grade machine	SF	.04	.16	.20	.11	.15
01.2100 135	Fine grade hand	SF		.79	.79	.56	.56
01.2200	**MASS EXCAVATION**						
01.2200 100	Site cut and fill, earth. 5M - 20M	CY	2.36	2.46	4.82	1.76	4.12
01.2200 105	Site cut and fill, earth. 20M - 50M	CY	1.66	1.72	3.38	1.23	2.89
01.2200 110	Site cut and fill, rock and earth mixture	CY	5.75	5.43	11.18	3.88	9.63
01.2300	**SITE FILL**						
01.2300 100	Engineered fill, 100 - 2.5M, imported one mile	CY	10.16	1.31	11.47	.92	11.08
01.2300 105	Engineered fill, 2.5M - 10M, imported one mile	CY	9.87	.78	10.65	.55	10.42
01.2300 110	Engineered fill, 10M - 25M, imported one mile	CY	9.50	1.02	10.52	.72	10.22
01.2300 115	Engineered fill, 25M - 50M, imported one mile	CY	9.25	.90	10.15	.64	9.89
01.2300 120	Engineered fill, 100M - 2.5M, imported one mile	CY	7.01	.51	7.52	.36	7.37
01.2300 125	Engineered fill, 2.5M - 25M, imported one mile	CY	7.01	.34	7.35	.24	7.25
01.2300 130	Engineered fill, 25M - 50M, imported one mile	CY	7.01	.17	7.18	.12	7.13
01.2300 135	Engineered fill, compaction, by roller	CY	.72	1.11	1.83	.78	1.50
01.2300 140	Engineered fill, compaction, by sheepsfoot	CY	.94	1.41	2.35	1.00	1.94
01.2300 145	Engineered fill, dozer spread, no material	CY	.56	.75	1.31	.54	1.10
01.2300 150	Backfill, machine, no compaction	CY	3.31	11.97	15.28	8.43	11.74
01.2300 155	Backfill, hand, no compaction	CY	5.65	62.51	68.16	27.18	32.83
01.2300 160	Backfill, select import, compacted	CY	13.63	32.41	46.04	22.82	36.45
01.2300 165	Backfill, site material, compacted	CY	6.83	20.87	27.70	14.70	21.53
01.2400	**SITE PAVING, ASPHALT**						
01.2400 100	Pavement, asphalt, driveway, 2" thick, 4" base	SF	1.67	1.53	3.20	.92	2.59
01.2400 105	Pavement, asphalt, parking lot, 2" thick, 6" base	SF	1.75	1.90	3.65	1.15	2.90
01.2400 110	Pavement, asphalt, truck & ramp, 3" thick, 8" base	SF	2.23	2.41	4.64	1.45	3.68
01.2400 115	Pavement, asphalt, street, 3" thick, 8" base, 10" sub-base	SF	2.87	3.31	6.18	2.00	4.87
01.2400 120	Pavement, asphalt, armor coat, 2 shot, 4" base	SF	.89	1.05	1.94	.64	1.53
01.2400 125	Add or deduct for each additional 1" of baserock	SF	.20		.20		.20
01.2400 130	Add or deduct for each additional 1" of asphaltic concrete	SF	.78		.78		.78
01.2500	**SITE PAVING, CONCRETE**						
01.2500 100	Pavement, concrete, driveway, 2" thick, 4" base	SF	2.59	2.37	4.96	1.43	4.02
01.2500 105	Pavement, concrete, parking lot, 2" thick, 6" base	SF	2.71	2.95	5.66	1.78	4.49
01.2500 110	Pavement, concrete, truck & ramp, 3" thick, 8" base	SF	3.46	3.74	7.20	2.25	5.71
01.2500 115	Pavement, concrete, street, 3" thick, 8" base, 10" sub-base	SF	4.45	5.13	9.58	3.10	7.55
01.2500 120	Bumper block, parking, precast, 3' long	EACH	25.82	15.72	41.54	6.83	32.65
01.2500 125	Bumper block, parking, precast, 6' long	EACH	41.47	19.23	60.70	8.36	49.83
01.2500 130	Striping, parking stall, one line per stall, 1 coat	EACH	.10	9.90	10.00	4.31	4.41
01.2500 135	Street sign with pole	EACH	129.61	122.68	252.29	53.34	182.95
01.2600	**SITE OTHER, SURFACE**						
01.2600 100	Sidewalk, concrete walk 4", 100% seeded color	SF	1.41	.29	1.70	.20	1.61
01.2600 105	Sidewalk, concrete walk 4", 80 - 100% seeded aggregate	SF	2.21	3.24	5.45	1.99	4.20

CSI #	1.21 SITEWORK Description	Unit	Material	Union Install	Union Total	Open Install	Open Total
01.2600	**SITE OTHER, SURFACE (Cont.)**						
01.2600 110	Sidewalk, concrete walk 4", exposed aggregate wash	SF	1.91	1.96	3.87	1.20	3.11
01.2600 115	Sidewalk, concrete walk 4", broom finish	SF	1.91	1.30	3.21	.79	2.70
01.2600 120	Curb and gutter, 4' sidewalk, mono	LF	35.14	11.86	47.00	7.27	42.41
01.2600 125	Curb 6", asphaltic concrete	LF	4.88	7.63	12.51	5.37	10.25
01.2600 130	Curb and gutter, machine work	LF	9.92	6.16	16.08	3.78	13.70
01.2600 140	Curb forms fabricacted edge 6" x 12"	LF	1.26	2.47	3.73	1.51	2.77
01.2600 145	Pavements miscellaneous, tennis court, bases, AC, color, seal	SF	6.88		6.88		6.88
01.2600 150	Pavements miscellaneous, tennis court, 7200 SF, fence/stripe	SF	72,017.08		72,017.08		72,017.08
01.2600 155	Pavements miscellaneous, parking gravel, 6" of 1 1/2" rock	SF	.53		.53		.53
01.2600 160	Sidewalk and concrete finishes, precast pavers, grouted	SF	3.17	6.71	9.88	4.11	7.28
01.2600 165	Sidewalk and concrete finishes, precast pavers, sand bed, 1" compact	SF	2.63	4.60	7.23	2.56	5.19
01.2600 170	Sidewalk and concrete finishes, brick pavers, grouted	SF	3.63	7.56	11.19	4.21	7.84
01.2600 175	brick pavers, sand bed, 1" compact	SF	3.21	5.60	8.81	3.12	6.33
01.2600 180	Sidewalk and concrete finishes, concrete hardner, iron base	SF	.34	.52	.86	.38	.72
01.2600 185	Sidewalk and concrete finishes, concrete hardner, granolithic	SF	.01	.27	.28	.19	.20
01.2600 190	Sidewalk and concrete finishes, concrete hardner, chemical	SF	.09	.27	.36	.19	.28
01.2600 195	finish broom	SF		.71	.71	.52	.52
01.2600 200	Sidewalk and concrete finishes, finish steel trowel	SF		.71	.71	.52	.52
01.2700	**SITE UTILITIES**						
01.2700 100	Underground service, concrete encased, 100 Amp, 600 V, 4-THHN #2 copper wire, grounded	LF	30.29	11.30	41.59	7.87	38.16
01.2700 105	Underground service, concrete encased, 175 Amp, 600 V, 3-THHN 2/0 copper wire, grounded	LF	39.63	13.52	53.15	9.35	48.98
01.2700 110	Underground service, concrete encased, 400 Amp, 600 V, 3-500 MCM copper wire, grounded	LF	72.25	19.36	91.61	13.61	85.86
01.2700 115	Underground service, concrete encased, 800 Amp, 600 V, 6-500 MCM copper wire, grounded	LF	134.45	35.92	170.37	25.54	159.99
01.2700 120	Underground service, concrete encased, 1200 Amp, 600 V, 12-350 MCM copper wire, grounded	LF	206.02	64.71	270.73	46.12	252.14
01.2700 125	Underground service, fiber conduit, 175 Amp, 600 V, 3-THW/THHN 2/0 copper wire, grounded	LF	17.00	16.86	33.86	12.27	29.27
01.2700 130	Underground service, fiber conduit, 300 Amp, 600 V, 4-THHN 350 MCM copper wire, grounded	LF	52.74	26.09	78.83	18.98	71.72
01.2700 135	Underground service, rigid steel conduit, 30 Amp, 600 V, 1-THHN #10 copper wire	LF	9.49	15.74	25.23	11.23	20.72
01.2700 140	Underground service, rigid steel conduit, 60 Amp, 600 V, 4-THHN #6 copper wire	LF	14.36	19.28	33.64	13.96	28.32
01.2700 145	Underground service, rigid steel conduit, 100 Amp, 600 V, 4-THHN #2 copper wire	LF	21.20	22.12	43.32	16.01	37.21
01.2700 150	Underground service, rigid steel conduit, 400 Amp, 600 V, 4-THHN 500 MCM copper wire	LF	89.24	45.09	134.33	32.71	121.95
01.2700 152	Underground service, rigid steel conduit, 600 Amp, 600 V, 6-THHN 350 MCM copper wire	LF	117.16	74.21	191.37	53.89	171.05
01.2700 155	Utility pole, with transformer, 250 KVA,	EACH	22,257.35	12,132.18	34,389.53	8,695.26	30,952.61
01.2700 160	Utility pole, with transformer, 100 KVA,	EACH	7,791.94	9,558.44	17,350.38	6,825.99	14,617.93
01.2700 165	Utility pole, with transformer, 75 KVA,	EACH	8,270.33	7,180.49	15,450.82	5,126.39	13,396.72
01.2700 170	Utility pole, with transformer, 25 KVA,	EACH	4,027.17	5,631.93	9,659.10	4,029.20	8,056.37
01.2700 175	Site drainage, underdrain, 4" polyethelene pipe	LF	8.45	23.87	32.32	16.01	24.46
01.2700 180	Site drainage, underdrain, 6" polyethelene pipe	LF	9.19	24.22	33.41	16.22	25.41

CSI #	1.21 SITEWORK Description	Unit	Material	Union Install	Union Total	Open Install	Open Total
01.2700	SITE UTILITIES (Cont.)						
01.2700 185	Site drainage, underdrain, 10" polyethelene pipe	LF	12.45	24.86	37.31	16.62	29.07
01.2700 190	Sanitary sewer, cast iron pipe, 4" Diameter	LF	16.31	18.12	34.43	11.10	27.41
01.2700 192	Sanitary sewer, cast iron pipe, 6" Diameter	LF	28.22	24.41	52.63	14.96	43.18
01.2700 195	Sanitary sewer, cast iron pipe, 10" Diameter	LF	71.12	30.50	101.62	18.69	89.81
01.2700 200	Storm drainage, reinforced concrete pipe, 12" Diameter	LF	21.14	25.18	46.32	15.43	36.57
01.2700 205	Storm drainage, reinforced concrete pipe, 15" Diameter	LF	29.95	30.98	60.93	18.98	48.93
01.2700 210	Storm drainage, reinforced concrete pipe, 18" Diameter	LF	38.68	38.49	77.17	23.59	62.27
01.2700 215	Storm drainage, reinforced concrete pipe, 36" Diameter	LF	112.41	64.46	176.87	39.50	151.91
01.2700 220	Storm drainage, corrugated metal pipe, 8" Diameter	LF	7.41	17.54	24.95	10.75	18.16
01.2700 225	Storm drainage, corrugated metal pipe, 15" Diameter	LF	10.11	23.83	33.94	15.95	26.06
01.2700 230	Sanitary sewer, PVC pipe, 4" Diameter	LF	9.13	19.50	28.63	11.95	21.08
01.2700 235	Sanitary sewer, PVC pipe, 8" Diameter	LF	14.24	24.17	38.41	14.81	29.05
01.2700 240	Sanitary sewer, PVC pipe, 12" Diameter	LF	26.43	43.78	70.21	26.83	53.26
01.2700 245	Water service, copper pipe, 2" Diameter	LF	42.80	17.84	60.64	10.93	53.73
01.2700 250	Water service, copper pipe, 3" Diameter	LF	77.43	20.36	97.79	12.48	89.91
01.2700 255	Water service, copper pipe, 4" Diameter	LF	119.25	19.42	138.67	11.90	131.15
01.2700 260	Water service, PVC MUNI C900, 4" Diameter	LF	24.14	15.12	39.26	10.12	34.26
01.2700 265	Water service, PVC MUNI C900, 6" Diameter	LF	29.32	17.02	46.34	11.39	40.71
01.2700 270	Water service, PVC MUNI C900, 8" Diameter	LF	38.73	18.78	57.51	12.57	51.30
01.2700 275	Water service, ductile iron pipe, 3" Diameter	LF	28.15	26.28	54.43	17.29	45.44
01.2700 280	Water service, ductile iron pipe, 4" Diameter	LF	31.44	27.02	58.46	17.73	49.17
01.2700 285	Water service, ductile iron pipe, 6" Diameter	LF	40.20	35.09	75.29	22.94	63.14
01.2700 290	Water service, ductile iron pipe, 8" Diameter	LF	49.55	37.31	86.86	24.24	73.79
01.2700 295	Gas/Steam service, black steel pipe, wrapped, 1" Diameter	LF	6.78	16.28	23.06	10.09	16.87
01.2700 300	Gas/Steam service, black steel pipe, wrapped, 2" Diameter	LF	19.10	20.26	39.36	12.53	31.63
01.2700 305	Gas/Steam service, black steel pipe, wrapped, 3" Diameter	LF	31.96	24.96	56.92	15.82	47.78
01.2700 310	Gas/Steam service, black steel pipe, wrapped, 4" Diameter	LF	44.59	31.39	75.98	19.93	64.52
01.2700 315	Fire hydrant, 4 outlets, 2 valves	EACH	3,309.24	1,974.14	5,283.38	1,203.25	4,512.49
01.2700 320	Catch basin, with grate, 2'X2'X2'	EACH	552.17	469.77	1,021.94	276.20	828.37
01.2700 325	Catch basin, with grate, 2'X2'X4'	EACH	697.79	731.12	1,428.91	429.87	1,127.66
01.2700 330	Drop inlet, precast with grate, 12"X12"X4"	EACH	348.59	306.19	654.78	179.69	528.28
01.2700 335	Drop inlet, precast with grate, 16"X16"X5"	EACH	458.19	382.74	840.93	224.61	682.80
01.2700 340	Manhole, with lid, 4' diameter X 6'-8' deep	EACH	1,574.07	1,264.69	2,838.76	743.58	2,317.65
01.2700 345	Manhole, with lid, 4' diameter X 6'-8' deep	EACH	1,967.67	1,616.34	3,584.01	950.33	2,918.00
01.2700 350	Fuel storage tank, underground, 500 gallon	EACH	7,704.14	685.70	8,389.84	403.16	8,107.30
01.2700 355	Fuel storage tank, underground, 1000 gallon	EACH	9,811.50	857.13	10,668.63	503.95	10,315.45
01.2700 360	Fuel storage tank, underground, 2000 gallon	EACH	12,588.32	936.68	13,525.00	550.72	13,139.04
01.2800	SITE LIGHTING						
01.2800 100	Site lighting, underground wire, 30' pole, mercury vapor, 175 watt	EACH	1,907.63	2,979.66	4,887.29	2,147.59	4,055.22
01.2800 105	Site lighting, underground wire, 30' pole, mercury vapor, 1000 watt	EACH	2,711.62	3,129.63	5,841.25	2,256.75	4,968.37
01.2800 110	Site lighting, underground wire, 42" bollards incandescent, 150 watt	EACH	1,150.48	599.47	1,749.95	427.14	1,577.62
01.2800 115	Site lighting, underground wire, 42" bollards metal halide, 175 watt	EACH	1,378.07	599.47	1,977.54	427.14	1,805.21
01.2800 120	Site lighting, parking lot, small	SF	.69	.83	1.52	.60	1.29
01.2800 125	Site lighting, parking lot, large	SF	.44	.48	.92	.35	.79

CSI #	2.1 SUBSTRUCTURE Description	Unit	Material	Union Install	Union Total	Open Install	Open Total
	The costs in this section include materials, labor, equipment rental, supervision, and subcontractor overhead and profit. There are no allowances for the general contractor. These costs are typical of those associated with the construction of a building. Costs are complete, and represent normal conditions related to weather and soil. For cast in place concrete items, allowances for forms and finishing are included. Pile costs include equipment costs and below grade walls include waterproofing and an allowance for excavation. Foundation wall and footing costs are combined as one assembly and include trenching and backfill. The costs, for these items, should be adjusted for excessive climate conditions and non-standard construction practices.						
02.1100	**EXCAVATION FOR BUILDINGS**						
02.1100 100	Excavation & backfill, sand or gravel, 4' deep, no removal	SF	2.97	1.22	4.19	.93	3.90
02.1100 105	Excavation & backfill, sand or gravel, 4' deep, remove excess	SF	4.05	1.65	5.70	1.25	5.30
02.1100 110	Excavation & backfill, clay, 4' deep, gravel backfill	SF	3.86	1.57	5.43	1.19	5.05
02.1100 115	Excavation & backfill, sand or gravel, 8' deep, no removal	SF	5.97	2.44	8.41	1.85	7.82
02.1100 120	Excavation & backfill, sand or gravel, 8' deep, remove excess	SF	8.15	3.33	11.48	2.53	10.68
02.1100 125	Excavation & backfill, clay, 8' deep, gravel backfill	SF	9.00	3.67	12.67	2.78	11.78
02.1100 130	Excavation & backfill, sand or gravel, 16' deep, no removal	SF	9.17	3.74	12.91	2.84	12.01
02.1100 135	Excavation & backfill, sand or gravel, 16' deep, remove excess	SF	11.86	4.84	16.70	3.67	15.53
02.1100 140	Excavation & backfill, clay, 16' deep, gravel backfill	SF	14.56	5.95	20.51	4.51	19.07
02.1200	**PILES**						
02.1200 100	Piles, precast concrete, square 10"	LF	31.93	16.42	48.35	11.90	43.83
02.1200 105	Piles, precast concrete, square 12"	LF	37.14	18.74	55.88	13.58	50.72
02.1200 110	Piles, precast concrete, square 16"	LF	38.10	20.01	58.11	14.50	52.60
02.1200 115	Piles, precast concrete, square 18"	LF	41.14	21.06	62.20	15.26	56.40
02.1200 120	Piles, steel H section, 8"x8"x36#	LF	25.81	20.52	46.33	14.87	40.68
02.1200 125	Piles, steel H section, 10"x10"x57#	LF	40.54	23.07	63.61	16.71	57.25
02.1200 130	Piles, steel H section, 12"x12"x74#	LF	49.76	24.31	74.07	17.62	67.38
02.1200 135	Piles, steel H section, 14"x14"x89#	LF	58.02	25.62	83.64	18.57	76.59
02.1200 140	Piles, pipe, 12", concrete filled	LF	16.71	21.52	38.23	15.59	32.30
02.1200 145	Piles, pipe, 12", unfilled	LF	14.38	19.20	33.58	13.91	28.29
02.1200 150	Piles, pipe, 16", concrete filled	LF	24.14	23.07	47.21	16.71	40.85
02.1200 155	Piles, pipe, 16", unfilled	LF	20.64	20.53	41.17	14.87	35.51
02.1200 160	Piles, steel step tapered, concrete filled, 12" butt	LF	14.52	15.10	29.62	10.94	25.46
02.1200 165	Piles, steel step tapered, concrete filled, 16" butt	LF	23.46	17.11	40.57	12.40	35.86
02.1200 170	Piles, wood, untreated to 39', 12" butt	LF	4.92	15.10	20.02	10.94	15.86
02.1200 175	Piles, wood, untreated to 70', 13" butt	LF	5.29	16.42	21.71	11.90	17.19
02.1200 180	Piles, wood, treated to 39', 12" butt	LF	6.96	15.10	22.06	10.94	17.90
02.1200 185	Piles, wood, treated to 70', 13" butt	LF	7.75	16.42	24.17	11.90	19.65
02.1200 190	Piles, soldier, steel, recovered, no lagging, 15'max, pulled	LF	20.39	12.33	32.72	8.94	29.33
02.1200 195	Piles, soldier, steel, recovered, no lagging, 20'max, pulled	LF	13.11	9.90	23.01	7.18	20.29
02.1200 200	Piles, soldier, steel, recovered, no lagging, 30'max, pulled	LF	12.58	9.20	21.78	6.67	19.25
02.1200 205	Piles, soldier, steel, recovered, no lagging, 50'max, pulled	LF	13.54	10.07	23.61	7.30	20.84

CSI #	2.1 SUBSTRUCTURE Description	Unit	Material	Union Install	Union Total	Open Install	Open Total
02.1300	**FOUNDATIONS AND PILE CAPS**						
02.1300 100	Foundation, residential, continuous footing, base 8"x16", wall 8"wide, 20" deep	LF	14.73	56.59	71.32	35.80	50.53
02.1300 105	Foundation, commercial, continuous footing, base 12"x24", wall 12" wide, 24" deep	LF	27.37	73.76	101.13	46.59	73.96
02.1300 110	Foundation, institutional, continuous footing, base 18"x36", wall 18" wide, 30" deep	LF	52.17	118.60	170.77	75.37	127.54
02.1300 115	Foundation, continuous footing, wall 8" wide, add for each additional foot deep	LF	6.16	26.85	33.01	17.66	23.82
02.1300 120	Foundation, continuous footing, wall 12" wide, add for each additional foot deep	LF	10.33	28.88	39.21	19.10	29.43
02.1300 125	Foundation, continuous footing, wall 18" wide, add for each additional foot deep	LF	13.82	30.67	44.49	20.37	34.19
02.1300 130	Foundation, spread footing, 2'x2'x12" deep, 3000 psi	EA	37.30	114.16	151.46	75.56	112.86
02.1300 135	Foundation, spread footing, 3'x3'x12" deep, 3000 psi	EA	76.86	179.02	255.88	118.68	195.54
02.1300 140	Foundation, spread footing, 4'x4'x12" deep, 3000 psi	EA	139.25	251.40	390.65	166.85	306.10
02.1300 145	Foundation, spread footing, 6'x6'x12" deep, 3000 psi	EA	294.18	410.90	705.08	273.69	567.87
02.1300 155	Foundation, spread footing, 6'x6'x18" deep, 3000 psi	EA	429.64	607.46	1,037.10	403.79	833.43
02.1300 160	Foundation, spread footing, 8'x8'x18" deep, 3000 psi	EA	738.94	872.23	1,611.17	581.05	1,319.99
02.1300 165	Foundation, spread footing, 10'x10'x24" deep, 3000 psi	EA	1,527.03	1,578.17	3,105.20	1,055.24	2,582.27
02.1300 170	Foundation, spread footing, 12'x12'x24" deep, 3000 psi	EA	2,156.35	2,005.69	4,162.04	1,341.74	3,498.09
02.1300 175	Foundation, pilecap, 6'x4'x24" deep, cap for two piles, 3000 psi	EA	395.60	488.53	884.13	325.84	721.44
02.1300 180	Foundation, pilecap, 6'x4'x36" deep, cap for two piles, 3000 psi	EA	576.67	730.08	1,306.75	487.25	1,063.92
02.1300 185	Foundation, pilecap, 6'x6'x24" deep, cap for 4 piles, 3000 psi	EA	573.00	627.83	1,200.83	419.95	992.95
02.1300 195	Foundation, pilecap, 6'x6'x36" deep, cap for 4 piles, 3000 psi	EA	854.55	939.27	1,793.82	628.27	1,482.82
02.1300 200	Foundation, pilecap, 8'x6'x36" deep, cap for 6 piles, 3000 psi	EA	1,127.78	1,147.50	2,275.28	768.71	1,896.49
02.1300 205	Foundation, pilecap, 8'x8'x36" deep, cap for 8 piles, 3000 psi	EA	1,481.56	1,389.15	2,870.71	932.40	2,413.96
02.1300 210	Foundation, pilecap, 12'x8'x42" deep, cap for 10 piles, 3000 psi	EA	2,198.40	1,893.14	4,091.54	1,274.55	3,472.95
02.1300 215	Foundation, underpinning, 6' deep, complete	LF	283.05	416.98	700.03	265.32	548.37
02.1300 220	Foundation, underpinning, each additional foot deep, complete	LF	38.31	63.68	101.99	40.69	79.00
02.1300 225	Foundation, cast in place concrete pier, poured neat, 16"	LF	18.01	11.40	29.41	8.13	26.14
02.1300 230	Foundation, cast in place concrete pier, poured neat, 24"	LF	35.54	19.43	54.97	13.90	49.44
02.1300 235	Foundation, cast in place concrete pier, poured neat, 36"	LF	75.77	37.42	113.19	26.84	102.61
02.1400	**WALLS BELOW GRADE**						
02.1400 100	Walls below grade, reinforced concrete, finished one side, 8" thick	SF	10.66	27.41	38.07	22.84	33.50
02.1400 105	Walls below grade, reinforced concrete, finished one side, 12" thick	SF	11.95	30.72	42.67	25.60	37.55
02.1400 110	Walls below grade, concrete block, reinforced, filled, 8" thick	SF	13.35	14.46	27.81	11.12	24.47
02.1400 115	Walls below grade, concrete block, reinforced, filled, 12" thick	SF	13.61	14.74	28.35	11.34	24.95
02.1500	**WATERPROOFING**						
02.1500 100	Waterproofing, hot coatings, vertical surfaces, bitumals, walls, per coat	SF	.05	1.03	1.08	.83	.88
02.1500 105	Waterproofing, hot coatings, vertical surfaces, hot mop, 15# felt, 2 ply	SF	.25	1.45	1.70	1.17	1.42
02.1500 110	Waterproofing, hot coatings, vertical surfaces, hot mop, 30# felt, 2 ply	SF	.33	1.45	1.78	1.17	1.50
02.1500 115	Waterproofing, hot coatings, vertical surfaces, hot mop, glass fiber, 2 ply	SF	.27	1.45	1.72	1.17	1.44
02.1500 120	Waterproofing, cold application, verticals, waterproof, 1/32" butyl	SF	.75	1.79	2.54	1.45	2.20
02.1500 125	Waterproofing, cold application, verticals, waterproof, 1/16" butyl	SF	1.10	1.79	2.89	1.45	2.55
02.1500 130	Waterproofing, cold application, verticals, waterproof, 1/16" neoprene	SF	1.13	1.79	2.92	1.45	2.58

CSI #	**2.1 SUBSTRUCTURE** Description	Unit	Material	Union Install	Union Total	Open Install	Open Total
02.1500	**WATERPROOFING (Cont.)**						
02.1500 135	Waterproofing, cold application, verticals, elastic polyurethane, 60 ML, vertical	SF	1.40	2.37	3.77	1.92	3.32
02.1500 140	Waterproofing, emulsion, verticals, waterproof, asphalt mastic, 1/8"	SF	.31	1.11	1.42	.90	1.21
02.1500 145	Waterproofing, emulsion, verticals, waterproof, asphalt paint, brush/coat	SF	.11	.43	.54	.35	.46
02.1500 150	Waterproofing, emulsion, verticals, waterproof, silicone, spray, 2 coat	SF	.26	.43	.69	.35	.61
02.1500 155	Waterproofing, specialties, verticals, volclay bent panels, 3/16"	SF	1.51	1.14	2.65	.92	2.43
02.1500 160	Waterproofing, specialties, verticals, volclay bent panels, 9/16"	SF	1.93	1.14	3.07	.92	2.85
02.1500 165	Waterproofing, specialties, verticals, bentonite panel, 3/8"	SF	2.61	1.26	3.87	1.02	3.63
02.1500 170	Waterproofing, specialties, verticals, exterior, cement pargetting, 1/2", 2 coat	SF	.49	1.76	2.25	1.43	1.92
02.1500 175	Waterproofing, specialties, verticals, ironite, 2 coats	SF	.77	2.92	3.69	2.37	3.14
02.1600	**SUBSTRUCTURE DRAINAGE**						
02.1600 100	Underdrain, corrugated polyethylene pipe, perforated, 3" diameter	LF	.44	8.47	8.91	5.19	5.63
02.1600 105	Underdrain, corrugated polyethylene pipe, perforated, 4" diameter	LF	.58	8.68	9.26	5.32	5.90
02.1600 110	Underdrain, corrugated polyethylene pipe, perforated, 6" diameter	LF	1.32	9.03	10.35	5.53	6.85
02.1600 115	Underdrain, corrugated polyethylene pipe, perforated, 8" diameter	LF	2.38	9.28	11.66	5.68	8.06
02.1600 120	Underdrain, corrugated polyethylene pipe, perforated, 10" diameter	LF	4.58	9.67	14.25	5.93	10.51
02.1600 125	Underdrain, corrugated polyethylene pipe, perforated, 12" diameter	LF	6.53	9.96	16.49	6.10	12.63
02.1700	**SLABS ON GRADE**						
02.1700 100	Slab on grade, reinforced concrete, 4" thick	SF	3.08	2.88	5.96	1.88	4.96
02.1700 105	Slab on grade, reinforced concrete, 5" thick	SF	3.54	2.98	6.52	1.95	5.49
02.1700 110	Slab on grade, reinforced concrete, 6" thick	SF	4.28	3.41	7.69	2.23	6.51
02.1700 115	Slab on grade, reinforced concrete, kalman floor, 6" thick	SF	4.82	5.32	10.14	3.48	8.30

CSI #	3.0 STRUCTURE Description	Unit	Material	Union Install	Union Total	Open Install	Open Total
	The costs in this section include materials, labor, equipment rental, supervision, and subcontractor overhead and profit. There are no allowances for the general contractor. These costs are typical of those associated with the construction of a building. Costs are complete, and represent normal conditions related to weather and soil. For cast in place concrete items, allowances for forms and finishing are included. Concrete columns include allowances for forms and reinforcing. All column costs have a pro-rated allowance for column base. Steel members include allowances for welding where appropriate. Roof structure costs do not include roof cover or insulation. These costs are found in section 4.2, Horizontal Enclosure.						
03.0105	**COLUMNS, CAST IN PLACE**						
03.0105 100	Concrete Column cast in place, round, 12" diameter	LF	25.56	28.21	53.77	21.12	46.68
03.0105 105	Concrete Column, cast in place, round, 14" diameter	LF	33.94	33.26	67.20	24.78	58.72
03.0105 110	Concrete Column, cast in place, round, 16" diameter	LF	43.03	38.71	81.74	28.73	71.76
03.0105 115	Concrete Column, cast in place, round, 20" diameter	LF	66.89	54.40	121.29	40.49	107.38
03.0105 120	Concrete Column, cast in place, round, 24" diameter	LF	92.19	70.68	162.87	52.37	144.56
03.0105 125	Concrete Column, cast in place, round, 30" diameter	LF	140.85	102.05	242.90	75.20	216.05
03.0105 130	Concrete Column, cast in place, round, 36" diameter	LF	193.80	138.70	332.50	101.53	295.33
03.0105 135	Concrete Column, cast in place, square, 10"x10"	LF	18.11	44.69	62.80	30.28	48.39
03.0105 140	Concrete Column, cast in place, square, 12"x12"	LF	23.97	54.97	78.94	37.04	61.01
03.0105 145	Concrete Column, cast in place, square, 16"x16"	LF	25.67	70.98	96.65	48.50	74.17
03.0105 150	Concrete Column, cast in place, square, 20"x20"	LF	53.63	100.47	154.10	66.75	120.38
03.0105 155	Concrete Column, cast in place, square, 24"x24"	LF	73.22	127.33	200.55	84.40	157.62
03.0105 160	Concrete Column, cast in place, square, 30"x30"	LF	108.28	171.52	279.80	113.48	221.76
03.0105 165	Concrete Column, cast in place, square, 36"x36"	LF	150.47	221.09	371.56	146.08	296.55
03.0110	**COLUMNS, PRECAST**						
03.0110 100	Column, Precast concrete, 12"x12",	LF	84.01	12.07	96.08	8.90	92.91
03.0110 105	Column, Precast concrete, 14"x14"	LF	117.53	16.89	134.42	12.45	129.98
03.0110 110	Column, Precast concrete, 16"x16"	LF	143.08	20.56	163.64	15.16	158.24
03.0110 115	Column, Precast concrete, 18"x18"	LF	165.57	23.79	189.36	17.54	183.11
03.0110 120	Column, Precast concrete, 20"x20"	LF	178.85	25.70	204.55	18.95	197.80
03.0115	**COLUMNS, STEEL**						
03.0115 100	Steel column, wide flange, W6x20	LF	67.61	13.11	80.72	9.73	77.34
03.0115 105	Steel column, wide flange, W8x24	LF	77.69	14.63	92.32	10.85	88.54
03.0115 110	Steel column, wide flange, W10x45	LF	130.61	22.61	153.22	16.73	147.34
03.0115 115	Steel column, wide flange, W12x72	LF	215.98	33.15	249.13	24.49	240.47
03.0115 120	Steel column, wide flange, W14x120	LF	336.94	51.39	388.33	37.93	374.87
03.0115 125	Steel column, wide flange, W14x176	LF	478.06	72.67	550.73	53.61	531.67
03.0115 130	Steel column, pipe, 3" diameter	LF	33.13	10.59	43.72	7.92	41.05
03.0115 135	Steel column, pipe, 4" diameter	LF	39.89	12.75	52.64	9.53	49.42
03.0115 140	Steel column, pipe, 6" diameter	LF	57.11	18.24	75.35	13.63	70.74
03.0115 145	Steel column, pipe, 8" diameter	LF	75.17	14.93	90.10	11.27	86.44
03.0115 150	Steel column, pipe, 10" diameter	LF	99.38	18.87	118.25	14.25	113.63
03.0115 155	Steel column, pipe, 12" diameter	LF	150.01	27.10	177.11	20.49	170.50
03.0115 160	Steel column, pipe, concrete filled, 3" diameter	LF	33.73	10.85	44.58	8.12	41.85
03.0115 165	Steel column, pipe, concrete filled, 4" diameter	LF	39.94	12.87	52.81	9.62	49.56
03.0115 170	Steel column, pipe, concrete filled, 6" diameter	LF	57.22	18.51	75.73	13.84	71.06
03.0115 175	Steel column, pipe, concrete filled, 8" diameter	LF	75.37	15.43	90.80	11.64	87.01
03.0115 180	Steel column, pipe, concrete filled, 10" diameter	LF	99.74	19.64	119.38	14.83	114.57
03.0115 190	Steel column, pipe, concrete filled, 12" diameter	LF	150.47	28.24	178.71	21.35	171.82
03.0115 195	Steel column, square tube, 3"	LF	34.87	8.88	43.75	6.67	41.54
03.0115 200	Steel column, square tube, 5"	LF	47.97	11.38	59.35	8.56	56.53
03.0115 205	Steel column, square tube, 6"	LF	54.81	12.68	67.49	9.54	64.35

CSI #	3.0 STRUCTURE Description	Unit	Material	Union Install	Union Total	Open Install	Open Total
03.0115	**COLUMNS, STEEL (Cont.)**						
03.0115 210	Steel column, square tube, 8"	LF	83.57	18.16	101.73	13.68	97.25
03.0115 215	Steel column, square tube, 10"	LF	120.91	25.28	146.19	19.06	139.97
03.0115 220	Steel column, square tube, 12"	LF	166.53	33.98	200.51	25.63	192.16
03.0115 225	Steel column, square tube, concrete filled, 3"	LF	56.06	13.09	69.15	9.79	65.85
03.0115 230	Steel column, square tube, concrete filled, 6"	LF	55.99	13.58	69.57	9.98	65.97
03.0115 235	Steel column, square tube, concrete filled, 8"	LF	85.67	19.75	105.42	14.46	100.13
03.0115 240	Steel column, square tube, concrete filled, 10"	LF	124.19	27.77	151.96	20.28	144.47
03.0115 245	Steel column, square tube, concrete filled, 12"	LF	171.39	37.66	209.05	27.44	198.83
03.0120	**COLUMNS, WOOD**						
03.0120 100	Wood column, 4"x4" post	LF	2.60	7.77	10.37	5.40	8.00
03.0120 105	Wood column, 4"x6" post	LF	3.60	11.53	15.13	8.02	11.62
03.0120 110	Wood column, 4"x8" post	LF	33.58	16.17	49.75	11.34	44.92
03.0120 115	Wood column, 6"x6" post	LF	5.02	16.91	21.93	11.77	16.79
03.0120 120	Wood column, 6"x8" post	LF	35.26	17.78	53.04	12.47	47.73
03.0120 125	Wood column, 6"x10" post	LF	9.86	20.33	30.19	14.15	24.01
03.0120 130	Wood column, 6"x12" post	LF	11.24	24.37	35.61	16.96	28.20
03.0120 135	Wood column, 8"x8" post	LF	10.43	20.72	31.15	14.42	24.85
03.0120 140	Wood column, 8"x10" post	LF	12.21	25.62	37.83	17.83	30.04
03.0120 145	Wood column, 8"x12" post	LF	14.17	31.01	45.18	21.59	35.76
03.0120 150	Wood column, 12"x12" post	LF	19.78	46.44	66.22	32.32	52.10
03.0205	**BEAMS & GIRDERS, CAST IN PLACE**						
03.0205 100	Concrete beams & girders, cast in place, 12"x24"	LF	43.17	169.33	212.50	111.02	154.19
03.0205 110	Concrete beams & girders, cast in place, 12"x30"	LF	55.67	232.23	287.90	152.36	208.03
03.0205 115	Concrete beams & girders, cast in place, 12"x36"	LF	65.70	267.17	332.87	175.32	241.02
03.0205 120	Concrete beams & girders, cast in place, 18"x24"	LF	63.61	238.97	302.58	156.93	220.54
03.0205 125	Concrete beams & girders, cast in place, 18"x30"	LF	77.62	277.27	354.89	182.17	259.79
03.0205 130	Concrete beams & girders, cast in place, 18"x36"	LF	88.59	313.35	401.94	206.44	295.03
03.0210	**BEAMS & GIRDERS, PRECAST**						
03.0210 100	Concrete beams & girders, precast, rectangular, 12"x24"	LF	64.84	8.70	73.54	6.41	71.25
03.0210 105	Concrete beams & girders, precast, rectangular, 12"x30"	LF	81.49	10.93	92.42	8.06	89.55
03.0210 110	Concrete beams & girders, precast, rectangular, 12"x36"	LF	97.26	13.05	110.31	9.62	106.88
03.0210 115	Concrete beams & girders, precast, rectangular, 18"x24"	LF	97.26	13.05	110.31	9.62	106.88
03.0210 120	Concrete beams & girders, precast, rectangular, 18"x30"	LF	120.92	16.22	137.14	11.96	132.88
03.0210 125	Concrete beams & girders, precast, rectangular, 18"x36"	LF	146.34	19.63	165.97	14.47	160.81
03.0210 130	Concrete beams & girders, precast, inverted tee, 12"x24"	LF	75.63	10.87	86.50	8.01	83.64
03.0210 135	Concrete beams & girders, precast, inverted tee, 12"x30"	LF	95.05	13.66	108.71	10.07	105.12
03.0210 140	Concrete beams & girders, precast, inverted tee, 12"x36"	LF	113.44	16.30	129.74	12.02	125.46
03.0210 145	Concrete beams & girders, precast, inverted tee, 18x24"	LF	113.44	16.30	129.74	12.02	125.46
03.0210 150	Concrete beams & girders, precast, inverted tee, 18x30"	LF	141.04	20.27	161.31	14.94	155.98
03.0210 155	Concrete beams & girders, precast, inverted tee, 18x36"	LF	170.68	24.53	195.21	18.08	188.76
03.0215	**BEAMS & GIRDERS, STEEL**						
03.0215 100	Steel beams & girders, wide flange, W6x20	LF	62.25	12.75	75.00	9.50	71.75
03.0215 105	Steel beams & girders, wide flange, W8x24	LF	59.76	12.24	72.00	9.12	68.88
03.0215 110	Steel beams & girders, wide flange, W10x45	LF	112.05	22.95	135.00	17.10	129.15
03.0215 115	Steel beams & girders, wide flange, W12x72	LF	179.28	36.72	216.00	27.36	206.64
03.0215 120	Steel beams & girders, wide flange, W14x109	LF	271.41	55.59	327.00	41.42	312.83
03.0215 125	Steel beams & girders, wide flange, W14x176	LF	438.24	89.76	528.00	66.88	505.12
03.0220	**BEAMS & GIRDERS, WOOD**						
03.0220 100	Wood beams & girders, 4"x4"	LF	1.84	6.99	8.83	4.86	6.70
03.0220 105	Wood beams & girders, 4"x6"	LF	2.84	10.75	13.59	7.48	10.32
03.0220 110	Wood beams & girders, 4"x8"	LF	3.83	14.52	18.35	10.10	13.93
03.0220 115	Wood beams & girders, 6"x6"	LF	4.13	12.10	16.23	8.42	12.55
03.0220 120	Wood beams & girders, 6"x8"	LF	5.51	16.13	21.64	11.23	16.74
03.0220 125	Wood beams & girders, 6"x10"	LF	6.89	20.16	27.05	14.03	20.92
03.0220 130	Wood beams & girders, 6"x12"	LF	8.27	24.20	32.47	16.84	25.11
03.0220 135	Wood beams & girders, 8"x8"	LF	7.42	20.43	27.85	14.22	21.64
03.0220 140	Wood beams & girders, 8"x10"	LF	9.24	25.45	34.69	17.71	26.95
03.0220 145	Wood beams & girders, 8"x12"	LF	11.20	30.84	42.04	21.47	32.67
03.0220 150	Wood beams & girders, 12"x12"	LF	16.81	46.27	63.08	32.20	49.01
03.0220 155	Wood beams & girders, glu-lams, 3 1/8"x12"	LF	7.50	1.74	9.24	1.21	8.71

CSI #	3.0 STRUCTURE Description	Unit	Material	Union Install	Union Total	Open Install	Open Total
03.0220	**BEAMS & GIRDERS, WOOD (Cont.)**						
03.0220 160	Wood beams & girders, glu-lams, 3 1/8"x18"	LF	15.56	3.61	19.17	2.52	18.08
03.0220 165	Wood beams & girders, glu-lams, 5 1/8"x12"	LF	12.30	2.86	15.16	1.99	14.29
03.0220 170	Wood beams & girders, glu-lams, 5 1/8"x18"	LF	18.44	4.28	22.72	2.98	21.42
03.0220 175	Wood beams & girders, glu-lams, 6 3/4"x12"	LF	16.21	3.77	19.98	2.62	18.83
03.0220 180	Wood beams & girders, glu-lams, 6 3/4"x12"	LF	24.25	5.63	29.88	3.92	28.17
03.0220 185	Wood beams & girders, glu-lams, 6 3/4"x18"	LF	36.50	8.48	44.98	5.90	42.40
03.0220 190	Wood beams & girders, glu-lams, 8 3/4"x12"	LF	21.01	4.88	25.89	3.40	24.41
03.0220 195	Wood beams & girders, glu-lams, 8 3/4"x18	LF	31.46	7.31	38.77	5.09	36.55
03.0220 200	Wood beams & girders, glu-lams, 8 3/4"x24	LF	42.03	9.76	51.79	6.79	48.82
03.0305	**FLOORS, CAST IN PLACE**						
03.0305 100	Floor, cast in place, slab, one way beams, with topping, 6" thick	SF	6.66	10.05	16.71	7.41	14.07
03.0305 105	Floor, cast in place, slab, one way beams, with topping, 8" thick	SF	8.85	13.35	22.20	9.84	18.69
03.0305 110	Floor, cast in place, slab, one way beams, with topping, 10" thick	SF	11.10	16.76	27.86	12.35	23.45
03.0305 115	Floor, cast in place, slab, two way beams, with topping, 6" thick	SF	7.95	12.02	19.97	8.86	16.81
03.0305 120	Floor, cast in place, slab, two way beams, with topping, 8" thick	SF	10.56	15.96	26.52	11.77	22.33
03.0305 125	Floor, cast in place, slab, two way beams, with topping, 10" thick	SF	13.25	20.03	33.28	14.77	28.02
03.0305 130	Floor, cast in place, slab, flat, with topping, 8" thick	SF	6.56	9.93	16.49	7.32	13.88
03.0305 135	Floor, cast in place, slab, flat, with topping, 12" thick	SF	8.98	23.60	32.58	17.40	26.38
03.0305 140	Floor, cast in place, slab, post tension with topping, 7" thick	SF	6.86	10.44	17.30	7.76	14.62
03.0305 145	Floor, cast in place, slab, with steel beam jacket topping, 6" thick	SF	6.44	9.80	16.24	7.28	13.72
03.0305 150	Floor, cast in place, slab, with steel beam jacket topping, 8" thick	SF	8.66	13.17	21.83	9.79	18.45
03.0305 155	Floor, cast in place, slab, on metal form, topping, 6" thick	SF	6.02	9.16	15.18	6.81	12.83
03.0305 160	Floor, cast in place, slab, on metal form, topping, 8" thick	SF	8.08	12.31	20.39	9.15	17.23
03.0305 165	Floor, cast in place, waffle slab, 30" square pan, 3" thick, 6"x12" joist	SF	8.36	12.69	21.05	9.44	17.80
03.0305 170	Floor, cast in place, waffle slab, 30" square pan, 3" thick, 6"x20" joist	SF	9.03	13.71	22.74	10.19	19.22
03.0305 175	Floor, cast in place, waffle slab, 20" square pan, 4-1/2" thick, 6"x12" joist	SF	9.71	14.76	24.47	10.97	20.68
03.0305 180	Floor, cast in place, waffle slab, 20" square pan, 4-1/2" thick, 6"x20" joist	SF	12.50	18.99	31.49	14.12	26.62
03.0310	**FLOORS, PRECAST**						
03.0310 100	Floor, precast concrete, single tees, with topping	SF	13.20	5.70	18.90	4.20	17.40
03.0310 105	Floor, precast concrete, double tees, with topping	SF	10.85	3.90	14.75	2.87	13.72
03.0310 110	Floor, precast concrete, plank, with topping, 6" solid	SF	7.37	3.11	10.48	2.29	9.66
03.0310 115	Floor, precast concrete, hollow plank, with topping, 4" thick	SF	6.76	2.51	9.27	1.85	8.61
03.0310 120	Floor, precast concrete, hollow plank, with topping, 6" thick	SF	7.14	2.80	9.94	2.06	9.20
03.0310 125	Floor, precast concrete, hollow plank, with topping, 8" thick	SF	7.63	3.11	10.74	2.29	9.92
03.0310 130	Floor, precast concrete, hollow plank, with topping, 10" thick	SF	8.11	3.50	11.61	2.58	10.69
03.0315	**FLOORS, CONCRETE ON STEEL JOISTS**						
03.0315 100	Floor, concrete on metal deck, open web steel joists, 40 PSF load	SF	11.97	4.01	15.98	2.86	14.83
03.0315 105	Floor, concrete on metal deck, open web steel joists, 75 PSF load	SF	13.64	4.38	18.02	3.15	16.79
03.0315 110	Floor, concrete on metal deck, open web steel joists, 125 PSF load	SF	16.19	5.01	21.20	3.62	19.81
03.0315 115	Floor, concrete slab, steel beam and deck, 40 PSF load	SF	22.68	6.59	29.27	4.69	27.37
03.0315 120	Floor, concrete slab, steel beam and deck, 75 PSF load	SF	27.58	7.69	35.27	5.51	33.09
03.0315 125	Floor, concrete slab, steel beam and deck, 125 PSF load	SF	30.41	8.37	38.78	6.01	36.42
03.0315 130	Floor, concrete slab, steel beam and deck, 200 PSF load	SF	38.35	10.24	48.59	7.39	45.74
03.0320	**FLOORS, WOOD**						
03.0320 100	Floor, wood, plywood, 2"x6" joists 16" OC	SF	2.48	2.97	5.45	2.06	4.54
03.0320 105	Floor, wood, plywood, 2"x8" joists 16" OC	SF	2.90	4.10	7.00	2.85	5.75
03.0320 110	Floor, wood, plywood, 2"x10" joists 16" OC	SF	3.14	4.23	7.37	2.94	6.08
03.0320 115	Floor, wood, plywood, 2"x12" joists 16" OC	SF	3.36	4.55	7.91	3.16	6.52
03.0320 120	Floor, wood, plywood, 2"x14" joists 16" OC	SF	3.65	5.23	8.88	3.63	7.28
03.0320 125	Add to above, 1" diagonal sheathing	SF	.15	.30	.45	.21	.36
03.0320 130	Add to above, 2" tongue & groove sheathing	SF	.88	.23	1.11	.16	1.04

CSI #	3.0 STRUCTURE Description	Unit	Material	Union Install	Union Total	Open Install	Open Total
03.0325	**ROOFS, METAL DECK ON STEEL JOISTS**						
03.0325 100	Roof, metal deck, open web steel joists, 20' span	SF	5.51	1.52	7.03	1.14	6.65
03.0325 105	Roof, metal deck, open web steel joists, 30' span	SF	7.92	1.99	9.91	1.49	9.41
03.0325 110	Roof, metal deck, open web steel joists, 40' span	SF	9.04	2.25	11.29	1.69	10.73
03.0325 115	Roof, metal deck, open web steel joists, 50 span	SF	11.78	2.84	14.62	2.13	13.91
03.0325 120	Roof, metal deck, open web steel joists, 60 span	SF	13.70	3.24	16.94	2.43	16.13
03.0325 125	Roof, metal deck, open web steel joists, 70' span	SF	14.82	3.50	18.32	2.63	17.45
03.0330	**ROOFS, WOOD**						
03.0330 100	Roof, plywood, 2"x6" wood rafters 24" OC flat	SF	2.16	5.38	7.54	3.74	5.90
03.0330 105	Roof, plywood, 2"x6" wood rafters 24" OC 4 in 12 slope	SF	2.28	5.68	7.96	3.94	6.22
03.0330 110	Roof, plywood, 2"x6" wood rafters 24" OC 8 in 12 slope	SF	2.59	6.47	9.06	4.50	7.09
03.0330 115	Roof, plywood, 2"x6" wood rafters 24" OC 12 in 12 slope	SF	3.05	7.61	10.66	5.29	8.34
03.0330 120	Roof, plywood, 2"x8" wood rafters 24" OC flat	SF	2.46	6.90	9.36	4.80	7.26
03.0330 125	Roof, plywood, 2"x8" wood rafters 24" OC 4 in 12 slope	SF	2.59	7.28	9.87	5.06	7.65
03.0330 130	Roof, plywood, 2"x8" wood rafters 24" OC 8 in 12 slope	SF	2.95	8.30	11.25	5.77	8.72
03.0330 135	Roof, plywood, 2"x8" wood rafters 24" OC 12 in 12 slope	SF	3.47	9.76	13.23	6.79	10.26
03.0330 140	Roof, plywood, 2"x10" wood rafters 24" OC flat	SF	2.80	8.26	11.06	5.75	8.55
03.0330 145	Roof, plywood, 2"x10" wood rafters 24" OC 4 in 12 slope	SF	2.95	8.71	11.66	6.06	9.01
03.0330 150	Roof, plywood, 2"x10" wood rafters 24" OC 8 in 12 slope	SF	3.36	9.94	13.30	6.91	10.27
03.0330 155	Roof, plywood, 2"x10" wood rafters 24" OC 12 in 12 slope	SF	3.95	11.68	15.63	8.13	12.08
03.0330 160	Roof, plywood, 2"x12" wood rafters 24" OC flat	SF	3.07	9.61	12.68	6.69	9.76
03.0330 165	Roof, plywood, 2"x12" wood rafters 24" OC 4 in 12 slope	SF	3.24	10.14	13.38	7.05	10.29
03.0330 170	Roof, plywood, 2"x12" wood rafters 24" OC 8 in 12 slope	SF	3.68	11.56	15.24	8.04	11.72
03.0330 175	Roof, plywood, 2"x12" wood rafters 24" OC 12 in 12 slope	SF	4.34	13.59	17.93	9.46	13.80
03.0400	**FLOOR, TOPPING**						
03.0400 100	Monolithic topping, 1/16"	SF	.07	1.33	1.40	.97	1.04
03.0400 105	Monolithic topping, 3/16"	SF	.29	1.40	1.69	1.02	1.31
03.0400 110	Monolithic topping, 1/2"	SF	.56	1.47	2.03	1.08	1.64
03.0400 115	White cement	SF	19.13		19.13		19.13
03.0400 120	Felton sand	SF	64.11		64.11		64.11
03.0400 125	Wear course, monolithic rock, 3/8" thick	SF	.38	1.29	1.67	.94	1.32
03.0400 130	Wear course, Kal Man, 3/4" thick	SF	.80	2.33	3.13	1.70	2.50
03.0400 135	Hardener, chemical	SF	.09	.27	.36	.19	.28
03.0400 140	Hardener, granolithic	SF	.01	.27	.28	.19	.20
03.0400 145	Hardener, iron base	SF	.34	.52	.86	.38	.72
03.0500	**FIREPROOFING**						
03.0500 100	Fireproof, columns, sprayed fiber, 1-3/8", no finish	SYCA	11.21	22.80	34.01	14.81	26.02
03.0500 105	Fireproof, beams and girders, sprayed fiber, 1-3/8", no finish	SYCA	10.20	17.90	28.10	11.62	21.82
03.0500 110	Fireproof, metal deck, sprayed fiber, 1-/8", no finish	SYCA	8.25	14.61	22.86	9.49	17.74
03.0500 115	Fireproof, columns, 1 hour, furring, lath & plaster, painted	LF	38.76	65.29	104.05	43.35	82.11
03.0500 120	Fireproof, beams & girders, framing, lath & plaster, painted	LF	47.42	79.89	127.31	53.05	100.47
03.0500 125	Fireproof, deck, 1 hour, furring, lath & plaster, paint	SF	6.30	10.73	17.03	6.96	13.26
03.0500 130	Fireproof, columns, 1 hour, furring, gypsum board, paint	LF	22.64	34.96	57.60	24.32	46.96
03.0500 135	Fireproof, beams & girders, 1 hour, framing, gypsum board, paint	LF	28.30	43.70	72.00	30.40	58.70
03.0500 140	Fireproof, deck, 1 hour, furring, gypsum board, paint	SF	2.55	4.03	6.58	2.69	5.24
03.0500 145	Fireproof, columns, cementitious monokote	TON	126.90	196.34	323.24	127.51	254.41
03.0500 150	Fireproof, beams & girders, cementitious monokote	TON	126.90	196.34	323.24	127.51	254.41
03.0500 155	Fireproof, metal deck, cementitious monokote	SF	.80	1.49	2.29	.96	1.76

Accurately Estimate Repair & Remodeling Work

Estimating repair & remodeling work can be tricky, especially the labor costs. You always have to account for the various degrees of difficulty that you'll find on each job or you can lose your shirt. Saylor Remodeling/Repair Construction Costs gives you grading factors for **degrees of difficulty** that let you base your estimate on the right labor cost for the job:

- Small jobs or big jobs
- Easy or difficult access
- Common or unique structure
- Additions/improvements or fire-gutted

This unique grading system lets you pick the best labor cost for the job (which you add to the updated material prices provided) for the most accurate repair and remodeling prices available in any book. You'll find thousands of unit costs, listed in 16 Division format, and a labor cost adjusted to the **degree of difficulty** that you may encounter. Also included are location multipliers to convert costs to your area. **Try this book for 30 days**. If you don't find the prices the most accurate you've seen, return it for a full refund. If you like it keep it and use it. It should save you several times the cost, during the year.

2010
remodeling
repair
construction
costs

20th ANNUAL EDITION   SAYLOR PUBLICATIONS, INC.

20th Annual Edition
$64.95
over 365 pages!

This unique manual addresses complexity in every cost item!

CSI #	4.1 ENCLOSURE, VERTICAL Description	Unit	Material	Union Install	Union Total	Open Install	Open Total
	The costs in this section include materials, labor, equipment rental, supervision, and subcontractor overhead and profit. There are no allowances for the general contractor. These costs are typical of those associated with the construction of a building. Costs are complete, and represent normal conditions related to weather and soil. For cast in place concrete items, allowances for forms and finishing are included. Precast and tilt-up costs include equipment costs. Curtain wall costs must be assembled to be complete, ie. the frame costs are separate from the glazing. Brick and concrete block costs represent standard running bond. For other bonding patterns the costs should be adjusted to account for additional installation time requirements. The fenestration costs are a combination of framing and glazing.						
04.1105	WALLS, CAST IN PLACE						
04.1105 100	Concrete Wall, cast in place, cut & patch, 8' high, 6" thick	SF	7.57	27.25	34.82	17.60	25.17
04.1105 105	Concrete Wall, cast in place, cut & patch, 8' high, 8" thick	SF	9.09	27.93	37.02	18.03	27.12
04.1105 110	Concrete Wall, cast in place, cut & patch, 8' high, 10" thick	SF	10.86	28.91	39.77	18.68	29.54
04.1105 115	Concrete Wall, cast in place, cut & patch, 8' high, 12" thick	SF	13.45	31.04	44.49	19.92	33.37
04.1105 120	Concrete Wall, cast in place, cut & patch, 12' high, 6" thick	SF	7.73	27.93	35.66	17.48	25.21
04.1105 125	Concrete Wall, cast in place, cut & patch, 12' high, 8" thick	SF	9.25	28.61	37.86	17.91	27.16
04.1105 130	Concrete Wall, cast in place, cut & patch, 12' high, 10" thick	SF	11.02	29.59	40.61	18.56	29.58
04.1105 135	Concrete Wall, cast in place, cut & patch, 12' high, 12" thick	SF	13.13	30.82	43.95	19.41	32.54
04.1105 140	Concrete Wall, cast in place, cut & patch, 16' high, 6" thick	SF	8.65	31.08	39.73	19.50	28.15
04.1105 145	Concrete Wall, cast in place, cut & patch, 16' high, 8" thick	SF	10.10	31.73	41.83	19.91	30.01
04.1105 150	Concrete Wall, cast in place, cut & patch, 16' high, 10" thick	SF	11.94	32.73	44.67	20.57	32.51
04.1105 155	Concrete Wall, cast in place, cut & patch, 16' high, 12" thick	SF	13.98	33.94	47.92	21.40	35.38
04.1105 200	Finish Add, one side, concrete wall, cast in place, sandblast, light	SF	.16	1.68	1.84	.73	.89
04.1105 205	Finish Add, one side, concrete wall, cast in place, sandblast, medium	SF	.36	2.39	2.75	1.04	1.40
04.1105 210	Finish Add, one side, concrete wall, cast in place, sandblast, heavy	SF	.64	2.90	3.54	1.26	1.90
04.1105 215	Finish Add, one side, concrete wall, cast in place, bush hammer, light	SF	.64	1.69	2.33	.74	1.38
04.1105 220	Finish Add, one side, concrete wall, cast in place, bush hammer, medium	SF	1.34	2.91	4.25	1.26	2.60
04.1105 225	Finish Add, one side, concrete wall, cast in place, bush hammer, heavy	SF	2.53	4.12	6.65	1.79	4.32
04.1105 230	Design mix Add, concrete wall, cast in place, Hi Early strength, 6" thick	SF	.21		.21		.21
04.1105 235	Design mix Add, concrete wall, cast in place, Hi Early strength, 8" thick	SF	.28		.28		.28
04.1105 240	Design mix Add, concrete wall, cast in place, Hi Early strength, 10" thick	SF	.34		.34		.34
04.1105 245	Design mix Add, concrete wall, cast in place, Hi Early strength, 12" thick	SF	.41		.41		.41
04.1105 250	Design mix Add, concrete wall, cast in place, lightweight aggregate, 6" thick	SF	.90		.90		.90
04.1105 255	Design mix Add, concrete wall, cast in place, lightweight aggregate, 8" thick	SF	1.20		1.20		1.20

CSI #	4.1 ENCLOSURE, VERTICAL Description	Unit	Material	Union Install	Union Total	Open Install	Open Total
04.1105	**WALLS, CAST IN PLACE (Cont.)**						
04.1105 260	Design mix Add, concrete wall, cast in place, lightweight aggregate, 10" thick	SF	1.50		1.50		1.50
04.1105 265	Design mix Add, concrete wall, cast in place, lightweight aggregate, 12" thick	SF	1.80		1.80		1.80
04.1105 270	Design mix Add, concrete wall, cast in place, granite aggregate, 6" thick	SF	.23		.23		.23
04.1105 275	Design mix Add, concrete wall, cast in place, granite aggregate, 8" thick	SF	.31		.31		.31
04.1105 280	Design mix Add, concrete wall, cast in place, granite aggregate, 10" thick	SF	.39		.39		.39
04.1105 285	Design mix Add, concrete wall, cast in place, granite aggregate, 12" thick	SF	.46		.46		.46
04.1110	**WALLS, TILT-UP CONCRETE PANEL**						
04.1110 100	Tilt-up, concrete wall, no pilasters, 6" thick	SF	7.10	7.85	14.95	5.84	12.94
04.1110 105	Tilt-up, concrete wall, no pilasters, 8" thick	SF	8.25	8.02	16.27	5.96	14.21
04.1110 110	Tilt-up, concrete wall, with pilasters, 6" thick	SF	7.54	9.13	16.67	6.79	14.33
04.1110 115	Tilt-up, concrete wall, with pilasters, 8" thick	SF	8.82	9.96	18.78	7.40	16.22
04.1115	**WALLS, PRECAST CONCRETE PANELS**						
04.1115 100	Precast concrete panel, single form	SF	19.55	10.91	30.46	8.11	27.66
04.1115 105	Precast concrete panel, double form	SF	26.14	10.91	37.05	8.11	34.25
04.1115 110	Precast concrete panel, single form, exposed aggregate	SF	28.26	10.91	39.17	8.11	36.37
04.1115 115	Precast concrete panel, single form, sandblast	SF	28.26	10.91	39.17	8.11	36.37
04.1115 120	Precast concrete panel, double form, exposed aggregate	SF	42.36	10.91	53.27	8.11	50.47
04.1115 125	Precast concrete panel, double form, sandblast	SF	42.36	10.91	53.27	8.11	50.47
04.1115 130	Precast concrete panel, single form, granite finish	SF	49.49	10.91	60.40	8.11	57.60
04.1120	**WALLS, CONCRETE BLOCK**						
04.1120 100	Concrete Block, 8"X16", reinforced, 4" thick	SF	8.96	6.17	15.13	3.43	12.39
04.1120 110	Concrete Block, 8"X16", reinforced, 8" thick	SF	10.94	7.00	17.94	3.90	14.84
04.1120 115	Concrete Block, 8"X16", reinforced, 12" thick	SF	17.01	7.81	24.82	4.35	21.36
04.1120 120	Concrete Block, 8"X16", reinforced, filled 4" thick	SF	9.49	6.63	16.12	3.69	13.18
04.1120 130	Concrete Block, 8"X16", reinforced, filled, 8" thick	SF	12.87	7.16	20.03	3.98	16.85
04.1120 135	Concrete Block, 8"X16", reinforced, filled, 12" thick	SF	16.24	8.67	24.91	4.83	21.07
04.1120 140	Concrete Block, 8"X16", reinforced, grout lock, 8" thick	SF	13.57	5.58	19.15	3.11	16.68
04.1120 145	Concrete Block, 8"X16", reinforced, grout lock, 12" thick	SF	17.44	6.62	24.06	3.69	21.13
04.1120 150	Concrete Block, Slumpstone, reinforced, filled, 8"X4"X16"	SF	22.31	10.16	32.47	5.66	27.97
04.1120 155	Concrete Block, Slumpstone, reinforced, filled, 8"X8"X16"	SF	17.36	8.54	25.90	4.76	22.12
04.1120 157	Concrete Block, split face, reinforced, filled, 8"X4"X16"	SF	20.16	10.15	30.31	5.65	25.81
04.1120 160	Concrete Block, Glazed one side, reinforced, filled, 4"X8"X16"	SF	15.20	9.42	24.62	5.24	20.44
04.1120 165	Concrete Block, Glazed one side, reinforced, filled, 6"X8"X16"	SF	17.49	10.07	27.56	5.61	23.10
04.1120 170	Concrete Block, Glazed one side, reinforced, filled, 8"X8"X16"	SF	20.47	10.92	31.39	6.08	26.55
04.1120 175	Concrete Block, Glazed one side, reinforced, filled, 12"X8"X16"	SF	24.74	15.50	40.24	8.63	33.37
04.1120 180	Concrete Block, Glazed one side, reinforced, filled, 4"X4"X16"	SF	22.52	10.77	33.29	6.00	28.52
04.1120 185	Concrete Block, Glazed one side, reinforced, filled, 6"X4"X16"	SF	26.30	12.51	38.81	6.97	33.27
04.1120 190	Concrete Block, Glazed one side, reinforced, filled, 8"X4"X16"	SF	30.05	13.30	43.35	7.41	37.46
04.1120 195	Add for glazing both sides	SF	8.19		8.19		8.19
04.1120 200	Add for pilaster per square foot of pilaster	SF	33.13		33.13		33.13

CSI #	4.1 ENCLOSURE, VERTICAL Description	Unit	Material	Union Install	Union Total	Open Install	Open Total
04.1125	**WALLS, BRICK VENEER WITH BLOCK BACK-UP**						
04.1125 100	Brick veneer, 4" standard, 4"X8"X16" block back-up	SF	14.94	13.18	28.12	7.33	22.27
04.1125 110	Brick veneer, 4" standard, 8"X8"X16" block back-up	SF	16.92	14.01	30.93	7.80	24.72
04.1125 115	Brick veneer, 4" modular, 4"X8"X16" block back-up	SF	15.29	16.05	31.34	8.93	24.22
04.1125 120	Brick veneer, 4" modular, 6"X8"X16" block back-up	SF	16.73	16.50	33.23	9.19	25.92
04.1125 125	Brick veneer, 4" modular, 8"X8"X16" block back-up	SF	17.27	16.88	34.15	9.40	26.67
04.1125 130	Brick veneer, 4"X4"X12" Jumbo, 4"X8"X16" block back-up	SF	13.21	13.12	26.33	7.30	20.51
04.1125 140	Brick veneer, 4"X4"X12" Jumbo, 8"X8"X16" block back-up	SF	15.19	13.95	29.14	7.77	22.96
04.1125 145	Brick veneer, 6"X4"X12" Jumbo, 4"X8"X16" block back-up	SF	15.01	13.91	28.92	7.74	22.75
04.1125 155	Brick veneer, 6"X4"X12" Jumbo, 8"X8"X16" block back-up	SF	16.99	14.74	31.73	8.21	25.20
04.1125 160	Brick veneer, 8"X4"X12" Jumbo, 4"X8"X16" block back-up	SF	16.85	14.73	31.58	8.19	25.04
04.1125 165	Brick veneer, 8"X4"X12" Jumbo, 6"X8"X16" block back-up	SF	18.29	15.18	33.47	8.45	26.74
04.1125 170	Brick veneer, 8"X4"X12" Jumbo, 8"X8"X16" block back-up	SF	18.83	15.56	34.39	8.66	27.49
04.1125 175	Brick veneer, face brick modular, 4"X8"X16" block back-up	SF	15.90	16.80	32.70	9.35	25.25
04.1125 180	Brick veneer, face brick modular, 6"X8"X16" block back-up	SF	17.34	17.25	34.59	9.61	26.95
04.1125 185	Brick veneer, face brick modular, 8"X8"X16" block back-up	SF	17.88	17.63	35.51	9.82	27.70
04.1125 190	Brick veneer, Norman, 4"X8"X16" block back-up	SF	14.73	16.67	31.40	9.28	24.01
04.1125 195	Brick veneer, Norman, 6"X8"X16" block back-up	SF	16.17	17.12	33.29	9.54	25.71
04.1125 200	Brick veneer, Norman, 8"X8"X16" block back-up	SF	16.71	17.50	34.21	9.75	26.46
04.1125 205	Brick veneer, Roman, 4"X8"X16" block back-up	SF	15.64	21.11	36.75	11.75	27.39
04.1125 210	Brick veneer, Roman, 6"X8"X16" block back-up	SF	17.08	21.56	38.64	12.01	29.09
04.1125 215	Brick veneer, Roman, 8"X8"X16" block back-up	SF	17.62	21.94	39.56	12.22	29.84
04.1125 220	Brick veneer, Glazed, 4"X8"X16" block back-up	SF	19.65	23.07	42.72	12.84	32.49
04.1125 225	Brick veneer, Glazed, 6"X8"X16" block back-up	SF	21.09	23.52	44.61	13.10	34.19
04.1125 230	Brick veneer, Glazed, 8"X8"X16" block back-up	SF	21.63	23.90	45.53	13.31	34.94
04.1130	**WALLS, BRICK**						
04.1130 100	Brick wall, cavity, 10" thick	SF	11.81	18.04	29.85	10.04	21.85
04.1130 105	Brick wall, reinforced, 10" thick	SF	13.30	19.52	32.82	10.87	24.17
04.1130 110	Brick wall, reinforced, 13" thick	SF	16.03	21.34	37.37	11.88	27.91
04.1130 115	Brick wall, reinforced, 16" thick	SF	19.85	22.68	42.53	12.63	32.48
04.1130 120	Brick wall, reinforced, 20" thick	SF	22.25	28.60	50.85	15.92	38.17
04.1135	**WALLS, STONE VENEER WITH BLOCK BACK-UP**						
04.1135 100	Stone veneer, Granite, 4"X8"X16" block back-up	SF	34.55	34.81	69.36	26.34	60.89
04.1135 105	Stone veneer, Granite, 6"X8"X16" block back-up	SF	35.99	35.26	71.25	26.60	62.59
04.1135 110	Stone veneer, Granite, 8"X8"X16" block back-up	SF	36.53	35.64	72.17	26.81	63.34
04.1135 115	Stone veneer, Limestone, 4"X8"X16" block back-up	SF	27.67	38.30	65.97	29.13	56.80
04.1135 120	Stone veneer, Limestone, 6"X8"X16" block back-up	SF	29.11	38.75	67.86	29.39	58.50
04.1135 125	Stone veneer, Limestone, 8"X8"X16" block back-up	SF	29.65	39.13	68.78	29.60	59.25
04.1135 130	Stone veneer, Marble, 4"X8"X16" block back-up	SF	36.24	34.39	70.63	26.01	62.25
04.1135 135	Stone veneer, Marble, 6"X8"X16" block back-up	SF	37.68	34.84	72.52	26.27	63.95
04.1135 140	Stone veneer, Marble, 8"X8"X16" block back-up	SF	38.22	35.22	73.44	26.48	64.70
04.1135 145	Stone veneer, Sandstone, 4"X8"X16" block back-up	SF	27.34	32.23	59.57	17.94	45.28
04.1135 155	Stone veneer, Sandstone, 8"X8"X16" block back-up	SF	18.38	26.06	44.44	14.51	32.89
04.1135 160	Stone veneer, Lava stone, 4"X8"X16" block back-up	SF	16.23	22.82	39.05	16.75	32.98
04.1135 165	Stone veneer, Lava stone, 6"X8"X16" block back-up	SF	17.67	23.27	40.94	17.01	34.68
04.1135 170	Stone veneer, Lava stone, 8"X8"X16" block back-up	SF	18.21	23.65	41.86	17.22	35.43

CSI #	**4.1 ENCLOSURE, VERTICAL** Description	Unit	Material	Union Install	Union Total	Open Install	Open Total
04.1135	**WALLS, STONE VENEER WITH BLOCK BACK-UP (Cont.)**						
04.1135 175	Stone veneer, Arizona stone, 4"X8"X16" block back-up	SF	21.71	24.90	46.61	18.42	40.13
04.1135 185	Stone veneer, Arizona stone, 8"X8"X16" block back-up	SF	23.69	25.73	49.42	18.89	42.58
04.1135 190	Stone veneer, Rubble, 4"X8"X16" block back-up	SF	15.52	26.00	41.52	19.29	34.81
04.1135 195	Stone veneer, Rubble, 6"X8"X16" block back-up	SF	16.96	26.45	43.41	19.55	36.51
04.1135 200	Stone veneer, Rubble, 8"X8"X16" block back-up	SF	17.50	26.83	44.33	19.76	37.26
04.1140	**WALLS, BRICK VENEER ON STUD FRAME**						
04.1140 100	Brick veneer, 4" standard, sheathing, building paper, insulation, 2"X4" wood stud 16"OC	SF	8.97	12.26	21.23	7.56	16.53
04.1140 105	Brick veneer, 4" standard, sheathing, building paper, insulation, 2"X6" wood stud 16"OC	SF	9.65	13.30	22.95	8.28	17.93
04.1140 110	Brick veneer, 4" standard, sheathing, building paper, insulation, 16 ga 3-5/8 metal stud 16"OC	SF	11.37	14.76	26.13	8.89	20.26
04.1140 115	Brick veneer, 4" modular, sheathing, building paper, insulation, 2"X4" wood stud 16"OC	SF	9.32	15.13	24.45	9.16	18.48
04.1140 120	Brick veneer, 4" modular, sheathing, building paper, insulation, 2"X6" wood stud 16"OC	SF	10.00	16.17	26.17	9.88	19.88
04.1140 125	Brick veneer, 4" modular, sheathing, building paper, insulation, 16 ga 3-5/8 metal stud 16"OC	SF	11.72	17.63	29.35	10.49	22.21
04.1140 130	Brick veneer, 4"X4"X12" Jumbo, sheathing, building paper, insulation, 2"X4" wood stud 16"OC	SF	7.24	12.20	19.44	7.53	14.77
04.1140 135	Brick veneer, 4"X4"X12" Jumbo, sheathing, building paper, insulation, 2"X6" wood stud 16"OC	SF	7.92	13.24	21.16	8.25	16.17
04.1140 140	Brick veneer, 4"X4"X12" Jumbo, sheathing, building paper, insulation, 16 ga 3-5/8 metal stud 16"OC	SF	9.64	14.70	24.34	8.86	18.50
04.1140 160	Brick veneer, 8"X4"X12" Jumbo, sheathing, building paper, insulation, 2"X4" wood stud 16"OC	SF	10.88	13.81	24.69	8.42	19.30
04.1140 165	Brick veneer, 8"X4"X12" Jumbo, sheathing, building paper, insulation, 2"X6" wood stud 16"OC	SF	11.56	14.85	26.41	9.14	20.70
04.1140 170	Brick veneer, 8"X4"X12" Jumbo, sheathing, building paper, insulation, 16 ga 3-5/8 metal stud 16"OC	SF	13.28	16.31	29.59	9.75	23.03
04.1140 175	Brick veneer, face brick modular, sheathing, building paper, insulation, 2"X4" wood stud 16"OC	SF	9.93	15.88	25.81	9.58	19.51
04.1140 180	Brick veneer, face brick modular, sheathing, building paper, insulation, 2"X6" wood stud 16"OC	SF	10.61	16.92	27.53	10.30	20.91
04.1140 185	Brick veneer, face brick modular, sheathing, building paper, insulation, 16 ga 3-5/8 metal stud 16"OC	SF	12.33	18.38	30.71	10.91	23.24
04.1140 190	Brick veneer, Norman, sheathing, building paper, insulation, 2"X4" wood stud 16"OC	SF	8.76	15.75	24.51	9.51	18.27
04.1140 195	Brick veneer, Norman, sheathing, building paper, insulation, 2"X6" wood stud 16"OC	SF	9.44	16.79	26.23	10.23	19.67
04.1140 200	Brick veneer, Norman, sheathing, building paper, insulation, 16 ga 3-5/8 metal stud 16"OC	SF	11.16	18.25	29.41	10.84	22.00
04.1140 205	Brick veneer, Roman, sheathing, building paper, insulation, 2"X4" wood stud 16"OC	SF	9.67	20.19	29.86	11.98	21.65
04.1140 210	Brick veneer, Roman, sheathing, building paper, insulation, 2"X6" wood stud 16"OC	SF	10.35	21.23	31.58	12.70	23.05
04.1140 215	Brick veneer, Roman, sheathing, building paper, insulation, 16 ga 3-5/8 metal stud 16"OC	SF	12.07	22.69	34.76	13.31	25.38
04.1140 220	Brick veneer, Glazed, sheathing, building paper, insulation, 2"X4" wood stud 16"OC	SF	13.68	22.15	35.83	13.07	26.75
04.1140 225	Brick veneer, Glazed, sheathing, building paper, insulation, 2"X6" wood stud 16"OC	SF	14.36	23.19	37.55	13.79	28.15
04.1140 230	Brick veneer, Glazed, sheathing, building paper, insulation, 16 ga 3-5/8 metal stud 16"OC	SF	16.08	24.65	40.73	14.40	30.48

CSI #	4.1 ENCLOSURE, VERTICAL Description	Unit	Material	Union Install	Union Total	Open Install	Open Total
04.1145	**WALLS, SIDING ON STUD FRAME**						
04.1145 100	Siding, Redwood Beveled, paint, sheathing, building paper, insulation, 2"X4" wood stud 16"OC	SF	7.09	9.48	16.57	6.69	13.78
04.1145 105	Siding, Redwood Beveled, paint, sheathing, building paper, insulation, 2"X6" wood stud 16"OC	SF	7.77	10.52	18.29	7.41	15.18
04.1145 110	Siding, Redwood Beveled, paint, sheathing, building paper, insulation, 16 ga 3-5/8 metal stud 16"OC	SF	9.49	11.98	21.47	8.02	17.51
04.1145 115	Siding, Cedar Beveled, paint, sheathing, building paper, insulation, 2"X4" wood stud 16"OC	SF	5.31	9.39	14.70	6.62	11.93
04.1145 120	Siding, Cedar Beveled, paint, sheathing, building paper, insulation, 2"X6" wood stud 16"OC	SF	5.99	10.43	16.42	7.34	13.33
04.1145 125	Siding, Cedar Beveled, paint, sheathing, building paper, insulation, 16 ga 3-5/8 metal stud 16"OC	SF	7.71	11.89	19.60	7.95	15.66
04.1145 130	Siding, board & batten, paint, sheathing, building paper, insulation, 2"X4" wood stud 16"OC	SF	9.41	8.89	18.30	6.27	15.68
04.1145 135	Siding, board & batten, paint, sheathing, building paper, insulation, 2"X6" wood stud 16"OC	SF	10.09	9.93	20.02	6.99	17.08
04.1145 140	Siding, board & batten, sheathing, paint, building paper, insulation, 16 ga 3-5/8 metal stud 16"OC	SF	11.81	11.39	23.20	7.60	19.41
04.1145 145	Siding, tongue & grove, paint, sheathing, building paper, insulation, 2"X4" wood stud 16"OC	SF	8.91	8.70	17.61	6.14	15.05
04.1145 150	Siding, tongue & grove, paint, sheathing, building paper, insulation, 2"X6" wood stud 16"OC	SF	9.59	9.74	19.33	6.86	16.45
04.1145 155	Siding, tongue & grove, paint, sheathing, building paper, insulation, 16 ga 3-5/8 metal stud 16"OC	SF	11.31	11.20	22.51	7.47	18.78
04.1145 160	Siding, Plywood texture 1-11 paint, sheathing, building paper, insulation, 2"X4" wood stud 16"OC	SF	6.08	9.27	15.35	6.54	12.62
04.1145 165	Siding, Plywood texture 1-11 paint, sheathing, building paper, insulation, 2"X6" wood stud 16"OC	SF	6.76	10.31	17.07	7.26	14.02
04.1145 170	Siding, Plywood texture 1-11 paint, sheathing, building paper, insulation, 16 ga 3-5/8 metal stud 16"OC	SF	8.48	11.77	20.25	7.87	16.35
04.1145 175	Siding, cedar shingles, stain, sheathing, building paper, insulation, 2"X4" wood stud 16"OC	SF	5.95	12.38	18.33	8.70	14.65
04.1145 180	Siding, cedar shingles, stain, sheathing, building paper, insulation, 2"X6" wood stud 16"OC	SF	6.63	13.42	20.05	9.42	16.05
04.1145 185	Siding, cedar shingles, stain, sheathing, building paper, insulation, 16 ga 3-5/8 metal stud 16"OC	SF	8.35	14.88	23.23	10.03	18.38
04.1145 190	Siding, hardboard, paint, sheathing, building paper, insulation, 2"X4" wood stud 16"OC	SF	4.39	9.42	13.81	6.64	11.03
04.1145 195	Siding, hardboard, paint, sheathing, building paper, insulation, 2"X6" wood stud 16"OC	SF	5.07	10.46	15.53	7.36	12.43
04.1145 200	Siding, hardboard, paint, sheathing, building paper, insulation, 16 ga 3-5/8 metal stud 16"OC	SF	6.79	11.92	18.71	7.97	14.76
04.1145 205	Siding, Glasweld, finish one side, sheathing, building paper, insulation, 2"X4" wood stud 16"OC	SF	8.42	9.65	18.07	6.72	15.14
04.1145 210	Siding, Glasweld, finish one side, sheathing, building paper, insulation, 2"X6" wood stud 16"OC	SF	9.10	10.69	19.79	7.44	16.54
04.1145 215	Siding, Glasweld, finish one side, sheathing, building paper, insulation, 16 ga 3-5/8 metal stud 16"OC	SF	10.82	12.15	22.97	8.05	18.87
04.1145 220	Siding, Glasweld, finish two sides, sheathing, building paper, insulation, 2"X4" wood stud 16"OC	SF	9.86	10.19	20.05	7.10	16.96
04.1145 225	Siding, Glasweld, finish two sides, sheathing, building paper, insulation, 2"X6" wood stud 16"OC	SF	10.54	11.23	21.77	7.82	18.36
04.1145 230	Siding, Glasweld, finish two sides, sheathing, building paper, insulation, 16 ga 3-5/8 metal stud 16"OC	SF	12.26	12.69	24.95	8.43	20.69

CSI #	4.1 ENCLOSURE, VERTICAL Description	Unit	Material	Union Install	Union Total	Open Install	Open Total
04.1150	**WALLS, STONE VENEER ON STUD FRAME**						
04.1150 100	Stone veneer, Granite, sheathing, building paper, insulation, 2"X4" wood stud 16"OC	SF	28.58	33.89	62.47	26.57	55.15
04.1150 105	Stone veneer, Granite, sheathing, building paper, insulation, 2"X6" wood stud 16"OC	SF	29.26	34.93	64.19	27.29	56.55
04.1150 110	Stone veneer, Granite, sheathing, building paper, insulation, 16 ga 3-5/8 metal stud 16"OC	SF	30.98	36.39	67.37	27.90	58.88
04.1150 115	Stone veneer, Limestone, sheathing, building paper, insulation, 2"X4" wood stud 16"OC	SF	21.70	37.38	59.08	29.36	51.06
04.1150 120	Stone veneer, Limestone, sheathing, building paper, insulation, 2"X6" wood stud 16"OC	SF	22.38	38.42	60.80	30.08	52.46
04.1150 125	Stone veneer, Limestone, sheathing, building paper, insulation, 16 ga 3-5/8 metal stud 16"OC	SF	24.10	39.88	63.98	30.69	54.79
04.1150 145	Stone veneer, Sandstone, sheathing, building paper, insulation, 2"X4" wood stud 16"OC	SF	21.37	31.31	52.68	18.17	39.54
04.1150 150	Stone veneer, Sandstone, sheathing, building paper, insulation, 2"X6" wood stud 16"OC	SF	22.05	32.35	54.40	18.89	40.94
04.1150 155	Stone veneer, Sandstone, sheathing, building paper, insulation, 16 ga 3-5/8 metal stud 16"OC	SF	23.77	33.81	57.58	19.50	43.27
04.1150 160	Stone veneer, Lava stone, sheathing, building paper, insulation, 2"X4" wood stud 16"OC	SF	10.26	21.90	32.16	16.98	27.24
04.1150 165	Stone veneer, Lava stone, sheathing, building paper, insulation, 2"X6" wood stud 16"OC	SF	10.94	22.94	33.88	17.70	28.64
04.1150 170	Stone veneer, Lava stone, sheathing, building paper, insulation, 16 ga 3-5/8 metal stud 16"OC	SF	12.66	24.40	37.06	18.31	30.97
04.1150 175	Stone veneer, Arizona stone, sheathing, building paper, insulation, 2"X4" wood stud 16"OC	SF	15.74	23.98	39.72	18.65	34.39
04.1150 180	Stone veneer, Arizona stone, sheathing, building paper, insulation, 2"X6" wood stud 16"OC	SF	16.42	25.02	41.44	19.37	35.79
04.1150 185	Stone veneer, Arizona stone, sheathing, building paper, insulation, 16 ga 3-5/8 metal stud 16"OC	SF	18.14	26.48	44.62	19.98	38.12
04.1150 190	Stone veneer, Rubble, sheathing, building paper, insulation, 2"X4" wood stud 16"OC	SF	9.55	25.08	34.63	19.52	29.07
04.1150 195	Stone veneer, Rubble, sheathing, building paper, insulation, 2"X6" wood stud 16"OC	SF	10.23	26.12	36.35	20.24	30.47
04.1150 200	Stone veneer, Rubble, sheathing, building paper, insulation, 16 ga 3-5/8 metal stud 16"OC	SF	11.95	27.58	39.53	20.85	32.80
04.1155	**WALLS, STUCCO ON STUD FRAME**						
04.1155 100	Stucco, paint, sheathing, building paper, insulation, 2"X4" wood stud 16"OC	SF	5.13	8.59	13.72	5.95	11.08
04.1155 105	Stucco, paint, sheathing, building paper, insulation, 2"X6" wood stud 16"OC	SF	5.81	9.63	15.44	6.67	12.48
04.1155 110	Stucco, paint, sheathing, building paper, insulation, 16 ga 3-5/8 metal stud 16"OC	SF	7.53	11.09	18.62	7.28	14.81
04.1155 115	Stucco, paint, lath, building paper, insulation, 2"X4" wood stud 16"OC	SF	4.23	7.01	11.24	4.82	9.05
04.1155 120	Stucco, paint, lath, building paper, insulation, 2"X6" wood stud 16"OC	SF	4.91	8.05	12.96	5.54	10.45
04.1155 125	Stucco, paint, lath, building paper, insulation, 16 ga 3-5/8 metal stud 16"OC	SF	6.63	9.51	16.14	6.15	12.78
04.1160	**WALLS, METAL SIDING**						
04.1160 100	Metal Siding, corrugated aluminum, .032" thick	SF	3.50	3.26	6.76	2.65	6.15
04.1160 105	Metal Siding, corrugated aluminum, .032" thick, painted	SF	4.19	3.26	7.45	2.65	6.84
04.1160 110	Metal Siding, aluminum, simulated wood, insulated	SF	3.91	3.26	7.17	2.65	6.56
04.1160 115	Metal Siding, corrugated composition, 3/8" thick	SF	2.72	4.36	7.08	3.54	6.26
04.1160 120	Metal Siding, corrugated fiberglass, 8 oz.	SF	3.13	3.26	6.39	2.65	5.78

CSI #	4.1 ENCLOSURE, VERTICAL Description	Unit	Material	Union Install	Union Total	Open Install	Open Total
04.1160	WALLS, METAL SIDING (Cont.)						
04.1160 125	Metal Siding, corrugated galvanized iron, 26 ga	SF	2.45	3.59	6.04	2.92	5.37
04.1160 130	Metal Siding, baked enamel	SF	39.54	4.17	43.71	3.12	42.66
04.1160 135	Metal Siding, porcelain	SF	43.92	4.39	48.31	3.29	47.21
04.1160 140	Metal Siding, insulated, baked enamel	SF	40.89	6.28	47.17	4.70	45.59
04.1160 145	Metal Siding, insulated, porcelain	SF	56.62	7.08	63.70	5.30	61.92
04.1165	CURTAIN WALLS						
04.1165 100	Curtain Wall, frame, anodized aluminum, bronze	SF	22.59		22.59		22.59
04.1165 105	Curtain Wall, frame, anodized aluminum, black	SF	26.01		26.01		26.01
04.1165 115	Curtain Wall, frame, aluminum, sloping section	SF	36.02		36.02		36.02
04.1165 120	Curtain Wall, frame, steel, painted	SF	21.93		21.93		21.93
04.1165 125	Curtain Wall, frame, steel, porcelain enamel	SF	23.67		23.67		23.67
04.1165 130	Curtain Wall, glazing, plate, 1/4" thick clear	SF	7.86		7.86		7.86
04.1165 135	Curtain Wall, glazing, plate, 1/4" thick tinted	SF	9.66		9.66		9.66
04.1165 140	Curtain Wall, glazing, plate, 1/4" solarcool reflective	SF	18.11		18.11		18.11
04.1165 145	Curtain Wall, glazing, plate, 1/4" veri-tran, reflective	SF	24.18		24.18		24.18
04.1165 150	Curtain Wall, glazing, tempered plate, 1/4" thick, clear	SF	14.46		14.46		14.46
04.1165 155	Curtain Wall, glazing, tempered plate, 1/4" thick, tinted	SF	16.94		16.94		16.94
04.1165 160	Curtain Wall, glazing, tempered plate, 1/4" solarcool, reflective	SF	27.22		27.22		27.22
04.1165 165	Curtain Wall, glazing, double glazed, 5/8" thick, clear	SF	14.46		14.46		14.46
04.1165 170	Curtain Wall, glazing, double glazed, 5/8" thick, tinted	SF	15.71		15.71		15.71
04.1165 175	Curtain Wall, glazing, double glazed, 5/8" solarcool, reflective	SF	19.29		19.29		19.29
04.1165 180	Curtain Wall, glazing, double glazed, tempered, 5/8" thick, clear	SF	24.79		24.79		24.79
04.1165 185	Curtain Wall, glazing, double glazed, tempered, 5/8" thick, tinted	SF	26.60		26.60		26.60
04.1165 190	Curtain Wall, glazing, double glazed, tempered, 5/8" solarcool, reflective	SF	37.53		37.53		37.53
04.1165 195	Curtain Wall, glazing, double glazed, 1" thick, clear	SF	15.71		15.71		15.71
04.1165 200	Curtain Wall, glazing, double glazed, 1" thick, tinted	SF	16.94		16.94		16.94
04.1165 205	Curtain Wall, glazing, double glazed, 1" solarcool, reflective	SF	22.38		22.38		22.38
04.1165 210	Curtain Wall, glazing, double glazed, tempered, 1" thick, clear	SF	28.42		28.42		28.42
04.1165 215	Curtain Wall, glazing, double glazed, tempered, 1" thick, tinted	SF	30.85		30.85		30.85
04.1165 220	Curtain Wall, glazing, double glazed, tempered, 1" solarcool, reflective	SF	15.71		15.71		15.71
04.1165 225	Curtain Wall, glazing, spandrel	SF	16.94		16.94		16.94
04.1165 230	Curtain Wall, glazing, glasweld, 1/4" finished, one side	SF	29.67		29.67		29.67
04.1165 235	Curtain Wall, glazing, glasweld, 1" insulated, finished, one side, dual	SF	38.57		38.57		38.57
04.1165 240	Curtain Wall, glazing, mirawal, 5/16" finished, one side, dual	SF	30.24		30.24		30.24
04.1165 245	Curtain Wall, glazing, mirawal, 1" insulated, finished, one side, dual	SF	39.63		39.63		39.63
04.1165 250	Curtain Wall, glazing, aluca bond,	SF	43.52		43.52		43.52
04.1165 255	Curtain Wall, prefinished and insulated building panels with support, frame, aluca bond	SF	48.16		48.16		48.16
04.1165 260	Curtain Wall, Dryvit, with studs & 3" insulation	SF	29.21		29.21		29.21
04.1165 265	Curtain Wall, precast panel, fiberglass reinforced, 1 form, standard finish	SF	35.38		35.38		35.38
04.1165 270	Curtain Wall, precast panel, fiberglass reinforced, 2 form, standard finish	SF	47.32		47.32		47.32
04.1165 275	Curtain Wall, precast panel, fiberglass reinforced, 1 form, sandblast	SF	57.05		57.05		57.05
04.1165 280	Curtain Wall, precast panel, fiberglass reinforced, 2 form, sandblast	SF	62.91		62.91		62.91

CSI #	4.1 ENCLOSURE, VERTICAL Description	Unit	Material	Union Install	Union Total	Open Install	Open Total
04.1165	**CURTAIN WALLS (Cont.)**						
04.1165 285	Curtain Wall, precast panel, fiberglass reinforced, 1 form, mo-sai finish	SF	49.26		49.26		49.26
04.1165 290	Curtain Wall, precast panel, fiberglass reinforced, 1 form, granite overlay	SF	72.63		72.63		72.63
04.1165 295	Curtain Wall, GFRC panel, fiberglass reinforced, 1 form, standard finish	SF	40.40		40.40		40.40
04.1165 300	Curtain Wall, GFRC panel, fiberglass reinforced, 2 form, standard finish	SF	47.28		47.28		47.28
04.1165 305	Curtain Wall, GFRC panel, fiberglass reinforced, 1 form, sandblast	SF	58.00		58.00		58.00
04.1165 310	Curtain Wall, GFRC panel, fiberglass reinforced, 2 form, sandblast	SF	61.66		61.66		61.66
04.1165 315	Curtain Wall, GFRC panel, fiberglass reinforced, 1 form, mo-sai finish	SF	47.32		47.32		47.32
04.1165 320	Curtain Wall, GFRC panel, fiberglass reinforced, 1 form, granite overlay	SF	72.74		72.74		72.74
04.1170	**WALLS, EXTERIOR COATING**						
04.1170 100	Exterior coating, concrete surface, paint, prime	SF	.09	.35	.44	.28	.37
04.1170 105	Exterior coating, concrete surface, paint, prime + 1 finish	SF	.17	.68	.85	.53	.70
04.1170 110	Exterior coating, concrete surface, paint, prime + 2 finish	SF	.24	.99	1.23	.77	1.01
04.1170 115	Exterior coating, plaster surface, paint, prime	SF	.09	.35	.44	.28	.37
04.1170 120	Exterior coating, plaster surface, paint, prime + 1 finish	SF	.14	.68	.82	.53	.67
04.1170 125	Exterior coating, plaster surface, paint, prime + 2 finish	SF	.24	.99	1.23	.77	1.01
04.1170 130	Exterior coating, masonry surface, paint, prime	SF	.14	.40	.54	.31	.45
04.1170 135	Exterior coating, masonry surface, paint, prime + 1 finish	SF	.14	.71	.85	.55	.69
04.1170 140	Exterior coating, masonry surface, paint, prime + 2 finish	SF	.24	1.01	1.25	.79	1.03
04.1170 145	Exterior coating, wood siding, paint, prime	SF	.08	.32	.40	.25	.33
04.1170 150	Exterior coating, wood siding, paint, prime + 1 finish	SF	.14	.68	.82	.53	.67
04.1170 155	Exterior coating, wood siding, paint, prime + 2 finish	SF	.24	.99	1.23	.77	1.01
04.1170 160	Exterior coating, wood siding, stain	SF	.09	.32	.41	.25	.34
04.1170 165	Exterior coating, wood siding, stain + 2 seal coats	SF	.09	.95	1.04	.74	.83
04.1170 170	Exterior coating, wood shingle, stain	SF	.08	.32	.40	.25	.33
04.1170 175	Exterior coating, wood shingle, stain + 2 seal coats	SF	.09	.95	1.04	.74	.83
04.1170 180	Exterior coating, silicone seal, spray 1 coat	SF	.26	.32	.58	.25	.51
04.1170 185	Exterior coating, silicone seal, spray 2 coats	SF	.63	.59	1.22	.46	1.09
04.1170 190	Exterior coating, polyurethane, 1/8" thick	SF	1.62	3.14	4.76	2.45	4.07
04.1170 195	Exterior coating, sheet metal, paint, prime	SF	.08	.63	.71	.49	.57
04.1170 200	Exterior coating, sheet metal, paint, prime + 1 finish	SF	.14	1.06	1.20	.83	.97
04.1170 205	Exterior coating, sheet metal, paint, prime + 2 finish	SF	.20	1.57	1.77	1.22	1.42
04.1170 210	Exterior coating, wood trim, paint, prime	SF	.09	.40	.49	.31	.40
04.1170 215	Exterior coating, wood trim, paint, prime + 1 finish	SF	.20	.69	.89	.54	.74
04.1170 220	Exterior coating, wood trim, paint, prime + 2 finish	SF	.26	1.11	1.37	.86	1.12
04.1175	**INTERIOR SURFACE OF EXTERIOR WALLS**						
04.1175 100	Finish interior wall, gypsum board, on stud, painted, rubber base	SF	.94	1.55	2.49	1.15	2.09
04.1175 105	Finish interior wall, gypsum board, on furring, painted, rubber base	SF	1.70	2.63	4.33	1.81	3.51
04.1175 110	Finish interior wall, lath and plaster, on stud, painted, rubber base	SF	3.64	6.41	10.05	4.28	7.92
04.1175 115	Finish interior wall, lath and plaster, on stud, painted, rubber base	SF	4.28	7.49	11.77	4.94	9.22
04.1175 120	Wall covering, ceramic tile, 4"x 4", mortar	SF	5.13	7.69	12.82	6.16	11.29
04.1175 125	Wall covering, ceramic tile, 4"x 4", mastic	SF	5.04	4.42	9.46	3.53	8.57
04.1175 130	Wall covering, ceramic tile, 6"x 4", mortar	SF	5.38	6.89	12.27	5.51	10.89

CSI #	4.1 ENCLOSURE, VERTICAL Description	Unit	Material	Union Install	Union Total	Open Install	Open Total
04.1175	**INTERIOR SURFACE OF EXTERIOR WALLS (Cont.)**						
04.1175 135	Wall covering, ceramic tile, 6"x 4", mastic	SF	5.38	3.68	9.06	2.94	8.32
04.1175 140	Wall painting, concrete, prime	SF	.04	.32	.36	.25	.29
04.1175 145	Wall painting, concrete, prime + 1 finished	SF	.12	.59	.71	.46	.58
04.1175 150	Wall painting, concrete, prime + 2 finished	SF	.22	.95	1.17	.74	.96
04.1175 155	Concrete block painting, prime, brush	SF	.04	.35	.39	.28	.32
04.1175 160	Concrete block painting, prime + 1 finished, brush	SF	.14	.68	.82	.53	.67
04.1175 165	Concrete block painting, prime + 2 finished, brush	SF	.24	1.00	1.24	.78	1.02
04.1175 170	Concrete block painting, prime, roll	SF	.04	.24	.28	.18	.22
04.1175 175	Concrete block painting, prime + 1 finished, roll	SF	.14	.45	.59	.35	.49
04.1175 180	Concrete block painting, prime + 2 finished, roll	SF	.24	.67	.91	.52	.76
04.1200	**FENESTRATION**						
04.1200 100	Window, steel frame, fixed, 1/4" glass, clear	SF	16.74	13.01	29.75	9.85	26.59
04.1200 105	Window, steel frame, fixed, 1/4" glass, tempered	SF	18.54	13.01	31.55	9.85	28.39
04.1200 110	Window, steel frame, fixed, security, 1/4" glass, wire	SF	38.42	13.01	51.43	9.85	48.27
04.1200 115	Window, steel frame, fixed, 1/4" glass, spandrel	SF	35.76	13.68	49.44	10.37	46.13
04.1200 120	Window, steel frame, fixed, 1/4" glass, obscure	SF	22.94	13.01	35.95	9.85	32.79
04.1200 125	Window, aluminum frame, fixed, 1/4" glass, clear	SF	16.45	10.10	26.55	7.58	24.03
04.1200 130	Window, aluminum frame, fixed, 1/4" glass, tempered	SF	18.25	10.10	28.35	7.58	25.83
04.1200 135	Window, aluminum frame, fixed, 1/4" glass, spandrel	SF	35.47	10.77	46.24	8.10	43.57
04.1200 140	Window, aluminum frame, fixed, 1/4" glass, obscure	SF	22.65	10.10	32.75	7.58	30.23
04.1200 145	Window, steel frame, fixed, 1/4" double glass, clear	SF	23.27	17.33	40.60	13.13	36.40
04.1200 150	Window, steel frame, fixed, 1/4" double glass, tinted	SF	25.33	17.33	42.66	13.13	38.46
04.1200 155	Window, steel frame, fixed, 1/4" double glass, tempered	SF	25.07	17.33	42.40	13.13	38.20
04.1200 160	Window, steel frame, fixed, security 1/4" double glass, wire	SF	44.95	17.33	62.28	13.13	58.08
04.1200 165	Window, steel frame, fixed, 1/4" double glass, spandrel	SF	42.29	18.00	60.29	13.65	55.94
04.1200 170	Window, steel frame, fixed, 1/4" double glass, obscure	SF	29.47	17.33	46.80	13.13	42.60
04.1200 175	Window, aluminum frame, fixed, 1/4" double glass, clear	SF	23.12	14.42	37.54	10.86	33.98
04.1200 180	Window, aluminum frame, fixed, 1/4" double glass, tinted	SF	25.18	14.42	39.60	10.86	36.04
04.1200 185	Window, aluminum frame, fixed, 1/4" double glass, tempered	SF	24.92	14.42	39.34	10.86	35.78
04.1200 190	Window, aluminum frame, fixed, 1/4" double glass, spandrel	SF	42.14	15.09	57.23	11.38	53.52
04.1200 195	Window, aluminum frame, fixed, 1/4" double glass, obscure	SF	29.32	14.42	43.74	10.86	40.18
04.1200 350	Window, metal, sliding, one vent, insulated glass, with screen, 2'0"X1'6"	EACH	66.16	34.78	100.94	25.40	91.56
04.1200 355	Window, metal, sliding, one vent, insulated glass, with screen, 2'0"X3'0"	EACH	87.14	34.78	121.92	25.40	112.54
04.1200 360	Window, metal, sliding, one vent, insulated glass, with screen, 3'0"X4'0"	EACH	123.23	41.69	164.92	30.45	153.68
04.1200 365	Window, metal, sliding, one vent, insulated glass, with screen, 4'0"X4'0"	EACH	137.41	48.71	186.12	35.58	172.99
04.1200 370	Window, metal, sliding, one vent, insulated glass, with screen, 5'0"X4'0"	EACH	154.46	48.71	203.17	35.58	190.04
04.1200 375	Window, metal, sliding, one vent, insulated glass, with screen, 6'0"X4'0"	EACH	168.66	55.63	224.29	40.64	209.30
04.1200 380	Window, metal, sliding, two vent, insulated glass, with screen, 8'0"X4'0"	EACH	252.97	69.54	322.51	50.79	303.76
04.1200 385	Window, metal, sliding, two vent, insulated glass, with screen, 10'0"X4'0"	EACH	289.29	83.38	372.67	60.90	350.19
04.1200 390	Window, metal, sliding, insulated glass, with screen, average	SF	10.66	2.43	13.09	1.77	12.43

CSI #	4.1 ENCLOSURE, VERTICAL Description	Unit	Material	Union Install	Union Total	Open Install	Open Total
04.1200	**FENESTRATION (Cont.)**						
04.1200 395	Window, metal, casement, one vent, insulated glass, with screen, 2'0"X2'6"	EACH	169.23	34.78	204.01	25.40	194.63
04.1200 400	Window, metal, casement, one vent, insulated glass, with screen, 2'6"X4'0"	EACH	226.16	34.78	260.94	25.40	251.56
04.1200 405	Window, metal, casement, one vent, insulated glass, with screen, 4'0"X5'0"	EACH	295.70	48.71	344.41	35.58	331.28
04.1200 410	Window, metal, casement, one vent, insulated glass, with screen, 6'0"X3'0"	EACH	272.99	48.71	321.70	35.58	308.57
04.1200 415	Window, metal, casement, two vent, insulated glass, with screen, 4'0"X5'0"	EACH	371.12	48.71	419.83	35.58	406.70
04.1200 420	Window, metal, casement, two vent, insulated glass, with screen, 6'0"X3'0"	EACH	345.57	48.71	394.28	35.58	381.15
04.1200 425	Window, metal, casement, insulated glass, with screen, average	SF	23.53	2.43	25.96	1.77	25.30
04.1200 430	Window, metal, awning, one vent, insulated glass, 2'0"X2'6"	EACH	169.23	34.78	204.01	25.40	194.63
04.1200 435	Window, metal, awning, one vent, insulated glass, 4'0"X5'0"	EACH	295.70	48.71	344.41	35.58	331.28
04.1200 440	Window, metal, awning, one vent, insulated glass, 6'0"X3'0"	EACH	272.99	48.71	321.70	35.58	308.57
04.1200 445	Window, metal, awning, insulated glass, average	SF	23.53	2.43	25.96	1.77	25.30
04.1200 450	Window, vinyl, sliding, one vent, insulated glass, 2'6"X3'0"	EACH	230.72	34.74	265.46	25.37	256.09
04.1200 455	Window, vinyl, sliding, one vent, insulated glass, 3'0"X4'0"	EACH	267.61	41.84	309.45	30.56	298.17
04.1200 460	Window, vinyl, sliding, one vent, insulated glass, 5'0"X5'0"	EACH	356.43	55.26	411.69	40.36	396.79
04.1200 465	Window, vinyl, sliding, one vent, insulated glass, 6'0"X5'0"	EACH	402.06	69.47	471.53	50.74	452.80
04.1200 470	Window, vinyl, sliding, one vent, insulated glass, average	EACH	24.25	2.43	26.68	1.78	26.03
04.1200 475	Window, vinyl, casement, one vent, insulated glass, 2'0" X 2'6"	SF	357.71	34.74	392.45	25.37	383.08
04.1200 480	Window, vinyl, casement, one vent, insulated glass, 3'0" X 4'0"	EACH	382.57	41.84	424.41	30.56	413.13
04.1200 485	Window, vinyl, fixed, insulated glass, 3'0" X 3'0"	EACH	150.56	27.78	178.34	20.29	170.85
04.1200 490	Window, vinyl, fixed, insulated glass, 5'0" X 5'0"	EACH	286.85	44.21	331.06	32.29	319.14
04.1200 495	Window, vinyl, fixed, insulated glass, 10'0" X 5'0"	EACH	527.54	66.95	594.49	48.90	576.44
04.1200 500	Window, wood, double hung, insulated glass, 1'6"X2'6"	EACH	230.44	90.39	320.83	66.02	296.46
04.1200 505	Window, wood, double hung, insulated glass, 2'0"X2'6"	EACH	233.51	90.39	323.90	66.02	299.53
04.1200 510	Window, wood, double hung, insulated glass, 2'0"X3'0"	EACH	245.71	90.39	336.10	66.02	311.73
04.1200 515	Window, wood, double hung, insulated glass, 2'0"X3'6"	EACH	282.31	90.39	372.70	66.02	348.33
04.1200 520	Window, wood, double hung, insulated glass, 2'6"X4'0"	EACH	309.80	90.39	400.19	66.02	375.82
04.1200 525	Window, wood, double hung, insulated glass, 2'6"X4'6"	EACH	331.17	97.31	428.48	71.07	402.24
04.1200 530	Window, wood, double hung, insulated glass, 3'0"X4'0"	EACH	344.89	97.31	442.20	71.07	415.96
04.1200 535	Window, wood, double hung, insulated glass, 3'0"X4'6"	EACH	369.32	97.31	466.63	71.07	440.39
04.1200 540	Window, wood, double hung, insulated glass, 3'0"X5'0"	EACH	392.20	97.31	489.51	71.07	463.27
04.1200 545	Window, wood, double hung, insulated glass, 3'0"X6'0"	EACH	486.82	111.23	598.05	81.24	568.06
04.1200 550	Window, wood, double hung, insulated glass, 4'0"X4'6"	EACH	445.64	131.99	577.63	96.40	542.04
04.1200 555	Window, wood, double hung, insulated glass, 4'0"X6'0"	EACH	595.18	131.99	727.17	96.40	691.58
04.1200 560	Window, wood, double hung, insulated glass, Average	SF	34.07		34.07		34.07
04.1200 565	Window, wood, casement, insulated glass, 1'6"X2'0"	EACH	186.19	97.31	283.50	71.07	257.26
04.1200 570	Window, wood, casement, insulated glass, 2'0"X3'0"	EACH	239.59	104.22	343.81	76.12	315.71
04.1200 575	Window, wood, casement, insulated glass, 5'0"X4'0"	EACH	561.62	180.60	742.22	131.91	693.53
04.1200 580	Window, wood, casement, insulated glass, 8'0"X5'0"	EACH	1,024.01	194.53	1,218.54	142.08	1,166.09
04.1200 585	Window, wood, casement, insulated glass, 10'0"X5'0"	EACH	1,190.35	250.13	1,440.48	182.70	1,373.05
04.1200 590	Window, wood, fixed, insulated glass, 2'0"X2'0"	EACH	141.94	77.85	219.79	56.86	198.80
04.1200 595	Window, wood, fixed, insulated glass, 3'0"X3'6"	EACH	231.98	77.85	309.83	56.86	288.84

CSI #	4.1 ENCLOSURE, VERTICAL Description	Unit	Material	Union Install	Union Total	Open Install	Open Total
04.1200	**FENESTRATION (Cont.)**						
04.1200 600	Window, wood, fixed, insulated glass, 5'0"X6'0"	EACH	546.35	104.22	650.57	76.12	622.47
04.1200 605	Window, wood, fixed, insulated glass, average	SF	25.24		25.24		25.24
04.1300	**EXTERIOR DOORS**						
04.1300 100	Door, prehung, solid core, 3' X 7' X 1 3/8"	EACH	141.59	88.10	229.69	64.35	205.94
04.1300 105	Door, prehung, solid core, 3' X 7' X 1 3/4"	EACH	149.93	88.10	238.03	64.35	214.28
04.1300 107	Door, prehung, 9 lite, 3' X 7' X 1 3/4"	EACH	193.24	88.10	281.34	64.35	257.59
04.1300 110	Door, prehung, 12 lite, 3' X 7' X 1 3/4"	EACH	219.89	88.10	307.99	64.35	284.24
04.1300 115	Door, prehung, Dutch, 3' X 7' X 1 3/4"	EACH	320.38	132.15	452.53	96.52	416.90
04.1300 120	Door, prehung, 12 lite, 3'-6" X 9' X 1 3/4"	EACH	273.20	88.10	361.30	64.35	337.55
04.1300 130	Door, metal, panic hardware, single, 3' X 7'	EACH	1,499.10	326.71	1,825.81	238.63	1,737.73
04.1300 135	Door, metal, panic hardware, single, 4' X 7'	EACH	1,467.54	347.64	1,815.18	253.91	1,721.45
04.1300 140	Door, metal, panic hardware, double, 6' X 7'	EACH	2,760.41	601.32	3,361.73	439.20	3,199.61
04.1300 145	Door, metal and glass, panic hardware, single, 3' X 7'	EACH	1,928.13	417.01	2,345.14	308.98	2,237.11
04.1300 150	Door, metal and glass, panic hardware, single, 4' X 7'	EACH	2,039.58	468.04	2,507.62	347.71	2,387.29
04.1300 155	Door, metal and glass, panic hardware, double, 6' X 7'	EACH	3,618.47	781.92	4,400.39	579.90	4,198.37
04.1400	**STORE FRONT SYSTEMS**						
04.1400 100	Storefront, wall, aluminum & glass, stub wall to 9'	SF	21.67	10.24	31.91	7.98	29.65
04.1400 105	Storefront, wall, aluminum & glass, floor to 13'	SF	25.06	11.84	36.90	9.23	34.29
04.1400 110	Storefront, entrance, 3'x7', concealed closer, center pivot, narrow stile	EACH	840.94	525.05	1,365.99	409.35	1,250.29
04.1400 115	Storefront, entrance, 3'x7', concealed closer, center pivot, heavy duty	EACH	987.28	552.39	1,539.67	430.67	1,417.95
04.1400 120	Storefront, entrance, 3'x7', concealed closer, center pivot, 1/2" tempered	EACH	2,085.78	683.57	2,769.35	532.95	2,618.73
04.1400 125	Add to entrance cost, center stop	EACH	27.68	20.80	48.48	16.22	43.90
04.1400 130	Add to entrance cost, floor check	EACH	224.71	109.38	334.09	85.28	309.99
04.1400 135	Add to entrance cost, bronze anodized aluminum	EACH	165.48		165.48		165.48
04.1400 140	Add to entrance cost, black anodized aluminum	EACH	240.38		240.38		240.38
04.1400 145	Add to entrance cost, automatic opener	EACH	3,170.29	1,776.77	4,947.06	1,297.73	4,468.02
04.1500	**SPECIAL DOORS**						
04.1500 100	Garage door, wood, spring balanced, 7' X 8'	EACH	193.10	391.29	584.39	285.80	478.90
04.1500 105	Garage door, wood, spring balanced, 7' X 16'	EACH	326.96	586.93	913.89	428.69	755.65
04.1500 110	Garage door, wood, track operated, 7' X 8'	EACH	200.86	404.78	605.64	295.65	496.51
04.1500 115	Garage door, wood, track operated, 7' X 16'	EACH	381.05	667.81	1,048.86	487.76	868.81
04.1500 120	Roll-up doors, chain operated, galvanized steel 20 GA, 10'x10'	EACH	792.31	2,075.05	2,867.36	1,553.85	2,346.16
04.1500 125	Roll-up doors, chain operated, galvanized steel 20 GA, 12'x12'	EACH	1,084.53	2,170.82	3,255.35	1,625.57	2,710.10
04.1500 130	Roll-up doors, chain operated, galvanized steel 20 GA, 14'x14'	EACH	1,355.61	2,170.82	3,526.43	1,625.57	2,981.18
04.1500 135	Roll-up grill, crank operated, aluminum, 8'x8'	EACH	1,238.84	1,085.42	2,324.26	812.80	2,051.64
04.1500 140	Roll-up grill, crank operated, aluminum, 10'x10'	EACH	1,437.78	1,436.60	2,874.38	1,075.77	2,513.55
04.1500 145	Overhead doors, sectional, steel, 8' X 8'	EACH	432.39	440.59	872.98	329.93	762.32
04.1500 150	Overhead doors, sectional, steel, 12'x12'	EACH	595.55	734.23	1,329.78	549.82	1,145.37
04.1500 155	Add to overhead door cost for motor	EACH	818.06	134.10	952.16	100.41	918.47
04.1500 160	Sliding door with track steel, 12'x14'	EACH	823.06	341.87	1,164.93	256.00	1,079.06
04.1500 165	Sliding door with track steel, 14'x16'	EACH	1,057.55	391.90	1,449.45	293.47	1,351.02
04.1500 170	Sliding door with track steel, 16'x20'	EACH	1,344.69	475.29	1,819.98	355.91	1,700.60
04.1500 175	Sliding door with track steel, industrial to 50' X 30'	SF	22.13	50.86	72.99	38.09	60.22
04.1500 177	Sliding door with track steel, industrial to 90' X 30'	SF	25.67	54.20	79.87	40.59	66.26
04.1500 180	Revolving door, aluminum, 7'	EACH	17,401.47	4,450.19	21,851.66	3,332.43	20,733.90
04.1500 185	Revolving door, stainless steel, satin finish, 7'	EACH	34,986.17	4,450.19	39,436.36	3,332.43	38,318.60
04.1500 190	Revolving door, stainless steel, mirror finish, 7'	EACH	42,313.12	6,626.15	48,939.27	4,961.85	47,274.97
04.1500 195	Revolving door, bronze, satin finish, 7'	EACH	34,535.05	6,499.69	41,034.74	4,867.15	39,402.20
04.1500 200	Revolving door, bronze, mirror finish, 7'	EACH	41,946.74	8,435.11	50,381.85	6,316.45	48,263.19

CSI #	4.2 ENCLOSURE, HORIZONTAL Description	Unit	Material	Union Install	Union Total	Open Install	Open Total
	The costs in this section include materials, labor, equipment rental, supervision, and subcontractor overhead and profit. There are no allowances for the general contractor. These costs are typical of those associated with the construction of a building. Costs are complete, and represent normal conditions related to weather. Roof costs do not include the roof structure. These costs are found in section 3.0 Structure. The insulation costs are separate from the roofing material.						
04.2100	**ROOF & ROOF MATERIALS**						
04.2100 100	Roof cover, built-up, low rise, 3 ply	SQ	134.57	89.64	224.21	72.79	207.36
04.2100 105	Roof cover, built-up, low rise, 4 ply	SQ	156.27	97.77	254.04	79.40	235.67
04.2100 110	Roof cover, built-up, low rise, 5 ply	SQ	183.79	111.32	295.11	90.40	274.19
04.2100 115	Roof cover, built-up, high rise, 3 ply	SQ	134.57	201.67	336.24	163.77	298.34
04.2100 120	Roof cover, built-up, high rise, 4 ply	SQ	156.27	220.00	376.27	178.65	334.92
04.2100 125	Roof cover, built-up, high rise, 5 ply	SQ	183.79	250.46	434.25	203.39	387.18
04.2100 130	Roof cover, plastic, elastomeric membrane, 1/16"	SQ	222.83	287.91	510.74	233.80	456.63
04.2100 135	Roof cover, plastic, elastomeric membrane, 1/32"	SF	198.15	287.91	486.06	233.80	431.95
04.2100 140	Roof cover, plastic, elastomeric membrane, loose, trocal	SQ	211.70	102.28	313.98	83.06	294.76
04.2100 145	Roof cover, plastic, elastomeric membrane, neoprene	SQ	319.00	492.00	811.00	400.00	719.00
04.2100 150	Roof cover, bituthene, 1/16", selfseal	SQ	208.03	287.91	495.94	233.80	441.83
04.2100 155	Roof cover, silicone, 3 ply, rolled	SQ	2.82	3.53	6.35	2.87	5.69
04.2100 160	Roof cover, urethane foam, silicone cover, 1' thick	SQ	533.62	150.12	683.74	121.90	655.52
04.2100 165	Roof cover, acrylic, over existing cap sheet	SQ	251.51	66.36	317.87	53.89	305.40
04.2100 170	Roof cover, acrylic, over existing gravel	SQ	251.51	132.74	384.25	107.79	359.30
04.2100 175	Roof cover, acrylic, over existing deck	SQ	257.46	65.81	323.27	53.44	310.90
04.2100 180	Roof cover, acrylic, over existing corrugated metal	SQ	251.51	60.33	311.84	48.99	300.50
04.2100 185	Roof cover, arcylic, new	SQ	251.51	132.74	384.25	107.79	359.30
04.2100 190	Roof cover, shingles, composition asphalt, 240 #	SQ	76.39	87.95	164.34	71.42	147.81
04.2100 200	Roof cover, shingles, composition asphalt, 240 #, 'A'	SQ	98.41	92.37	190.78	75.01	173.42
04.2100 205	Roof cover, shingles, composition asphalt, 300 #	SQ	108.72	92.37	201.09	75.01	183.73
04.2100 210	Roof cover, shingles, composition asphalt, 325 #, 'A'	SQ	124.28	92.37	216.65	75.01	199.29
04.2100 215	Roof cover, shingles, composition asphalt, president	SQ	169.10	84.54	253.64	68.65	237.75
04.2100 220	Roof cover, shingles, valley roll	LF	.52	1.37	1.89	1.11	1.63
04.2100 225	Roof cover, shingles, aluminum tab, 020"	SF	3.02	2.74	5.76	2.23	5.25
04.2100 230	Roof cover, shingles, aluminum tab, 030"	SF	3.51	2.74	6.25	2.23	5.74
04.2100 235	Roof cover, shingles, porcelain enamel, 18 GA	SQ	388.61	298.71	687.32	242.56	631.17
04.2100 240	Roof cover, shingles, fiberglass tabs, 300 #	SQ	113.97	113.94	227.91	83.22	197.19
04.2100 245	Roof cover, tile, clay, spanish, 2 piece	SQ	373.47	609.51	982.98	494.95	868.42
04.2100 250	Roof cover, tile, clay, flat bed	SQ	158.81	339.49	498.30	275.68	434.49
04.2100 255	Roof cover, tile, clay, glazed, interlock	SQ	258.95	368.59	627.54	299.31	558.26
04.2100 260	Roof cover, tile, clay, spanish	SQ	224.46	334.65	559.11	271.76	496.22
04.2100 265	Roof cover, tile, concrete, premium	SQ	325.10	361.88	686.98	293.87	618.97
04.2100 270	Roof cover, tile, concrete, flat	SQ	218.10	310.75	528.85	252.34	470.44
04.2100 275	Roof cover, tile, concrete, interlock	SQ	199.89	285.83	485.72	232.11	432.00
04.2100 280	Roof cover, tile, slate	SQ	619.96	233.44	853.40	189.56	809.52
04.2100 285	Roof cover, corrugated aluminum, 020"	SF	1.42	2.17	3.59	1.76	3.18
04.2100 290	Roof cover, corrugated aluminum, 032"	SF	2.37	2.52	4.89	2.05	4.42
04.2100 295	Roof cover, corrugated composition, 3/16", non-walk	SF	2.07	2.95	5.02	2.39	4.46
04.2100 300	Roof cover, corrugated composition, 3/8"	SF	2.50	3.26	5.76	2.65	5.15
04.2100 305	Roof cover, corrugated fiberglass, 8 oz	SF	3.45	2.95	6.40	2.39	5.84
04.2100 310	Roof cover, corrugated galvanized iron, 26 GA	SF	2.45	3.26	5.71	2.65	5.10
04.2100 315	Roof cover, copper clad stainless steel, 16 oz panels	SF	9.28	5.95	15.23	4.83	14.11
04.2100 320	Roof cover, copper clad stainless steel, 24 oz panels	SF	13.50	7.37	20.87	5.99	19.49
04.2100 325	Roof cover, 16 oz copper, standing seam, 16" panels	SF	8.25	5.95	14.20	4.83	13.08
04.2200	**RIGID INSULATION**						
04.2200 100	Rigid, insulation board, deck, mineral fiber, 1"	SF	.70	.26	.96	.21	.91
04.2200 105	Rigid, insulation board, deck, mineral fiber, 1-1/2"	SF	1.00	.34	1.34	.28	1.28
04.2200 110	Rigid, insulation board, deck, mineral fiber, 2"	SF	1.35	.34	1.69	.28	1.63
04.2200 115	Rigid, insulation board, deck, mineral fiber, 6"	SF	4.15	.62	4.77	.50	4.65
04.2200 120	Rigid, insulation board, deck, fiberglass, 1-1/2"	SF	1.75	.36	2.11	.30	2.05

CSI #	4.2 ENCLOSURE, HORIZONTAL Description	Unit	Material	Union Install	Union Total	Open Install	Open Total
04.2200	**RIGID INSULATION (Cont.)**						
04.2200 125	insulation board, deck, fiberglass, 2"	SF	2.32	.34	2.66	.28	2.60
04.2200 130	Rigid, insulation board, deck, fiberglass, 3"	SF	3.06	.36	3.42	.30	3.36
04.2200 135	Rigid, insulation board, deck, firtex, 2"	SF	1.71	.43	2.14	.35	2.06
04.2200 140	Rigid, insulation board, deck, tectum, paint, 2"	SF	3.06	.68	3.74	.55	3.61
04.2200 145	Rigid, insulation board, deck, tectum, paint, 2-1/2"	SF	3.56	.77	4.33	.62	4.18
04.2200 150	Rigid, insulation board, deck, urethane, paint, 1-1/4" R9	SF	1.75	.30	2.05	.24	1.99
04.2200 155	Rigid, insulation board, deck, urethane, paint, 1-1/2" R11	SF	2.25	.36	2.61	.30	2.55
04.2200 160	Rigid, insulation board, deck, urethane, paint, 2" R14	SF	2.89	.43	3.32	.35	3.24
04.2200 165	Rigid, insulation board, deck, urethane, paint, 1" non-rated R7	SF	1.28	.24	1.52	.19	1.47
04.2200 170	Rigid, insulation board, deck, urethane, paint, 1-1/2" non-rated R11	SF	2.01	.33	2.34	.27	2.28
04.2200 175	Rigid, insulation board, deck, urethane, paint, 2" non-rated R14	SF	2.25	.43	2.68	.35	2.60
04.2200 180	Rigid, insulation board, deck, urethane, paint, 2-1/2" non-rated R19	SF	2.88	.57	3.45	.46	3.34
04.2200 185	Rigid, insulation board, deck, urethane, paint, 3" non-rated R25	SF	3.79	.63	4.42	.51	4.30
04.2200 190	Rigid, insulation board, deck, styrofoam, paint, 1-1/2"	SF	1.71	.36	2.07	.30	2.01
04.2200 195	Rigid, insulation board, deck, styrofoam, paint, 2"	SF	2.18	.40	2.58	.33	2.51
04.2200 200	insulation board, deck, styrofoam, paint, 3"	SF	3.30	.43	3.73	.35	3.65
04.2200 205	Cant strip, 3" fiber	LF	.41	1.44	1.85	1.17	1.58
04.2200 210	Cant strip, 4" fiber	LF	.51	1.44	1.95	1.17	1.68

CSI #	4.3 SUPPORT ITEMS Description	Unit	Material	Union Install	Union Total	Open Install	Open Total
	The costs in this section include materials, labor, equipment rental, supervision, and subcontractor overhead and profit. There are no allowances for the general contractor. These costs are typical of those associated with the construction of a building. Costs are complete, and represent normal conditions related to weather. Where appropriate paint is included in the item cost.						
04.3100	**MISCELLANEOUS IRON**						
04.3100 100	Stairs, steel, concrete tread, 14 risers	FLT	4,976.32	606.18	5,582.50	453.93	5,430.25
04.3100 105	Stairs, steel, concrete tread, 18 risers	FLT	12,783.42	1,389.73	14,173.15	1,040.67	13,824.09
04.3100 110	Stairs, steel, steel tread, 18 risers	FLT	10,865.89	1,829.06	12,694.95	1,369.66	12,235.55
04.3100 115	Ladders, galvanized steel, 2-1/2"x3-3/8" bar, 3/4"rung, protective cage	RISER	275.53	66.96	342.49	50.14	325.67
04.3100 120	Railing, pipe 2 high, welded, with kick plate 1-1/2"	LF	69.12	16.32	85.44	12.22	81.34
04.3100 125	Railing, pipe 3 high, welded, with kick plate 1-1/2"	LF	88.90	16.32	105.22	12.22	101.12
04.3100 130	Railing, pipe 4 high, welded, with kick plate 1-1/2"	LF	108.68	16.32	125.00	12.22	120.90
04.3100 135	Railing, pipe 1-1/2", wall type	LF	32.34	16.32	48.66	12.22	44.56
04.3100 140	Railing, welded, flat bar and angle	LF	40.34	15.24	55.58	11.41	51.75
04.3100 145	Railing, welded, flat and square bar, ornamental	LF	48.48	16.50	64.98	12.35	60.83
04.3100 150	Railing, wrought iron, stock pattern	LF	170.65	17.31	187.96	12.96	183.61
04.3100 155	Railing, wrought iron, custom pattern	LF	377.76	36.73	414.49	27.51	405.27
04.3100 160	Railing, wrought iron, stair	LF	117.52	17.95	135.47	13.44	130.96
04.3100 165	Handrails, decorative, easy designs, brass/bronze, floor mounted	LF	380.31	34.70	415.01	25.98	406.29
04.3100 170	Handrails, decorative, easy designs, brass/bronze, wall mounted	LF	133.39	23.10	156.49	17.30	150.69
04.3100 175	Handrails, decorative, easy designs, stainless steel, floor mounted	LF	232.57	38.15	270.72	28.57	261.14
04.3100 180	Handrails, decorative, easy designs, stainless steel, wall mounted	LF	83.83	30.62	114.45	22.93	106.76
04.3100 185	Handrails, decorative, easy designs, aluminum, floor mounted	LF	138.86	28.87	167.73	21.62	160.48
04.3100 190	Handrails, decorative, easy designs, stainless steel, wall mounted	LF	50.04	19.28	69.32	14.44	64.48
04.3100 195	Fire escape, ladder and balcony	EACH	4,600.09	650.22	5,250.31	486.91	5,087.00
04.3100 200	Ornamental sight screen, aluminum	LF	58.46	11.78	70.24	8.82	67.28
04.3100 205	Ornamental sight screen, extruded metal	LF	44.96	11.78	56.74	8.82	53.78
04.3100 210	Ornamental sun screen, aluminum, manual	LF	58.82	5.85	64.67	4.38	63.20
04.3100 215	Ornamental sun screen, aluminum, motorized	LF	106.11	7.73	113.84	5.79	111.90
04.3100 220	Wrought iron gate, 6'x7'	EACH	2,705.18	336.65	3,041.83	252.09	2,957.27
04.3100 225	Expansion joint, 1-1/2", floor	LF	59.47	10.34	69.81	7.74	67.21
04.3100 230	Expansion joint, 1-1/2", wall	LF	41.94	12.59	54.53	9.43	51.37
04.3100 235	Expansion joint, 1-1/2", roof	LF	83.40	12.19	95.59	9.13	92.53
04.3100 240	Expansion joint, 4", floor	LF	115.46	20.75	136.21	15.54	131.00
04.3100 245	Expansion joint, 4", wall	LF	80.94	25.18	106.12	18.85	99.79
04.3100 250	Expansion joint, 4", roof	LF	122.46	23.36	145.82	17.49	139.95
04.3200	**SHEETMETAL**						
04.3200 100	Gutter, galvanized iron, facia, 5"	LF	1.56	4.04	5.60	2.40	3.96
04.3200 105	Gutter, aluminum, facia, 5"	LF	1.06	4.04	5.10	2.40	3.46
04.3200 110	Gutter, copper, facia, 5"	LF	7.60	4.18	11.78	2.48	10.08
04.3200 115	Downspout, galvanized iron, fabricated, 3"x4"	LF	2.20	3.49	5.69	2.07	4.27
04.3200 120	Downspout, aluminum, fabricated, 3"x4"	LF	1.63	3.49	5.12	2.07	3.70

CSI #	4.3 SUPPORT ITEMS Description	Unit	Material	Union Install	Union Total	Open Install	Open Total
04.3200	**SHEETMETAL (Cont.)**						
04.3200 125	Downspout, copper, fabricated, 3"x4"	LF	8.45	3.70	12.15	2.19	10.64
04.3200 130	Downspout, add for over 2 stories, fabricated, 3"x4"	LF		1.45	1.45	.86	.86
04.3200 135	Gravel stop, galvanized iron, facia 10"	LF	1.84	3.49	5.33	2.07	3.91
04.3200 140	Gravel stop, aluminum, facia 10"	LF	2.57	3.49	6.06	2.07	4.64
04.3200 145	Gravel stop, copper, facia 10"	LF	4.83	3.77	8.60	2.24	7.07
04.3200 150	Sheet metal, fabricated, galvanized iron, 26 gauge	SF	1.19	5.54	6.73	3.29	4.48
04.3200 155	Sheet metal, fabricated, aluminum, .032	SF	2.04	5.54	7.58	3.29	5.33
04.3200 160	Sheet metal, fabricated, copper, 16 oz	SF	4.15	5.83	9.98	3.46	7.61
04.3200 165	Reglets, galvanized iron, 26 gauge	LF	.88	2.12	3.00	1.26	2.14
04.3200 170	Reglets, aluminum, .032"	LF	1.10	2.12	3.22	1.26	2.36
04.3200 175	Reglets, copper, 16oz	LF	2.76	2.12	4.88	1.26	4.02
04.3200 177	Add for neoprene gasket	LF	.54	.69	1.23	.41	.95
04.3200 180	Roof safe & cap, 4", aluminum, .032"	EA	11.36	11.63	22.99	6.90	18.26
04.3200 185	Plumber's flash cone, galvanized, 3"	EA	9.04	14.78	23.82	8.77	17.81
04.3200 190	Scupper, aluminum, .032"	EA	16.66	22.58	39.24	13.40	30.06
04.3200 195	Vent, frieze, galvanized, 4"x24"	EA	1.91	3.97	5.88	2.36	4.27
04.3200 197	Vent, block/brick, galvanized, 8"x16"	EA	15.96	30.10	46.06	17.86	33.82
04.3200 200	Vent, block/brick, galvanized, 12"x16"	EA	20.65	30.10	50.75	17.86	38.51
04.3200 205	Louvers, manual, galvanized	SF	10.02	17.79	27.81	10.55	20.57
04.3200 210	Screens, cooling tower, galvanized	SF	7.97	17.79	25.76	10.55	18.52
04.3200 212	Screens, bird	SF	1.59	2.06	3.65	1.22	2.81
04.3200 215	Gravity ventilator, galvanized 8"	EA	152.05	42.41	194.46	25.17	177.22
04.3200 220	Gravity ventilator, galvanized 36"	EA	645.75	86.19	731.94	51.15	696.90
04.3200 225	Gravity ventilator, galvanized 60"	EA	1,727.92	307.80	2,035.72	182.66	1,910.58
04.3200 230	Gravity ventilator, add for hand damper	EA	51.21		51.21		51.21
04.3200 235	Gravity ventilator, add for motor damper	EA	76.86		76.86		76.86
04.3200 240	Mushroom vent, 8", to 180 cubic feet per minute	EA	378.72	220.25	598.97	130.70	509.42
04.3200 245	Mushroom vent, 12", to 360 cubic feet per minute	EA	613.81	220.25	834.06	130.70	744.51
04.3200 250	Mushroom vent, 24", to 1200 cubic feet per minute	EA	1,358.29	360.47	1,718.76	213.92	1,572.21
04.3200 255	Expansion joints, dry wall, aluminum cover, 2"	LF	16.06	4.11	20.17	2.44	18.50
04.3200 260	Expansion joints, concrete wall, aluminum cover, 4"-6"	LF	33.82	24.63	58.45	14.62	48.44
04.3200 265	Expansion joints, roof,neoprene & aluminum, 2"	LF	22.86	5.47	28.33	3.25	26.11
04.3200 270	Roof hatches, frame/cover, galvanized, 3'x3'-6"	EA	462.95	384.34	847.29	228.08	691.03
04.3200 275	Roof hatches, frame/cover, galvanized, 3'x9'-6"	EA	1,166.84	495.07	1,661.91	293.79	1,460.63
04.3200 280	Smoke vent, automatic 160 degree, galvanized, 420#, 4'-8"x4'-8"	EA	1,227.93	426.68	1,654.61	253.21	1,481.14
04.3200 285	Smoke vent, automatic 160 degree, galvanized, 650#, 4'-8"x9'	EA	1,936.46	563.47	2,499.93	334.39	2,270.85
04.3200 290	Fire vent, automatic 160 degree, aluminum, 260#, 4'-8"x4'-8"	EA	1,308.25	359.10	1,667.35	213.10	1,521.35
04.3200 295	Fire vent, automatic 160 degree, aluminum, 380#, 4'-8"x9'-6"	EA	1,681.38	513.00	2,194.38	304.43	1,985.81
04.3200 300	Fire vent, automatic 160 degree, aluminum, 425#, 6'x9'-6"	EA	1,945.85	564.30	2,510.15	334.88	2,280.73
04.3300	**SKYLIGHTS**						
04.3300 100	Skylights, aluminum frame, plastic dome, 2'x2'	EA	137.44	89.06	226.50	52.85	190.29
04.3300 105	Skylights, aluminum frame, plastic dome, 4'x4'	EA	279.69	89.06	368.75	52.85	332.54
04.3300 110	Skylights, aluminum frame, plastic dome, 5'x5'	EA	529.24	89.06	618.30	52.85	582.09
04.3300 115	Skylights, aluminum frame, plastic dome, 3'x6'	EA	350.51	89.06	439.57	52.85	403.36
04.3300 120	Skylights, aluminum frame, plastic dome, 7'x7'	EA	1,367.12	120.18	1,487.30	71.32	1,438.44

CSI #	4.3 SUPPORT ITEMS Description	Unit	Material	Union Install	Union Total	Open Install	Open Total
04.3300	**SKYLIGHTS (Cont.)**						
04.3300 125	Skylights, aluminum frame, plastic dome, 8'x10'	EA	2,473.36	120.18	2,593.54	71.32	2,544.68
04.3300 130	Skylights, aluminum frame, pyramid dome, 2'x2'	EA	199.52	89.06	288.58	52.85	252.37
04.3300 135	Skylights, aluminum frame, pyramid dome, 3'x3'	EA	224.73	89.06	313.79	52.85	277.58
04.3300 140	Skylights, aluminum frame, pyramid dome, 4'x4'	EA	405.91	89.06	494.97	52.85	458.76
04.3300 145	Skylights, double glazed, aluminum frame 2'x2'	EA	241.04	101.24	342.28	60.08	301.12
04.3300 150	Skylights, double glazed, aluminum frame 3'x3'	EA	389.91	127.22	517.13	75.50	465.41
04.3300 155	Skylights, double glazed, aluminum frame 4'x4'	EA	601.70	151.85	753.55	90.12	691.82
04.3300 160	Skylights, double glazed, aluminum frame 6'x6'	EA	1,505.40	180.58	1,685.98	107.16	1,612.56
04.3300 165	Skylights, double glazed, aluminum frame 4'x8'	EA	1,434.57	180.58	1,615.15	107.16	1,541.73
04.3300 170	Skylights, fabricated, steel frame, laminated glass, 20' span	SF	88.42		88.42		88.42
04.3300 175	Skylights, fabricated, steel frame, laminated glass, 30' span	SF	109.02		109.02		109.02
04.3300 180	Skylights, fabricated, steel frame, laminated glass, 40' span	SF	127.64		127.64		127.64
04.3400	**INSULATION**						
04.3400 100	Acoustic insulation, sound board, vertical, 1/2"	SF	.22	.72	.94	.53	.75
04.3400 105	Insulation, batt, wall and ceiling, mineral fiber, 2-1/2" R7	SF	.24	.39	.63	.28	.52
04.3400 110	Insulation, batt, wall and ceiling, mineral fiber, 3" R11	SF	.32	.39	.71	.28	.60
04.3400 115	Insulation, batt, wall and ceiling, mineral fiber, 3-1/2" R13	SF	.34	.39	.73	.28	.62
04.3400 120	Insulation, batt, wall and ceiling, mineral fiber, 3-1/2", R13, fiberglass	SF	.41	.39	.80	.28	.69
04.3400 125	Insulation, batt, wall and ceiling, mineral fiber, 6" R19	SF	.51	.39	.90	.28	.79
04.3400 130	Insulation, batt, wall and ceiling, mineral fiber, 8-9" R30	SF	.44	.80	1.24	.58	1.02
04.3400 135	Insulation, batt, wall and ceiling, mineral fiber, 11" blown fiber	SF	.33	.54	.87	.39	.72
04.3400 140	Insulation, batt, wall and ceiling, mineral fiber, add for supporting Batts on wire	SF	.01	.20	.21	.15	.16
04.3500	**CAULKING & SEALANTS**						
04.3500 100	Caulk, linseed base, 1/8"x1/8"	LF	.02	.98	1.00	.71	.73
04.3500 105	Caulk, linseed base, 1/4"x1/4"	LF	.09	1.46	1.55	1.07	1.16
04.3500 110	Caulk, linseed base, 1/2"x1/2"	LF	.22	1.94	2.16	1.42	1.64
04.3500 115	Caulk, linseed base, 3/4"x3/4"	LF	.35	2.91	3.26	2.12	2.47
04.3500 120	Caulk, linseed base, 1"x1"	LF	.95	3.88	4.83	2.84	3.79
04.3500 125	Caulk, butyl base, 1/8"x1/8"	LF	.02	.98	1.00	.71	.73
04.3500 135	Caulk, butyl base, 1/2"x1/2"	LF	.37	1.94	2.31	1.42	1.79
04.3500 145	Caulk, butyl base, 1"x1"	LF	1.58	3.88	5.46	2.84	4.42
04.3500 150	Caulk, acrylic, 1/8"x1/8"	LF	.06	.98	1.04	.71	.77
04.3500 160	Caulk, acrylic, 1/2"x1/2"	LF	.90	1.94	2.84	1.42	2.32
04.3500 170	Caulk, acrylic, 1"x1"	LF	3.27	3.88	7.15	2.84	6.11
04.3500 175	Caulk, polysulfide, 1/8"x1/8"	LF	.32	.98	1.30	.71	1.03
04.3500 185	Caulk, polysulfide, 1/2"x1/2"	LF	1.04	1.94	2.98	1.42	2.46
04.3500 195	Caulk, polysulfide, 1"x1"	LF	4.29	3.88	8.17	2.84	7.13
04.3500 200	Caulk, silicone, 1/8"x1/8"	LF	.09	.98	1.07	.71	.80
04.3500 210	Caulk, silicone, 1/2"x1/2"	LF	1.40	1.94	3.34	1.42	2.82
04.3500 220	Caulk, silicone, 1"x1"	LF	5.54	3.88	9.42	2.84	8.38
04.3500 225	Caulk, mildew resistant, 1/8"x1/8"	LF	.12	.98	1.10	.71	.83
04.3500 235	Caulk, mildew resistant, 1/2"x1/2"	LF	2.17	1.94	4.11	1.42	3.59
04.3500 240	Caulk, mildew resistant, 3/4"x3/4"	LF	4.85	2.91	7.76	2.12	6.97
04.3500 245	Caulk, mildew resistant, 1"x1"	LF	7.26	3.88	11.14	2.84	10.10

CSI #	4.3 SUPPORT ITEMS Description	Unit	Material	Union Install	Union Total	Open Install	Open Total
04.3500	**CAULKING & SEALANTS (Cont.)**						
04.3500 250	Caulk, elastomeric, for concrete	LF	2.54	1.62	4.16	1.18	3.72
04.3500 255	Caulk, acoustical, butyl rubber, 1/4"x1/2"	LF	.49	2.19	2.68	1.60	2.09
04.3500 260	Sealants, self-leveling, polysulfide polymer, 1/4"x3/8"	LF	1.55	2.71	4.26	1.98	3.53
04.3500 265	Sealants, self-leveling, acrylic latex polymer, 1/4"x3/8"	LF	1.37	2.71	4.08	1.98	3.35
04.3500 270	Sealants, self-leveling, polyurethane, 1/4"x3/8"	LF	1.72	2.71	4.43	1.98	3.70

CSI #	5.1 INTERNALS, VERTICAL Description	Unit	Material	Union Install	Union Total	Open Install	Open Total
	The costs in this section include materials, labor, equipment rental, supervision, and subcontractor overhead and profit. There are no allowances for the general contractor. Costs are complete, walls are painted where applicable with allowances for rubber base and gypsum board or plaster on both sides.						
05.1105	**GYPSUM BOARD ON STUD**						
05.1105 100	Interior wall, non-rated, residential, 2"x4" wood stud 16"OC, 8' high, insulation, 5/8" gypsum board, both sides, painted, rubber base	SF	3.02	5.11	8.13	3.67	6.69
05.1105 120	Interior wall, non-rated, residential, 2"x6" wood stud 16"OC, 8' high, insulation, 5/8" gypsum board, both sides, painted, rubber base	SF	3.48	5.94	9.42	4.25	7.73
05.1105 135	Interior plumbing wall, water resistant, residential, 2"x6" wood stud 16"OC, 8' high, insulation, 5/8" gypsum board, one side, painted	SF	2.68	4.35	7.03	3.07	5.75
05.1105 150	Interior shearwall, non-rated, residential, 2"x4" wood stud 16"OC, 10' high, 3/8" structural plywood, insulation, 5/8" gypsum board, both sides painted, rubber base	SF	4.04	6.95	10.99	4.94	8.98
05.1105 165	Interior shearwall, 2 hour rated, residential, 2"x6" wood stud 16"OC, 10' high, 3/8" structural plywood, insulation, 5/8" gypsum board, both sides painted, rubber base	SF	5.75	9.04	14.79	6.39	12.14
05.1105 170	Interior wall, non-rated, commercial, 2"x4" wood stud 16"OC, 8' high, insulation, 5/8" gypsum board, both sides, painted, rubber base	SF	3.33	6.89	10.22	4.92	8.25
05.1105 175	Interior wall, 1 hour rated, commercial, 2"x4" wood stud 16"OC, 10' high, insulation, 5/8" gypsum board, both sides, painted, rubber base	SF	3.46	6.80	10.26	4.84	8.30
05.1105 180	Interior wall, 2 hour rated, commercial, 2"x4" wood stud 16"OC, 10' high, insulation, 5/8" gypsum board, both sides, painted, rubber base	SF	4.78	7.68	12.46	5.44	10.22
05.1105 190	Interior wall, non-rated, commercial, 2"x6" wood stud 16"OC, 8' high, insulation, 5/8" gypsum board, both sides, painted, rubber base	SF	3.91	7.93	11.84	5.64	9.55
05.1105 195	Interior wall, 1 hour rated, commercial, 2"x6" wood stud 16"OC, 10' high, insulation, 5/8" gypsum board, both sides, painted, rubber base	SF	3.94	8.09	12.03	5.75	9.69
05.1105 200	Interior wall, 2 hour rated, commercial, 2"x6" wood stud 16"OC, 10' high, insulation, 5/8" gypsum board, both sides, painted, rubber base	SF	5.26	8.97	14.23	6.35	11.61
05.1105 205	Interior plumbing wall, water resistant, commercial, 2"x6" wood stud 16"OC, 8' high, insulation, 5/8" water resistant gypsum board, one side, painted	SF	3.06	5.69	8.75	4.00	7.06
05.1105 220	Interior shearwall, non-rated, commercial, 2"x4" wood stud 16"OC, 3/8" structural plywood, insulation, 5/8" gypsum board, both sides, painted, rubber base	SF	4.34	8.72	13.06	6.18	10.52
05.1105 225	Interior shearwall, 2 hour rated, commercial, 2"x4" wood stud 16"OC, 3/8" structural plywood, insulation, 5/8" gypsum board, both sides, painted, rubber base	SF	5.66	9.60	15.26	6.78	12.44
05.1105 230	Interior shearwall, non-rated, commercial, 2"x6" wood stud 16"OC, 3/8" structural plywood, insulation, 5/8" gypsum board, both sides, painted, rubber base	SF	4.82	10.01	14.83	7.09	11.91
05.1105 235	Interior shearwall, 2 hour rated, commercial, 2"x6" wood stud 16"OC, 3/8" structural plywood, insulation, 5/8" gypsum board, both sides, painted, rubber base	SF	6.14	10.89	17.03	7.69	13.83
05.1105 240	Interior wall, non-rated, institutional, 2"x4" wood stud 16"OC, 8' high, insulation, 5/8" gypsum board, both sides, painted, rubber base	SF	3.65	7.54	11.19	5.37	9.02
05.1105 245	Interior wall, 1 hour rated, institutional, 2"x4" wood stud 16"OC, 10' high, insulation, 5/8" gypsum board, both sides, painted, rubber base	SF	3.65	7.45	11.10	5.29	8.94
05.1105 250	Interior wall, 2 hour rated, institutional, 2"x4" wood stud 16"OC, 10' high, insulation, 5/8" gypsum board, both sides, painted, rubber base	SF	5.13	8.05	13.18	5.71	10.84
05.1105 255	Interior plumbing wall, water resistant, institutional, 2"x4" wood stud 16"OC, 8' high, insulation, 5/8" gypsum board, one side, painted	SF	2.67	5.06	7.73	3.56	6.23
05.1105 260	Interior wall, non-rated, institutional, 2"x6" wood stud 16"OC, 8' high, insulation, 5/8" gypsum board, both sides, painted, rubber base	SF	4.27	8.66	12.93	6.14	10.41

CSI #	**5.1 INTERNALS, VERTICAL** Description	Unit	Material	Union Install	Union Total	Open Install	Open Total
05.1105	**GYPSUM BOARD ON STUD (Cont.)**						
05.1105 265	Interior wall, 1 hour rated, institutional, 2"x6" wood stud 16"OC, 10' high, insulation, 5/8" gypsum board, both sides, painted, rubber base	SF	4.17	8.83	13.00	6.27	10.44
05.1105 270	Interior wall, 2 hour rated, institutional, 2"x6" wood stud 16"OC, 10' high, insulation, 5/8" gypsum board, both sides, painted, rubber base	SF	5.65	9.43	15.08	6.69	12.34
05.1105 275	Interior plumbing wall, water resistant, institutional, 2"x6" wood stud 16"OC, 8' high, insulation, 5/8" gypsum board, one side, painted	SF	4.44	8.34	12.78	5.87	10.31
05.1105 290	Interior shearwall, non-rated, institutional, 2"x4" wood studs 16" OC, 3/8" structural plywood, 10' high, insulation, 5/8" gypsum board, both sides, painted, rubber base	SF	4.53	9.37	13.90	6.63	11.16
05.1105 295	Interior shearwall, 2 hour rated institutional, 2"x4" wood studs 16" OC, 3/8" structural plywood, 10' high, insulation, 5/8" gypsum board, both sides, painted, rubber base	SF	6.01	9.97	15.98	7.05	13.06
05.1105 300	Interior shearwall, non-rated institutional, 2"x6" wood studs 16" OC, 3/8" structural plywood, 10' high, insulation, 5/8" gypsum board, both sides, painted, rubber base	SF	5.05	10.75	15.80	7.61	12.66
05.1105 305	Interior shearwall, 2 hour rated institutional, 2"x6" wood studs 16" OC, 3/8" structural plywood, 10' high, insulation, 5/8" gypsum board, both sides, painted, rubber base	SF	6.53	11.35	17.88	8.03	14.56
05.1105 310	Interior partitions, non-rated commercial, drywall studs 25 GA 3 5/8", insulation, 5/8" gypsum board, both sides, painted, rubber base	SF	2.97	6.55	9.52	4.65	7.62
05.1105 315	Interior partitions, 1 hour rated commercial, drywall studs 25 GA 3 5/8", insulation, 5/8" gypsum board, both sides, painted, rubber base	SF	3.21	6.55	9.76	4.65	7.86
05.1105 320	Interior partitions, 2 hour rated commercial, drywall studs 25 GA 3 5/8", insulation, 5/8" gypsum board, both sides, painted, rubber base	SF	4.46	7.25	11.71	5.13	9.59
05.1105 325	Interior plumbing wall, water resistant, commercial, drywall studs 25 GA 3 5/8", insulation, 5/8" gypsum board, one side, painted	SF	1.87	4.13	6.00	2.89	4.76
05.1105 330	Interior chase wall, 1 hour rated, commercial, drywall studs 25 GA 3 5/8", insulation, 5/8" gypsum board, one side, painted, rubber base	SF	2.06	4.26	6.32	3.00	5.06
05.1105 335	Interior chase wall, 2 hour rated, commercial, drywall studs 25 GA 3 5/8", insulation, 5/8" gypsum board, one side, painted, rubber base	SF	2.72	4.70	7.42	3.30	6.02
05.1105 375	Interior partitions, non-rated, institutional, drywall studs 25 GA 3 5/8", insulation, 5/8" gypsum board, both sides, painted, rubber base	SF	3.19	6.99	10.18	4.95	8.14
05.1105 380	Interior partitions, 1 hour rated, institutional, drywall studs 25 GA 3 5/8", insulation, 5/8" gypsum board, both sides, painted, rubber base	SF	3.33	7.04	10.37	4.99	8.32
05.1105 385	Interior partitions, 2 hour rated, institutional, drywall studs 25 GA 3 5/8", insulation, 5/8" gypsum board, both sides, painted, rubber base	SF	4.74	7.46	12.20	5.29	10.03
05.1105 390	Interior plumbing wall, water resistant, institutional, drywall studs 25 GA 3 5/8", insulation, 5/8" gypsum board, one side, painted	SF	1.99	4.38	6.37	3.06	5.05
05.1105 400	Interior chase wall, 2 hour rated, institutional, drywall studs 25 GA 3 5/8", insulation, 5/8" gypsum board, one side, painted, rubber base	SF	2.86	4.81	7.67	3.38	6.24
05.1105 440	Interior structural wall, non-rated, commercial, studs 14 GA 3 5/8", insulation, 5/8" gypsum board, both sides, painted, rubber base	SF	4.38	8.42	12.80	5.65	10.03
05.1105 450	Interior structural wall, 2 hour rated, commercial, studs 14 GA 3 5/8", insulation, 5/8" gypsum board, both sides, painted, rubber base	SF	5.94	9.30	15.24	6.25	12.19
05.1105 500	Interior shaft wall, 1 hour rated, commercial, studs CH 20 GA 4", insulation, 5/8" gypsum board, one side, 1/2" ashpalt core sheathing, one side, paint one side, rubber base	SF	3.86	7.25	11.11	4.74	8.60
05.1105 510	Interior structural wall, non-rated, institutional, studs 14 GA 3 5/8", insulation, 5/8" gypsum board, both sides, painted, rubber base	SF	4.62	8.91	13.53	5.99	10.61
05.1105 520	Interior structural wall, 2 hour rated, institutional, studs 14 GA 3 5/8", insulation, 5/8" gypsum board, both sides, painted, rubber base	SF	6.22	9.51	15.73	6.41	12.63
05.1105 575	Interior shaft wall, 1 hour rated, institutional, studs CH 25 GA 4", insulation, 5/8" gypsum board, one side, 1/2" asphalt core sheathing, one side, paint one side, rubber base	SF	3.32	7.65	10.97	5.02	8.34
05.1105 580	Column enclosure, non-rated, commercial, drywall studs 25 GA 1 5/8", 5/8" gypsum board, painted, rubber base	SF	2.84	4.95	7.79	3.50	6.34

CSI #	5.1 INTERNALS, VERTICAL Description	Unit	Material	Union Install	Union Total	Open Install	Open Total
05.1105	**GYPSUM BOARD ON STUD (Cont.)**						
05.1105 590	Column enclosure, 2 hour rated, commercial, drywall studs 25 GA 1 5/8", 5/8" gypsum board, painted, rubber base	SF	3.62	5.39	9.01	3.80	7.42
05.1110	**LATH AND PLASTER ON STUD**						
05.1110 100	Interior wall, non-rated, residential, 2"x4" wood stud 16"OC, 8' high, insulation, lath & plaster, both sides, painted, rubber base	SF	7.23	10.68	17.91	7.21	14.44
05.1110 120	Interior wall, non-rated, residential, 2"x6" wood stud 16"OC, 8' high, insulation, lath & plaster, both sides, painted, rubber base	SF	7.69	11.51	19.20	7.79	15.48
05.1110 135	Interior plumbing wall, residential, 2"x6" wood stud 16"OC, 8' high, insulation, lath & plaster, one side, painted	SF	4.60	7.39	11.99	5.04	9.64
05.1110 150	Interior shearwall, non-rated, residential, 2"x4" wood stud 16"OC, 10' high, 3/8" structural plywood, insulation, lath & plaster, both sides painted, rubber base	SF	8.12	12.75	20.87	8.64	16.76
05.1110 160	Interior shearwall, non-rated, residential, 2"x6" wood stud 16"OC, 10' high, 3/8" structural plywood, insulation, lath & plaster, both sides painted, rubber base	SF	8.55	13.91	22.46	9.46	18.01
05.1110 170	Interior wall, non-rated, commercial, 2"x4" wood stud 16"OC, 8' high, insulation, lath & plaster, both sides, painted, rubber base	SF	8.60	12.22	20.82	8.24	16.84
05.1110 175	Interior wall, 1 hour rated, commercial, 2"x4" wood stud 16"OC, 10' high, insulation, furring, lath & plaster, both sides, painted, rubber base	SF	9.77	14.29	24.06	9.48	19.25
05.1110 190	non-rated, commercial, 2"x6" wood stud 16"OC, 8' high, insulation, lath & plaster, both sides, painted, rubber base	SF	9.18	13.26	22.44	8.96	18.14
05.1110 195	Interior wall, 1 hour rated, commercial, 2"x6" wood stud 16"OC, 10' high, insulation, furring, lath & plaster, both sides, painted, rubber base	SF	10.25	15.58	25.83	10.39	20.64
05.1110 205	Interior plumbing wall, commercial, 2"x6" wood stud 16"OC, 8' high, insulation, lath & plaster, one side, painted	SF	5.51	8.36	13.87	5.67	11.18
05.1110 220	Interior shearwall, non-rated, commercial, 2"x4" wood stud 16"OC, 3/8" structural plywood, insulation, lath & plaster, both sides, painted, rubber base	SF	9.37	14.05	23.42	9.50	18.87
05.1110 230	Interior shearwall, non-rated, commercial, 2"x6" wood stud 16"OC, 3/8" structural plywood, insulation, lath & plaster, both sides, painted, rubber base	SF	9.85	15.34	25.19	10.41	20.26
05.1110 240	Interior wall, non-rated, institutional, 2"x4" wood stud 16"OC, 8' high, insulation, lath & plaster, both sides, painted, rubber base	SF	13.99	13.02	27.01	8.76	22.75
05.1110 245	Interior wall, 1 hour rated, institutional, 2"x4" wood stud 16"OC, 10' high, insulation, furring, lath & plaster, both sides, painted, rubber base	SF	15.15	15.09	30.24	10.00	25.15
05.1110 255	Interior plumbing wall, institutional, 2"x4" wood stud 16"OC, 8' high, insulation, lath & plaster, one side, painted	SF	7.66	7.80	15.46	5.26	12.92
05.1110 260	Interior wall, non-rated, institutional, 2"x6" wood stud 16"OC, 8' high, insulation, lath & plaster, both sides, painted, rubber base	SF	14.61	14.14	28.75	9.53	24.14
05.1110 265	Interior wall, 1 hour rated, institutional, 2"x6" wood stud 16"OC, 10' high, insulation, furring, lath & plaster, both sides, painted, rubber base	SF	15.67	16.47	32.14	10.98	26.65
05.1110 275	Interior plumbing wall, institutional, 2"x6" wood stud 16"OC, 8' high, insulation, lath & plaster, one side, painted	SF	8.51	9.31	17.82	6.34	14.85
05.1110 290	Interior shearwall, non-rated, institutional, 2"x4" wood studs 16" OC, 3/8" structural plywood, 10' high, insulation, lath & plaster, both sides, painted, rubber base	SF	14.75	14.85	29.60	10.02	24.77
05.1110 300	Interior shearwall, non-rated institutional, 2"x6" wood studs 16" OC, 3/8" structural plywood, 10' high, insulation, lath & plaster, both sides, painted, rubber base	SF	15.27	16.23	31.50	11.00	26.27
05.1110 310	Interior partitions, non-rated commercial, drywall studs 25 GA 3 5/8", insulation, lath & plaster, both sides, painted, rubber base	SF	8.17	11.70	19.87	7.85	16.02

CSI #	5.1 INTERNALS, VERTICAL Description	Unit	Material	Union Install	Union Total	Open Install	Open Total
05.1110	**LATH AND PLASTER ON STUD (Cont.)**						
05.1110 315	Interior partitions, 1 hour rated commercial, drywall studs 25 GA 3 5/8", insulation, furring, lath & plaster, both sides, painted, rubber base	SF	9.45	13.86	23.31	9.17	18.62
05.1110 325	Interior plumbing wall, commercial, drywall studs 25 GA 3 5/8", insulation, lath & plaster, one side, painted	SF	7.14	7.10	14.24	4.75	11.89
05.1110 330	Interior chase wall, 1 hour rated, commercial, drywall studs 25 GA 3 5/8", insulation, furring, lath & plaster, one side, painted, rubber base	SF	4.64	7.47	12.11	4.98	9.62
05.1110 375	Interior partitions, non-rated, institutional, drywall studs 25 GA 3 5/8", insulation, lath & plaster, both sides, painted, rubber base	SF	13.46	12.31	25.77	8.24	21.70
05.1110 380	Interior partitions, 1 hour rated, institutional, drywall studs 25 GA 3 5/8", insulation, furring, lath & plaster, both sides, painted, rubber base	SF	14.76	14.50	29.26	9.58	24.34
05.1110 390	Interior plumbing wall, institutional, drywall studs 25 GA 3 5/8", insulation, lath & plaster, one side, painted	SF	7.15	7.12	14.27	4.76	11.91
05.1110 395	Interior chase wall, 1 hour rated, institutional, drywall studs 25 GA 3 5/8", insulation, furring, lath & plaster, one side, painted, rubber base	SF	7.86	8.33	16.19	5.53	13.39
05.1110 455	Interior structural wall, non-rated, commercial, studs 16 GA 3 5/8", insulation, lath & plaster, both sides, painted, rubber base	SF	9.14	13.75	22.89	8.97	18.11
05.1110 460	Interior structural wall, 1 hour rated, commercial, studs 16 GA 3 5/8", insulation, lath & plaster, both sides, painted, rubber base	SF	9.14	13.75	22.89	8.97	18.11
05.1110 500	Interior shaft wall, 1 hour rated, commercial, studs CH 20 GA 4", insulation, lath & plaster, one side, 1/2" ashpalt core sheathing, one side, paint one side, rubber base	SF	6.37	9.92	16.29	6.41	12.78
05.1110 510	Interior structural wall, non-rated, institutional, studs 14 GA 3 5/8", insulation, lath & plaster, both sides, painted, rubber base	SF	14.96	14.39	29.35	9.38	24.34
05.1110 545	Interior structural wall, 1 hour rated, institutional, studs 14 GA 3 5/8", insulation, lath & plaster, both sides, painted, rubber base	SF	14.96	14.39	29.35	9.38	24.34
05.1110 575	Interior shaft wall, 1 hour rated, institutional, studs CH 25 GA 4", insulation, lath & plaster, one side, 1/2" asphalt core sheathing, one side, paint one side, rubber base	SF	8.42	10.39	18.81	6.72	15.14
05.1110 580	Column furring, non-rated, commercial, drywall studs 25 GA 1 5/8", lath & plaster painted, rubber base	SF	5.40	7.43	12.83	5.02	10.42
05.1110 610	Column furring, non-rated, institutional, drywall studs 25 GA 1 5/8", lath & plaster, painted, rubber base	SF	8.05	7.75	15.80	5.22	13.27
05.1115	**CONCRETE BLOCK**						
05.1115 105	Concrete masonry unit, 4"x8"x16", #4 bar, 32" on center, both ways, unfilled	SF	8.96	6.17	15.13	3.43	12.39
05.1115 110	Concrete masonry unit, 6"x8"x16", #4 bar, 32" on center, both ways, unfilled	SF	10.40	6.62	17.02	3.69	14.09
05.1115 115	Concrete masonry unit, 8"x8"x16", #4 bar, 32" on center, both ways, unfilled	SF	10.94	7.00	17.94	3.90	14.84
05.1115 120	Concrete masonry unit, 12"x8"x16", #4 bar, 32" on center, both ways, unfilled	SF	17.01	7.81	24.82	4.35	21.36
05.1115 125	Concrete masonry unit, 4"x8"x16", #4 bar, 32" on center, both ways, filled	SF	9.49	6.63	16.12	3.69	13.18
05.1115 130	Concrete masonry unit, 6"x8"x16", #4 bar, 32" on center, both ways, filled	SF	11.98	6.78	18.76	3.77	15.75
05.1115 135	Concrete masonry unit, 8"x8"x16", #4 bar, 32" on center, both ways, filled	SF	12.87	7.16	20.03	3.98	16.85
05.1115 140	Concrete masonry unit, 12"x8"x16", #4 bar, 32" on center, both ways, filled	SF	16.24	8.67	24.91	4.83	21.07
05.1115 145	Concrete masonry unit, 8"x4"x16", #4 bar, 32" on center, both ways, filled	SF	18.44	9.43	27.87	5.25	23.69
05.1115 150	Concrete masonry unit, 12"x4"x16", #4 bar, 32" on center, both ways, filled	SF	20.22	10.91	31.13	6.08	26.30

CSI #	5.1 INTERNALS, VERTICAL Description	Unit	Material	Union Install	Union Total	Open Install	Open Total
05.1115	**CONCRETE BLOCK (Cont.)**						
05.1115 155	Concrete masonry unit, grout lock, 6"x8"x24", #4 bar, filled	SF	12.84	4.60	17.44	2.56	15.40
05.1115 160	Concrete masonry unit, grout lock, 8"x8"x16", #4 bar, filled	SF	13.57	5.58	19.15	3.11	16.68
05.1115 165	Concrete masonry unit, grout lock, 12"x8"x16", #4 bar, filled	SF	17.44	6.62	24.06	3.69	21.13
05.1115 170	Concrete masonry unit, slumpstone, 8"x4"x16", #4 bar, filled	SF	22.31	10.16	32.47	5.66	27.97
05.1115 175	Concrete masonry unit, slumpstone, 8"x8"x16", #4 bar, filled	SF	17.36	8.54	25.90	4.76	22.12
05.1115 180	Concrete masonry unit, splitface, 8"x4"x16", #4 bar, filled	SF	20.16	10.15	30.31	5.65	25.81
05.1115 185	Concrete masonry unit, glazed 1 side, 4"x8"x16", reinforced, filled	SF	15.20	9.42	24.62	5.24	20.44
05.1115 190	Concrete masonry unit, glazed 1 side, 6"x8"x16", reinforced, filled	SF	17.49	10.07	27.56	5.61	23.10
05.1115 195	Concrete masonry unit, glazed 1 side, 8"x8"x16", reinforced, filled	SF	20.47	10.92	31.39	6.08	26.55
05.1115 200	Concrete masonry unit, glazed 1 side, 4"x4"x16", reinforced, filled	SF	22.52	10.77	33.29	6.00	28.52
05.1115 205	Concrete masonry unit, glazed 1 side, 6"x4"x16", reinforced, filled	SF	26.30	12.51	38.81	6.97	33.27
05.1115 210	Concrete masonry unit, glazed 1 side, 8"x4"x16", reinforced, filled	SF	30.05	13.30	43.35	7.41	37.46
05.1115 215	Concrete masonry unit, glazed 1 side, 12"x8"x16", reinforced, filled	SF	24.74	15.50	40.24	8.63	33.37
05.1115 220	Concrete masonry unit, add for glazing both sides,	SF	8.19		8.19		8.19
05.1115 225	Concrete masonry unit, screen block, 4"x12"x12"	SF	8.72	7.98	16.70	4.44	13.16
05.1115 250	add for pilasters	SF	33.13		33.13		33.13
05.1115 255	add for sill blocks	LF	3.57	6.09	9.66	3.39	6.96
05.1115 260	add for cutting blocks	LF	4.12	10.01	14.13	5.58	9.70
05.1115 265	add for bond beams	LF	7.85	13.54	21.39	7.54	15.39
05.1115 270	add for lintels, over openings	LF	15.32	22.89	38.21	12.75	28.07
05.1120	**STRUCTURAL TILE**						
05.1120 100	Structural tile, glazed 1 side, 2"x6"x12"	SF	6.23	11.61	17.84	6.46	12.69
05.1120 105	Structural tile, glazed 1 side, 4"x6"x12"	SF	9.17	13.26	22.43	7.38	16.55
05.1120 110	Structural tile, glazed 2 side, 4"x6"x12"	SF	10.65	15.28	25.93	8.51	19.16
05.1120 115	Structural tile, glazed 1 side, 6"x6"x12"	SF	8.81	13.99	22.80	7.79	16.60
05.1120 120	Structural tile, glazed 1 side, 3"x6"x12"	SF	6.51	13.47	19.98	7.50	14.01
05.1120 125	Structural tile, glazed 1 side, base	LF	8.85	13.47	22.32	7.50	16.35
05.1120 127	Structural tile, glazed 2 side, cap	SF	8.61	13.69	22.30	7.62	16.23
05.1120 130	Structural tile, clay backing, load bearing, 4"x12"x12"	SF	2.98	6.86	9.84	3.82	6.80
05.1120 135	Structural tile, clay backing, load bearing, 6"x12"x12"	SF	3.46	7.53	10.99	4.19	7.65
05.1120 140	Structural tile, clay backing, load bearing, 8"x12"x12"	SF	3.97	8.43	12.40	4.69	8.66
05.1120 145	Structural tile, clay backing, non-load bearing, 4"x12"x12"	SF	2.92	6.18	9.10	3.44	6.36
05.1120 150	Structural tile, clay backing, non-load bearing, 6"x12"x12"	SF	3.10	6.87	9.97	3.82	6.92
05.1120 155	Structural tile, clay backing, non-load bearing, 8"x12"x12"	SF	4.89	7.52	12.41	4.19	9.08
05.1125	**WALL FINISHES**						
05.1125 100	Wall finish, Granite, 3/4" thick	SF	24.96	25.56	50.52	20.45	45.41
05.1125 105	Wall finish, Granite, 1-1/4" thick	SF	25.59	28.64	54.23	22.91	48.50
05.1125 110	Wall finish, Limestone, 2" thick	SF	17.60	25.69	43.29	20.55	38.15
05.1125 115	Wall finish, Limestone, 3" thick	SF	18.71	32.13	50.84	25.70	44.41
05.1125 120	Wall finish, Marble, 7/8" thick	SF	23.86	25.31	49.17	20.25	44.11
05.1125 125	Wall finish, Marble, 1-1/4" thick	SF	27.28	28.22	55.50	22.58	49.86
05.1125 130	Wall finish, Travertine,	SF	20.78	24.95	45.73	13.89	34.67
05.1125 135	Wall finish, Travertine, base 9"x3/4"	SF	29.62	35.42	65.04	19.72	49.34
05.1125 145	Wall finish, Sandstone, 2" thick	SF	15.50	23.42	38.92	13.04	28.54
05.1125 147	Wall finish, Sandstone, 3" thick	SF	18.38	26.06	44.44	14.51	32.89

CSI #	5.1 INTERNALS, VERTICAL Description	Unit	Material	Union Install	Union Total	Open Install	Open Total
05.1125	**WALL FINISHES (Cont.)**						
05.1125 155	Wall cover, paper hanging, normal conditions	SF		.89	.89	.69	.69
05.1125 160	Wall cover, wall paper, 36 SF/roll,	ROLL	32.06	26.17	58.23	20.39	52.45
05.1125 165	Wall cover, vinyl, 7oz, light	SF	1.72	.57	2.29	.45	2.17
05.1125 170	Wall cover, vinyl, 14oz, medium	SF	1.88	.73	2.61	.57	2.45
05.1125 175	Wall cover, vinyl, 22oz, heavy	SF	2.14	.84	2.98	.65	2.79
05.1125 180	Wall cover, vinyl, 14oz, aluminum back	SF	1.58	2.14	3.72	1.66	3.24
05.1125 185	Wall cover, linen, acrylic back	SF	1.34	1.14	2.48	.89	2.23
05.1125 190	Wall cover, glass cloth	SF	1.46	.79	2.25	.61	2.07
05.1125 195	Wall cover, felt	SF	2.54	1.61	4.15	1.26	3.80
05.1125 200	Wall cover, cork sheating, 1/8"	SF	2.02	1.61	3.63	1.26	3.28
05.1125 205	Wall cover, flexible wood, veneer	SF	4.81	2.91	7.72	2.27	7.08
05.1125 210	Laminated plastics, standard patterns & colors, w/o backing, adhesive 1/16"	SF	2.22	2.08	4.30	1.62	3.84
05.1125 230	Wall cover, hardboard, photo repro, w/o backing, plastic, 1/8", trim	SF	2.58	1.30	3.88	1.01	3.59
05.1125 235	Wall cover, hardboard, photo repro, w/o backing, plastic, 1/4", trim	SF	3.42	1.30	4.72	1.01	4.43
05.1125 240	Wall cover, pegboard, photo repro, w/o backing, plastic, 1/4", trim	SF	.78	1.30	2.08	1.01	1.79
05.1125 245	Wall cover, pegboard, photo repro, w/o backing, plastic, 1/8", trim	SF	.85	1.30	2.15	1.01	1.86
05.1125 250	Wall covering, tile, plastic tile, 4 1/4"x4 1/4"x.11"	SF	1.68	2.08	3.76	1.62	3.30
05.1125 255	Wall covering, tile, plastic tile, 4 1/4"x4 1/4"x.05"	SF	1.08	2.08	3.16	1.62	2.70
05.1125 260	Wall covering, tile, aluminum tile, 4 1/2"x4 1/2"	SF	7.53	2.49	10.02	1.94	9.47
05.1125 265	Wall covering, tile, copper/aluminum tile, 4 1/4"x4 1/4"	SF	7.53	2.49	10.02	1.94	9.47
05.1125 270	Wall covering, tile, stain steel tile, 4 1/4"x4 1/4"	SF	15.31	2.95	18.26	2.30	17.61
05.1125 275	Wainscote, galvanized sheet metal	SF	1.31	2.09	3.40	1.24	2.55
05.1125 280	Wall covering, ceramic tile, 1"x 1", mortar	SF	5.82	9.60	15.42	7.68	13.50
05.1125 285	Wall covering, ceramic tile, 1"x 1", mastic	SF	5.73	4.98	10.71	3.98	9.71
05.1125 290	Wall covering, ceramic tile, 2"x 1", mortar	SF	5.51	7.89	13.40	6.31	11.82
05.1125 295	Wall covering, ceramic tile, 2"x 1", mastic	SF	5.38	4.42	9.80	3.53	8.91
05.1125 300	Wall covering, ceramic tile, 4"x 4", mortar	SF	5.13	7.69	12.82	6.16	11.29
05.1125 305	Wall covering, ceramic tile, 4"x 4", mastic	SF	5.04	4.42	9.46	3.53	8.57
05.1125 310	Wall covering, ceramic tile, 6"x 3", mortar	SF	5.51	7.49	13.00	5.99	11.50
05.1125 315	Wall covering, ceramic tile, 6"x 3", mastic	SF	5.38	3.81	9.19	3.05	8.43
05.1125 320	Wall covering, ceramic tile, 6"x 4", mortar	SF	5.38	6.89	12.27	5.51	10.89
05.1125 325	Wall covering, ceramic tile, 6"x 4", mastic	SF	5.38	3.68	9.06	2.94	8.32
05.1125 330	Wall painting, concrete, prime	SF	.04	.32	.36	.25	.29
05.1125 332	Wall painting, concrete, prime + 1 finished	SF	.12	.59	.71	.46	.58
05.1125 335	Wall painting, concrete, prime + 2 finished	SF	.22	.95	1.17	.74	.96
05.1125 340	Wall painting, gypsum wall board , prime brush	SF	.04	.32	.36	.25	.29
05.1125 345	Wall painting, gypsum wall board , prime + 1 finished, roll	SF	.12	.40	.52	.31	.43
05.1125 350	Wall painting, gypsum wall board , prime + 2 finished, roll	SF	.22	.63	.85	.49	.71
05.1125 355	Wall painting, plaster, prime, roll	SF	.04	.21	.25	.16	.20
05.1125 360	Wall painting, plaster, prime + 1 finished, roll	SF	.12	.40	.52	.31	.43
05.1125 365	Wall painting, plaster, prime + 2 finished, roll	SF	.22	.63	.85	.49	.71
05.1125 370	Concrete block painting, prime, brush	SF	.04	.35	.39	.28	.32
05.1125 375	Concrete block painting, prime + 1 finished, brush	SF	.14	.68	.82	.53	.67
05.1125 380	Concrete block painting, prime + 2 finished, brush	SF	.24	1.00	1.24	.78	1.02

CSI #	5.1 INTERNALS, VERTICAL Description	Unit	Material	Union Install	Union Total	Open Install	Open Total
05.1125	**WALL FINISHES (Cont.)**						
05.1125 385	Concrete block painting, prime, roll	SF	.04	.24	.28	.18	.22
05.1125 390	Concrete block painting, prime + 1 finished, roll	SF	.14	.45	.59	.35	.49
05.1125 395	Concrete block painting, prime + 2 finished, roll	SF	.24	.67	.91	.52	.76
05.1125 400	Sheet metal painting, prime	SF	.08	.59	.67	.46	.54
05.1125 405	Sheet metal painting, prime + 1 finished	SF	.14	1.02	1.16	.80	.94
05.1125 410	Sheet metal painting, prime + 2 finished	SF	.20	1.54	1.74	1.20	1.40
05.1125 415	Wood trim painting, prime	SF	.09	.35	.44	.28	.37
05.1125 420	Wood trim painting, prime + 1 finished	SF	.20	.65	.85	.51	.71
05.1125 425	Wood trim painting, prime + 2 finished	SF	.26	.99	1.25	.77	1.03
05.1200	**DOORS, INCLUDING HARDWARE**						
05.1200 105	Door, hollow metal, stock, hardware, painted, door 18 GA, frame 16 GA, 3'0"x7'0", non-rated	EACH	672.76	349.17	1,021.93	257.02	929.78
05.1200 115	Door, hollow metal, stock, hardware, painted, door 18 GA, frame 16 GA, 4'0"x8'0", non-rated	EACH	733.94	415.57	1,149.51	305.51	1,039.45
05.1200 125	Door, hollow metal, stock, hardware, painted, door 18 GA, frame 16 GA, 3'0"x7'0", 1 hour rated	EACH	725.77	349.17	1,074.94	257.02	982.79
05.1200 135	Door, hollow metal, stock, hardware, painted, door 18 GA, frame 16 GA, 4'0"x8'0", 1 hour rated	EACH	786.95	415.57	1,202.52	305.51	1,092.46
05.1200 145	Door, hollow metal, stock, hardware, painted, door 18 GA, frame 16 GA, 3'0"x7'0", 3 hour rated	EACH	849.35	349.17	1,198.52	257.02	1,106.37
05.1200 155	Door, hollow metal, stock, hardware, painted, door 18 GA, frame 16 GA, 4'0"x8'0", 3 hour rated	EACH	786.95	415.57	1,202.52	305.51	1,092.46
05.1200 165	Door, hollow metal, custom, hardware, painted, door 18 GA, frame 16 GA, 3'0"x7'0", non-rated	EACH	801.63	349.17	1,150.80	257.02	1,058.65
05.1200 175	Door, hollow metal, custom, hardware, painted, door 18 GA, frame 16 GA, 4'0"x8'0", non-rated	EACH	913.01	415.57	1,328.58	305.51	1,218.52
05.1200 185	Door, hollow metal, custom, hardware, painted, door 18 GA, frame 16 GA, 3'0"x7'0", 1 hour rated	EACH	860.80	374.16	1,234.96	275.27	1,136.07
05.1200 195	Door, hollow metal, custom, hardware, painted, door 18 GA, frame 16 GA, 4'0"x8'0", 1 hour rated	EACH	966.02	415.57	1,381.59	305.51	1,271.53
05.1200 205	Door, hollow metal, custom, hardware, painted, door 18 GA, frame 16 GA, 3'0"x7'0", 3 hour rated	EACH	978.22	349.17	1,327.39	257.02	1,235.24
05.1200 215	Door, hollow metal, custom, hardware, painted, door 18 GA, frame 16 GA, 4'0"x8'0", 3 hour rated	EACH	966.02	415.57	1,381.59	305.51	1,271.53
05.1200 220	Door, hollow metal, institutional, hardware, painted, door 16 GA, frame 14 GA, 3'0"x7'0", non-rated	EACH	898.12	393.03	1,291.15	289.05	1,187.17
05.1200 230	Door, hollow metal, institutional, hardware, painted, door 16 GA, frame 14 GA, 4'0"x7'0", non-rated	EACH	1,027.67	413.96	1,441.63	304.33	1,332.00
05.1200 235	Door, hollow metal, institutional, hardware, painted, door 16 GA, frame 14 GA, 3'0"x7'0", 1 hour rated	EACH	901.72	400.74	1,302.46	294.68	1,196.40
05.1200 245	Door, hollow metal, institutional, hardware, painted, door 16 GA, frame 14 GA, 4'0"x7'0", 1 hour rated	EACH	1,080.68	413.96	1,494.64	304.33	1,385.01
05.1200 250	Door, hollow metal, institutional, hardware, painted, door 16 GA, frame 14 GA, 3'0"x7'0", 3 hour rated	EACH	1,076.31	393.03	1,469.34	289.05	1,365.36
05.1200 260	Door, hollow metal, institutional, hardware, painted, door 16 GA, frame 14 GA, 4'0"x7'0", 3 hour rated	EACH	1,204.26	413.96	1,618.22	304.33	1,508.59
05.1200 265	Add for galvanizing	EACH	59.95		59.95		59.95
05.1200 267	Add for baked enamel	EACH	20.21		20.21		20.21
05.1200 270	Add for porcelain	EACH	166.18		166.18		166.18
05.1200 272	Add for 10" x 10" vision light	EACH	87.98		87.98		87.98
05.1200 274	Add for half glass opening	EACH	109.87		109.87		109.87

CSI #	5.1 INTERNALS, VERTICAL Description	Unit	Material	Union Install	Union Total	Open Install	Open Total
05.1200	**DOORS, INCLUDING HARDWARE (Cont.)**						
05.1200 275	Door, wood, commercial, door and frame, hardware, solid core, prehung, 3'0"x6'8", painted	EACH	220.34	156.60	376.94	115.31	335.65
05.1200 285	Door, wood, commercial, door and frame, hardware, solid core, prehung, 3'6"x6'8", painted	EACH	235.06	156.60	391.66	115.31	350.37
05.1200 290	Door, wood, commercial, door and frame, hardware, solid core, prehung, 3'0"x7'0", painted	EACH	235.03	165.41	400.44	121.74	356.77
05.1200 295	Door, wood, commercial, solid core, hardware, job hung, metal frame 16 GA, 2'8"x6'8", painted	EACH	552.01	459.30	1,011.31	337.45	889.46
05.1200 305	Door, wood, commercial, solid core, hardware, job hung, metal frame 16 GA, 3'0"x7'0", painted	EACH	535.40	468.11	1,003.51	343.89	879.29
05.1200 310	Door, wood, commercial, solid core, hardware, job hung, metal frame 16 GA, 3'6"x7'0", painted	EACH	574.68	475.82	1,050.50	349.52	924.20
05.1200 335	Door, wood, institutional, solid core, hardware, job hung, metal frame 14 GA, 3'0"x7'0", painted	EACH	783.36	503.16	1,286.52	369.48	1,152.84
05.1200 340	Door, wood, institutional, solid core, hardware, job hung, metal frame 14 GA, 3'6"x7'0", painted	EACH	795.79	503.16	1,298.95	369.48	1,165.27
05.1200 345	Add for formica clad	EACH	89.51		89.51		89.51
05.1200 350	Add for C label 1 hour	EACH	88.83		88.83		88.83
05.1200 355	Add for B label 1-1/2 hour	EACH	127.33		127.33		127.33
05.1200 360	Add for A label 3 hour	EACH	165.79		165.79		165.79
05.1200 365	Add for sound proof, STC 40	EACH	175.06	8.02	183.08	5.86	180.92
05.1200 370	Add for sound proof, STC 45	EACH	212.19	10.75	222.94	7.85	220.04
05.1200 375	Add for sound proof, STC 51	EACH	424.41	32.69	457.10	23.88	448.29
05.1300	**INTERNAL FENESTRATION**						
05.1300 100	Glazing, interior, clear, fixed, commercial, glass 1/4", steel frame, painted	SF	14.12	11.42	25.54	8.67	22.79
05.1300 105	Glazing, interior, tempered, fixed, commercial, glass 1/4", steel frame, painted	SF	15.74	11.42	27.16	8.67	24.41
05.1300 110	Glazing, interior, security, fixed, commercial, glass wire 1/4", steel frame, painted	SF	33.64	11.42	45.06	8.67	42.31
05.1300 115	Glazing, interior, spandrel, fixed, commercial, glass 1/4", steel frame, painted	SF	31.24	12.02	43.26	9.13	40.37
05.1300 120	Glazing, interior, obscure, fixed, commercial, glass 1/4", steel frame, painted	SF	19.70	11.42	31.12	8.67	28.37
05.1300 125	Sidelight, 2'x7', commercial, tempered glass 1/4", steel frame, painted	EACH	259.56	182.14	441.70	137.90	397.46
05.1300 130	Sidelight, 3'x7', commercial, tempered glass 1/4", steel frame, painted	EACH	389.34	273.21	662.55	206.85	596.19
05.1300 135	Glazing, interior, clear, fixed, commercial, glass 1/4", aluminun frame	SF	13.73	8.51	22.24	6.40	20.13
05.1300 140	Glazing, interior, tempered, fixed, commercial, glass 1/4", aluminum frame	SF	15.35	8.51	23.86	6.40	21.75
05.1300 145	Glazing, interior, spandrel, fixed, commercial, glass 1/4", aluminum frame	SF	30.85	9.11	39.96	6.86	37.71
05.1300 150	Glazing, interior, obscure, fixed, commercial, glass 1/4", aluminum frame	SF	19.31	8.51	27.82	6.40	25.71
05.1300 155	Sidelight, 2'x7', commercial, tempered glass 1/4", aluminum frame	EACH	255.50	141.40	396.90	106.12	361.62
05.1300 160	Sidelight, 3'x7', commercial, tempered glass 1/4", aluminum frame	EACH	383.25	212.10	595.35	159.18	542.43

CSI #	5.2 INTERNALS, HORIZONTAL Description	Unit	Material	Union Install	Union Total	Open Install	Open Total
	The costs in this section include materials, labor, equipment rental, supervision, and subcontractor overhead and profit. There are no allowances for the general contractor. Costs are complete, the suspension systems and painting are part of the ceiling costs and appropriate adhesives and finishes are included in flooring costs.						
05.2100	**CEILING**						
05.2100 100	Acoustical ceiling, suspended, 2'x2'	SF	1.93	1.59	3.52	1.16	3.09
05.2100 105	Acoustical ceiling, suspended, 2'x4'	SF	1.72	1.15	2.87	.84	2.56
05.2100 110	Acoustical ceiling, concealed spline, suspended, 1'x1'	SF	3.52	2.56	6.08	1.87	5.39
05.2100 115	Acoustical ceiling, concealed spline, suspended, 2'x2'	SF	5.39	2.41	7.80	1.76	7.15
05.2100 120	Acoustical ceiling, glue on, wood studs, 5/8" gypsum board, vinyl tile 1'x1', painted	SF	3.98	5.44	9.42	3.85	7.83
05.2100 125	Acoustical ceiling, glue on, metal studs, 5/8" gypsum board, vinyl tile 1'x1', painted	SF	3.55	4.92	8.47	3.46	7.01
05.2100 130	Gypsum board ceiling, wood frame, 5/8" gypsum board, painted	SF	1.79	4.08	5.87	2.85	4.64
05.2100 135	Gypsum board ceiling, metal frame, 5/8" gypsum board, painted	SF	1.43	3.59	5.02	2.49	3.92
05.2100 140	Acoustical ceiling, suspended, 2'x2', insulated	SF	2.27	1.98	4.25	1.44	3.71
05.2100 145	Acoustical ceiling, suspended, 2'x4', insulated	SF	2.06	1.54	3.60	1.12	3.18
05.2100 150	concealed spline, suspended, 1'x1', insulated	SF	3.86	2.95	6.81	2.15	6.01
05.2100 155	Acoustical ceiling, concealed spline, suspended, 2'x2', insulated	SF	5.73	2.80	8.53	2.04	7.77
05.2100 160	Acoustical ceiling, glue on, wood studs, 5/8" gypsum board, tile vinyl 1'x1' painted, insulated	SF	4.32	5.83	10.15	4.13	8.45
05.2100 165	glue on, metal studs, 5/8" gypsum board, tile vinyl 1'x1' painted, insulated	SF	3.89	5.31	9.20	3.74	7.63
05.2100 170	Gypsum board ceiling, wood frame, 5/8" gypsum board, painted, insulated	SF	2.13	4.47	6.60	3.13	5.26
05.2100 175	Gypsum board ceiling, framed, metal frame, 5/8" gypsum board, painted, insulated	SF	1.77	3.98	5.75	2.77	4.54
05.2200	**FLOOR, RESILIENT**						
05.2200 100	Resilient floor, tile, asphalt, 1/8", 'B'	SF	1.45	1.56	3.01	1.30	2.75
05.2200 105	Resilient floor, tile, asphalt, 1/8", 'C'	SF	1.61	1.56	3.17	1.30	2.91
05.2200 110	Resilient floor, tile, vinyl, grease resistant, 1/8"	SF	4.62	1.56	6.18	1.30	5.92
05.2200 115	Resilient floor, tile, cork, 5/16"	SF	6.58	1.56	8.14	1.30	7.88
05.2200 120	Resilient floor, tile, cork 3/16"	SF	4.38	1.56	5.94	1.30	5.68
05.2200 125	Resilient floor, tile, vinyl composition, standard 1/16"	SF	1.23	1.56	2.79	1.30	2.53
05.2200 130	Resilient floor, tile, vinyl composition, standard 3/32"	SF	1.61	1.56	3.17	1.30	2.91
05.2200 135	Resilient floor, tile, vinyl composition, standard 1/8"	SF	1.80	1.56	3.36	1.30	3.10
05.2200 140	Resilient floor, tile, vinyl composition, metallic 1/8"	SF	1.53	1.56	3.09	1.30	2.83
05.2200 145	Resilient floor, tile, vinyl solid, standard 1/16"	SF	4.29	1.56	5.85	1.30	5.59
05.2200 150	Resilient floor, tile, vinyl solid, heavy duty 1/8"	SF	6.35	1.56	7.91	1.30	7.65
05.2200 155	Resilient floor, tile, vinyl decorative, best 125"	SF	13.01	3.13	16.14	2.61	15.62
05.2200 160	Resilient floor, vinyl, 065", w/cove	SY	22.99	13.75	36.74	11.47	34.46
05.2200 165	Resilient floor, vinyl, 040", w/cove	SY	18.81	13.75	32.56	11.47	30.28
05.2200 170	Resilient floor, vinyl, metallic 065", w/cove	SY	29.13	13.75	42.88	11.47	40.60
05.2200 175	Resilient floor, vinyl, metallic 090", custom	SY	40.54	3.30	43.84	2.75	43.29
05.2200 180	Resilient floor, linoleum, standard grade, w/o cove	SY	24.86	13.74	38.60	11.46	36.32
05.2200 185	Resilient floor, polyvinylchloride, edge sealed, hot welded	SF	2.06	5.31	7.37	4.43	6.49
05.2200 190	Resilient base, top set, vinyl 2-1/2"	LF	1.05	1.29	2.34	1.08	2.13
05.2200 195	Resilient base, top set, vinyl 6"	LF	1.53	1.29	2.82	1.08	2.61

CSI #	5.2 INTERNALS, HORIZONTAL Description	Unit	Material	Union Install	Union Total	Open Install	Open Total
05.2200	**FLOOR, RESILIENT (Cont.)**						
05.2200 200	Resilient base, top set, vinyl 4"	LF	1.05	1.29	2.34	1.08	2.13
05.2200 205	Resilient base, top set, rubber 2 1/2"	LF	.66	1.29	1.95	1.08	1.74
05.2200 210	Resilient base, top set, rubber 6"	LF	2.12	1.29	3.41	1.08	3.20
05.2200 215	Resilient base, top set, rubber 4"	LF	1.52	1.29	2.81	1.08	2.60
05.2200 220	Resilient base, cove set, rubber 2-1/2"	LF	1.05	1.29	2.34	1.08	2.13
05.2200 225	Seamless floor, resilient, large area	SF	1.47	4.41	5.88	3.68	5.15
05.2200 230	Seamless floor, resilient, small area	SF	4.27	12.15	16.42	10.13	14.40
05.2200 235	Seamless floor, chemical resistant, 4" base	SF	1.79	5.31	7.10	4.43	6.22
05.2200 240	Elasto/poly cove base, large area	SF	1.47	4.41	5.88	3.68	5.15
05.2200 245	Elasto/poly cove base, small area	SF	1.73	5.13	6.86	4.28	6.01
05.2200 250	Magnesite floor, medium area	SF	3.35	5.13	8.48	4.28	7.63
05.2200 255	Magnesite floor, large area	SF	2.94	3.96	6.90	3.31	6.25
05.2200 260	Magnesite base medium area	LF	3.37	5.31	8.68	4.43	7.80
05.2200 265	Magnesite base, large area	LF	3.06	4.41	7.47	3.68	6.74
05.2200 270	Asphalt plank, 1/2"x12"x24"	SF	2.27	1.16	3.43	.97	3.24

CSI #	5.3 FINISHES, SPECIAL Description	Unit	Material	Union Install	Union Total	Open Install	Open Total
	The costs in this section include materials, labor, equipment rental, supervision, and subcontractor overhead and profit. There are no allowances for the general contractor. Costs are complete, floors are finished, walls are painted or appropriately finished all ancillary costs are included.						
05.3100	**TILE**						
05.3100 100	Tile, ceramic, floor, 1"x1", mortar set	SF	5.73	7.49	13.22	5.99	11.72
05.3100 105	Tile, ceramic, floor, 4"x4", mortar set	SF	5.55	6.79	12.34	5.43	10.98
05.3100 110	Tile, ceramic, wall, 1"x1", mortar set, base included	SF	6.74	10.21	16.95	8.17	14.91
05.3100 115	Tile, ceramic, wall, 4"x4", mortar set, base included	SF	6.05	8.30	14.35	6.65	12.70
05.3200	**TERRAZZO**						
05.3200 100	Terrazzo, floor, mud bonded, 2", non-slip abrasive	SF	6.88	2.05	8.93	1.33	8.21
05.3200 105	Terrazzo, floor, thin set, polyester, 3/8", polished	SF	6.73	12.78	19.51	8.32	15.05
05.3200 110	Terrazzo, floor, thin set, latex, 3/8", polished	SF	8.02	15.18	23.20	9.88	17.90
05.3200 115	Terrazzo, floor, thin set, epoxy chemical resistant, 3/8", polished	SF	6.64	12.52	19.16	8.15	14.79
05.3200 120	Divider strip, brass, 12 gauge adder	LF	4.05	.46	4.51	.30	4.35
05.3200 125	Divider strip, white metal, 12 gauge adder	LF	1.61	.46	2.07	.30	1.91
05.3300	**HARDWOOD FLOORS**						
05.3300 100	Hardwood floor, oak, common, finished	SF	4.21	4.20	8.41	2.94	7.15
05.3300 105	Hardwood floor, oak, select, finished	SF	4.28	4.43	8.71	3.10	7.38
05.3300 110	Hardwood floors, oak parquet 5/16", pre-finished	SF	4.17	4.92	9.09	3.44	7.61
05.3300 115	Hardwood floor, oak parquet 25/32", pre-finished	SF	4.50	5.06	9.56	3.53	8.03
05.3300 120	Hardwood floor, maple parquet 5/16", pre-finished	SF	6.97	5.28	12.25	3.69	10.66
05.3300 125	Hardwood floor, walnut parquet 5/16", pre-finished	SF	7.12	5.49	12.61	3.84	10.96
05.3300 130	Hardwood floor, teak parquet 5/16", pre-finished	SF	7.42	5.84	13.26	4.08	11.50
05.3300 135	Hardwood floor, gym, maple	SF	7.74	5.48	13.22	3.83	11.57
05.3300 140	Hardwood floor, gym, on steel springs	SF	8.93	8.00	16.93	5.59	14.52
05.3300 145	Hardwood floor, gym, on steel channels	SF	7.96	7.14	15.10	4.99	12.95
05.3400	**WALL COVERING**						
05.3400 100	Vinyl wall covering, light, 7 ounces	SF	1.72	.57	2.29	.45	2.17
05.3400 105	Vinyl wall covering, medium, 14 ounces	SF	1.88	.73	2.61	.57	2.45
05.3400 110	Vinyl wall covering, heavy, 22 ounces	SF	2.14	.84	2.98	.65	2.79
05.3400 115	Wall covering, plastic hardboard, 1/8"	SF	2.58	1.30	3.88	1.01	3.59
05.3400 120	Wall covering, plastic hardboard, 1/4"	SF	3.42	1.30	4.72	1.01	4.43
05.3500	**WOOD**						
05.3500 100	Paneling, birch or ash, select	SF	1.94	5.06	7.00	3.60	5.54
05.3500 105	Paneling, birch or ash, economy	SF	1.29	4.72	6.01	3.36	4.65
05.3500 110	Paneling, mahogony, African	SF	3.07	6.01	9.08	4.26	7.33
05.3500 115	Paneling, mahogony, Phillipine, select	SF	1.43	4.38	5.81	3.13	4.56
05.3500 120	Paneling, mahogony, ribbon cut, good	SF	1.47	4.38	5.85	3.13	4.60
05.3500 125	Paneling, mahogony, rotary cut, economy	SF	1.28	4.38	5.66	3.13	4.41
05.3500 130	Paneling, teak, select	SF	2.62	6.01	8.63	4.26	6.88
05.3500 135	Paneling, teak, finish V plank, good	SF	4.24	5.14	9.38	3.58	7.82
05.3500 140	Paneling, walnut, select	SF	6.56	5.14	11.70	3.58	10.14
05.3500 145	Paneling, walnut, domestic	SF	4.03	4.80	8.83	3.34	7.37
05.3500 150	Paneling, redwood, clear, all heart	SF	3.05	1.26	4.31	.96	4.01
05.3500 155	Paneling, douglas fir, clear, vertical grain	SF	2.97	4.15	7.12	2.97	5.94
05.3500 160	Paneling, hardboard, printed finish	SF	.86	3.74	4.60	2.61	3.47
05.3500 165	Base, 1-5/8", pre-finished, hardwood	LF	1.78	2.70	4.48	1.92	3.70
05.3500 170	Base, 2-1/4", softwood	LF	1.47	2.70	4.17	1.92	3.39
05.3500 175	Base, 3-1/4", softwood	LF	1.68	2.70	4.38	1.92	3.60
05.3500 180	Molding, chair rail	LF	1.56	3.92	5.48	2.77	4.33
05.3500 185	Molding, cove, 3/4"	LF	.99	2.46	3.45	1.75	2.74
05.3500 190	Molding, cove, 1-3/4"	LF	1.16	2.46	3.62	1.75	2.91
05.3500 195	Molding, picture	LF	1.19	3.92	5.11	2.77	3.96
05.3500 200	Trim, apron, 1-3/8"	LF	1.12	3.04	4.16	2.16	3.28
05.3500 205	Trim, jamb, 2" pine w/stop	LF	2.48	2.58	5.06	1.84	4.32
05.3500 210	Trim, jamb, 4-5/8" pine	LF	3.62	9.41	13.03	6.59	10.21

CSI #	5.4 INTERIORS Description	Unit	Material	Union Install	Union Total	Open Install	Open Total
	The costs in this section include materials, labor, equipment rental, supervision, and subcontractor overhead and profit. There are no allowances for the general contractor. Costs are complete, as expected under standard construction conditions. Certain adders are noted among the costs.						
05.4100	**CABINETS & TOPS**						
05.4100 100	Cabinets and laminated plastic tops, multi-unit, hardwood, economy, base	LF	37.98	20.01	57.99	14.61	52.59
05.4100 105	Cabinets and laminated plastic tops, multi-unit, hardwood, economy, wall	LF	24.51	35.35	59.86	25.82	50.33
05.4100 110	Cabinets and laminated plastic tops, multi-unit, hardwood, economy, full height	LF	94.67	45.43	140.10	33.18	127.85
05.4100 115	Cabinets and laminated plastic tops, multi-unit, hardwood, custom, base	LF	54.66	20.01	74.67	14.61	69.27
05.4100 120	Cabinets and laminated plastic tops, multi-unit, hardwood, custom, wall	LF	39.61	35.35	74.96	25.82	65.43
05.4100 125	Cabinets and laminated plastic tops, multi-unit, hardwood, custom, full height	LF	95.70	45.43	141.13	33.18	128.88
05.4100 130	Cabinets and laminated plastic tops, premium, birch institutional, base	LF	109.65	39.20	148.85	28.63	138.28
05.4100 135	Cabinets and laminated plastic tops, premium, birch institutional, wall	LF	92.01	68.76	160.77	50.22	142.23
05.4100 140	Cabinets and laminated plastic tops, premium, birch institutional, full height	LF	155.54	49.49	205.03	36.14	191.68
05.4100 143	Add for ash	LF	10.02		10.02		10.02
05.4100 144	Add for walnut	LF	54.52		54.52		54.52
05.4100 145	Add for overlay	LF	6.70		6.70		6.70
05.4100 146	Add for flush overlay	LF	10.02		10.02		10.02
05.4100 147	Add for edge banding	LF	6.70		6.70		6.70
05.4100 148	Add for pre-finished exterior	LF	5.13		5.13		5.13
05.4100 149	Add for pre-finished interior	LF	10.99		10.99		10.99
05.4100 150	Add for standard hardware	LF	4.55		4.55		4.55
05.4100 151	Add for institutional hardware	LF	6.70		6.70		6.70
05.4100 152	Add for roller guides	SET	5.13		5.13		5.13
05.4100 153	Add for roller guides, full suspension	SET	25.48		25.48		25.48
05.4100 154	Cabinets and laminated plastic tops, units, premium, open with one shelf	LF	68.55		68.55		68.55
05.4100 155	Cabinets and laminated plastic tops, units, premium, with door and one shelf	LF	84.98		84.98		84.98
05.4100 160	Cabinets and laminated plastic tops, units, premium, with door, 1 shelf & 1 drawer	LF	117.98		117.98		117.98
05.4100 165	Cabinets and laminated plastic tops, units, premium, sink	LF	75.44		75.44		75.44
05.4100 170	Cabinets and laminated plastic tops, units, premium, 4 drawers	LF	135.83		135.83		135.83
05.4100 175	Cabinets and laminated plastic tops, units, premium, add for apron (knee space)	LF	19.17		19.17		19.17
05.4100 180	Cabinets and laminated plastic tops, units, premium, add for backsplash	LF	10.99		10.99		10.99
05.4100 185	Cabinets and laminated plastic tops, metal, base, commercial, with door, shelf	LF	108.97	20.86	129.83	15.24	124.21
05.4100 190	Cabinets and laminated plastic tops, metal, wall, commercial, with door, 2 shelves	LF	80.25	25.05	105.30	18.29	98.54
05.4100 195	Cabinets and laminated plastic tops, metal, full, commercial, with door, 5 shelves	LF	189.08	32.73	221.81	23.91	212.99
05.4100 200	Cabinets and laminated plastic tops, metal, full, library, shelving	LF	70.18	18.30	88.48	13.37	83.55

CSI #	5.4 INTERIORS Description	Unit	Material	Union Install	Union Total	Open Install	Open Total
05.4100	**CABINETS & TOPS (Cont.)**						
05.4100 205	Cabinets and laminated plastic tops, metal, full, wardrobe, 4' wide	EA	458.67	55.27	513.94	40.37	499.04
05.4100 210	Cabinets and laminated plastic tops, wood, formica faced, base, w/door, 1 shelf, school	LF	208.72	34.68	243.40	25.33	234.05
05.4100 215	Cabinets and laminated plastic tops, wood, formica faced, wall, w/door, 1 shelves, school	LF	151.56	41.64	193.20	30.42	181.98
05.4100 220	Cabinets and laminated plastic tops, wood, formica faced, full, w/doors, school	LF	247.70	42.85	290.55	31.29	278.99
05.4100 225	Cabinets and laminated plastic tops, wood, formica faced, add for laboratory cabinets, school	LF	48.94	23.94	72.88	17.48	66.42
05.4100 230	Cabinets and laminated plastic tops, wood and metal, w/door, 1 shelf, 1 drawer, hospital	LF	158.26	70.17	228.43	51.25	209.51
05.4100 235	Cabinets and laminated plastic tops, wood and metal, w/door, 2 shelves, hospital	LF	92.75	46.75	139.50	34.15	126.90
05.4100 240	Cabinets and laminated plastic tops, wood and metal, w/door, full, hospital	LF	191.37	36.52	227.89	26.67	218.04
05.4100 245	Cabinets and laminated plastic tops, furniture grade, base, laboratory	LF	221.63	123.27	344.90	90.04	311.67
05.4100 250	Cabinets and laminated plastic tops, furniture grade, wall, laboratory	LF	105.58	59.54	165.12	43.49	149.07
05.4100 255	Cabinets and laminated plastic tops, furniture grade, wardrobe, laboratory	LF	237.04	51.01	288.05	37.26	274.30
05.4100 260	Cabinets and laminated plastic tops, furniture grade, lab island, laboratory	LF	316.90	148.77	465.67	108.66	425.56
05.4100 265	Cabinets and laminated plastic tops, furniture grade, fume hood, laboratory	LF	438.03	331.51	769.54	242.13	680.16
05.4100 270	Cabinets and laminated plastic tops, furniture grade, fume hood, stainless steel, laboratory	LF	584.92	318.79	903.71	232.85	817.77
05.4100 275	Cabinets and laminated plastic tops, furniture grade, add for premium quality, laboratory	LF	25.23	22.95	48.18	16.76	41.99
05.4100 280	Laminated plastic & simulated marble tops, multi-residential	LF	32.03		32.03		32.03
05.4100 285	Laminated plastic & simulated marble tops, small projects	LF	36.99		36.99		36.99
05.4100 290	Laminated plastic & simulated marble tops, custom jobs	LF	49.38		49.38		49.38
05.4100 295	Laminated plastic & simulated marble tops, vanity top, cultered marble, no bowl	LF	44.21		44.21		44.21
05.4100 300	Laminated plastic & simulated marble tops vanity top, add to vanity for molded bowl	EA	40.99		40.99		40.99
05.4100 305	Laminated plastic & simulated marble tops, vanity top, add to vanity for molded clam shell	EA	71.75		71.75		71.75
05.4100 310	Laminated plastic & simulated marble tops, acid proof tops	LF	99.18		99.18		99.18
05.4100 315	Laminated plastic & simulated marble tops, komar/simulated marble, molded section	SF	18.51		18.51		18.51
05.4300	**CARPET**						
05.4300 100	Carpet, 30 oz polyester, with 50 oz pad	SY	24.26	10.08	34.34	8.41	32.67
05.4300 105	Carpet, 35 oz polyester, with 50 oz pad	SY	26.93	10.08	37.01	8.41	35.34
05.4300 110	Carpet, 40 oz polyester, with 50 oz pad	SY	28.70	10.08	38.78	8.41	37.11
05.4300 115	Carpet, 50 oz polyester, with 50 oz pad	SY	33.69	10.08	43.77	8.41	42.10
05.4300 120	Carpet, 20 oz nylon shag, with 50 oz pad	SY	14.11	10.08	24.19	8.41	22.52
05.4300 125	Carpet, 24 oz nylon shag, with 50 oz pad	SY	16.07	10.08	26.15	8.41	24.48
05.4300 130	Carpet, 24 oz nylon shag, with 50 oz pad	SY	16.07	10.08	26.15	8.41	24.48
05.4300 135	Carpet, 20 oz nylon filament, with 50 oz pad	SY	14.11	10.08	24.19	8.41	22.52
05.4300 140	Carpet, 24 oz nylon filament, with 50 oz pad	SY	19.49	10.08	29.57	8.41	27.90
05.4300 145	Carpet, 15 oz nylon level loop, with rubber back	SY	16.07	8.64	24.71	7.21	23.28
05.4300 150	Carpet, 21 oz nylon level loop, with rubber back	SY	19.49	8.64	28.13	7.21	26.70

CSI #	5.4 INTERIORS Description	Unit	Material	Union Install	Union Total	Open Install	Open Total
05.4300	CARPET (Cont.)						
05.4300 155	Carpet, 28 oz nylon level loop, with rubber back	SY	26.59	8.64	35.23	7.21	33.80
05.4300 160	Carpet, 15 oz nylon level loop, with 50 oz pad	SY	16.83	10.08	26.91	8.41	25.24
05.4300 165	Carpet, 21 oz nylon level loop, with 50 oz pad	SY	20.45	10.08	30.53	8.41	28.86
05.4300 170	Carpet, 28 oz nylon level loop, with 50 oz pad	SY	28.01	10.08	38.09	8.41	36.42
05.4300 175	Carpet, 48 oz nylon level loop, with 50 oz pad	SY	33.88	10.08	43.96	8.41	42.29
05.4300 180	Carpet, 21 oz antron, anti-static, with 50 oz pad	SY	26.59	10.08	36.67	8.41	35.00
05.4300 185	Carpet, wool commercial, with 50 oz pad	SY	56.90	10.08	66.98	8.41	65.31
05.4300 190	Carpet, exterior, premium, without pad	SY	26.26	11.54	37.80	9.62	35.88
05.4300 195	Carpet pad, 40 oz, jute	SY	3.50	2.14	5.64	1.79	5.29
05.4300 200	Carpet pad, 50 oz, jute/hair	SY	4.92	2.14	7.06	1.79	6.71
05.4300 205	Carpet pad, 50 oz, hair	SY	6.18	2.14	8.32	1.79	7.97
05.4300 210	Carpet pad, 72 oz, rubber waffle	SY	4.50	2.14	6.64	1.79	6.29
05.4300 215	Carpet pad, 100 oz, rubber waffle	SY	8.51	2.14	10.65	1.79	10.30
05.4300 220	Carpet pad, 72 oz, rubber slab	SY	5.68	2.14	7.82	1.79	7.47
05.4300 225	Carpet pad, 88 oz, rubber slab	SY	8.51	2.14	10.65	1.79	10.30
05.4300 230	Carpet pad, urethane, 15#	SY	2.90	2.14	5.04	1.79	4.69
05.4300 235	Carpet pad, urethane, 2#	SY	4.68	2.14	6.82	1.79	6.47
05.4300 240	Carpet pad, urethane, 25#	SY	5.48	2.14	7.62	1.79	7.27
05.4300 245	Carpet pad, urethane, rebound	SY	5.99	2.14	8.13	1.79	7.78
05.4300 250	Carpet average, housing	SY	21.68		21.68		21.68
05.4300 255	Carpet average, commercial	SY	30.70		30.70		30.70
05.4300 260	Carpet average, school	SY	33.46		33.46		33.46
05.4300 265	Carpet average, hotel/motel/theatre	SY	36.28		36.28		36.28
05.4300 270	Carpet average, custom housing	SY	53.03		53.03		53.03
05.4300 275	Floor mat, rubber, 1/4" recessed	SF	6.98	3.01	9.99	2.41	9.39
05.4300 280	Floor mat, rubber, 1/2" recessed	SF	11.03	3.79	14.82	3.03	14.06
05.4300 285	Floor mat, vinyl, 1/4" recessed	SF	10.26	3.01	13.27	2.41	12.67
05.4300 290	Floor mat, vinyl, 1/2" recessed	SF	13.59	3.79	17.38	3.03	16.62

CSI #	6.0 SPECIALTIES Description	Unit	Material	Union Install	Union Total	Open Install	Open Total
	The costs of Specialties, in this section, include material, installation, and subcontractor overhead and profit. There are no allowances for general contractor markup and profit.						
	The items in this section are typical of those found in offices, hotel meeting rooms and buildings that are designed for high concentrations of public use.						
	Costs represent standard grade materials and normal installation. Adjustments should be made for economy quality or custom and heavy duty materials and commensurate installation.						
06.0100	**CHALK & TACK BOARDS**						
06.0100 110	Tackboard, 1/4" vinyl cork, 1/4" hardboard, without frame	SF	22.77	3.11	25.88	2.27	25.04
06.0100 115	Tackboard, vinyl and fiberboard 1/2", without frame, installed	SF	12.86	1.87	14.73	1.36	14.22
06.0100 120	Tackboard, 1/8", burlap back, without frame, installed	SF	12.70	1.33	14.03	.97	13.67
06.0100 125	Tackboard, 1/8", cork unbacked 1/4", without frame, installed	SF	12.01	1.09	13.10	.80	12.81
06.0100 128	Tackboard, cork or vinyl, with trim, installed	SF	21.78	4.96	26.74	3.63	25.41
06.0100 130	Aluminum map, display rail, deluxe	LF	5.59	1.00	6.59	.73	6.32
06.0100 135	Aluminum chalk tray	LF	10.54	2.31	12.85	1.69	12.23
06.0100 140	Aluminum chalk board frame with trim	LF	4.63	.80	5.43	.58	5.21
06.0100 145	Chalkboard, slate 3/8", without frame, installed	SF	23.87	5.02	28.89	3.67	27.54
06.0100 150	Chalkboard, hardboard, tempered 1/4", without frame, installed	SF	15.84	2.31	18.15	1.69	17.53
06.0100 155	Chalkboard, metal 24 GA 1/2", without trim, installed	SF	18.22	2.71	20.93	1.98	20.20
06.0100 160	Chalkboard, reversible, roll, 4'x8'	EACH	897.96	438.58	1,336.54	320.34	1,218.30
06.0100 165	Chalkboard, horizontal sliding, installed	SF	56.44	15.36	71.80	11.22	67.66
06.0100 170	Chalkboard, vertical sliding, installed	SF	86.85	23.49	110.34	17.16	104.01
06.0100 180	Chalkboard, without trim, average, installed	SF	9.14	2.49	11.63	1.82	10.96
06.0100 185	Chalkboard, with trim, map, rail, installed	SF	21.78	4.96	26.74	3.63	25.41
06.0200	**TOILET PARTITIONS**						
06.0200 100	Toilet partition, baked enamel, floor mounted	EACH	630.17	123.68	753.85	90.33	720.50
06.0200 105	Toilet partition, baked enamel, ceiling mounted	EACH	665.22	144.27	809.49	105.38	770.60
06.0200 110	Toilet partition, porcelin enamel, floor mounted	EACH	931.02	151.19	1,082.21	110.43	1,041.45
06.0200 115	Toilet partition, porcelin enamel, ceiling mounted	EACH	980.24	176.37	1,156.61	128.82	1,109.06
06.0200 120	Toilet partition, laminated plastic, floor mounted	EACH	814.88	151.19	966.07	110.43	925.31
06.0200 125	Toilet partition, laminated plastic, ceiling mounted	EACH	827.90	176.37	1,004.27	128.82	956.72
06.0200 130	Toilet partition, stainless steel, floor mounted	EACH	2,137.48	151.19	2,288.67	110.43	2,247.91
06.0200 135	Toilet partition, stainless steel, ceiling mounted	EACH	1,984.80	176.37	2,161.17	128.82	2,113.62
06.0200 140	Add for best quality	EACH	143.29		143.29		143.29
06.0200 145	Urinal screen, baked enamel, wall mounted	EACH	227.42	42.53	269.95	31.07	258.49
06.0200 150	Urinal screen, porcelin enamel, wall mounted	EACH	427.95	51.98	479.93	37.96	465.91
06.0200 155	Urinal screen, laminated plastic, wall mounted	EACH	315.51	51.98	367.49	37.96	353.47
06.0200 160	Urinal screen, stainless steel, wall mounted	EACH	579.48	51.98	631.46	37.96	617.44
06.0200 165	Add for best quality	EACH	57.96	21.24	79.20	15.51	73.47
06.0200 170	Sight screen, 3'x7', baked enamel, floor mounted	EACH	358.19	89.25	447.44	65.18	423.37
06.0200 175	Sight screen, laminated plastic, floor mounted	EACH	465.68	109.11	574.79	79.69	545.37
06.0200 180	Dressing cubicle, baked enamel, floor mounted	EACH	1,164.47	99.33	1,263.80	72.55	1,237.02
06.0200 185	Dressing cubicle, porcelin enamel, floor mounted	EACH	1,724.11	121.44	1,845.55	88.70	1,812.81
06.0200 190	Dressing cubicle, stainless steel, floor mounted	EACH	2,157.64	121.44	2,279.08	88.70	2,246.34
06.0200 195	Dressing cubicle, laminated plastic, floor mounted	EACH	1,513.86	121.44	1,635.30	88.70	1,602.56

CSI #	6.0 SPECIALTIES Description	Unit	Material	Union Install	Union Total	Open Install	Open Total
06.0300	**DEMOUNTABLE PARTITIONS**						
06.0300 100	Relocatable partitions, 5/8"	SF	19.14	5.63	24.77	4.11	23.25
06.0300 105	Accordian partitions, vinyl, 8', STC 36, economy	SF	19.14	5.63	24.77	4.11	23.25
06.0300 110	Accordian partitions, vinyl, 30'x17', STC 43, good	SF	29.64	8.72	38.36	6.37	36.01
06.0300 115	Accordian partitions, vinyl, large, open, STC 45, bottom	SF	36.08	10.57	46.65	7.72	43.80
06.0300 120	Accordian partitions, wide slat, birch/ash, prefinished	SF	19.14	5.63	24.77	4.11	23.25
06.0300 125	Folding partitions, vinyl, metal panel, STC 52	SF	59.84	23.65	83.49	17.28	77.12
06.0300 130	Folding partitions, vinyl, wide panel, STC 40	SF	44.03	17.35	61.38	12.68	56.71
06.0300 135	Add for laminated plastic	SF	3.67	1.17	4.84	.85	4.52
06.0300 140	Add for wood veneer	SF	4.81	1.46	6.27	1.07	5.88
06.0300 145	Folding partitions, wide, side coil, single, crank (operable walls)	SF	27.87	11.15	39.02	8.14	36.01
06.0300 150	Folding partitions, motor, under 30'x9'	EACH	1,714.75	683.02	2,397.77	498.87	2,213.62
06.0400	**TOILET ACCESSORIES**						
06.0400 100	Toilet accessories, paper towel and waste combination, stainless steel/lam, 14"x24", recessed	EACH	456.00	33.00	489.00	23.00	479.00
06.0400 105	Toilet accessories, paper towel and waste combination, stainless steel, 17"x54", semi-recessed	EACH	687.00	33.00	720.00	23.00	710.00
06.0400 110	Toilet accessories, paper towel and waste combination, stainless steel/lam, 12"x72", semi-recessed	EACH	795.00	33.00	828.00	23.00	818.00
06.0400 115	Toilet accessories, paper towel and waste combination, stainless steel, 17"x54", semi-recessed	EACH	1,145.00	33.00	1,178.00	23.00	1,168.00
06.0400 120	Toilet accessories, paper towel dispenser, stainless steel, 12"x17", surface	EACH	112.00	33.00	145.00	23.00	135.00
06.0400 125	Toilet accessories, paper towel dispenser, stainless steel, 12"x15", recessed	EACH	217.00	33.00	250.00	23.00	240.00
06.0400 130	Toilet accessories, paper towel dispenser, stainless steel, 14"x26", recessed	EACH	325.00	33.00	358.00	23.00	348.00
06.0400 140	Toilet accessories, paper towel dispenser, stainless steel trim, 17"x28"	EACH	774.00	33.00	807.00	23.00	797.00
06.0400 150	Toilet accessories, paper towel and soap combo, laminated	EACH	577.00	33.00	610.00	23.00	600.00
06.0400 160	Toilet accessories, towel, soap and mirror, laminated	EACH	741.00	33.00	774.00	23.00	764.00
06.0400 165	Toilet accessories, waste receptacles, stainless steel, 3 GAL, recessed	EACH	336.00	33.00	369.00	23.00	359.00
06.0400 170	Toilet accessories, waste receptacles, stainless steel, 10 GAL, semi-recessed	EACH	509.00	33.00	542.00	23.00	532.00
06.0400 200	Toilet accessories, toilet seat cover dispensers, stainless steel, surface	EACH	70.00	33.00	103.00	23.00	93.00
06.0400 210	Toilet accessories, toilet seat cover dispensers, laminated, recessed	EACH	308.00	33.00	341.00	23.00	331.00
06.0400 220	Toilet accessories, toilet paper dispensers, aluminum, single, surface	EACH	25.00	33.00	58.00	23.00	48.00
06.0400 225	Toilet accessories, toilet paper dispensers, stainless steel, single, surface	EACH	45.00	33.00	78.00	23.00	68.00
06.0400 245	Toilet accessories, toilet paper dispenser, stainless steel, double, recessed	EACH	77.00	33.00	110.00	23.00	100.00
06.0400 250	Toilet accessories, feminine napkin dispenser, stainless steel, surface	EACH	679.00	33.00	712.00	23.00	702.00
06.0400 265	Toilet accessories, feminine napkin dispensers/dispoasl, stainless steel	EACH	1,025.00	33.00	1,058.00	23.00	1,048.00
06.0400 285	Toilet accessories, feminine napkin dispoasl, stainless steel, recessed, large	EACH	287.00	33.00	320.00	23.00	310.00
06.0400 295	Toilet accessories, soap dispensers, plastic, liquid, surface, stainless steel lid	EACH	43.00	33.00	76.00	23.00	66.00
06.0400 310	Toilet accessories, soap dispensers, stainless steel, liquid, recessed	EACH	147.00	33.00	180.00	23.00	170.00

CSI #	6.0 SPECIALTIES Description	Unit	Material	Union Install	Union Total	Open Install	Open Total
06.0400	**TOILET ACCESSORIES (Cont.)**						
06.0400 325	Toilet accessories, soap dispensers, stainless steel, liquid, recessed, shelf	EACH	287.00	33.00	320.00	23.00	310.00
06.0400 345	Toilet accessories, facial tissue dispensers, stainless steel, surface	EACH	36.00	33.00	69.00	23.00	59.00
06.0400 360	Toilet accessories, facial tissue dispensers, stainless steel, recessed, with shelf	EACH	204.00	33.00	237.00	23.00	227.00
06.0400 370	Toilet accessories, grab bars, stainless steel, 1 1/2"x24", exposed mounted	EACH	72.00	33.00	105.00	23.00	95.00
06.0400 380	Toilet accessories, grab bars, swing away, exposed floor mounted	EACH	803.00	33.00	836.00	23.00	826.00
06.0400 405	Toilet accessories, miscellaneous, towel bar, stainless steel, 24"	EACH	68.00	33.00	101.00	23.00	91.00
06.0400 415	Toilet accessories, miscellaneous, shower rod, stainless steel, 1"x6'	EACH	47.00	33.00	80.00	23.00	70.00
06.0400 435	Toilet accessories, miscellaneous, mirror, stainless steel frame, tilt	EACH	182.00	33.00	215.00	23.00	205.00
06.0400 445	Toilet accessories, miscellaneous, mirror, stainless steel frame, 16"x24", shelf	EACH	130.00	33.00	163.00	23.00	153.00
06.0400 455	Toilet accessories, miscellaneous, medicine cabinet and mirror, baked enamel, recessed	EACH	199.00	33.00	232.00	23.00	222.00
06.0400 460	Toilet accessories, miscellaneous, medicine cabinet and mirror, stainless steel, recessed	EACH	579.00	33.00	612.00	23.00	602.00
06.0400 515	Toilet accessories, miscellaneous, shelf, stainless steel, 24"	EACH	105.00	33.00	138.00	23.00	128.00
06.0400 530	Toilet accessories, miscellaneous, towel shelf, stainless steel, 24"	EACH	138.00	33.00	171.00	23.00	161.00
06.0400 545	Toilet accessories, miscellaneous, electric hand dryer, surface, 40 second cycle	EACH	1,819.00	33.00	1,852.00	23.00	1,842.00

CSI #	7.0 EQUIPMENT Description	Unit	Material	Union Install	Union Total	Open Install	Open Total
	The equipment costs, in this section, include material, installation, and subcontractor overhead and profit. There are no allowances for general contractor markup and profit. Costs represent standard grade materials and normal installation. Adjustments should be made for economy quality or custom and heavy duty materials and commensurate installation.						
07.0100	**BANK EQUIPMENT**						
07.0100 100	Vault door for safekeeping, 78"x44"x3 1/2", steel, class 1	EACH	33,229.32	1,101.02	34,330.34	824.48	34,053.80
07.0100 105	Vault door for safekeeping, 78"x44"x3 1/2", steel, class 2	EACH	37,516.96	1,101.02	38,617.98	824.48	38,341.44
07.0100 110	Vault door for safekeeping, 78"x44"x3 1/2", steel, class 3	EACH	45,020.37	1,101.02	46,121.39	824.48	45,844.85
07.0100 115	Vault door for safekeeping, 78"x44"x3 1/2", steel, 6 hour	EACH	25,078.71	1,101.02	26,179.73	824.48	25,903.19
07.0100 120	Vaults for record keeping only, 78"x33", 1 hour, single	EACH	4,414.62	569.34	4,983.96	426.34	4,840.96
07.0100 125	Vaults for record keeping only, 84"x51 1/8", 2 hour, single	EACH	5,380.36	569.34	5,949.70	426.34	5,806.70
07.0100 130	Vaults for record keeping only, 84"x51 1/8", 4 hour, single	EACH	5,623.89	558.58	6,182.47	418.28	6,042.17
07.0100 135	Vaults for record keeping only, 84"x51 1/8", 6 hour, single	EACH	6,527.19	565.75	7,092.94	423.65	6,950.84
07.0100 140	Modular vaults, class 1, 15 minute	EACH	31,220.79	9,281.60	40,502.39	6,950.33	38,171.12
07.0100 145	Modular vaults, class 2, 1 hour	EACH	52,034.64	9,280.71	61,315.35	6,949.66	58,984.30
07.0100 150	Modular vaults, class 3, 2 hour	EACH	72,848.47	9,285.19	82,133.66	6,953.02	79,801.49
07.0100 155	Teller Window, drive-up, manual	EACH	10,257.18	1,219.79	11,476.97	913.41	11,170.59
07.0100 160	Teller Window, drive-up, motorized	EACH	11,552.12	1,219.79	12,771.91	913.41	12,465.53
07.0100 165	Teller Window, walk-up, 1 teller	EACH	7,051.67	975.81	8,027.48	730.72	7,782.39
07.0100 170	Teller Window, walk-up, 2 teller	EACH	7,790.85	975.81	8,766.66	730.72	8,521.57
07.0100 175	Night deposit, bag/envelope, illuminated	EACH	5,807.06	1,010.47	6,817.53	756.67	6,563.73
07.0100 180	Nigth deposit, envelope	EACH	2,399.79	278.83	2,678.62	208.80	2,608.59
07.0100 185	Night deposit, bag, flush mounted	EACH	2,932.62	458.25	3,390.87	343.15	3,275.77
07.0100 190	Teller counter, modular component	LF	350.47	92.35	442.82	69.15	419.62
07.0100 195	Check desk, round 48", 4 person	EACH	2,568.44	559.21	3,127.65	418.75	2,987.19
07.0100 200	Check desk, square 48", 4 person	EACH	2,164.59	528.75	2,693.34	347.38	2,511.97
07.0100 205	Check desk, 72"x24", 4 person	EACH	2,572.58	320.17	2,892.75	210.35	2,782.93
07.0100 210	Check desk, 72"x36", 4 person	EACH	3,197.00	418.86	3,615.86	275.18	3,472.18
07.0100 215	Safe deposit, 42 opening, 2"x5"	EACH	3,425.93	333.78	3,759.71	219.29	3,645.22
07.0100 220	Safe deposit, 30 opening, 2"x5"	EACH	2,447.66	249.29	2,696.95	163.78	2,611.44
07.0100 225	Safe deposit, 18 opening, 5"x5"	EACH	1,769.16	207.72	1,976.88	136.47	1,905.63
07.0100 230	Safe deposit, base, 32"x24"x3"	EACH	228.94	75.57	304.51	49.65	278.59
07.0100 235	Safe deposit, canopy top	EACH	58.78	41.58	100.36	27.31	86.09
07.0100 240	Safe deposit, 9 open, 5"x10 3/8"	EACH	1,332.06	260.20	1,592.26	194.85	1,526.91
07.0100 245	Safe deposit, 15 open, 3"x10 3/8"	EACH	1,540.23	257.86	1,798.09	193.09	1,733.32
07.0100 250	Safe deposit, 1 section, 3 open, 5"x10"	EACH	1,352.90	468.92	1,821.82	351.14	1,704.04
07.0100 255	Deposit, 1 section, 3 open, 10"x10 3/8"	EACH	1,352.90	477.08	1,829.98	357.25	1,710.15
07.0100 260	Safe, floor, 10"x24", minimum security	EACH	558.46	111.56	670.02	81.49	639.95
07.0100 265	Safe, wall, minimum security	EACH	2,924.69	794.76	3,719.45	580.48	3,505.17
07.0100 270	Safe, cabinet, medium security, full door	EACH	4,214.40	1,145.28	5,359.68	836.50	5,050.90
07.0100 275	Book drop, minimum security	EACH	1,045.91	284.24	1,330.15	207.60	1,253.51
07.0100 280	Night depository	EACH	1,706.01	463.62	2,169.63	338.62	2,044.63
07.0200	**EDUCATIONAL EQUIPMENT**						
07.0200 100	Equipment, educational, wardrobes, teacher, 40"x78"x26 1/4"	EACH	1,128.72	66.71	1,195.43	49.95	1,178.67
07.0200 105	Equipment, educational, wardrobes, student, 40"x78"x26 1/4"	EACH	739.66	50.03	789.69	37.46	777.12
07.0200 110	Equipment, educational, seating, pedestal, folding arm	EACH	124.76	22.19	146.95	16.20	140.96
07.0200 115	Equipment, educational, seating, horizontal 2 section, 5 chair	EACH	134.09	23.82	157.91	17.39	151.48
07.0200 120	Equipment, educational, tables, fixed pedestal, 48"x16"	EACH	520.10	92.39	612.49	67.48	587.58
07.0200 125	Equipment, educational, tables, fixed pedestal, chair, 48"x16"	EACH	716.51	127.30	843.81	92.98	809.49
07.0200 130	Equipment, educational, slide screen, pull, 70"x70", ceiling	SF	6.06	1.31	7.37	.95	7.01
07.0200 135	Equipment, educational, slide screen, electric, ceiling	SF	52.09	5.37	57.46	3.92	56.01
07.0200 140	Equipment, educational, drafting furniture, table, steel base, 60"x37 1/2"	EACH	579.97		579.97		579.97

CSI #	7.0 EQUIPMENT Description	Unit	Material	Union Install	Union Total	Open Install	Open Total
07.0200	**EDUCATIONAL EQUIPMENT (Cont.)**						
07.0200 145	Equipment, educational, drafting furniture, table, hardwood, 60"x37 1/2"	EACH	1,196.85		1,196.85		1,196.85
07.0200 150	Equipment, educational, drafting furniture, table, 2 station, 10 drawer, flex	EACH	810.49		810.49		810.49
07.0200 155	Equipment, educational, drafting furniture, table, 1 station, 6 drawer, flex	EACH	647.63		647.63		647.63
07.0200 160	Equipment, educational, drafting furniture, desk, metal frame, mechanical drawing	EACH	869.10		869.10		869.10
07.0200 165	Equipment, educational, drafting furniture, desk, wood, mechanical drawing	EACH	434.51		434.51		434.51
07.0200 170	Equipment, educational, drafting furniture, tracing table, pedestal, 24"x22"	EACH	775.81		775.81		775.81
07.0200 175	Equipment, educational, file cabinet, steel, 10 drawer	EACH	2,107.23		2,107.23		2,107.23
07.0200 180	Equipment, educational, file cabinet, wood, 10 drawer	EACH	1,638.02		1,638.02		1,638.02
07.0200 185	Equipment, educational, files, modular, 8 tube, 48"	EACH	128.23		128.23		128.23
07.0200 190	Equipment, educational, files, 26 binder, 48 3/4"	EACH	2,339.01		2,339.01		2,339.01
07.0200 195	Equipment, educational, audio visual, video tape recorder	EACH	4,638.35	393.68	5,032.03	287.54	4,925.89
07.0200 200	Equipment, educational, audio visual, camera	EACH	1,854.67	421.76	2,276.43	308.05	2,162.72
07.0200 205	Equipment, educational, audio visual, monitor	EACH	821.62	398.31	1,219.93	290.92	1,112.54
07.0200 210	Equipment, educational, audio visual, tape recorder	EACH	512.56		512.56		512.56
07.0200 215	Equipment, educational, audio visual, head set	EACH	49.49		49.49		49.49
07.0200 220	Equipment, educational, audio visual, projector, movie, 8MM	EACH	605.78		605.78		605.78
07.0200 225	Equipment, educational, audio visual, projector, slide, carousel	EACH	465.96		465.96		465.96
07.0200 230	Equipment, educational, study carrel, plastic laminated wood, 48"x30"x54", 1 station	EACH	885.56	93.70	979.26	68.44	954.00
07.0200 235	Equipment, educational, study carrel, plastic laminated wood, 73"x30"x47", 2 station	EACH	1,549.99	140.59	1,690.58	102.68	1,652.67
07.0200 240	Equipment, educational, study carrel, plastic laminated wood, 66"x66"x47", 4 station	EACH	1,834.55	210.84	2,045.39	154.00	1,988.55
07.0200 245	Equipment, educational, audio-visual center, mobile, with control panels, 10 listening stations with earphones, folding table, electric, 4'x8'	EACH	1,276.68		1,276.68		1,276.68
07.0200 250	Equipment, educational, audio-visual center, stack chairs	EACH	136.34		136.34		136.34
07.0200 255	Equipment, educational, accessories for carrels, rear projection module with light	EACH	309.81		309.81		309.81
07.0200 260	Equipment, educational, accessories for carrels, power column, study carrel	EACH	61.92		61.92		61.92
07.0300	**FOOD SERVICE EQUIPMENT**						
07.0300 100	Food service equipment, oven, single, self clean	EACH	1,166.96		1,166.96		1,166.96
07.0300 105	Food service equipment, oven, double, self clean	EACH	1,359.53		1,359.53		1,359.53
07.0300 110	Food service equipment, oven, microwave, built-in	EACH	2,163.09		2,163.09		2,163.09
07.0300 115	Food service equipment, cook top	EACH	785.86		785.86		785.86
07.0300 120	Food service equipment, range & oven, drop-in	EACH	1,125.70		1,125.70		1,125.70
07.0300 125	Food service equipment, range hood with microwave	EACH	799.58		799.58		799.58
07.0300 130	Food service equipment, hood	EACH	137.53		137.53		137.53
07.0300 140	Food service equipment, electric grill	EACH	805.50		805.50		805.50
07.0300 145	Food service equipment, refrigerator, 12 CF	EACH	823.16		823.16		823.16
07.0300 150	Food service equipment, refrigerator, 18 CF	EACH	1,074.63		1,074.63		1,074.63
07.0300 155	Food service equipment, refrigerator with icemaker	EACH	1,035.34		1,035.34		1,035.34
07.0300 160	Food service equipment, freezer, 16 CF	EACH	760.29		760.29		760.29

CSI #	7.0 EQUIPMENT Description	Unit	Material	Union Install	Union Total	Open Install	Open Total
07.0300	**FOOD SERVICE EQUIPMENT (Cont.)**						
07.0300 165	Food service equipment, dishwasher, built-in	EACH	654.19		654.19		654.19
07.0300 170	Food service equipment, garbage disposal	EACH	192.54		192.54		192.54
07.0300 175	Food service equipment, trash compactor	EACH	575.62		575.62		575.62
07.0300 180	Food service equipment, washer	EACH	719.06		719.06		719.06
07.0300 185	Food service equipment, dryer, electric	EACH	571.69		571.69		571.69
07.0300 190	Food service equipment, dryer, gas	EACH	1,037.34		1,037.34		1,037.34
07.0300 195	Food service equipment, tables, counters with sinks, shelves, racks, economy	LF	354.33	77.17	431.50	52.73	407.06
07.0300 200	Food service equipment, tables, counters with sinks, shelves, racks, best	LF	570.90	117.78	688.68	80.48	651.38
07.0300 205	Food service equipment, service center, open storage	LF	869.63	174.63	1,044.26	119.32	988.95
07.0300 210	Food service equipment, service center, closed storage	LF	869.63	223.38	1,093.01	152.63	1,022.26
07.0300 215	Food service equipment, cook's table, with sink, 6'	EACH	4,990.60	528.08	5,518.68	360.83	5,351.43
07.0300 220	Food service equipment, vegetable prep table, with sink, 12'	EACH	5,238.76	678.51	5,917.27	463.62	5,702.38
07.0300 225	Food service equipment, average cost	SF	445.50		445.50		445.50
07.0300 230	Food service equipment, table and counter, stainless steel, rolled edge, 6" splash	LF	347.91	105.26	453.17	71.92	419.83
07.0300 240	Food service equipment, serving fixture, stainless steel, economy	LF	298.24	140.30	438.54	95.86	394.10
07.0300 245	Food service equipment, serving fixture, all stainless steel, best	LF	422.55	140.30	562.85	95.86	518.41
07.0300 250	Food service equipment, adders for basic built-up fixtures, shelves, stainless steel, 85 square feet, base	LF	69.09		69.09		69.09
07.0300 255	Food service equipment, adders for basic built-up fixtures, shelves, galvanized iron, 375 square feet, base	LF	37.69		37.69		37.69
07.0300 260	Food service equipment, adders for basic built-up fixtures, angle or pipe stretchers	LF	23.53		23.53		23.53
07.0300 265	Food service equipment, adders for basic built-up fixtures, tray slide, stainless steel	LF	80.12		80.12		80.12
07.0300 270	Food service equipment, adders for basic built-up fixtures, display shelf, sneeze guard	LF	97.41		97.41		97.41
07.0300 275	Food service equipment, adders for basic built-up fixtures, each additional shelf	LF	58.15		58.15		58.15
07.0300 280	Food service equipment, adders for basic built-up fixtures, plastic laminate on plywood	LF	48.80		48.80		48.80
07.0300 285	Food service equipment, adders for basic built-up fixtures, stainless steel facing, 18 GA, 3' high	LF	72.36		72.36		72.36
07.0300 290	Food service equipment, adders for basic built-up fixtures, stainless steel facing, 22 GA, 3' high	LF	45.92		45.92		45.92
07.0300 295	Food service equipment, adders for basic built-up fixtures, stainless steel dirty dish table, 12" splash	LF	36.16		36.16		36.16
07.0300 300	Food service equipment, adders for basic built-up fixtures, slop cutter, 4" square, with sump	LF	68.90		68.90		68.90
07.0300 305	Food service equipment, shop installed accessories, ventilating grill, 24"x12"	EACH	102.07		102.07		102.07
07.0300 310	Food service equipment, shop installed accessories, vegetable sink	EACH	1,038.91		1,038.91		1,038.91
07.0300 315	Food service equipment, disposer, with stainless steel cone, 1 HP	EACH	1,688.22	473.61	2,161.83	323.61	2,011.83
07.0300 320	Food service equipment, disposer, with stainless steel cone, 1-1/2 HP	EACH	2,316.58	473.61	2,790.19	323.61	2,640.19
07.0300 325	Food service equipment, disposer, with stainless steel cone, 3 HP	EACH	3,525.23	473.61	3,998.84	323.61	3,848.84
07.0300 330	Food service equipment, disposer, with stainless steel cone, 3 HP	EACH	3,525.23	473.61	3,998.84	323.61	3,848.84
07.0300 335	Food service equipment, water heater, electric, sink mounted	EACH	984.75	473.61	1,458.36	323.61	1,308.36
07.0300 340	Food service equipment, pot & pan rack, 6', table mounted	EACH	614.36		614.36		614.36

CSI #	7.0 EQUIPMENT Description	Unit	Material	Union Install	Union Total	Open Install	Open Total
07.0300	**FOOD SERVICE EQUIPMENT (Cont.)**						
07.0300 345	Food service equipment, glass rack dispenser, self level	EACH	895.29	252.57	1,147.86	172.57	1,067.86
07.0300 350	Food service equipment, cup & plate dispenser, heater	EACH	682.10	157.84	839.94	107.85	789.95
07.0300 355	Food service equipment, hot food well, electric, 12"x20"	EACH	554.18	236.80	790.98	161.80	715.98
07.0300 360	Food service equipment, drop-in water cooler	EACH	1,449.50	157.84	1,607.34	107.85	1,557.35
07.0300 370	Food service equipment, refrigerator, undercounter, without compressor	EACH	358.94		358.94		358.94
07.0300 375	Food service equipment, refrigerator, undercounter, without compressor, add for each door	EACH	424.74		424.74		424.74
07.0300 380	Food service equipment, refrigerator, undercounter, without compressor, add for each drawer	EACH	375.09		375.09		375.09
07.0300 385	Food service equipment, refrigerator, undercounter, without compressor, add for each 16"x16" coil	EACH	244.05		244.05		244.05
07.0300 390	Food service equipment, refrigerator, undercounter, without compressor, add for each remote compressor, 1/4 HP	EACH	937.88	1,499.79	2,437.67	1,024.78	1,962.66
07.0300 395	Food service equipment, refrigerator, undercounter, without compressor, soft drink dispenser, 4 spout, 1 remote	EACH	9,464.61	3,157.31	12,621.92	2,157.34	11,621.95
07.0400	**GYMNASIUM & PLAYGROUND EQUIPMENT**						
07.0400 100	Field equipment, basketball, post and steel backstop, single	EACH	958.11	398.79	1,356.90	291.09	1,249.20
07.0400 105	Field equipment, basketball, post and steel backstop, double	EACH	1,345.28	427.76	1,773.04	312.23	1,657.51
07.0400 110	Field equipment, basketball, add for Fiberglass backstop	EACH	58.02		58.02		58.02
07.0400 115	Field equipment, basketball backstop, 34x10, with hood	EACH	2,893.84	1,193.47	4,087.31	871.14	3,764.98
07.0400 120	Field equipment, basketball backstop, 60x15, with hood	EACH	8,100.86	2,094.64	10,195.50	1,528.93	9,629.79
07.0400 125	Field equipment, football goal, single post, two	SET	3,449.38	974.26	4,423.64	711.14	4,160.52
07.0400 130	Field equipment, soccer goal, two	SET	2,680.90	1,266.55	3,947.45	924.49	3,605.39
07.0400 135	Field equipment, tennis post, two	SET	338.74	204.59	543.33	149.33	488.07
07.0400 140	Field equipment, tennis net, nylon	EACH	292.25		292.25		292.25
07.0400 145	Field equipment, tennis net, metal	EACH	619.38		619.38		619.38
07.0400 150	Field equipment, volley ball post, two	SET	290.31	214.81	505.12	156.80	447.11
07.0400 155	Field equipment, tether ball post	EACH	121.72	112.53	234.25	82.14	203.86
07.0400 160	Field equipment, add for ground sock, tether ball	EACH	93.17	112.53	205.70	82.14	175.31
07.0400 165	Field equipment, court striping, tennis, basketball	EACH	303.96		303.96		303.96
07.0400 170	Field equipment, court striping, volleyball	EACH	182.36		182.36		182.36
07.0400 175	Field equipment, swings, 10' high, 4 seats	SET	1,254.30	664.94	1,919.24	485.36	1,739.66
07.0400 180	Field equipment, swings, 10' high, 6 seats	SET	1,538.81	792.83	2,331.64	578.70	2,117.51
07.0400 185	Field equipment, horizontal ladder, 8'x16'	EACH	809.11	409.18	1,218.29	298.67	1,107.78
07.0400 190	Field equipment, horizontal bar, single, 6 1/2'	EACH	239.02	194.37	433.39	141.87	380.89
07.0400 195	Field equipment, bleachers, on concrete riser, benches only, fiberglass	SEAT	28.83		28.83		28.83
07.0400 200	Field equipment, bleachers, on concrete riser, benches only, wood	SEAT	54.65		54.65		54.65
07.0400 205	Field equipment, bleachers, on concrete riser, benches only, aluminum	SEAT	60.75		60.75		60.75
07.0400 210	Field equipment, bleachers, on concrete riser, benches only, fiberglass, with back	SEAT	72.94		72.94		72.94
07.0400 215	Field equipment, bleachers, on concrete riser, individual seats	SEAT	103.28		103.28		103.28
07.0400 220	Field equipment, bleachers, on concrete riser, benches, portable, 16 rows, 500 minimum	SEAT	57.72		57.72		57.72
07.0400 225	Field equipment, outdoor equipment, miscellaneous, benches, wood slats, 6'	EACH	712.80	38.27	751.07	27.94	740.74
07.0400 230	Field equipment, outdoor equipment, miscellaneous, benches, pre-cast concrete, 6'	EACH	1,603.80	57.41	1,661.21	41.91	1,645.71

CSI #	7.0 EQUIPMENT Description	Unit	Material	Union Install	Union Total	Open Install	Open Total
07.0400	**GYMNASIUM & PLAYGROUND EQUIPMENT (Cont.)**						
07.0400 235	Field equipment, outdoor equipment, miscellaneous, picnic table and benches, 6'	EACH	1,602.90	76.55	1,679.45	55.87	1,658.77
07.0400 240	Field equipment, outdoor equipment, miscellaneous, picnic table and benches, 6'	EACH	1,236.44	76.55	1,312.99	55.87	1,292.31
07.0400 245	Field equipment, outdoor equipment, miscellaneous, bicycle rack, galvanized iron, 10', 2 side	EACH	1,419.66	76.55	1,496.21	55.87	1,475.53
07.0400 250	Field equipment, outdoor equipment, miscellaneous, bicycle rack, pre-cast concrete, single	EACH	201.36		201.36		201.36
07.0400 255	Field equipment, athletic field, synthetic surface, uniturf, embossed, running, 3/8"	SF	8.91		8.91		8.91
07.0400 260	Field equipment, athletic field, synthetic surface, turf, 3 layer	SF	13.42		13.42		13.42
07.0400 265	Field equipment, athletic field, synthetic surface, turf, 2 layer	SF	11.73		11.73		11.73
07.0400 270	Field equipment, athletic field, synthetic surface, running track, volcanic cinder, 7"	SF	2.30		2.30		2.30
07.0400 275	Field equipment, athletic field, synthetic surface, running track, bitum/cork, 2"	SF	3.67		3.67		3.67
07.0400 280	Field equipment, athletic field, synthetic surface, running track, AC, 1/4 mile, 55 MSF, 1/4" synth	EACH	563,091.48		563,091.48		563,091.48
07.0400 285	Field equipment, athletic field, synthetic surface, running track, 1/4 mile, 55 MSF, 2" cinder, 6" curb	EACH	158,474.83		158,474.83		158,474.83
07.0400 290	Field equipment, athletic field, synthetic surface, running track, bitum/cork, 1/4 mile, 55 MSF,	EACH	202,308.32		202,308.32		202,308.32
07.0400 295	Field equipment, athletic field, synthetic surface, tennis court, AC base, all weather	SF	4.18		4.18		4.18
07.0400 300	Field equipment, score board	EACH	16,858.97		16,858.97		16,858.97
07.0400 305	Field equipment, basketball backstops, wall, out-rigger, fixed	EACH	722.32	692.00	1,414.32	505.10	1,227.42
07.0400 310	Field equipment, basketball backstops, wall, out-rigger, swing	EACH	2,214.36	1,321.69	3,536.05	964.73	3,179.09
07.0400 315	Field equipment, basketball backstops, ceiling, swing up, manual	EACH	4,453.35	1,770.35	6,223.70	1,292.22	5,745.57
07.0400 320	Field equipment, basketball backstops, add for glass, fan backstop	EACH	1,011.25		1,011.25		1,011.25
07.0400 325	Field equipment, basketball backstops, add for glass, rectangular backs	EACH	1,207.73		1,207.73		1,207.73
07.0400 330	Field equipment, basketball backstops, add for power operation	EACH	803.19		803.19		803.19
07.0400 335	Field equipment, gym walls, padded	SF	9.51		9.51		9.51
07.0400 340	Field equipment, gym floors, sub-floor or base not included, synthetic gym floor, 3/16"	SF	7.84		7.84		7.84
07.0400 345	Field equipment, gym floor, sub-floor or base not included, synthetic gym floor, 3/8"	SF	8.59		8.59		8.59
07.0400 350	Field equipment, gym floor, sub-floor or base not included, maple, wood, spring	SF	22.63		22.63		22.63
07.0400 355	Field equipment, gym floor, sub-floor or base not included, rubber cusion maple	SF	12.67		12.67		12.67
07.0400 360	Field equipment, gym floor, sub-floor or base not included, maple over sleepers	SF	18.18		18.18		18.18
07.0400 365	Field equipment, gym floor, add for apparatus inserts	EACH	60.65		60.65		60.65
07.0400 370	Field equipment, gym seating, bleachers, telescoping, manual	SEAT	74.13	16.70	90.83	12.20	86.33
07.0400 375	Field equipment, gym seating, bleachers, portable, hydraulic	SEAT	75.35		75.35		75.35
07.0400 380	Field equipment, score boards basketball, economy	EACH	2,806.70	679.83	3,486.53	496.54	3,303.24
07.0400 385	Field equipment, score boards basketball, good	EACH	2,819.87	1,246.35	4,066.22	910.33	3,730.20
07.0400 390	Field equipment, score boards basketball, best	EACH	4,197.05	1,982.90	6,179.95	1,448.29	5,645.34

CSI #	7.0 EQUIPMENT Description	Unit	Material	Union Install	Union Total	Open Install	Open Total
07.0500	**INDUSTRIAL EQUIPMENT**						
07.0500 100	Industrial equipment, service station, 3 island, 4 tanks	EACH	652,398.49		652,398.49		652,398.49
07.0500 105	Industrial equipment, service station, remodel to self-serve, average	EACH	186,399.57		186,399.57		186,399.57
07.0500 110	Industrial equipment, service station, air compressor, 2 HP, with receiver	EACH	3,280.60	321.73	3,602.33	139.89	3,420.49
07.0500 115	Industrial equipment, service station, air compressor, 3 HP, with receiver	EACH	3,448.37	321.73	3,770.10	139.89	3,588.26
07.0500 120	Industrial equipment, service station, gas pump, full size, 1/2 HP	EACH	2,423.17	160.83	2,584.00	69.93	2,493.10
07.0500 125	Industrial equipment, service station, gas pump, submerge turbine, 1/3 HP	EACH	1,146.30	86.36	1,232.66	50.77	1,197.07
07.0500 130	Industrial equipment, service station, gas pump, submerge turbine, 3/4 HP	EACH	1,327.15	86.36	1,413.51	50.77	1,377.92
07.0500 135	Industrial equipment, service station, gas dispenser, computing, single hose	EACH	4,072.81	87.05	4,159.86	45.99	4,118.80
07.0500 140	Industrial equipment, service station, add for vapor recovery	EACH	838.77		838.77		838.77
07.0500 145	Industrial equipment, service station, gas dispenser, computing, dual hose	EACH	8,145.65	87.05	8,232.70	45.99	8,191.64
07.0500 147	Industrial equipment, service station, fill boxes, 12", cast iron	EACH	64.29	78.15	142.44	41.29	105.58
07.0500 150	service station, air/water, bibbs, underground reels	EACH	438.00	69.67	507.67	36.81	474.81
07.0500 155	Industrial equipment, service station, add for electric thermal unit	EACH	177.08		177.08		177.08
07.0500 160	Industrial equipment, service station, hoist, 1 post, 8000#, semi-hydraulic	EACH	3,700.04	720.46	4,420.50	473.33	4,173.37
07.0500 165	Industrial equipment, service station, hoist, 2 post, 8000#, semi-hydraulic	EACH	6,100.05	1,545.73	7,645.78	1,015.52	7,115.57
07.0500 170	Industrial equipment, service station, cash box & pedestal stand	EACH	177.08	80.43	257.51	34.97	212.05
07.0500 175	Industrial equipment, service station, tire changer, air operated	EACH	1,781.44	104.46	1,885.90	55.19	1,836.63
07.0500 180	Industrial equipment, service station, lube, oil and air reels/rem pump	EACH	2,143.56	783.53	2,927.09	413.96	2,557.52
07.0500 185	Industrial equipment, service station, exhaust fume system, underground	STA.	1,160.32		1,160.32		1,160.32
07.0500 190	Industrial equipment, service station, island metal furring for 3 islands	1 STA	1,118.34	156.22	1,274.56	102.63	1,220.97
07.0500 195	Industrial equipment, service station, dynamometer	EACH	70,150.32	9,629.46	79,779.78	6,780.05	76,930.37
07.0500 200	Industrial equipment, shop miscellaneous, sawdust collector	EACH	12,899.83	927.32	13,827.15	609.23	13,509.06
07.0500 205	Industrial equipment, shop miscellaneous, sawdust collector, large capacity	EACH	17,098.08	927.32	18,025.40	609.23	17,707.31
07.0500 210	Industrial equipment, shop miscellaneous, paint spray booths	SF	13.27		13.27		13.27
07.0500 215	Industrial equipment, shop miscellaneous, paint spray booth car	EACH	58,124.60	2,526.34	60,650.94	1,659.76	59,784.36
07.0500 220	Industrial equipment, shop miscellaneous, paint spray booth, 60' bus	EACH	250,537.07	61,524.13	312,061.20	43,318.82	293,855.89
07.0600	**PARKING LOT EQUIPMENT**						
07.0600 100	Parking lot equipment, automatic gate, automatic arm, 8'	EACH	3,735.45	156.22	3,891.67	102.63	3,838.08
07.0600 105	Parking lot equipment, traffic detector	EACH	1,195.35	195.28	1,390.63	128.29	1,323.64
07.0600 110	Parking lot equipment, ticket dispenser, control unit	EACH	4,452.69	130.18	4,582.87	85.53	4,538.22
07.0600 115	Parking lot equipment, gate operator card/coin	EACH	1,195.35	475.58	1,670.93	334.86	1,530.21
07.0700	**MATERIAL HANDLING EQUIPMENT**						
07.0700 100	Dock bumper, 10"x4 1/2" x2'	EA	92.45	55.60	148.05	40.61	133.06
07.0700 105	Scissors lift, 56", 2000#, 4'x4' deck	EA	8,813.01		8,813.01		8,813.01
07.0700 110	Dock leveler, heavy duty, hydraulic	EA	7,647.21	722.41	8,369.62	527.64	8,174.85
07.0700 115	Dock leveler, accordian door, 7'6"x8'	EA	1,192.43	746.86	1,939.29	545.50	1,737.93
07.0800	**LABORATORY EQUIPMENT**						
07.0800 100	Laboratory equipment, instructor's table, includes sinks, fixtures and acid resistant tops, 12'x36"x36"	EACH	3,044.73	264.30	3,309.03	193.04	3,237.77
07.0800 105	Laboratory equipment, student table, for 8 students, 15'x5'x36"	EACH	6,422.53	264.30	6,686.83	193.04	6,615.57

CSI #	7.0 EQUIPMENT Description	Unit	Material	Union Install	Union Total	Open Install	Open Total
07.0800	**LABORATORY EQUIPMENT (Cont.)**						
07.0800 110	Laboratory equipment, steel cabinet, base	LF	262.82	152.52	415.34	111.40	374.22
07.0800 115	Laboratory equipment, wood cabinet, base	LF	216.75	152.52	369.27	111.40	328.15
07.0800 120	Laboratory equipment, plastic laminated cabinet, base	LF	196.63	152.52	349.15	111.40	308.03
07.0800 125	Laboratory equipment, steel cabinet, knee space, drawer unit	LF	168.37	96.91	265.28	70.78	239.15
07.0800 130	Laboratory equipment, wood cabinet, knee space, drawer unit	LF	140.26	96.81	237.07	70.71	210.97
07.0800 135	Laboratory equipment, plastic laminated cabinet, knee space, drawer unit	LF	126.24	96.72	222.96	70.64	196.88
07.0800 140	Laboratory equipment, steel cabinet, wall hung	LF	193.14	74.08	267.22	54.11	247.25
07.0800 145	Laboratory equipment, wood cabinet, wall hung	LF	201.16	74.08	275.24	54.11	255.27
07.0800 150	Laboratory equipment, plastic laminated cabinet, wall hung	LF	127.00	74.08	201.08	54.11	181.11
07.0800 155	Laboratory equipment, plastic laminated cabinet top	LF	72.16		72.16		72.16
07.0800 160	Laboratory equipment, epoxy resin, acid resistant cabinet top	LF	168.37		168.37		168.37
07.0800 165	Laboratory equipment, stainless steel cabinet top	LF	242.52		242.52		242.52
07.0800 170	Laboratory equipment, stainless steel cabinet top	LF	96.18		96.18		96.18
07.0800 175	Laboratory equipment, centrifuge, high speed, portable	EACH	2,465.28		2,465.28		2,465.28
07.0800 180	Laboratory equipment, centrifuge, ultra high speed, explosion proof	EACH	11,224.05		11,224.05		11,224.05
07.0800 185	Laboratory equipment, centrifuge, ultra high speed, refer	EACH	17,838.24		17,838.24		17,838.24
07.0800 190	Reagent rack, metal upright, wall, 1 tier	EACH	96.18	43.86	140.04	32.03	128.21
07.0800 195	Reagent rack, metal upright center, 1 tier	EACH	118.24	43.86	162.10	32.03	150.27
07.0800 200	Laboratory stoarage, wardrobe	LF	269.50	62.19	331.69	45.42	314.92
07.0800 205	Laboratory equipment miscellaneous, fume hood	LF	1,202.56	323.03	1,525.59	235.94	1,438.50
07.0800 210	Laboratory equipment miscellaneous, add for stainless steel	LF	601.27		601.27		601.27
07.0800 215	Laboratory equipment miscellaneous, water distiller, 10 GPM	EACH	7,591.13	404.52	7,995.65	253.60	7,844.73
07.0800 220	Laboratory equipment miscellaneous, water tank, stainless steel, 50 GAL	EACH	8,284.71	404.52	8,689.23	253.60	8,538.31
07.0800 225	Laboratory equipment miscellaneous, washer	EACH	9,870.63	809.01	10,679.64	507.18	10,377.81
07.0800 230	Laboratory equipment miscellaneous, portable water distiller, 18 LPH	EACH	1,271.99	132.15	1,404.14	96.52	1,368.51
07.0800 235	Laundry equipment, unloading washer, 60"x44", 400#	EACH	103,651.99	15,036.87	118,688.86	10,982.81	114,634.80
07.0800 240	Laundry equipment, extractor, 200#, with accessories	EACH	83,473.25	12,265.06	95,738.31	8,958.30	92,431.55
07.0800 245	Laundry equipment, washer/extractor, 600#	EACH	151,351.01	21,978.91	173,329.92	16,053.21	167,404.22
07.0800 250	Laundry equipment, dryer, gas or steam, 200/400#	EACH	68,405.05	9,934.67	78,339.72	7,256.20	75,661.25
07.0800 255	Laundry equipment, flat ironer, 6 roller	EACH	153,926.59	22,341.94	176,268.53	16,318.36	170,244.95
07.0800 260	Laundry equipment, ironer/folder, 2 lane	EACH	61,793.61	9,076.10	70,869.71	6,629.11	68,422.72
07.0800 265	Laundry equipment, folder, 3 lane	EACH	38,893.95	5,641.89	44,535.84	4,120.79	43,014.74
07.0900	**LIBRARY EQUIPMENT**						
07.0900 100	Library equipment, study carrels, hardwood, 36"x24"x29", 2 face	EACH	448.21	99.55	547.76	72.71	520.92
07.0900 105	Library equipment, study carrels, hardwood, individual lights	EACH	79.95	59.77	139.72	43.66	123.61
07.0900 110	Library equipment, study carrels, hardwood, power post recept	EACH	22.32	59.77	82.09	43.66	65.98
07.0900 115	Library equipment, table, 60"x36"x39"	EACH	1,430.03		1,430.03		1,430.03
07.0900 120	Library equipment, table, 48" round	EACH	1,295.56		1,295.56		1,295.56
07.0900 125	Library equipment, chairs, wood	EACH	241.70		241.70		241.70
07.0900 130	Library equipment, card catalog cabinet, wood, 60 tray	EACH	1,093.63		1,093.63		1,093.63
07.0900 135	Library equipment, card catalog cabinet, wood, 30 tray	EACH	629.18		629.18		629.18
07.0900 140	Library equipment, charging counters, hardwood	LF	159.33	59.77	219.10	43.66	202.99
07.0900 145	Library equipment, charging counter top	SF	14.16	9.96	24.12	7.27	21.43
07.0900 150	Library equipment, shelving, metal, bracket, 3 tier, 3x3	EACH	184.92	54.75	239.67	39.99	224.91

CSI #	7.0 EQUIPMENT Description	Unit	Material	Union Install	Union Total	Open Install	Open Total
07.0900	**LIBRARY EQUIPMENT (Cont.)**						
07.0900 155	Library equipment, shelving, metal, bracket, 5 tier, 3x3	EACH	199.19	59.77	258.96	43.66	242.85
07.1000	**HOSPITAL EQUIPMENT**						
07.1000 100	Nurses monitoring equipment, CCU/ICU, cardioscope, 1 channel, bed side	EACH	4,726.00		4,726.00		4,726.00
07.1000 105	Nurses monitoring equipment, CCU/ICU, BP monitor, bed side, with readout	EACH	7,256.00		7,256.00		7,256.00
07.1000 110	Nurses monitoring equipment, CCU/ICU, CCU bed & nurse display, 8 bed	EACH	147,650.00		147,650.00		147,650.00
07.1000 115	Nurses monitoring equipment, CCU/ICU, telemetry, wireless, 8 bed	EACH	403,829.00		403,829.00		403,829.00
07.1000 120	Nursing acute care equipment, modular wall unit, 1 bed core, prewire	EACH	5,370.00	685.00	6,055.00	500.00	5,870.00
07.1000 125	Nursing acute care equipment, modular wall unit, 24" nurse treatment	EACH	712.00	158.00	870.00	116.00	828.00
07.1000 130	Nursing acute care equipment, mod wall unit, 24" storage center	EACH	771.00	174.00	945.00	127.00	898.00
07.1000 135	Nursing acute care equipment, patient communications & convenience unit	EACH	1,665.00		1,665.00		1,665.00
07.1000 140	Nursing acute care equipment, cubicle track & curtain, to 8' high	LF	13.00	4.00	17.00	3.00	16.00
07.1000 145	Nursing acute care equipment, mirror, medicine cabinet, stainless steel, resess, light	EACH	513.00	115.00	628.00	84.00	597.00
07.1000 150	Nursing station/core equipment, nurse chart desk	EACH	1,171.00		1,171.00		1,171.00
07.1000 155	Nursing station/core equipment, nurse call, 40 station, two way	EACH	22,069.00	5,834.00	27,903.00	4,261.00	26,330.00
07.1000 160	Nursing station/core equipment, nourishment station, 84" x 80", stainless steel	EACH	20,016.00	352.00	20,368.00	257.00	20,273.00
07.1000 165	Nursing station/core equipment, medical prep cab, 72" x 80", stainless steel, lock	EACH	9,238.00	352.00	9,590.00	257.00	9,495.00
07.1000 170	Nursing station/core equipment, IV prep center, 60" x 80", stainless steel	EACH	7,955.00	352.00	8,307.00	257.00	8,212.00
07.1000 175	Nursing station/core equipment, sani-prep maintenance station, stainless steel	EACH	5,774.00	1,526.00	7,300.00	1,115.00	6,889.00
07.1000 180	Nursing station/core equipment, multi-use tote carts, average cost	EACH	1,622.00		1,622.00		1,622.00
07.1000 185	Nursing station/core equipment, modular storage systems	LF	369.00		369.00		369.00
07.1000 190	Corridors, hospital corner guard, plastic, 8'	EACH	144.00	43.00	187.00	31.00	175.00
07.1000 195	Corridors, hospital corner guard, plastic, 4'	EACH	82.00	32.00	114.00	23.00	105.00
07.1000 200	Corridors, hospital corner guard, stainless steel, 8'	EACH	348.00	138.00	486.00	100.00	448.00
07.1000 205	Corridors, hospital corner guard, stainless steel, 4'	EACH	174.00	74.00	248.00	54.00	228.00
07.1000 210	Surgery tables & accessories, surgery table, electric, stationary	EACH	24,222.00	2,247.00	26,469.00	1,641.00	25,863.00
07.1000 215	Surgery tables & accessories, surgery service island, complete	EACH	8,769.00	1,828.00	10,597.00	1,335.00	10,104.00
07.1000 220	Surgery tables & accessories, surgical monitor, conduct casters	EACH	9,140.00		9,140.00		9,140.00
07.1000 225	Surgery tables & accessories, conductivity meter, current leakage detector	EACH	1,012.00	254.00	1,266.00	186.00	1,198.00
07.1000 230	Surgery tables & accessories, surgical clock, stainless steel, auto reset	EACH	1,222.00	261.00	1,483.00	191.00	1,413.00
07.1000 235	Obstetrical & nursery equipment, delivery table	EACH	7,015.00	1,764.00	8,779.00	1,288.00	8,303.00
07.1000 240	Obstetrical & nursery equipment, incubator, isolation servo-care	EACH	6,487.00		6,487.00		6,487.00
07.1000 245	Obstetrical & nursery equipment, incubator, warming	EACH	2,123.00		2,123.00		2,123.00
07.1000 250	Surgical lighting, surgery light, surface mounted, 3 arm	EACH	27,393.00	2,925.00	30,318.00	2,124.00	29,517.00
07.1000 255	Surgical lighting, surgery light, surface mounted, 2 arm	EACH	19,024.00	2,693.00	21,717.00	1,956.00	20,980.00
07.1000 260	Surgical lighting, surgery light, surface mounted, 1 arm	EACH	13,271.00	1,954.00	15,225.00	1,419.00	14,690.00
07.1000 265	Surgical lighting, add for auxiliary light head	EACH	6,904.00	812.00	7,716.00	590.00	7,494.00
07.1000 270	Surgical lighting, surgical light intensity control, 600W	EACH	767.00	609.00	1,376.00	442.00	1,209.00
07.1000 275	Surgical lighting, surgical light intensity control, 300W	EACH	575.00	352.00	927.00	257.00	832.00

CSI #	7.0 EQUIPMENT Description	Unit	Material	Union Install	Union Total	Open Install	Open Total
07.1000	**HOSPITAL EQUIPMENT (Cont.)**						
07.1000 280	Scrub & clean room equipment, scrub station, stainless steel, 3 bay, base mounted	EACH	9,999.00	1,682.00	11,681.00	1,054.00	11,053.00
07.1000 285	Scrub & clean room equipment, scrub station, stainless steel, 1 bay, base mounted	EACH	7,142.00	1,103.00	8,245.00	691.00	7,833.00
07.1000 290	Scrub & clean room equipment, solution warm cab, stainless steel, 24"X30"X74"	EACH	7,385.00	276.00	7,661.00	173.00	7,558.00
07.1000 295	Scrub & clean room equipment, surgery storage console, stainless steel, 12'	EACH	4,918.00	176.00	5,094.00	129.00	5,047.00
07.1000 300	Scrub & clean room equipment, suture/drug cab, stainless steel, 36"X18"X81"	EACH	1,627.00	132.00	1,759.00	97.00	1,724.00
07.1000 305	Scrub & clean room equipment, instrument cab, stainless steel, 48"X18"X60"	EACH	2,206.00	132.00	2,338.00	97.00	2,303.00
07.1000 310	Scrub & clean room equipment, sterilizer, 16"X16"X26"	EACH	22,811.00	440.00	23,251.00	322.00	23,133.00
07.1000 315	Cardiac emergency equipment, monitor/resuscitation unit, with DC defibrillator	EACH	17,872.00		17,872.00		17,872.00
07.1000 320	Cardiac emergency equipment, mobile emergency utility, crash cart	EACH	9,748.00		9,748.00		9,748.00
07.1000 325	Cardiac emergency equipment, DC defibrillator	EACH	5,199.00		5,199.00		5,199.00
07.1000 330	Cardiac emergency equipment, external cardiac compressor	EACH	5,849.00		5,849.00		5,849.00
07.1000 335	Emergency accessories, treatment cabinet, mobile unit	EACH	1,787.00		1,787.00		1,787.00
07.1000 340	Emergency accessories, treatment cabinet, with suction compressor	EACH	3,168.00		3,168.00		3,168.00
07.1000 345	Emergency accessories, exam lights, 22", ceiling mounted	EACH	3,481.00	685.00	4,166.00	498.00	3,979.00
07.1000 350	Emergency accessories, plaster sink with trap & fittings	EACH	1,393.00	558.00	1,951.00	350.00	1,743.00
07.1000 355	Emergency accessories, splint cabinet with plaster bins	EACH	1,214.00	226.00	1,440.00	165.00	1,379.00
07.1000 360	Sterilizers, recessed, with automatic doors, sterilizer, 24"x36"x36", 1 door, steam	EACH	92,316.00	27,505.00	119,821.00	17,243.00	109,559.00
07.1000 365	Sterilizers, recessed, with automatic doors, sterilizer, 24"x36"x48", 1 door, steam	EACH	94,086.00	27,505.00	121,591.00	17,243.00	111,329.00
07.1000 370	Sterilizers, recessed, with automatic doors, sterilizer, gas, 24"x36"x60", 1 door	EACH	110,617.00	22,216.00	132,833.00	13,928.00	124,545.00
07.1000 375	Sterilizers, recessed, with automatic doors, sterilizer, gas, 24"x36"x60", pass-thru	EACH	116,025.00	22,216.00	138,241.00	13,928.00	129,953.00
07.1000 380	Sterilizers, recessed, with automatic doors, sterilizer, steam, 24"x36"x48", pass-thru	EACH	118,134.00	27,505.00	145,639.00	17,243.00	135,377.00
07.1000 385	Sterilizers, recessed, with automatic doors, sterilizer, steam, 24"x36"x60", pass-thru	EACH	120,217.00	27,505.00	147,722.00	17,243.00	137,460.00
07.1000 390	Sterilizers, recessed, with automatic doors, sterilizer, gas/cyro, 24"x36"x60", pass-thru	EACH	99,148.00	23,844.00	122,992.00	14,948.00	114,096.00
07.1000 395	Sterilizers, recessed, with automatic doors, sterilizer, gas/cyro, 24"x36"x48", 1 door	EACH	84,382.00	10,963.00	95,345.00	6,873.00	91,255.00
07.1000 400	Sterilizers, recessed, with automatic doors, gas, aerator, 24"x36"x60"	EACH	10,548.00	2,965.00	13,513.00	1,859.00	12,407.00
07.1000 405	Sterilizers, recessed, with automatic doors, gas, aerator, 24"x36"x48"	EACH	5,696.00	1,590.00	7,286.00	997.00	6,693.00
07.1000 410	Sterilizers, accessories, loading car & carriage, large	EACH	6,961.00		6,961.00		6,961.00
07.1000 415	Sterilizers, accessories, loading car & carriage, medium	EACH	5,696.00		5,696.00		5,696.00
07.1000 420	Sterilizers, accessories, steam general, 10 BHP/110, PSIG/208V, 3PH	EACH	5,010.00	1,200.00	6,210.00	752.00	5,762.00
07.1000 425	Instrument & utensil washer/sterilizer, instrument cleaner, sonic, 12x11x24, 1 comp	EACH	16,349.00	5,598.00	21,947.00	3,509.00	19,858.00
07.1000 430	Instrument & utensil washer/sterilizer, instrument cleaner, sonic, 12x11x24, 2 comp	EACH	22,054.00	5,598.00	27,652.00	3,509.00	25,563.00
07.1000 435	Instrument & utensil washer/sterilizer, glass wash, steam, 24x20x24, pass-thru	EACH	34,692.00	8,078.00	42,770.00	5,064.00	39,756.00

CSI #	7.0 EQUIPMENT / Description	Unit	Material	Union Install	Union Total	Open Install	Open Total
07.1000	**HOSPITAL EQUIPMENT (Cont.)**						
07.1000 440	Instrument & utensil washer/sterilizer, utensil wash, 27x27x60, free stand	EACH	14,767.00	3,188.00	17,955.00	1,998.00	16,765.00
07.1000 445	Instrument & utensil washer/sterilizer, utensil wash, conveyor, Pass-thru	EACH	50,102.00	11,878.00	61,980.00	7,446.00	57,548.00
07.1000 450	Instrument & utensil washer/sterilizer, drying Oven, 25"x25"x50", steam	EACH	12,235.00	2,706.00	14,941.00	1,696.00	13,931.00
07.1000 455	Instrument & utensil washer/sterilizer, charging Oven, 5', stainless steel, 2 sink	EACH	2,320.00	669.00	2,989.00	419.00	2,739.00
07.1000 460	Hospital cart wash, pit mounted, cart wash, 92"x72"x98", pass-thru, pit	EACH	96,153.00	23,182.00	119,335.00	14,533.00	110,686.00
07.1000 465	Hospital cart wash, pit mounted, cart wash, 92"x72"x196", auto, 2 stage	EACH	241,041.00	28,022.00	269,063.00	17,568.00	258,609.00
07.1000 470	Central pharmacy equipment, pharmacy unit w/basic modules	LF	592.00		592.00		592.00
07.1000 475	Central pharmacy equipment, medication refer, 115 CF, stainless steel	EAcH	4,107.00	326.00	4,433.00	204.00	4,311.00
07.1000 480	Central pharmacy equipment, water purification mod, rev Osm, 6 LPM	EACH	3,392.00	812.00	4,204.00	509.00	3,901.00
07.1000 485	Central pharmacy equipment, laminated flow hood, 36" work area	EACH	7,713.00	1,550.00	9,263.00	972.00	8,685.00
07.1000 490	Central pharmacy equipment, hi-density storage, caster/track	EACH	3,214.00	255.00	3,469.00	160.00	3,374.00
07.1000 495	Central laboratory equipment, lab work counter, with base units	LF	522.00		522.00		522.00
07.1000 500	Central laboratory equipment, lab sterilizer, 16"x26", 208V, 3PH	EACH	6,428.00	815.00	7,243.00	511.00	6,939.00
07.1000 505	Central laboratory equipment, liquid nitrogen refer, 30 CF, 190 DEG	EACH	28,568.00	849.00	29,417.00	532.00	29,100.00
07.1000 510	Central laboratory equipment, water distribution, steam, 10 GPH, wall	EACH	15,821.00	1,161.00	16,982.00	728.00	16,549.00
07.1000 515	Central laboratory equipment, water tank, stainless steel, 50 GAL, wall, mounted	EACH	9,493.00	1,042.00	10,535.00	653.00	10,146.00
07.1000 520	Central laboratory equipment, specimen pass-thru box, stainless steel	EACH	196.00	137.00	333.00	86.00	282.00
07.1000 525	X-ray equipment, x-ray, ceiling mounted, telescoping	EACH	38,567.00	5,064.00	43,631.00	3,678.00	42,245.00
07.1000 530	X-ray equipment, x-ray, ceiling wall mounted, chest	EACH	11,427.00	2,501.00	13,928.00	1,816.00	13,243.00
07.1000 535	X-ray equipment, mobile x-ray unit	EACH	47,768.00		47,768.00		47,768.00
07.1000 540	X-ray equipment, x-ray control unit	EACH	12,641.00	2,766.00	15,407.00	2,009.00	14,650.00
07.1000 545	X-ray equipment, multix table	EACH	24,104.00	5,275.00	29,379.00	3,831.00	27,935.00
07.1000 550	X-ray processing equipment, auto film processor, complete	EACH	37,953.00		37,953.00		37,953.00
07.1000 555	X-ray processing equipment, developer tank, 10 G, stainless steel, 2 comp, mix valve	EACH	2,052.00		2,052.00		2,052.00
07.1000 560	X-ray processing equipment, x-ray pass box, 2 comp, RO-IN frame	EACH	1,714.00		1,714.00		1,714.00
07.1000 565	X-ray processing equipment, x-ray film loading bin	EACH	696.00		696.00		696.00
07.1000 570	X-ray processing equipment, revolving door, 36"x80", safe hinge	EACH	3,535.00		3,535.00		3,535.00
07.1000 575	X-ray viewing equipment, x-ray film illuminating, wet, drip tray	EACH	341.00		341.00		341.00
07.1000 580	X-ray viewing equipment, x-ray film illluminating, 1 panel 14x17	EACH	272.00		272.00		272.00
07.1000 585	X-ray viewing equipment, x-ray film illluminating, 2 panel 30x18	EACH	518.00		518.00		518.00
07.1000 590	X-ray viewing equipment, x-ray film illluminating, multibank, 4/4	EACH	2,468.00		2,468.00		2,468.00
07.1000 595	X-ray viewing equipment, x-ray film illluminating, multibank, 6/6	EACH	3,285.00		3,285.00		3,285.00
07.1000 600	X-ray viewing equipment, x-ray shield, view glass, deluxe	EACH	1,125.00		1,125.00		1,125.00
07.1000 605	Nuclear equipment, gamma camera, 10" view, complete	EACH	424,660.00		424,660.00		424,660.00
07.1000 610	Nuclear equipment, gamma camera, 15" view, complete	EACH	478,225.00		478,225.00		478,225.00
07.1000 615	Ultra sound equipment, ultra sound unit complete	EACH	247,558.00		247,558.00		247,558.00
07.1000 620	Hydrotherapy units, hubbard tank, 400 gallon, twin eject	EACH	28,925.00		28,925.00		28,925.00
07.1000 625	Hydrotherapy units, treatment/wade tank, 1000 gallon	EACH	35,353.00		35,353.00		35,353.00

CSI #	7.0 EQUIPMENT Description	Unit	Material	Union Install	Union Total	Open Install	Open Total
07.1000	**HOSPITAL EQUIPMENT (Cont.)**						
07.1000 630	Hydrotherapy units, whirlpool, stainless steel, 85 gallon, leg & hip	EACH	5,464.00		5,464.00		5,464.00
07.1000 635	Hydrotherapy units, whirlpool, stainless steel, 80 gallon, arm, leg & hip	EACH	4,714.00		4,714.00		4,714.00
07.1000 640	Hydrotherapy units, whirlpool, stainless steel, 80 gallon, arm	EACH	3,482.00		3,482.00		3,482.00
07.1000 645	Hydrotherapy units, moisture heat therapy unit, table	EACH	4,558.00		4,558.00		4,558.00
07.1000 650	Hydrotherapy units, mobile paraffin bath	EACH	1,670.00		1,670.00		1,670.00
07.1000 655	Hydrotherapy units, mobile sitz bath	EACH	455.00		455.00		455.00
07.1000 660	Inhalation therapy equipment, ventilator, complete	EACH	15,489.00		15,489.00		15,489.00
07.1000 665	Inhalation therapy equipment, suction unit, stainless steel cabinet	EACH	1,428.00		1,428.00		1,428.00
07.1000 670	Inhalation therapy equipment, IPPB inhaler	EACH	1,883.00		1,883.00		1,883.00
07.1000 675	Inhalation therapy equipment, air volume tester, lung	EACH	7,592.00		7,592.00		7,592.00
07.1000 680	Physical therapy equipment, exercise unit, complete	EACH	7,761.00		7,761.00		7,761.00
07.1000 685	Physical therapy equipment, exercise chair	EACH	2,278.00		2,278.00		2,278.00
07.1000 690	Physical therapy equipment, treadmill, motorized, 5 speed	EACH	4,938.00		4,938.00		4,938.00
07.1000 695	Physical therapy equipment, treadmill, adjustable angle	EACH	1,063.00		1,063.00		1,063.00
07.1000 700	Physical therapy equipment, rowing machine	EACH	987.00		987.00		987.00
07.1000 705	Physical therapy equipment, rehabilitation loom	EACH	1,594.00		1,594.00		1,594.00
07.1100	**DENTAL EQUIPMENT**						
07.1100 100	Dental equipment, dental chair, deluxe, with lift	EACH	10,081.00		10,081.00		10,081.00
07.1100 105	Dental equipment, dental chair, standard, tilt	EACH	5,867.00		5,867.00		5,867.00
07.1100 110	Dental equipment, instrument unit, 4 port, tray, chair mounted	EACH	6,585.00		6,585.00		6,585.00
07.1100 115	Dental equipment, assistant instrument unit, chair mounted	EACH	5,014.00		5,014.00		5,014.00
07.1100 117	Dental equipment, mobile instrument unit, cabinet	EACH	7,538.00		7,538.00		7,538.00
07.1100 120	Dental equipment, mobile assistant's instrument unit, cabinet	EACH	6,478.00		6,478.00		6,478.00
07.1100 125	Dental equipment, instrument unit, cabinet, wall mounted	EACH	18,851.00		18,851.00		18,851.00
07.1100 130	Dental equipment, dental light, chair or unit mounted	EACH	1,710.00		1,710.00		1,710.00
07.1100 135	Dental equipment, dental light, ceiling mounted	EACH	1,710.00		1,710.00		1,710.00
07.1100 140	Dental equipment, dental x-ray, wall mounted	EACH	13,955.00		13,955.00		13,955.00
07.1100 141	Dental equipment, dental x-ray, wall mounted, extra remote HD	EACH	22,061.00		22,061.00		22,061.00
07.1100 142	Dental equipment, dental sterilizer, chemiclave	EACH	1,966.00		1,966.00		1,966.00
07.1100 143	Dental equipment, dental sterilizer, vibraclean	EACH	1,199.00		1,199.00		1,199.00
07.1100 144	Dental equipment, dental compressor with dryer	EACH	3,557.00		3,557.00		3,557.00
07.1100 145	Dental equipment, laboratory, dust collector, pedestal	EACH	2,492.00	484.00	2,976.00	303.00	2,795.00
07.1100 150	Dental equipment, laboratory, waxing unit, 3 compartment	EACH	99.00		99.00		99.00
07.1100 155	Dental equipment, laboratory, pneumatic curing unit	EACH	212.00		212.00		212.00
07.1100 160	Dental equipment, laboratory, double pneumatic press	EACH	1,481.00		1,481.00		1,481.00
07.1100 165	Dental equipment, laboratory, curing tank assembly	EACH	1,152.00	219.00	1,371.00	137.00	1,289.00
07.1100 170	Dental equipment, laboratory, boilout assembly	EACH	946.00	180.00	1,126.00	113.00	1,059.00
07.1100 175	Dental equipment, laboratory, plaster bin, 4 compartment, 300#	EACH	657.00	125.00	782.00	78.00	735.00
07.1100 180	Dental equipment, laboratory furniture, dental lab tech bench, 5 drawer	EACH	1,249.00	190.00	1,439.00	139.00	1,388.00
07.1100 185	Dental equipment, laboratory furniture, dental lab, 2 door cabinet, 36"x24"x36"	EACH	1,414.00	244.00	1,658.00	178.00	1,592.00
07.1100 190	Dental equipment, laboratory furniture, dental lab, 1 door cabinet, 24"x24"x36"	EACH	1,100.00	190.00	1,290.00	139.00	1,239.00
07.1100 195	Dental equipment, laboratory furniture, dental lab, 1 door cabinet, corner	EACH	1,728.00	298.00	2,026.00	218.00	1,946.00

CSI #	7.0 EQUIPMENT Description	Unit	Material	Union Install	Union Total	Open Install	Open Total
07.1200	**STAGE EQUIPMENT**						
07.1200 100	Stage equipment, lighting instruments, footlights, disappearing, reflect	PER 5	181.00		181.00		181.00
07.1200 105	Stage equipment, lighting instruments, add for motorized	PER 5	312.00		312.00		312.00
07.1200 110	Stage equipment, lighting instruments, border lights, 1 row, reflect, 3 color	PER 8	95.00		95.00		95.00
07.1200 115	Stage equipment, lighting instruments, border lights, 1 row, roundel, 3 color	PER 8	132.00		132.00		132.00
07.1200 120	Stage equipment, lighting instruments, border lights, 2 row, roundel, 4 color	PER 8	335.00		335.00		335.00
07.1200 123	Stage equipment, lighting instruments, ball, mirrored, rotating, 30"	EACH	2,379.00	1,569.00	3,948.00	1,139.00	3,518.00
07.1200 125	Stage equipment, lighting instruments, spotlight, follow, carbon arc	EACH	6,542.00		6,542.00		6,542.00
07.1200 130	Stage equipment, lighting instruments, spotlight, follow, quartz halogen	EACH	2,082.00		2,082.00		2,082.00
07.1200 135	Stage equipment, lighting instruments, quartz spot, ellip, iod lamp, 3000W	EACH	1,933.00		1,933.00		1,933.00
07.1200 140	Stage equipment, lighting instruments, quartz spot, ellip, iod lamp, 1500W	EACH	669.00		669.00		669.00
07.1200 145	Stage equipment, lighting instruments, quartz spot, ellip, iod lamp, 500W	EACH	416.00		416.00		416.00
07.1200 150	Stage equipment, lighting instruments, quartz spot, fresnl, iod lamp, 1000W	EACH	476.00		476.00		476.00
07.1200 155	Stage equipment, lighting instruments, quartz spot, fresnl, iod lamp, 500W	EACH	282.00		282.00		282.00
07.1200 160	Stage equipment, lighting instruments, color wheel, motorized, 20"	EACH	282.00		282.00		282.00
07.1200 165	Stage equipment, lighting instruments, quartz beam proj, iod lamp, 1500W	EACH	461.00		461.00		461.00
07.1200 170	Stage equipment, lighting instruments, floodlight, utility, incandescent, 1000W	EACH	253.00		253.00		253.00
07.1200 175	Stage equipment, lighting instruments, floodlight, scoop, iod lamp, 18", 750W	EACH	282.00		282.00		282.00
07.1200 180	Stage equipment, lighting and control accessories, light tower, 4'x6'x15'	EACH	7,434.00		7,434.00		7,434.00
07.1200 185	Stage equipment, lighting and control accessories, light stand, cast iron base, 24"	EACH	342.00		342.00		342.00
07.1200 190	Stage equipment, lighting and control accessories, plug strip	LF	50.00		50.00		50.00
07.1200 195	Stage equipment, lighting and control accessories, floor pocket, plug, 4 outlet, 100A	EACH	238.00		238.00		238.00
07.1200 200	Stage equipment, lighting and control accessories, floor pocket, plug, 2 outlet, 50A	EACH	208.00		208.00		208.00
07.1200 205	Stage equipment, lighting and control accessories, wall pocket, surf plug, 3 outlet, 50A	EACH	74.00		74.00		74.00
07.1200 210	Stage equipment, lighting and control accessories, wall pocket, surf plug, 1 outlet, 50A	EACH	164.00		164.00		164.00
07.1200 215	Stage equipment, lighting and control accessories, wall pocket, flush, 2 outlet, 100A	EACH	288.00		288.00		288.00
07.1200 220	Stage equipment, lighting and control accessories, wall pocket, flush, 4 outlet, 50A	EACH	253.00		253.00		253.00
07.1200 225	Stage equipment, lighting and control accessories, catwalk, wood, metal pipe mount rail	LF	21.00	89.00	110.00	65.00	86.00
07.1200 230	Stage equipment, rigging curtains and drops, acoustic cloud, adjust, wood frame	SF	4.00	7.00	11.00	5.00	9.00
07.1200 235	Stage equipment, rigging curtains and drops, curtain track, heavy duty, straight	LF	15.00	19.00	34.00	14.00	29.00
07.1200 240	Stage equipment, rigging curtains and drops, curtain track, medium duty, straight	LF	10.00	19.00	29.00	14.00	24.00

CSI #	7.0 EQUIPMENT Description	Unit	Material	Union Install	Union Total	Open Install	Open Total
07.1200	**STAGE EQUIPMENT (Cont.)**						
07.1200 245	Stage equipment, rigging curtains and drops, curtain track, heavy duty, curved	LF	62.00	28.00	90.00	21.00	83.00
07.1200 250	Stage equipment, rigging curtains and drops, curtain track, medium duty, curved	LF	16.00	28.00	44.00	21.00	37.00
07.1200 255	Stage equipment, rigging curtains and drops, add for electric driven heavy duty	EACH	1,365.00	273.00	1,638.00	198.00	1,563.00
07.1200 260	Stage equipment, rigging curtains and drops, add for electric driven medium duty	EACH	1,312.00	273.00	1,585.00	198.00	1,510.00
07.1200 265	Stage equipment, rigging curtains and drops, T-bar rig, 4 loft blk, 55x35	SET	47,581.00		47,581.00		47,581.00
07.1200 270	Stage equipment, rigging curtains and drops, rig, wire guard, 4 loft blk 45x30	SET	41,633.00		41,633.00		41,633.00
07.1200 275	Stage equipment, rigging curtains and drops, T-bar rig, 4 loft blk caster mounted	SET	50,554.00		50,554.00		50,554.00
07.1200 280	Stage equipment, rigging curtains and drops, add for electric control	LUMP	47,581.00		47,581.00		47,581.00
07.1200 285	Stage equipment, rigging curtains and drops, curtain, asbestos, straight, lift, 23'x47'	LUMP	66,910.00		66,910.00		66,910.00
07.1200 290	Stage equipment, rigging curtains and drops, curtain, asbestos, trip, 23'x47'	LUMP	63,937.00		63,937.00		63,937.00
07.1200 295	Stage equipment, rigging curtains and drops, curtain, main, velour, heavy	SY	23.00		23.00		23.00
07.1200 300	Stage equipment, rigging curtains and drops, curtain, main, velour, medium	SY	16.00		16.00		16.00
07.1200 305	Stage equipment, rigging curtains and drops, curtain, light weight, cyclorama	SY	12.00		12.00		12.00
07.1200 310	Stage equipment, rigging curtains and drops, drops, velour, heavy, 6'x40'	EACH	1,906.00		1,906.00		1,906.00
07.1200 315	Stage equipment, rigging curtains and drops, drops, velour, medium, 6'x40'	EACH	1,784.00		1,784.00		1,784.00
07.1200 320	Stage equipment, rigging curtains and drops, wings, velour, heavy, 10'x30'	EACH	1,338.00		1,338.00		1,338.00
07.1200 325	Stage equipment, rigging curtains and drops, wings, velour, medium, 10'x30'	EACH	1,249.00		1,249.00		1,249.00
07.1200 330	Stage equipment, rigging curtains and drops, scissors lift, not including any structural work, 5'x10', 12' lift	LUMP	17,843.00		17,843.00		17,843.00
07.1200 335	Stage equipment, television studio lighting, including lamps, studio, 8000 SF, very well equipped	LUMP	581,427.00	15,688.00	597,115.00	11,394.00	592,821.00
07.1200 340	Stage equipment, television studio lighting, including lamps, studio, 6, 60'x72', well equipped	LUMP	137,699.00	4,393.00	142,092.00	3,190.00	140,889.00
07.1200 345	Stage equipment, television studio lighting, including lamps, studio, medium equipped	LUMP	107,066.00	3,138.00	110,204.00	2,279.00	109,345.00
07.1200 350	Stage equipment, television studio lighting, including lamps, studio, 2, 20'x30', medium equipped	LUMP	24,714.00	1,506.00	26,220.00	1,094.00	25,808.00
07.1200 355	Stage equipment, television studio lighting, including lamps, studio, port, minimum equipped, no control	LUMP	3,866.00	628.00	4,494.00	456.00	4,322.00
07.1300	**GARBAGE COMPACTORS**						
07.1300 100	Garbage compactor, 1-1/2 CY	EACH	13,901.00	1,103.00	15,004.00	691.00	14,592.00
07.1300 105	Garbage compactor, 2 CY	EACH	20,640.00	1,103.00	21,743.00	691.00	21,331.00
07.1300 110	Garbage compactor, 2-1/2" CY	EACH	25,323.00	1,323.00	26,646.00	830.00	26,153.00

CSI #	8.0 SPECIAL CONSTRUCTION Description	Unit	Material	Union Install	Union Total	Open Install	Open Total
	The special construction costs, in this section, include material, installation, and subcontractor overhead and profit. There are no allowances for general contractor markup and profit. The items in this section are associated with computer rooms, X-Ray rooms and swimming pools. The treatment of these items is not extensive, in this publication, but the costs can be used for non detailed estimating. Costs represent standard grade materials and normal installation. Adjustments should be made for economy quality or custom and heavy duty materials and commensurate installation.						
08.0100	**RAISED FLOORS**						
08.0100 100	Pedestal floors, vinyl tile, gridless	SF	19.95		19.95		19.95
08.0100 105	Pedestal floors, vinyl tile, grid	SF	23.95		23.95		23.95
08.0100 110	Pedestal floors, perma kleen, grid	SF	26.10		26.10		26.10
08.0100 115	Pedestal floors, carpeted system	SF	26.95		26.95		26.95
08.0100 120	Pedestal floors, ramps	SF	28.47		28.47		28.47
08.0100 125	Add for cutouts	EACH	226.05		226.05		226.05
08.0100 130	Add for floor grills	EACH	100.51		100.51		100.51
08.0100 140	Add for sheetmetal trim and casing	LF	111.55		111.55		111.55
08.0100 145	Add for seismic bracing	SF	.06		.06		.06
08.0100 150	Add for CO2 fire system (smoke detector)	SF	6.39		6.39		6.39
08.0100 155	Add for automatic fire alarm	SF	.42		.42		.42
08.0200	**X-RAY ROOM CONSTRUCTION**						
08.0200 100	Lead lined lath 2#	SF	9.04		9.04		9.04
08.0200 105	Lead lined lath 4#	SF	13.38		13.38		13.38
08.0200 110	Lead lined lath 6#	SF	16.02		16.02		16.02
08.0200 115	Lead lined lath 8#	SF	20.64		20.64		20.64
08.0200 120	Lead glass windows with lead frames	SF	335.87		335.87		335.87
08.0200 125	Lead lined doors to 4#	SF	34.99		34.99		34.99
08.0200 130	Lead lined door frames	EACH	457.86		457.86		457.86
08.0300	**POOLS**						
08.0300 100	Swimming pool, residential	SF	65.04		65.04		65.04
08.0300 105	Swimming pool, multiple residential	SF	73.45		73.45		73.45
08.0300 110	Swimming pool, community	SF	78.44		78.44		78.44
08.0300 115	Swimming pool, hotel/resort	SF	84.55		84.55		84.55
08.0300 120	Swimming pool, school 42'x75'	SF	86.63		86.63		86.63
08.0300 125	Swimming pool, school 42'x165'	SF	89.95		89.95		89.95
08.0300 130	Swimming pool, school 30'x30'	SF	93.75		93.75		93.75
08.0300 135	Pool deck concrete	SF	7.01		7.01		7.01
08.0300 140	Pool cool concrete	SF	10.28		10.28		10.28

CSI #	9.0 CONVEYING Description	Unit	Material	Union Install	Union Total	Open Install	Open Total
	The costs in this section include materials, labor, equipment rental, supervision, and subcontractor overhead and profit. There are no allowances for the general contractor. Costs are complete, stairs are painted or finished where appropriate and ancillary installation and equipment costs are included where expected.						
09.0100	**STAIRS**						
09.0100 100	Wood stair, straight, wood rail, 36" wide	RISER	117.00	146.00	263.00	101.00	218.00
09.0100 105	Wood stair, switch back, wood rail, 36" wide	RISER	127.00	167.00	294.00	116.00	243.00
09.0100 110	Wood stair, circular, wood rail, 36" wide	RISER	716.00	447.00	1,163.00	311.00	1,027.00
09.0100 115	Wood stair, circular, wood rail, 36" wide	RISER	716.00	447.00	1,163.00	311.00	1,027.00
09.0100 120	Concrete stair, straight, wood rail, 36" wide	RISER	343.00	209.00	552.00	141.00	484.00
09.0100 125	Concrete stair, straight, wood rail, 48" wide	RISER	364.00	237.00	601.00	159.00	523.00
09.0100 130	Concrete stair, straight, wood rail, 72" wide	RISER	405.00	292.00	697.00	195.00	600.00
09.0100 135	Steel stair, concrete tread, wrought iron rail, 44" wide	RISER	630.00	70.00	700.00	53.00	683.00
09.0100 140	Steel stair, steel pan, concrete tread, wrought iron rail, 44" wide	RISER	985.00	139.00	1,124.00	104.00	1,089.00
09.0100 145	Steel stair, steel pan, concrete tread, wrought iron rail, 48" wide	RISER	1,054.00	144.00	1,198.00	108.00	1,162.00
09.0100 150	Steel stair, cast iron, circular, wrought iron rail, 32" wide	RISER	765.00	82.00	847.00	61.00	826.00
09.0100 155	Steel stair, steel Riser, wrought iron rail, 36" wide	RISER	873.00	143.00	1,016.00	107.00	980.00
09.0205	**ELEVATORS, HYDRAULIC**						
09.0205 100	Elevator, hydraulic, 125'min, 2000 lb, 5'x6'cab, auto exit, 2 stop	EACH	68,585.00		68,585.00		68,585.00
09.0205 105	Elevator, hydraulic, 125'min, 2000 lb, 5'x6'cab, auto exit, 4 stop	EACH	89,555.00		89,555.00		89,555.00
09.0205 110	Elevator, hydraulic, 125'min, 2000 lb, 5'x6'cab, auto exit, 5 stop	EACH	103,260.00		103,260.00		103,260.00
09.0205 115	Elevator, hydraulic, 125'min, 2000 lb, 5'x6'cab, auto exit, additional stops	EACH	13,893.00		13,893.00		13,893.00
09.0205 120	Elevator, hydraulic, 125'min, 2500 lb, 5'x7'cab, auto exit, 2 stop	EACH	70,578.00		70,578.00		70,578.00
09.0205 125	Elevator, hydraulic, 125'min, 2500 lb, 5'x7'cab, auto exit, 3 stop	EACH	81,348.00		81,348.00		81,348.00
09.0205 130	Elevator, hydraulic, 125'min, 2500 lb, 5'x7'cab, auto exit, 4 stop	EACH	92,157.00		92,157.00		92,157.00
09.0205 135	Elevator, hydraulic, 125'min, 2500 lb, 5'x7'cab, auto exit, 5 stop	EACH	106,267.00		106,267.00		106,267.00
09.0205 140	Elevator, hydraulic, 125'min, 2500 lb, 5'x7'cab, auto exit, additional stops	EACH	14,296.00		14,296.00		14,296.00
09.0205 145	Elevator, hydraulic, 125'min, 4000 lb, 6'x8'cab, auto exit, 3 stop	EACH	95,144.00		95,144.00		95,144.00
09.0205 150	Elevator, hydraulic, 125'min, 20000 lb, 10'x16'cab, auto exit, 3 stop	EACH	180,774.00		180,774.00		180,774.00
09.0210	**ELEVATORS, ELECTRIC GEAR**						
09.0210 100	Elevator, electric gear, 350'min, 3500 lb, 5'x8'cab, auto exit, 10 stop	EACH	236,960.00		236,960.00		236,960.00
09.0210 105	Elevator, electric gear, 350'min, 3500 lb, 5'x8'cab, auto exit, 15 stop	EACH	282,530.00		282,530.00		282,530.00
09.0210 110	Elevator, electric gear, 350'min, 3500 lb, 5'x8'cab, auto exit, additional stops	EACH	9,114.00		9,114.00		9,114.00
09.0210 115	Elevator, electric gear, 350'min, 4000 lb, 6'x8'cab, auto exit, 5 stop	EACH	304,461.00		304,461.00		304,461.00
09.0210 120	Elevator, electric gear, 200'min, 4000 lb, 6'x8'cab, auto exit, 3 stop	EACH	266,404.00		266,404.00		266,404.00
09.0210 125	Elevator, electric gear, 350'min, 4500 lb, 6'x9'cab, auto exit, 10 stop	EACH	271,358.00		271,358.00		271,358.00
09.0210 130	Elevator, electric gear, 350'min, 4500 lb, 6'x9'cab, auto exit, 15 stop	EACH	333,979.00		333,979.00		333,979.00
09.0210 135	Elevator, electric gear, 350'min, 4500 lb, 6'x9'cab, auto exit, additional stops	EACH	13,568.00		13,568.00		13,568.00
09.0210 140	Elevator, electric gear, 350'min, 6000 lb, 8'x10'cab, auto exit, 3 stop	EACH	285,433.00		285,433.00		285,433.00
09.0215	**ELEVATORS, ELECTRIC GEARLESS**						
09.0215 100	Elevator, electric gearless, 500'min, 3500 lb, 6'x9'cab, auto exit, 10 stop	EACH	333,248.00		333,248.00		333,248.00
09.0215 105	Elevator, electric gearless, 500'min, 3500 lb, 6'x9'cab, auto exit, 15 stop	EACH	397,748.00		397,748.00		397,748.00
09.0215 110	Elevator, electric gearless, 500'min, 3500 lb, 6'x9'cab, auto exit, additional stops	EACH	16,125.00		16,125.00		16,125.00

CSI #	9.0 CONVEYING Description	Unit	Material	Union Install	Union Total	Open Install	Open Total
09.0215	**ELEVATORS, ELECTRIC GEARLESS (Cont.)**						
09.0215 115	Elevator, electric gearless, 700'min, 4500 lb, 6'x9'cab, auto exit, 10 stop	EACH	354,651.00		354,651.00		354,651.00
09.0215 120	Elevator, electric gearless, 700'min, 4500 lb, 6'x9'cab, auto exit, 15 stop	EACH	409,661.00		409,661.00		409,661.00
09.0215 125	Elevator, electric gearless, 700'min, 4500 lb, 6'x9'cab, auto exit, 20 stop	EACH	464,670.00		464,670.00		464,670.00
09.0215 130	Elevator, electric gearless, 700'min, 4500 lb, 6'x9'cab, auto exit, additional stops	EACH	11,265.00		11,265.00		11,265.00
09.0215 135	Elevator, electric gearless, 1200'min, 4500 lb, 6'x9'cab, auto exit, 20 stops	EACH	661,735.00		661,735.00		661,735.00
09.0215 140	Elevator, electric gearless, 1200'min, 4500 lb, 6'x9'cab, auto exit, additional stops	EACH	12,465.00		12,465.00		12,465.00
09.0215 145	Elevator, freight, electric gearless, 100'min, 4500 lb, 6'x9'cab, manual door, 2 stop	EACH	140,809.00		140,809.00		140,809.00
09.0215 150	Elevator, freight, electric gearless, 100'min, 4500 lb, manual door, additional stops	EACH	12,110.00		12,110.00		12,110.00
09.0220	**HOISTS AND CRANES**						
09.0220 100	Air hoist, 30'lift, rail, 2000 lb,	EACH	10,084.00	90.00	10,174.00	90.00	10,174.00
09.0220 105	Air hoist, 30'lift, rail, 500 lb,	EACH	10,981.00	90.00	11,071.00	90.00	11,071.00
09.0220 110	Electric hoist, 30'lift, rail, 1000 lb,	EACH	6,563.00	90.00	6,653.00	90.00	6,653.00
09.0220 115	Electric hoist, 30'lift, rail, 500 lb,	EACH	5,698.00	90.00	5,788.00	90.00	5,788.00
09.0220 120	Crane, hydraulic, portable, 2000 lb,	EACH	3,594.00		3,594.00		3,594.00
09.0220 125	Crane, hydraulic, gantry, 4000 lb,	EACH	3,736.00		3,736.00		3,736.00
09.0220 130	Crane, monorail, overhead, 200#/LF, manual	LF	27.00	90.00	117.00	90.00	117.00
09.0220 135	Crane, monorail, overhead, 100#/LF, manual	LF	11.00	90.00	101.00	90.00	101.00
09.0220 140	bridge Crane, 1 ton,	EACH	9,387.00		9,387.00		9,387.00
09.0220 150	Bridge crane, 2 ton	EACH	18,775.00		18,775.00		18,775.00
09.0220 155	Bridge crane, 3 ton	EACH	28,162.00		28,162.00		28,162.00
09.0225	**MANLIFT**						
09.0225 100	manlift, 2 stop	EACH	22,588.00		22,588.00		22,588.00
09.0225 105	manlift, 3 stop	EACH	24,797.00		24,797.00		24,797.00
09.0225 110	manlift, 4 stop	EACH	27,006.00		27,006.00		27,006.00
09.0300	**DUMB-WAITERS**						
09.0300 100	Dumbwaiter, manual, 200#, 2 stop	EACH	9,964.00		9,964.00		9,964.00
09.0300 105	Dumbwaiter, manual, 200#, additional stops	EACH	1,707.00		1,707.00		1,707.00
09.0300 110	Dumbwaiter, electric, 300#, 2 stops	EACH	24,785.00		24,785.00		24,785.00
09.0300 115	Dumbwaiter, electric, 300#, additional stops	EACH	3,438.00		3,438.00		3,438.00
09.0400	**ESCALATORS**						
09.0400 100	Escalator, 12' floor to floor, 24" wide	FLOOR	162,511.00		162,511.00		162,511.00
09.0400 105	Escalator, 12' floor to floor, 32" wide	FLOOR	165,539.00		165,539.00		165,539.00
09.0400 110	Escalator, 12' floor to floor, 36" wide	FLOOR	169,782.00		169,782.00		169,782.00
09.0400 115	Escalator, 12' floor to floor, 40" wide	FLOOR	170,297.00		170,297.00		170,297.00
09.0400 120	Escalator, 12' floor to floor, 44" wide	FLOOR	174,065.00		174,065.00		174,065.00
09.0400 125	Escalator, 12' floor to floor, 48" wide	FLOOR	181,444.00		181,444.00		181,444.00
09.0400 130	Escalator, 12' floor to floor, add for baked enamel sides	FLOOR	6,762.00		6,762.00		6,762.00
09.0400 135	Escalator, 12' floor to floor, add for glass sides	FLOOR	6,965.00		6,965.00		6,965.00
09.0400 140	Escalator, 12' floor to floor, add for stainless steel sides	FLOOR	9,286.00		9,286.00		9,286.00
09.0500	**PNEUMATIC SYSTEMS**						
09.0500 100	Pnuematic tube systems, Twin 3", 2 station	LUMP	25,048.00		25,048.00		25,048.00
09.0500 105	Pnuematic tube systems, Twin 3", add for additional station	STATION	10,441.00		10,441.00		10,441.00
09.0500 110	Pnuematic tube systems, Twin 4", 2 station	LUMP	25,851.00		25,851.00		25,851.00
09.0500 115	Pnuematic tube systems, Twin 4", add for additional station	STATION	10,842.00		10,842.00		10,842.00

CSI #	10.1 PLUMBING & FIRE PROTECTION Description	Unit	Material	Union Install	Union Total	Open Install	Open Total
	The equipment costs, in this section, include material, installation, and subcontractor overhead and profit. There are no allowances for general contractor markup and profit. Costs represent standard grade materials and normal installation. Adjustments should be made for economy quality or custom and heavy duty materials and commensurate installation.						
10.1100	**EQUIPMENT**						
10.1100 100	Water heater, commercial, electric, 6 gallon, 17 GPH	EACH	652.00	237.00	889.00	149.00	801.00
10.1100 105	Water heater, commercial, electric, 50 gallon, 100 GPH	EACH	3,393.00	591.00	3,984.00	370.00	3,763.00
10.1100 110	Water heater, commercial, gas, 50 gallon, 100 GPH	EACH	1,738.00	636.00	2,374.00	399.00	2,137.00
10.1100 115	Water heater, commercial, gas, 85 gallon, 168 GPH	EACH	5,879.00	682.00	6,561.00	427.00	6,306.00
10.1100 120	Interceptor grease, cast iron, 10 gallons per minute, 20#	EACH	1,226.00	273.00	1,499.00	171.00	1,397.00
10.1100 125	Interceptor grease, cast iron, 50 gallons per minute, 100#	EACH	4,089.00	1,090.00	5,179.00	684.00	4,773.00
10.1100 130	Pump, circulating, in line, flanged, iron body, 3/4" to 1-1/2"	EACH	598.00	173.00	771.00	108.00	706.00
10.1100 135	Pumps, circulating, in line, flanged, iron body, 3/4" to 2-1/2"	EACH	1,906.00	254.00	2,160.00	160.00	2,066.00
10.1100 140	Pump, sewage ejector, w/tank & fittings, single, 1/2 horsepower, 3"	EACH	10,543.00	1,227.00	11,770.00	769.00	11,312.00
10.1100 145	Pump, sewage ejector, w/tank & fittings, single, 2 horsepower, 4"	EACH	11,671.00	1,408.00	13,079.00	883.00	12,554.00
10.1100 150	Pump, sewage ejector, w/tank & fittings, duplex, 2 horsepower	EACH	17,368.00	1,936.00	19,304.00	1,213.00	18,581.00
10.1100 155	Pump, sewage ejector, w/tank & fittings, duplex, 5 horsepower	EACH	20,832.00	2,753.00	23,585.00	1,726.00	22,558.00
10.1100 160	Pump, sump, electric, w/iron guard accessories, 1/3 horsepower, 3'deep, 1/2" outlet	EACH	1,943.00	227.00	2,170.00	142.00	2,085.00
10.1100 165	Pump, sump, electric, w/iron guard accessories, 1/2 horsepower, 6'deep, 2" outlet	EACH	2,448.00	318.00	2,766.00	199.00	2,647.00
10.1100 170	Pressure booster system, 2 pump, 100 GPM, 50 PSI	EACH	21,294.00	2,846.00	24,140.00	1,784.00	23,078.00
10.1100 175	Pressure booster system, 3 pump, 300 GPM, 100 PSI	EACH	33,080.00	3,795.00	36,875.00	2,379.00	35,459.00
10.1100 180	Septic tank, steel, 200 gallon, buried	EACH	1,035.00	309.00	1,344.00	181.00	1,216.00
10.1100 185	Septic tank, steel, 500 gallon, buried	EACH	1,476.00	514.00	1,990.00	302.00	1,778.00
10.1100 190	Septic tank, steel, 1000 gallon, buried	EACH	3,251.00	737.00	3,988.00	433.00	3,684.00
10.1100 195	Septic tank, steel, 10,000 gallon, buried	EACH	22,192.00	2,811.00	25,003.00	1,653.00	23,845.00
10.1100 200	Compressor air, simplex, 5 horsepower, reciprocating, tank mounted	EACH	8,001.00	1,897.00	9,898.00	1,189.00	9,190.00
10.1100 205	Compressor air, simplex, 10 horsepower, reciprocating, tank mounted	EACH	14,505.00	2,372.00	16,877.00	1,487.00	15,992.00
10.1100 210	Tank, water, glass lined, 200 gallon, ASME	EACH	2,724.00	813.00	3,537.00	510.00	3,234.00
10.1100 215	Tank, water, glass lined, 400 gallon, ASME	EACH	3,713.00	1,299.00	5,012.00	815.00	4,528.00
10.1100 220	Water softener, w/brine tank, 25 GPM, start-up	EACH	3,448.00	727.00	4,175.00	456.00	3,904.00
10.1100 225	Water softeners, w/brine tank, 50 GPM, start-up	EACH	6,284.00	1,318.00	7,602.00	826.00	7,110.00
10.1205	**FIXTURES, ECONOMY GRADE**						
10.1205 100	Fixture, economy grade, bath tub, steel, w/shower	EACH	395.66	318.06	713.72	199.39	595.05
10.1205 105	Fixture, economy grade, bath tub, steel, w/o shower	EACH	338.56	272.62	611.18	170.91	509.47
10.1205 110	Fixture, economy grade, tub, fiberglass, integral walls	EACH	775.98	318.06	1,094.04	199.39	975.37
10.1205 115	Fixture, economy grade, bidet, floor mounted	EACH	537.47	181.75	719.22	113.94	651.41
10.1205 120	Fixture, economy grade, lavatory, steel, wall hung	EACH	221.66	181.75	403.41	113.94	335.60
10.1205 125	Fixture, economy grade, lavatory, steel, vanity mounted	EACH	173.26	181.75	355.01	113.94	287.20
10.1205 130	Fixture, economy grade, service sink	EACH	409.79	227.18	636.97	142.42	552.21
10.1205 135	Fixture, economy grade, shower & drain receptor, 32" square	EACH	319.02	272.62	591.64	170.91	489.93
10.1205 140	Fixture, economy grade, shower cabinet, w/door, 32" square	EACH	678.50	408.92	1,087.42	256.36	934.86
10.1205 145	Fixture, economy grade, sink, porcelain on steel, counter, single	EACH	151.09	136.31	287.40	85.45	236.54

CSI #	10.1 PLUMBING & FIRE PROTECTION Description	Unit	Material	Union Install	Union Total	Open Install	Open Total
10.1205	**FIXTURES, ECONOMY GRADE (Cont.)**						
10.1205 150	Fixture, economy grade, sink, porcelain on cast iron, counter, single	EACH	214.91	136.31	351.22	85.45	300.36
10.1205 155	Fixture, economy grade, sink, stainless steel, counter, single	EACH	225.02	136.31	361.33	85.45	310.47
10.1205 160	Fixture, economy grade, sink, porcelain on steel, counter, double	EACH	166.83	136.31	303.14	85.45	252.28
10.1205 165	Fixture, economy grade, sink, porcelain on cast iron, counter, double	EACH	228.35	136.31	364.66	85.45	313.80
10.1205 170	Fixture, economy grade, sink, stainless steel, counter double	EACH	257.90	136.31	394.21	85.45	343.35
10.1205 175	Fixture, economy grade, sink, bar	EACH	218.67	136.31	354.98	85.45	304.12
10.1205 180	Fixture, economy grade, sink, floor mounted	EACH	161.16	90.88	252.04	56.97	218.13
10.1205 185	Fixture, economy grade, urinal, floor, w/flush valve	EACH	486.73	181.75	668.48	113.94	600.67
10.1205 190	Fixture, economy grade, urinal, wall, w/flush valve, carrier	EACH	514.14	181.75	695.89	113.94	628.08
10.1205 195	Fixture, economy grade, water closet, floor, w/tank	EACH	500.44	181.75	682.19	113.94	614.38
10.1205 200	Fixture, economy grade, water closet, wall, w/flush valve, carrier	EACH	530.69	181.75	712.44	113.94	644.63
10.1210	**FIXTURES, STANDARD GRADE**						
10.1210 100	Fixture, standard grade, bathtub, cast iron, enamel, with shower	EACH	1,496.87	679.68	2,176.55	426.09	1,922.96
10.1210 105	Fixture, standard grade, lavatory, wall hung	EACH	794.25	523.21	1,317.46	328.00	1,122.25
10.1210 110	Fixture, standard grade, lavatory, vanity mounted	EACH	613.91	523.21	1,137.12	328.00	941.91
10.1210 115	Fixture, standard grade, service sink	EACH	1,301.77	593.00	1,894.77	371.72	1,673.49
10.1210 120	Fixture, standard grade, shower and drain receptor, 32" square	EACH	999.39	654.40	1,653.79	410.25	1,409.64
10.1210 125	Fixture, standard grade, sink, stainless steel, counter top with trim, single	EACH	965.73	522.29	1,488.02	327.39	1,293.12
10.1210 130	Fixture, standard grade, sink, stainless steel, counter top with trim, double	EACH	1,247.36	542.45	1,789.81	340.03	1,587.39
10.1210 135	Fixture, standard grade, bar sink	EACH	693.56	477.77	1,171.33	299.51	993.07
10.1210 140	Fixture, standard grade, urinal, wall mounted	EACH	919.87	430.25	1,350.12	269.74	1,189.61
10.1210 145	Fixture, standard grade, water closet with tank and accessories	EACH	755.03	507.44	1,262.47	318.14	1,073.17
10.1215	**FIXTURES, INSTITUTIONAL GRADE**						
10.1215 100	Fixture, institutional, hospital, lavatory, wall hung	EACH	1,100.95	810.49	1,911.44	508.09	1,609.04
10.1215 105	Fixture, institutional, hospital, lavatory, counter top with trim	EACH	927.66	810.49	1,738.15	508.09	1,435.75
10.1215 110	Fixture, institutional, hospital, service sink	EACH	1,656.05	877.10	2,533.15	549.84	2,205.89
10.1215 115	Fixture, institutional, hospital, sink, clinic	EACH	1,706.92	863.06	2,569.98	541.06	2,247.98
10.1215 120	Fixture, institutional, hospital, sink, stainless steel, single	EACH	1,144.12	700.87	1,844.99	439.38	1,583.50
10.1215 125	Fixture, institutional, hospital, sink, stainless steel, double	EACH	1,487.83	741.19	2,229.02	464.66	1,952.49
10.1215 130	Fixture, institutional, hospital, sitz bath	EACH	2,216.85	1,135.38	3,352.23	711.79	2,928.64
10.1215 135	Fixture, institutional, hospital, urinal, wall hung	EACH	1,454.26	788.23	2,242.49	494.17	1,948.43
10.1215 140	Fixture, institutional, hospital, water closet, floor mounted	EACH	1,301.17	1,012.69	2,313.86	634.88	1,936.05
10.1215 145	Fixture, institutional, hospital, water closet, wall mounted	EACH	1,250.99	969.78	2,220.77	608.00	1,858.99
10.1215 150	Fixture, institutional, hospital, water closet, floor with bed pan	EACH	1,310.19	1,080.08	2,390.27	677.15	1,987.34
10.1215 155	Fixture, institutional, hospital, water closet, wall with bed pan	EACH	2,244.95	1,081.40	3,326.35	677.98	2,922.93
10.1215 160	Fixture, institutional, hospital, shower cabinet, corner with door	EACH	5,233.14	1,968.95	7,202.09	1,234.42	6,467.56
10.1215 165	Fixture, institutional, hospital, shower cabinet, 36" square, with door	EACH	1,990.62	1,386.75	3,377.37	869.40	2,860.02
10.1215 170	Fixture, institutional, hospital, shower and drain receptor, 36" square	EACH	1,304.83	1,089.18	2,394.01	682.83	1,987.66
10.1215 175	Fixture, institutional, jail, water closet, in floor, stainless steel	EACH	3,028.98	652.17	3,681.15	408.88	3,437.86
10.1215 180	Fixture, institutional, jail, water closet/lavatory, in floor, stainless steel	EACH	4,234.06	841.37	5,075.43	527.44	4,761.50
10.1215 185	Fixture, institutional, jail, shower, wall unit, stainless steel, floor drain	EACH	1,403.37	949.27	2,352.64	595.08	1,998.45
10.1305	**ROUGH-INS**						
10.1305 100	Rough-in for fixtures, piping and valves, fixture to 5' beyond building perimeter, tract housing	FIX	331.00	205.00	536.00	128.00	459.00

CSI #	10.1 PLUMBING & FIRE PROTECTION Description	Unit	Material	Union Install	Union Total	Open Install	Open Total
10.1305	**ROUGH-INS (Cont.)**						
10.1305 105	Rough-in for fixtures, piping and valves, fixture to 5' beyond building perimeter, custom housing	FIX	633.00	380.00	1,013.00	238.00	871.00
10.1305 110	Rough-in for fixtures, piping and valves, fixture to 5' beyond building perimeter, apartment building	FIX	458.00	284.00	742.00	178.00	636.00
10.1305 115	Rough-in for fixtures, piping and valves, fixture to 5' beyond building perimeter, industrial building	FIX	844.00	489.00	1,333.00	307.00	1,151.00
10.1305 120	Rough-in for fixtures, piping and valves, fixture to 5' beyond building perimeter, commercial building	FIX	1,035.00	531.00	1,566.00	333.00	1,368.00
10.1305 125	Rough-in for fixtures, piping and valves, fixture to 5' beyond building perimeter, institutional structures	FIX	2,313.00	1,818.00	4,131.00	1,140.00	3,453.00
10.1305 130	Rough-in for fixtures, piping and valves, fixture to 5' beyond building perimeter, schools	FIX	2,173.00	1,312.00	3,485.00	823.00	2,996.00
10.1305 135	Rough-in for fixtures, piping and valves, fixture to 5' beyond building perimeter, 1 or 2 story hospital	FIX	2,812.00	2,203.00	5,015.00	1,381.00	4,193.00
10.1305 140	Rough-in for fixtures, piping and valves, fixture to 5' beyond building perimeter, high rise hospital	FIX	3,255.00	2,550.00	5,805.00	1,598.00	4,853.00
10.1305 145	Rough-in for fixtures, piping and valves, fixture to 5' beyond building perimeter, high rise office building	FIX	2,230.00	1,764.00	3,994.00	1,106.00	3,336.00
10.1305 150	Rough-in at fixtures, bath tub, fittings and valving, fixture to waste line, vent riser and water runs	EA	326.00	318.00	644.00	199.00	525.00
10.1305 155	Rough-in at fixtures, fountains and coolers, fittings and valving, fixture to waste line, vent riser and water runs	EA	190.00	204.00	394.00	128.00	318.00
10.1305 160	Rough-in at fixtures, lavatory, fittings and valving, fixture to waste line, vent riser and water runs	EA	269.00	295.00	564.00	185.00	454.00
10.1305 165	Rough-in at fixtures, shower, fittings and valving, fixture to waste line, vent riser and water runs	EA	299.00	318.00	617.00	199.00	498.00
10.1305 170	Rough-in at fixtures, sinks, fittings and valving, fixture to waste line, vent riser and water runs	EA	270.00	295.00	565.00	185.00	455.00
10.1305 175	Rough-in at fixtures, urinal, fittings and valving, fixture to waste line, vent riser and water runs	EA	211.00	295.00	506.00	185.00	396.00
10.1305 180	Rough-in at fixtures, washing machine, fittings and valving, fixture to waste line, vent riser and water runs	EA	281.00	273.00	554.00	171.00	452.00
10.1305 185	Rough-in at fixtures, water closet, fittings and valving, fixture to waste line, vent riser and water runs	EA	339.00	382.00	721.00	239.00	578.00
10.1305 190	Rough-in at fixtures, wash fountain, fittings and valving, fixture to waste line, vent riser and water runs	EA	614.00	454.00	1,068.00	285.00	899.00
10.1310	**PIPE, CAST IRON**						
10.1310 100	Cast iron pipe, soil, service weight, single hub, 2"	LF	9.94	21.81	31.75	13.67	23.61
10.1310 105	Cast iron pipe, soil, service weight, single hub, 3"	LF	12.17	23.17	35.34	14.53	26.70
10.1310 110	Cast iron pipe, soil, service weight, single hub, 4"	LF	16.21	25.00	41.21	15.67	31.88
10.1310 115	Cast iron pipe, soil, service weight, single hub, 5"	LF	22.94	28.17	51.11	17.66	40.60
10.1310 120	Cast iron pipe, soil, service weight, single hub, 6"	LF	28.15	32.27	60.42	20.23	48.38
10.1310 125	Cast iron pipe, soil, service weight, single hub, 8"	LF	54.30	35.44	89.74	22.22	76.52
10.1310 130	Cast iron pipe, soil, service weight, single hub, 10"	LF	71.28	41.03	112.31	25.72	97.00
10.1310 135	Cast iron pipe, soil, service weight, hubless, 1-1/2"	LF	10.17	20.16	30.33	12.64	22.81
10.1310 140	Cast iron pipe, soil, service weight, hubless, 2"	LF	10.49	20.16	30.65	12.64	23.13
10.1310 145	Cast iron pipe, soil, service weight, hubless, 3"	LF	11.84	22.06	33.90	13.83	25.67
10.1310 150	Cast iron pipe, soil, service weight, hubless, 4"	LF	15.84	23.21	39.05	14.55	30.39
10.1310 155	Cast iron pipe, soil, service weight, hubless, 5"	LF	24.64	26.62	51.26	16.69	41.33
10.1310 160	Cast iron pipe, soil, service weight, hubless, 6"	LF	29.04	30.57	59.61	19.16	48.20
10.1310 165	Cast iron pipe, soil, service weight, hubless, 8"	LF	52.14	34.53	86.67	21.65	73.79
10.1310 170	Cast iron pipe, soil, service weight, hubless, 10"	LF	75.06	39.17	114.23	24.55	99.61
10.1310 175	Cast iron pipe, soil, extra heavy, single hub, 2"	LF	11.49	21.81	33.30	13.67	25.16
10.1310 180	Cast iron pipe, soil, extra heavy, single hub, 3"	LF	14.17	23.17	37.34	14.53	28.70
10.1310 185	Cast iron pipe, soil, extra heavy, single hub, 4"	LF	18.73	25.00	43.73	15.67	34.40
10.1310 190	Cast iron pipe, soil, extra heavy, single hub, 5"	LF	24.79	28.17	52.96	17.66	42.45
10.1310 195	Cast iron pipe, soil, extra heavy, single hub, 6"	LF	32.54	32.27	64.81	20.23	52.77

CSI #	10.1 PLUMBING & FIRE PROTECTION Description	Unit	Material	Union Install	Union Total	Open Install	Open Total
10.1310	**PIPE, CAST IRON (Cont.)**						
10.1310 200	Cast iron pipe, soil, extra heavy, single hub, 8"	LF	62.70	35.44	98.14	22.22	84.92
10.1310 205	Cast iron pipe, soil, extra heavy, single hub, 10"	LF	82.31	41.03	123.34	25.72	108.03
10.1310 210	Cast iron pipe, soil, extra heavy, single hub, 12"	LF	118.55	46.34	164.89	29.05	147.60
10.1310 215	Cast iron pipe, soil, dur iron, 2"	LF	53.21	20.91	74.12	13.11	66.32
10.1310 220	Cast iron pipe, soil, dur iron, 3"	LF	66.67	23.17	89.84	14.53	81.20
10.1310 225	Cast iron pipe, soil, dur iron, 4"	LF	93.02	24.63	117.65	15.44	108.46
10.1310 230	Cast iron pipe, soil, dur iron, 6"	LF	147.65	31.82	179.47	19.95	167.60
10.1310 235	Cast iron pipe, soil, dur iron, 8"	LF	278.47	34.41	312.88	21.57	300.04
10.1315	**PIPE, COPPER**						
10.1315 100	Copper pipe, underground, "K", soft, w/trenching, 1/2" coils	LF	5.11	7.49	12.60	4.70	9.81
10.1315 105	Copper pipe, underground, "K", soft, w/trenching, 3/4" coils	LF	9.08	8.63	17.71	5.41	14.49
10.1315 110	Copper pipe, underground, "K", soft, w/trenching, 1" coils	LF	12.21	8.63	20.84	5.41	17.62
10.1315 115	Copper pipe, underground, "K", soft, w/trenching, 1-1/4" coils	LF	16.00	15.44	31.44	9.68	25.68
10.1315 120	Copper pipe, underground, "K", hard, straight, 1-1/2"	LF	20.14	15.91	36.05	9.98	30.12
10.1315 125	Copper pipe, underground, "K", hard, straight, 2"	LF	31.13	19.08	50.21	11.96	43.09
10.1315 130	Copper pipe, underground, "K", hard, straight, 2-1/2"	LF	44.38	19.08	63.46	11.96	56.34
10.1315 135	Copper pipe, underground, "K", hard, straight, 3"	LF	61.82	19.54	81.36	12.25	74.07
10.1315 140	Copper pipe, underground, "K", hard, straight, 4"	LF	102.24	21.76	124.00	13.64	115.88
10.1315 145	Copper pipe, underground, "K", hard, straight, 5"	LF	225.01	28.63	253.64	17.95	242.96
10.1315 155	Copper pipe, underground, "K", hard, straight, 6"	LF	297.85	31.35	329.20	19.66	317.51
10.1315 160	Copper pipe, in building, "L", w/fittings & supports, 1/2"	LF	4.33	9.38	13.71	5.88	10.21
10.1315 165	Copper pipe, in building, "L", w/fittings & supports, 3/4"	LF	6.74	11.41	18.15	7.15	13.89
10.1315 170	Copper pipe, in building, "L", w/fittings & supports, 1"	LF	9.76	13.54	23.30	8.49	18.25
10.1315 175	Copper pipe, in building, "L", w/fittings & supports, 1-1/4"	LF	13.98	14.62	28.60	9.17	23.15
10.1315 180	Copper pipe, in building, "L", w/fittings & supports, 1-1/2"	LF	17.41	15.55	32.96	9.75	27.16
10.1315 185	Copper pipe, in building, "L", w/fittings & supports, 2"	LF	21.60	18.75	40.35	11.75	33.35
10.1315 190	Copper pipe, in building, "L", w/fittings & supports, 2-1/2"	LF	38.08	20.78	58.86	13.02	51.10
10.1315 195	Copper pipe, in building, "L", w/fittings & supports, 3"	LF	52.38	23.86	76.24	14.96	67.34
10.1315 200	Copper pipe, in building, "L", w/fittings & supports, 4"	LF	87.98	29.08	117.06	18.23	106.21
10.1315 205	Copper pipe, in building, "L", w/fittings & supports, 5"	LF	209.76	36.44	246.20	22.84	232.60
10.1315 210	Copper pipe, in building, "L", w/fittings & supports, 6"	LF	247.27	44.61	291.88	27.97	275.24
10.1315 215	Copper pipe, in building, "M", w/fittings & supports, 1/2"	LF	3.36	9.38	12.74	5.88	9.24
10.1315 220	Copper pipe, in building, "M", w/fittings & supports, 3/4"	LF	5.28	11.41	16.69	7.15	12.43
10.1315 225	Copper pipe, in building, "M", w/fittings & supports, 1"	LF	7.87	13.54	21.41	8.49	16.36
10.1315 230	Copper pipe, in building, "M", w/fittings & supports, 1-1/4"	LF	11.83	14.62	26.45	9.17	21.00
10.1315 235	Copper pipe, in building, "M", w/fittings & supports, 1-1/2"	LF	15.72	15.55	31.27	9.75	25.47
10.1315 240	Copper pipe, in building, "M", w/fittings & supports, 2"	LF	24.77	18.75	43.52	11.75	36.52
10.1315 245	Copper pipe, in building, "M", w/fittings & supports, 3"	LF	44.33	23.86	68.19	14.96	59.29
10.1315 250	Copper pipe, in building, "M", w/fittings & supports, 4"	LF	79.65	29.08	108.73	18.23	97.88
10.1315 255	Copper pipe, in building, "M", w/fittings & supports, 5"	LF	188.80	37.26	226.06	23.36	212.16
10.1315 260	Copper pipe, in building, "M", w/fittings & supports, 6"	LF	242.52	36.18	278.70	22.68	265.20
10.1315 265	Copper pipe, "DWV", drainage tube, 2"	LF	33.59	18.75	52.34	11.75	45.34
10.1315 270	Copper pipe, "DWV", drainage tube, 3"	LF	45.00	23.86	68.86	14.96	59.96
10.1320	**PIPE, PVC**						
10.1320 100	PVC pipe, schedule 40, in building, w/fittings & supports, 1/2"	LF	1.33	6.59	7.92	4.13	5.46

CSI #	10.1 PLUMBING & FIRE PROTECTION Description	Unit	Material	Union Install	Union Total	Open Install	Open Total
10.1320	**PIPE, PVC (Cont.)**						
10.1320 105	PVC pipe, schedule 40, in building, w/fittings & supports, 3/4"	LF	1.55	7.36	8.91	4.62	6.17
10.1320 110	PVC pipe, schedule 40, in building, w/fittings & supports, 1"	LF	2.05	7.36	9.41	4.62	6.67
10.1325	**PIPE, POLYPROPYLENE**						
10.1325 100	Pipe, polypropylene, acid waste, 2"	LF	20.54	5.99	26.53	3.75	24.29
10.1325 105	Pipe, polypropylene, acid waste, 3"	LF	28.35	8.99	37.34	5.63	33.98
10.1325 115	Pipe, polypropylene, acid waste, 4"	LF	38.08	10.81	48.89	6.78	44.86
10.1330	**PIPE, PLASTIC**						
10.1330 100	Plastic, "DWV", ABS, pipe, 1-1/2"	LF	8.09	14.54	22.63	9.11	17.20
10.1330 105	Plastic, "DWV", ABS, pipe, 2"	LF	10.46	18.90	29.36	11.85	22.31
10.1330 110	Plastic, "DWV", ABS, pipe, 3"	LF	15.65	22.81	38.46	14.30	29.95
10.1330 115	Plastic, "DWV", ABS, pipe, 4"	LF	26.62	25.26	51.88	15.83	42.45
10.1330 120	Plastic, "DWV", ABS, pipe, 6"	LF	100.60	25.90	126.50	16.24	116.84
10.1335	**PIPE, PYREX UNIT COST**						
10.1335 100	Pyrex, glass, pipe, 1"	LF	23.21	24.76	47.97	15.52	38.73
10.1335 105	Pyrex, glass, pipe, 1-1/2"	LF	32.81	27.25	60.06	17.08	49.89
10.1335 110	Pyrex, glass, pipe, 2"	LF	40.23	29.74	69.97	18.64	58.87
10.1335 115	Pyrex, glass, pipe, 3"	LF	44.12	38.31	82.43	24.02	68.14
10.1335 120	Pyrex, glass, pipe, 4"	LF	76.91	51.88	128.79	32.52	109.43
10.1340	**PIPE, STEEL UNIT COST**						
10.1340 100	Steel pipe, black, weld, schedule 40, A-120, screwed, 3/4"	LF	2.42	11.04	13.46	6.92	9.34
10.1340 105	Steel pipe, black, weld, schedule 40, A-120, screwed, 1"	LF	3.11	13.30	16.41	8.34	11.45
10.1340 110	Steel pipe, black, weld, schedule 40, A-120, screwed, 2"	LF	6.50	22.63	29.13	14.18	20.68
10.1340 115	Steel pipe, black, weld, schedule 40, A-120, screwed, 3"	LF	13.48	31.71	45.19	19.88	33.36
10.1340 120	Steel pipe, galvanized, weld, schedule 40, A-120, screwed, 3/4"	LF	3.04	11.04	14.08	6.92	9.96
10.1340 125	Steel pipe, galvanized, weld, schedule 40, A-120, screwed, 1-1/2"	LF	5.65	16.62	22.27	10.42	16.07
10.1400	**MISCELLANEOUS PLUMBING SPECIALTIES**						
10.1400 100	Access door, painted steel, 8"x8"	EACH	69.00	36.00	105.00	23.00	92.00
10.1400 105	Access door, painted steel, 12"x12"	EACH	77.00	36.00	113.00	23.00	100.00
10.1400 110	Access door, painted steel, 18"x18"	EACH	110.00	45.00	155.00	28.00	138.00
10.1400 115	Access door, painted steel, 24"x24"	EACH	157.00	45.00	202.00	28.00	185.00
10.1400 120	Access door, painted steel, 36"x36"	EACH	305.00	64.00	369.00	40.00	345.00
10.1400 125	Cleanout, cast iron, floor & wall, 2" & 3"	EACH	144.00	95.00	239.00	60.00	204.00
10.1400 130	Cleanout, cast iron, floor & wall, 4"	EACH	196.00	97.00	293.00	61.00	257.00
10.1400 135	Cleanout, cast iron, to grade, 4"	EACH	304.00	100.00	404.00	63.00	367.00
10.1400 140	Cleanout, cast iron, to grade, 6"	EACH	498.00	114.00	612.00	71.00	569.00
10.1400 145	Cleanout, cast iron, wall, 2"	EACH	42.00	91.00	133.00	57.00	99.00
10.1400 150	Drains, cast iron, area, w/5"x5" strainer	EACH	126.00	136.00	262.00	85.00	211.00
10.1400 155	Drains, cast iron, floor, 2"-4", with trap	EACH	149.00	136.00	285.00	85.00	234.00
10.1400 160	Drains, cast iron, roof, 2"-4", aluminum dome	EACH	182.00	173.00	355.00	108.00	290.00
10.1500	**MEDICAL GASES, ACCESSORIES**						
10.1500 100	Manifold, 4 cylinder	EACH	8,918.00	582.00	9,500.00	365.00	9,283.00
10.1500 105	Manifold, 6 cylinder	EACH	9,378.00	818.00	10,196.00	513.00	9,891.00
10.1500 110	Zone valve, w/box 3 @ 1/2"	EACH	870.00	179.00	1,049.00	112.00	982.00
10.1500 115	Zone valve, w/box 5 @ 1/2"	EACH	1,593.00	249.00	1,842.00	156.00	1,749.00
10.1500 120	Shut-off valve, w/o box 1"	EACH	166.00	41.00	207.00	26.00	192.00

CSI #	10.1 PLUMBING & FIRE PROTECTION Description	Unit	Material	Union Install	Union Total	Open Install	Open Total
10.1500	**MEDICAL GASES, ACCESSORIES (Cont.)**						
10.1500 122	Shut-off valve, w/o box 1-1/4"	EACH	242.00	55.00	297.00	34.00	276.00
10.1500 125	Gas outlet, wall	EACH	115.00	56.00	171.00	35.00	150.00
10.1500 130	Alarm, line press, local, 1 gas	EACH	3,137.00	70.00	3,207.00	44.00	3,181.00
10.1500 135	Alarm, line press, local, 2 gas	EACH	3,887.00	91.00	3,978.00	57.00	3,944.00
10.1500 140	Alarm, line press, local, 3 gas & liquid	EACH	4,871.00	136.00	5,007.00	85.00	4,956.00
10.1500 145	Alarm, line press, local, 5 gas	EACH	5,746.00	231.00	5,977.00	145.00	5,891.00
10.1500 150	Alarm, master 15 signal	EACH	4,232.00	298.00	4,530.00	187.00	4,419.00
10.1500 155	Vacuum pump, duplex, w/all related accessories, 30 CFM, 5 HP	EACH	30,021.00	2,726.00	32,747.00	1,709.00	31,730.00
10.1500 160	Vacuum pump, duplex, w/all related accessories, 210 CFM, 15 HP	EACH	38,568.00	3,635.00	42,203.00	2,279.00	40,847.00
10.1500 165	Air compressor, duplex, medical, 2 @ 3 HP	EACH	16,371.00	1,454.00	17,825.00	912.00	17,283.00
10.1500 170	Air compressor, duplex, medical, 2 @ 10 HP	EACH	66,256.00	2,726.00	68,982.00	1,709.00	67,965.00
10.1515	**MEDICAL GAS PIPING**						
10.1515 100	Gas pipe, medical, copper, 'L', 1/2"	LF	10.97	18.76	29.73	11.76	22.73
10.1515 105	Gas pipe, medical, copper, 'L', 3/4"	LF	14.91	22.79	37.70	14.29	29.20
10.1515 110	Gas pipe, medical, copper, 'L', 1"	LF	19.50	27.06	46.56	16.96	36.46
10.1515 115	Gas pipe, medical, copper, 'L', 1-1/4"	LF	25.91	29.22	55.13	18.32	44.23
10.1515 120	Stainless steel pipe, non-spooled,'304', schedule 10, seamless, 1/2"	LF	9.98	9.85	19.83	7.16	17.14
10.1515 125	Stainless steel pipe, non-spooled,'304', schedule 10, seamless, 3/4"	LF	11.37	12.20	23.57	8.86	20.23
10.1515 130	Stainless steel pipe, non-spooled,'304', schedule 10, seamless, 1"	LF	15.86	14.69	30.55	10.67	26.53
10.1515 140	Stainless steel pipe, non-spooled,'304', schedule 10, seamless, 1-1/4"	LF	19.48	15.87	35.35	11.52	31.00
10.1515 145	Stainless steel pipe, '304', schedule 80, seamless, 1/2"	LF	15.61	11.81	27.42	7.40	23.01
10.1515 150	Stainless steel pipe, '304', schedule 80, seamless, 3/4"	LF	19.70	14.62	34.32	9.17	28.87
10.1515 155	Stainless steel pipe, '304', schedule 80, seamless, 1"	LF	25.87	17.60	43.47	11.03	36.90
10.1515 160	Stainless steel pipe, '304', schedule 80, seamless, 1-1/4"	LF	32.85	19.02	51.87	11.92	44.77
10.1515 165	Stainless steel pipe, '316', extra low carbon, schedule 10, seamless, 1/2"	LF	11.40	10.71	22.11	6.71	18.11
10.1515 170	Stainless steel pipe, '316', extra low carbon, schedule 10, seamless, 3/4"	LF	13.18	13.26	26.44	8.31	21.49
10.1515 175	Stainless steel pipe, '316', extra low carbon, schedule 10, seamless, 1"	LF	18.80	15.96	34.76	10.01	28.81
10.1515 180	Stainless steel pipe, '316', extra low carbon, schedule 10, seamless, 1-1/4"	LF	22.49	17.24	39.73	10.81	33.30
10.1515 190	Stainless steel pipe, '316', extra low carbon, schedule 40, seamless, 1/2"	LF	16.13	11.23	27.36	7.04	23.17
10.1515 195	Stainless steel pipe, '316', extra low carbon, schedule 40, seamless, 3/4"	LF	18.57	13.91	32.48	8.72	27.29
10.1515 200	Stainless steel pipe, '316', extra low carbon, schedule 40, seamless, 1"	LF	25.08	16.77	41.85	10.51	35.59
10.1515 205	Stainless steel pipe, '316', extra low carbon, schedule 40, seamless, 1-1/4"	LF	30.10	18.11	48.21	11.35	41.45
10.1515 210	Stainless steel pipe, '316', extra low carbon, schedule 80, seamless, 1/2"	LF	20.52	11.81	32.33	7.40	27.92
10.1515 215	Stainless steel pipe, '316', extra low carbon, schedule 80, seamless, 3/4"	LF	23.91	14.62	38.53	9.17	33.08
10.1515 220	Stainless steel pipe, '316', extra low carbon, schedule 80, seamless, 1"	LF	31.40	17.60	49.00	11.03	42.43
10.1515 225	Stainless steel pipe, '316', extra low carbon, schedule 80, seamless, 1-1/4"	LF	42.15	19.02	61.17	11.92	54.07

CSI #	10.1 PLUMBING & FIRE PROTECTION Description	Unit	Material	Union Install	Union Total	Open Install	Open Total
10.1600	**FEES, PERMITS, STERILIZATION**						
10.1600 105	Water meter fee, 3/4" connection	EACH	1,314.00		1,314.00		1,314.00
10.1600 110	Water meter fee, 1" connection	EACH	2,023.00		2,023.00		2,023.00
10.1600 115	Water meter fee, 1-1/2" connection	EACH	3,896.00		3,896.00		3,896.00
10.1600 120	Water meter fee, 2" connection	EACH	6,035.00		6,035.00		6,035.00
10.1600 125	Water meter fee, 3" connection	EACH	9,993.00		9,993.00		9,993.00
10.1600 130	Water meter fee, 4" connection	EACH	15,856.00		15,856.00		15,856.00
10.1600 135	Water meter fee, 6" connection	EACH	31,608.00		31,608.00		31,608.00
10.1600 140	Sewer fee, average, connection	FIX	350.00		350.00		350.00
10.1600 145	Sewer fee, average, connection, no plant or line charge	FIX	100.00		100.00		100.00
10.1600 150	Sterilization, testing & cleaning, per fixture	FIX	100.00		100.00		100.00
10.1700	**FIRE PROTECTION SYSTEMS**						
10.1700 100	Fire protection, concealed system, wet, normal hazard, 1 to 5,000 SF	SF	3.64	2.62	6.26	1.73	5.37
10.1700 105	Fire protection, concealed system, wet, normal hazard, 6,000 to 15,000 SF	SF	3.20	1.95	5.15	1.29	4.49
10.1700 110	Fire protection, concealed system, wet, normal hazard, over 15,000 SF	SF	3.00	1.83	4.83	1.21	4.21
10.1700 115	Fire protection, concealed system, wet, high hazard, 1 to 5,000 SF	SF	4.73	3.01	7.74	1.99	6.72
10.1700 120	Fire protection, concealed system, wet, high hazard, 6,000 to 15,000 SF	SF	4.16	2.24	6.40	1.48	5.64
10.1700 125	Fire protection, concealed system, wet, high hazard, over 15,000 SF	SF	3.90	2.10	6.00	1.39	5.29
10.1700 130	Fire protection, concealed system, wet, light hazard, 1 to 5,000 SF	SF	3.09	2.62	5.71	1.73	4.82
10.1700 135	Fire protection, concealed system, wet, light hazard, 6,000 to 15,000 SF	SF	2.72	1.95	4.67	1.29	4.01
10.1700 140	Fire protection, concealed system, wet, light hazard, over 15,000 SF	SF	2.55	1.83	4.38	1.21	3.76
10.1700 145	Fire protection, exposed system, wet, normal hazard, 1 to 5,000 SF	SF	2.35	2.42	4.77	1.60	3.95
10.1700 150	Fire protection, exposed system, wet, normal hazard, 6,000 to 15,000 SF	SF	1.96	1.76	3.72	1.16	3.12
10.1700 155	Fire protection, exposed system, wet, normal hazard, over 15,000 SF	SF	1.88	1.67	3.55	1.10	2.98
10.1700 160	Fire protection, exposed system, wet, high hazard, 1 to 5,000 SF	SF	3.06	2.78	5.84	1.84	4.90
10.1700 165	Fire protection, exposed system, wet, high hazard, 6,000 to 15,000 SF	SF	2.55	2.02	4.57	1.33	3.88
10.1700 170	Fire protection, exposed system, wet, high hazard, over 15,000 SF	SF	2.44	1.92	4.36	1.27	3.71
10.1700 175	Fire protection, exposed system, wet, light hazard, 1 to 5,000 SF	SF	2.00	2.42	4.42	1.60	3.60
10.1700 180	Fire protection, exposed system, wet, light hazard, 6,000 to 15,000 SF	SF	1.67	1.76	3.43	1.16	2.83
10.1700 185	Fire protection, exposed system, wet, light hazard, over 15,000 SF	SF	1.60	1.67	3.27	1.10	2.70
10.1700 190	Fire protection, halon system, 2000 SF, 8' ceiling & 1" raised floor	SF	23.81		23.81		23.81
10.1700 195	Fire protection, halon system, 4000 SF, 8' ceiling & 1" raised floor	SF	17.64		17.64		17.64
10.1700 200	Fire protection, halon system, 10,000 SF, 8' ceiling & 1" raised floor	SF	14.53		14.53		14.53
10.1700 205	Standpipe, dry, 6" diameter, hook up, connection, pumper 6"	EACH	1,735.00	492.00	2,227.00	326.00	2,061.00
10.1700 210	Standpipe, dry, 6" diameter, hook up, connection, pumper 4"	EACH	1,653.00	479.00	2,132.00	317.00	1,970.00
10.1700 215	Fire pump, electric, 2500 GPM, @ 40 psi	EACH	18,103.00	4,172.00	22,275.00	2,759.00	20,862.00
10.1700 220	Fire pump, electric, 750 GPM, @ 100 psi	EACH	26,368.00	5,006.00	31,374.00	3,310.00	29,678.00
10.1700 225	Fire pump, diesel, 500 GPM, @ 100 psi	EACH	50,476.00	4,636.00	55,112.00	3,065.00	53,541.00
10.1700 230	Fire pump, diesel, 1000 GPM, @ 150 psi	EACH	82,280.00	6,119.00	88,399.00	4,046.00	86,326.00

CSI #	10.2 HEAT, VENT & AIR CONDITIONING Description	Unit	Material	Union Install	Union Total	Open Install	Open Total
	The costs, in this section, include material, installation, and subcontractor overhead and profit. There are no allowances for general contractor markup and profit. Costs represent standard grade materials and normal installation. Adjustments should be made for economy quality or custom and heavy duty materials and commensurate installation.						
10.2105	**FURNACES**						
10.2105 100	Furnace, up flow, 80 MBTU, gas fired	EACH	703.00	436.00	1,139.00	274.00	977.00
10.2105 105	Furnace, up flow, 120 MBTU, gas fired	EACH	829.00	590.00	1,419.00	370.00	1,199.00
10.2105 110	Furnace, horizontal flow, 80 MBTU, gas fired	EACH	815.00	539.00	1,354.00	338.00	1,153.00
10.2105 115	Furnace, horizontal flow, 100 MBTU, gas fired	EACH	895.00	610.00	1,505.00	382.00	1,277.00
10.2105 120	Unit heater, suspended, 75 MBTU, gas fired	EACH	1,023.00	487.00	1,510.00	305.00	1,328.00
10.2105 125	Unit heater, suspended, 175 MBTU, gas fired	EACH	1,636.00	781.00	2,417.00	489.00	2,125.00
10.2105 130	Duct heater, indoor, 100 MBTU, gas fired	EACH	1,393.00	471.00	1,864.00	295.00	1,688.00
10.2105 135	Duct heater, indoor, 175 MBTU, gas fired	EACH	1,755.00	563.00	2,318.00	353.00	2,108.00
10.2105 140	Duct heater, roof, 125 MBTU, gas fired	EACH	2,292.00	527.00	2,819.00	330.00	2,622.00
10.2105 145	Duct heater, roof, 225 MBTU, gas fired	EACH	2,885.00	842.00	3,727.00	528.00	3,413.00
10.2105 150	Electric furnace, unit heater, 10 MBH, 3 KW, 240 V	EACH	470.00	225.00	695.00	141.00	611.00
10.2105 155	Electric furnace, unit heater, 34 MBH, 10 KW, 240 V	EACH	695.00	337.00	1,032.00	211.00	906.00
10.2105 160	Electric furnace, duct heater, 3.4 MBH, 1 KW, no enclosure	EACH	186.00	93.00	279.00	58.00	244.00
10.2105 165	Electric furnace, duct heater, 18 MBH, 5 KW, no enclosure	EACH	278.00	129.00	407.00	81.00	359.00
10.2105 170	Electric furnace, baseboard heater, hot water, 1030 BTU	LF	33.00	14.00	47.00	9.00	42.00
10.2105 175	Electric furnace, baseboard heater, hot water, 2 row	LF	47.00	18.00	65.00	11.00	58.00
10.2105 180	Electric furnace, baseboard heater, 240/160 V, aluminum finish	LF	47.00	12.00	59.00	8.00	55.00
10.2105 185	Electric furnace, baseboard heater, 240/140 V	LF	30.00	12.00	42.00	8.00	38.00
10.2110	**BOILERS**						
10.2110 100	Boiler, steel tube, gas fired, 670 MBH, 150# steam, pump 200 GPM at 95 TDH, expansion tank, air separator, pipe, valves	EACH	35,113.00	8,033.00	43,146.00	5,036.00	40,149.00
10.2110 105	Boiler, steel tube, gas fired, 2700 MBH, 150# steam, pump 108 GPM at 60 TDH, expansion tank, air separator, pipe, valves	EACH	55,818.00	7,036.00	62,854.00	4,411.00	60,229.00
10.2110 110	Boiler, steel tube, gas fired, 6700 MBH, 150# steam, pump 250 GPM at 90 TDH, expansion tank, air separator, pipe, valves	EACH	102,449.00	12,568.00	115,017.00	7,879.00	110,328.00
10.2110 115	Boiler, steel tube, gas fired, 3350 MBH, 15# steam, 30" water, pump 108 GPM at 60 TDH, expansion tank, air separator, pipe, valves	EACH	37,276.00	8,308.00	45,584.00	5,208.00	42,484.00
10.2110 120	Boiler, steel tube, gas fired, 670 MBH, 15# steam, 30" water, pump 200 GPM at 95 TDH, expansion tank, air separator, pipe, valves	EACH	26,220.00	8,033.00	34,253.00	5,036.00	31,256.00
10.2115	**CHILLERS**						
10.2115 100	Chiller, reciprocating, air cool, 20 TON	EACH	21,223.00	4,580.00	25,803.00	2,871.00	24,094.00
10.2115 105	Chiller, reciprocating, air cool, 50 TON	EACH	44,662.00	6,543.00	51,205.00	4,102.00	48,764.00
10.2115 110	Chiller, reciprocating, air cool, 150 TON	EACH	98,615.00	13,085.00	111,700.00	8,203.00	106,818.00
10.2115 115	Chiller, centrifugal, water cool, 60 TON	EACH	52,205.00	5,452.00	57,657.00	3,418.00	55,623.00
10.2115 120	Chiller, centrifugal, water cool, 150 TON	EACH	97,789.00	12,540.00	110,329.00	7,862.00	105,651.00
10.2115 125	Chiller, centrifugal, water cool, 400 TON	EACH	198,928.00	26,580.00	225,508.00	16,663.00	215,591.00
10.2115 130	Chiller, absorption, hot water, 100 TON	EACH	135,347.00	9,269.00	144,616.00	5,811.00	141,158.00
10.2115 135	Chiller, absorption, hot water, 200 TON	EACH	248,137.00	16,357.00	264,494.00	10,254.00	258,391.00
10.2115 140	Chiller, absorption, hot water 650 TON	EACH	703,956.00	28,897.00	732,853.00	18,116.00	722,072.00
10.2120	**COOLING TOWERS**						
10.2120 100	Cooling tower, 20 TON, compressor chiller	EACH	7,896.00	1,090.00	8,986.00	684.00	8,580.00
10.2120 105	Cooling tower, 60 TON, compressor chiller	EACH	23,687.00	2,181.00	25,868.00	1,367.00	25,054.00
10.2120 110	Cooling tower, 150 TON, compressor chiller	EACH	50,755.00	4,035.00	54,790.00	2,529.00	53,284.00
10.2120 115	Cooling tower, 400 TON, compressor chiller	EACH	112,969.00	8,178.00	121,147.00	5,127.00	118,096.00
10.2120 120	Cooling tower, 200 TON, absorption chiller	EACH	34,976.00	5,125.00	40,101.00	3,213.00	38,189.00
10.2120 125	Cooling tower, 350 TON, absorption chiller	EACH	43,283.00	7,960.00	51,243.00	4,990.00	48,273.00
10.2120 130	Cooling tower, 1000 TON, absorption chiller	EACH	116,996.00	16,793.00	133,789.00	10,528.00	127,524.00

CSI #	10.2 HEAT, VENT & AIR CONDITIONING Description	Unit	Material	Union Install	Union Total	Open Install	Open Total
10.2125	**AIR CONDITIONERS**						
10.2125 100	Air conditioner, 8 TON, roof mounted, D-X	EACH	12,394.00	1,090.00	13,484.00	684.00	13,078.00
10.2125 105	Air conditioner, 15 TON, roof mounted, D-X	EACH	19,661.00	1,454.00	21,115.00	912.00	20,573.00
10.2125 110	Air conditioner, 2 TON, thru-wall, D-X	EACH	2,047.00	545.00	2,592.00	342.00	2,389.00
10.2125 115	Air conditioner, 4 TON, thru-wall, D-X	EACH	4,069.00	727.00	4,796.00	456.00	4,525.00
10.2130	**SPLIT SYSTEMS**						
10.2130 100	Split system, air conditioner, residential, 2 TON	EACH	2,868.00	409.00	3,277.00	256.00	3,124.00
10.2130 105	Split system, air conditioner, residential, 3 TON	EACH	3,632.00	432.00	4,064.00	271.00	3,903.00
10.2130 110	Split system, air conditioner, residential, 4 TON	EACH	4,807.00	636.00	5,443.00	399.00	5,206.00
10.2130 115	Split system, air conditioner, residential, 5 TON	EACH	5,593.00	772.00	6,365.00	484.00	6,077.00
10.2130 120	Split system, air conditioner, commercial, 10 TON	EACH	9,912.00	1,523.00	11,435.00	955.00	10,867.00
10.2130 125	Split system, air conditioner, commercial, 20 TON	EACH	16,710.00	1,499.00	18,209.00	940.00	17,650.00
10.2130 130	Split system, air conditioner, commercial, 30 TON	EACH	25,102.00	2,908.00	28,010.00	1,823.00	26,925.00
10.2130 135	Split system, air conditioner, commercial, 50 TON	EACH	36,183.00	3,544.00	39,727.00	2,222.00	38,405.00
10.2130 140	Split system, air conditioner, commercial, 70 TON	EACH	45,026.00	4,544.00	49,570.00	2,848.00	47,874.00
10.2135	**COMPUTER ROOM AIR CONDITIONING**						
10.2135 100	Computer room, air conditioning unit, 5 TON	EACH	16,199.00	2,908.00	19,107.00	1,823.00	18,022.00
10.2135 105	Computer room, air conditioning unit, 10 TON	EACH	29,634.00	5,816.00	35,450.00	3,646.00	33,280.00
10.2135 110	Computer room, air conditioning unit, 20 TON	EACH	48,304.00	8,724.00	57,028.00	5,469.00	53,773.00
10.2140	**ROOF MOUNTED UNITS**						
10.2140 100	Roof mounted, air-conditioner, gas heat, DX cooling, 3 TON cooling, 100 MBH heating	EACH	6,518.00	1,272.00	7,790.00	798.00	7,316.00
10.2140 105	Roof mounted, air-conditioner, gas heat, DX cooling, 4 TON cooling, 140 MBH heating	EACH	8,733.00	1,363.00	10,096.00	855.00	9,588.00
10.2140 110	Roof mounted, air-conditioner, gas heat, DX cooling, 5 TON cooling, 140 MBH heating	EACH	9,306.00	1,545.00	10,851.00	968.00	10,274.00
10.2140 115	Roof mounted, air-conditioner, gas heat, DX cooling, 8 TON cooling, 200 MBH heating	EACH	14,911.00	1,817.00	16,728.00	1,139.00	16,050.00
10.2140 120	Roof mounted, air-conditioner, gas heat, DX cooling, 10 TON cooling, 360 MBH heating	EACH	17,987.00	2,363.00	20,350.00	1,481.00	19,468.00
10.2140 125	Roof mounted, air-conditioner, gas heat, DX cooling, 20 TON cooling, 400 MBH heating	EACH	41,711.00	3,635.00	45,346.00	2,279.00	43,990.00
10.2140 130	Roof mounted, air-conditioner, gas heat, DX cooling, 40 TON cooling, 760 MBH heating	EACH	75,599.00	7,724.00	83,323.00	4,842.00	80,441.00
10.2140 135	Roof mounted, air-conditioner, gas heat, DX cooling, 60 TON cooling, 1000 MBH heating	EACH	106,881.00	9,996.00	116,877.00	6,267.00	113,148.00
10.2145	**HEAT PUMPS**						
10.2145 100	Heat pump, 2 TON, 26000 BTU, thru-wall	EACH	2,023.00	727.00	2,750.00	456.00	2,479.00
10.2145 105	Heat pump, 4 TON, 52000 BTU, thru-wall	EACH	4,120.00	1,090.00	5,210.00	684.00	4,804.00
10.2145 110	Heat pump, 10 TON, 120000 BTU, roof, duct	EACH	15,121.00	2,363.00	17,484.00	1,481.00	16,602.00
10.2145 115	Heat pump, 20 TON, 240000 BTU, roof, duct	EACH	28,675.00	3,635.00	32,310.00	2,279.00	30,954.00
10.2145 120	Heat pump, 2 TON, 26000 BTU, plenum	EACH	3,389.00	636.00	4,025.00	399.00	3,788.00
10.2145 125	Heat pump, 4 TON, 52000 BTU, plenum	EACH	5,735.00	727.00	6,462.00	456.00	6,191.00
10.2150	**HYDRONIC SYSTEMS**						
10.2150 100	Hydronic unit, 50 TON, 300 MBH	EACH	34,114.00	1,897.00	36,011.00	1,189.00	35,303.00
10.2150 105	Hydronic unit, 100 TON, 600 MBH	EACH	60,880.00	2,846.00	63,726.00	1,784.00	62,664.00
10.2150 110	Hydronic unit, 150 TON, 900 MBH	EACH	77,676.00	2,846.00	63,726.00	1,784.00	62,664.00
10.2150 115	Hydronic unit, 200 TON, 1200 MBH	EACH	94,468.00	3,795.00	98,263.00	2,379.00	96,847.00
10.2155	**INFRA-RED AND RADIANT SYSTEMS**						
10.2155 100	Infra-red heater, 30,000 BTU, gas	EACH	1,032.00	266.00	1,298.00	167.00	1,199.00
10.2155 105	Infra-red heater, 60,000 BTU, gas	EACH	1,862.00	400.00	2,262.00	251.00	2,113.00
10.2155 110	Radiant heat panel, 24x24, 357 W	EACH	326.00	91.00	417.00	57.00	383.00
10.2155 115	Radiant heat panel, 24x48, 500 W	EACH	364.00	91.00	455.00	57.00	421.00

CSI #	10.2 HEAT, VENT & AIR CONDITIONING Description	Unit	Material	Union Install	Union Total	Open Install	Open Total
10.2160	**HUMIDIFIERS**						
10.2160 100	Humidifier, steam, 50#/hr	EACH	906.00	727.00	1,633.00	456.00	1,362.00
10.2160 105	Humidifier, steam, 300#/hr	EACH	2,480.00	1,704.00	4,184.00	1,068.00	3,548.00
10.2160 110	Humidifier, electric, 50#/hr	EACH	4,487.00	545.00	5,032.00	342.00	4,829.00
10.2160 115	Humidifier, electric, 150#/hr	EACH	7,793.00	1,090.00	8,883.00	684.00	8,477.00
10.2165	**PUMPS**						
10.2165 100	Pump, condensate, duplex, 40 GPM	EACH	6,529.00	1,817.00	8,346.00	1,139.00	7,668.00
10.2165 105	Pump, condensate, duplex, 75 GPM	EACH	7,657.00	2,726.00	10,383.00	1,709.00	9,366.00
10.2165 110	Pump, condensate, duplex, 120 GPM	EACH	9,998.00	3,362.00	13,360.00	2,108.00	12,106.00
10.2165 115	Pump, water service, 20 GPM, 50' head	EACH	1,232.00	409.00	1,641.00	256.00	1,488.00
10.2165 120	Pump, water service, 60 GPM, 50' head	EACH	1,753.00	909.00	2,662.00	570.00	2,323.00
10.2165 125	Pump, water service, 200 GPM, 50' head	EACH	2,964.00	1,545.00	4,509.00	968.00	3,932.00
10.2165 130	Pump, water service, 400 GPM, 50' head	EACH	4,343.00	2,272.00	6,615.00	1,424.00	5,767.00
10.2165 135	Pump, water service, 2000 GPM, 50' head	EACH	13,243.00	3,998.00	17,241.00	2,507.00	15,750.00
10.2165 140	Pump, water service, 4000 GPM, 50' head	EACH	17,714.00	4,998.00	22,712.00	3,133.00	20,847.00
10.2165 145	Pump, fuel oil, 1 GPM, 1/4 horse power	EACH	1,048.00	591.00	1,639.00	370.00	1,418.00
10.2165 150	Pump, fuel oil, 5 GPM, 1/4 HP	EACH	1,213.00	909.00	2,122.00	570.00	1,783.00
10.2165 155	Pump, fuel oil, 10 GPM, 1/4 HP	EACH	1,343.00	1,000.00	2,343.00	627.00	1,970.00
10.2170	**AIR HANDLERS**						
10.2170 100	Air handler, 2000 CFM, 5 TON	EACH	6,988.00	803.00	7,791.00	516.00	7,504.00
10.2170 105	Air handler, 5200 CFM, 12 TON	EACH	19,665.00	1,352.00	21,017.00	869.00	20,534.00
10.2170 110	Air handler, 15,000 CFM, 30 TON	EACH	60,460.00	2,535.00	62,995.00	1,630.00	62,090.00
10.2170 115	Air handler, 28,000 CFM, 75 TON	EACH	104,950.00	5,492.00	110,442.00	3,531.00	108,481.00
10.2170 120	Air handler, 2500 CFM, 8 TON	EACH	5,165.00	676.00	5,841.00	435.00	5,600.00
10.2170 125	Air handler, 4000 CFM, 10 TON	EACH	8,832.00	760.00	9,592.00	489.00	9,321.00
10.2170 130	Air handler, 6250 CFM, 15 TON	EACH	12,088.00	1,014.00	13,102.00	652.00	12,740.00
10.2170 140	Air handler, 15,000 CFM, 30 TON	EACH	26,035.00	1,859.00	27,894.00	1,195.00	27,230.00
10.2175	**COILS**						
10.2175 100	Coil, chill water, 22,000 CFM, 44 SF	EACH	14,114.00	1,599.00	15,713.00	1,003.00	15,117.00
10.2175 105	Coil, chill water, 28,000 CFM, 56 SF	EACH	18,205.00	2,036.00	20,241.00	1,276.00	19,481.00
10.2175 110	Coil, chill water, 32,000 CFM, 64 SF	EACH	20,222.00	2,181.00	22,403.00	1,367.00	21,589.00
10.2175 115	Coil, hot water, 16,000 CFM, 16 SF	EACH	2,331.00	582.00	2,913.00	365.00	2,696.00
10.2175 120	Coil, hot water, 22,000 CFM, 22 SF	EACH	2,770.00	800.00	3,570.00	501.00	3,271.00
10.2175 125	Coil, hot water, 28,000 CFM, 28 SF	EACH	4,025.00	1,018.00	5,043.00	638.00	4,663.00
10.2180	**FANS**						
10.2180 100	Fan, supply, low pressure, 10,000 CFM, 1-1/2" utility set	EACH	4,474.00	1,169.00	5,643.00	752.00	5,226.00
10.2180 105	Fan, supply, low pressure, 20,000 CFM, 1-1/2" utility set	EACH	7,634.00	1,787.00	9,421.00	1,149.00	8,783.00
10.2180 110	Fan, supply, low pressure, 40,000 CFM, 1-1/2" utility set	EACH	13,030.00	2,949.00	15,979.00	1,896.00	14,926.00
10.2180 115	Fan, supply, high pressure, 10,000 CFM, 3-1/2" utility set	EACH	6,418.00	1,235.00	7,653.00	794.00	7,212.00
10.2180 120	Fan, supply, high pressure, 30,000 CFM, 3-1/2" utility set	EACH	11,327.00	2,319.00	13,646.00	1,491.00	12,818.00
10.2180 125	Fan, supply, high pressure, 40,000 CFM, 3-1/2" utility set	EACH	16,277.00	3,087.00	19,364.00	1,985.00	18,262.00
10.2180 130	Fan, exhaust, wall, 100 CFM	EACH	104.00	71.00	175.00	46.00	150.00
10.2180 135	Fan, exhaust, wall, 300 CFM	EACH	177.00	197.00	374.00	127.00	304.00
10.2180 140	Fan, exhaust, roof, 1/2"SP, 1600 CFM	EACH	1,311.00	427.00	1,738.00	275.00	1,586.00
10.2180 145	Fan, exhaust, roof, 1/2"SP, 6000 CFM	EACH	5,026.00	1,604.00	6,630.00	1,031.00	6,057.00
10.2180 150	Fan, exhaust, vibration mount, 3/4"SP, 2000 CFM	EACH	2,041.00	487.00	2,528.00	313.00	2,354.00
10.2180 155	Fan, exhaust, vibration mount, 3/4"SP, 10,000 CFM	EACH	3,781.00	914.00	4,695.00	588.00	4,369.00
10.2180 160	Fan, return, vibration mount, 5 HP, 17,500 CFM	EACH	8,429.00	972.00	9,401.00	625.00	9,054.00
10.2180 165	Fan, return, vibration mount, 10 HP, 31,000 CFM	EACH	17,191.00	1,690.00	18,881.00	1,086.00	18,277.00
10.2180 170	Fan, centrifugal in-line, 4,000 CFM	EACH	3,519.00	581.00	4,100.00	364.00	3,883.00
10.2180 175	Fan, centrifugal in-line, 10,000 CFM	EACH	6,354.00	983.00	7,337.00	616.00	6,970.00
10.2180 180	Fan, centrifugal in-line, 20,000 CFM	EACH	10,324.00	1,199.00	11,523.00	752.00	11,076.00
10.2180 185	Fan coil unit, duct mount, 2 pipe, 1 coil, 600 CFM	EACH	1,347.00	209.00	1,556.00	134.00	1,481.00
10.2180 190	Fan coil unit, duct mount, 2 pipe, 1 coil, 1000 CFM	EACH	1,964.00	313.00	2,277.00	201.00	2,165.00

CSI #	10.2 HEAT, VENT & AIR CONDITIONING Description	Unit	Material	Union Install	Union Total	Open Install	Open Total
10.2180	**FANS (Cont.)**						
10.2180 195	Fan coil unit, w/cabinets, 2 pipe, 1 coil, 600 CFM	EACH	1,420.00	258.00	1,678.00	166.00	1,586.00
10.2180 200	Fan coil unit, w/cabinets, 2 pipe, 1 coil, 1500 CFM	EACH	2,926.00	418.00	3,344.00	268.00	3,194.00
10.2185	**TANKS**						
10.2185 100	Expansion tank, chilled water, 44 GAL	EACH	1,244.00	186.00	1,430.00	117.00	1,361.00
10.2185 105	Expansion tank, ASME code, 88 GAL	EACH	3,763.00	813.00	4,576.00	510.00	4,273.00
10.2185 110	Expansion tank, ASME code, 250 GAL	EACH	7,252.00	1,608.00	8,860.00	1,008.00	8,260.00
10.2200	**CONTROLS**						
10.2200 100	Controls, pneumatic, air conditioning unit, to 10 Tons	LUMP	6,400.00		6,400.00		6,400.00
10.2200 105	Controls, pneumatic, air conditioning unit, to 20 Tons	LUMP	6,920.00		6,920.00		6,920.00
10.2200 110	Controls, pneumatic, air conditioning unit, to 30 Tons	LUMP	7,490.00		7,490.00		7,490.00
10.2200 115	Controls, pneumatic, boiler, to 1,000 MBH	LUMP	3,490.00		3,490.00		3,490.00
10.2200 120	Controls, pneumatic, boiler, to 4,000 MBH	LUMP	7,200.00		7,200.00		7,200.00
10.2200 125	Controls, pneumatic, boiler, to 10,000 MBH	LUMP	9,600.00		9,600.00		9,600.00
10.2200 130	Controls, pneumatic, chiller, to 50 Ton	LUMP	3,270.00		3,270.00		3,270.00
10.2200 135	Controls, pneumatic, chiller, to 300 Ton	LUMP	6,760.00		6,760.00		6,760.00
10.2200 140	Controls, pneumatic, chiller, to 600 Ton	LUMP	12,000.00		12,000.00		12,000.00
10.2200 145	Controls, pneumatic, cooling tower, to 100 Ton	LUMP	2,400.00		2,400.00		2,400.00
10.2200 150	Controls, pneumatic, cooling tower, to 300 Ton	LUMP	4,800.00		4,800.00		4,800.00
10.2200 155	Controls, pneumatic, cooling tower, to 600 Ton	LUMP	7,200.00		7,200.00		7,200.00
10.2200 160	Controls, pneumatic, exhaust fan	LUMP	700.00		700.00		700.00
10.2200 165	Controls, pneumatic, variable air volume box	LUMP	720.00		720.00		720.00
10.2200 170	Controls, pneumatic, variable air volume box with reheat coil	LUMP	1,180.00		1,180.00		1,180.00
10.2200 175	Controls, pneumatic, air compressor, 1/2 HP	LUMP	14,510.00		14,510.00		14,510.00
10.2200 180	Controls, pneumatic, air compressor, 1-1/2 HP	LUMP	18,150.00		18,150.00		18,150.00
10.2200 185	Controls, pneumatic, air compressor, 5 HP	LUMP	35,030.00		35,030.00		35,030.00
10.2300	**DUCTWORK**						
10.2300 100	Duct rectangular, galvanized iron, with supports, to 10000 LBS	POUND	6.12	5.23	11.35	3.36	9.48
10.2300 105	Duct rectangular, galvanized iron, with supports, to 20000 LBS	POUND	5.69	4.40	10.09	2.83	8.52
10.2300 110	Duct rectangular, galvanized iron, with supports, to 40000 LBS	POUND	5.05	3.86	8.91	2.48	7.53
10.2300 115	Duct flexible, insulated, with clamps, 4"	LF	3.73	5.63	9.36	3.62	7.35
10.2300 120	Duct flexible, insulated, with clamps, 6"	LF	5.01	6.97	11.98	4.48	9.49
10.2300 125	Duct flexible, insulated, with clamps, 8"	LF	7.13	10.07	17.20	6.47	13.60
10.2300 130	Duct flexible, insulated, with clamps, 10"	LF	7.44	13.24	20.68	8.51	15.95
10.2300 135	Duct flexible, insulated, with clamps, 12"	LF	9.13	18.61	27.74	11.96	21.09
10.2300 140	Duct flexible, insulated, with clamps, 14"	LF	10.09	22.84	32.93	14.69	24.78
10.2300 145	Duct flexible, insulated, with clamps, 16"	LF	12.84	28.46	41.30	17.84	30.68
10.2300 150	Duct flexible, insulated, with clamps, 18"	LF	15.64	34.49	50.13	21.63	37.27
10.2300 155	Duct flexible, insulated, with clamps, 20"	LF	16.75	40.66	57.41	25.49	42.24
10.2300 160	Fire dampers, insulated, UL rated, fusible link to 1 SF	EACH	202.00	93.00	295.00	60.00	262.00
10.2300 165	Fire dampers, insulated, UL rated, fusible link to 2 SF	EACH	267.00	115.00	382.00	74.00	341.00
10.2300 170	Fire dampers, insulated, UL rated, fusible link to 4 SF	EACH	342.00	170.00	512.00	109.00	451.00
10.2300 175	Fire dampers, insulated, UL rated, fusible link to 6 SF	EACH	649.00	197.00	846.00	127.00	776.00
10.2300 180	Fire dampers, insulated, UL rated, fusible link to 10 SF	EACH	701.00	285.00	986.00	183.00	884.00
10.2300 185	Fire dampers, insulated, UL rated, fusible link to 16 SF	EACH	866.00	345.00	1,211.00	222.00	1,088.00
10.2300 190	Fire dampers, insulated, UL rated, fusible link to 25 SF	EACH	1,055.00	484.00	1,539.00	311.00	1,366.00

CSI #	10.2 HEAT, VENT & AIR CONDITIONING Description	Unit	Material	Union Install	Union Total	Open Install	Open Total
10.2300	DUCTWORK (Cont.)						
10.2300 195	Air outlets, supply, to 12" louver face	EACH	82.00	66.00	148.00	42.00	124.00
10.2300 200	Air outlets, supply, to 18" louver face	EACH	118.00	82.00	200.00	53.00	171.00
10.2300 205	Air outlets, supply, to 24" louver face	EACH	178.00	104.00	282.00	67.00	245.00
10.2300 210	Air outlets, exhaust, to 12" louver face	EACH	51.00	44.00	95.00	28.00	79.00
10.2300 215	Air outlets, exhaust, to 18" louver face	EACH	70.00	60.00	130.00	39.00	109.00
10.2300 220	Air outlets, exhaust, to 24" louver face	EACH	95.00	82.00	177.00	53.00	148.00
10.2300 225	Duct insulation, wrap with vapor barrier, 1" thick	SFCA	1.58	1.69	3.27	1.08	2.66
10.2300 230	Duct insulation, lining with vapor barrier, 1" thick	SFCA	2.16	2.54	4.70	1.63	3.79
10.2300 235	Duct insulation, lining with vapor barrier, 2" thick	SFCA	3.16	3.38	6.54	2.16	5.32
10.2300 240	Plenum insulation, rigid, 2" thick	SFCA	2.81	4.23	7.04	2.72	5.53
10.2400	PIPING						
10.2400 100	Steel pipe, seamless, A-53, schedule 40, welded, 2"	LF	16.00	23.00	39.00	14.00	30.00
10.2400 105	Steel pipe, seamless, A-53, schedule 40, welded, 3"	LF	22.00	33.00	55.00	21.00	43.00
10.2400 110	Steel pipe, seamless, A-53, schedule 40, welded, 4"	LF	32.00	42.00	74.00	27.00	59.00
10.2400 115	Steel pipe, seamless, A-53, schedule 40, welded, 6"	LF	40.00	52.00	92.00	33.00	73.00
10.2400 120	Valve, gate, globe & check, iron body, flange, 125#, bolt & gasket, 2"	EACH	334.00	143.00	477.00	90.00	424.00
10.2400 125	Valve, gate, globe & check, iron body, flange, 125#, bolt & gasket, 2-1/2"	EACH	365.00	160.00	525.00	100.00	465.00
10.2400 130	Valve, gate, globe & check, iron body, flange, 125#, bolt & gasket, 3"	EACH	417.00	178.00	595.00	112.00	529.00
10.2400 135	Valve, gate, globe & check, iron body, flange, 125#, bolt & gasket, 5"-6"	EACH	1,061.00	415.00	1,476.00	260.00	1,321.00
10.2400 140	Valve, gate, globe & check, iron body, flange, 125#, bolt & gasket, 8"	EACH	2,096.00	545.00	2,641.00	342.00	2,438.00
10.2400 145	Steam traps, cast iron, screwed, 3/4", bucket	EACH	217.00	54.00	271.00	34.00	251.00
10.2400 150	Steam traps, cast iron, screwed, 1", bucket	EACH	365.00	68.00	433.00	43.00	408.00
10.2400 155	Butterfly valve, iron body, nylon, 2", wafer body	EACH	153.00	126.00	279.00	79.00	232.00
10.2400 160	Butterfly valve, iron body, nylon, 3", wafer body	EACH	174.00	174.00	348.00	109.00	283.00
10.2400 165	Butterfly valve, iron body, nylon, 6", wafer body	EACH	383.00	338.00	721.00	212.00	595.00
10.2400 170	Butterfly valve, iron body, nylon, 8", wafer, chain	EACH	572.00	498.00	1,070.00	312.00	884.00
10.2400 175	Butterfly valve, iron body, nylon, 2", lug type	EACH	183.00	126.00	309.00	79.00	262.00
10.2400 180	Butterfly valve, iron body, nylon, 3", lug type	EACH	208.00	174.00	382.00	109.00	317.00
10.2400 185	Butterfly valve, iron body, nylon, 6", lug type	EACH	444.00	338.00	782.00	212.00	656.00
10.2400 190	Butterfly valve, iron body, nylon, 8", lug, chain	EACH	616.00	498.00	1,114.00	312.00	928.00
10.2400 195	Valve, balancing, circuit setter, 1/2"	EACH	82.00	30.00	112.00	19.00	101.00
10.2400 200	Valve, balancing, circuit setter, 3/4"	EACH	100.00	36.00	136.00	23.00	123.00
10.2400 205	Valve, balancing, circuit setter, 1 1/2"	EACH	154.00	80.00	234.00	50.00	204.00
10.2400 210	Valve, balancing, circuit setter, 2"	EACH	254.00	135.00	389.00	85.00	339.00

CSI #	11.0 ELECTRICAL Description	Unit	Material	Union Install	Union Total	Open Install	Open Total
	The costs, in this section, include material, installation, and subcontractor overhead and profit. There are no allowances for general contractor markup and profit. Costs represent standard grade materials and normal installation. Adjustments should be made for economy quality or custom and heavy duty materials and commensurate installation.						
11.0100	**SWITCHGEAR**						
11.0100 100	Substation, 150 KVA, 1200 AMP, with transformer, breakers, pad, grounding	EACH	49,850.00	11,533.00	61,383.00	8,262.00	58,112.00
11.0100 105	Substation, 1000 KVA, 3000 AMP, with transformer, breakers, pad, grounding	EACH	94,880.00	18,969.00	113,849.00	13,662.00	108,542.00
11.0100 110	Service switchboard, 600 A, 3PH, 277/480V MCMB, breakers, bus, meter, enclosure	EACH	19,769.00	5,035.00	24,804.00	3,657.00	23,426.00
11.0100 115	Service switchboard, 1200 A, 3PH, 277/480V MCMB, breakers, bus, meter, enclosure	EACH	31,747.71	7,584.15	39,331.86	5,508.25	37,255.96
11.0100 120	Service switchboard, 2000 A, 3PH, 277/480V MCMB, breakers, bus, meter, enclosure	EACH	40,400.00	11,018.00	51,418.00	8,002.00	48,402.00
11.0100 125	Distribution switchboard, 600 A, 3PH, 120/208 V, enclosure, breakers	EACH	6,919.00	1,774.00	8,693.00	1,289.00	8,208.00
11.0100 130	Distribution switchboard, 800 A, 3PH, 120/208 V, enclosure, breakers	EACH	8,110.00	2,341.00	10,451.00	1,700.00	9,810.00
11.0100 135	Distribution switchboard, 1600 A, 3PH, 120/208 V, enclosure, breakers	EACH	15,322.00	4,896.00	20,218.00	3,556.00	18,878.00
11.0100 140	Distribution switchboard, 400 A, 3PH, 277/480 V, enclosure, breakers	EACH	5,741.00	1,614.00	7,355.00	1,172.00	6,913.00
11.0100 145	Distribution switchboard, 800 A, 3PH, 277/480 V, enclosure, breakers	EACH	9,102.00	2,929.00	12,031.00	2,127.00	11,229.00
11.0100 150	Distribution switchboard, 1200 A, 3PH, 277/480 V, enclosure, breakers	EACH	14,264.00	3,985.00	18,249.00	2,895.00	17,159.00
11.0100 151	Transformer, 480/120 V, 3 phase, 500 KVA	EACH	26,280.00	4,365.00	30,645.00	3,170.00	29,450.00
11.0100 152	Transformer, 480/120 V, 3 phase, 750 KVA	EACH	42,704.00	5,238.00	47,942.00	3,804.00	46,508.00
11.0100 153	Transformer, 480/120 V, 3 phase, 1,000 KVA	EACH	51,516.00	5,675.00	57,191.00	4,122.00	55,638.00
11.0100 155	Panelboards, bolt-on breakers, 277/480V, 3PH, 4W, 100 A, 24 circuits	EACH	3,101.00	486.00	3,587.00	353.00	3,454.00
11.0100 160	Panelboards, bolt-on breakers, 277/480V, 3PH, 4W, 225 A, 42 circuits	EACH	4,298.00	1,624.00	5,922.00	1,179.00	5,477.00
11.0100 165	Panelboards, bolt-on breakers, 277/480V, 3PH, 4W, 400 A, 42 circuits	EACH	4,507.00	1,798.00	6,305.00	1,306.00	5,813.00
11.0100 205	Panelboards, bolt-on breakers, 120/208 V, 3PH, 4W, 100 A, 30 circuits	EACH	1,633.00	1,157.00	2,790.00	840.00	2,473.00
11.0100 210	Panelboards, bolt-on breakers, 120/208 V, 3PH, 4W, 225 A, 42 circuits	EACH	2,946.00	1,711.00	4,657.00	1,243.00	4,189.00
11.0100 215	Panelboards, bolt-on breakers, 120/208 V, 3PH, 4W, 400 A, 42 circuits	EACH	4,109.00	1,886.00	5,995.00	1,370.00	5,479.00
11.0100 220	Transformer, 480/120 V, 3 phase, 45 KVA	EACH	3,702.00	1,746.00	5,448.00	1,268.00	4,970.00
11.0100 225	Transformer, 480/120 V, 3 phase, 75 KVA	EACH	5,579.00	1,964.00	7,543.00	1,427.00	7,006.00
11.0100 230	Transformer, 480/120 V, 3 phase, 112.5 KVA	EACH	7,424.00	2,183.00	9,607.00	1,585.00	9,009.00
11.0200	**EMERGENCY SYSTEMS**						
11.0200 100	Emergency generator to 30 KW	EACH	29,454.00	3,572.00	33,026.00	2,595.00	32,049.00
11.0200 105	Emergency generator to 100 KW	EACH	50,215.00	7,145.00	57,360.00	5,189.00	55,404.00
11.0200 110	Emergency generator to 400 KW	EACH	145,624.00	12,504.00	158,128.00	9,081.00	154,705.00
11.0200 115	Emergency generator to 750 KW	EACH	316,355.00	17,862.00	334,217.00	12,973.00	329,328.00
11.0200 120	Emergency generator to 1,000 KW	EACH	363,708.00	21,435.00	385,143.00	15,568.00	379,276.00
11.0200 125	Automatic transfer switch 30 A	EACH	7,222.00	357.00	7,579.00	259.00	7,481.00
11.0200 130	Automatic transfer switch 100 A	EACH	7,989.00	715.00	8,704.00	519.00	8,508.00

CSI #	11.0 ELECTRICAL Description	Unit	Material	Union Install	Union Total	Open Install	Open Total
11.0200	**EMERGENCY SYSTEMS (Cont.)**						
11.0200 135	Automatic transfer switch 400 A	EACH	15,514.00	1,429.00	16,943.00	1,038.00	16,552.00
11.0200 140	Automatic transfer switch 1,000 A	EACH	47,103.00	1,965.00	49,068.00	1,427.00	48,530.00
11.0200 145	Automatic transfer switch 2,000 A	EACH	63,135.00	3,215.00	66,350.00	2,335.00	65,470.00
11.0200 150	Exit sign, incandescent, battery, surface mounted	EACH	375.00	147.00	522.00	107.00	482.00
11.0200 155	Exit sign, incandescent, battery, recessed	EACH	365.00	192.00	557.00	139.00	504.00
11.0200 160	Exit sign, fluorescent, battery, surface mounted	EACH	375.00	147.00	522.00	107.00	482.00
11.0200 165	Exit sign, fluorescent, battery, recessed	EACH	376.00	192.00	568.00	139.00	515.00
11.0300	**FEEDER CONDUIT & WIRE**						
11.0300 100	Conduit and wire, in slab, 60 A, 3 CU wire 600 V THHN #6, 1 CU soft #10, in 1" PVC	LF	5.34	7.35	12.69	5.36	10.70
11.0300 105	Conduit and wire, in slab, 100 A, 4 CU wire 600 V THHN #2, 1 CU soft #8, in 1" PVC	LF	13.42	10.47	23.89	7.61	21.03
11.0300 110	Conduit and wire, in slab, 225 A, 4 CU wire 600 V THHN #4/0, 1 CU soft #1, in 2" PVC	LF	37.90	20.10	58.00	14.60	52.50
11.0300 115	Conduit and wire, in slab, 300 A, 4 CU wire 600 V THHN 350 MCM, 1 CU soft #4, in 3" PVC	LF	56.86	25.41	82.27	18.48	75.34
11.0300 120	Conduit and wire, in slab, 400 A, 4 CU wire 600 V THHN 500 MCM, 1 CU soft #2, in 3" PVC	LF	77.61	28.85	106.46	20.96	98.57
11.0300 125	Conduit and wire, in slab, 600 A, 8 CU wire 600 V THHN 350 MCM, 1 CU soft #1, in 2" PVC	LF	114.04	46.44	160.48	33.76	147.80
11.0300 130	Conduit and wire, in slab, 800 A, 6 CU wire 600 V THHN 500 MCM, 2 CU soft #1/0, in 3" PVC	LF	124.74	49.78	174.52	36.16	160.90
11.0300 135	Conduit and wire, in slab, 1000 A, 12 CU wire 600 V THHN 400 MCM, 3 bare CU soft #2/0, in 3" PVC	LF	207.36	82.77	290.13	60.12	267.48
11.0300 140	Conduit and wire, in slab, 1200 A, 16 CU wire 600 V THHN 350 MCM, 4 bare CU soft #3/0, in 3" PVC	LF	245.28	105.56	350.84	76.76	322.04
11.0300 145	Conduit and wire, in slab, 1600 A, 20 CU wire 600 V THHN 400 MCM, 5 bare CU soft #4/0, in 3" PVC	LF	358.30	140.00	498.30	101.70	460.00
11.0300 150	Conduit and wire, in slab, 2000 A, 18 CU wire 600 V THHN 400 MCM, 6 bare CU soft 250 MCM, in 3" PVC	LF	356.46	146.22	502.68	106.20	462.66
11.0300 155	Conduit and wire, 60 A, 3 CU wire 600 V THHN #6, 1 bare CU soft #10, in 1" EMT	LF	5.15	8.77	13.92	6.39	11.54
11.0300 160	Conduit and wire, 100 A, 4 CU wire 600 V THHN #2, 1 bare CU soft #8, in 1" EMT	LF	13.50	12.98	26.48	9.43	22.93
11.0300 165	Conduit and wire, 225 A, 4 CU wire 600 V THHN #4/0, 1 bare CU soft #1, in 2" EMT	LF	41.78	22.06	63.84	16.02	57.80
11.0300 170	Conduit and wire, 300 A, 4 CU wire 600 V THHN 350 MCM, 1 bare CU soft #4, in 3" EMT	LF	61.65	26.93	88.58	19.59	81.24
11.0300 175	Conduit and wire, 400 A, 4 CU wire 600 V THHN 500 MCM, 1 bare CU soft #2, in 3" EMT	LF	82.40	30.37	112.77	22.07	104.47
11.0300 180	Conduit and wire, 600 A, 8 CU wire 600 V THHN 350 MCM, 1 bare CU soft #1, in 2" EMT	LF	121.80	50.36	172.16	36.60	158.40
11.0300 185	Conduit and wire, 800 A, 6 CU wire 600 V THHN 500 MCM, 2 bare CU soft #1/0, in 3" EMT	LF	129.32	48.46	177.78	35.20	164.52
11.0300 190	Conduit and wire, 1000 A, 12 CU wire 600 V THHN 400 MCM, 3 bare CU soft #2/0, in 3" EMT	LF	221.73	87.33	309.06	63.45	285.18
11.0300 195	Conduit and wire, 1200 A, 16 CU wire 600 V THHN 350 MCM, 4 bare CU soft #3/0, in 3" EMT	LF	264.44	111.64	376.08	81.20	345.64
11.0300 200	Conduit and wire, 1600 A, 20 CU wire 600 V THHN 400 MCM, 5 bare CU soft #4/0, in 3" EMT	LF	382.25	147.60	529.85	107.25	489.50
11.0300 205	Conduit and wire, 2000 A, 18 CU wire 600 V THHN 400 MCM, 6 bare CU soft 250 MCM, in 3" EMT	LF	385.20	155.34	540.54	112.86	498.06
11.0300 210	Conduit and wire, 60 A, 3 CU wire 600 V THHN #6, 1 bare CU soft #10, in 1" GRS	LF	7.24	10.84	18.08	7.89	15.13

CSI #	11.0 ELECTRICAL Description	Unit	Material	Union Install	Union Total	Open Install	Open Total
11.0300	**FEEDER CONDUIT & WIRE (Cont.)**						
11.0300 215	Conduit and wire, 100 A, 4 CU wire 600 V THHN #2, 1 bare CU soft #8, in 1" GRS	LF	15.72	15.71	31.43	11.41	27.13
11.0300 220	Conduit and wire, 225 A, 4 CU wire 600 V THHN #4/0 1 bare CU soft #1, in 2" GRS	LF	44.96	26.21	71.17	19.04	64.00
11.0300 225	Conduit and wire, 300 A, 4 CU wire 600 V THHN 350 MCM 1 bare CU soft #4, in 3" GRS	LF	65.23	32.39	97.62	23.55	88.78
11.0300 230	Conduit and wire, 400 A, 4 CU wire 600 V THHN 500 MCM 1 bare CU soft #2, in 3" GRS	LF	85.98	35.83	121.81	26.03	112.01
11.0300 235	Conduit and wire, 600 A, 8 CU wire 600 V THHN 350 MCM 2 bare CU soft #1, in 2" GRS	LF	128.16	58.66	186.82	42.64	170.80
11.0300 240	Conduit and wire, 800 A, 6 CU wire 600 V THHN 500 MCM, 2 bare CU soft #1/0, in 3" GRS	LF	141.48	63.74	205.22	46.30	187.78
11.0300 245	Conduit and wire, 1000 A, 12 CU wire 600 V THHN 400 MCM, 3 bare CU soft #2/0, in 3" GRS	LF	232.47	103.71	336.18	75.33	307.80
11.0300 250	Conduit and wire, 1200 A, 16 CU wire 600 V THHN 350 MCM, 4 bare CU soft #3/0, in 3" GRS	LF	278.76	133.48	412.24	97.04	375.80
11.0300 255	Conduit and wire, 1600 A, 20 CU wire 600 V THHN 400 MCM, 5 bare CU soft #4/0, in 3" GRS	LF	400.15	174.90	575.05	127.05	527.20
11.0300 260	2000 A, 18 CU wire 600 V THHN 400 MCM, 6 bare CU soft 250 MCM, in 3" GRS	LF	406.68	188.10	594.78	136.62	543.30
11.0300 265	Cable trays ladder type 12", with ells, tees, 4" drop cover, unistrut hangers	LF	29.99	30.62	60.61	22.24	52.23
11.0300 270	Cable trays ladder type 24", with ells, tees, 4" drop cover, unistrut hangers	LF	33.83	39.09	72.92	28.39	62.22
11.0400	**FIXTURES**						
11.0400 100	Fixture, incandescent, commercial grade, surface mounted, with junction box, wire, conduit, 100 watt	EACH	92.00	151.00	243.00	110.00	202.00
11.0400 105	Fixture, incandescent, commercial grade, recessed downlight, with junction box, wire, conduit, 100 watt	EACH	103.00	196.00	299.00	142.00	245.00
11.0400 110	Fixture, incandescent, commercial grade, surface mounted, with junction box, wire, conduit, 200 watt	EACH	112.00	156.00	268.00	113.00	225.00
11.0400 115	Fixture, incandescent, commercial grade, recessed downlight, with junction box, wire, conduit, 200 watt	EACH	120.00	218.00	338.00	159.00	279.00
11.0400 120	Fixture, fluorescent, commercial grade, recessed, with junction box, wire, conduit, 2' x 2'	EACH	151.00	165.00	316.00	120.00	271.00
11.0400 125	Fixture, fluorescent, commercial grade, recessed, with junction box, wire, conduit, 2' x 4'	EACH	184.00	181.00	365.00	132.00	316.00
11.0400 130	Fixture, fluorescent strip, surface mounted, with junction box, wire, conduit, 4', 2 lamp	EACH	94.00	178.00	272.00	129.00	223.00
11.0400 135	Fixture, fluorescent strip, surface mounted, with junction box, wire, conduit, 8', 4 lamp	EACH	242.00	257.00	499.00	187.00	429.00
11.0400 140	Fixture, fluorescent strip, surface mounted, with junction box, wire, conduit, 4', 4 lamp	EACH	161.00	203.00	364.00	148.00	309.00
11.0400 145	Fixture, mercury vapor, hi-bay, with junction box, wire, conduit, 250 watt	EACH	394.00	298.00	692.00	217.00	611.00
11.0400 150	Fixture, mercury vapor, hi-bay, with junction box, wire, conduit, 400 watt	EACH	446.00	333.00	779.00	242.00	688.00
11.0400 155	Fixture, mercury vapor, hi-bay, with junction box, wire, conduit, 1000 watt	EACH	966.00	333.00	1,299.00	242.00	1,208.00
11.0400 160	Fixture, metal halide, hi-bay, with junction box, wire, conduit, 250 watt	EACH	298.00	297.00	595.00	216.00	514.00
11.0400 165	Fixture, metal halide, hi-bay, with junction box, wire, conduit, 400 watt	EACH	618.00	332.00	950.00	241.00	859.00
11.0400 170	Fixture, high pressure sodium, hi-bay, with junction box, wire, conduit, 250 watt	EACH	439.00	298.00	737.00	217.00	656.00

CSI #	11.0 ELECTRICAL Description	Unit	Material	Union Install	Union Total	Open Install	Open Total
11.0400	**FIXTURES (Cont.)**						
11.0400 175	Fixture, high pressure sodium, hi-bay, with junction box, wire, conduit, 400 watt	EACH	481.00	333.00	814.00	242.00	723.00
11.0400 180	Fixture, high pressure sodium, hi-bay, with junction box, wire, conduit, 1000 watt	EACH	798.00	377.00	1,175.00	274.00	1,072.00
11.0400 185	Perimeter security lights, industrial, 400 watt HPS wallpack, 40' on center	LF	16.00	9.00	25.00	6.00	22.00
11.0400 190	Perimeter security lights, school, 250 watt HPS wallpack, 30' on center	LF	19.00	10.00	29.00	8.00	27.00
11.0500	**SIGNAL & COMMUNICATIONS**						
11.0500 100	Telephone system, warehouse, 10,000 SF	SYS	3,432.00	2,458.00	5,890.00	1,688.00	5,120.00
11.0500 105	Telephone system, hospital, 220,000 SF	SYS	24,574.00	50,673.00	75,247.00	36,569.00	61,143.00
11.0500 110	Telephone system, office, 250,000 SF	SYS	46,220.00	49,658.00	95,878.00	35,778.00	81,998.00
11.0500 115	Telephone system, school, 80,000 SF	SYS	6,538.00	8,560.00	15,098.00	6,118.00	12,656.00
11.0500 120	Telephone system, library, 10,000 SF	SYS	5,285.00	3,691.00	8,976.00	2,535.00	7,820.00
11.0500 125	Fire alarm system, warehouse, 10,000 SF	SYS	8,111.00	6,663.00	14,774.00	4,766.00	12,877.00
11.0500 130	Fire alarm system, hospital, 220,000 SF	SYS	116,594.00	132,590.00	249,184.00	96,122.00	212,716.00
11.0500 135	Fire alarm system, office, 250,000 SF	SYS	94,692.00	108,197.00	202,889.00	78,368.00	173,060.00
11.0500 140	Fire alarm system, school, 80,000 SF	SYS	41,930.00	43,745.00	85,675.00	31,701.00	73,631.00
11.0500 145	Fire alarm system, library, 10,000 SF	SYS	13,019.00	8,864.00	21,883.00	6,327.00	19,346.00
11.0500 150	Public address/intercom system, warehouse, 10,000 SF	SYS	5,405.00	2,452.00	7,857.00	1,742.00	7,147.00
11.0500 155	Public address/intercom system, hospital, 220,000 SF	SYS	41,476.00	32,250.00	73,726.00	23,207.00	64,683.00
11.0500 160	Public address/intercom system, office, 250,000 SF	SYS	45,798.00	35,943.00	81,741.00	25,851.00	71,649.00
11.0500 165	Public address/intercom system, school, 80,000 SF	SYS	16,042.00	12,354.00	28,396.00	8,888.00	24,930.00
11.0500 175	Public address/intercom system, library, 10,000 SF	SYS	8,348.00	3,749.00	12,097.00	2,610.00	10,958.00
11.0500 180	Security system, warehouse, 10,000 SF	SYS	3,908.00	2,350.00	6,258.00	1,669.00	5,577.00
11.0500 185	Security system, hospital, 220,000 SF	SYS	34,517.00	18,822.00	53,339.00	13,552.00	48,069.00
11.0500 190	Security system, office, 250,000 SF	SYS	56,786.00	27,727.00	84,513.00	19,972.00	76,758.00
11.0500 195	Security system, school, 80,000 SF	SYS	20,020.00	13,133.00	33,153.00	9,492.00	29,512.00
11.0500 200	Security system, library, 10,000 SF	SYS	3,599.00	2,274.00	5,873.00	1,613.00	5,212.00
11.0600	**DEVICES**						
11.0600 100	Receptacle, duplex, commercial, standard grade	EACH	29.00	133.00	162.00	97.00	126.00
11.0600 105	Receptacle, duplex, hospital grade	EACH	54.00	151.00	205.00	109.00	163.00
11.0600 110	Receptacle, locking type, tamperproof	EACH	39.00	133.00	172.00	97.00	136.00
11.0600 115	60 A, welding, heavy duty	EACH	328.00	242.00	570.00	176.00	504.00
11.0600 120	Receptacle, 100 A, welding, heavy duty	EACH	572.00	294.00	866.00	213.00	785.00
11.0600 125	Switch, commercial, single pole	EACH	30.00	95.00	125.00	69.00	99.00
11.0600 130	Switch, commercial, double pole	EACH	34.00	111.00	145.00	81.00	115.00
11.0600 135	Switch, commercial, three way toggle	EACH	33.00	113.00	146.00	82.00	115.00

commercial square foot building costs

This Cost Manual is ideal for evaluating "Trade-offs" on materials and design. There are 65 square foot tables each has its own detailed description with the construction parameters clearly stated. The functional assemblies section can be used for unusual situations.

SAYLOR
Publications, Inc.

2010

commercial square foot building costs

20th ANNUAL EDITION
SAYLOR PUBLICATIONS, INC.

20th Annual Edition
$64.95
over 320 pages!

Square Foot Costs by:

- Building Type
- Size
- Exterior Wall
- Height
- Number of Stories
- Seismic Zone

Functional Assemblies
Landscape
ADA Section
Location Multipliers

---

65 Building types, including: Apartments, Auditoriums, Auto Showrooms, Banks, Bowling Alleys, Car Washes, Clubs, Convenience Markets, Day Care Centers, Dispensaries, Fire Stations, Fraternal Buildings, Garages, Government Buildings, Gymnasiums, Racquetball Clubs, Hangars, Health Clubs, Hospitals, Hotels, Indoor Tennis Clubs, Jails, Laundromats, Libraries, Manufacturing Buildings, Motels, Multiple Residences, Offices, Post Offices, Restaurants, Rinks, Schools, Shopping Centers, Stores, Supermarkets, Surgical Centers, Terminals, Theaters, Warehouses.

COMMERCIAL SQUARE FOOT BUILDING COSTS

1.0 APARTMENT, 2-3 STORY
Building Parameters: 2 Story, 10 Ft Story Height, 15,000 Square Feet

Exterior	Zone 0,1	Zone 2	Zone 3	Zone 4
Wood siding on stud frame	142.00	143.70	146.50	148.90
Brick veneer on stud frame	145.70	147.40	150.20	152.60
Stucco on stud frame	141.40	143.10	145.90	148.30
Brick, concrete block back-up	150.20	151.90	154.70	157.10
Decorative concrete block	147.30	149.00	151.80	154.20

2.0 APARTMENT, 4-7 STORY
Building Parameters: 6 Story, 11 Ft Story Height, 65,000 Square Feet

Exterior	Zone 0,1	Zone 2	Zone 3	Zone 4
Decorative concrete block, steel frame	166.50	169.80	175.30	180.00
Brick, concrete block back-up, steel frame	169.00	172.30	177.80	182.50
Brick, concrete block back-up, reinforced concrete frame	148.60	151.90	157.40	162.10
Precast panels, steel frame	173.30	176.60	182.10	186.80
Precast panels, reinforced concrete frame	143.30	146.60	152.10	156.80

3.0 APARTMENT, 8-30 Story
Building Parameters: 15 Story, 11 Ft Story Height, 175,000 Square Feet

Exterior	Zone 0,1	Zone 2	Zone 3	Zone 4
Decorative concrete block, steel frame	211.30	216.30	224.80	232.00
Decorative concrete block, reinforced concrete frame	173.30	178.30	186.80	194.00
Brick, concrete block back-up, steel frame	213.80	218.80	227.30	234.50
Precast panels, steel frame	208.50	213.50	222.00	229.20
Precast panels, reinforced concrete frame	159.10	164.10	172.60	179.80

4.0 AUDITORIUM
Building Parameters: 1 Story, 35 Ft Story Height, 25,000 Square Feet

Exterior	Zone 0,1	Zone 2	Zone 3	Zone 4
Precast panels, steel frame	309.00	313.70	321.70	328.50
Brick, concrete block back-up, steel frame	300.60	305.30	313.30	320.10
Decorative concrete block, steel frame	295.40	300.10	308.10	314.90
Stone veneer, block back-up, steel frame	339.50	344.20	352.20	359.00
Tilt-up panels, steel frame	265.60	270.30	278.30	285.10

5.0 AUTO SALES/SHOWROOM
Building Parameters: 1 Story, 14 Ft Story Height, 25,000 Square Feet

Exterior	Zone 0,1	Zone 2	Zone 3	Zone 4
Brick veneer on stud frame	146.30	147.90	150.40	152.60
Stucco on stud frame	143.50	145.10	147.60	149.80
Decorative concrete block, steel frame	179.50	181.10	183.60	185.80
Brick, concrete block back-up, steel frame	178.70	180.30	182.80	185.00
Precast panels, steel frame	180.90	182.50	185.00	187.20

Costs include General Contractor's Overhead and Profit and Architect Fees.
See page VI for seismic zones. See pages X and XI for Location Indexes.
For expanded coverage of costs see **2010 COMMERCIAL SQUARE FOOT BUILDING COSTS.**

COMMERCIAL SQUARE FOOT BUILDING COSTS

6.0 BANK
Building Parameters: 1 Story, 14 Ft Story Height, 4,000 Square Feet

Exterior	Zone 0,1	Zone 2	Zone 3	Zone 4
Brick veneer on stud frame	241.90	243.10	245.10	246.80
Stone veneer, block back-up, steel frame	310.10	311.30	313.30	315.00
Precast panels, steel frame	319.10	320.30	322.30	324.00
Tilt-up panels, steel frame	291.00	292.20	294.20	295.90
Wood siding on stud frame	239.40	240.60	242.60	244.30

7.0 BOWLING ALLEY
Building Parameters: 1 Story, 14 Ft Story Height, 20,000 Square Feet

Exterior	Zone 0,1	Zone 2	Zone 3	Zone 4
Tilt-up panels, steel frame	178.90	181.70	186.50	190.50
Concrete block, steel roof frame	183.20	186.00	190.80	194.80
Decorative concrete block, steel frame	183.80	186.60	191.40	195.40
Stucco on stud frame	141.90	144.70	149.50	153.50
Wood siding on stud frame	142.40	145.20	150.00	154.00

8.0 CAR WASH
Building Parameters: 1 Story, 12 Ft Story Height, 2,500 Square Feet

Exterior	Zone 0,1	Zone 2	Zone 3	Zone 4
Metal siding on steel frame	126.20	127.90	130.70	133.10
Insulated metal panel, steel frame	161.50	163.20	166.00	168.40
Brick, concrete block back-up	140.10	141.80	144.60	147.00
Concrete block, steel roof frame	134.60	136.30	139.10	141.50
Precast panels, steel frame	154.40	156.10	158.90	161.30

9.0 CLUB, COUNTRY
Building Parameters: 1 Story, 14 Ft Story Height, 12,000 Square Feet

Exterior	Zone 0,1	Zone 2	Zone 3	Zone 4
Wood siding on stud frame	261.10	255.20	256.60	261.10
Stucco on stud frame	260.60	254.70	256.10	260.60
Brick, concrete block back-up	279.40	273.50	274.90	279.40
Decorative concrete block	276.80	270.90	272.30	276.80
Insulated metal panel, steel frame	249.40	243.50	244.90	249.40

10.0 CLUB, SOCIAL
Building Parameters: 1 Story, 12 Ft Story Height, 20,000 Square Feet

Exterior	Zone 0,1	Zone 2	Zone 3	Zone 4
Decorative concrete block, steel frame	199.50	201.70	205.40	208.50
Stone veneer, block back-up, steel frame	214.00	216.20	219.90	223.00
Decorative concrete block	162.30	164.50	168.20	171.30
Wood siding on stud frame	162.60	164.80	168.50	171.60
Brick veneer on stud frame	164.80	167.00	170.70	173.80

Costs include General Contractor's Overhead and Profit and Architect Fees.
See page VI for seismic zones. See pages X and XI for Location Indexes.
For expanded coverage of costs see **2010 COMMERCIAL SQUARE FOOT BUILDING COSTS.**

COMMERCIAL SQUARE FOOT BUILDING COSTS

11.0 CONVENIENCE MARKET
Building Parameters: 1 Story, 12 Ft Story Height, 5,000 Square Feet

Exterior	Zone 0,1	Zone 2	Zone 3	Zone 4
Wood siding on stud frame	150.60	152.00	154.50	156.50
Decorative concrete block	158.40	159.80	162.30	164.30
Stucco on stud frame	149.80	151.20	153.70	155.70
Insulated metal panel, steel frame	156.90	158.30	160.80	162.80
Brick veneer on stud frame	156.00	157.40	159.90	161.90

12.0 COURTHOUSE
Building Parameters: 2 Story, 12 Ft Story Height, 40,000 Square Feet

Exterior	Zone 0,1	Zone 2	Zone 3	Zone 4
Precast panels, steel frame	282.50	286.60	293.70	299.70
Brick, concrete block back-up	273.20	277.30	284.40	290.40
Stone veneer, block back-up, steel frame	287.10	291.20	298.30	304.30
Decorative concrete block, steel frame	271.40	275.50	282.60	288.60
Curtain wall, metal and glass	247.70	251.80	258.90	264.90

13.0 DAY CARE CENTER
Building Parameters: 1 Story, 10 Ft Story Height, 6,000 Square Feet

Exterior	Zone 0,1	Zone 2	Zone 3	Zone 4
Decorative concrete block	170.70	172.10	174.40	176.30
Brick, concrete block back-up, steel frame	189.10	190.50	192.80	194.70
Wood siding on stud frame	166.20	167.60	169.90	171.80
Brick veneer on stud frame	169.30	170.70	173.00	174.90
Stucco on stud frame	165.70	167.10	169.40	171.30

14.0 DISPENSARY
Building Parameters: 2 Story, 10 Ft Story Height, 10,000 Square Feet

Exterior	Zone 0,1	Zone 2	Zone 3	Zone 4
Decorative concrete block, steel frame	268.80	271.60	276.30	280.40
Brick, concrete block back-up, steel frame	272.10	274.90	279.60	283.70
Wood siding on stud frame	231.60	234.40	239.10	243.20
Brick veneer on stud frame	235.90	238.70	243.40	247.50
Stucco on stud frame	231.00	233.80	238.50	242.60

15.0 DORMITORY
Building Parameters: 3 Story, 10 Ft Story Height, 30,000 Square Feet

Exterior	Zone 0,1	Zone 2	Zone 3	Zone 4
Brick, concrete block back-up	144.00	145.20	147.10	148.80
Decorative concrete block	141.70	142.90	144.80	146.50
Brick, concrete block back-up, steel frame	178.90	180.10	182.00	183.70
Decorative concrete block, steel frame	176.60	177.80	179.70	181.40
Precast panels, steel frame	182.70	183.90	185.80	187.50

Costs include General Contractor's Overhead and Profit and Architect Fees.
See page VI for seismic zones. See pages X and XI for Location Indexes.
For expanded coverage of costs see **2010 COMMERCIAL SQUARE FOOT BUILDING COSTS.**

COMMERCIAL SQUARE FOOT BUILDING COSTS

16.0 FIRE STATION
Building Parameters: 2 Story, 14 Ft Story Height, 9,000 Square Feet

Exterior	Zone 0,1	Zone 2	Zone 3	Zone 4
Tilt-up panels, steel frame	235.00	239.70	247.60	254.40
Insulated metal panel, steel frame	253.50	258.20	266.10	272.90
Brick, concrete block back-up	203.80	208.50	216.40	223.20
Decorative concrete block	199.90	204.60	212.50	219.30
Brick veneer on stud frame	197.60	202.30	210.20	217.00

17.0 FRATERNAL BUILDING
Building Parameters: 1 Story, 12 Ft Story Height, 20,000 Square Feet

Exterior	Zone 0,1	Zone 2	Zone 3	Zone 4
Decorative concrete block, steel frame	196.90	200.30	206.00	210.90
Stone veneer, block back-up, steel frame	214.50	217.90	223.60	228.50
Brick, concrete block back-up	178.30	181.70	187.40	192.30
Decorative concrete block	155.70	159.10	164.80	169.70
Insulated metal panel, steel frame	149.10	152.50	158.20	163.10

18.0 GARAGE, MINI-LUBE
Building Parameters: 1 Story, 14 Ft Story Height, 1,500 Square Feet

Exterior	Zone 0,1	Zone 2	Zone 3	Zone 4
Metal siding on steel frame	184.50	186.20	189.00	191.40
Insulated metal panel, steel frame	234.10	235.80	238.60	241.00
Concrete block, steel roof frame	216.50	218.20	221.00	223.40
Stucco on stud frame	197.90	199.60	202.40	204.80
Decorative concrete block	210.90	212.60	215.40	217.80

19.0 GARAGE, PARKING
Building Parameters: 4 Story, 10 Ft Story Height, 185,000 Square Feet

Exterior	Zone 0,1	Zone 2	Zone 3	Zone 4
Precast panels, steel frame	84.50	88.90	96.30	102.60
Precast panels, reinforced concrete frame	53.40	57.80	65.20	71.50
Brick, concrete block back-up, reinforced concrete frame	56.40	60.80	68.20	74.50
Reinforced concrete, cast in place	55.60	60.00	67.40	73.70
Decorative concrete block, reinforced concrete frame	49.90	54.30	61.70	68.00

20.0 GARAGE, REPAIR
Building Parameters: 1 Story, 14 Ft Story Height, 8,000 Square Feet

Exterior	Zone 0,1	Zone 2	Zone 3	Zone 4
Wood siding on stud frame	101.20	102.10	103.60	104.80
Stucco on stud frame	100.60	101.50	103.00	104.20
Metal siding on steel frame	98.50	99.40	100.90	102.10
Reinforced concrete, cast in place	115.80	116.70	118.20	119.40
Concrete block, steel roof frame	123.70	124.60	126.10	127.30

Costs include General Contractor's Overhead and Profit and Architect Fees.
See page VI for seismic zones. See pages X and XI for Location Indexes.
For expanded coverage of costs see **2010 COMMERCIAL SQUARE FOOT BUILDING COSTS.**

COMMERCIAL SQUARE FOOT BUILDING COSTS

21.0 GARAGE, SERVICE STATION
Building Parameters: 1 Story, 10 Ft Story Height, 1,500 Square Feet

Exterior	Zone 0,1	Zone 2	Zone 3	Zone 4
Metal siding on steel frame	137.10	138.80	141.60	144.00
Insulated metal panel, steel frame	172.50	174.20	177.00	179.40
Concrete block, steel roof frame	148.50	150.20	153.00	155.40
Wood siding on stud frame	132.90	134.60	137.40	139.80
Brick veneer on stud frame	138.80	140.50	143.30	145.70

22.0 GARAGE, UNDERGROUND PARKING
Building Parameters: 2 Story, 10 Ft Story Height, 90,000 Square Feet

Exterior	Zone 0,1	Zone 2	Zone 3	Zone 4
Reinforced concrete, cast in place (Two levels below grade)	79.10	81.50	85.60	89.10
Reinforced concrete, cast in place (Three levels below grade)	74.70	77.10	81.20	84.70
Reinforced concrete, cast in place (Four levels below grade)	58.70	61.10	65.20	68.70

23.0 GOVERNMENT BUILDING
Building Parameters: 2 Story, 12 Ft Story Height, 25,000 Square Feet

Exterior	Zone 0,1	Zone 2	Zone 3	Zone 4
Brick veneer on stud frame	217.40	218.70	220.80	222.60
Brick, concrete block back-up	246.00	247.30	249.40	251.20
Stone veneer, block back-up, steel frame	263.50	264.80	266.90	268.70
Decorative concrete block, steel frame	243.70	245.00	247.10	248.90
Decorative concrete block, reinforced concrete frame	222.50	223.80	225.90	227.70

24.0 GYMNASIUM
Building Parameters: 1 Story, 35 Ft Story Height, 30,000 Square Feet

Exterior	Zone 0,1	Zone 2	Zone 3	Zone 4
Brick, concrete block back-up, steel frame	239.70	242.60	247.50	251.70
Decorative concrete block, steel frame	234.20	237.10	242.00	246.20
Insulated metal panel, steel frame	225.20	228.10	233.00	237.20
Reinforced concrete block, steel roof frame	233.10	236.00	240.90	245.10
Precast panels, steel frame	248.70	251.60	256.50	260.70

25.0 HANDBALL/RACQUETBALL CLUB
Building Parameters: 2 Story, 12 Ft Story Height, 30,000 Square Feet

Exterior	Zone 0,1	Zone 2	Zone 3	Zone 4
Precast panels, steel frame	213.60	217.40	223.90	229.40
Brick, concrete block back-up	209.20	213.00	219.50	225.00
Decorative concrete block, steel frame	206.50	210.30	216.80	222.30
Tilt-up panels, steel frame	201.40	205.20	211.70	217.20
Insulated metal panel, steel frame	217.90	221.70	228.20	233.70

Costs include General Contractor's Overhead and Profit and Architect Fees.
See page VI for seismic zones. See pages X and XI for Location Indexes.
For expanded coverage of costs see **2010 COMMERCIAL SQUARE FOOT BUILDING COSTS.**

COMMERCIAL SQUARE FOOT BUILDING COSTS

26.0 HANGAR, AIRCRAFT
Building Parameters: 1 Story, 30 Ft Story Height, 50,000 Square Feet

Exterior	Zone 0,1	Zone 2	Zone 3	Zone 4
Metal siding on steel frame	132.60	134.90	138.90	142.20
Insulated metal panel, steel frame	150.90	153.20	157.20	160.50
Concrete block, steel roof frame	140.60	142.90	146.90	150.20
Tilt-up panels, steel frame	136.70	139.00	143.00	146.30
Precast panels, steel frame	147.20	149.50	153.50	156.80

27.0 HEALTH CLUB
Building Parameters: 2 Story, 12 Ft Story Height, 27,000 Square Feet

Exterior	Zone 0,1	Zone 2	Zone 3	Zone 4
Brick, concrete block back-up	267.00	271.70	279.60	286.40
Precast panels, steel frame	271.60	276.30	284.20	291.00
Decorative concrete block, steel frame	264.10	268.80	276.70	283.50
Insulated metal panel, steel frame	276.10	280.80	288.70	295.50
Tilt-up panels, steel frame	258.70	263.40	271.30	278.10

28.0 HOSPITAL, CONVALESCENT
Building Parameters: 2 Story, 10 Ft Story Height, 28,000 Square Feet

Exterior	Zone 0,1	Zone 2	Zone 3	Zone 4
Wood siding on stud frame	204.30	205.60	207.80	209.70
Brick veneer on stud frame	206.80	208.10	210.30	212.20
Stucco on stud frame	203.90	205.20	207.40	209.30
Brick, concrete block back-up	205.60	206.90	209.10	211.00
Decorative concrete block, steel frame	230.70	232.00	234.20	236.10

29.0 HOSPITAL, GENERAL
Building Parameters: 4 Story, 15 Ft Story Height, 140,000 Square Feet

Exterior	Zone 0,1	Zone 2	Zone 3	Zone 4
Precast panels, steel frame	459.40	466.80	479.20	489.80
Precast panels, reinforced concrete frame	386.60	394.00	406.40	417.00
Brick, concrete block back-up, steel frame	451.20	458.60	471.00	481.60
Brick, concrete block back-up, reinforced concrete frame	384.00	391.40	403.80	414.40
Curtain wall, metal and glass	462.20	469.60	482.00	492.60

30.0 HOTEL 4-7 STORY
Building Parameters: 5 Story, 10 Ft Story Height, 100,000 Square Feet

Exterior	Zone 0,1	Zone 2	Zone 3	Zone 4
Brick, concrete block back-up, steel frame	236.00	241.10	249.60	256.90
Brick, concrete block back-up, reinforced concrete frame	223.80	228.90	237.40	244.70
Precast panels, steel frame	238.50	243.60	252.10	259.40
Precast panels, reinforced concrete frame	226.30	231.40	239.90	247.20
Curtain wall, metal and glass	248.50	253.60	262.10	269.40

Costs include General Contractor's Overhead and Profit and Architect Fees.
See page VI for seismic zones. See pages X and XI for Location Indexes.
For expanded coverage of costs see **2010 COMMERCIAL SQUARE FOOT BUILDING COSTS.**

COMMERCIAL SQUARE FOOT BUILDING COSTS

31.0 HOTEL 8-30 STORY
Building Parameters: 15 Story, 10 Ft Story Height, 470,000 Square Feet

Exterior	Zone 0,1	Zone 2	Zone 3	Zone 4
Brick, concrete block back-up, steel frame	226.80	234.00	246.20	256.50
Precast panels, steel frame	228.50	235.70	247.90	258.20
Precast panels, reinforced concrete frame	207.50	214.70	226.90	237.20
Curtain wall, metal and glass	234.80	242.00	254.20	264.50
Decorative concrete block, steel frame	225.70	232.90	245.10	255.40

32.0 INDOOR TENNIS CLUB
Building Parameters: 1 Story, 24 Ft Story Height, 23,000 Square Feet

Exterior	Zone 0,1	Zone 2	Zone 3	Zone 4
Tilt-up panels, steel frame	153.50	155.50	159.00	161.90
Metal siding on steel frame	145.90	147.90	151.40	154.30
Insulated metal panel, steel frame	145.70	147.70	151.20	154.10
Concrete block, steel roof frame	160.80	162.80	166.30	169.20
Precast panels, steel frame	173.10	175.10	178.60	181.50

33.0 JAIL
Building Parameters: 2 Story, 12 Ft Story Height, 20,000 Square Feet

Exterior	Zone 0,1	Zone 2	Zone 3	Zone 4
Reinforced concrete, cast in place	327.70	334.30	345.40	354.90
Precast panels, reinforced concrete frame	277.80	284.40	295.50	305.00
Brick, concrete block back-up, steel frame	334.10	340.70	351.80	361.30
Brick, concrete block back-up, reinforced concrete frame	273.00	279.60	290.70	300.20
Decorative concrete block, steel frame	322.70	329.30	340.40	349.90

34.0 LAUNDROMAT
Building Parameters: 1 Story, 12 Ft Story Height, 8,000 Square Feet

Exterior	Zone 0,1	Zone 2	Zone 3	Zone 4
Wood siding on stud frame	146.20	147.50	149.80	151.70
Stucco on stud frame	145.60	146.90	149.20	151.10
Decorative concrete block	153.60	154.90	157.20	159.10
Precast panels, steel frame	169.90	171.20	173.50	175.40
Insulated metal panel, steel frame	147.50	148.80	151.10	153.00

35.0 LIBRARY
Building Parameters: 2 Story, 14 Ft Story Height, 15,000 Square Feet

Exterior	Zone 0,1	Zone 2	Zone 3	Zone 4
Decorative concrete block, steel frame	264.50	269.30	277.30	284.10
Brick, concrete block back-up, steel frame	268.50	273.30	281.30	288.10
Precast panels, steel frame	275.00	279.80	287.80	294.60
Tilt-up panels, steel frame	256.90	261.70	269.70	276.50
Stone veneer, block back-up, steel frame	298.40	303.20	311.20	318.00

Costs include General Contractor's Overhead and Profit and Architect Fees.
See page VI for seismic zones. See pages X and XI for Location Indexes.
For expanded coverage of costs see **2010 COMMERCIAL SQUARE FOOT BUILDING COSTS.**

36.0 MANUFACTURING, HEAVY
Building Parameters: 1 Story, 20 Ft Story Height, 40,000 Square Feet

Exterior	Zone 0,1	Zone 2	Zone 3	Zone 4
Concrete block, steel roof frame	199.50	206.30	217.90	227.80
Reinforced concrete, cast in place	205.50	212.30	223.90	233.80
Reinforced concrete block, steel roof frame	199.50	206.30	217.90	227.80
Precast panels, reinforced concrete frame	206.10	212.90	224.50	234.40
Decorative concrete block, steel frame	200.00	206.80	218.40	228.30

37.0 MANUFACTURING, LIGHT
Building Parameters: 1 Story, 12 Ft Story Height, 35,000 Square Feet

Exterior	Zone 0,1	Zone 2	Zone 3	Zone 4
Precast panels, steel frame	148.30	151.40	156.60	161.00
Tilt-up panels, steel frame	141.60	144.70	149.90	154.30
Metal siding on steel frame	139.00	142.10	147.30	151.70
Insulated metal panel, steel frame	150.60	153.70	158.90	163.30
Concrete block, steel roof frame	144.10	147.20	152.40	156.80

38.0 MEDICAL OFFICE
Building Parameters: 2 Story, 10 Ft Story Height, 8,000 Square Feet

Exterior	Zone 0,1	Zone 2	Zone 3	Zone 4
Brick veneer on stud frame	304.40	306.00	308.70	311.00
Stucco on stud frame	299.20	300.80	303.50	305.80
Brick, concrete block back-up	309.80	311.40	314.10	316.40
Precast panels, steel frame	333.20	334.80	337.50	339.80
Curtain wall, metal and glass	362.80	364.40	367.10	369.40

39.0 MOTEL
Building Parameters: 3 Story, 9 Ft Story Height, 46,000 Square Feet

Exterior	Zone 0,1	Zone 2	Zone 3	Zone 4
Wood siding on stud frame	175.90	177.40	179.90	182.10
Brick veneer on stud frame	177.90	179.40	181.90	184.10
Stucco on stud frame	175.60	177.10	179.60	181.80
Brick, concrete block back-up	180.40	181.90	184.40	186.60
Decorative concrete block, steel frame	211.10	212.60	215.10	217.30

40.0 MULTIPLE RESIDENCE
Building Parameters: 2 Story, 9 Ft Story Height, 7,000 Square Feet

Exterior	Zone 0,1	Zone 2	Zone 3	Zone 4
Wood siding on stud frame	165.30	166.50	168.60	170.30
Brick veneer on stud frame	169.80	171.00	173.10	174.80
Decorative concrete block	171.90	173.10	175.20	176.90
Stucco on stud frame	164.60	165.80	167.90	169.60
Decorative concrete block, steel frame	185.00	186.20	188.30	190.00

Costs include General Contractor's Overhead and Profit and Architect Fees.
See page VI for seismic zones. See pages X and XI for Location Indexes.
For expanded coverage of costs see **2010 COMMERCIAL SQUARE FOOT BUILDING COSTS.**

COMMERCIAL SQUARE FOOT BUILDING COSTS

41.0 MULTIPLE RESIDENCE, ELDERLY
Building Parameters: 3 Story, 9 Ft Story Height, 12,000 Square Feet

Exterior	Zone 0,1	Zone 2	Zone 3	Zone 4
Brick, concrete block back-up	169.10	170.20	172.20	173.80
Decorative concrete block	165.80	166.90	168.90	170.50
Brick, concrete block back-up, steel frame	211.70	212.80	214.80	216.40
Decorative concrete block, steel frame	208.40	209.50	211.50	213.10
Precast panels, steel frame	217.00	218.10	220.10	221.70

42.0 OFFICE, 2-3 STORY
Building Parameters: 3 Story, 12 Ft Story Height, 23,000 Square Feet

Exterior	Zone 0,1	Zone 2	Zone 3	Zone 4
Wood siding on stud frame	168.50	170.10	172.90	175.30
Brick veneer on stud frame	172.30	173.90	176.70	179.10
Stucco on stud frame	167.90	169.50	172.30	174.70
Decorative concrete block	175.10	176.70	179.50	181.90
Brick, concrete block back-up, steel frame	210.90	212.50	215.30	217.70

43.0 OFFICE, 4-7 STORY
Building Parameters: 6 Story, 12 Ft Story Height, 64,000 Square Feet

Exterior	Zone 0,1	Zone 2	Zone 3	Zone 4
Decorative concrete block, steel frame	227.30	232.40	241.00	248.30
Brick, concrete block back-up, steel frame	229.80	234.90	243.50	250.80
Precast panels, steel frame	233.90	239.00	247.60	254.90
Curtain wall, metal and glass	255.00	260.10	268.70	276.00
Decorative concrete block, reinforced concrete frame	211.20	216.30	224.90	232.20

44.0 OFFICE, 8-30 STORY
Building Parameters: 20 Story, 12 Ft Story Height, 135,000 Square Feet

Exterior	Zone 0,1	Zone 2	Zone 3	Zone 4
Precast panels, steel frame	273.40	280.20	291.90	301.80
Precast panels, reinforced concrete frame	224.60	231.40	243.10	253.00
Brick, concrete block back-up, steel frame	268.30	275.10	286.80	296.70
Brick, concrete block back-up, reinforced concrete frame	219.50	226.30	238.00	247.90
Curtain wall, metal and glass	300.10	306.90	318.60	328.50

45.0 POST OFFICE
Building Parameters: 1 Story, 18 Ft Story Height, 13,000 Square Feet

Exterior	Zone 0,1	Zone 2	Zone 3	Zone 4
Brick, concrete block back-up, steel frame	249.60	252.70	258.10	262.60
Decorative concrete block, steel frame	245.90	249.00	254.40	258.90
Precast panels, steel frame	255.60	258.70	264.10	268.60
Decorative concrete block, steel frame	245.90	249.00	254.40	258.90
Tilt-up panels, steel frame	238.80	241.90	247.30	251.80

Costs include General Contractor's Overhead and Profit and Architect Fees.
See page VI for seismic zones. See pages X and XI for Location Indexes.
For expanded coverage of costs see **2010 COMMERCIAL SQUARE FOOT BUILDING COSTS.**

COMMERCIAL SQUARE FOOT BUILDING COSTS

46.0 PRISON
Building Parameters: 2 Story, 12 Ft Story Height, 40,000 Square Feet

Exterior	Zone 0,1	Zone 2	Zone 3	Zone 4
Reinforced concrete, cast in place	361.60	368.20	379.30	388.80
Precast panels, reinforced concrete frame	311.50	318.10	329.20	338.70
Brick, concrete block back-up, steel frame	370.30	376.90	388.00	397.50
Brick, concrete block back-up, reinforced concrete frame	308.00	314.60	325.70	335.20
Decorative concrete block, steel frame	355.30	361.90	373.00	382.50

47.0 RESTAURANT
Building Parameters: 1 Story, 12 Ft Story Height, 5,000 Square Feet

Exterior	Zone 0,1	Zone 2	Zone 3	Zone 4
Wood siding on stud frame	247.00	248.40	250.80	252.90
Brick veneer on stud frame	252.10	253.50	255.90	258.00
Brick, concrete block back-up, steel frame	261.20	262.60	265.00	267.10
Decorative concrete block, steel frame	257.30	258.70	261.10	263.20
Stone veneer, block back-up, steel frame	290.50	291.90	294.30	296.40

48.0 RESTAURANT, FAST FOOD
Building Parameters: 1 Story, 10 Ft Story Height, 3,000 Square Feet

Exterior	Zone 0,1	Zone 2	Zone 3	Zone 4
Brick veneer on stud frame	288.10	289.50	291.90	293.90
Stucco on stud frame	282.60	284.00	286.40	288.40
Brick, concrete block back-up, steel frame	296.20	297.60	300.00	302.00
Decorative concrete block, steel frame	292.50	293.90	296.30	298.30
Insulated metal panel, steel frame	308.10	309.50	311.90	313.90

49.0 RINK, HOCKEY
Building Parameters: 1 Story, 24 Ft Story Height, 30,000 Square Feet

Exterior	Zone 0,1	Zone 2	Zone 3	Zone 4
Tilt-up panels, steel frame	186.50	188.50	192.00	194.90
Brick, concrete block back-up	197.50	199.50	203.00	205.90
Insulated metal panel, steel frame	184.70	186.70	190.20	193.10
Concrete block, steel roof frame	193.00	195.00	198.50	201.40
Precast panels, steel frame	203.70	205.70	209.20	212.10

50.0 SCHOOL, ELEMENTARY
Building Parameters: 1 Story, 14 Ft Story Height, 43,000 Square Feet

Exterior	Zone 0,1	Zone 2	Zone 3	Zone 4
Brick veneer on stud frame	249.60	252.90	258.50	263.20
Stucco on stud frame	285.60	288.90	294.50	299.20
Brick, concrete block back-up	291.00	294.30	299.90	304.60
Decorative concrete block, steel frame	289.20	292.50	298.10	302.80
Tilt-up panels, steel frame	285.90	289.20	294.80	299.50

Costs include General Contractor's Overhead and Profit and Architect Fees.
See page VI for seismic zones. See pages X and XI for Location Indexes.
For expanded coverage of costs see **2010 COMMERCIAL SQUARE FOOT BUILDING COSTS.**

COMMERCIAL SQUARE FOOT BUILDING COSTS

51.0 SCHOOL, SECONDARY
Building Parameters: 2 Story, 14 Ft Story Height, 100,000 Square Feet

Exterior	Zone 0,1	Zone 2	Zone 3	Zone 4
Brick, concrete block back-up, steel frame	294.40	302.50	316.20	327.80
Precast panels, steel frame	293.20	301.30	315.00	326.60
Stone veneer, block back-up, steel frame	335.20	343.30	357.00	368.60
Decorative concrete block, steel frame	293.80	301.90	315.60	327.20
Insulated metal panel, steel frame	295.50	303.60	317.30	328.90

52.0 SCHOOL, VOCATIONAL
Building Parameters: 2 Story, 14 Ft Story Height, 50,000 Square Feet

Exterior	Zone 0,1	Zone 2	Zone 3	Zone 4
Decorative concrete block, steel frame	318.80	328.20	344.10	357.70
Brick, concrete block back-up, steel frame	319.50	328.90	344.80	358.40
Tilt-up panels, steel frame	308.50	317.90	333.80	347.40
Concrete block, steel roof frame	312.00	321.40	337.30	350.90
Precast panels, steel frame	317.90	327.30	343.20	356.80

53.0 SHOPPING CENTER, STRIP
Building Parameters: 1 Story, 10 Ft Story Height, 6,000 Square Feet

Exterior	Zone 0,1	Zone 2	Zone 3	Zone 4
Brick, concrete block back-up, steel frame	206.90	209.60	214.10	218.00
Wood siding on stud frame	176.30	179.00	183.50	187.40
Brick veneer on stud frame	179.30	182.00	186.50	190.40
Decorative concrete block, steel frame	204.70	207.40	211.90	215.80
Stucco on stud frame	175.90	178.60	183.10	187.00

54.0 STORE, DEPARTMENT
Building Parameters: 2 Story, 16 Ft Story Height, 150,000 Square Feet

Exterior	Zone 0,1	Zone 2	Zone 3	Zone 4
Brick, concrete block back-up, steel frame	174.00	178.10	185.10	191.00
Decorative concrete block, steel frame	172.60	176.70	183.70	189.60
Precast panels, steel frame	176.30	180.40	187.40	193.30
Stone veneer, block back-up, steel frame	184.60	188.70	195.70	201.60
Tilt-up panels, steel frame	169.90	174.00	181.00	186.90

55.0 STORE, DISCOUNT
Building Parameters: 1 Story, 18 Ft Story Height, 80,000 Square Feet

Exterior	Zone 0,1	Zone 2	Zone 3	Zone 4
Decorative concrete block, steel frame	145.80	148.20	152.10	155.40
Precast panels, steel frame	149.60	152.00	155.90	159.20
Brick, concrete block back-up, steel frame	147.20	149.60	153.50	156.80
Tilt-up panels, steel frame	143.00	145.40	149.30	152.60
Insulated metal panel, steel frame	148.70	151.10	155.00	158.30

Costs include General Contractor's Overhead and Profit and Architect Fees.
See page VI for seismic zones. See pages X and XI for Location Indexes.
For expanded coverage of costs see 2010 COMMERCIAL SQUARE FOOT BUILDING COSTS.

COMMERCIAL SQUARE FOOT BUILDING COSTS

56.0 STORE, RETAIL
Building Parameters: 1 Story, 14 Ft Story Height, 35,000 Square Feet

Exterior	Zone 0,1	Zone 2	Zone 3	Zone 4
Brick, concrete block back-up, steel frame	152.50	154.80	158.70	162.10
Precast panels, steel frame	155.60	157.90	161.80	165.20
Decorative concrete block, steel frame	150.60	152.90	156.80	160.20
Tilt-up panels, steel frame	146.90	149.20	153.10	156.50
Stucco on stud frame	127.40	129.70	133.60	137.00

57.0 SUPERMARKET
Building Parameters: 1 Story, 14 Ft Story Height, 20,000 Square Feet

Exterior	Zone 0,1	Zone 2	Zone 3	Zone 4
Brick, concrete block back-up	149.80	151.70	154.90	157.70
Decorative concrete block	147.60	149.50	152.70	155.50
Tilt-up panels, steel frame	146.50	148.40	151.60	154.40
Insulated metal panel, steel frame	156.60	158.50	161.70	164.50
Precast panels, steel frame	153.30	155.20	158.40	161.20

58.0 SURGICAL CENTER
Building Parameters: 2 Story, 14 Ft Story Height, 10,000 Square Feet

Exterior	Zone 0,1	Zone 2	Zone 3	Zone 4
Decorative concrete block, steel frame	414.20	418.30	425.10	430.90
Brick, concrete block back-up, steel frame	419.40	423.50	430.30	436.10
Precast panels, steel frame	428.00	432.10	438.90	444.70
Stone veneer, block back-up, steel frame	458.60	462.70	469.50	475.30
Tilt-up panels, steel frame	404.30	408.40	415.20	421.00

59.0 SWIMMING POOL, ENCLOSED
Building Parameters: 1 Story, 24 Ft Story Height, 20,000 Square Feet

Exterior	Zone 0,1	Zone 2	Zone 3	Zone 4
Brick, concrete block back-up, steel frame	271.30	273.10	276.20	278.90
Decorative concrete block, steel frame	266.80	268.60	271.70	274.40
Insulated metal panel, steel frame	399.50	401.30	404.40	407.10
Reinforced concrete block, steel roof frame	266.00	267.80	270.90	273.60
Precast panels, steel frame	278.50	280.30	283.40	286.10

60.0 TERMINAL, AIRPORT
Building Parameters: 3 Story, 16 Ft Story Height, 140,000 Square Feet

Exterior	Zone 0,1	Zone 2	Zone 3	Zone 4
Decorative concrete block, steel frame	307.30	312.30	320.70	327.80
Precast panels, steel frame	306.50	311.50	319.90	327.00
Brick, concrete block back-up, steel frame	308.00	313.00	321.40	328.50
Insulated metal panel, steel frame	309.30	314.30	322.70	329.80
Curtain wall, metal and glass	321.50	326.50	334.90	342.00

Costs include General Contractor's Overhead and Profit and Architect Fees.
See page VI for seismic zones. See pages X and XI for Location Indexes.
For expanded coverage of costs see **2010 COMMERCIAL SQUARE FOOT BUILDING COSTS.**

COMMERCIAL SQUARE FOOT BUILDING COSTS

61.0 TERMINAL, BUS
Building Parameters: 1 Story, 14 Ft Story Height, 15,000 Square Feet

Exterior	Zone 0,1	Zone 2	Zone 3	Zone 4
Brick, concrete block back-up, steel frame	206.30	209.30	214.20	218.40
Decorative concrete block, steel frame	203.70	206.70	211.60	215.80
Tilt-up panels, steel frame	198.60	201.60	206.50	210.70
Wood siding on stud frame	159.40	162.40	167.30	171.50
Brick veneer on stud frame	162.80	165.80	170.70	174.90

62.0 THEATER, MOVIE
Building Parameters: 1 Story, 20 Ft Story Height, 16,000 Square Feet

Exterior	Zone 0,1	Zone 2	Zone 3	Zone 4
Decorative concrete block, steel frame	235.90	237.80	241.10	243.90
Precast panels, steel frame	247.30	249.20	252.50	255.30
Brick, concrete block back-up, steel frame	240.20	242.10	245.40	248.20
Tilt-up panels, steel frame	227.60	229.50	232.80	235.60
Insulated metal panel, steel frame	254.10	256.00	259.30	262.10

63.0 VETERINARY HOSPITAL
Building Parameters: 1 Story, 12 Ft Story Height, 6,000 Square Feet

Exterior	Zone 0,1	Zone 2	Zone 3	Zone 4
Brick veneer on stud frame	282.60	284.40	287.50	290.20
Wood siding on stud frame	277.40	279.20	282.30	285.00
Brick, concrete block back-up, steel frame	306.80	308.60	311.70	314.40
Decorative concrete block, steel frame	302.70	304.50	307.60	310.30
Insulated metal panel, steel frame	319.80	321.60	324.70	327.40

64.0 WAREHOUSE
Building Parameters: 1 Story, 24 Ft Story Height, 45,000 Square Feet

Exterior	Zone 0,1	Zone 2	Zone 3	Zone 4
Concrete block, steel roof frame	124.80	127.40	131.80	135.50
Insulated metal panel, steel frame	137.80	140.40	144.80	148.50
Tilt-up panels, steel frame	119.90	122.50	126.90	130.60
Precast panels, steel frame	133.20	135.80	140.20	143.90
Metal siding on steel frame	114.70	117.30	121.70	125.40

65.0 WAREHOUSE, SELF STORAGE
Building Parameters: 1 Story, 12 Ft Story Height, 33,000 Square Feet

Exterior	Zone 0,1	Zone 2	Zone 3	Zone 4
Concrete block, steel roof frame	153.00	154.80	157.90	160.60
Insulated metal panel, steel frame	161.00	162.80	165.90	168.60
Tilt-up panels, steel frame	150.00	151.80	154.90	157.60
Precast panels, steel frame	158.20	160.00	163.10	165.80
Metal siding on steel frame	146.80	148.60	151.70	154.40

Costs include General Contractor's Overhead and Profit and Architect Fees.
See page VI for seismic zones. See pages X and XI for Location Indexes.
For expanded coverage of costs see **2010 COMMERCIAL SQUARE FOOT BUILDING COSTS.**

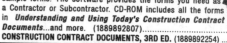

SAYLOR in Windows and Job Cost Wizard Quick Start

SAYLOR in Windows is a construction cost estimating program with all the cost items in this book. This estimating program is licensed to Saylor Publications, Inc. by Craftsman Book Company. You can page through the cost database one screen at a time or use the electronic index to search by keyword for the information that you need. Split the screen in two so your estimate is on the bottom half of the screen and the database is on the top half. Then copy and paste into your estimate. The program extends prices and totals columns automatically.

Job Cost Wizard takes your estimates to the next level:

1. Turning estimates into invoices you can send out in a window envelope.

2. Exporting to *QuickBooks* where you can track actual costs against estimates.

Job Cost Wizard.

The installation program creates a Construction Estimating program group and puts several icons in that group. If you have trouble installing *SAYLOR in Windows*, call Saylor tech support at 818-718-5966. Saylor Publications, Inc. is located at 9420 Topanga Canyon Blvd., Suite 203, Chatsworth, CA 91311.

Installing *SAYLOR in Windows* and *Job Cost Wizard*

With Windows running, put the *SAYLOR in Windows* disk in your CD drive (such as D:). If **Install Software** doesn't appear as an option after a few seconds:

1. Click on **start**
2. Click on **Control Panel**
3. Double-click on **Add or Remove Programs**
4. Click on **Add New Programs**
5. Click on **CD or Floppy**
6. Click on **Next**
7. Select **D:\Setup**
8. Click on **Finish**

Follow the instructions on the screen. We recommend accepting the installation defaults and "Typical" setup. When installation is complete, click on **Finish**.

The SAYLOR in Windows installation screen.

339

Uninstalling *SAYLOR in Windows* and *Job Cost Wizard*

Click on **Start, Control Panel**. Double-click on **Add or Remove Programs**. Then click on the name of the program to remove and **Remove**.

Using *SAYLOR in Windows*

SAYLOR in Windows icon.

SAYLOR in Windows begins when you click on the *SAYLOR in Windows* icon or click on **Start, All Programs**, the **Construction Estimating** group and then *SAYLOR in Windows*.

On the title bar at the top of the screen you see the program name, *Saylor in Windows*, and [*2010 Saylor in Windows - Commercial - Union*]. That's your default costbook. It opens automatically when you start **SAYLOR in Windows**. The commercial open shop costbook is also on the disk and is installed by default. For information on opening other costbooks and changing the default, see page 350. Let's take a closer look at the other information at the top of your screen.

The Menu Bar

Below the title bar you see the menu bar. Every option in *SAYLOR in Windows* is available on the menu bar. Click with your left mouse button on any item on the menu to open a list of available commands.

Title Bar →
Menu Bar →
Toolbar →
Page and Subject →
Column Heads →

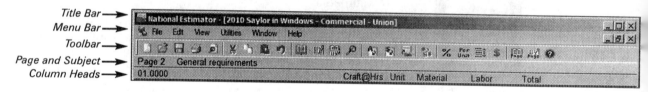

Buttons on the Toolbar

Below the menu bar you see 24 buttons that make up the toolbar. The options you use most in *SAYLOR in Windows* are only a mouse click away on the toolbar.

Column Headings

Below the toolbar you'll see column headings for the costbook:

Craft@Hrs for craft (the crew doing the work) and manhours (to complete the task)

Unit for unit of measure, such as per linear foot or per square foot

Material for material cost

Labor for labor cost

Total for the total of all cost columns

The Status Bar

The bottom line on your screen is the status bar. Here you'll find helpful information about the choices available. Notice "Page 2/242" near the center of the status line. That's a clue that you're looking at page 2 of a 242-page book.

Check the status bar occasionally for helpful tips and explanations of what you see on screen.

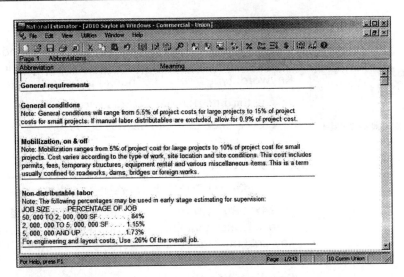

The Costbook Window has the entire Commercial Construction Costs database.

The Costbook

The entire *2010 Commercial Construction Costs* is available in the Costbook Window. Notice the words *Page 2 General requirements* at the left side of the screen just below the toolbar. That's your clue that the general requirements section of page 2 is on the screen.

To turn to the next page, either:

∎ Press `PgDn` (with Num Lock off), -or-

∎ Click on the lower half of the scroll bar at the right edge of the screen.

To move down one line at a time, either:

∎ Press the ↓ arrow key (with Num Lock off), -or-

∎ Click on the arrow on the down scroll bar at the lower right corner of the screen.

To turn quickly to any page, either:

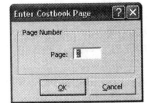

Type the page number you want to see.

∎ Click on the ![icon] (Turn to Costbook Page) button near the right end of the toolbar, -or-

∎ Click on **View** on the menu bar. Then click on **Turn to Costbook Page**.

Type the number of the page you want to see and press `Enter ↵`. *SAYLOR in Windows* will turn to the top of the page you requested.

An Even Better Way

Drag the square to see any page.

Find the small square in the slide bar at the right side of the Costbook Window. Click and hold on that square while rolling the mouse up or down. Keep dragging the square until you see the page you want in the Page: box. Release the mouse button to turn to the top of that page.

A Still Better Way: Keyword Search

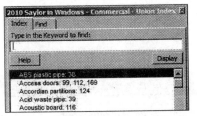

Use the electronic index to find cost estimates for any item.

To find any cost estimate in seconds, search by keyword in the index. To go to the index, either:

∎ Click on the ![icon] (Index) button near the center of the toolbar, -or-

∎ Click on **View** on the menu bar. Then press `Enter ↵`.

Notice that the cursor is blinking in the Enter Keyword box at the right of the screen. Obviously, the index is ready to begin a search.

Your First Estimate

Suppose we're estimating the cost of 4" standard commercial brick veneer. Let's put the index to work with a search for brick. In the box under Enter Keyword, type *brick*. The index jumps to the *brick* heading.

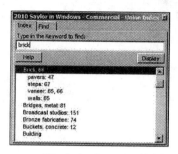

The index jumps to Brick.

The third item under *Brick* is *veneer: 65, 66*.

■ Click once on that line and press [Enter⏎], -or-

■ Double-click on that line, -or-

■ Press [Tab⇥] and the [↓] arrow key to move the highlight to *veneer: 65, 66*. Then press [Enter⏎].

SAYLOR in Windows turns to the top of page 65. See the example at the left below. Notice that line items on this page are for brick masonry. Press [↓] arrow key until the cursor is on "Veneer, 4", standard brick, commercial."

Splitting the Screen

Most of the time you'll want to see what's in both the costbook and your estimate. To split the screen into two halves, either:

■ Click on the ▦ (Split Window) button near the center of the toolbar, -or-

■ Click on **View** on the menu bar. Then click on **Split Window** and your screen should look like the example on the right below.

Notice the costbook is at the top of the screen and your estimate form is at the bottom. Column headings are at the top of the costbook and across the middle of the screen (for your estimate).

To Switch from Window to Window

■ Click in the window of your choice, -or-

■ Hold the [Ctrl] key down and press [Tab⇥].

Notice that a window title bar turns dark when that window is selected. The selected window is where keystrokes appear as you type. Click in the bottom half of the screen so your estimate is selected.

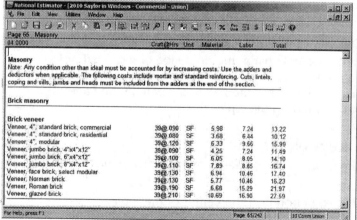

Costs for brick veneer on page 65.

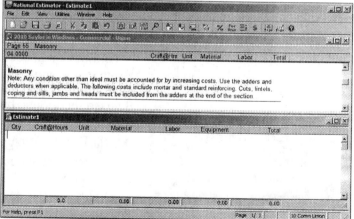

The split window: Costbook above and estimate below.

Beginning an Estimate

The Blinking Cursor (insert point)

Mouse Pointer

Mouse Pointer

You can type anything in the Estimate Window. Let's start by putting a heading on this estimate:

1. Press [Enter ⏎] once to space down one line.

2. Press [Tab ⇆] four times (or hold the space bar down) to move the Blinking Cursor (the insert point) near the middle of the line.

3. Type "Estimate One" and press [Enter ⏎]. That's the title of this estimate, "Estimate One."

4. Press [Enter ⏎] again to move the cursor down a line. That opens up a little space below the title.

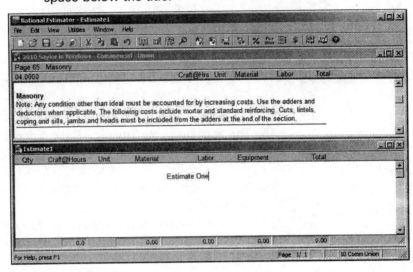

Begin by putting a title on your estimate, such as "Estimate One."

Copying Costs to Your Estimate

Next, we'll estimate the cost of 100 square feet of brick veneer. Click on the 🗔 (Split Window) button on the toolbar to be sure you're in the split window. Click anywhere in the costbook (the top half of your screen). Then press the ⬇ arrow key until the cursor is on the line:

| Veneer, 4", standard brick, commercial | 39@.090 | SF | 5.98 | 7.24 | 13.22 |

Hint: Instead of clicking on the 🗋 (Copy) and 📋 (Paste) buttons, you can both copy and paste by pressing the [F8] key.

To copy this line to your estimate:

1. Click on the line.

2. Click the 🗋 (Copy) button.

3. Click on the 📋 (Paste) button to open the Enter Cost Information dialog box.

Notice that the blinking cursor is in the Quantity box:

1. Type a quantity of 100 because 100 square feet are needed.

2. Press [Tab ⇆] and check the estimate for accuracy. See the example on the right, next page.

3. Notice that the column headed Unit Costs shows costs per unit, per "SF" (square foot) in this case.

4. The column headed Extended Costs shows costs for 100 square feet.

343

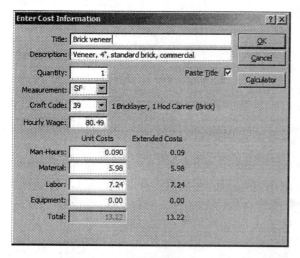

Use the Enter Cost Information dialog box to copy or change costs.

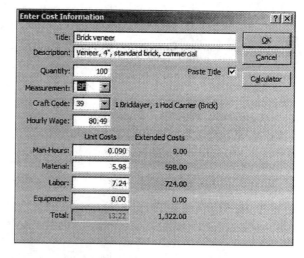

Costs for 100 square feet (extended costs) are on the right.

5. The lines opposite Title and Description show what's getting installed. You can change the words in either of these boxes. Just click on what you want to change and start typing or deleting.

6. You can also change any numbers in the Unit Cost column. Just click and start typing.

7. When the words and costs are exactly right, press Enter ↵ or click on **OK** to copy these figures to the end of your estimate.

Extended costs for 100 square feet of veneer as they appear on your estimate form.

Brick veneer						
Veneer, 4", standard brick, commercial						
100.00	39@9.000	SF	598.00	724.00	0.00	1,322.00

100.00 is the number of square feet of veneer

39 is the recommended crew, a bricklayer and a hod carrier

@9.000 shows the manhours required for the work

SF is the unit of measure, square feet in this case

598.00 is the material cost (the brick)

724.00 is labor cost for the job

0.00 shows there is no equipment cost

1,322.00 is the total of material, labor and equipment columns

Copy Anything to Anywhere in Your Estimate

Anything in the costbook can be copied to your estimate. Just click on the line (or select the words) you want to copy and press the F8 key. It's copied to the last line of your estimating form. If your selection includes costs, you'll have a chance to enter the quantity. To copy to the *middle* of your estimate:

1. Select what you want to copy.

2. Click on the ⬚ (Copy) button.

3. Click in the estimate where you want to paste.

4. Click on the ⬚ (Paste) button.

Circle with a bar.

Vertical bar with mouse cursor.

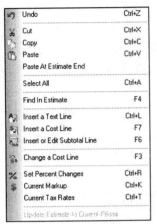

Right-click editing menu.

Search for information on setting wage rates.

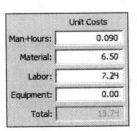

Change the material cost to 6.50.

Drag and Drop Estimating

You can also drag lines or words out of the costbook and drop them in your estimate:

1. Click on the line to copy and move your mouse slightly so the line is selected (turns black).

2. Release the mouse button. The line remains selected.

3. Click again on the selected line. This time hold your mouse button down.

4. Your mouse cursor turns into a circle with a diagonal bar.

5. Holding the mouse button down, move the circle with a bar into the Estimate Window.

6. Once in the Estimate Window, you'll see a vertical bar to the left of your mouse cursor.

7. Move this vertical bar to where the copied line should be pasted.

8. Then release the mouse button. The line is pasted in that position.

9. If the line pasted includes costs, you'll have a chance to enter a quantity.

Right-Click Editing

Most of what you do in *SAYLOR in Windows* is editing — such as Cut, Copy, Paste and Undo. Most editing features have their own button on the toolbar. Of course, all editing functions are available from the Edit selection on the menu bar. But you might find it easier and quicker to open the floating edit menu by right-clicking with your mouse. Press the right mouse button. All edit functions currently a valid choice will be available. Simply click on the selection you need.

Changing Wage Rates

The labor cost in the example above is based on a bricklayer and a hod carrier working at an average cost of $80.49 per manhour. (See pages IV and V in *Commercial Construction Costs* for labor rates used in the costbook.) Suppose $80.49 per hour isn't right for your estimate. What then? No problem! It's easy to use your own wage rate for any crew or even make up your own crew codes. To get more information on setting wage rates, press F1. At *SAYLOR in Windows* Help, click on the **Key** button. Type *wage,* then double-click on **Setting Hourly Wage Rates** under Wage Rates. To return to your estimate, click on **File** on the *SAYLOR in Windows* Help menu bar. Then click on **Exit**.

Changing Cost Estimates

With Num Lock off, use the ↑ or ↓ arrow key to move the cursor to the line you want to change (or click on that line). In this case, move to the line that begins with a quantity of 100. To open the Enter Cost Information Dialog box, either:

▮ Press Enter ↵ , -or-

▮ Click on the 🦴 (Change Cost) button on the toolbar.

To make a change, either:

▮ Click on what you want to change, -or-

▐ Press [Tab⇆] until the cursor advances to what you want to change.

Then type the correct figure. In this case, change the material cost to $6.50.

Press [Tab⇆] and check the Extended Costs column. If it looks OK, press [Enter ↵] and the change is made on your estimating form.

Changing Text (Descriptions)

Click on the ▦ (Estimate Window) button on the toolbar to be sure you're in the estimate. With Num Lock off, use the [↑] or [↓] arrow key or click the mouse button to put the cursor where you want to make a change. In this case, we're going to make a change on the line that begins "Brick veneer."

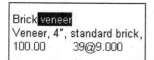

Brick veneer
Veneer, 4", standard brick,
100.00   39@9.000

To select, click and hold the mouse button while dragging the mouse.

To make a change, click where the change is needed. Then either:

▐ Press the [Del] or [←Bksp] key to erase what needs deleting, -or-

▐ Select what needs deleting and click on the ✂ (Cut) button on the toolbar.

▐ Type what needs to be added.

In this case, click just after the word "brick." Then hold the left mouse button down and drag the mouse to the right until you've put a dark background behind the word "veneer." The dark background shows that this word is selected and ready for editing.

Press the [Del] key, or click on the ✂ (Cut) button on the toolbar, and the selection is cut from the estimate. If that's not what you wanted, click on the ↶ (Undo) button and the word "veneer" is back again.

Adding Text (Descriptions)

Some of your estimates will require descriptions (text) and costs that can't be found in *Commercial Construction Costs*. What then? With *SAYLOR in Windows* it's easy to add descriptions and costs of your choice anywhere in the estimate. For practice, let's add a line item for four reinforced corners to Estimate One.

Brick veneer
Veneer, 4", standard brick,
100.00   39@9.000
Reinforced corners

Adding "Reinforced corners."

Click on the ▦ (Estimate Window) button to be sure the estimate window is maximized. We can add lines anywhere on the estimate. But in this case, let's make the addition at the end. Press the [↓] arrow key to move the cursor down until it's just above the horizontal line that separates estimate detail lines from estimate totals. To open a blank line, either:

▐ Press [Enter ↵], -or-

▐ Click on the 🗅 (Insert Text) button on the toolbar, -or-

▐ Click on **Edit** on the menu bar. Then click on **Insert a Text Line**.

Type "Reinforced corners" and press [Enter ↵].

Adding a Cost Estimate Line

Now let's add a cost for "Reinforced corners" to your estimate. Begin by opening the Enter Cost Information dialog box. Either:

▐ Click on the 🗐 (Insert Cost) button on the toolbar, -or-

▐ Click on **Edit** on the menu bar. Then click on **Insert a Cost Line**.

1. The cursor is in the Quantity box. Type the number of units (4 in this case) and press [Tab⇆].

2. The cursor moves to the next box, Measurement.

3. In the Measurement box, type *Each* and press Tab↹.
4. Press Tab↹ twice to leave the Craft Code blank and Hourly Wage at zero.
5. Since these reinforced corners will be installed by the supplier, there's no material, labor or equipment cost. So press Tab↹ four times to skip over the Man-Hours, Material, Labor and Equipment boxes.
6. In the Total box, type 20.00. That's the cost per corner quoted by your supplier.
7. Press Tab↹ once more to advance to OK.
8. Press Enter↵ and the cost of four reinforced corners is written to your estimate.

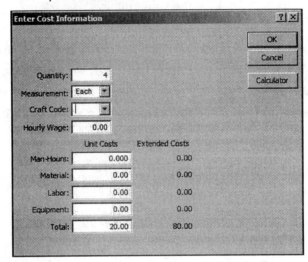

Unit and extended costs for four reinforced corners.

Note: The sum of material, labor and equipment costs appears automatically in the Total box. If there's no cost entered in the Material, Labor or Equipment boxes (such as for a subcontracted item), you can enter any figure in the Total box.

Adding Lines to the Costbook

Add lines or make changes in the costbook the same way you add lines or make changes in an estimate. The additions and changes you make become part of the user costbook. For more information on user costbooks, press F1. Click on **Search**. Type "user" and press Enter↵.

Subtotals Become *QuickBooks* Cost Categories

At the end of each section in your estimate, insert a subtotal. For a general contractor, estimate sections might be Demolition, Excavation, Foundation, Framing, etc. Estimate sections for a repair and remodeling contractor might include Bathroom, Kitchen, Basement and Attic. Section subtotals help organize your estimates and make them easier to read and understand. Insert section subtotals wherever they make the most sense to you. These subtotals become cost categories when printing bids and invoices. The first 28 characters of subtotal names become *QuickBooks* cost category names when exporting to *QuickBooks*.

To insert a subtotal:

1. Click on the last cost line of the section (or on any blank line below the section).

Insert a subtotal.

2. Click on the 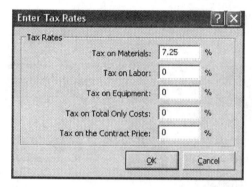 (Subtotal) button on the toolbar (or click on **Edit** and **Insert Subtotal**).

3. Type a name or description for the section (such as "Exterior Finish") or select from the list of CSI or Residential Divisions categories.

4. Press [Enter↵].

Adding Tax

To include sales tax in your estimate:

1. Click on **Edit**.

2. Click on **Current Tax Rates**.

3. Type the tax rate in the appropriate box.

4. Press [Tab⇆] to advance to the next box.

5. Press [Enter↵] or click on **OK** when done.

In this case, the tax rate is 7.25% on materials only. Tax will appear as the last line of the estimate.

Type the tax rate that applies.

Adding Overhead and Profit

Set markup percentages in the Set Markup Amounts dialog box. To open the box, either:

- Click on the 💲 (Markup) button on the toolbar, -or-
- Click on **Edit** on the menu bar. Then click on **Markup**.

Type the percentages you want to add for overhead. For this estimate:

1. Type 15 on the Overhead line.

2. Press [Tab⇆] to advance to Contingency.

3. Type 5 on the Contingency line.

4. Press [Tab⇆] to advance to Profit.

5. Type 10% on the Profit line.

6. Press [Enter↵].

Adding overhead & profit.

Preview Your Estimate

You can display an estimate on screen just the way it will look when printed on paper. To preview your estimate, either:

- Click on the 📄 (Print Preview) button on the toolbar, -or-
- Click on **File** on the menu bar. Then click on **Print Preview**.

Use buttons on Print Preview to see your estimate as it will look when printed.

In Print Preview:

- Click on **Next Page** or **Prev Page** to turn pages.
- Click on **Two Page** to see two estimate pages side by side.
- Click on **Zoom In** to get a closer look.
- Click on **Close** when you've seen enough.

Printing Your Estimate

When you're ready to print the estimate, either:

▮ Click on the 🖨 (Print) button on the toolbar, -or-

▮ Click on **File** on the menu bar. Then click on **Print**, -or-

▮ Hold the [Ctrl] key down and type the letter P.

▮ Press [Enter←] or click on **OK** to begin printing.

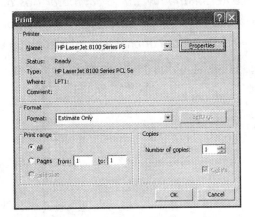

Options available depend on the printer you're using.

Save Your Estimate to Disk

To store your estimate on the hard disk where it can be re-opened and changed at any time, either:

▮ Click on the 💾 (Save) button on the toolbar, -or-

▮ Click on **File** on the menu bar. Then click on **Save**, -or-

▮ Hold the [Ctrl] key down and type the letter S.

The cursor is in the File Name box. Type the name you want to give this estimate, such as *First Estimate*. Press [Enter←] or click on **OK** and the estimate is written to disk. Note that the default location for estimates is the *My Documents* folder.

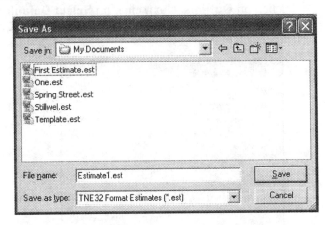

Type the estimate name in the File Name box to assign a file name.

Opening Other Costbooks

Many construction cost estimating databases are available for the *SAYLOR in Windows* program. The order form at the back of this manual has more information on these costbooks.

If you own several of these manuals and have installed the database that comes with each, you can open several costbooks at the same time. To open another costbook:

▮ Click on **File**.

▮ Click on **Open Costbook**.

▮ Be sure the drive and directory are correct, usually *C:\Program Files\Craftsman\National Estimator\Costbooks*.

▮ Double-click on the costbook of your choice.

To see a list of the open costbooks, click on **Window**. The name of the current

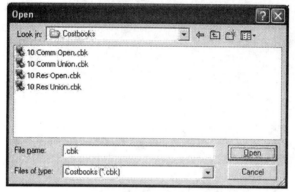

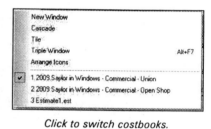

Click to switch costbooks.

Open the costbook of your choice.

estimate or costbook will be checked. Click on any other costbook name to display that costbook. Click on **Window**, then click on **Tile** to display all open costbooks and estimates.

Select Your Default Costbook

Your default costbook is the last costbook installed. It opens automatically every time you begin using *SAYLOR in Windows*. Save time by making the default costbook the one you use most.

To change your default costbook, click on **Utilities** on the menu bar. Then click on **Options**. Next, click on **Select Default Costbook**. Click on the costbook of your choice. Click on **OK**. Then click on **OK** again.

Select the default costbook.

Select File Locations

By default, your estimates are saved in the My Documents folder. That's a change from older versions of *SAYLOR in Windows*. Previously estimates and costbooks were kept in the National folder by default. To change the default location for estimates, costbooks and user costbooks, click **Utilities**, click **Options** and click the **File Locations** tab.

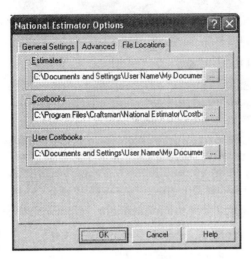

Decide where you want to store estimates.

Use *National Estimator* Help

That completes the basics of *SAYLOR in Windows*. You've learned enough to complete most estimates. When you need more information about the fine points, click on the 🔘 (Help) button to see Help Contents. Then click on the menu selection of your choice.

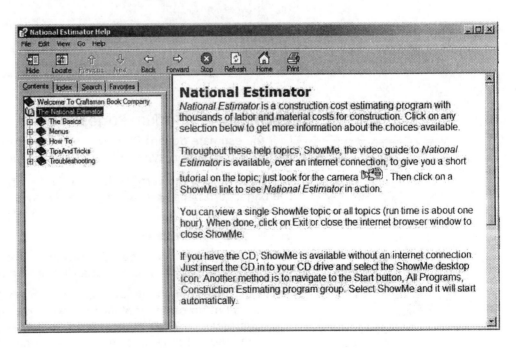

The National Estimator Help screen.

Converting Estimates with *Job Cost Wizard*

Use *Job Cost Wizard* to:

▐ Convert estimates into bids and invoices you can send to a client, and,

▐ Export to *QuickBooks* where you can track job costs, receivables, payables, create payrolls and print financial reports.

To view your completed estimate in *Job Cost Wizard*, either:

▐ Click on **File**, Click on **Send Estimate to JCW**, or

▐ Hold the Ctrl key down and tap J.

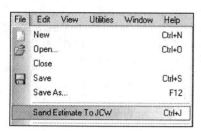

Send the estimate to Job Cost Wizard.

You can also start *Job Cost Wizard* by clicking on the *Job Cost Wizard* icon in the Construction Estimating program group. Then click on the name of the estimate you want to open.

The Company Information dialog box will open the first time you use *Job Cost Wizard*. Type your company name and address. This will appear at the top of every estimate and invoice. When you've filled in infomation about your company, click on **OK** and your estimate will open in *Job Cost Wizard*.

To change any of the information about your company:

▐ Click on **File**

▐ Click on **Print Setup**

▐ Click on **Company Info**

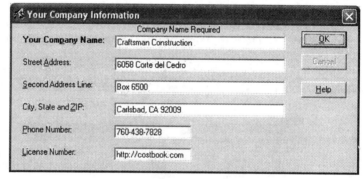

Fill in information about your company.

Zoom, Scroll and Turn Pages

If the estimate doesn't fit your screen, set the percentage of zoom. For 640 x 480 resolution, type 81% in the zoom window and press [Enter ↵].

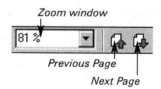

Zoom window

Previous Page

Next Page

Click and drag the vertical slide bar at the right of your screen to scroll down the page. Turn pages by clicking on the Previous Page or Next Page buttons.

Enter Job Information

Job Cost Wizard needs some information about the job to create a nice-looking bid or invoice. For practice, enter job information for the Stillwel estimate:

1. **Customer name and address.** Click on the ▨ (Customer Info) button on the toolbar to enter information about the customer. Only the customer first name and last name are required. All other information is optional. When done, click on OK.

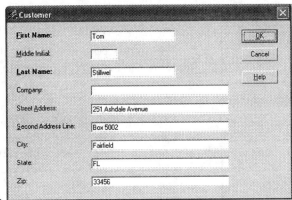

Fill in Customer Information.

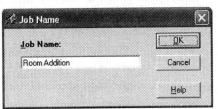

Enter a Job Name.

2. Job Name. Click on the 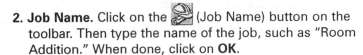 (Job Name) button on the toolbar. Then type the name of the job, such as "Room Addition." When done, click on **OK**.

For transfers to QuickBooks You can change the customer or job name after the file has been imported into *QuickBooks*. In *QuickBooks*, click on **Lists**. Click on **Customers:Jobs**. Right-click on customer name or job name. Click on **Edit**. Then click on the tab of your choice.

3. Estimate Number. Click on the (Estimate Number) button on the toolbar. *Job Cost Wizard* keeps track of the last number used and recommends using the next number in sequence. Click **OK** when done.

For transfers to QuickBooks When *QuickBooks* imports an estimate or invoice, subtotals in your estimate become cost categories ("items") in *QuickBooks*. By default, cost category names in *QuickBooks* are the first 28 characters of estimate subtotal names plus the work type, either Mat, Lab, Equ, or Sub. You can change this default in the Estimate Number dialog box.

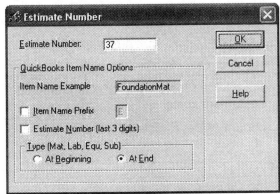

Check the Estimate Number.

Job Cost Wizard Prints Invoices Your Way

Your estimates should cover every cost in a job. But your bids and invoices don't have to show all the details and reveal your markup. So *Job Cost Wizard* gives you choices about showing or hiding the details and markup.

Amount of Detail

To set the amount of detail, click on the (Detail) button.

If *Show All* is selected, every item in your bid or invoice will show a cost and each will become a cost category on the *QuickBooks* Items list. *Subtotals Only* is the default and will usually be a better choice.

If *Subtotals Only* is selected, subtotals will be the only costs in your bid or invoice. Each subtotal in your estimate becomes a cost category on the *QuickBooks* Items list. That's usually the best choice. If Subtotals Only is selected

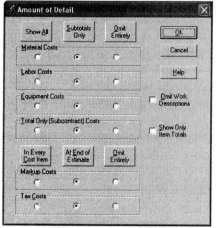

How much detail do you want to show?

for all four cost categories, click on **Omit Work Descriptions** to show subtotal categories but hide all work descriptions.

The names you give to subtotals in *SAYLOR in Windows* become cost category names in *QuickBooks*. Cost lines in *SAYLOR in Windows* not followed by a subtotal become the "Project" subtotal.

If *Omit Entirely* is selected, neither costs nor descriptions will appear for that type of cost — either material, labor, equipment or total only (subcontract). Use Omit Entirely for materials, for example, when materials are being furnished by the owner.

"Total only" costs are assumed to be subcontract items. Subcontract items have a cost in the total column but no cost for material, labor, or equipment.

Markup and Tax

Use the three buttons at the bottom of the Amount of Detail dialog box to show or hide markup (overhead, contingency and profit) and tax.

In Every Cost Item distributes markup and tax proportionately throughout the estimate. There's no mention of overhead, profit or markup anywhere in the estimate or invoice.

At End of Estimate puts markup and tax at the end of the estimate, as in *National Estimator*.

Omit Entirely omits markup and tax from the estimate or invoice. Use this option if you prefer to add markup and tax in *QuickBooks*.

Click **Show Only Item Totals** if you don't want the invoice or estimate to show any breakdown of material, labor or equipment costs.

Click on **OK** when done with the Amount of Detail dialog box.

QuickBooks Account Names

Estimates and invoices imported into *QuickBooks* include expense and income account names. If the imported accounts do not exist already in your *QuickBooks* company, *QuickBooks* will create new accounts. You can control the names of these accounts by making changes in the *QuickBooks* Account Names box.

▌ Click on the ▨ (Account Names) button on the toolbar, -or-

▌ Click on **Options** on the menu bar. Then click on **QuickBooks** Options.

Enter the names you prefer for construction income and construction expense accounts. Change "ST Sales Tax" to "FL Sales Tax", for example, if the job is taxable under Florida law. *QuickBooks* will keep track of tax due in each state where you do business.

Click **Use "Contractors Guide" Accounts** if you prefer the account names recommended in *Contractor's Guide to QuickBooks Pro*. An order form for this title is at http://costbook.com. To restore the default account names, click **Reset**.

If *QuickBooks Pro* version 2002 or later is installed on the computer, you should see a check mark beside *Use qbXML to integrate with QuickBooks*. XML exports to *QuickBooks*, as will be explained on the next page. If *QuickBooks Pro* is installed but there is no check mark, click on **Use qbXML to integrate with**

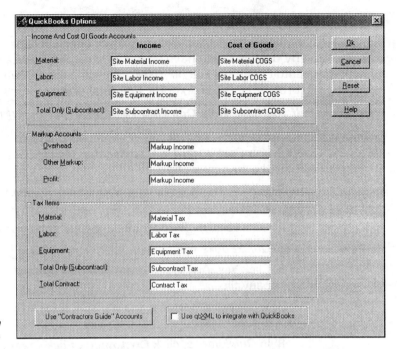

Click on OK when done with QuickBooks Options.

QuickBooks. You'll be asked to identify the *QuickBooks* Company to receive imports from *Job Cost Wizard*. Select the company file you prefer and click **Open**. See Exporting an Estimate to *QuickBooks* on the next page for more on opening the XML link to *QuickBooks*.

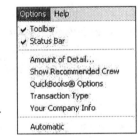

Set up for automatic operation.

Automatic

Job Cost Wizard always requires customer information, a job name and a job number before exporting an estimate. In automatic mode, *Job Cost Wizard* opens the Customer Info, Job Name and Estimate Number dialog boxes automatically after opening any estimate.

Job Cost Wizard runs in automatic mode when there is a check mark beside Automatic on the Options menu. To change to automatic mode, click on **Options** on the menu bar. Then click on **Automatic**.

Transaction Type and Your Company Info

On the Options menu, click **Transaction Type** to change the form title from Estimate to Invoice to Proposal or anything you want (Custom). For *QuickBooks* exports, the transaction type has to be either estimate or invoice.

On the Options menu, click **Your Company Info** to change the company name or address.

Click on the **Print** icon or **File** and **Print**. Then click **OK** to print the document.

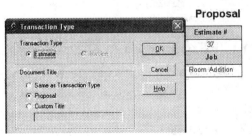

Changing the form title to "Proposal."

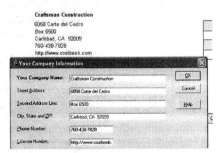

Enter your company name.

Exporting an Estimate to *QuickBooks*

If you have *QuickBooks 2002* or later, *Job Cost Wizard* will select XML export by default. If you have an earlier version of *QuickBooks*, exports will create an Intuit Interface File (IIF). XML exports happen over a direct link between the two programs. For IIF exports, *Job Cost Wizard* writes a file in the *QuickBooks* folder.

If you have 2002 QuickBooks or later, *use the XML export:*

1. Begin by clicking the QB icon.

2. *Job Cost Wizard* will advise that *QuickBooks* is asking permission to access the company file.

3. If you receive a warning about security level, follow instructions on the screen.

4. Click **Launch QuickBooks** and select the company file to receive the export.

5. *QuickBooks* will open.

6. Click **Yes, Always** to grant *Job Cost Wizard* access to the *QuickBooks* company file.

7. A bar will report that the transfer is in progress. Click **OK** when the export is successful.

8. In *QuickBooks*, click **Customers**. Click **Create Estimates**. Then click **Previous** to see the imported estimate. You can skip information on IIF exports and go right to turning estimates into invoices at the bottom of page 357.

If you have an older version of QuickBooks, *use the IIF export:*

QB icon.

1. Begin by clicking the QB icon.

2. Change the drive or the folder if the *QuickBooks* folder is not listed at the right of Save in.

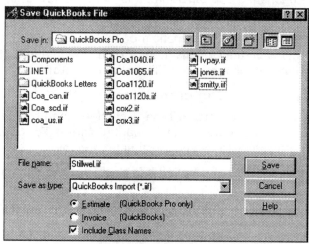
Exporting as an estimate to QuickBooks Pro.

3. Check the file name to be sure it is what you want.

4. If you use *QuickBooks Pro*, click on **Estimate**.

5. If you use regular *QuickBooks*, click on **Invoice**.

6. When complete, click on **Save**.

Exporting an estimate to *QuickBooks Pro* does not affect the original estimate in any way. *Job Cost Wizard* can open and export an estimate as many times as you want. To create a second copy of the same estimate with different *Job Cost Wizard* options, save with a slightly different file name. But note that you can import an estimate for any customer and job only once.

Opening IIF Export Files in *QuickBooks*

Once an estimate or invoice has been written to file with *Job Cost Wizard*, start *QuickBooks*:

1. Click on **File**.

2. Click on **Utilities**.

3. Click on **Import**.

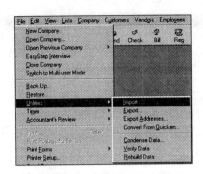

Importing into QuickBooks.

4. Double-click on the name of the estimate or invoice you want.

5. Click on **OK** when the import is complete.

6. Click on **Customers**.

7. Click on **Create Estimates** if you saved the file as an estimate.

8. Click on **Create Invoices** if you saved the file as an invoice.

9. Click on **Previous** to see the file just imported.

Important Note: With *QuickBooks Pro 2000* and higher, you can import an estimate only once from an IIF. On second import of the same estimate, you'll see an error message, "Can't record invalid transaction." If you make a mistake and want to import an estimate again, delete the previous imported estimate before importing again. Instructions for deleting an estimate are on the next page. If you want two versions of any one estimate in *QuickBooks Pro*, save the alternate estimate with a slightly different job name or customer name. That makes the estimate different enough so it will import perfectly into *QuickBooks*.

Filling in the "Amount" Column (IIF only)

An imported estimate is not complete until some figure appears in the Amount column of each cost line. So long as the Amount column is blank, *QuickBooks* will consider the estimated cost for that line to be zero (even when numbers appear in the Total column). If the Amount column for an entire estimate is left blank, *QuickBooks* reports will show the estimated cost for that job to be zero.

Forcing a figure into the "Amount" column.

Cost	Amount	Markup	Total
3,544.38	3,544.38		3,544.38
3,924.38			3,924.38
			7,468.76

The fastest way to fill in the Amount column for a *QuickBooks* estimate is to click on a number in the "Cost" column and change the figure by a penny. Continue clicking and changing costs by a penny until every row of costs includes a figure in the Amount column.

Turn an Estimate into an Invoice in *QuickBooks*

First, decide if you want an invoice for the whole job or for just part of the job (progress billing). If you prefer progress billing:

1. Click on **Edit**.

2. Click on **Preferences**.

3. Click on **Jobs & Estimates**.

4. Click on the **Company Preferences** tab.

5. Click on **Yes** under **Do You Do Progress Invoicing?**

6. Click on **OK**.

To create the invoice:

1. Click on the **Create Invoice** button at the top of the *QuickBooks* estimate screen.

2. Click on **Yes** to record changes to the estimate.

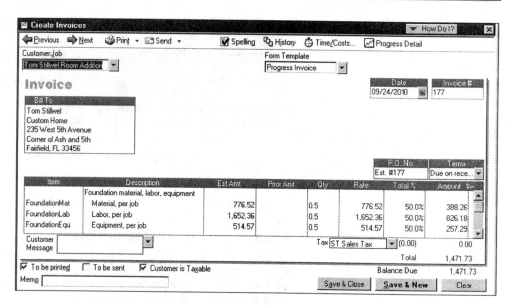

An invoice for the first half of the foundation work.

3. If you selected progress billing, enter a percentage or select items to be invoiced.

4. Click on **OK** and *QuickBooks* creates the invoice.

5. Make changes to the invoice if you want.

6. Click to print one copy for your file and another for your customer.

7. Click on **OK** when done. (Processing the file may take a little time.) *QuickBooks* reports will now include totals from the job just invoiced.

Don't Worry About Making a Mistake

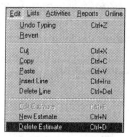

It's easy to delete an estimate.

QuickBooks is very forgiving. Practice all you want. Experiment any way you want. Then delete any estimate or invoice to remove every trace of it from *QuickBooks*. With the offending estimate or invoice displayed:

1. Click on **Edit**.

2. Click on **Delete Estimate** (or Invoice).

3. Click on **OK**.

4. The estimate (or invoice) is deleted.

Your Jobs in *QuickBooks*

▌ Click on **Reports, Company & Financial, Profit & Loss By Job** to see job income and expense.

▌ Click on **Reports, Company & Financial, Balance Sheet Standard** to see the new receivables total.

▌ Click on **Reports, Jobs & Time, Job Estimates vs. Actuals Detail**, select the customer and job to see a detailed cost comparison for the job. Until you start paying bills, the Actual Cost column will be all zeros.

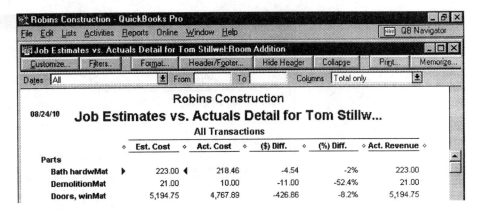

Estimates vs. actual details.

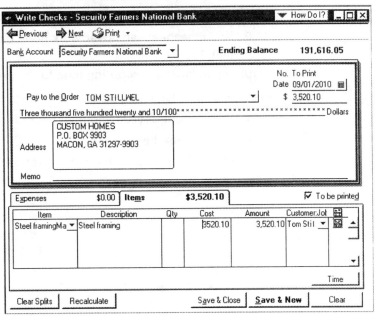

*Select a cost category
from the Item list.*

Paying Bills by Cost Category

When you pay vendors and subcontractors, the amount paid is charged to the job and deducted from your bank balance.

1. Click on **Banking**.

2. Click on **Write Checks**.

3. Fill in the **Pay to the Order of** line.

4. Click on the **Items** tab.

5. Click on the down triangle in the Item column of the check stub to open the Item list.

6. Select a Mat, Sub or Equ cost category from the Item list. These are the material, subcontract and equipment subtotal costs from your estimate.

7. Click in the amount column and enter the amount paid for the item described. Click on the down triangle under Customer:Job and select the correct customer and job.

8. This amount is not billable to your customer. So click on the icon representing an invoice to put a red X over the icon.

9. One check can cover items in several cost categories and even costs on several jobs. Click again on the next line down in the Item column and find the next cost item.

*Paying a bill for the steel framing
on the Stillwel job.*

359

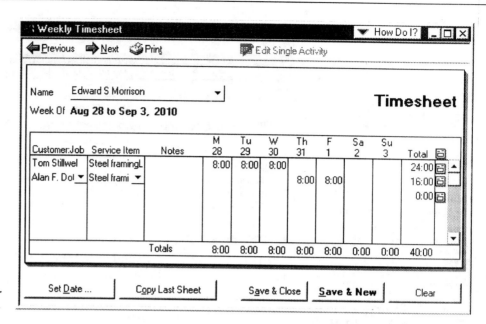

Fill out the timesheet by customer and service item.

Under Service Item, select a labor cost category from the list.

Creating Payroll by Cost Category

When you write payroll checks, the amount paid is charged to the job and deducted from your bank balance.

1. Click on **Employees**.

2. Click on **Time Tracking**.

3. Click on **Use Weekly Time Sheets**.

4. Click on the down triangle opposite Name and select the employee to be paid.

5. On the Timesheet, click on the ⬇ arrow under Customer:Job and select the first job where the employee worked.

6. Under Service Item, select a Lab cost category from the list. These are labor subtotal costs from your estimate.

7. Under Payroll Item, select the type of pay, such as hourly.

8. Enter the number of hours worked for that cost category.

9. Any timesheet can cover work done on several jobs and many service items.

10. When finished recording time for an employee, click on **Save & Close**.

To actually produce paychecks:

1. Click on **Employees** and then **Payroll**.

2. Click on **Pay Employees**.

3. Check the names of the employees to be paid.

4. When done, click on **Create**.

A

ABS plastic pipe 38
Access doors 99, 112, 169
Accordion partitions 124
Acid waste pipe 39
Acoustic board 116
Acoustic ceilings 115
Acoustic insulation, sound board 85
Acrylic glazing 105
Acrylic latex sealants 93
Acute care equipment 141
Aftercoolers 8
Aggregate panels 88
Aggregate, sub base 46
Air and water reels 139
Air compressors 138, 160
    electric 7
    portable 6
    silenced 6
Air concrete vibrators 9
Air conditioners
    (d-x) 181
    computer rooms 182
    electric heat, d-x 182
    slit systems 181
Air drills 9
Air entrainment 54
Air floor scrabblers 13
Air grinders 9
Air handlers 184
Air hoists 156
Air hoses & accessories 7
Air impact wrenches 9
Air manifolds 8
Air separators 187
Air structures 153
Air tamper 9
Air terminals 186
Air tool, rock drilling 35
Air tools 8
Air torches 19
Air vibrators 11
Alarm risers 196
Alarms 239
    fire 207, 237
    plumbing 171
Altars 131, 132
Aluco bond 107
Aluminum
    busway tap box 230
    busways 229
    conduit 221
    fabrication 74
    power cable 229
    railings 72
    roofing 87
    sash 102
    tile 121
    wire 227
Anchor bolts 72, 76
Angles 70
Antenna, television systems 238
Aqua lath 110
Arc lamps 20
Area drains 42, 170

Arks 131
Arrestor, lightning 45
Artificial stone work 67
Asphalt
    cutters 8
    felt, walls 77
    mastic, decks 84
    mastic, walls 83
    paint, walls 83
    paving 46
    sheet 47
    tile 117
Athletic field lighting 45
Athletic fields, synthetic surface 138
Audio visual equipment 133
Audiometric rooms 151
Auger holes 35
Auto transfer switches 204, 218
Autopsy tables 144
Awnings & canopies 129

B

Backfill 34, 55
Backflow preventors 49, 167, 196
Backhoe loader 15
Backing rods 93
Backstops
    baseball 137
    basketball 138
Baggage carousels 157
Bank equipment 131
Bar sinks 161
Bar, reinforcing 59
Barrel pumps 21
Base plates 70
Base, top set 118
Baseball backstops 137
Baseboard heaters 179
Bases, column 73
Basins, catch 42
Basketball backstops 138
Basketball posts 137
Bathing pools 162
Baths
    fixtures 160
    recessed 162
    sitz 161
Battens 92
Batts 85
Beam forms 58
Beams
    and battens 92
    concrete 53
    steel 69
    wood 76, 77
Bell footings 35
Belt conveyors 156
Bench, landscaping 51
Benches 138
Benders, redwood 47
Bentonite, walls 83
Bibbs, hose 41
Bicycle
    locks 47
    racks 138

Bidets 161
Bins 129
Bits, carbide 8
Bitumals, walls 83
Bituthene 86
Black iron 180
Black steel pipe 40
Bleachers
    field 138
    gym 138
Blocking 76
Boat berths 51
Boilers 179
Bolts 82
    anchor 72, 76
    expansion 72
    high strength 70, 72
Bonds, roof 87
Booths, paint spray 139
Boulders, ornamental 34
Bowling alleys 151
Boxes
    pull or junction 44
    valve 42
    valve, curb 42
Brace, metal 81
Bracing 76
Branch circuit devices/outlets 236
Branch circuit panels 203
Brass
    fabrication 74
    railings 72
Breakers, vacuum 165
    circuit 212
    current limiting 213
Breakers, vacuum 165
Breeching 180
Brick 66
    pavers 47
    steps 67
    veneer 65
    walls 65
Bridges, metal 81
Broadcast studios 151
Bronze fabrication 74
Buckets, concrete 12
Building
    demolition 29
    paper 77
    permits 2
    cut & fill 33
    steel, light frame 70
Built/up girders 70
Built/up roof 86
Bulkheads 35
Bullet resistive glass 105
Bumpers
    dock 139
    parking 47
Bun warmers 136
Busway
    aluminum 229
    aluminum, tap box 230
    copper 229
    plug-in 231
    tap box, copper 230
Butterfly valves 193

Butyl, decks 83

C

Cabinets 147
    blowers 186
    drug 141
    file 133
    hot food 136
    install only 80
    lab 140
    plastic faced 147
    shower 161
    wood 147
Cable
    control, copper 228
    power, aluminum 229
Cable tray 225
Caissons 35
    drill only 35
    drill, shoring 35
    reinforcing 59
Calcium chloride 61
Canopies & awnings 129
Canopy framing 73
Canopy hoods 136
Cant strips 87
Capacitors 215
Capillary fill 55
Capsheet 86
Carbide bits 8
Card catalogs 140
Cardiac care equipment 141
Cardioscopes 141
Carousels, baggage 157
Carpeting 148
Carts
    concrete 13
    food service 136
    hospital 141
    wash 142
Carved doors 98
Casement sash 102
Cash box w/stand 139
Cast iron flanges 165, 191
Cast iron pipe 37, 162
Cast steel valves 175
Cast stone 67
Casting, iron 74
Catch basin grates 73
Catch basins 42
Cathedral chairs 132
Caulk
    acrylic 92
    butyl 92
    butyl rubber 93
    linseed 92
    mildew resistant 93
    polysulfide 92
    silicone 92
Cedar siding 79
CEE studs 109
Ceiling
    access hatch 92
    board 116
    hatches 73

INDEX

removal 30
returns 189
T-bar 116, 151
tile 116
Ceiling diffuser 190
Ceilings
    suspended.. 151
Cell accessories 144
Cellular floor systems 205
Cement
    pargeting 83
    white 61
Central vacuum 144
Centrifugal fans 186
Centrifugal pumps 16
Centrifuges 140
Ceramic tile 114
Ceramic veneer 66
Chain link partitions 129
Chairlift 155
Chairs 51
Chairs, library 140
Chalk board 123
Check valves 41, 166, 192
Chemical toilets 3
Chillers 180
Chimneys 152
Chipping hammers 8
Chisels 8
Chrome-molybdenum pipe 173
Church glass 132
Chutes
    debris 31
    garbage 125
Cinder tracks 138
Circuit breakers 212
    distribution switchboard 212
    plug-in 218, 230
Circuit outlets 207
Circuits, lighting 206
Circular column forms 57
Circulating pumps 159
Clay
    facing tile 66
    pipe 39
    tile 66, 86
Clean up 22
Cleanouts 42
    floor 170
    wall 170
Clear & grub 33
Clips 70, 81
Clock & program systems 240
Closed circuit TV 133
Closed circuit TV systems 238
Closers 104
Coat, prime, pavements 47
Cocks, gas 41, 166
Coffee urns 136
Coils 184
Coils, reheat 187
Colored glass 133
Colorlith panels 88
Colors, concrete 54
Column, showers 161
Columns
    base 73

base, wood...73
concrete...53
forms..57
pipe..70, 73
shapes, steel..69
tube..70, 73
Combination starters.............................204, 214
Combination switchboards..............................211
Communication systems.................................207
    intercom..238
    public address...............................207, 238
Communion rails.......................................132
Compaction
    backfill...34
    equipment...9
    fill...33
Compactors, trash.....................................134
Composite deck...70
Compressors, air......................................160
Computer floors.......................................151
Computer room air conditioners........................182
Concrete
    air entrainment....................................54
    beams..53
    buckets..11, 12
    carts..12, 13
    columns..53
    conveyors...4
    deck...64
    dust coat..54
    envelopes..43
    epoxy coat...54
    fill...61
    finishes.......................................54, 61
    fireproofing.......................................55
    floor grinders.....................................13
    floor planers......................................13
    forms..55
    foundations..53
    girders..53
    grading..55
    hardeners..47
    insulating...63
    integral colors....................................54
    lightweight..54
    manholes...44
    masonry..65
    masonry adders.....................................66
    miscellaneous items................................62
    mixers...11
    panels, precast...................................107
    pipe...37
    pour...61
    poured in place....................................53
    precast..54
    precast panels.....................................54
    pumping...4
    readymix...60
    reinforced pipe....................................37
    sawing...30, 62
    saws...12, 21
    special wear surfaces..............................62
    stairs...53
    tiles..86
    tilt-up..53
    troweling machines.................................12
    vaults...44

walls 53
   waterproofing 54
Condensate pumps 183
Conductivity meters 141
Conduit
   aluminum 221
   bodies 223
   bodies, explosion proof 224
   EMT 222
   fiber 43
   fittings 224
   hangers, unistrut 226
   hubs 222
   intermediate metal 220
   PVC 43
   rigid steel 43, 220
   steel 43
   steel, flexible 226
   terminations 221
   terminations, PVC 219
   trench 43
Conectors, moment 70
Confessionals 132
Connections, motor 207, 215
Connectors, timber 82
Construction shacks, temporary 3
Contractor lighting 236
Control cable, copper 228
Control centers, motor 204, 214
Control joints 59
Control relays 214
Controls
   zone 188
Controls, HVAC 188
Conveyor belts 156
Conveyor toasters 137
Conveyors 139, 156
   concrete 4
   earthmoving 13
   mail 157
Cookers, steam 137
Coolers, walk-in 137
Cooling tower screens 90
Cooling towers 181
Copings 89
Copper clad stainless steel roofing 87
Copper
   busway tap box 230
   busways 229
   control cable 228
   ground rod 44
   panels, foam core 87
   panels, paper core 87
   pipe 39, 163, 190
   roofing 87
   tile 121
   tubing 164
   tubing, type K 39
   veneer panels 87
   wire 227. 228
   wire & IMC 232
   wire & PVC 231
   wire & RSC 232
Copper clad stainless steel roofing 87
Core drilling 30
Cork tile 117
Cork, acoustic insulation 85

Corner guards 92, 141
Corner guards, cast 73
Coronary care equipment 141
Corrugated metal
   pipe 38
   roof 86
   siding 87
Corrugated polyethylene pipe 37
Corspan panels 88
Counter
   bank teller 131
   doors 99
   flashing 90
   flow furnaces 178
   sinks 161
Couplings, flexible 224
Couplings, victaulic 192
Court striping 137
Cranes 156
   crawler 4
   hydraulic 156
   piling 34
   tower 3
Crawler cranes 4
Crawler tractor 14
Cross arms 44
Cryogenic valves 175
Cubicle track & curtain 141
Cultured marble 148
Curb forms 59
Curb valve boxes 42
Curbs 47
Current limiting breakers 213
Curtain track, stage 145
Curtain wall 107
Curtain wall, glazed 107
Cut
   for buildings 33
   for levees 33
   openings, demolition 30
Cut & fill 33
Cut back 46
Cut off saws 21
Cutouts, fused 45
Cutters, asphalt 8

D

Dampers, fire 189
Deadbolt 103
Debris
   chutes 31
   removal 22
Deck
   floor 77
   floor, metal 70
   roof, metal 71
   waterproofing 83
Decks
   concrete 64
   fiber 64
Decontamination shower 162
Decorative handrail 72
Deep fryers 136
Deep well system 36
Defibrillators 141

INDEX

Demolition
  building 29
  drilling 30
  electrical 32
  floors only 31
  HVAC 32
  plumbing 32
  site 29
Demolition hammer 11
Demolition, walls only 30
Demountable partitions 125
Dental chairs 143
Dental furniture 143
Dental sterilizers 143
Derricks 3
Detailing, forms 59
Dewatering 36
Dexotex 84
Diaphragm pumps 16
Diffuser
  ceiling 190
  suction 193
Dimmer
  fluorescent 236
  incandescent 236
Directories, building 127
Discharge hoses 17
Disconnect switches 45
Dishwashers 134
  commercial 137
  institutional 137
Display cases 127
Disposal
  earth 55
  garbage 134
Distillers, water 142
Distribution
  panels 203
  switchboard 212
  transformers 202, 204
  wiremold overhead 226
Dividers, redwood 47
Dock bumpers 139
Dock levelers 139
Doctors' registry system 239
Dome observatories 133
Dome slab 53
Domes 153
Doors
  access 99, 112, 169
  carved 98
  controls, remote 144
  counter 99
  Dutch 99
  fire label 98
  frames with borrowed light 95
  frames with side light 95
  frames with transom light 95
  frames, metal 95
  French 98
  garage 98
  hollow core, masonite 96
  hollow wood 96
  install only 80
  jamb & trim 98
  jambs 98
  louvers 92

metal 83
night deposit 131
overhead 99
pocket 97
prison 240
refrigerator 100
removal 30
revolving 100
roll-up 99
roll-up, fire 100
sliding glass 101
sliding, fire 99
solid core, wood 97
solid, exterior 97
vault 100, 131
wardrobe 99
Douglas fir floors 117
Downspouts 89
Drafting furniture 133
Drain
  rock 34
  trench 73
Drains
  area 42, 170
  floor 170
  roof 170
  shower 170
Draperies 149
Dredging 51
Dressing cubicles 123
Drill for caissons 35
Drill steel 8
Drilling
  demolition 30
  for piers 35
  rock 35
Drills, air 9
Drinking fountains 161
Drop inlets 42
Drug cabinets 141
Dryers, clothes 134
Dryvit 107
Drywall studs, standard 112
Drywall, gypsum wall board 112
Duct
  fiberglass reinforced plastic 189
  floor systems 205
  flush trench 225
  galvanized iron 188
  heaters 178, 179
  insulation 190
  underfloor 225
Duct work 188
Duct, flexible 189
Ductile iron pipe 39
Dumbwaiters 155
Dummy knobs 104
Dur iron pipe 163
Dust coat, concrete 54
Dust partitions 31
Dust proof strikes 104
Dutch doors 99

E

E-Z wall systems 87

INDEX

Earth
- disposal 55
- moving equipment 13

Earthquake, gas shut off valve 168
Edging 50
Elastomeric membrane 86
Elastoplastic floor 118
Elbows
- conduit 222

Elbows, PVC 219
Electrical demolition 32
Electrical hoist 155
Elevator beams 73
Elevators 155
Elevators, incline 156
Embedded steel 73
Emergency
- accessories 141
- generator 204, 218
- lighting fixtures 236

EMT conduit 222
Enclosures, telephone 129
Energy management systems 241
Engineered fill 33
Entrance hardware 103
Entrances 106
Envelopes, concrete 43
Epoxy coat, concrete 54
Epoxy injection, repair 64
Equipment rental
- conveyors, earthmoving 13
- aftercooler 8
- air compressors 6
- air concrete vibrators 9
- air drills 9
- air grinders 9
- air hoses 7
- air impact wrenches 9
- air manifolds 8
- air tamper 9
- air tools 8
- air torches 19
- air vibrators 11
- asphalt cutters 8
- backhoe loader 15
- barrel pumps 21
- carbide bits 8
- centrifugal pumps 16
- chipping hammers 8
- chisels 8
- compaction 9
- concrete 11
- concrete buckets 11, 12
- concrete carts 13
- concrete conveyors 4
- concrete floor grinders 13
- concrete floor planers 13
- concrete mixers 11
- concrete pumping 4
- concrete saws 12
- crawler cranes 4
- crawler tractor 14
- derricks 3
- diaphragm pumps 16
- discharge hoses 17
- drill steel 8
- electric air compressors 7
- excavator 14
- forklifts 4
- fuel tanks 21
- generators 17
- gin poles 3
- heaters 20
- hoist towers 3
- hydrostatic testers 21
- jackhammers 8
- jitterbugs 13
- lighting 20
- membrane remover 13
- moil points 8
- paving breakers 8
- plaster mixers 11, 12
- platforms 22
- portable air compressors 6
- posthole diggers 13
- pumps 16
- rammers 9
- rollers 9
- rollers, machinery 21
- sandblasters 19
- saws 21
- silenced air compressors 6
- skid steer 15
- skid steer loader 15
- spades 8
- submersible pumps 16
- suction hoses 17
- sump pumps 16
- tower cranes 3
- trash pumps 16
- tree spade 15
- trencher 13
- troweling machines 12
- truck cranes 3
- trucks 4
- vocational 146
- washers 21
- welders 18
- wheel loader 16
- wheel tractor 14
- wheelbarrows 13
- window washing 145

Equipotential grounding systems 239
Escalators 156
Excavate
- roadway 33

Excavation & backfill 55
Excavator 14
Exercise units 143
Exhaust
- fans 185
- grills, wall 190
- registers, ceiling 189
- registers, wall 190

Exit signs 206, 235
Expansion
- bolts 72
- joints 59, 74, 91
- tanks 187

Extension cords 18
Exterior insulation finish system 88
Extinguisher cabinets 128
Extinguishers 128

INDEX

F

Facade screens.. 92
Facespan panels.. 88
Facet glass... 133
Facia... 78
Facia assembly, granostrut.. 87
Facial tissue dispensers... 126
Facing tile, clay... 66
False work.. 70
Fan coils.. 186
Fans... 185
    centrifugal............................... 186
    exhaust................................... 185
    return.................................... 186
Fees
    inspection................................ 208
    sewer....................................... 2
    sewer connection.......................... 173
    water meter............................. 2, 173
Felt, 30#... 86
Feminine napkin dispenser.. 125
Feminine napkin disposals.. 125
Fence
    metal..................................... 48
    removal................................... 29
    temporary.................................. 3
    wood...................................... 48
Fertilizer.. 50
Fiber conduit... 43
Fiber deck.. 64
Fiberboard forms.. 57
Fiberglass
    blown..................................... 84
    forms..................................... 59
    pans.................................... 58, 59
    reinforced plastic duct................... 189
    tanks..................................... 42
Fiberboard insulation... 77
File cabinets.. 133
Fill... 55
    concrete.................................. 61
    engineered................................ 33
Filters and frames... 185
Finish hardware.. 103
Finishes
    concrete................................ 54, 61
    floor.................................... 117
    slab...................................... 61
Fire
    alarm systems........................... 207, 237
    dampers.................................. 189
    doors, sliding............................ 99
    escapes................................... 73
    hose cabinets............................ 128
    hose equipment........................... 128
    hydrants.................................. 42
    labels for doors.......................... 98
    protection systems....................... 195
    protection, halon........................ 196
    pumps.................................... 196
    vents..................................... 91
    vents, skylight......................... 86, 91
Fireplaces
    brick..................................... 68
    pre-fab................................. 68, 92

Fireproof jackets... 70
Fireproofing concrete... 55
Fireproofing
    sprayed................................... 85
    wood...................................... 78
Fittings, conduit.. 224
Fixture.. 236
Fixture outlets.. 206
    emergency................................ 236
    floodlights.............................. 235
    lighting................................. 206
    lighting, fluorescent.................... 233
    lighting, HPS/lucalux.................... 206
    lighting, incandescent................. 206, 232
    lighting, mercury vapor.................. 206
    lighting, commercial mercury vapor....... 233
    lighting, commercial, incandescent....... 233
    lighting, fluorescent strip.............. 206
Flag poles... 127
Flanges.. 191
    cast iron................................ 165
    steel, slip-on........................... 165
Flashing
    counter................................... 90
    roof...................................... 89
Flashings... 89
Flatbed truck rental.. 4
Flex connections... 194
Flexible couplings... 224
Flexible duct.. 189
Flexible steel conduit... 226
Floodlight fixtures.. 235
Floodlights... 20
Floor
    box..................................... 207
    cleanouts................................ 170
    drains................................... 170
    elastoplastic............................ 118
    finishes................................. 117
    furnaces................................. 178
    gym...................................... 138
    joists.................................. 75, 76
    mats..................................... 148
    parquet.................................. 117
    pine...................................... 79
    removal................................... 31
    seamless................................. 118
    sheathing................................. 77
    sinks.................................... 161
    specialties.............................. 118
    system outlets........................... 205
    systems duct............................. 205
    systems, cellular........................ 205
    wood..................................... 117
Floor grinders.. 13
Floor planers... 13
Flotation rig, piling... 34
Fluorescent lighting fixtures.................................... 233
Flow meter... 194
Fluorescent strip lighting fixtures.............................. 206
Flush bolts.. 104
Flush trench duct.. 225
Flying forms, columns... 57
Flying forms, structural slabs................................. 58, 59
Foam insulation... 85
Folding partitions... 124
Food

preparation tables 134
service carts 136
service equipment 134
service fixtures, stainless steel 135
Footing
   forms 56
Footing removal 30
Footings, bell 35
Forklifts 4
Forms
   beam 58
   column 57
   concrete 55
   curb 59
   detailing 59
   fiberglass 59
   flying, wall 56, 57
   footing 56
   foundation 56
   liners 59
   retaining wall 56
   slab 56, 58
   slab depression 59
   stair 59
   structural slabs 58, 59
   wall 56, 57
Foundation 53
   bolts 82
   forms 56
   pressure injected 36
   vents 90
Fountains
   drinking 161
   eye wash 162
   water 162
FP
   encapsulation 31
   removal 31
Frame supports 73
Frames
   door, metal 95
   metal, install only 80
   wood, install only 80
Framing
   clips 81
   joists 75
   rafters 75
   walls 75
Freezers 136
French doors 99
Fuel oil pumps 183
Fuel storage tanks 21
Fuel tanks 42
Fume hoods, lab 140
Furnaces
   counter flow 178
   floor 178
   horizontal flow 178
   up flow 178, 179
   wall 178
Furnishings 149
Furring 77
   channels, ceiling 112
   channels, wall 112
   coffered 110
   hat channel 110
   metal 110

resilient spring 110
   wall 110
Fused cutouts 45
Fused switchboards 213
Fusible switches 215

G

Galvanized iron duct 188
Galvanized steel ladders 72
Galvanized steel pipe 40
Galvanizing 70
Gamma camera 143
Garage doors 98
Garage hoists 139
Garbage
   chutes 126
   compactors 145
   disposals 134
Gas
   cocks 41, 166
   pipe, medical 171
   pumps 138
   regulator valves 167
Gas shut off valve, earthquake 168
Gas station equipment 138
Gasket, neoprene 93
Gate operator, parking lot 139
Gate valves 41, 166, 192
Gates 48
Gates, hose 41
Gates, wrought iron 74
Generator, emergency 204, 218
Generators 17
Gin poles 3
Girders
   built/up 70
   concrete 53
   steel 69
Glass
   beads, insulation 84
   colored 133
   facet 133
   masonry 67
   stained 133
Glasweld panels 88
Glasweld siding 79
Glazing
   acrylic 105
   bullet resistive glass 105
   insulated glass 105
   job 105
   leaded glass 105
   mirrors 105
   shower doors 105
Globe valves 41, 166, 192
Glu-lams 80
Goalposts 137
Grab bar 126
Grading 33
Grading for pavement 46
Granite 67
Granite aggregate 61
Granostrut panels 87
Grass, seeding 50
Grates, catch basin 73

INDEX

Grating 73
Gravel 34
Gravel stops 89
Gravel, parking 46
Gravity sewer pipe 38
Gravity vents 90
Grease interceptors 159
Greenhouses 151
Grills
    roll-up 99
    wall exhaust 190
Grinders, air 9
Ground cover 50
Ground rod, copper 44
Ground wire 44
Grounds 77
Grouting, pressure 54
Guard rails 48
Gunite 54
Gussets 70
Gutters 47, 89
Gutters, steel 226
Gym
    equipment 137
    floors 117, 138
    seating 138
Gypsum
    lath 110
    sheathing 77
    vinyl clad 113
    wall board 112

H

Hair interceptors 159
    demolition 11
Hammers, chipping 8
Handrail, decorative 72
Handrail, wood 81
Hangers, stainless 81
Hangers, unistrut conduit 226
Hardboard siding 79
Hardeners, concrete 47
Hardware
    finish 103
    install only 80
Hat channels 110
Hatches
    ceiling 73
    roof 73, 91
Headers 47, 76, 77
Heat pumps 182
Heaters
    baseboard 179
    duct 178, 179
    for dx units 181
    infra-red 183
    unit 178, 179
    water 159
Heaters, space 20
Heating units
    hydronic 182
Heavy timbers 80
Heavywall PVC conduit 43
Hi early strength concrete 61
High mast lighting 46

High strength bolts 70, 72
High voltage transformer 202
High voltage unit substation 202
Highway buttons 48
Hinges 103
Hoisting towers 3
Hoists
    air 156
    electrical 155
    garage 139
Hook strip 79
Horizontal flow furnaces 178
Hose bibbs 41
Hose gate valves 166
Hose gates 41
Hoses, discharge 17
Hoses, suction 17
Hospital
    corner guards 141
    electrical, special systems 239
    isolating panels 240
Hot food cabinets 136
Hot mop, walls 83
Hot water heaters 159
Hotplates, built-in 135
HPS/lucalux lighting fixtures 206
Hubs, conduit 222
Hubbard tanks 143
Humidifiers 183
HVAC demolition 32
Hydrant removal 29
Hydrants, fire 42
Hydronic units
    heating 182
Hydrostatic testers 21
Hydrotherapy equipment 143

I

I studs 110
Ice cream machines 137
Ice machines 136
IMC & copper wire 232
Incandescent lighting fixtures 206
Incandescent lighting fixtures, commercial 233
Incinerators 151
Incline elevators 156
Incubators 141
Indicators, post 42
Induction units 186
Industrial racking 129
Infra-red heaters 183
Inhalation therapy equipment 143
Inlets, drop 42
Inspection fees 208
Institutional switchgear 203
Instrument washer/sterilizer 142
Insulated glass 105
Insulated metal wall siding 71
Insulated rooms 151
Insulating concrete 63
Insulation
    acoustic, sound board 85
    batts 85
    board 77, 84
    duct 190

INDEX

fiberglass 84
glass beads 84
industrial piping 176
mineral 84
pipe 168, 194
polystyrene beads 85
urethane foam 85
valve 176
vermiculite beads 84
Integral colors, concrete 54
Interceptors 159
Intercom systems 207, 238
Interior trim, paint 119
Intermediate metal conduit 220
Iron casting 74
Iron pipe 37, 39
Ironite 83
Irrigation 48
Irrigation valves 49

J

Jack posts 75
Jack studs 75
Jackhammers 8
Jacking, pipe 36
Jamb and trim 98
Jitterbugs 13
Joints
   construction 59
   expansion 74, 91
Joists
   floor 75, 76
   hangers 81
   open web 70
   roof 76
Junction boxes 44

K

Kettles, steam 137
Key joints 59
Kick plates 104
Kitchen equipment 134
Kitchen units, prefab 135
Kitchens, pre-fab 137
Kleftstone panels 88
Kneelers 132
Knobs
   dummy 104
Kraft paper, walls 83

L

Lab
   cabinets 140
   equipment 140
   fume hoods 140
   furniture 140
   laundry equipment 143
Ladders, galvanized steel 72
Laminated plastic tops 148
Landscaping
   bench 51
   chairs 51
   planters 51
   tables 51
   umbrellas 51
Language labs 133
Latch sets 103
Lath
   aqua 110
   gypsum 110
   metal 110
   rock 110
   wire mesh 110
Laundry equipment, lab 143
Lead-base paint removal 31
Lead coated copper roofing 87
Lead lined materials 152
Leaded glass 105
Lecterns 131
Ledger bolts 82
Ledgers 77
Letters, metal 127
Levees, cutting 33
Levelers, dock 139
Library equipment 140
Lifts 156
Lifts, scissors 156
Lighting
   athletic fields 45
   contractor 236
   dental 143
   fixtures 206
   fixtures, commercial, mercury vapor 233
   fixtures, emergency 236
   fixtures, floodlight 235
   fixtures, fluorescent 233
   fixtures, fluorescent strip 206
   fixtures, HPS/lucalux 206
   fixtures, incandescent 206, 232
   fixtures, incandescent 233
   fixtures, mercury vapor 206
   high mast 46
   outdoor 45
   outdoor, specialty 45
   parking lot 45
   stage, controls 144
   surgical 141
   traffic signals 45
   TV studio 145
   walkway 45
Lighting circuits 206, 236
Lightning arrestors 45
Lights
   arc lamps 20
   flood 20
   mercury vapor 20
   portable 20
Lightweight
   aggregate 61
   concrete 54
   concrete fill 61
Lime treatment 46
Limestone 67
Liners, form 59
Linoleum 117
Load centers 217
   backhoe 15
   skid steer 15
Loam 50
Lock sets 103

Lockers 128
Louvers
   aluminum 92
   door 90, 92
Low voltage switching systems 240

M

Machine tool control transformer 214
Machinery rollers 21
Magnetic starter 214
Mail
   boxes 128
   chutes 128
   conveyors 157
Main
   panels 203
   switchboards 203
   switchgear 202, 203
Main panels 203
Maintenance, plants 50
Manhole
   covers 73
   removal 29
   steps 73
Manholes 42
   concrete 44
Manifolds 171
Manlifts 156
Manual starter 214
Marble 67
Marine facilities 51
Masonry
   concrete 65
   glass 67
   reinforcing 67
   wall finishes 67
   wall ties 67
Material handling equipment 139
Mats, floor 148
Meat slicers 137
Mechanical drawing desks 133
Medical care system 239
Membrane removers 13
Membrane
   waterproof 55
Mercury vapor lighting fixtures 45
Mercury vapor lighting fixtures, commercial 233
Mercury vapor lights 20
Mesh, wire 72
Mesh, wire 60
Metal
   braces 81
   cabinets 147
   conduit, intermediate 220
   door frames 95
   doors 83
   furring 110
   lockers 128
   pans 58, 59
   pipe, corrugated 38
   roof deck 70
   roof, corrugated 86
   siding 71
   siding, corrugated 87
   stairs 72

studs 109, 112
Meter fees, water 2
Meters
   flow 194
Mileage allowances 4
Mineral
   blown 84
   fiber insulation 84
   fiber tile 116
Mirawal 107
Mirrors 105
Miscellaneous alarms 239
Mixers, plaster 12
Mixing boxes 186
Modular vaults 131
Moil points 8
Molding, plaster 112
Moldings 79
Moldings & ornaments, plaster 112
Moment connectors 70
Monitoring systems
   seismic 239
Mortar lined steel pipe 40
Mortuary equipment 144
Motor connections 215
Motor control centers 204, 214
Motor starters 214
Moving sidewalks 157
Moving structures 31
Mud sills 76
Mud, terrazzo 115
Mulch 50
Mullions 77
Mushroom vents 91

N

Nails 81
Neoprene
   neon 127
   decks 75
   gaskets 93
   roof 86
   walls 83
Nets
   safety 22
   tennis 137
Night deposit doors 131
Non-corrosive rebar 60
Nonfused switches 215
Nosings, stair 73
Nuclear equipment 143
Nurse call stations 141
Nurse monitoring equipment 141

O

Oak floors 117
Observatories 133
Occupancy sensor system 236
Occupancy sensors 236
Office expense allowance 22
Office furniture 149
Office trailers, rental 3
Open web joists 70
Operable walls 124

Outdoor lighting 45
Outlets 241
    circuit 207
    devices, branch circuit 236
    duplex 207
    fixture 206
    floor system 205
Ovens, convection 136
Ovens, micro-wave 136
Overhead distribution systems 226
Overhead doors 99

P

Pads
    carpeting 148
Pads, transformer 44
Paging systems, radio 239
Paint
    cabinets 119
    concrete 118
    doors and trim 119
    field touch-up, steel 70
    interior 119
    lead-base 31
    masonry 118
    pipe 120
    plaster 118
    sheet metal 119
    sheetrock 119
    spray booths 139
    steel tanks 120
    structural steel 120
    wood 118
    wood trim 119
Painting 118
Panelboards 203, 215, 216
Paneling 80
Panels
    aggregate 88
    branch circuit 203
    colorlith 88
    copper veneer 87
    copper, foam core 87
    copper, paper core 87
    corspan 88
    distribution 203
    electrical 203
    facespan 88
    glasweld 88
    granostrut 87
    kleftstone 88
    permastone 88
    porcelain on aluminum 88
    porcelain on steel 88
    precast concrete 54, 107
    qasal 88
    radiant heat, ceiling 183
    santone 88
    sculptured 88
    splitwood 88
    stonehenge 88
Panic devices 104
Pans, waffle and joist 58, 59
Paper hanging 120
Paper towel & waste combination 125

Paper towel dispensers 125
Paper, building 77
Pargeting 68
Parking bumpers 47
Parking lot equipment 139
Parking lot lighting 45
Parquet floors 117
Partition accessories 123
Partitions
    accordion 124
    chain link 129
    demountable 125
    dust 31
    folding 124
    relocatable 124
    toilet 123
Pavement
    asphalt 46
    coatings 47
    removal 29
    sealer 46
    tennis court 46
Paving breakers 8
Paving tile 66
Pedestal floors 151
Peelers, vegetable 136
Perlite cores 85
Permastone panels 88
Permits
    building 2
    miscellaneous 2
    testing 241
Pews 132
Pharmacy equipment 142
Photography 24
Physical therapy equipment 143
Picnic table & benches 138
Picture windows 102
Pier caps 75
Piers
    drill only 35
    test boring 35
Piles 34
    cranes 34
    flotation rig 34
    pipe 34
    precast 34
    salvage 34
    sheet 35
    soldier 34
    steel 34
    steel step tapered 34
    test 34
    wood 34
Pipe
    ABS plastic 38
    acid waste 39
    cast iron 37, 162
    chrome-molybdenum 173
    clay 39
    columns 70, 73
    concrete 37
    copper 39, 163, 190
    corrugated metal 38
    corrugated polyethylene 37
    ductile iron 39
    dur iron pipe 163

gravity sewer 38
insulation 194
insulation, industrial 176
iron, ductile 39
irrigation 49
jacking 36
medical gas 171
mortar lined 40
piles 34
plastic 164
plastic, ABS 38
polypropylene 39, 164
PVC 38, 39, 164
pyrex 164
railings 72
stainless steel 171, 174
steel 40, 164, 171, 173, 190, 191
vacuum jacketed 175
Pipe insulation 168
Plan checks... 2
Planetarium equipment 134
Planetariums 134
Plant bed.. 50
Planters.. 51
Plants, maintenance............................... 50
Plaques, metal 127
Plaster
exterior, float................................... 110
interceptors 159
interior, ceilings 111
interior, walls 111
molding.. 112
moldings and ornaments 112
thin coat... 111
Plaster mixers 11, 12
Plastic
pipe 38, 164
roofing 86
tile 120
tops 148
Plastic faced cabinets 147
Plates 76
Plates, base 70
Plates, shear 82
Platform scales 129
telescoping and scissor 22
Playground equipment 137
Plug-in
busway 231
circuit breakers 218, 230
Plugmold 226
Plumber's cone 90
Plumbing demolition 32
Ply clips.. 81
Plywood sheathing 77
Plywood siding 79
Pneumatic tubes 157
Point of connection................................ 49
Pointing 68
Poisoning soil 34
Poles, wood 44
Polyethylene pipe, corrugated 37
Polyisobutylene tape 93
Polypropylene pipe............................ 39, 164
Polystyrene beads.................................. 85
Polystyrene insulation, refrigeration....... 85
Polysulfide sealants 93

Polyurethane sealants 93
Pools 153
bathing 162
Porcelain on aluminum panels 88
Porcelain on steel panels 88
Portable lights... 20
Post anchors... 81
Post caps.. 81
Post indicators.. 42
Post-tensioning....................................... 59
Posthole diggers..................................... 13
Posts.. 76
Poured in place concrete 54
Pouring concrete..................................... 61
Power cable
aluminum 229
Power columns.. 241
Power poles, temporary 3
Power systems, uninterrupted................. 219
Pre-fab
buildings.. 151
kitchen units 135
kitchens... 137
Pre-fab fireplaces.................................... 92
Pre-insulated steel pipe 40
Pre-stressing.. 59
Precast
area drains... 42
concrete 54
drop inlets 42
panels 54
piles 34
Pressure grouting.................................... 54
Pressure injected foundations................. 36
Pressure pumps...................................... 160
Pressure reducing valves................... 167, 193
Prime coat, pavements 47
Prison door control.................................. 240
Prison equipment.................................... 144
Projection screens, school 133
Public address systems 207, 238
Pull
bars... 104
boxes 44, 226
plates 104
Pumping concrete.................................... 4
Pumps
barrel... 21
centrifugal.. 16
circulating.. 159
condensate.. 183
diaphragm.. 16
fire... 196
fuel oil 183
heat... 182
pressure 160
rental... 16
sewage ejector 160
submersible 16
sump 16, 160
trash.. 16
vacuum 171
water service 183
Purification, water 187
Purlins.. 76
Push
plates 104

PVC
    and copper wire 231
    conduit 43
    floor 117
    pipe 38, 39, 164
    water pipe 39
    waterproofing, walls 83
Pyrex pipe 164

Q

Qasal panels 88
Quarry tile 66

R

Raceway 43, 219
    and wire 204
    industrial 129
    telephone 237
    wiremold surface 226
Racks, food storage 136
Racks, reagent 140
Radiant heat panels, ceiling 183
Radiation protection 152
Radio paging system 239
Rafters 75, 76
Rail, guard 48
Railings
    aluminum 72
    angle 72
    brass 72
    flatbar 72
    pipe 72
    stainless 72
    temporary 3
    wrought iron 72
Railroad work 51
    communion 132
    guard 48
    wall, stainless 73
    wood 81
Rakers, steel 35
Rammers 9
Ranges 134
Ranges, hot top 136
Re-heat coils 187
Readymix 60
Reagent racks 140
Rebar 59
Rebar, welding 60
    non-corrosive 60
Receptors, shower & drain 161
Recessed baths 162
Redwood siding 78
Refrigeration insulation 85
Refrigerator doors 100
Refrigerators 134
    liquid nitrogen 142
    pass thru 136
    under counter 135
Registers
    ceiling exhaust 189
    wall exhaust 190
    wall supply 190
Reglets 90

Reinforcing
    caissons 59
    masonry 67
    welding 60
Reinforcing bar 59
Reinforcing steel accessories 60
Relays, control 214
Relief valves 167, 193
Relocatable partitions 124
Remote door controls 144
Removal, miscellaneous 30
Removal: see specific material being removed 29
Resuscitators 141
Retaining wall forms 56
Return fans 186
Returns, ceiling 189
Revolving doors 100
Ribbons 77
Rigging, theater 145
Rigid steel conduit 43, 220
Rip rap 34
Risers, alarm & valve 196
Roadway cut & fill 33
Roadway excavation 33
Rock
    drainage 34
    drilling 35
    lath 110
Roll warmers 136
Roll-up doors 99
Roll-up grills 99
Rollers
    machinery 21
Rollers, compaction 9
Roof
    bonds 87
    built/up 86
    copper 87
    copper clad stainless steel 87
    covers 91
    deck, metal 70
    drains 170
    flashing 89
    hatches 73
    jacks 170
    joists 76
    plastic 86
    removal 30
    safes 90
    scuppers 90
    sheathing 77
    sheet metal 87
Roof hatches 91
Roof, corrugated metal 86
Room occupancy system 239
Rough-in at fixtures 162
Rowing machines 143
RSC 43
RSC & copper wire 232
Running tracks 138

S

Safe deposit boxes 131
Safes 131
Safes, roof 90

Safety nets 22
Sand fill 55
Sandblasters 19
Sandblasting 120
Sandblasting equipment 19
Sandblasting, masonry 68
Sandstone 67
Sanitary line removal 29
Santone panels 88
Sash
   aluminum 102
   awning, aluminum 101
   casement 102
   casement, aluminum 101
   install only 80
   metal 108
   sliding, aluminum 101
   steel 102
   wood 102
Sawdust collectors 139
Sawing concrete 30, 62
Saws
   concrete 21
   cut off 21
Saws, concrete 12
Scaffolds 22
Scales, steel, platform 129
Scarifying 33
Scissor platforms 22
Scissors lifts 139, 156
Scoreboards, field 138
Scoreboards, gym 138
Scrabblers, air 13
Screen accessories 123
Screens
   bird/insect 90
   cooling tower 90
   facade 92
   projection 133
   sight 123
   sight, metal 74
   sun, metal 74
   urinal 123
Scrub stations 141
Sculptured panels 88
Scuppers 90
Seal spray, silicone 119
Sealants
   acrylic latex 93
   polyurethane 93
Sealer, pavement 46
Seamless floor 118
Seating 128
Seating, pedestal 133
Security systems 239, 241
Seeding grass 50
Seismic monitoring 239
Selector switch 202
Sensor, occupancy system 236
   occupancy 236
Separators
   air 187
Separators, moisture 20
Septic tanks 160
Service sections 209
Service sinks 161
Sewage ejector pumps 160

Sewer connection fees 173
Sewer fees 2
SFS studs 109
Shacks, construction, temporary 3
Shacks, temporary, rental 3
Shades 147
Shakes 86
Shale beads 84
Shapes
   column 69
   steel 69
   structural 69
Shear plates 82
Shear studs 70
Sheathing
   floor 77
   gypsum 77
   plywood 77
   roof 77
   wall 77
Sheepsfoot rollers 10
Sheet
   asphalt 47
   metal 89
   metal roofing 87
   metal wainscot 92
   pilings 35
   rock 112
   vinyl 117
Shelving
   library 140
   metal, bins 129
   pine 79
Shingle siding 79
Shingles 85
Shingles, wood 86
Shop equipment 134, 139
Shot fasteners 76
Shower
   cabinet 161
   column 161
   compartments 124
   doors 105
   drains 170
   head drench 162
   pans 75
Shrubs 50
Shut-off valves 171
Sidewalks 47
Sidewalks, moving 157
Siding
   corrugated metal 87
   glasweld 79
   hardboard 79
   insulated metal wall 71
   metal 71
   plywood 79
   redwood/cedar 78
   shingles 79
Sight screens 48
Sight screens, metal 74
   sight 123
Sign, 'construction' 22
Signs, graphics 127
Signs
   exit 206
   neon 127

street 47
Silicone
    roof 86
    seal spray 119
    walls 83
Simulated marble 148
Sinks
    bar 161
    counter 161
    floor 161
    service 161
Sisalkraft flashing 77
Site demolition 29
Sitz baths 161
Skid steer loader 15
Skylights 91
Skylights, fire vent 86, 91
Slab
    depress forms 59
    dome 53
    finishes 61
    forms 56, 58
    forms, structural 58, 59
    on grade combos 54
    removal 31
Slabs, structural 53
Slate 86
Slicing machines 137
Sliding fire doors 99
Sliding glass doors 101
Slip rings 82
Slurry trenching 36
Small tool allowance 22
Smoke vents 91
Soap dispensers 126
Sodding 50
Soft wire systems 240
Softeners, water 160
Soil poisoning 34
Soil treatment 34
Solar stone 65
Soldier piles 34
Sonic equipment 143
Sound attentuators 190
Sound board 85, 113
Space frame systems 69
Space heaters 20
Spades 8
Special wear surfaces 62
Specialty outdoor lighting 45
Splitwood panels 88
Sprinkler heads 49
Stacks 180
Stage equipment 144
Stain, wood 118
Stained glass 132
Stainless steel
    fabrication 74
    pipe 174
    railings 72
    roofing 87
Stainless steel pipe 171
Stairs
    forms 59
Stair nosings 73
Stairs, concrete 53
Stairs, hardwood 81

Stairs, metal 72
Stakes, reflector 48
Stakeside truck rental 4
Stand-by charges, concrete 61
Standpipe 196
Starters
    combination 204, 214
    magnetic 214
    manual 214
    motor 214
Steam
    cookers 137
    kettles 137
    trap valves 167, 193
Steel
    beams 69
    beams & girders 69
    buildings, light frame 70
    conduit, flexible 226
    conduit, rigid 220
    embedded 73
    girders 69
    gutter 226
    piles 34
    pipe 40, 164, 171, 173, 190, 191
    pipe mortar lined 40
    rakers 35
    shapes 69
    shapes, column 69
    step tapered piles 34
Steps, brick 67
Sterilizers 141, 142
Sterilizers, dental 143
Stone
    architectural 67
    veneer 67
    work, artificial 67
Stone cast 67
Stonehenge panels 88
Storage, surgical 141
Store front systems 105
Storefront 106
Storm drain removal 29
Strainers, 'Y' 166
Strap anchors 81
Street signs 47
Strikes, dust proof 104
Strip & stockpile 33
Strip deck 13
Striping 47
Striping, court 137
Stripping 77
Strong backs 77
Structural
    shapes 69
    slab forms 58, 59
    studs 109
Structures
    moving 31
    temporary 3
Stucco, exterior 111
Stud
    bolts 82
    wall components 76
    walls 75
Studio lighting 145
Studios, broadcast 151

Studs
  CEE 109
  drywall 112
  I 110
  SFS 109
  WFS 109
Study carrels 133, 140
Sub base, aggregate 46
Submersible pumps 16
Substations, high voltage 202, 208
Suction diffuser 193
Suction hoses 17
Sump pumps 16, 160
Sun screens, metal 74
Supplies, consumable, allowance 22
Supply registers, wall 190
Surface bolts 104
Surgical light supports 73
Suspended ceilings 115, 151
Swimming pools 153
Swings 137
Switch 236
Switch, time 236
Switchboards
  combination 211
  distribution 212
  fused 213
  main 203
Switches
  auto transfer 204, 218
  disconnect 45
  fusible 215
  nonfused 215
Switchgear
  commercial 203
  large commercial 203
  light commercial 202
  small institutional 203
Switching 240
  low voltage 240
  ceilings 151

T

T-bar
  ceilings 115, 151
Tables 51
  counters w/sinks 134
  delivery 141
  library 140
  school 133
  surgery 141
Tack board 123
Tack coat 46
Tamper, air 9
Tampers, jitterbug 13
Tanks 187
  fiberglass 42
  fuel 42
  fuel storage 21
  septic 160
  water 160
Tap box, aluminum busway 230
Tap box, copper busway 230
Taping & texturing 114
Tee system 64
Telephone

enclosures 129
  monthly 3
  raceway 237
  systems 207, 237
Telescopes 134
Telescoping platforms 22
Television antenna systems 238
Television systems, closed-circuit 238
Teller counters 131
Teller windows 131
Temporary
  construction shacks 3
  fence 3
  power poles 3
  railings 3
  structures 3
  utilities 3
Tempower boxes 18
Tennis court pavements 46
Tennis courts 138
Tennis posts 137
Terminations, conduit 222
Terminations, PVC conduit 219
Termite treatment 78
Terne roofing 87
Terrazzo
  accessories 115
  floor 115
  thinset 115
  tiles 66
Test boring for piers 35
Test piles 34
Tester, hydrostatic 21
Testing, lighting 208
Tether ball posts 137
Thermostatic mixing valves 167
Thin coat plaster 111
Thinset, terrazzo 115
Ticket dispenser, parking lot 139
Tie
  plates 70
  rods 70
  straps 81
Tie back walls 35
Tile
  accessories 115
  aluminum 121
  asphalt 117
  ceilings 116
  ceramic 114
  clay 66, 86
  concrete 121
  copper 117
  cork 117
  floor 114
  mineral fiber 116
  paving 66
  plastic 120
  quarry 66
  vinyl composition 117
  vinyl diaphragm 116
Tiles
  terrazzo 66
Tilt-up
  casting 62
  erection 63
  special finishes 63

INDEX

walls 53
Timber connectors 82
Timbers, heavy 80
Time switch 236
Tire changers 139
Titanaloy 87
Toasters, conveyor 137
Toilet
   accessories, install only 80
   accessories 126
   paper dispenser 125
   partition supports 73
   partitions 123
   seat cover dispensers 125
Toilets
   chemical 3
Tools, air 8
Toothed rings 82
Top set base 118
Topping removal 31
Topsoil 50
Torches, arc air 19
Tower cranes 3
Tracing table 133
Traffic signals 45
Trailers, office, rental 3
Transfer switches, auto 204
Transformers 45, 209
   distribution 202, 204
   high voltage 202
   low voltage 216
   pads 44
Trash compactors 134
Trash pumps 16
Trash receptacle 51
Treadmills 143
Treatment, soil 34
Tree grate 51
Tree removal 29
Tree spade 15
Trees 50
Trench drain 73
Trench, conduit 43
Trencher 13
Trenching 55
Trenching, slurry 36
Trim 79
Trim, gypsum wall board 114
Trim, redwood 78
Troweling machines 12
Truck cranes 3
Trucks, rental 4
Trusses 80
Trusses, steel 69
Tube columns 70, 73
Tubes, pneumatic 157
Tubing, copper 164
Tubs 161
Turnstiles 128

U

Ultra sound equipment 143
Umbrellas 51
Underfloor duct 225
Underfloor duct, steel 225

Underground tanks 42
Underlayment 118
Underpinning 36
Uninterrupted power systems 219
Unistrut conduit hangers 226
Unit
   heaters 178, 179
   substations 208
   substations, high voltage 202
Uniturf 138
Up flow furnaces 178, 179
Urethane foam 85
Urethane, rigid 84
Urinal screens 123
Urinals 161
Utilities, temporary 3

V

Vacuum
   breakers 165
   cleaning systems 144
   jacket pipe 175
   pumps 171
Valve, gas shut off, earthquake 168
   boxes 42
   boxes, curb 42
   insulation 176
   risers 196
Valves
   butterfly 193
   cast steel 175
   check 41, 166
   cryogenic 175
   gas regulator 167
   gate 41
   gate, globe & check 192
   gate, globe and check 166
   gate, globe & check 192
   globe 41, 166
   hose gate 166
   irrigation 49
   pressure reducing 167, 193
   relief 167, 193
   shut-off 171
   steam trap 167, 193
   thermostatic mixing 167
   zone 171
Vaults
   concrete 44
   doors 100, 131
   modular 131
Vegetable peelers 136
Vegetable sinks 134
Veneer
   architectural 67
   brick 65
   ceramic 66
   stone 67
Ventilators, inhalation 143
Vents
   attic 90
   block/brick 90
   fire 91
   foundation 90
   frieze 90

gravity 90
mushroom 91
smoke 91
Vermiculite beads 85
Vermiculite cores 85
Vertical surface finishes 61
Vibrating rollers 9
Vibrators, concrete, air 9
Vibrators, air 11
Victaulic couplings 167, 192
Video equipment 133
Vinyl
composition tile 117
diaphragm tile 116
sheet 117
wall covering 120
Vinyl, windows 100
Vocational equipment 146
Volclay, walls 83
Volleyball posts 137

W

Wainscot 92
Walk-in coolers 137
Walkway lighting 45
Wall
brick 65
concrete 53
coverings 118, 120
coverings, cloth 120
coverings, paper 120
coverings, plastic 120
coverings, vinyl 120
finishes, masonry 67
forms 56, 57
forms, flying 56, 57
framing 75
furnaces 178
glazed curtain 107
rails, stainless 73
removal 30
sheathing 77
stud 75
tie back 35
ties, masonry 67
Wall cleanouts 170
Wallpack 236
Wardrobe doors 99
Wardrobes, school 133
Washer/sterilizer
instrument 142
Washers 21
Waste receptacles 125
Water
buy 3
closets 161
coolers 161
distillers 142
fountains 162
meter fees 2, 173
meters 168
purification 187
reels 139
service pumps 183
softener 160

stations 137
tanks 160
Waterproof membrane 55
Waterproofing
concrete 54
deck 83
Weatherstripping
metal 93
Welders 18
Welding
booths 134
equipment 18
rebar 60
structural steel 70
Well points 36
WFS studs 109
Wharves 51
Wheel loader 16
Wheel tractor 14
Wheelbarrows 13
White cement 61
Window washing equipment 145
Windows
bank teller 131
picture 102
vinyl 100
Wire
and raceway 204
copper 228
copper & IMC 232
copper & RSC 232
for irrigation controls 49
ground 44
mesh 60, 72
PVC and copper 231
Wiremold overhead distribution systems 226
Wiremold surface raceway 226
Wood
beams 76
cabinets 147
doors, hollow 96
floors 117
piles 34
poles 44
shingles 86
stairs 81
Wrenches, air impact 9
Wrought iron gates 74
Wrought iron railings 72

X

X-ray equipment 142
X-rays, dental 143
X-ray track supports 73

Y

Y strainers 166

Z

Zip-rib 87
Zone controls 188
Zone valve 171

commercial square foot building costs

This Cost Manual is ideal for evaluating "Trade-offs" on materials and design. There are 65 square foot tables each has its own detailed description with the construction parameters clearly stated. The functional assemblies section can be used for unusual situations.

2010

commercial square foot building costs

20th ANNUAL EDITION
SAYLOR PUBLICATIONS, INC.

20th Annual Edition
$64.95
over 320 pages!

Square Foot Costs by:

- Building Type
- Size
- Exterior Wall
- Height
- Number of Stories
- Seismic Zone

Functional Assemblies
Landscape
ADA Section
Location Multipliers

65 Building types, including: Apartments, Auditoriums, Auto Showrooms, Banks, Bowling Alleys, Car Washes, Clubs, Convenience Markets, Day Care Centers, Dispensaries, Fire Stations, Fraternal Buildings, Garages, Government Buildings, Gymnasiums, Racquetball Clubs, Hangars, Health Clubs, Hospitals, Hotels, Indoor Tennis Clubs, Jails, Laundromats, Libraries, Manufacturing Buildings, Motels, Multiple Residences, Offices, Post Offices, Restaurants, Rinks, Schools, Shopping Centers, Stores, Supermarkets, Surgical Centers, Terminals, Theaters, Warehouses.

residential square foot building costs

SAYLOR
Publications, Inc.

2010

residential square foot building costs

18th ANNUAL EDITION SAYLOR PUBLICATIONS, INC.

Square Foot Costs by:
- Building Class
- Size
- Exterior Wall
- Number of Stories

Six Building Classes:

- Economy
- Fair
- Standard
- Custom
- Estate
- Luxury

18th Annual Edition
$44.95
over 200 pages!

Location Multipliers
Special Landscape Cost Section
Special Features with extra items

FUNCTIONAL ASSEMBLIES SECTION:
Use this section to "build-up" the cost of unique dwellings or buildings that have special structural requirements or non-standard design.

Accurately Estimate Repair & Remodeling Work

Estimating repair & remodeling work can be tricky, especially the labor costs. You always have to account for the various degrees of difficulty that you'll find on each job or you can lose your shirt. Saylor Remodeling/Repair Construction Costs gives you grading factors for *degrees of difficulty* that let you base your estimate on the right labor cost for the job:

- Small jobs or big jobs
- Easy or difficult access
- Common or unique structure
- Additions/improvements or fire-gutted

This unique grading system lets you pick the best labor cost for the job (which you add to the updated material prices provided) for the most accurate repair and remodeling prices available in any book. You'll find thousands of unit costs, listed in 16 Division format, and a labor cost adjusted to the *degree of difficulty* that you may encounter. Also included are location multipliers to convert costs to your area. **Try this book for 30 days**. If you don't find the prices the most accurate you've seen, return it for a full refund. If you like it keep it and use it. It should save you several times the cost, during the year.

2010
remodeling
repair
construction
costs

20th ANNUAL EDITION   SAYLOR PUBLICATIONS, INC.

20th Annual Edition
$64.95
over 365 pages!

This unique manual addresses complexity in every cost item!

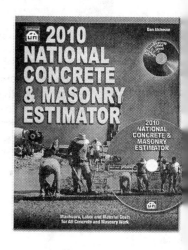
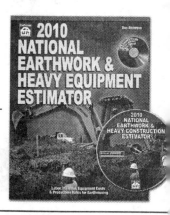

ORDER FORM
These prices are valid until December 31, 2010

30 DAY money back guarantee!

Order Now! by MAIL
send this form to:

SAYLOR Publications, Inc.
Order Fulfillment Dept.
PO Box 4508
West Hills, CA 91308-4508

for credit card orders:

Fax 818-718-8024 or Call 800-624-3352

* Shipping & handling ($ 9.85) applies to UPS Ground in continental USA. Additional charges for expedited services, International, Hawaii, Alaska and Puerto Rico.

_____ Current Construction Costs 2010 .... $ 79.95 _____

_____ Residential Construction Costs 2010 .... $ 79.95 _____

_____ Remodeling/Repair Construction Costs 2010 .... $ 64.95 _____

_____ Commercial Square Foot Building Costs 2010 .... $ 64.95 _____

_____ Residential Square Foot Building Costs 2010 .... $ 44.95 _____

SUB-TOTAL:_____

California residents must add **LOCAL SALES TAX:**_____

* *Shipping and Handling (UPS GROUND):* $ 9.85

TOTAL:_____

❏ Check Enclosed ❏ Visa ❏ MC ❏ Amex ❏ Disc
Make checks payable to Saylor Publications, Inc.

Card # _____ Exp Date _____

Signature: _____ Phone _____

Name: _____

Street: _____

City: _____ State: _____ Zip: _____

Phone: _____ - _____

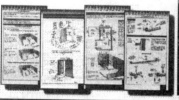

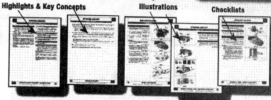